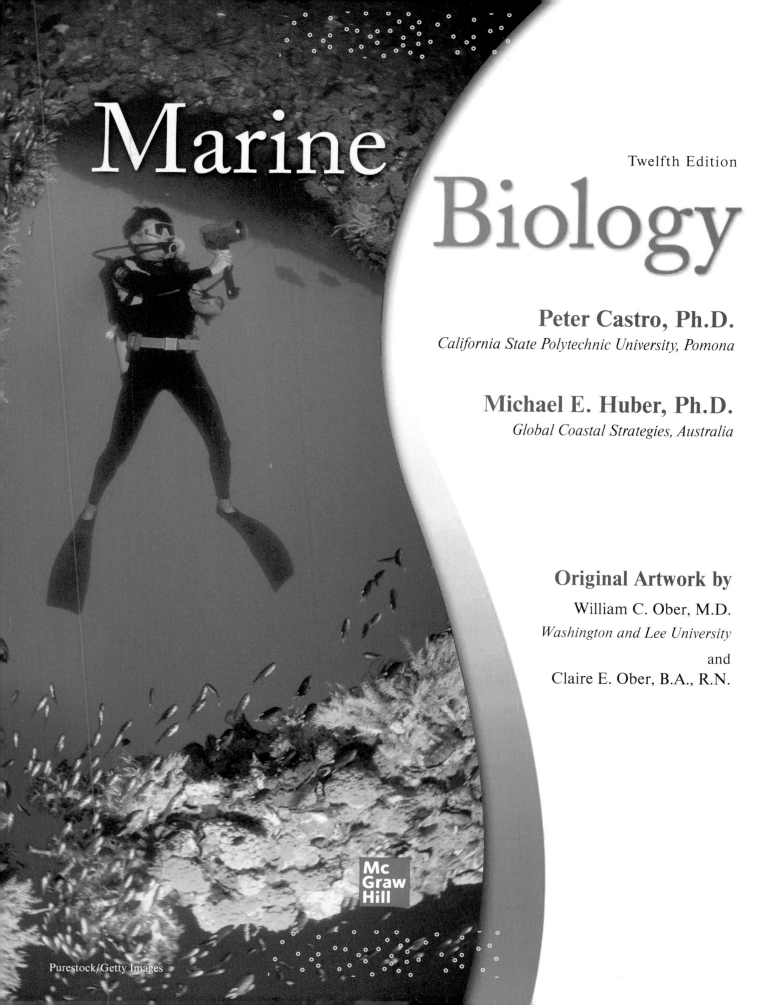

Marine

Twelfth Edition

Biology

Peter Castro, Ph.D.
California State Polytechnic University, Pomona

Michael E. Huber, Ph.D.
Global Coastal Strategies, Australia

Original Artwork by

William C. Ober, M.D.
Washington and Lee University
and
Claire E. Ober, B.A., R.N.

McGraw Hill

MARINE BIOLOGY, TWELFTH EDITION

Published by McGraw Hill LLC, 1325 Avenue of the Americas, New York, NY 10019. Copyright ©2024 by McGraw Hill LLC. All rights reserved. Printed in the United States of America. Previous editions ©2019, 2016, and 2013. No part of this publication may be reproduced or distributed in any form or by any means, or stored in a database or retrieval system, without the prior written consent of McGraw Hill LLC, including, but not limited to, in any network or other electronic storage or transmission, or broadcast for distance learning.

Some ancillaries, including electronic and print components, may not be available to customers outside the United States.

This book is printed on acid-free paper.

1 2 3 4 5 6 7 8 9 LWI 28 27 26 25 24 23

ISBN 978-1-260-72219-2 (bound edition)
MHID 1-260-72219-8 (bound edition)
ISBN 978-1-266-57470-2 (loose-leaf edition)
MHID 1-266-57470-0 (loose-leaf edition)

Portfolio Director: *Michelle Vogler*
Product Developer: *Katherine Habr*
Marketing Manager: *Kelly Brown*
Content Project Managers: *Maria McGreal; Rachael Hillebrand*
Manufacturing Project Manager: *Sandy Ludovissy*
Content Licensing Specialist: *Gina Oberbroeckling*
Cover Image: *Getty Images*
Compositor: *Straive*

All credits appearing on page or at the end of the book are considered to be an extension of the copyright page.

Library of Congress Cataloging-in-Publication Data
Names: Castro, Peter, author. | Huber, Michael, author. | Ober, William C.,
 illustrator. | Ober, Claire E., illustrator.
Title: Marine biology / Peter Castro, Ph.D., California State Polytechnic
 University, Pomona, Michael E. Huber, Ph.D., Global Coastal Strategies,
 Australia ; original artwork by William C. Ober, M.D., Washington and
 Lee University and Claire E. Ober, B.A., R.N.
Description: Twelfth edition. | New York, NY : McGraw Hill, LLC, [2024]
Identifiers: LCCN 2022045201 | ISBN 9781260722192 (bound edition ;
 acid-free paper) | ISBN 1260722198 (bound edition ; acid-free paper) |
 ISBN 9781266574702 (loose-leaf edition ; acid-free paper) | ISBN
 1266574700 (loose-leaf edition ; acid-free paper)
Classification: LCC QH91 .C37 2024 | DDC 578.77–dc23/eng/20221007
LC record available at https://lccn.loc.gov/2022045201

The Internet addresses listed in the text were accurate at the time of publication. The inclusion of a website does not indicate an endorsement by the authors or McGraw Hill LLC, and McGraw Hill LLC does not guarantee the accuracy of the information presented at these sites.

mheducation.com/highered

Dedication

To all future marine biologists
—Peter Castro—

To Mason and Erin
—Michael Huber—

Contents

Instructors
The Power of Connections

A complete course platform

Connect enables you to build deeper connections with your students through cohesive digital content and tools, creating engaging learning experiences. We are committed to providing you with the right resources and tools to support all your students along their personal learning journeys.

65% **Less Time Grading**

Laptop: Getty Images; Woman/dog: George Doyle/Getty Images

Every learner is unique

In Connect, instructors can assign an adaptive reading experience with SmartBook® 2.0. Rooted in advanced learning science principles, SmartBook 2.0 delivers each student a personalized experience, focusing students on their learning gaps, ensuring that the time they spend studying is time well-spent. **mheducation.com/highered/connect/smartbook**

Affordable solutions, added value

Make technology work for you with LMS integration for single sign-on access, mobile access to the digital textbook, and reports to quickly show you how each of your students is doing. And with our Inclusive Access program, you can provide all these tools at the lowest available market price to your students. Ask your McGraw Hill representative for more information.

Solutions for your challenges

A product isn't a solution. Real solutions are affordable, reliable, and come with training and ongoing support when you need it and how you want it. Visit **supportateverystep.com** for videos and resources both you and your students can use throughout the term.

Students
Get Learning that Fits You

Effective tools for efficient studying

Connect is designed to help you be more productive with simple, flexible, intuitive tools that maximize your study time and meet your individual learning needs. Get learning that works for you with Connect.

Study anytime, anywhere

Download the free ReadAnywhere® app and access your online eBook, SmartBook® 2.0, or Adaptive Learning Assignments when it's convenient, even if you're offline. And since the app automatically syncs with your Connect account, all of your work is available every time you open it. Find out more at **mheducation.com/readanywhere**

"I really liked this app—it made it easy to study when you don't have your text-book in front of you."

- Jordan Cunningham,
 Eastern Washington University

iPhone: Getty Images

Everything you need in one place

Your Connect course has everything you need—whether reading your digital eBook or completing assignments for class—Connect makes it easy to get your work done.

Learning for everyone

McGraw Hill works directly with Accessibility Services Departments and faculty to meet the learning needs of all students. Please contact your Accessibility Services Office and ask them to email accessibility@mheducation.com, or visit **mheducation.com/about/accessibility** for more information.

Eye on Science Boxes

About the Authors

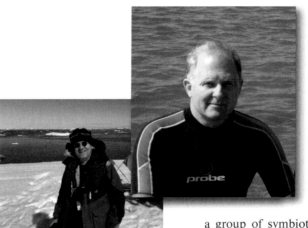

Peter Castro, Ph.D.

Peter Castro realized that he had to become a marine biologist during a high school field trip to the coral reefs in his native Puerto Rico. He obtained a B.S. in biology from the University of Puerto Rico, Mayagüez, but left the warm Caribbean for warm Hawai'i to obtain a Ph.D. in marine zoology from the University of Hawai'i, Mānoa. His first experience with cold water was a year of post-doctoral research at Hopkins Marine Station of Stanford University in Monterey Bay, California. He is currently Professor Emeritus at California State Polytechnic University, Pomona. He also holds a B.A. in history and art history from his home institution, something that took him 18 years to accomplish as a part-time student. He is fluent in four languages and has taught marine biology (in English and Spanish) as a Fulbright Scholar at Odessa State University in the former Soviet Union. His research specialty is the biology of crustaceans symbiotic with reef corals and other invertebrates, research that has taken him anywhere where the water is warm enough to dive. He has also been doing research for almost the last two decades on the systematics of deep-water crabs, mostly, of all places, in Paris, France. Dr. Castro has so far published 70 peer-reviewed papers on his research. He is currently editor-in-chief of the *Journal of Crustacean Biology*.

Michael Huber, Ph.D.

Michael became fascinated by aquatic organisms when he caught his first trout on an Alaskan lake at age 2. His interest in marine biology grew, and he went on to obtain B.S. degrees in both zoology and oceanography from the University of Washington. He received his doctorate from Scripps Institution of Oceanography for research on a group of symbiotic coral crabs. After his Ph.D., he worked at Scripps on the genetics and cell biology of unicellular algae and bioluminescence in midwater organisms. In 1988 he moved to the Biology Department at the University of Papua New Guinea, where he had the opportunity to work on some of the world's most spectacular coral reefs and was Head of the University's Motupore Island Research Station. He also became increasingly involved in marine environmental science. This interest continued to grow when he left Papua New Guinea in 1994 to become the Scientific Director of James Cook University's Orpheus Island Research Station on Australia's Great Barrier Reef. In 1998 he became a full-time environmental advisor, providing scientific information and advice on marine environmental protection to international agencies, governments, and private industry. Much of his work has been in marine environmental protection at the global level, while regionally much of his work has been in the Asia-Pacific region. He has worked on a wide range of environmental issues including pollution control and waste management, underwater noise, habitat conservation and restoration, marine invasive species, endangered species management, long-term environmental monitoring, effects of mariculture, and deep-sea mining. Dr. Huber is a past Chairman of GESAMP, a United Nations scientific body that advises international agencies on marine environmental issues. Currently, he is helping coordinate GESAMP's role in the United Nations of Ocean Science for Sustainable Development. Mike has worked in more than 40 countries.

Mike lives in Brisbane, Australia. His hobbies are fishing, diving, swimming, listening to and attempting to play music, reading, and gardening.

Preface

We are absolutely delighted to introduce *Marine Biology, twelfth edition.* When we first start working on the very first edition back in 1988, our focus was on getting through that task—and the book on shelves somewhere—and never dreamed we would find ourselves introducing a twelfth edition. We are profoundly grateful to the many instructors, reviewers, and most of all students who have carried us to this point.

Whether their interest originated from visiting the shore, scuba diving, recreational fishing, sailing, aquarium keeping, viewing television documentaries and movies, or just dreaming about the ocean, we hope this book reinforces, enhances, and informs the fascination of readers all over the world with the ocean. And, of course, we have tried in *Marine Biology* to provide a rigorous introduction to marine biology as a science.

Marine Biology is used by undergraduate, graduate, high school, and adult-education students, as well as by interested laypersons not enrolled in formal courses. We are gratified that many professional marine biologists use the book. The book is used in many countries outside the United States, and has been translated into six other languages. While keeping this range of users in mind, we have written the text primarily for lower-division, non-science majors at colleges and universities. For many of these students, marine biology will be their only tertiary science course, often taken to satisfy a general education requirement. We have therefore been careful to provide solid basic science coverage, including principles of the scientific method, the physical sciences, and basic biology. Our aim has been to integrate this basic science content with a stimulating, up-to-date overview of marine biology. We hope this approach demonstrates the relevance of the physical sciences to biology and makes all sciences less intimidating. To this end, we use an informal writing style that emphasizes an understanding of concepts over rigorous detail and terminology.

Not all marine biology courses, of course, are intended to fulfill a basic science requirement, and in many the students already have a science background. To balance the needs of instructors teaching courses with and without prerequisites in biology or other sciences, we have designed the book to provide as much flexibility as possible in the use of the basic science material, the order in which topics are presented, and overall emphasis and approach. We have tried to meet the needs and expectations of a wide variety of students, from the scuba-diving philosophy major to the biology major considering a marine science career. We hope a variety of readers other than university students also find the book useful and enjoyable.

Four major themes run through *Marine Biology.* One is the above-mentioned coverage of basic science applied to the marine environment. Another is a focus on the organisms themselves, and their vast diversity not only in taxonomic terms but also in structure, function, and ecology. The third theme is an ecosystem approach that integrates this organismal diversity with the challenges imposed by the surrounding environment, both physical and biological. A final theme that, unfortunately, becomes more urgent with each passing year is the impact of humans on the marine environment.

Marine Biology, **twelfth edition,** adopts a global perspective to emphasize that the world's oceans and seas are an integrated system that cannot be understood by looking in any one person's own backyard. For many students this is a new perspective. One aspect of our global approach is the deliberate inclusion of examples from many different regions and ecosystems so that as many students as possible, not just in North America but around the world, will find something relevant to their local areas or places they have visited. We hope this will stimulate them to think about the many relationships between their own shores and the one world ocean that so greatly influences all our lives.

CHANGES IN THE TWELFTH EDITION

Like all new editions of Marine Biology, we have made extensive revisions to the twelfth edition to correct errors, incorporate new information, and improve readability. In many cases, our revisions reflect comments by reviewers, whose suggestions we greatly appreciate. Unfortunately, perhaps the dominant theme of this revision reflects the inescapable reality of the existential threat of climate change to both the health of the ocean and human society. Even in the last edition, our coverage of global climate change reflected some scientific uncertainty, and tended to point to impacts in the future. Since then, the uncertainty has vanished and it is clear that climate change is happening *now,* at a faster rate and with more dire consequences than we thought. Other aspects of global change have also become more urgent. We have reflected this throughout our revision, in every chapter, to reflect that negative global change is not something that *might* happen, *in future decades,* but is happening now and urgently needs to be addressed to avert catastrophe. This theme carries into the other aspects of global change described in *Special Report: Our Changing Planet.*

Aspects of this overarching theme included in the revision include:

- A new Box 1.1 on the 2019–2020 *Polarstern* expedition to study changes in Arctic Sea ice

- A new section in Chapter 6 on the economic importance of seagrass, saltmarsh, and mangrove communities

- A new Box 10.3 on carbon sinks and blue carbon, introducing both terms and including two new figures, and further discussion of blue carbon sinks in other relevant sections throughout the book

- The addition in Chapter 14 of a new section on Human Impact on Coral Reefs, consolidating and updating coverage that was previously spread across multiple chapters

- New coverage of illegal, unreported, unregulated fishing in Chapter 17

There are many other changes, throughout the book, that update information on the health of the oceans.

Of course, as in every edition, we have updated the information in the book to reflect new research and recent data, to incorporate suggestions from reviewers, and especially to make the book more user-friendly. There are too many changes to fully list here, but examples include:

- Significant revision of the line art in every chapter to improve accessibility for readers with visual challenges

- Line art in many chapters was updated to include the latest available data

- Significant revision of the explanation of the Coriolis Effect—something we have always struggled to explain on the written page. We hope this time we made it better.

- A new Figure 3.36 showing part of an actual tide table

- New coverage of the importance non-coding ("junk") DNA and epigenetic markers, including their heritability

- Added information on the importance of glycoproteins

- Updated coverage of the shortcomings of the traditional "biological species concept," especially in light of prokaryote reproduction, horizontal gene transfer, and hybridization

- New Box 5.1 on the origins of eukaryotes

- New Figure 6.13 comparing marine seaweeds and flowering plants

- New Box 7.3 on mantis shrimp eyes

- Information on "predator fear" effects—ecological effects of predator avoidance by prey species

- Updated examples of transplantation, caging, and removal experiments in marine ecology

- New Figure 17.13 comparing marine and freshwater capture fisheries with aquaculture production

As in every revision, there are many smaller changes throughout the book to include corrections, updates, and clarifications. We have also included a number of new photographs, in our continuing effort to make the book more visually appealing.

ORGANIZATION

Marine Biology is organized into four parts. **Part one** (*Chapters 1 through 4*) introduces students to marine biology and the basic sciences that underpin it. *Chapter 1* describes the history of marine biology. It also explains the fundamentals of the scientific method. This feature emphasizes that science is a process, an ongoing human endeavor. We think it is critical that students understand how and why science works, that science has limitations, and that there is still much to be learned. *Chapters 2 and 3* are a basic introduction to marine geology, physics, and chemistry. *Marine Biology* includes more information on these subjects, and places greater stress on their importance to understanding marine ecosystems, than other texts but we have kept *Chapters 2* and *3* as short as possible and have covered many abiotic aspects of the marine environment in the chapters where they are most relevant to biology. Wave refraction, for example, is described in conjunction with intertidal communities (*Chapter 11*) and estuarine circulation is discussed as part of the ecology of estuaries (*Chapter 12*). This approach emphasizes the importance of the physical and chemical environment to the organisms of the sea throughout the book. At the same time, it provides flexibility for instructors to make best use of the material in light of general education requirements, course prerequisites, and students' backgrounds. *Chapter 4*, "Fundamentals of Biology," briefly reviews some essential biological concepts. In covering basic biology we have tried to balance the needs of a spectrum of students ranging from those with no prior university-level instruction to those who have taken a number of biology courses. Depending on the level of their students, instructors may choose to cover *Chapter 4* in class, assign it as review reading, or omit it and rely on the in-text glossary entries in later chapters to remind students of the definitions of key terms.

Part Two (*Chapters 5 through 9*) surveys the diversity of marine life from the perspective of organismal biology. As in Part One, we provide introductory information that is reviewed and expanded upon in later chapters. In discussing the various taxa we emphasize functional morphology, ecological and physiological adaptations, and economic importance or other significance to humanity. Classification and phylogeny are not stressed, though we do present cladograms illustrating widely accepted phylogenetic schemes for invertebrates and vertebrates. As in the rest of the book we have selected organisms from around the world for photographs, line drawings, and color paintings, but organisms from the coasts of North America are emphasized. Organisms are referred to by their most widely accepted common names. One or two common or important genera are noted in parentheses the first time a group is mentioned in a chapter, but we have not attempted to provide comprehensive lists of genera.

Part Three of the book (*Chapters 10 through 16*) presents an ecological tour of the major environments of the world ocean, commencing with an introduction to some fundamental principles of marine ecology in *Chapter 10*. As in *Chapter 4*, important concepts

presented here are reviewed elsewhere in the in-text glossary boxes. The remaining six chapters of Part Three proceed from nearshore to offshore and from shallow to deep water, describing the physical characteristics of each environment and the adaptations and interactions of the organisms that live there. This admittedly arbitrary sequence follows the teaching sequence of the greatest number of our reviewers, but the chapters are designed so that they can be covered in any sequence according to instructors' preferences and needs. Most chapters include generalized food webs with standardized color coding to indicate the nature of the trophic relationships. Part Three also contains the *Special Report: Our Changing Planet,* a feature on anthropogenic global change that was introduced in the seventh edition.

Finally, **Part Four** looks at the many ways in which humans interact with the world ocean: our use of and impact on the marine environment and the influence of the ocean on the human experience. The section presents an up-to-date, comprehensive view of issues and concerns shared by many students. The chapter on resource utilization (*Chapter 17*) looks not only at traditional uses, such as fisheries, aquaculture, and oil and gas extraction but also at more modern aspects, such as the emerging technologies to generate energy from the sea, the pharmacological use of marine natural products, and the application of genetic engineering and other technologies in aquaculture. *Chapter 18* discusses human-induced degradation of the marine environment, balanced by an examination of marine conservation and habitat restoration.

The *Special Report: Our Changing Planet,* lying roughly in the middle of the book, presents some of the global-scale threats to the ocean resulting from human activities. Much of the material in the *Special Report* could appear in chapters where it is most relevant to specific ecosystems or species. In our opinion, bringing this material together in a single section emphasizes both the global nature of human-induced change in the ocean and the multiple stresses we are imposing. Placing the *Special Report* in the middle

of the book results in important related material being covered in later chapters. We think the current placement gives prominence to this critically important issue even if the *Special Report* has to look forward to later chapters.

ACKNOWLEDGMENTS

Bill Ober and Claire Garrison have again done a superb job of bringing new life to the illustrations, including new ones. We also thank the many contributors of photographs that add so much to the book. Most of all we thank the students, friends, colleagues, former teachers, and reviewers who answered questions, pointed out errors, and made suggestions that have greatly improved the book. We take full credit, however, for any errors or shortcomings that remain.

REVIEWERS

The following people reviewed the eleventh edition and have provided valuable comments and suggestions for preparing the twelfth edition:

Ginger Fisher, *University of Northern Colorado, Greeley*

Richard Grippo, *Arkansas State University, Jonesboro*

John Gunderson, *Tennessee Tech University, Cookeville*

Tonya Huff, *Riverside City College, Riverside, California*

Jeffrey D. Leblond, *Middle Tennessee State University, Murfreesboro*

Randi Sue Papke, *Southwestern Illinois College, Belleville*

Kristian Taylor, *University of Tampa, Florida*

Seema G. Thomas, *Rochester Institute of Technology, New York*

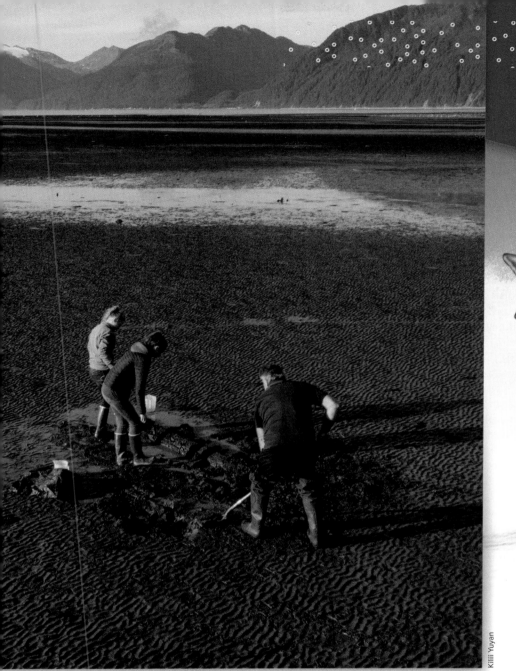

Kilii Yuyan

1

CHAPTER

The Science of Marine Biology

Researchers from the tribally managed Alutiiq Pride Marine Institute in Alaska collect clams, an important food for local indigenous people, to test for harmful toxins.

Marine biology is the scientific study of life in the sea. The ocean is vast, home to countless strange and wonderful creatures. The beauty, mystery, and variety of sea life often attract students to marine biology courses. This same sense of adventure and wonder is what leads marine biologists to their profession.

There are also many practical reasons to study marine biology. Life on Earth probably originated in the sea, so the study of marine organisms teaches us about all life on Earth, not just marine life. Many medical advances, for example, have been underpinned by research on marine organisms, such as studies of the animal immune system in sea anemones and sea star larvae, the fertilization of sea urchin eggs, nerve conduction in squids, and barnacle muscles.

Marine life is also a vast source of human wealth. It provides food, medicines, and raw materials, offers recreation to millions, and supports tourism all over the world. Marine organisms can also cause problems. Some marine organisms harm humans directly by causing disease or attacking people. Others harm us indirectly by injuring or killing other marine organisms that we value for food or other purposes. Marine organisms can erode piers, sea walls, and other structures in the ocean, foul ship bottoms, and clog pipes.

At a much more fundamental level, marine life is vital to the very nature of our planet. Marine organisms produce around half the oxygen we breathe and help regulate Earth's climate. Our shorelines are shaped and protected by marine life, and some marine organisms even help create new land. In economic terms, the ocean's living systems are worth *trillions* of dollars every year.

To make full and wise use of the sea, to solve the problems that marine organisms create, and to predict the effects of human

activities on the ocean, we must learn all we can about marine life. In addition, marine organisms provide valuable clues to Earth's past, the history of life, and even our own bodies. This is the challenge, the adventure, of marine biology.

1.1 THE SCIENCE OF MARINE BIOLOGY

Marine biology is really the more general science of biology applied to the sea rather than a separate science. All the disciplines of biology are represented in marine biology. There are marine biologists who study the basic chemistry of living things, for example. Others are interested in whole organisms: how they behave, where they live and why, and so on. Other marine biologists adopt a global perspective and look at the way entire oceans function as systems. Marine biology is thus both part of a broader science and itself made up of many different disciplines, approaches, and viewpoints.

Marine biology is closely related to oceanography, the scientific study of the oceans. Like marine biology, oceanography has many branches. Geological oceanographers, or marine geologists, study the sea floor. Chemical oceanographers study ocean chemistry, and physical oceanographers study waves, tides, currents, and other physical aspects of the sea. Marine biology is most closely related to biological oceanography, so closely, in fact, that the two are difficult to separate. Sometimes they are distinguished on the basis that marine biologists tend to study organisms living relatively close to shore, whereas biological oceanographers focus on life in the open ocean, far from land. Another common distinction is that marine biologists tend to study marine life from the perspective of the organisms (for example, studying what an organism eats), while biological oceanographers tend to take the perspective of the ocean (for example, studying how food energy cycles through the system). In practice there are so many exceptions to these distinctions that most marine scientists don't worry about the difference.

A marine biologist's interests may also overlap broadly with those of biologists who study terrestrial organisms. Many of the basic ways in which living things make use of energy, for example, are similar whether an organism lives on land or in the sea. Nevertheless, marine biology does have a flavor all its own, partly because of its history.

The History of Marine Biology

People have been living by the sea since the dawn of humanity, and seafood was crucial to early humans. The earliest known stone blades, from 165,000 years ago, were discovered in a seaside cave in South Africa, along with piles of shells from Stone Age clambakes and the earliest traces of ochre pigment, thought to be used for symbolic body painting and decoration. Ancient bone or shell harpoons and fishhooks have also been found, as well as the earliest known jewelry in the form of shell beads from as long as 110,000 years ago. There is evidence that even more ancient peoples voyaged across the sea.

One of the paths of early human migration from Africa into Europe probably followed the coast, with its abundant seafood. Humans also probably migrated down the west coast after arriving

FIGURE 1.1 A stick chart of the Marshall Islands, in the Western Pacific Ocean. The shells represent island groups, and the sticks represent prevailing wind and wave patterns. Pacific Islanders navigated over vast distances between tiny islands using such charts.

in the Americas. That migration seems to have been very rapid and may have been by boat.

The use of marine resources improved peoples' knowledge of marine organisms and drove improvements in seamanship and navigation. Ancient Pacific Islanders had detailed knowledge of marine life, which their descendants still retain. They were consummate mariners (Fig. 1.1), using clues such as wind, wave, and current patterns to navigate over vast distances, perhaps as far as South America.

The Phoenicians were the first accomplished Western navigators. By 2000 BCE (Before Common Era, that is, before year 1 in the Gregorian calendar that we use today), they were sailing around the Mediterranean Sea, Red Sea, eastern Atlantic Ocean, Black Sea, and Indian Ocean.

The ancient Greeks had considerable knowledge of nearshore organisms in the Mediterranean region. The Greek philosopher Aristotle is often considered to be the first marine biologist. He described many forms of marine life and recognized, among other things, that gills are the breathing apparatus of fish.

During the Dark Ages, scientific inquiry, including the study of marine life, came to a grinding halt in most of Europe. Much of the knowledge of the ancient Greeks was lost or distorted. Not all exploration of the ocean stopped, however. During the ninth and tenth centuries CE, or Common Era, the Vikings continued to explore the North Atlantic. In 995 CE a Viking party led by Leif Eriksson discovered Vinland, what we now call North America (Fig. 1.2). Arab traders were also active in the Middle Ages, voyaging to eastern Africa, Southeast Asia, and India. In the Far East and the Pacific, people also continued to explore and learn about the sea.

During the Renaissance, spurred in part by the rediscovery of ancient knowledge preserved by the Arabs, Europeans again began to investigate the world around them, and several undertook voyages of exploration. Christopher Columbus rediscovered the "New World" in 1492—word of the Vikings' find had never reached the rest of Europe. In 1519 Ferdinand Magellan led the first expedition to sail around the globe. Other epic voyages increased our knowledge of the oceans. Fairly accurate maps began to appear for the first time, especially for places outside Europe.

Explorers soon became curious about what lived in the ocean they sailed. An English sea captain, James Cook, was one of the

FIGURE 1.2 Viking explorers reached North America in ships like this reconstruction, *Sea Stallion*, centuries before Columbus.

PA Images/Alamy Stock Photo

first to make scientific observations and to include a full-time naturalist among his crew. In a series of three great voyages, beginning in 1768, he explored all the oceans. He and his crew were the first Europeans to see the Antarctic ice fields and to land in Hawai'i, New Zealand, Tahiti, and a host of other Pacific islands. Cook was the first to use a chronometer, an accurate timepiece that enabled him to determine his longitude precisely, and therefore prepare reliable charts. From the Arctic to the Antarctic, from Alaska to Australia, Cook extended and reshaped the European conception of the world. He brought back specimens of plants and animals and tales of new lands previously unimagined by Europeans. Cook was generally respectful and appreciative of indigenous cultures by the standards of the day, but not always. He was killed in 1779 in a fight after a dispute with native Hawaiians at Kealakekua Bay, Hawai'i.

By the nineteenth century, taking a naturalist along on expeditions was commonplace. Perhaps the most famous of these shipboard naturalists was Charles Darwin, also from England. Beginning in 1831, Darwin sailed around the world on HMS *Beagle* for five years, horribly seasick most of the time. *Beagle*'s primary mission was to map coastlines, but Darwin made detailed observations of all aspects of the natural world. This set off a train of thought that led him, years later, to propose the theory of evolution by natural selection (see "Natural Selection and Adaptation," in 4.5). Though best known for the theory of evolution, Darwin made many other contributions to marine biology. He explained the formation of the distinctive rings of coral reef called atolls (see "Atolls," in 14.2). He used nets to capture the tiny, drifting organisms known as plankton, which marine biologists still do today (Fig. 1.3). Darwin's many interests also included barnacles, crustaceans that attach to surfaces (see Fig. 7.33). Specialists still refer to his treatise on them.

In the United States the most important early exploratory voyage was the United States Exploring Expedition of 1838–42, often called the "Wilkes Expedition" after its leader, Lt. Charles Wilkes of the U.S. Navy. The expedition included 11 naturalists and scientific illustrators. Wilkes was by all accounts a vain and cruel man who promoted himself to Captain as soon as he left port and was later court-martialed for flogging his crew to excess. Only two of the expedition's six ships made it home. Nevertheless, the Wilkes Expedition's achievements are impressive. The expedition charted 2,400 km (1,500 mi) of the coast of Antarctica, confirming it as a continent, as well as the coast of the Pacific Northwest of North America. It explored some 280 islands in the South Pacific, collecting information about peoples and cultures as well as flora and fauna. The 10,000 biological specimens included some 2,000 previously unknown species (Fig. 1.4). The expedition, the first international survey sponsored by the U.S. government, also laid a foundation for government funding of scientific research.

The *Challenger* Expedition By the mid-nineteenth century, a few lucky scientists were able to make voyages specifically to study the oceans, instead of having to tag along on ships doing other jobs. One was Edward Forbes, who in the 1840s and 1850s carried out extensive trawling of the sea floor, mostly around his native Britain but also in the Aegean Sea and other places. Forbes died prematurely in 1854, at age 39, but was the most influential marine biologist of his day. He discovered many previously unknown organisms and recognized that sea-floor life varies at different depths (see Box 16.2, "Biodiversity in the Deep Sea"). Perhaps his most important contribution, however, was to inspire new interest in life on the sea floor.

Forbes's contemporaries and successors, especially from Britain, Germany, Scandinavia, and France, carried on his studies of sea-floor life. Their ships were poorly equipped and the voyages short, but their studies produced many valuable results. They were so successful, in fact, that British scientists managed to convince their government to fund the first major oceanographic expedition, under the scientific leadership of Charles Wyville Thompson. The British navy supplied a light warship to be fitted out for the purpose. The ship was named HMS *Challenger*.

Challenger underwent extensive renovations in preparation for the voyage. Laboratories and quarters for the scientific crew were added, and gear for collecting samples in deep water was installed. Though primitive by modern standards, the scientific equipment on board was the best of its day. Finally, in December 1872, *Challenger* set off.

FIGURE 1.3 These marine scientists are hauling in a net known as a "bongo net" used to capture minute marine plankton. One is signaling instructions to the winch operator.

Michael E. Huber

FIGURE 1.4 Peale's dolphin (*Lagenorhynchus australis*), named after the Wilkes Expedition naturalist who first described it, is one of 2,000 marine and terrestrial species discovered by the expedition.

from earlier efforts. The expedition set new standards for ocean research. *Challenger's* scientists collected data in a more systematic way than previous expeditions and kept meticulous records. For the first time, scientists began to get a coherent picture of what the ocean was like. They also learned about the enormous variety of marine life, for *Challenger* brought back thousands of previously unknown species. Thus, the *Challenger* expedition laid the foundations of modern marine science.

Other expeditions continued the work begun by *Challenger*, and major oceanographic cruises continue to this day. In many ways, though, the voyage of the *Challenger* remains one of the most important in the history of marine science.

The Growth of Marine Labs Even before *Challenger* set off, biologists were excited about the organisms brought back by ocean expeditions. Unfortunately, the ships had quarters for only a few scientists. Most biologists only got to see the preserved specimens the ships brought back to port. Such specimens revealed much about marine life around the world, but biologists wanted to know how the organisms actually lived: what they did and how they functioned. Living specimens were essential for this, but ships usually stayed in one place for only a short time, making long-term observations and experiments impossible.

As an alternative to ships, biologists began to work at the seashore. Among the first were two French biologists, Henri Milne

Over the next three and a half years, *Challenger* and her crew sailed around the world, gathering information and collecting water, sediment, and biological samples (Fig. 1.5). The sheer volume of data gathered was enormous—it took 19 years to publish the results, which fill 50 thick volumes. *Challenger* brought back more information about the ocean than had been recorded in all previous human history.

It was not just the duration of the voyage or the amount of information collected that set the *Challenger* expedition apart

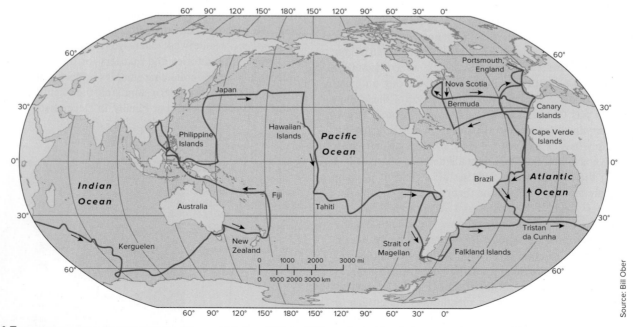

FIGURE 1.5 The route of the *Challenger* expedition, which from 1872 to 1876 conducted the first systematic survey of the world ocean.

Edwards and Victor Andouin, who around 1826 began making regular visits to the shore to study marine life. Others soon followed suit. These excursions offered the opportunity to study live organisms, but there were no permanent facilities and only a limited amount of equipment could be taken along. Eventually, biologists set up permanent laboratories where they could keep organisms alive and work over long periods. The first such laboratory was the Stazione Zoologica, founded in Naples, Italy, in 1872—the same year *Challenger* embarked. The laboratory of the Marine Biological Society of the United Kingdom was founded at Plymouth, England, in 1879.

The first major American marine laboratory was the Marine Biological Laboratory at Woods Hole, Massachusetts. It is hard to pinpoint the exact date when this laboratory was established. The first marine laboratory at Woods Hole was started by the United States Fish Commission in 1871, but didn't flourish. Several other short-lived laboratories later appeared in the area. Harvard biologist Louis Agassiz, who also studied many of the specimens collected by the Wilkes Expedition, established a laboratory on nearby Cape Ann in 1873. In 1888 this lab moved to Woods Hole and officially opened its doors as the Marine Biological Laboratory. It is still one of the world's most prestigious marine labs.

After these early beginnings, other marine laboratories were established. Among the earliest in the United States were Hopkins Marine Station in Pacific Grove, California (Fig. 1.6), Scripps Institution of Oceanography in La Jolla, California, and Friday Harbor Marine Laboratory in Friday Harbor, Washington. More laboratories appeared all over the world, and new ones are being established even today.

World War II had a major effect on the development of marine biology. A new technology, **sonar**, or *so*und *na*vigation and *r*anging, was developed for submarine warfare. Sonar is based on detecting underwater echoes (Fig. 1.7). The ocean, long thought of as a silent realm, was suddenly found to be full of sound, much of it made by animals. During wartime, learning about these animals was no longer the casual pursuit of a few interested marine biologists but a matter of national security. As a result of this urgency, several marine laboratories, such as Scripps and the Woods Hole Oceanographic Institution (established in 1929), grew rapidly. When the war ended, these labs not only remained vital research centers, but continued to grow.

The years immediately after World War II saw the refinement of the first practical **scuba**, or *s*elf-*c*ontained *u*nderwater *b*reathing *a*pparatus. The basic technology was developed in occupied France by the engineer Émile Gagnan to allow automobiles to run on compressed natural gas. After the war, Gagnan and fellow Frenchman Jacques Cousteau modified the apparatus, using it to breathe compressed air under water. Cousteau went on to devote his life to scuba diving and the oceans.

FIGURE 1.6 An early marine biology class at Stanford University's Hopkins Marine Station. The station, established in 1892, is the third-oldest in the United States.

Courtesy of the Stanford University Archives

Using scuba, marine biologists could, for the first time, go under water for more than a few minutes at a time to observe marine organisms in their natural environment (Fig. 1.8). They could work comfortably in the ocean, collecting specimens and performing experiments, though still limited to relatively shallow water, generally less than 50 m (165 ft).

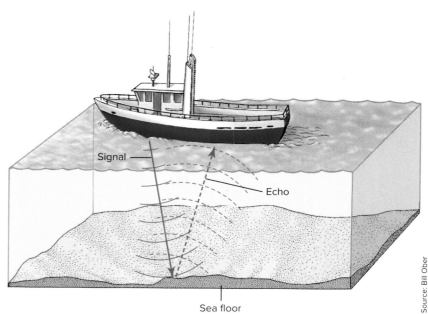

Source: Bill Ober

FIGURE 1.7 A ship uses sonar by "pinging," or emitting a loud pulse of sound, and timing how long it takes the echo to return from the sea floor. The water depth can be determined from the return time. This, the most common form of sonar, is called "active sonar" because the sounds used are actively generated by the equipment.

FIGURE 1.8 Scuba is an important tool for many marine biologists. This one is using an apparatus called a respirometer to measure the production and consumption of oxygen by organisms on a coral reef.

FIGURE 1.10 *Alvin*, a deep-sea submarine operated by the Woods Hole Oceanographic Institution, is one of the most famous vessels in the history of marine science.

Marine Biology Today

Oceanographic ships and shore-based laboratories are as important to marine biology now as ever. Today many universities and other institutions operate research vessels (Fig. 1.9). Modern ships are equipped with the latest technology for navigation, sampling, and studying marine life. Many, like *Challenger*, were originally built for other uses, but more and more research vessels are purpose-built for marine science.

In addition to ships as we normally think of them, some remarkable craft are used to study the marine world. High-tech submarines descend to the deepest parts of the ocean, revealing a once-inaccessible world (Fig. 1.10). Various odd-looking vessels ply the oceans, providing specialized research platforms (Fig. 1.11).

Marine laboratories, too, have come a long way since the early days. Today labs dot coastlines around the world and are used by an international community of scientists. Some are equipped with the most up-to-date facilities available. Others are simple field stations, providing "bed, breakfast, and boats" in remote locations. Often the scientists even have to bring their own breakfasts! There are undersea habitats where scientists can live for weeks at a time, literally immersed in their work (Fig. 1.12). Marine labs are important not only for research but also for education. Many offer hands-on undergraduate courses for students to study marine biology firsthand, and most provide facilities where graduate students begin their careers in marine science.

We all know technology is exploding. Even today's elementary school students have lived through major changes that have affected all of society—our personal lives, business, even politics. Needless to say, technology has and continues to transform marine science. Satellites peer down at the ocean and this **remote sensing** technology has revealed much of what we know about large-scale features like ocean currents and the geographic distribution of marine life (Fig. 1.13). Satellites only see the surface of the ocean, however, and a lot of the action is a long way down. Submarines are one way to penetrate the depths, but scientists increasingly use underwater robots, including remotely operated vehicles (ROVs), which are controlled from the surface, and autonomous underwater vehicles (AUVs; see Fig. 16.23), which operate independently of direct human control. Marine scientists continue to develop an array of instruments that sit on the bottom, float in place, drift with the currents, or are even attached to

FIGURE 1.9 The R/V *Thomas G. Thompson*, operated by the University of Washington, was the first of a new generation of dedicated research vessels that offer more work space and can travel to research sites faster and stay there longer than earlier research ships.

EYE ON SCIENCE

Box 1.1 The Best Laid Plans

The plan was audacious. For millennia, mariners venturing into polar waters feared being trapped in the ice, starving while their vessels were crushed by massive icebergs. But one group of researchers decided to deliberately wedge their research vessel, *RV Polarstern* in the Arctic ice and spend a year drifting with the floating icepack. The Arctic is warming much faster than the rest of our planet (see Special Report, Climate Change), and scientists are desperate to better understand the implications. An entire year of measurements and experiments would vastly improve our knowledge.

Over 10 years of careful planning and preparation—not to mention fundraising— went into the expedition, the Multidisciplinary Drifting Observatory for the Study of Arctic Climate (MOSAiC), the largest Arctic research expedition ever. But things don't always go according to plan. *Polarstern*, a converted icebreaker that can withstand the tremendous pressure of the ice, sailed from Norway in September 2019. A few weeks later, she was wedged in the ice and the scientists got to work.

To prevent their measurements from being effected by the operations of the ship itself, they set up much of the equipment on the surrounding ice up to 50 km (30 mi) away, getting around with snowmobiles and helicopters. As Arctic winter set in, the researchers had to learn to cope with constant darkness and temperatures down to −50°C (−60°F). They weren't expecting to encounter polar bears within days of their arrival, and scientists had to take turns away from their studies to stand watch. The bears also had an irritating habit of chewing the power and communication cables linking the various instruments. Despite their planning,

MOSAiC researchers drill through the ice.

dpa picture alliance archive/Alamy Stock Photo

severe storms sometimes disrupted their instruments. But overall the expedition was going more or less as planned, and data on the Arctic air, ice and water, and the things living in them, started flooding in.

Then the world changed. When the coronavirus hit, hundreds of scientists scheduled to rotate for a stint on *Polarstern* were faced with cancelled flights, travel restrictions, quarantine, expired visas, and closed borders. And the prospect of an outbreak onboard ship, in the remote Arctic, was unthinkable. It became essentially impossible to conduct resupply and crew swaps by air as planned. As the expedition's logistics coordinator said "there you have a plan B, C, D, and X, and then a virus like this comes along and just thwarts all the plans."

The project leaders were forced into the difficult decision to break free of the ice and head to the edge of the ice pack, where crew swap and resupply could be done by ships lacking *Polarstern*'s icebreaking capability. They left much of the research facility on the ice, hoping to return as soon as possible but not knowing for sure when. New logistics plans and coronavirus procedures were frantically developed. Other oceanographic expeditions were cancelled due to coronavirus, but almost miraculously *Polarstern* was able to return to its base camp after only two weeks! In the end, the expedition spent over a year in the ice pack, moving from the constant darkness of winter to the unending days of summer, before returning to port in October 2020. In all, nearly 500 scientists from 20 countries participated.

Unfortunately, MOSAiC brought bad news. Results show that Arctic ice is thinning faster, and more ice is lost in summer, than was expected. Researchers were surprised to see fishes from the North Atlantic, indicating that marine species are moving northward as their normal home waters warm. Such rapid changes in the Arctic are a worrying harbinger of what is in store for the rest of our planet.

For more information, explore the links provided in the Marine Biology Online Learning Center.

animals (see "Observing the Ocean," below). Space technology has a role to play here as well; many oceanographic instruments relay their data through satellites.

Marine biologists use every available tool to study the sea, even some decidedly low-tech ones (Fig. 1.14), and information about the ocean pours in at an ever-increasing pace.

The Census of Marine Life With all of these advances, marine biologists are equaling if not surpassing milestones from past centuries such as the *Challenger* expedition. Despite the achieve-

ments of the past, at the turn of the twenty-first century less than 1% of the oceans had been explored, and we had probably discovered an even smaller fraction of marine species. We knew hardly anything about most species that had been discovered. To make a dent in this ignorance, marine scientists launched the 10-year Census of Marine Life (COML) in the year 2000. COML was a massive undertaking, involving some 2,700 scientists, at nearly 700 institutions in 81 countries. It included some 24 projects focused on a particular region, a specific group of organisms, or individual ecosystem types. The individual scientists and research groups involved

(a)

(b)

Scripps Institution of Oceanography, UC San Diego

FIGURE 1.11 R/V *FLIP*, short for *floating instrument platform*, operated by Scripps Institution of Oceanography, provides a stable platform for research at sea. (*a*) Most of the hull consists of a hollow tube that floats while the vessel is towed into position. When the hull is flooded and sinks, *FLIP* swings into a vertical position (*b*) in which it is largely unaffected by the rise and fall of waves.

would have done their research anyway, but through networking, data sharing, and cooperation, their work was greatly magnified.

COML found an amazing amount of undiscovered marine biodiversity, discovering nearly two new species a day. Genetic studies, analysis of historical records and other investigations established that past populations of some species exploited by humans (for example, some whales and fishes) were much larger before exploitation than previously thought, and that they declined earlier. For example, fishing reduced the Nova Scotian cod population by 96% as early as 1850. This established new understanding of what constitutes "healthy" baseline populations. From a global decline in phytoplankton to evidence that most harvested fish species have become fewer and smaller, COML painted a picture of oceans even more profoundly affected by human activities than we thought. But COML also documented that populations can recover with sound conservation measures.

COML officially ended in 2010 but created a lasting legacy. New technologies were developed, the networks for international cooperation continue, and data platforms that were created provide free access to data by not only scientists but also the general public. The Ocean Biogeographic Information System (OBIS) makes the vast amount of information COML collected about what species live where not only continues to operate but is growing. You can still follow online the movements of tagged sharks, seals, and sea turtles on systems developed by COML. Some COML results are even on Google Earth.

1.2 THE SCIENTIFIC METHOD

Marine biology is an adventure, for sure, but it is still a science. Scientists, including marine biologists, share a certain way of looking at the world. Students of marine biology need to be familiar with this approach and how it affects our understanding of the natural world.

FIGURE 1.12 A diver swims outside *Aquarius*, the world's only underwater marine science laboratory. *Aquarius* is located in the Florida Keys Marine Sanctuary at a depth of about 20 m (60 ft). The living quarters are in the large cylinder at the upper left, which, fortunately for the crew, is larger than it appears here because it is further away than the diver.

Mark E. Ward

NASA/GSFC

NASA/GSFC

FIGURE 1.13 A satellite image showing the abundance of photosynthetic organisms in the ocean, as indicated by the amount of pigment in the water. This photo was taken by the Coastal Zone Color Scanner (CZCS), which was mounted on the *Nimbus-7* satellite. It is actually a composite of information gathered over nearly an eight-year period. Advances in computer and space technology made this image possible.

spite of these minor differences, most scientists do agree on the basic principles of the scientific method, which should be seen as a flexible framework guiding the study of nature and not a rigid set of rules.

Observation: The Currency of Science

The goal of science is to discover facts about the natural world and principles explaining these facts. At the heart of the scientific method is the conviction that we can learn about the world only through our senses or with tools that extend our senses. Microscopes, for example, extend our vision to help us see what is otherwise too small to see. Thus, scientific knowledge is fundamentally derived from the observation of nature. Science is based on observations, and not on preexisting ideas of how the world is or should be.

Relying on observations means that others can verify the observations. A person's thoughts, feelings, and beliefs are internal. No one has access to the minds of others. On the other hand, the world studied by scientists is external to any one person. Different people can look at the same object. Sensory perception may be imperfect, and scientists, like anyone else, are not always impartial, but the object is there for all to see and measure. Thus, there is a way to check and validate any one person's observations.

Observation is critical to all phases of the scientific method. To begin with, it allows us to describe the natural world. The only way to learn what organisms live in a particular part of the ocean, how many of them there are, how fast and how large they grow, when

We live in an age of science. Advertisers boast of "scientific" improvements to their products. News sites regularly report new breakthroughs, and many media outlets have dedicated science reporters. Governments and private companies spend billions of dollars a year on scientific research and education. Why does science have such prestige in our society? The answer, quite simply, is that it works! Science is among the most successful of human endeavors. Modern society could not exist without the knowledge and technology produced by science. Everyone's lives have been enriched by scientific advances in medicine, agriculture, industry, communication, transportation, art, and countless other fields.

Much of the practical success of science results from the way it is done. Scientists do not see the world as a place where things just happen for no reason. They assert instead that the universe can be explained by physical laws. Scientists don't go about discovering these laws haphazardly; they proceed according to time-tested procedures. The set of procedures that scientists use to learn about the world is called the **scientific method.**

Scientists may disagree over the fine points of the scientific method and may apply the method in slightly different ways. In

MBARI 1998

FIGURE 1.14 High-tech meets low-tech: The robotic arm of the ROV *Ventana* captures a pompom anemone *(Liponema brevicornis)* in an ordinary kitchen colander.

Box 1.2 Observing the Ocean

Most of the ocean is incredibly remote, and difficult and expensive to get to. The ocean is also a vast, interconnected network, and conditions at one place are affected by events far away. To cap things off, events such as storms and earthquakes—not to mention the interactions and movements of marine organisms—occur suddenly, so that being in the right place at the right time to observe them is often a matter of luck. Ships, submarines, scuba diving, and studies in the laboratory and on the shore are essential in marine science, but they can't provide the continuous coverage of broad areas of the ocean, throughout its depths, that is needed to really understand the sea. Satellites do observe vast areas of the ocean (see "Marine Biology Today," above), but only at the surface.

Technologies are allowing scientists—and the general public—to observe the oceans in ways that would have seemed like science fiction not long ago. In the Argo system, for example, some 3,800 automated floats, looking a bit like torpedoes turned on end, drift throughout the ocean. Each float continuously bobs between the surface and a depth of 2,000 m (6,600 ft), over about 10 days, measuring ocean properties and sending their data and position via satellite when they surface. Argo floats provide huge amounts of information at the scale of the entire global ocean. Robotic gliders cruise across the oceans for years at a time, like Argo floats, collecting data and surfacing to relay it by satellite.

Oceanographers have also wired parts of the sea floor, providing power and communications for an amazing array

Marine biologists fit a southern elephant seal (*Mirounga leonina*) with electronic instruments.

of instruments that measure currents and water chemistry, detect sea-floor tremors, and track biological activity. The first such system in the United States was the Long-term Ecosystem Observatory (LEO), installed off the New Jersey coast in 1996. LEO, now known as the Coastal Ocean

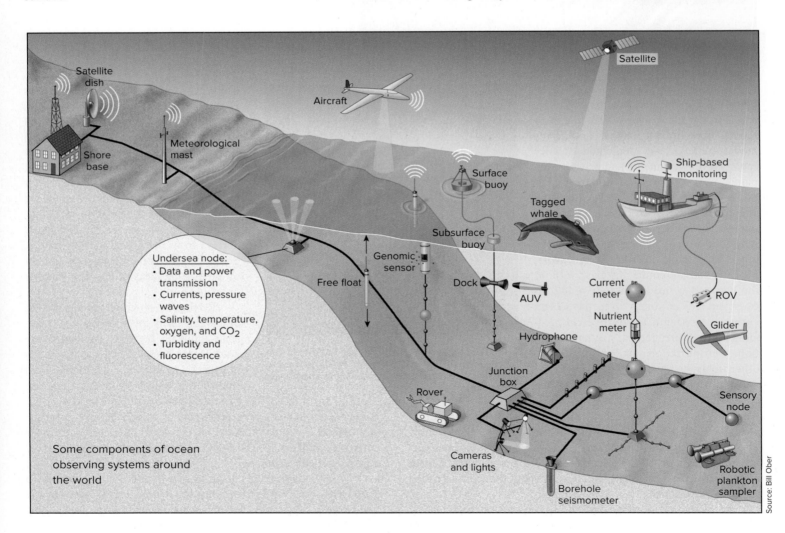

Some components of ocean observing systems around the world

Source: Bill Ober

Observation Lab (COOL), includes underwater gliders, shore-based radar, ship measurements, and moored instruments, and is being integrated with similar systems into a single network covering the United States from Maine to Florida. In the Pacific, the Victoria Experimental Network Under the Sea (VENUS) has operated in coastal waters in British Columbia since 2006. The affiliated North East Pacific Time-integrated Undersea Networked Experiments (NEPTUNE) Observatory, which extends off the coast from British Columbia to Oregon, has operated since 2008. The Monterey Accelerated Research System (MARS) has also operated since 2008, off the coast of northern California. Science and Technology University Research Network (SATURN) Collaboratory (marine scientists on the west coast of North America seem to like naming their networks after planets) was established to measure interactions between the Columbia River in the Pacific northwest and the coastal ocean. The Ocean Observatories Initiative (OOI) has instrument arrays at locations around the Americas, from Antarctica to the North Pacific and Atlantic oceans. There are similar networks in Europe, Japan, the Gulf of Mexico, and the Arctic Ocean. The vision is to integrate all these networks into a single Global Ocean Observing System (GOOS), but so far such observing systems cover only a small fraction of the ocean, mostly near the coast.

Many exciting devices have been developed for these networks, such as genomic sensors that identify plankton DNA and measure toxins, and free-ranging autonomous underwater vehicles (AUVs) that move across the seabed or in the water making measurements and collecting samples. Some networks include docking stations for AUVs to recharge batteries and upload data.

Like all cutting-edge endeavors, developing these observing networks has its challenges. High-tech electronics can be fickle even in the laboratory, much less the depths of the sea. A NEPTUNE scientist once said, "We're learning a lot, which is another way of saying that things are breaking." But more and more the networks are reliably collecting data and transmitting photos, audio, and video that are freely available online, often in real time. An Internet search can take you to some amazing places in the ocean depths.

The networks have also brought unexpected benefits, in part because they are used by scientists from widely varying disciplines. For example, marine geologists use the NEPTUNE network to monitor for earthquakes, but the endangered fin whale (*Balaenoptera physalus*) sings at a sound frequency that interferes with the earthquake measurements. Scientists developed software tools to identify and filter out fin whale songs to track the whales.

Not all ocean observing systems are inanimate—marine animals are recruited. Seals, sea lions, sharks, and other large marine animals move underwater faster than we can ever hope and are unlikely to behave naturally when humans are present. To get a firsthand look at what these animals do beneath the surface, scientists developed "crittercam," a compact underwater video camera attached to animals including sea turtles, sharks, whales, seals, and sea lions, and it provided the first underwater views of feeding humpback whales using curtains of bubbles to herd herring, social diving behavior in Adélie (*Pygoscelis adeliae*) and chinstrap (*P. antarctica*) penguins, and the movements of endangered sea turtles in Mexico. A crittercam attached to a sperm whale (*Physeter catodon*) provided new views of life in the deep sea.

Scientists use animals to study the ocean as well as the animals themselves. An "Autonomous Underwater Sampler" is another name for an animal, such as an elephant seal, with a sensor glued to its back. Originally the transmitters, which measure temperature, depth, and salinity, were used to record the diving behavior of the animals, but oceanographers realized that the sensors also provide valuable data on ocean currents, as the animals can go places scientists can't access otherwise.

Marine scientists are also finding ways to capitalize on equipment installed for other purposes. For example, using signal processing software an undersea cable installed by Google can measure deep-sea earthquakes and ocean waves.

Ocean observing systems aren't just for science. They bring concrete benefits to society. They help track storms, warn of tsunamis, (see Box 3.3, "Waves That Kill") track the effects of climate change, monitor fish populations, and make shipping more efficient. Ocean observatories will save lives and money and help humanity make wiser use of the oceans—and indeed the entire ocean planet.

and how they reproduce, what they eat, how they behave, and so on, is to observe that part of the ocean and the organisms living there. Exploration and description are vitally important parts of marine biology, constantly revealing new information. Previously unknown species, for example, are discovered almost every week. New technologies, such as underwater cameras that reveal the behavior of whales (see Box 1.2, "Observing the Ocean") or genetic techniques that have uncovered vast numbers of previously unknown marine microbes (see Box 5.2, "Tiny Cells, Big Surprises"), regularly improve our ability to observe the sea and make new discoveries. Each finding leads to new observations. The discovery of completely unknown and unexpected ecosystems at deep-sea hot springs, for example, led biologists to look for—and find—similar ecosystems in other parts of the ocean (see 16.4).

As they observe more and more about the world, scientists inevitably seek to explain their observations—*why is that species of seaweed found only in a certain depth range?*—and to make predictions—*will the fishing be good next year?* The desire to explain and predict in turn guides yet more observation.

Two Ways of Thinking

To describe, explain, and make predictions about the natural world, scientists use two basic ways of thinking. In **induction**, they use observations to arrive at general principles. Conversely, reasoning from general principles to specific conclusions is called **deduction.** Scientists once argued about which way of thinking is acceptable, but now generally agree that both induction and deduction are indispensable.

Induction In induction, a scientist starts with a series of observations. Ideally, they have no goal or preconceptions about the

FIGURE 1.15 The Atlantic sailfish (*Istiophorus albicans*) attacking a school of sardines. The long projection on the snout is called the bill.

outcome and are completely objective. The scientist then uses these observations to reach a general conclusion. For example, suppose a marine biologist examined a sailfish (Fig. 1.15), a shark (Fig. 1.16), and a tuna (Fig. 1.17) and found they all had gills. Because sailfishes, sharks, and tunas are all fishes, he might conclude *All fishes have gills*. This is an example of induction.

> In the process of induction, general conclusions are made on the basis of specific observations.

Scientists must be careful when using induction. The step from isolated observations to general conclusions critically depends on the number and quality of the observations and on recognizing their limitations. If our biologist stopped after examining the sailfish, which happens to have a bill, induction might lead to the false conclusion *All fishes have bills*. Even after examining all three fishes, he might have concluded *All marine animals have gills* instead of just *All fishes have gills*. This is where deduction comes into play.

Deduction In deduction, scientists start with a general statement about nature and predict what the specific consequences would

FIGURE 1.16 A tiger shark (*Galeocerdo cuvier*). The five vertical gill slits can be seen just in front of the pectoral fins.

FIGURE 1.17 The southern bluefin tuna (*Thunnus maccoyii*) has two plates on each side of the head that cover its gills.

be if that statement is true. The general statement might be based on hunch or intuition, but is usually based on observations. If our marine biologist used induction to make the general statement *All marine animals have gills*, knowing whales are marine animals he might reason that whales must have gills. Thus, a general statement about all marine animals was used to make a statement about a particular kind of marine animal.

> In deduction, specific predictions are made by applying general principles.

Testing Ideas

Scientists are never content to simply make statements about the world and let it go at that. Instead, they are obsessed with testing the statements to see if they are, in fact, true. Both induction and deduction lead the scientist to make statements about the world, based on available information or even an "educated guess," that *might* be true but requires further testing. A statement that might be true is called a **hypothesis.** A crucial feature of the scientific method is that all hypotheses are tested, usually again and again. This insistence on testing is one of the great strengths of the scientific method. Incorrect hypotheses are usually quickly weeded out and discarded.

Constructing the Hypothesis Scientific hypotheses must be stated in a way that allows them to be critically tested. What this means is that it must be possible, at least potentially, to *disprove* the hypothesis if it is false. Sometimes this is simple. For example,

the hypothesis that whales have gills is easy to test. All the biologist has to do is examine a whale to see if it has gills, and he would find that whales have lungs, not gills (Fig. 1.18). He would have proven the hypothesis *Whales have gills* false. This would also disprove the more general hypothesis *All marine animals have gills.* The steps our marine biologist used to construct and test these hypotheses are illustrated in Figure 1.19. This line of reasoning is not entirely imaginary. Aristotle used similar logic in the fourth century BCE, observing not only that whales breathe with lungs and not gills but also that unlike most fishes they give birth to live young instead of laying eggs. Unfortunately, Aristotle's recognition that whales and other marine mammals are not fishes was lost to Western science for more than two millennia.

Hypotheses are often much more complicated than whether or not an animal has gills. Marine organisms are affected by weather and current patterns, the abundance of food and predators, natural cycles of reproduction and death, human activities, and a host of other factors.

People sometimes make the mistake of proposing hypotheses that cannot actually be tested. Someone might say *There are mermaids in the ocean.* The problem with this hypothesis is that it could never be *proved* to be false. An army of marine biologists could spend their entire careers looking for a mermaid without finding one, but the true believer could always say *The mermaids are there, you just didn't find them.* No matter how hard they looked, the biologists could never prove that there are no mermaids. Therefore, the statement *There are mermaids in the ocean* is not a valid scientific hypothesis because it is not **testable.**

A scientific hypothesis is a statement about the world that might be true and is testable. A testable hypothesis is one that at least potentially can be proved false.

The Nature of Scientific Proof It must be possible to disprove a hypothesis, at least in principle, before the hypothesis is a scientific one. But how can a hypothesis be proved true? This question has always troubled scientists, and the answer may trouble you too. In general, no scientific hypothesis can be absolutely proved true. For example, consider the hypothesis that all fishes

The term *fish* is used for a single individual or for more than one individual of the same species.

The term *fishes* is used to refer to more than one species of fish.

FIGURE 1.18 A sperm whale (*Physeter catodon*) exhales bubbles of air from its lungs through the blowhole on top of its head.

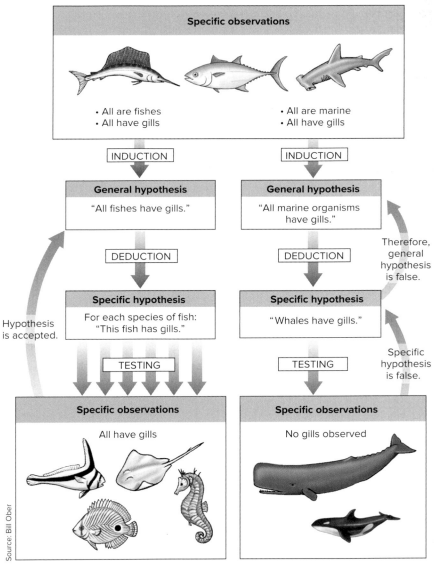

FIGURE 1.19 An example of the scientific method. Two hypotheses were derived from the same observations. When tested by further observations, one hypothesis (left) is accepted and one (right) is rejected.

Francois Gohier/VWPics/Alamy Stock Photo

Source: Bill Ober

have gills. It is easy to see that this hypothesis can be proved false by finding a fish without gills. But even though every fish so far examined has gills, this does not prove that *all* fishes have gills. Somewhere out there may lurk a fish without them. Just as it cannot be proved that there are no mermaids, it can never be proved that all fish have gills.

In science, then, there are no absolute truths. Knowing this, scientists could throw up their hands and look for another line of work. Fortunately, most scientists have learned to accept and deal with the lack of absolute certainty that is inherent in science by making the best of the available evidence. All scientific hypotheses are examined and tested, poked, and prodded, to see if they agree with actual observations of the world. When a hypothesis withstands all these tests, it is conditionally accepted as "true" in the sense that it is consistent with the available evidence. Scientists speak of *accepting* hypotheses, not *proving* them. They accept the hypothesis that all fish have gills because every attempt to reject it has failed. At least for now, the hypothesis fits the observations. The good scientist, however, never quite forgets that any hypothesis, even a personal favorite, could be thrown out the window by new information. No hypothesis is exempt from testing, or immune to being discarded if it conflicts with the evidence. The bottom line in science is observation of the world, *not* our preconceived ideas and beliefs.

No hypothesis can be scientifically *proved* to be true. Instead, hypotheses are *accepted* as long as they are supported by the available evidence.

Testing the Hypothesis Because hypotheses generally can't be proved true, scientists, somewhat surprisingly, spend their time trying to disprove, not prove, hypotheses. They have more confidence in hypotheses that have stood up to critical testing than in untested ones. Thus, the role of the scientist is to be a skeptic.

Often scientists are trying to decide among two or more **alternative hypotheses.** After looking at the sailfish, shark, and tuna, our imaginary marine biologist advanced two possible hypotheses: that all fish have gills and that all marine animals have gills. Both hypotheses were consistent with the observations to that point. After examining a whale, our biologist rejected the second hypothesis and, in doing so, strengthened the first one. He arrived at the best hypothesis by a process of elimination.

Real marine biologists rarely have it as easy as our imaginary one, who was able to construct and then test his hypotheses about gills with just a few simple observations. Hypothesis testing usually requires carefully planned, painstaking observations. Occasionally a new observation or set of observations leads to the complete rejection of an accepted hypothesis, which has been termed a "scientific revolution." Such discoveries make headlines, but most of the time the scientific process is a gradual one in which hypotheses are continually refined and modified, and new alternatives proposed, as more information becomes available.

Hypotheses can often be tested by making the right kind of observations of the natural world, at the right time and place.

Improved observing systems (see "Observing the Ocean," above) and continuing ocean exploration are constantly revealing more of the ocean's secrets.

Sometimes, however, the conditions needed to test a hypothesis do not occur naturally and scientists must manipulate nature, that is, perform an **experiment**, to make the necessary observations.

In experiments, scientists create artificial situations to test hypotheses because they cannot make the necessary observations under natural conditions.

Suppose another marine biologist observes that the same species of mussel is smaller at a location that has generally warmer water than at a colder spot. She wants to know if that size difference is due to the temperature difference. But the temperature at both locations changes all the time with seasons, weather, and so forth. The difference in temperature between locations would never stay the same. Even if it did, there would be many other differences between the two places. The mussels might be different strains, for example. They might be eating different foods or different amounts of food. There might be pollution or an outbreak of disease at one place or another, or stronger currents or waves. Or people could be harvesting the mussels at one location, so the mussels there are younger on average. In any natural situation, there are countless factors other than temperature that might explain the difference in mussel size. Factors that might affect observations are called **variables.**

Faced with all these variables, the biologist decides to perform an experiment. She collects mussels from a single location and divides them at random into two groups. This means the two groups of mussels in the experiment are pretty much the same. She places the two groups into separate tanks where she can control the water temperature. She grows one group in warm water, the other in cold. She feeds all the mussels the same amounts of the same food at the same time, protects the mussels from pollution and disease, supplies both holding tanks with seawater from the same source, and keeps all the other living conditions exactly the same for both groups. Because all these variables are the same for both groups, the biologist knows that they cannot be responsible for any differences observed in mussel growth. The only difference between the two groups is temperature.

To prevent a variable from affecting the experiment, the scientist has two options. One is to artificially keep the variable from changing—for example, by giving all the mussels exactly the same food. The other is to make sure that any changes that do occur are identical for both groups. By supplying both tanks with seawater from the same source, for example, our biologist ensures that any changes in the quality of the water affect both groups of mussels equally. Variables that are prevented from affecting an experiment are said to be **controlled**, and the experiment is called a **controlled experiment** (Fig. 1.20). Since the biologist has controlled the effects of other variables while growing the mussels at different temperatures, she can be confident that differences in growth between the two groups are due to temperature.

In this imaginary experiment, our biologist found that temperature was in fact the factor causing the observed size difference. But

Field Observations

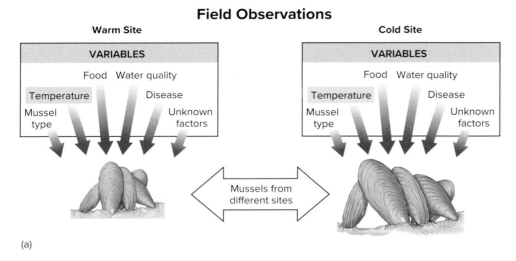

(a)

Controlled Laboratory Experiment

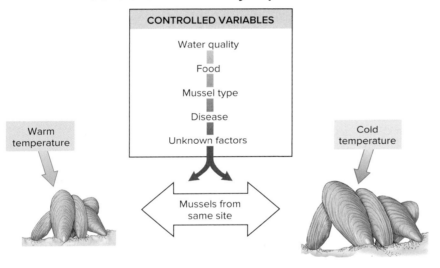

(b)

FIGURE 1.20 (*a*) Many different variables might produce differences between groups of mussels at different locations. (*b*) Controlling the variables in an experiment allows the effects of a single factor—in this case, temperature—to be tested, confirming that the size difference between the sites is due to temperature. This example describes a laboratory experiment, but experiments are often performed in the field.

Source: Bill Ober

Experiments aren't just for the laboratory—many (some would say most) important controlled experiments are done out in the real world (see Box 11.1, "Transplantation, Removal, and Caging Experiments").

Not all experiments are designed, much less controlled. Marine scientists are hungry for knowledge however they get it, and capitalize whenever they can on accidental and natural experiments. When a ship accidentally dumped a cargo of tennis shoes in a North Pacific storm, plotting where the floating shoes washed up on beaches improved our understanding of surface currents. Monitoring the recovery of a coral reef smashed by a cyclone provided information about how fast damaged reefs can recover.

Marine scientists often try to capture what they think they know in the form of models. These may start as very simple sketches along the lines of "the water flows from here to there, this eats that." Even such simple "models" help crystallize and communicate our understanding. They also help identify errors in our thinking and point to where more information is needed. If numbers can be attached—how much water flows, how much they eat—more sophisticated models are developed to predict what might happen in a particular situation. If the prediction doesn't bear out, what did we miss or were our measurements wrong: back to the drawing board. This cycle of capturing and testing our knowledge is another, powerful form of experiment.

The Scientific Theory Most of us have heard people ridicule some idea or other because it was "only theoretical." The public usually reserves such scorn for controversial or unpopular theories. The theory of gravity, for instance, is rarely criticized for being "only a theory" even though physicists have no accepted explanation of why gravity exists. People often say "theory" in everyday conversation to mean a guess, speculation, or just one of several possible explanations for something, but scientists don't use the term **scientific theory** to refer to a controversial or provisional hypothesis. A hypothesis is not considered a scientific theory until all reasonable alternatives have been ruled out and the hypothesis has passed every possible test. A scientific theory is supported by overwhelming evidence and represents the best comprehensive explanation of our observations of how the world works. It is an established scientific principle that guides the search for new knowledge by leading to new, testable hypotheses.

why? Perhaps the higher temperature increased the mussels' metabolism so they burned more energy and grew slower (a weight-watcher's dream). Or maybe the temperature was near the upper extreme that the mussels can tolerate, so they were stressed. More often than not, good science raises as many questions than it answers, which is why science continually progresses. This example is particularly relevant because Earth is warming (see "Climate Change," in Special Report: Our Changing Planet) and understanding the effects on organisms both in the sea and on land is increasingly urgent.

The way that variables interact can also be studied. The mussels could be maintained in different *combinations* of temperature and food supply, for example, to see how the effects of temperature depend on food supply. That would help answer the question of whether the smaller size in warmer water is an effect of higher metabolism.

Box 1.3 John Steinbeck and Ed Ricketts

People mostly know the American writer John Steinbeck as the author of such beloved works as *The Grapes of Wrath, Of Mice and Men*, and *East of Eden*. Less well known are Steinbeck's contributions to marine biology, which resulted largely from his close friendship with a man named Ed Ricketts.

Steinbeck and Ricketts first met in 1930—by Steinbeck's account, in a dentist's office in Pacific Grove, California. Steinbeck had a long-standing interest in marine biology and had wanted to meet Ricketts for some time. Ricketts owned the Pacific Biological Laboratory, located near the Hopkins Marine Station and the present site of the Monterey Bay Aquarium. Ricketts collected specimens of marine life along the Pacific coast and sold them to universities and museums. He was immensely popular in the area and knew more about marine biology than anyone around.

The two men became close friends almost immediately. Before long Steinbeck, then struggling as a writer, was spending a lot of time hanging around his friend's laboratory, going on collecting trips, and assisting in day-to-day operations. Steinbeck got so involved in this work that he could even get excited about a microscope:

> My dream for some time in the future is a research scope with an oil immersion lens, but that costs about 600 dollars and I'm not getting it right now.... Oh boy! Oh boy! Sometime I'll have one.[1]

John Steinbeck would eventually credit Ricketts with shaping his views of humanity and the world, and characters in at least six of Steinbeck's novels were based on Ricketts. The most famous is Doc, the main character of *Cannery Row*, who runs the "Western Biological Laboratory":

> It sells the lovely animals of the sea, the sponges, tunicates, anemones, the stars and buttlestars [sic], the sunstars, the bivalves, barnacles, the worms and shells, the fabulous and multiform little brothers, the living moving flowers of the sea, nudibranchs and tectibranchs, the spiked and nobbed and needly urchins, the crabs and demi-crabs, the little dragons, the snapping shrimps, the ghost shrimps so transparent that they hardly throw a shadow.... You can order anything living from Western Biological and sooner or later you will get it.[2]

The friendship was beneficial to marine biology as well as to literature. Their expedition to Mexico produced *The Sea of Cortez*, a scientific report that is also part literature and part travelogue. The book lists the more than 600 species collected by the pair, including some 60 that were new to science. The trip was not all work, however: The authors report taking "2,160 individuals of two species of beer."

Ed Ricketts's most enduring contribution to marine biology was the 1939 publication *Between Pacific Tides*. Written with Jack Calvin, a friend of Ricketts and Steinbeck, *Between Pacific Tides* is a comprehensive guide to the seashore life of the Pacific coast of North America. Revised and updated, it is still used by amateurs and professionals alike.

Though Ricketts was an able biologist and was largely responsible for the content of *Between Pacific Tides*, he had difficulty getting his observations and ideas down on paper. Steinbeck almost certainly helped him write the book and get it published. When Ricketts felt that the publisher, Stanford University Press, was dragging its feet, Steinbeck fired off this sarcastic letter:

> Gentlemen:
> May we withdraw certain selected parts of Between Pacific Tides *which with the passing years badly need revision. Science advances but Stanford Press does not.*

Vicki Buchsbaum Pearse

Ed Ricketts.

> There is the problem also of the impending New Ice Age.
> Sometime in the near future we should like to place our order for one (1) copy of the forthcoming (1948, no doubt) publication, The Internal Combustion Engine, Will it Work?[3]
> Sincerely,
> John Steinbeck
> Ed Ricketts
>
> P.S. Good Luck with A Brief Anatomy of the Turtle.

Ed Ricketts was killed in a train accident in 1948. Steinbeck, saddened at the death of his friend, wrote, "There died the greatest man I have ever known and the best teacher."

[1]Source: "2/17/1948 to Gwyndolyn Steinbeck" by John Steinbeck and Ed Ricketts and "12/15/1939 letter to Elizabeth Otis" by John Steinbeck, from *Steinbeck: A Life in Letters* edited by Elaine A. Steinbeck and Robert Wallsten.

[2]Source: "Chapter 5" from *Cannery Row* by John Steinbeck, 1945.

[3]Source: "2/17/1948 to Gwyndolyn Steinbeck" by John Steinbeck and Ed Ricketts and "12/15/1939 letter to Elizabeth Otis" by John Steinbeck, from *Steinbeck: A Life in Letters* edited by Elaine A. Steinbeck and Robert Wallsten.

It must be remembered, however, that a theory is still a hypothesis, albeit a well-tested one. As with other hypotheses, theories cannot be absolutely proved and are accepted as true only as long as they are supported by evidence. Good scientists accept theories only as long as the best available evidence supports them, and they recognize that any theory could be overturned by new evidence.

A scientific theory is a hypothesis that has been so extensively tested that it is generally regarded as true. Like any hypothesis, however, it is subject to rejection if enough evidence accumulates against it.

Limitations of the Scientific Method

No human enterprise, including science, is perfect. Just as it is important to understand how and why the scientific method works, it is important to understand the limitations of the scientific method. For one thing, remember that scientists are people too: they have the same human shortcomings as anyone else. Scientists may be attached to favorite theories even when confronted with contradictory evidence—being wrong can be hard to accept. Like anyone else, they may let personal biases affect their thinking. No one can be completely objective all the time. Fortunately, factual errors are usually corrected because hypotheses are tested not just by one person but by many. The practical success of science is evidence that the self-checking nature of the scientific method does work most of the time.

Science also has some built-in limitations. Ironically, these limitations arise from the same features that give the scientific method its power: the insistence on direct observation and testable hypotheses. This means that science cannot make judgments about values, ethics, or morality. Science can reveal how the world is, but not how it should be. Science cannot decide what is beautiful. Science can't even tell humanity how to use the knowledge and technology it produces. These things all depend on values, feelings, and beliefs, which are beyond the scope of science.

Interactive Exploration

McGraw-Hill Connect® is a great place to check your understanding of chapter material. Visit **www.mcgrawhillconnect.com** for access to interactive chapter summaries, chapter quizzing, and more! Further enhance your knowledge with videoclips and weblinks to chapter-related material.

Critical Thinking

1. Most of the major advances in marine biology have come in the last 200 years. What do you think are the reasons for this?

2. Recall that the statement "There are mermaids in the ocean" is not a valid scientific hypothesis. Can the same be said of the statement "There are *no* mermaids in the ocean?" Why?

3. Imagine you are a marine biologist and you notice that a certain type of crab tends to be larger in a local bay than in the waters outside the bay. What hypotheses might account for this difference? How would you go about testing these hypotheses?

4. Many species of whale have been hunted to the brink of extinction. Many people think that we do not have the right to kill whales and that all whaling should cease. On the other hand, in many cultures whales have been hunted for centuries and still have great cultural importance. People from such cultures argue that limited whaling should be allowed to continue. What is the role that science can play in deciding who is right? What questions cannot be answered by science?

For Further Reading

Some of the recommended reading may be available online. Look for live links on the *Marine Biology* Online Learning Center.

General Interest

Alzona, A., 2022. Solving the ocean. *Smithsonian*, vol. 53, no. 3, July-August, pp. 105–118. In a man's world, Mary Sears was a brilliant marine scientist who helped win World War II.

Aschwanden, C., 2015. A user's guide to rational thinking. *Discover*, July/August 2015, pp. 44–49. No matter how rational we might think we are, everyone falls prey to logical traps. Here are some strategies to recognize when that person is you, and to engage and not argue with the other person when it isn't.

Barnes, C. R., M. M. Best, and A. Zelinski, 2009. The NEPTUNE Canada regional cabled ocean observatory. *Sea Technology*, vol. 49, no. 7, July, pp. 10–14. An overview of one of the new deep-ocean observing systems.

Barras, C., 2018. Stone age sailors. *New Scientist*, Vol. 238, No. 3180, 2 June, pp. 36–39. Humans may have been crossing the oceans since the time of our earliest ancestors.

Di Ventra, M., 2018. *The Scientific Method: Reflections from a Practitioner.* Oxford University Press, Oxford.

Eident, K., 2012. A long voyage to get a new ship. *Oceanus*, vol. 49, no. 2, Spring, pp. 18–21. A lot of planning goes into building a new research ship.

Lawler, A., 2014. Sailing Sinbad's seas. *Science*, vol. 344, no. 6191, pp. 1440–1445. For three millennia, maritime trade extending all the way from east Africa to southeast Asia transported more goods than the more famous Silk Road traveled by Marco Polo.

Lippsett, C., 2012. The quest to map *Titanic*. *Oceanus*, vol. 49, no. 2, Spring, pp. 26–35. New technologies such as sidescan sonar are used by underwater vehicles to map the *Titanic* wreck.

Marean, C. W., 2010. When the sea saved humanity. *Scientific American*, vol. 303, no. 2, August, pp. 54–61. When a "mini ice age" nearly drove early humans extinct, marine resources on the south coast of Africa pulled them through.

New Scientist, vol. 231, no. 3084, 30 July 2016, pp. 31–39. Conquering the deep. Vignettes of new technology to study the ocean.

Oceanus, vol. 51, no. 1, Summer, 2014. The complete issue is devoted to *Alvin*, one of the most important research vessels in the exploration of the deep sea.

Pietsch, T. W., 2011. Plumier's passion. *Natural History*, vol. 119, no. 7, July–August, pp. 30–16. A seventeenth-century French monk conducted meticulous studies of fish, including anatomical diagrams.

Pringle, H., 2007. Follow that kelp. *New Scientist*, vol. 195, no. 2616, 11 August, pp. 40–43. America's first inhabitants may have traveled from Siberia in small boats following the belt of kelp forests along North Pacific coasts.

Schofield, O., S. Glenn, and M. Moline, 2013. The robot ocean network. *American Scientist*, vol. 101, no. 6, Nov./Dec., pp. 434–441. New technologies in the study of the ocean include robotics, autonomous underwater vehicles, and underwater gliders.

Shugart, J., 2013. Deep network. *Science News*, vol. 184, no. 8, October, pp. 22–27. Monitoring of the seafloor with cameras and other instruments provides new insights.

Smith, R., 2008. Beyond the blue horizon. *National Geographic*, vol. 213, no. 3, March, pp. 106–123. Recent archaeological finds help piece together the puzzle of how ancient Polynesian sailors navigated their way across the Pacific.

Sulloway, F. J., 2006. The evolution of Charles Darwin. *Smithsonian*, vol. 36, no. 9, December, pp. 58–69. Darwin rigorously followed the scientific method, even when his conclusions challenged his deeply held religious beliefs.

Tarlach, G., 2018. The secret history of the Vikings. *Discover*, vol. 39, no. 2, March, pp. 24–31. New insights into the Vikings' voyages comes from genetic studies of their descendants.

2

CHAPTER

The Sea Floor

Image courtesy of Galapagos Rift 2005 Exploration, NOAA-OE

Submarine eruptions produce fresh sea floor like this "pillow basalt," which formed as lava slowly oozed out of a fissure on the sea floor. The new sea floor has already been colonized by vent clams (*Calyptogena magnifica*) and other animals.

The oceans are not just places where the land happens to be underwater. Most of the sea floor is geologically distinct from the continents. It is locked in a perpetual cycle of birth and destruction that shapes the oceans and controls much of the geology of the continents. Marine geological processes affect not only the oceans but also dry land.

Many of the processes that mold ocean basins occur slowly, over hundreds of millions of years. On this timescale, where a human lifetime is but the blink of an eye, solid rocks flow like liquid, entire continents move across the face of the Earth, and mountains grow from flat plains. To understand the sea floor, we must learn to adopt the unfamiliar perspective of geological time.

At first glance geology might not seem to have much to do with marine biology, but geological processes profoundly influence marine

habitats, the natural environments where marine organisms live. Geological processes sculpt the shoreline, determine the water depth, control whether the bottom is muddy, sandy, or rocky, create new islands and undersea mountains for organisms to colonize, and determine the nature of marine habitats in countless other ways. Much of the history of life in the oceans has been determined by geological events.

2.1 THE WATER PLANET

Our planet is very much a water planet, unique in having large amounts of liquid water—the oceans—on its surface. The oceans not only cover 71% of the globe but also regulate its climate and atmosphere.

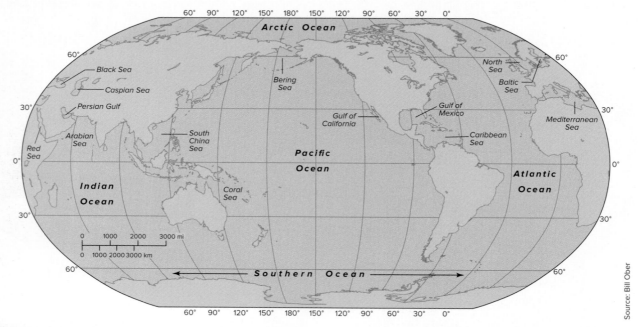

FIGURE 2.1 The major ocean basins and some of the marginal seas.

The Geography of the Ocean Basins

The oceans are not distributed equally with respect to the Equator. About two-thirds of Earth's land area is found in the Northern Hemisphere, which is only 61% ocean. About 80% of the Southern Hemisphere is ocean.

The oceans are traditionally classified into four large basins (Fig. 2.1). The **Pacific** is the deepest and largest, almost as large as all the others combined (Table 2.1). The **Atlantic** Ocean is a little larger than the **Indian** Ocean, but the two are similar in average depth. The **Arctic** is the smallest and shallowest ocean. A number of shallow seas, such as the Mediterranean Sea, Gulf of Mexico, and South China Sea, are marginal or connected to the main ocean basins.

Though we usually treat the oceans as four separate entities, they are actually interconnected. This connection is most obvious when the world is viewed from the South Pole (Fig. 2.2). From this view it is clear that the Pacific, Atlantic, and Indian oceans are large branches of one vast system. The connections among the major basins allow seawater, materials, and some organisms to move from one ocean to another. Because the oceans are actually one great interconnected system, oceanographers often speak of a single **world ocean.** They also refer to the continuous body of water that surrounds Antarctica as the **Southern Ocean.**

The world ocean, which covers 71% of the planet, is divided into four major basins: the Pacific, Atlantic, Indian, and Arctic oceans.

The Structure of Planet Earth

Earth and the rest of the solar system are thought to have originated about 4.5 billion years ago from a cloud or clouds of dust formed by the explosion of a star. The dust particles collided with each other, clumping into larger particles. These larger particles collided in turn, joining into pebble-sized rocks that collided to form larger rocks, and so on. The process eventually built up Earth and the other planets.

Earth's formation generated so much heat that the entire early planet was molten. This allowed materials to settle within the planet according to their **density.** Density is the mass of a given volume of a substance. Obviously, a pound of styrofoam weighs more than an ounce of lead, but most people think of lead as "heavier" than styrofoam even though a kilogram of lead weighs the same as a kilogram of styrofoam. This is because lead weighs more than styrofoam if *equal volumes* of the two are compared. In other words, lead is denser than styrofoam. The density of a substance is calculated by dividing its mass by its volume. If two substances are mixed, the denser material tends to sink and the less dense to float.

Table 2.1
Average Depths and Total Areas of the Four Major Ocean Basins

Ocean	AREA		AVERAGE DEPTH		
	Millions of km²	Millions of mi²	Meters	Feet	Deepest Place
Pacific	166.2	64.2	4,188	13,741	Marianas Trench, 10,994 m (36,070 ft)
Atlantic	86.5	33.4	3,736	12,258	Puerto Rico Trench, 8,605 m (28,233 ft)
Indian	73.4	28.3	3,872	12,704	Java Trench, 7,725 m (25,344 ft)
Arctic	9.5	3.7	1,330	4,364	Molloy Deep, 5,608 m (18,400 ft)

(a) Southern Ocean

(b) Arctic Ocean

Source: Bill Ober

FIGURE 2.2 (*a*) South polar view of the world. The major ocean basins can be seen as extensions of one interconnected world ocean. The ocean that surrounds Antarctica is often called the Southern Ocean. (*b*) North polar view of the world showing the partially enclosed Arctic Ocean.

Density is the mass of a substance per unit volume. Substances of low density will float on substances of higher density.

$$density = \frac{mass}{volume}$$

While the young Earth was molten, the densest material sank toward the center of the planet, while lighter materials floated toward the surface. The light surface material cooled into a thin crust. Eventually, the atmosphere and oceans began to form. If Earth had settled into orbit too far away from or too close to the sun, or our atmosphere had formed differently, the planet would be either so hot that all the water would have evaporated away or so cold that all Earth's water would be perpetually frozen. Fortunately for us, both our planet's orbit and its atmosphere allow liquid water, and therefore life as we know it, to exist.

Internal Structure The internal structure of Earth reflects the planet's early beginnings. As materials sank or floated according to their density, they formed layers (Fig. 2.3). The innermost layer, the **core,** is mostly iron. The pressure in the core is more than a million times that at Earth's surface, and the temperature is over 4,000 °C (7,200 °F). The core consists of a solid inner core and a liquid outer core. It is thought that swirling motions of the liquid material in the iron-rich outer core produce Earth's magnetic field.

The layer outside Earth's core is the **mantle.** Though most of the mantle is thought to be solid, it is very hot—near the melting point of the rocks. Because of this, much of the mantle slowly flows like a liquid, swirling and mixing over hundreds of millions of years.

The **crust** is the outermost, and therefore best-known, of Earth's layers. Compared with the deeper layers, it is extremely thin, like a rigid skin floating on top of the mantle. The composition and characteristics of the crust differ greatly between the oceans and the continents.

Earth is composed of three main layers: the iron-rich core, the semiplastic mantle, and the thin outer crust.

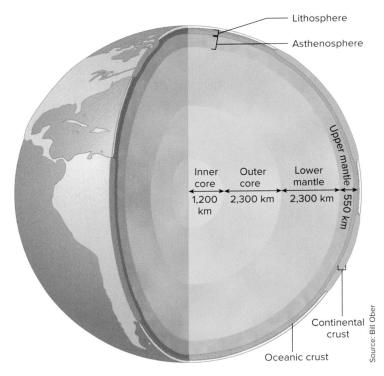

Source: Bill Ober

FIGURE 2.3 Earth's interior is divided into the core, mantle, and crust. The core is subdivided into the solid inner core and the liquid outer core. The mantle is also subdivided into upper and lower layers. The crust and uppermost layer of the mantle together form the lithosphere. Most of the upper mantle in the lithosphere is relatively solid, except for a fluid layer at the base of the lithosphere. The upper mantle below the lithosphere is relatively fluid, though not nearly as much as the lower layer of the lithosphere, and is called the asthenosphere. The thickness of the crust and lithosphere is exaggerated here, and the thickness of all layers varies from place to place.

Continental and Oceanic Crusts The geological distinction between ocean and continents results from physical and chemical differences in the rock that makes up the crust (Table 2.2). Oceanic crust, which makes up the sea floor, consists of a dark-colored mineral called **basalt** (see the photo at the beginning of the chapter).

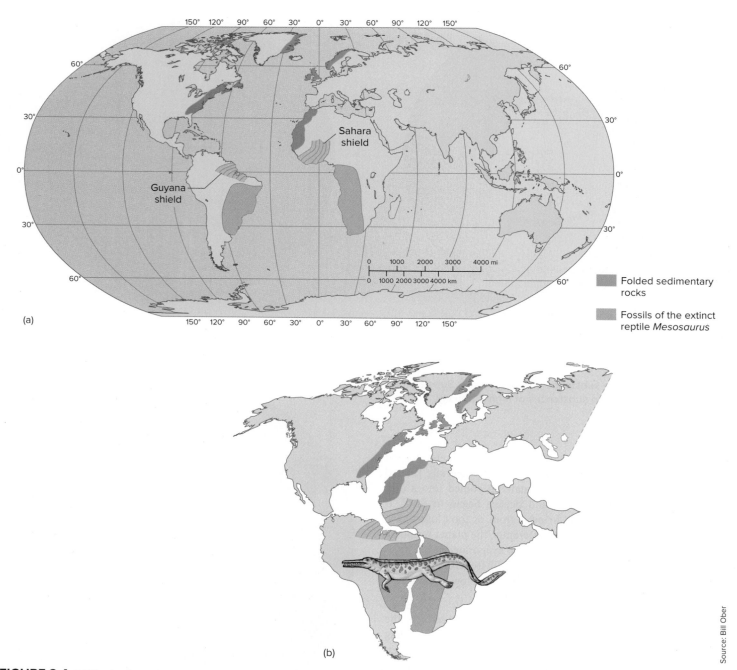

Source: Bill Ober

FIGURE 2.4 (*a*) The landmasses on opposite sides of the Atlantic have coastlines and geological features that (*b*) fit together like pieces of a puzzle.

Most continental rocks are of a general type called **granite,** which has a different chemical composition than basalt and is lighter in color. Oceanic crust is denser than continental crust. Ocean crust is also much thinner than continental crust, so it doesn't retain as much of the heat coming up from the mantle. The continents can be thought of as thick blocks of relatively warm, light crust floating on the mantle, much as icebergs float in water. Oceanic crust floats on the mantle, too, but because it is denser it doesn't float as high. That is why the continents lie high and dry above sea level and oceanic crust lies below sea level, covered with water.

Oceanic and continental crusts also differ in age. The oldest oceanic rocks are less than 200 million years old, quite young by geological standards. Continental rocks, on the other hand, can be as old as 3.8 billion years.

2.2 THE ORIGIN AND STRUCTURE OF THE OCEAN BASINS

We are surrounded by evidence of geological change—catastrophic earthquakes, volcanic eruptions, the erosion of river valleys, for example—but for centuries people somehow viewed the world as static and unchanging. People eventually understood that the face of the planet does indeed change. Today scientists recognize Earth as a planet of constant transformation where even the continents move.

Early Evidence of Continental Drift

As early as 1620 the English philosopher, writer, and politician Sir Francis Bacon noted that the coastlines on opposite sides of the Atlantic fit together like pieces of a puzzle (Fig. 2.4). It was

Table 2.2
Comparison of Continental and Oceanic Crusts

Oceanic Crust (Basalt)	Continental Crust (Granite)
Density about 3.0 g/cm³	Density about 2.7 g/cm³
Only about 5 km (3 mi) thick	20 to 50 km (12 to 30 mi) thick
Geologically young	Can be very old
Dark in color	Light in color
Rich in iron and magnesium	Rich in sodium, potassium, calcium, and aluminum

later suggested that the Western Hemisphere might once have been joined to Europe and Africa. Coal deposits and other geological formations, for example, match up on opposite sides of the Atlantic. Fossils collected on opposing coasts are also similar.

On the basis of such evidence, the German scientist Alfred Wegener proposed the first detailed hypothesis of **continental drift** in 1912. Wegener hypothesized that all the continents had once been joined in a single "supercontinent," which he named **Pangaea.** He thought Pangaea began breaking up into the continents we know today about 180 million years ago.

Plate Tectonics

Wegener's hypothesis was not widely accepted because he could not explain *how* the continents moved. Later proposals of continental drift also failed to provide a workable mechanism, but evidence continued to accumulate. In the late 1950s and the 1960s, scientists finally put the evidence together. They showed that the continents *do* drift, as part of larger plates in the process of **plate tectonics,** a phenomenon that involves the entire surface of our planet.

Discovery of the Mid-Ocean Ridge In the years after World War II, sonar allowed the first detailed surveys of large areas of the sea floor. These surveys resulted in the discovery of the **mid-ocean ridge** system, a continuous chain of submarine volcanic mountains that encircles the globe like seams on a baseball (Figs. 2.5 and 2.6). The mid-ocean ridge system is the largest geological feature on Earth. At regular intervals the mid-ocean ridge is displaced to one side or the other by cracks, or **faults,** in Earth's crust known as **transform faults.** Occasionally the submarine mountains of the ridge rise so high that they break the surface to form islands, such as Iceland and the Azores (Fig. 2.7).

The mid-ocean ridge in the Atlantic, called the **Mid-Atlantic Ridge,** runs right down the center of the Atlantic Ocean, parallel to the opposing coastlines. The ridge forms an inverted Y in the Indian Ocean and runs up the eastern side of the Pacific (Fig. 2.5). The main section of ridge in the Eastern Pacific is called the **East Pacific Rise.**

> The mid-ocean ridge system is a continuous, submarine range of volcanic mountains that runs through all the ocean basins.

Surveys of the sea floor also revealed the existence of a system of deep depressions in the sea floor called **trenches** (Fig. 2.5). Trenches are especially common in the Pacific. How they are formed is discussed in "Sea-Floor Spreading and Plate Tectonics," below.

Significance of the Mid-Ocean Ridge When the mid-ocean ridge system and trenches were discovered, geologists realized that geological activity is concentrated around them. Earthquakes are clustered at the ridge and volcanoes are associated with trenches (Fig. 2.8). Sea-floor rock at the ridge is very young and gets progressively older moving away from the ridge. Right at the ridge crest there is little, if any, **sediment,** loose material like sand and mud, that settles to the bottom, but sediment gets thicker and thicker at

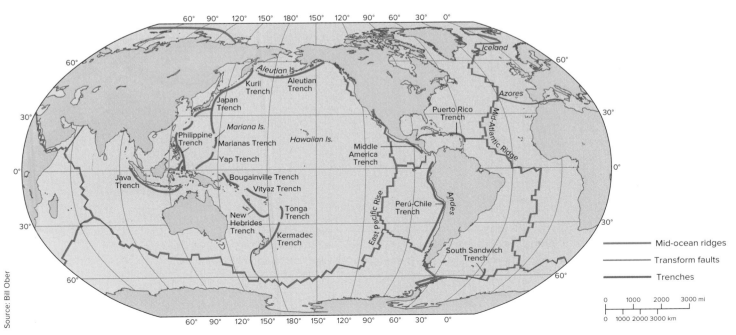

FIGURE 2.5 The major features of the sea floor. Compare this map with Figure 2.6.

FIGURE 2.6 The global sea floor. Dark blue areas are the deepest, and the trenches can be clearly seen. Orange areas are shallowest and include the mid-ocean ridges (compare to Fig. 2.5). The nearly straight lines are transform faults.

25

FIGURE 2.7 A portion of the Mid-Atlantic Ridge above the sea surface in Iceland.

Many rocks contain tiny magnetic particles. When the rock is molten these particles can move, and they act like tiny compasses, pointing north or south depending on whether Earth's field is normal or reversed. When the rocks cool, the particles are frozen in place and keep their orientation even when the magnetic field changes. It is therefore possible to tell the orientation of Earth's magnetic field at the time the rocks cooled.

Sea-floor rocks have patterns of magnetic bands, or "stripes," that run parallel to the mid-ocean ridge (Fig. 2.9). The bands represent zones in which the rocks alternate between normal and reversed magnetization. The bands are symmetric around the ridge, so that the pattern on one side of the ridge is a mirror image of the pattern on the other side. These bands, or **magnetic anomalies** (Fig. 2.10), could only have formed if the normally magnetized rock cooled from molten material at different times than the reverse-magnetized bands. The sea floor, then, was not formed all at once but in strips that parallel the mid-ocean ridge.

greater distance from the ridge. The deepest sediment, that resting directly on the sea-floor rock, gets older away from the ridge.

One of the most important findings came from studying the magnetism of rocks on the sea floor. Earth's magnetic field constantly "wobbles," moving around slightly so that the magnetic North Pole constantly moves around a little. In fact, in recent years this movement seems to be increasing. Every so often, however, the pole completely flips, so that instead of pointing north as it does today, a compass would point south. Our present magnetic field is arbitrarily called "normal," when the compass points south it is called a "reversal." In the recent past, geologically speaking, reversals have occurred about every 300,000 years, though the interval has varied, and there have been times in Earth's history when no reversals occurred over tens of millions of years. Reversals are thought to be caused by changes in the motion of material in the iron-rich outer core.

> Earthquakes and volcanoes are associated with the mid-ocean ridge. The sediments are thicker and the rock of the actual sea floor is older the farther they are from the ridge. Bands of rock alternating between normal and reversed magnetism parallel the ridge.

Creation of the Sea Floor The discovery of magnetic anomalies tied together the other evidence into an understanding of plate tectonics. The jump from observations of the sea floor and mid-ocean ridges to the theory of plate tectonics is a good example of the use of **induction** in science.

Huge slabs of oceanic crust separate at mid-ocean ridges, creating cracks in the crust called **rifts.** When a rift occurs it releases some of the pressure on the underlying mantle, like removing the cap from a bottle of soft drink. The reduced pressure allows hot mantle material to melt and rise up through the rift. The ascending

FIGURE 2.8 The world distribution of earthquakes and volcanoes. Compare these with the locations of mid-ocean ridges and trenches shown in Figure 2.5.

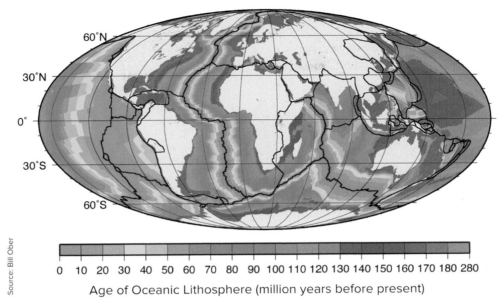

Source: Bill Ober

0 10 20 30 40 50 60 70 80 90 100 110 120 130 140 150 160 170 180 280

Age of Oceanic Lithosphere (million years before present)

FIGURE 2.9 Examination of the age of sea-floor rocks reveals stripes that parallel the mid-ocean ridges (shown as black lines). The youngest crust (red) is found nearest the ridge, and the oldest (blue) the farthest away. The alternating bands can be correlated to rocks with normal and reversed magnetization; the rocks right at the ridge crest have normal magnetization.

mantle material, or magma, pushes up the oceanic crust around the rift to form the mid-ocean ridge (Fig. 2.10). When this molten material reaches Earth's surface, it cools and solidifies to form new oceanic crust (see the photo at the beginning of the chapter). The process repeats itself as the sea floor continues to move away from the mid-ocean ridge. The entire process of the sea floor moving away from the mid-ocean ridges to create new sea floor is called **sea-floor spreading** (see Fig. 2.10), and the ridges are also called spreading centers.

Sea-floor spreading explains many features of the mid-ocean ridge. Right at the ridge crest the crust is new and has not had time to accumulate sediment. As the crust moves away from the ridge it ages and sediment builds up. This explains why the sediment gets thicker and the rocks get older moving away from the ridge. Sea-floor spreading also explains the pattern of magnetic stripes. As new sea floor is created, it "freezes" the magnetic field prevailing at the time and preserves that magnetization as it moves away from the ridge. Eventually Earth's magnetic field reverses, starting a new stripe.

Sea-Floor Spreading and Plate Tectonics Sea-floor spreading is only part of the story of plate tectonics. Earth's surface is covered by a fairly rigid layer composed of the crust and the uppermost part of the mantle. This layer, averaging about 100 km (60 mi) thick, is called the **lithosphere,** meaning "rock sphere" (see Fig. 2.3). The lithosphere is broken into a number of plates called **lithospheric plates** or **tectonic plates** (Fig. 2.11). Different plates contain continental crust, oceanic crust, or both. The lithosphere floats on a denser, more plastic layer of the upper mantle called the **asthenosphere** with a thin (in geological terms) layer of unusually fluid mantle material in between. While the crust, mantle, and core are distinguished by their chemical composition, the distinction between the lithosphere and the asthenosphere is based on how easily the rock flows.

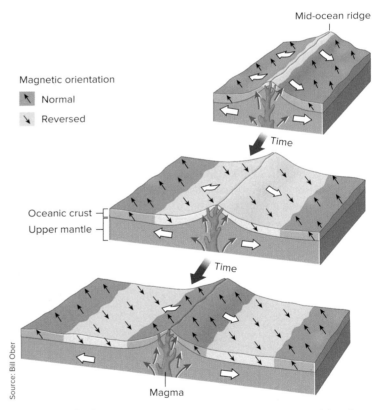

Magnetic orientation

↗ Normal

↘ Reversed

Mid-ocean ridge

Time

Oceanic crust

Upper mantle

Time

Source: Bill Ober

Magma

FIGURE 2.10 Cross section of the sea floor at a mid-ocean ridge showing the mechanism of sea-floor spreading. As the sea floor moves away from the rift, molten material rises from the mantle and cools to form new sea floor. When the rocks cool, they "freeze" whatever magnetic orientation, normal or reversed, is present at the time. The entire floor of the ocean was created at the mid-ocean ridge in this manner.

Induction The development of a generalized conclusion from a series of individual observations.

• 1.2, The Scientific Method

FIGURE 2.11 The division of Earth's surface into lithospheric plates. Some areas are not fully understood, and there are some small plates not shown here. Compare this map with those in Figures 2.5 and 2.8.

Earth's surface is broken up into a number of plates. These plates, composed of the crust and the top part of the mantle, make up the lithosphere. The plates are about 100 km (60 mi) thick.

Mid-ocean ridges form the edges of many plates. Here, the lithospheric plates move apart and new sea floor—that is, new oceanic lithosphere—is created. If the plate includes a block of continental crust, the continent is carried along with the plate as it moves away from the ridge. This is the mechanism of continental drift. The plates spread at around 2 to 18 cm (0.8 to 7 in) per year. For comparison, human fingernails grow at about 6 cm (2.4 in) per year. The spreading rate varies from place to place and over time.

As new lithosphere is created, old lithosphere is destroyed somewhere else. Otherwise, Earth would have to constantly expand to make room for new lithosphere. Lithosphere is destroyed at trenches, another main type of plate boundary. A trench is formed when two plates collide and one of the plates dips below the other and sinks back down into the mantle (Figs. 2.12 and 2.13). This downward movement of the plate into the mantle is called **subduction,** and trenches are also called **subduction zones.**

As the plate sinks, it weakens under the heat and pressure of the mantle and begins to break up, causing earthquakes. Eventually the plate gets so hot it melts. Some of the molten material rises back to the surface to form volcanoes. The rest continues to sink into the mantle. Some of this material is probably recycled eventually, rising again to the lithosphere millions of years later.

FIGURE 2.12 Some trenches are formed by the collision of continental and oceanic plates. Here, the Nazca Plate dips under the South American Plate. Earthquakes are produced as the plate descends into the mantle. Less dense material from the sinking plate rises to the surface as it melts, creating the volcanic Andes (see Figs. 2.5, 2.6, and 2.8).

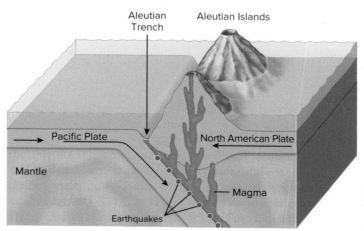

FIGURE 2.13 Trenches can also be caused when two oceanic plates collide. The oceanic portion of the North American Plate has collided with the Pacific Plate. The Pacific Plate dipped below the North American Plate, but either of the two plates might have done so. Earthquakes are produced by the descending plate. The volcanoes associated with the trench produced the Aleutian Island arc (see Figs. 2.5, 2.6, and 2.8).

EYE ON SCIENCE

Box 2.1 Life Below the Sea Floor

You might expect that the deepest-living organisms inhabit the deepest ocean trenches. In fact, life extends deeper—much deeper—than that. Single-celled organisms like bacteria live not only on, but *in* the sea floor, inhabiting deep layers of sediment and even the rocks of the crust. Rich communities of microbes live more than 3 km (1.9 mi) below the sea floor and probably extend to at least 10 km (6.2 mi). They live by **chemosynthesis**, using chemical energy in the rocks. Similar organisms abound on newly formed crust that has just cooled from magma erupting at mid-ocean ridges.

To study this "deep biosphere," scientists drill deep into Earth's crust. The drilling, of course, disturbs the microbial communities, but, using ROVs, scientists can install sea-floor observatories over the drill holes that can last a decade. These observatories allow the microbial communities to return to normal and can then make measurements, collect samples, and perform experiments.

This is a relatively new field of research because the tools required, such as ROVs, sea-floor observatories, and genetic bio-technologies, have only recently become available.

In a classic example of how scientific discoveries raise more questions, it appears that some 20 types of microbe occur in the deep crust all over the globe. How they came to be so widely distributed is a mystery.

Until recently microbes were the only life known from deep below the sea floor, but all those microbes are a food source so it is not surprising that worms that appear to feed on deep-Earth microbes were recently discovered up to 3.6 km (2.2 mi) deep in the crust.

Microbes on and below the sea floor not only support food chains but also alter the crust itself, breaking down some minerals and forming new ones. Geologists think that about two-thirds of the 4,300 minerals in Earth's crust would never have formed if

not for marine microbes. **Photosynthesis** by microbes has had an even greater impact than chemosynthesis. Photosynthesis produces the oxygen in Earth's atmosphere, and for billions of years microbes dominated oxygen production on Earth. Oxygen has been critical to the formation of minerals in Earth's crust, since most contain oxygen and are believed not to exist elsewhere in the solar system, where oxygen is not available. In particular, oxygen and energy produced by marine microbes are probably responsible for the formation of granite, the dominant mineral type in continental crust. There is no sign of granite in the rest of the solar system. The production of granite led to the formation and stabilization of the continents. Thus, we may be indebted to primordial marine microbes for the very rocks under our feet.

For more information, explore the links provided in the Marine Biology *Online Learning Center.*

At trenches, a lithospheric plate descends into the mantle, where it breaks up and melts. This process, called subduction, produces earthquakes and volcanoes.

The collision that produces a trench can be either between an oceanic plate and a continent or between two oceanic plates. When an oceanic plate collides with a continent, it is always the oceanic plate that descends into the mantle. The continental block is less dense than the oceanic plate and floats on top. That is why very old rocks are only found on continents: oceanic crust is continually destroyed at trenches and never gets old by geological standards. Continental crust, on the other hand, is not destroyed in trenches and can last for billions of years.

When oceanic and continental plates collide, continental volcanoes develop behind the trench. These volcanoes may form coastal mountain ranges. The Andes on the Pacific coast of South America are a good example (Fig. 2.12).

The oceanic plate lifts the edge of the continent slightly when it slides down under the continent. As the slab of cold lithosphere sinks deeper in the mantle, however, it tends to drag the interior of the continent down with it. The central part of the continent subsides, sometimes so much that seawater floods in to form shallow seas. After tens of millions of years the continent breaks free of the sinking plate and floats back up to its normal elevation, and the shallow sea disappears. This probably happened in North America when a huge slab of oceanic lithosphere called the Farallon Plate slid under

the west coast. That explains why Denver, Colorado, the "mile-high city," is surrounded by rocks formed from marine sediments.

When two oceanic plates collide, one of the plates dips beneath the other to form the trench. Again the trench is associated with earthquakes and volcanoes (Figs. 2.13 and 2.14). The volcanoes may rise from the sea floor to create chains of volcanic islands. As viewed on a map, trenches are curved because of Earth's spherical shape. The volcanic island chains associated with the trenches follow the trenches' curvature and are called **island arcs.** Examples include the Aleutian and Mariana islands (see Figs. 2.5 and 2.6).

Occasionally two continental plates collide. Because of the relatively low density of continental crust, both plates float and neither is subducted. Therefore, no trench is formed. Instead, the two continental blocks push against each other with such tremendous force that the continents become "welded" together. The force is eventually too much for the rocks, which buckle and fold. The huge folds form mountain ranges. The Himalayas, for example, were formed when India collided with the rest of Asia (see "The Geological History of the Earth," above).

Chemosynthesis The use by microbes of energy contained in inorganic chemicals rather than sunlight to make organic matter.

• 5.2, Prokaryotes; Table 5.1

Photosynthesis

$CO_2 + H_2O + $ Sun energy $\rightarrow$ organic matter $+ O_2$
(glucose)

• 4.1, The Ingredients of Life

M.E. Yount/USGS

FIGURE 2.14 Mount Veniaminof, an active volcano on the Alaska Peninsula. Geologically, the Alaska Peninsula is part of the Aleutian Island chain that has formed behind the Aleutian Trench (see Figs. 2.5 and 2.13).

There is a third type of plate boundary in addition to trenches and mid-ocean ridges. Sometimes two plates slide past each other, neither creating nor destroying lithosphere. This type of plate boundary is called a **shear boundary.** In the crack, or fault, where the two plates move past each other there is immense friction between the plates. This friction prevents the plates from sliding smoothly. Instead they lock, and stress builds up until the plates suddenly break free and slip, causing an earthquake. The San Andreas Fault in California is the largest and most famous example of a shear boundary (Fig. 2.15).

Geologists once thought the most likely explanation for what makes the plates move was **convection,** in which heat from Earth's core causes the mantle to swirl like thick soup heating in a saucepan. They thought the convection currents carried the overlying plates along like icebergs in a current (Fig. 2.16). Mantle convection, however, probably plays only a small part in plate motion. The main cause of plate motion is that as oceanic lithosphere ages and cools, it becomes denser. Eventually it sinks into the mantle, forming a trench and pulling the rest of the plate along behind it. This "slab pull" causes the plates to separate at the mid-ocean ridge, allowing fresh magma to well up from the mantle. The fluid layer at the base of the lithosphere may help "lubricate" this motion. Though not the main driver of plate movement as once thought, the upwelling of mantle at the ridge may help push the plates apart.

Earth's Geological History

Earth's surface has undergone dramatic alterations. The continents have been carried long distances by the moving sea floor, the ocean basins have changed in size and shape, and new oceans have been born.

Continental Drift and the Changing Oceans About 200 million years ago all the continents were joined in the supercontinent Pangaea, just as Wegener proposed. Antarctica was in approximately the same place it is today, but all the other continents were

in different positions (Fig. 2.17*a*). India was attached to Antarctica and Africa rather than to Eurasia as it is now.

Pangaea was surrounded by a single, vast ocean called **Panthalassa.** Panthalassa, which covered all the rest of the planet, was the ancestor of the modern Pacific Ocean. A relatively shallow sea, the **Tethys Sea,** separated Eurasia from Africa. The Tethys Sea, the precursor of the present-day Mediterranean, was home to many of the world's shallow-water organisms. Another indentation in the coast of Pangaea, the Sinus Borealis, was to become the Arctic Ocean. Before Pangaea began to break up, there was no sign of the modern Atlantic or Indian oceans.

About 180 million years ago, a rift appeared between North America and the combined continents of South America and Africa (Fig. 2.17*b*). This was the beginning of the Mid-Atlantic Ridge, and its formation marked the birth of the North Atlantic Ocean. Pangaea was now separated into two large continents. One was **Laurasia,** composed of what is now North America and Eurasia. South America, Africa, Antarctica, India, and Australia made up the southern continent of **Gondwana.**

At around the same time another rift began to split up Gondwana, marking the beginning of the Indian Ocean. South America and Africa began to move to the northeast, and India, separated from the other continents, began to move north.

Some 135 million years ago the South Atlantic was born when a new rift occurred between South America and Africa (Fig. 2.17*c*). This rift eventually joined the mid-ocean ridge in the North Atlantic to form a single mid-ocean ridge. As the Atlantic Ocean grew, the Americas were carried away from Eurasia and Africa. To make room for the new sea floor produced in the Atlantic, the Pacific Ocean—the descendant of Panthalassa—steadily shrank. The Atlantic is still growing, and the Pacific shrinking.

The Y-shaped ridge that produced the Indian Ocean gradually extended to separate Australia from Antarctica (Fig. 2.17*d*). The base of the inverted Y extended into the African continent, forming the Red Sea, which is actually a young ocean. India continued to move north faster and faster, reaching speeds of up to 20 cm/yr (8 in/yr) before colliding with Asia (Fig. 2.17*e*) to create the Himalayas. The Tethys Sea closed up and disappeared as Africa, and then India moved up into Asia. Most of the organisms that once lived in the Tethys Sea are now known only as fossils, although the descendants of a few species still live in the Caspian, Black, and Mediterranean seas.

The continents were once united in a single supercontinent called Pangaea that began to break up about 180 million years ago. The continents have since moved to their present positions.

The breakup of Pangaea to form today's continents is only the most recent turn of a continuing cycle. For hundreds of millions of years the continents have been adrift. They alternately collide and re-form into larger landmasses, only to break up and drift apart again.

Kip Evans/Alamy Stock Photo

FIGURE 2.15 Aerial view of a section of the San Andreas fault on the Carrizo Plain in central California.

The Record in the Sediments We have seen how the increase in sediment thickness away from mid-ocean ridges gave a clue to how plate tectonics works. Marine sediments provide a wealth of other information about Earth's past. The type of sediment on the sea floor often reflects conditions in the ocean above. By studying sediments that were deposited in the past, oceanographers have learned a great deal about the history of our planet.

Most marine sediments are of two basic types. The first is **lithogenous sediment,** which is derived from the physical and chemical breakdown, or **weathering,** of rocks, mostly on the continents. Coarse sediments, which consist of relatively large particles, tend to sink to the bottom rapidly rather than being carried out to sea by currents (see "The Shifting Sediments," in 11.2). Coarse lithogenous sediments, therefore, are usually deposited near the edges of the continents. Finer material sinks much more slowly and is carried far out to sea by currents. Some is even transported as dust

by the wind. The most common lithogenous sediment on the open ocean floor is a fine sediment called **red clay.**

The second major type of marine sediment, **biogenous sediment,** consists of the skeletons and shells of marine organisms, including **diatoms, radiolarians, foraminiferans,** and **coccolithophorids.** Some biogenous sediments are composed of the mineral **calcium carbonate ($CaCO_3$).** This type of sediment is called **calcareous ooze.** The other type of biogenous sediment is made of **silica (SiO_2),** which is similar to glass. It is called **siliceous ooze.**

The two most abundant types of marine sediment are lithogenous sediment, which comes from the weathering of rocks on land, and biogenous sediment, which is composed of the remains of marine organisms. Biogenous sediment is primarily either of calcium carbonate or silica.

Though large fossils like whale bones and shark teeth can be found, most of the organisms that produce biogenous sediments are microscopic or nearly so. Such sediment particles are sometimes called **microfossils,** since each particle represents the preserved remains of a dead organism (Fig. 2.18). Microfossils reveal the organisms that lived in the ocean in the past. Some of these organisms are known to prefer cold or warm water, so microfossils also give clues to ancient ocean temperatures. Ocean temperatures are determined by Earth's climate and ocean currents.

Earth's past climate can also be determined by the chemical composition of the microfossils. Various methods including **carbon dating,** a procedure in which the ratios of different atomic forms, or **isotopes,** of carbon are measured, can be used to determine the age of microfossils. It is also possible to tell the temperature of the water in which the organisms lived by measuring the ratios of magnesium (Mg) to calcium (Ca) or of different isotopes of oxygen in the microfossils. Thus, microfossils preserve a detailed record of Earth's climate history. This record isn't always easy to read, but it is supplemented by other information. The ratio of the elements

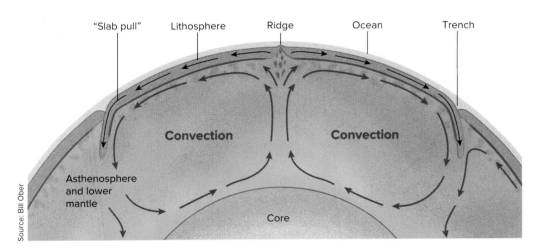

Source: Bill Ober

FIGURE 2.16 The movement of lithospheric plates was long thought to be driven by large-scale convection currents in the asthenosphere and lower mantle, caused by heat from Earth's core. Today, the prevailing hypothesis is that the plates move mainly because of slab pull, in which old, cold, and dense lithosphere sinks into the mantle and pulls the rest of the plate behind it. It may be this sinking cold rock rather than heat from the core that stirs the mantle. A layer of relatively fluid material at the base of the lithosphere may help the plates slide more easily.

Diatoms Single-celled algae with a shell, or test, made of silica.
• 5.3, Unicellular Algae; Figure 5.6

Coccolithophorids Single-celled algae covered with plates made of calcium carbonate.
• 5.3, Unicellular Algae; Figure 5.10

Foraminiferans (Forams) Protozoans, often microscopic, with a calcium carbonate test.
• 5.3, Unicellular Algae; Figure 5.11

Radiolarians Single-celled protozoans with a test made of silica.
• 5.3, Unicellular Algae; Figure 5.12

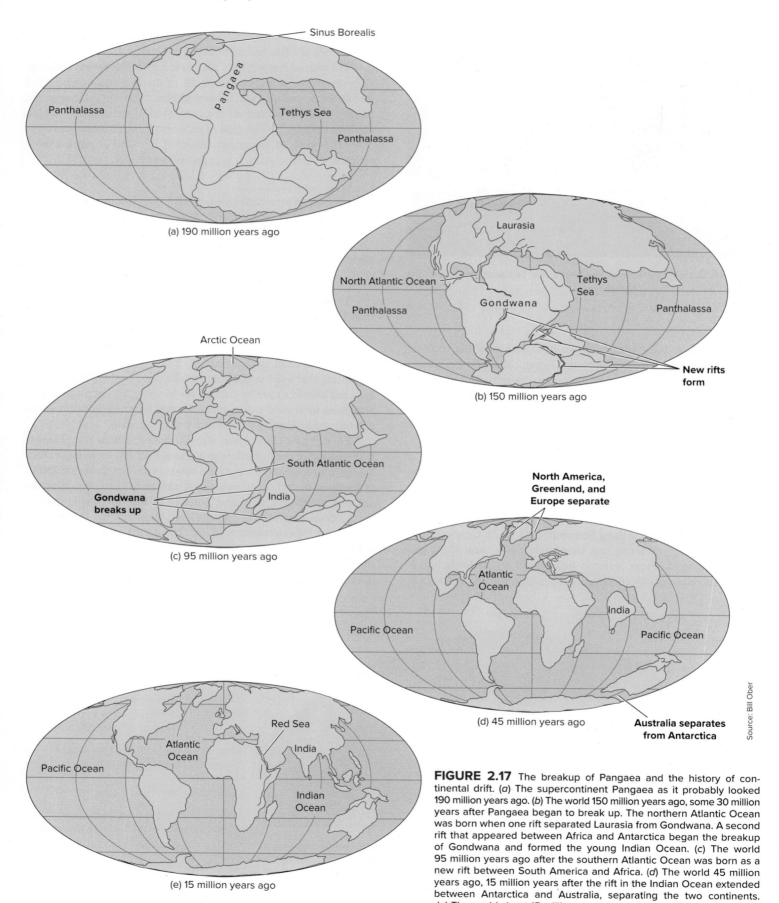

(a) 190 million years ago

(b) 150 million years ago

(c) 95 million years ago

(d) 45 million years ago

(e) 15 million years ago

FIGURE 2.17 The breakup of Pangaea and the history of continental drift. (*a*) The supercontinent Pangaea as it probably looked 190 million years ago. (*b*) The world 150 million years ago, some 30 million years after Pangaea began to break up. The northern Atlantic Ocean was born when one rift separated Laurasia from Gondwana. A second rift that appeared between Africa and Antarctica began the breakup of Gondwana and formed the young Indian Ocean. (*c*) The world 95 million years ago after the southern Atlantic Ocean was born as a new rift between South America and Africa. (*d*) The world 45 million years ago, 15 million years after the rift in the Indian Ocean extended between Antarctica and Australia, separating the two continents. (*e*) The world about 15 million years ago.

Source: Bill Ober

N-2-s/Shutterstock

FIGURE 2.18 The fossilized tests of several species of foraminiferans.

strontium (Sr) and calcium in ancient coral skeletons, for example, also records past ocean temperatures. Ice cores from polar areas like Greenland and Antarctica also preserve a record of past temperatures, as well as samples of the ancient atmosphere in the form of tiny bubbles trapped in the ice. These and other studies are providing an increasingly detailed picture of Earth's past climate (see Special Report, Climate Change).

Climate and Changes in Sea Level Earth's climate has fluctuated rhythmically through much of its history, alternating between warm, or **interglacial,** periods and cold periods, or **ice ages** (Fig. 2.19). We are currently in an interglacial period. During ice ages, great glaciers build up on the continents. Because large amounts of water are trapped as ice instead of flowing to the sea in rivers, there is less water in the ocean. Thus, sea level falls during ice ages.

The **Pleistocene Epoch,** which began 2.6 million years ago, was the last major period of glaciation. During the Pleistocene a series of ice ages was interspersed by brief warm periods of melting. The peak of the last ice age occurred about 18,000 years ago, when vast ice sheets as thick as 3 km (2 mi) covered much of North America and Europe. Sea level was about 130 m (425 ft) lower than it is today.

Sea level falls during ice ages because water is trapped in ice on the continents. The last major ice age was about 18,000 years ago.

Sea level continues to rise, though the rate of melting slowed during the past 3,000 years until about 150 years ago. Without human influence, Earth would be entering another ice age. Our impact on the atmosphere, however, has intensified the **greenhouse effect,** the retention of heat in the lower atmosphere as a result of an increase in carbon dioxide and other gases (see Special Report, Climate Change). Global temperatures and glacial melting are now increasing rapidly, and sea level is projected to continue rising for at least the next century. The loss of ice is also causing Earth's crust to warp slightly.

2.3 THE GEOLOGICAL PROVINCES OF THE OCEAN

The structure of the ocean floor is dominated by plate tectonics. Because this is a global process, the major features of the sea floor are quite similar from place to place around the world. The sea floor is divided into two main regions: the **continental margins,** which represent the submerged edges of the continents, and the deep-sea floor itself.

Continental Margins

The continental margins are the boundaries between continental and oceanic crust. Most sediments from the continents settle to the bottom soon after entering the sea and accumulate on the continental margins, where sediment deposits may be up to 10 km (6 mi) thick. Continental margins generally consist of a shallow, gently sloping **continental shelf,** a steeper **continental slope,** and another gently sloping region, the **continental rise,** at the base of the continental slope (Fig. 2.20).

The Continental Shelf The shallowest part of the continental margin is the continental shelf. Though they make up only about 8% of the ocean's sea floor, continental shelves are the biologically richest part of the ocean, with the most life and the best fishing. The shelf is composed of continental crust and is really just the edge of the continent that presently happens to be under water.

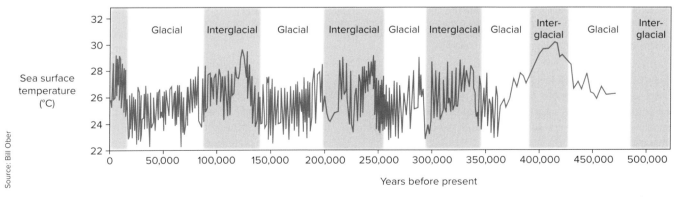

Source: Bill Ober

FIGURE 2.19 A history of Earth's climate over the past half-million years as determined from foraminiferan microfossils. The red line shows the average sea surface temperature in the equatorial Pacific Ocean as determined from the magnesium-to-calcium ratio in the microfossils. The white and blue bands indicate major glacial and interglacial periods, respectively, recorded in oxygen isotope ratios. Shifts between ice ages and interglacial periods involve relatively small changes in average temperature.

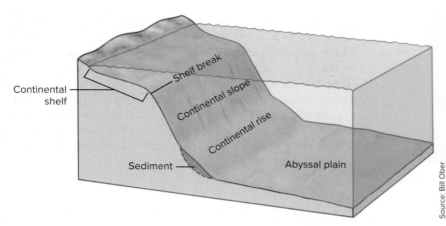

Source: Bill Ober

FIGURE 2.20 An idealized continental margin consists of a continental shelf, continental slope, and a continental rise. Seaward of the continental rise lies the deep-sea floor or abyssal plain. These basic features vary from place to place.

usually occurs at depths of 120 to 200 m (400 to 600 ft) but can be as deep as 400 m (1,300 ft). The precise edge is difficult to define but is of more than academic interest because, under international law, countries have the right to control the resources on their adjacent continental shelves. Recently there has been intense interest in detailed mapping of the continental shelves in the Arctic Ocean, because shrinking Arctic sea ice due to global warming is set to give countries, including Russia, the United States, and Canada, unprecedented access to oil and other Arctic seabed resources—if they can claim them.

The Continental Slope The continental slope is the closest thing to the exact edge of the continent. It begins at the shelf break and descends to the deep-sea floor. Submarine canyons beginning on the continental shelf cut across the continental slope to its base at a depth of 3,000 to 5,000 m (10,000 to 16,500 ft; Fig. 2.22). These canyons channel sediments from the continental shelf to the deep sea.

The Continental Rise Sediment moving down a submarine canyon accumulates at the canyon's base in a deposit called a **deep-sea fan**, similar to a river delta. Adjacent deep-sea fans may merge to form the continental rise. The rise consists of a thick layer of sediment piled up on the sea floor. Sediment may also be carried along the base of the slope by currents, extending the continental rise away from the deep-sea fans.

Continental margins have three main parts. The continental shelf is the submerged part of the continent and is almost flat. The relatively steep continental slope is the actual edge of the continent. The continental rise is formed by sediments building up on the sea floor at the base of the continental slope.

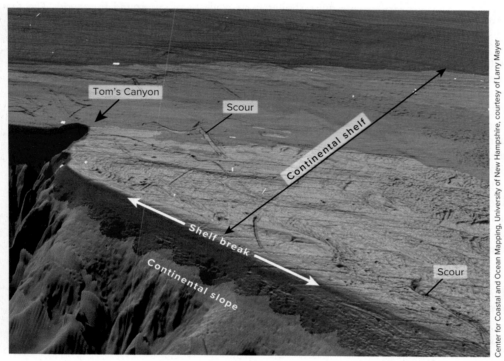

Center for Coastal and Ocean Mapping, University of New Hampshire, courtesy of Larry Mayer

FIGURE 2.21 A section of the continental shelf (upper right) off Atlantic City, New Jersey, approximately 30 km (19 mi) wide. The white arrows indicate the shelf break. The red arrow shows the head of a submarine canyon called Tom's Canyon. The linear marks on the shelf are iceberg scours made during the last ice age. This image was created with a sophisticated form of sonar known as multibeam sonar. The steepness of the continental slope is exaggerated.

During past times of low sea level, in fact, most of the continental shelves were exposed. At these times, rivers and glaciers flowed across the continental shelves and eroded deep canyons. When sea level rose, these canyons were submerged and gave rise to much larger **submarine canyons.**

The continental shelf extends outward at a gentle slope that in most places would be too gradual to see with the naked eye. The shelf varies in width from less than 1 km (0.6 mi) on the Pacific coast of South America and other places to more than 750 km (470 mi) on the Arctic coast of Siberia. The continental shelf ends at the **shelf break,** where the slope abruptly gets steeper (Fig. 2.21). The shelf break

Active and Passive Margins The nature of the continental margin, and therefore of coastal biological habitats, depends to a large extent on the plate tectonic processes occurring in the region. The continent of South America provides a good example of the relationship between the continental margin and plate tectonics (Fig. 2.23). The South American Plate (see Fig. 2.11) consists of both the continent itself and Atlantic sea floor created by the Mid-Atlantic Ridge. South America is carried westward with the plate as new sea floor is created at the ridge. The west coast of South America is colliding with the Nazca Plate, leading to the creation of a trench (see Figs. 2.5 and 2.12). Trenches are zones of intense geological activity, including earthquakes and volcanoes, so this type of continental margin is called an **active margin.** The west coast of North America also has a type of active margin, but it is more complex than that of South America.

South America's east coast, on the other hand, is not a boundary between plates and is therefore relatively inactive geologically. The continental margin here can be thought of as the trailing edge left when South America separated from Africa. This type of margin is called a **passive margin.** Passive margins typically have flat coastal plains (Fig. 2.24), wide shelves, and relatively gradual continental slopes. Because there are no tectonic processes to remove it, sediment accumulates at the base of the continental slope. Passive margins therefore usually have a thick continental rise.

Active continental margins have narrow shelves, steep slopes, and little or no continental rise. Passive margins have wide shelves, relatively gentle slopes, and a well-developed rise.

Deep-Ocean Basins

Most of the deep-sea floor lies at a depth of 3,000 to 5,000 m (10,000 to 16,500 ft), averaging about 4,000 m (13,000 ft). The deep-sea floor, or **abyssal plain,** rises at a very gentle slope of less than 1° toward the mid-ocean ridge. Though relatively flat, it often has submarine channels, low **abyssal hills,** plateaus, rises, and other features. The abyssal plain is also dotted with volcanic islands and submarine volcanoes called **seamounts.** Distinctive flat-topped seamounts called **guyots** are common in parts of the Pacific. Guyots and many other seamounts were once islands, but are now several hundred meters beneath the sea surface because the lithosphere has sunk into the mantle under the weight of the island, and also because sea level has risen. The abyssal plain and seamounts support a tremendous variety of marine life (see Box 16.2, "Biodiversity in the Deep Sea").

FIGURE 2.22 Multibeam sonar image of the continental margin off California. Numerous submarine canyons cut across the continental shelf and down the continental slope to the deep-sea floor. The largest is Monterey Canyon, which extends nearly to the shore at Monterey Bay (arrow).

As the colliding plate descends into the trench, some of the sediment gets scraped off, folded, and "plastered" onto the continental margin. The edge of the continent is lifted by the oceanic plate passing below (see "Sea-Floor Spreading and Plate Tectonics," above), and the coast is built up by volcanoes. These processes give active margins steep, rocky shorelines, narrow continental shelves, and steep continental slopes. Because the sediments at the base of the continental slope are either carried down into the trench or scraped onto the continent, active margins usually lack a well-developed continental rise.

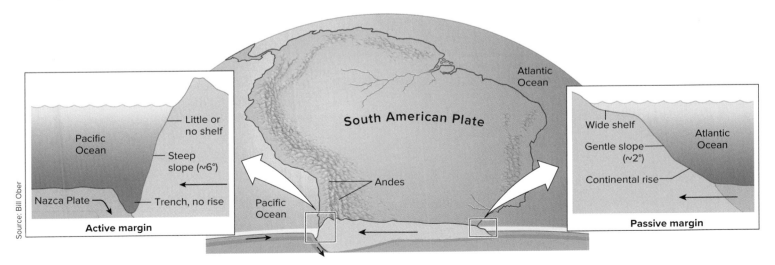

FIGURE 2.23 The opposite sides of South America have very different continental margins. The leading edge, or west coast, is colliding with the Nazca Plate. It has a narrow shelf and steep slope, and a trench rather than a continental rise. The trailing edge—that is, the Atlantic coast—has a wide shelf, a relatively gentle continental slope, and a well-developed continental rise. The steepness of all the slopes is exaggerated for illustrative purposes. Compare this with the map in Figure 2.5.

Box 2.2 The Hawaiian Islands, Hot Spots, and Mantle Plumes

Siberia

Alaska

Canada

Meiji Seamount
(70 million years)

Kaua'i (3.8–5.6 million years)

O'ahu (2.2–3.3 million years)

Moloka'i (1.3–1.8 million years)

Maui (less than 1 million years)

Hawai'i (0.8 million years to present)

Lō'ihi (submarine; present)

Emperor Seamounts

— 55–60 million years

— 50 million years

— 47 million years

Hawaiian Ridge

Midway Island
(25 million years)

Hawaiian
Islands

Moving lithospheric plate

Oceanic
crust

Asthenosphere

Volcanoes

Stationary
hot spot

Source: Bill Ober

The Emperor Seamounts and Hawaiian Island chain.

The Hawaiian Islands are part of a chain of volcanoes called the Hawaiian Ridge, which continues in a string of seamounts called the Emperor Seamount chain. The volcanoes get progressively older along the chain. A young submarine volcano called Lō'ihi lies southeast of the island of Hawai'i, the youngest Hawaiian island, and could grow into a new island. Hawai'i began forming less than a million years ago and is still erupting. Much of the island is bare volcanic rock too young to have eroded or for vegetation to grow. Kaua'i, at more than 5 million years old, is the oldest of the main Hawaiian Islands. It is densely vegetated, and erosion has produced steep, jagged cliffs. The remaining islands and seamounts of the chain continue to get older moving to the northwest. Midway Island, about two-thirds of the way up the Hawaiian Ridge, is about 25 million

FIGURE 2.24 The barrier islands, sand dunes, sandbars, and lagoons on the coast of southern Cape Cod, Massachusetts, are typical of passive margins.

Steve Dunwell/Getty Images

At trenches, where the plate descends into the mantle, the sea floor slopes steeply downward. Trenches are the deepest parts of the world ocean. The Mariana Trench in the western Pacific is the deepest place of all, at 10,994 m (36,070 ft) deep.

The Mid-Ocean Ridge and Hydrothermal Vents

The mid-ocean ridge itself is an environment that is unique in the ocean. As noted previously, the ridge is formed when material rising from the mantle pushes up the oceanic crust. Right at the center of the ridge, however, the plates are pulling apart. This leaves a great gap or depression known as the **central rift valley**. The floor and sides of the valley are riddled with crevices and fractures. Seawater seeps down through these cracks until it

Pele's house: volcanic eruption at Kīlauea, Hawai'i. A major eruption in 2018 wiped out surrounding houses and other infrastructure.

years old. Meiji Seamount, at the northernmost end, is 70 million years old.

This pattern was caused by a "hot spot" where a plume of hot magma rises from deep in the mantle to erupt in volcanic activity. As the Pacific Plate moves over the stationary hot spot, new eruptions of magma break out at a different places, producing the line of volcanoes.

Geologists long thought that the bend between the Hawaiian Ridge and Emperor Seamounts occurred when the Pacific Plate changed direction. Recent evidence, however, is that the Hawaiian hot spot wasn't always stationary but instead drifted to the south under the Emperor chain, with plate movement adding an easterly tilt. Then an ancient plate near east Asia slid completely into the mantle and off Earth's surface. This blocked the movement of the hot spot, and plate movement over the now-stationary

hot spot resulted in the more east-west alignment of the Hawaiian Ridge.

The ancient Hawaiians understood that their islands were formed by volcanoes, that the eroded, forested Kaua'i was the oldest of the islands, and the still-erupting Hawai'i the youngest. Hawaiian tradition is that Pele, the Goddess of Fire, originally lived on Kaua'i but was repeatedly attacked by the Goddess of the Sea, her sister, and progressively moved to younger islands until reaching her present home, the Kīlauea Volcano on Hawai'i. This explanation is a remarkable parallel for the modern Geological understanding of hot spots.

There are 50 or so other hot spots around the world, mostly under oceanic plates. Hot spots are credited for other island-seamount chains in the Pacific Ocean; the Gilbert and Tokelau chains even have bends like the Hawaiian-Emperor chain. Hot spots under mid-ocean ridges rather than moving plates are thought to have created islands or groups of islands rather than chains. Examples include Iceland, the Azores, and the Galápagos Islands. There are also a few hot spots beneath continents. The most famous is responsible for the geysers and bubbling pools of Yellowstone and a line of progressively older volcanoes to the northwest. Geologists hypothesize that even larger masses of hot magma called superplumes rise from deep in the mantle, lifting up great areas of lithosphere. A superplume

is thought to have uplifted a vast plateau region in southern Africa, for example. There is recent evidence that at least some of these plumes are not as hot as previously thought.

The role of hot spots and mantle plumes in creating the Hawaiian Islands and other features of the global ocean has been somewhat controversial, with some geologists even arguing that hot spots and plumes don't exist at all. New studies supported by new technology, however, have provided more and more evidence for hot spots and plumes, and the "hot-spot skeptics" are a shrinking minority. This is the power of science: evidence rules and good scientists revise their views as new information comes in even it means reversing a previously held opinion.

The formation of the Hawaiian Islands by a hot spot explains an unusual feature of the Hawaiian Islands. About a quarter of the shallow-water fish species and one-fifth of shallow-water molluscs there are endemic, meaning they are found nowhere else. This is one of the highest rates of marine endemism anywhere, but even the oldest island, Kaua'i, at only 5 million years old, is far too young for so many unique species to have evolved there. These species probably originated on much older islands in the chain. Like Pele, these species moved to new islands as they formed, ensuring their survival when the old islands eventually sank to become seamounts.

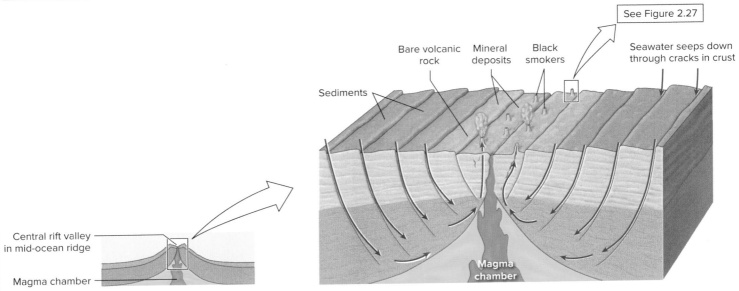

FIGURE 2.25 Cross section of a mid-ocean ridge showing how seawater seeps down through cracks in the crust, is heated, and reemerges in underwater hot springs.

FIGURE 2.26 Colorful red and white tubeworms grow around a black smoker on the Juan de Fuca Ridge, a section of mid-ocean ridge offshore of Oregon and Washington. Black smokers are common in hydrothermal vent areas. The black "smoke," actually composed of mineral particles, rises because the water emerging from the black smoker is much warmer than the surrounding water.

Verena Tunnicliffe, University of Victoria

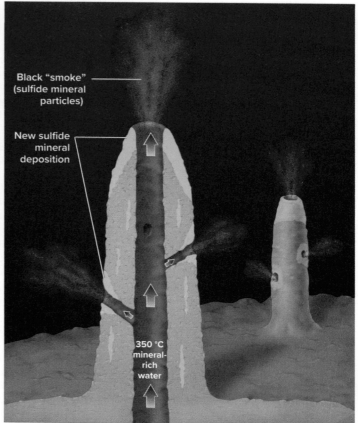

Black "smoke" (sulfide mineral particles)

New sulfide mineral deposition

350 °C mineral-rich water

Source: Bill Ober

FIGURE 2.27 Cross-section of a black smoker. Minerals are deposited as a precipitate when hot, mineral-laden water emerging from the rift zone meets the cold ocean water. Over time these mineral deposits build up the chimney of the black smoker.

gets heated to very high temperatures by the hot mantle (Fig. 2.25). The heated water then forces its way back up through the crust and emerges in **hydrothermal vents,** or deep-sea hot springs.

The water coming from many hydrothermal vents is warm, perhaps 10 to 20 °C (50 to 68 °F), much warmer than the surrounding water (see "Thermohaline Circulation and the Great Ocean Conveyor" in 3.2). At some vents, however, the water is blisteringly hot, up to 350 °C (660 °F). The water is so hot that when scientists first tried to measure its temperature the thermometer they were using started to melt! To take accurate readings, they had to return with a specially designed thermometer.

As the hot water seeps through cracks in Earth's crust, it dissolves a variety of minerals, mainly **sulfides.** When the mineral-laden hot water emerges at the vent, it mixes with the surrounding cold water and rapidly cools. This causes many of the minerals to solidify, forming mineral deposits around the vents. **Black smokers** (Figs. 2.26 and 2.27) are chimney-like structures that progressively build up around a vent as the minerals solidify. The "smoke" is actually a dense cloud of mineral particles. Vents can also produce "white smokers," "snowblowers," or even "blue smokers" depending on the minerals released and other factors.

When hydrothermal activity was first discovered it was thought to be confined to mid-ocean ridges. Hydrothermal vents, complete with black smokers and other mineral deposits, have since been

found behind trenches. They result from the same volcanic activity that creates island arcs (see "Sea-Floor Spreading and Plate Tectonics," above). Relatively cool (40 to 75 °C, or 105 to 170 °F) vents have also been discovered near, but not at, mid-ocean ridges. These vents produce chimneys of carbonate rather than sulfide minerals and are caused by chemical reactions between seawater and newly formed oceanic crust rather than by volcanic activity. One such chimney rises 60 m (200 ft) above the sea floor, making it the tallest hydrothermal vent known.

Deep-sea hot springs are of great interest not only to geologists but also to biologists. The discovery of unexpectedly rich marine life around hydrothermal vents was one of the most exciting finds in the history of marine biology. These organisms are discussed in Chapter 16 (see 16.4).

Interactive Exploration

McGraw-Hill Connect® is a great place to check your understanding of chapter material. Visit **www.mcgrawhillconnect.com** for access to interactive chapter summaries, chapter quizzing, and more! Further enhance your knowledge with videoclips and weblinks to chapter-related material.

Critical Thinking

1. Plate tectonics works today in the same way as in the past. Can you project the future positions of the continents by looking at a map of their present positions and the positions of the mid-ocean ridges (see Fig. 2.5)? Which oceans are growing and which are shrinking? Where will new oceans form?
2. Why are most oceanic trenches found in the Pacific Ocean?
3. Scientists who study forms of marine life that lived more than 200 million years ago usually obtain fossils not from the sea floor, but from areas that were once under sea and have been uplifted onto the continents. Why?
4. What are some of the major pieces of evidence for the theory of plate tectonics? How does the theory explain these observations?

For Further Reading

Some of the recommended reading may be available online. Look for live links on the *Marine Biology* Online Learning Center.

General Interest

Battersby, S., 2010. The great meltdown. *New Scientist*, vol. 206, no. 2761, 22 May 2010. Ocean sediments, corals, ice cores, and even stalagmites from Chinese caves provide clues to what starts and ends ice ages.

Betz, E., 2016. Drilling to doomsday. *Discover*, vol. 37, no. 8, October, pp. 42–47. Drilling deep into Earth's crust to learn about the giant asteroid impact that ended the age of the dinosaurs.

Brooks, M., 2019. What's wrong with the north pole? *New Scientist*, vol. 242, no. 3236, pp. 34–37. The pole is headed for Siberia. The cause lies in Earth's core.

Cameron, J., 2013. Deep sea challenge. *National Geographic*, vol. 223, no. 6, June, pp. 46–59. Filmmaker and explorer James Cameron designed a vehicle that descended to the deepest spot on Earth in the Marianas Trench.

Coltice, N., 2021. The chicken, the egg, and plate tectonics. *American Scientists*, vol. 109, pp. 166–173. Modern supercomputers and sophisticated models are providing new insights into plate tectonics.

Dacey, J., 2021. Earth's past on ice. *New Scientist*, vol. 250, no. 3339, 19 June. Glacial ice preserves critical information about Earth's past, but glaciers are melting fast.

Fountain, H., 2017. *The great quake*. Penguin Random House. One of the authors was a boy in Anchorage, Alaska, when the second-strongest earthquake on record (magnitude 9.2) struck southern Alaska. The quake caused massive geological changes and killed 130 people in the sparsely populated state. This book tells the human story as well as how studies of the quake changed our understanding of geology.

Gramling, C., 2021. Shaking up Earth. *Science News*, vol. 199, no. 1, pp. 16–22. Why the discovery of plate tectonics was among the greatest scientific advances of the 20th century, changing our understanding of our planet and the rest of the cosmos.

Kerr, R. A., 2013. The deep earth machine is coming together. *Science*, vol. 340, no. 6128, 5 April, pp. 22–24. Geologists are steadily learning more about how Earth's crust, mantle, and core interact.

Molnar, P., 2015. Plate tectonics: A very short introduction. Oxford University Press. An excellent summary of the basic processes and history of plate tectonics.

Perrottet, T., 2011. Into the volcano. *Smithsonian*, vol. 42, no. 8, December, pp. 40–51. An account of a descent into the crater of the Haleakala Volcano on the Hawaiian island of Maui, with an accompanying article on the Hawaiian hot spot.

Unknown earth. Our planet's seven biggest mysteries. *New Scientist*, vol. 199, no. 2675, 27 September 2008, pp. 28–35. "How come Earth got all the good stuff?" "Where did life come from?" These and five other big questions are answered by *New Scientist* writers.

Tarlach, G., 2019. Plate tectonics: our planet's big, slow square dance. *Discover*, vol. 40, no. 6, July/August, pp. 40–43. Plate tectonics in a nutshell.

Vince, G., 2011. United plates of America. *New Scientist*, vol. 210, no. 2816, 11 June, pp. 44–47. The collision of North and South America and the rise of the Isthmus of Panamá had profound effects on the oceans and climate.

Witze, A., 2012. Intraplate quakes signal tectonic breakup. *Science News*, vol. 182, no. 8, October 20, pp. 5–6. Giant earthquakes in the eastern Indian Ocean indicate that one large plate is breaking in two.

Witze, A., 2017. Supercontinent superpuzzle. *Science News*, vol. 191, no. 1, 21 January, pp. 18–21. Geologists piece together the supercontinents that came before Pangaea.

In Depth

Berger, W. H., 2011. Geologist at sea: aspects of ocean history. *Annual Review of Marine Science*, vol. 3, pp. 1–34.

Coulson, S., M. Lubeck, J. X. Mitrovica, et al., 2021. The global fingerprint of modern ice-mass loss on 3-D crustal motion. *Geophysical Research Letters*, https://doi.org/10.1029/2021GL095477.

Fernandez-Arcaya, U., E. Ramirez-Llodra, J. Aguzzi et al., 2017. Ecological role of submarine canyons and need for canyon conservation: a review. *Frontiers in Marine Science*, vol. 4, article 5, pp. 1–26.

Holder, R. M., D. R. Viete, M. Brown, and T. E. Johnson, 2019. Metamorphism and the evolution of plate tectonics. *Nature*, vol. 572, no. 7769, pp. 378–381.

Kawakatsu, H. and H. Utada, 2017. Seismic and electrical signatures of the lithosphere-asthenosphere system of the normal oceanic mantle. *Annual Review of Earth and Planetary Sciences*, vol. 45, pp. 139–167.

Li, Z. H. S., 2018. Tethyan changes shaped aquatic diversification. *Biological Reviews*, vol. 93, pp. 874–896.

Mann, M. E., 2007. Climate over the past two millennia. *Annual Review of Earth and Planetary Sciences*, vol. 35, pp. 111–136.

Müller, R. D., M. Seton, S. Zahirovic, et al., 2016. Ocean basin evolution and global-scale plate reorganization events since Pangaea breakup. *Annual Review of Earth and Planetary Sciences*, vol. 44, pp. 107–138.

Norcutt, B. N., J. B. Sylvan, and K. J. Edwards, 2011. Microbial ecology of the dark ocean above, at, and below the seafloor. *Microbiology and Molecular Biology Reviews*, vol. 75, pp. 361–422.

Design elements: chapter opener (ocean wave) ©EpicStockMedia/Shutterstock, (blue Parrotfish) ©ivvv1975/Shutterstock; Eye on Science box ©Westend61/Getty Images; Evolutionary Perspective box ©vilainecrevette/123RF; end-of-chapter (beach): ©photoaraki.com/Getty Images

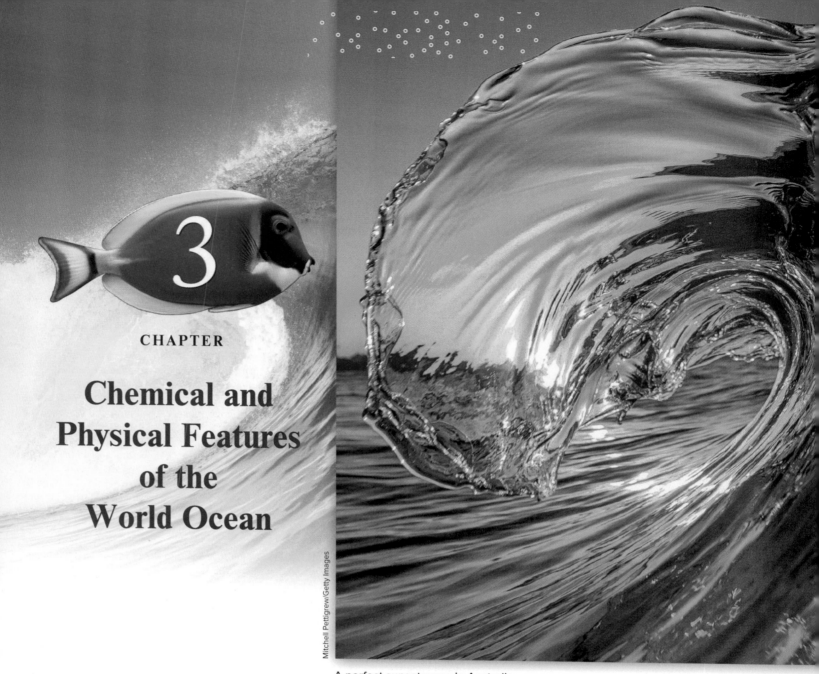

CHAPTER

Chemical and Physical Features of the World Ocean

Mitchell Pettigrew/Getty Images

A perfect sunset wave in Australia.

"Everybody talks about the weather, but nobody does anything about it." Often attributed to Mark Twain, this quote by Twain's collaborator, Charles Dudley Warner, expresses the plight of marine organisms as well as people. From the point of view of marine organisms, crashing waves, wind, tides, currents, salt, and other chemical and physical features of the ocean constitute the ocean's "weather."

Because marine organisms can't control the physical and chemical nature of their environment, they simply have to "grin and bear it"—that is, *adapt* to where they live—or live somewhere else. The organisms occur at a given place in the ocean and how they live largely depends on the prevailing physical and chemical conditions there. To understand the biology of marine organisms, therefore,

we must understand their environment. This chapter describes the chemistry and physics of the oceans in relation to life in the sea.

3.1 THE WATERS OF THE OCEAN

We think of water as commonplace because there is so much of it around us. From a cosmic perspective, though, water is not common at all. Earth is the only known planet with liquid water on its surface.

Even so, most of us never give water a second thought unless we're hot or thirsty. Water quenches our thirst because it makes up

40

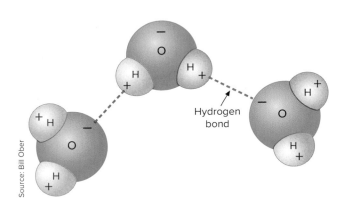

Source: Bill Ober

FIGURE 3.1 The different ends of water molecules have opposite electrical charges. The oxygen (O) end has a weak negative charge, while the hydrogen (H) end has a slight positive charge. Opposite charges attract each other like the opposite poles of a magnet, so the oxygen end of one molecule is attracted to the hydrogen end of neighboring molecules. These weak attractions between water molecules are known as hydrogen bonds.

most of our bodies. Marine organisms, too, are mostly water—80% or more in most cases, and in jellyfishes, or sea jellies, over 95%. Water not only fills the ocean, it makes life itself possible.

The Unique Nature of Pure Water

All matter is made of **atoms.** Only 118 known substances are composed of a single kind of atom; these are called **elements.** In all other substances two or more atoms are chemically combined into larger particles called **molecules.** Water molecules are made up of one oxygen atom, which is relatively large, and two hydrogen atoms, the smallest of all atoms. The oxygen and hydrogen atoms have weak, opposite charges that create electrical attractions, or **hydrogen bonds,** between adjacent water molecules (Fig. 3.1). Hydrogen bonds are much weaker than the bonds that hold the oxygen and the hydrogen atoms in the water molecule together, but they make water different from any other substance on Earth.

The Three States of Water Any substance can exist in three different states, or phases: solid, liquid, or gas. Water is the only substance that naturally occurs in all three states on Earth.

In liquid water, hydrogen bonds hold most of the molecules together in small groups (Fig. 3.2). The molecules are in constant motion, however, and because the hydrogen bonds are weak the groups constantly break apart and re-form. The higher the water temperature, the faster the molecules move. When a molecule moves fast enough it breaks free of all the hydrogen bonds and escapes from the liquid phase into the gaseous or vapor phase. This is the process of **evaporation.**

In water vapor, the molecules are not held together by hydrogen bonds. They are separate and much farther apart than in the liquid (Fig. 3.2). As temperature rises so does the evaporation rate, since the molecules move faster and more escape the hydrogen bonds. When the water gets hot enough, nearly all the bonds are broken and many molecules enter the vapor state at once: in other words, the water boils.

When liquid water cools, the molecules not only move slower, they pack closer together and take up less space, so that the volume of water decreases. Because the volume decreases without changing the mass, the amount of matter, the water gets **denser.** As seawater gets colder, therefore, it gets more dense. As we shall see, cold seawater tends to sink in the ocean. Freshwater also gets denser as it gets colder, but only down to a temperature of about 4 °C (39 °F). Below 4 °C freshwater gets *less* dense as it cools.

Water freezes when the molecules move so slowly that the hydrogen bonds take over, locking the molecules into a fixed, three-dimensional pattern known as a **crystal.** In ice crystals the molecules are farther apart than in liquid water, so water expands as it freezes. Because the same mass of water occupies more volume as ice than as liquid water, ice is less dense and floats. Water is extremely unusual in being less dense as a solid than a liquid, a property that is very important for aquatic organisms, both freshwater and marine. A floating layer of ice leaves liquid below, where organisms can live, and insulates it so it doesn't freeze. If ice were denser than liquid water, the ocean would freeze from the bottom up and be much less hospitable to life.

Seawater becomes denser as it cools, until it freezes. Ice is less dense than liquid water.

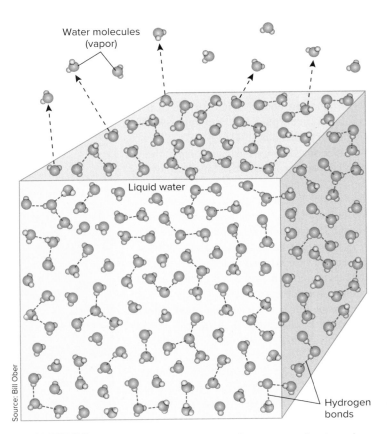

Source: Bill Ober

FIGURE 3.2 The molecules in liquid water form groups of various sizes held together by hydrogen bonds. The molecules move too rapidly to stay in place, so the groups constantly break up and re-form. Evaporation occurs when molecules break free of hydrogen bonds and enter the gaseous state. Molecules of water vapor are much farther apart than in the liquid state and are not held in groups by hydrogen bonds.

FIGURE 3.3 The molecular structure of water changes with temperature. In ice, hydrogen bonds hold the vibrating molecules in a hexagonal pattern. As heat is added, the ice warms up and the molecules vibrate more rapidly until they break free of the crystal structure, and the ice melts. While the ice is melting, added heat is absorbed by breaking hydrogen bonds, not by increasing the temperature. Once the ice is completely melted, added heat raises the temperature again. Some molecules gain enough speed to break free of all the bonds and evaporate. At 100 °C (212 °F) nearly all of the hydrogen bonds are broken and the water boils.

Heat and Water In ice, vibrating water molecules are held in place in the ice crystal by hydrogen bonds. The bonds must be broken before the molecules can begin to move around, which is what happens when ice melts (Fig. 3.3). Because of this, ice melts—or, moving in the opposite direction, freezes—at a much higher temperature than similar substances that do not form hydrogen bonds. If not for the hydrogen bonds, ice would melt at about −90 °C (−130 °F) instead of 0 °C (32 °F)!

Not only does ice melt at a comparatively high temperature, it absorbs a lot of heat when it melts. The amount of heat required to melt a substance is called its **latent heat of melting.** Water has a higher latent heat of melting than any other commonly occurring substance. The reverse is also true: A great deal of heat must be removed from liquid water to freeze it. It thus takes a long period of very cold weather before a body of water freezes.

In melting ice, added heat breaks more hydrogen bonds rather than increasing the speed of molecular motion, so the temperature of the ice–water mixture remains at a constant 0 °C (32 °F) until all the ice melts. That is why ice keeps drinks cold: Added heat goes into melting the ice, not raising the temperature.

Once all the ice has melted, added heat again makes the molecules move faster and so raises the water temperature. Some of the heat energy, however, still goes into breaking hydrogen bonds rather than increasing the speed of molecular motion. It therefore takes a lot of heat to raise the temperature. The amount of heat needed to raise a substance's temperature by a given amount, or its **heat capacity,** reflects how much heat the substance can store. Water has one of the highest heat capacities of any naturally occurring substance. Water's ability to absorb a lot of heat with a relatively small increase in temperature is why it is used as a coolant, in car engines for example. More importantly for marine organisms, water's high heat capacity means that most of them are not subjected to the rapid and sometimes drastic temperature changes that occur on land (Fig. 3.4).

Water also absorbs a lot of heat when it evaporates—that is, it has a high **latent heat of evaporation.** Again this is due to hydrogen bonds: Only the fastest-moving molecules, those with the most energy, can break the bonds to enter the gaseous phase. Because the fastest molecules leave the liquid phase, those left behind have a lower average velocity and therefore a lower temperature. This **evaporative cooling** is why evaporating perspiration cools our skin. Water's ability to absorb and release large amounts of heat is also why temperatures vary less near coasts than inland.

> Water has the highest latent heat of melting and evaporation and one of the highest heat capacities of any natural substance.

FIGURE 3.4 In the heat of the sun, this seaweed (*Hormosira banksii*) in New Zealand is beginning to shrivel. Shore organisms exposed to the air at low tide must endure much more extreme temperatures than those that stay submerged.

⊕ Sodium ion
⊖ Chloride ion
◍ Water molecule

Sodium ion

Chloride ion

FIGURE 3.5 In a crystal of table salt, or sodium chloride, the ions are bound by attractions between opposite charges. The charges on the ions are much stronger than the charges on a water molecule, so the bonds between ions are much stronger than hydrogen bonds. In water, the weakly charged water molecules are attracted to the charges on the ions, and they cluster around the ions. This weakens the bonds between ions, which separate, or dissociate.

Water as a Solvent Water can dissolve more things than any other natural substance and is often called the universal solvent. Water is especially good at dissolving **salts.** Salts are made up of particles with opposite electrical charges. Such electrically charged particles, which can be either single atoms or groups of atoms, are known as **ions.** For example, ordinary table salt, or sodium chloride ($NaCl$), consists of a positively charged sodium ion (Na^+) combined with a negatively charged chloride ion (Cl^-). The oppositely charged ions are joined by the same electrical attraction that creates hydrogen bonds between water molecules. Ions have much stronger electrical charges than the opposite ends of the water molecule, however, so these ionic bonds are much stronger than hydrogen bonds. If no water is present, the ions bind strongly together to form salt crystals (Fig. 3.5).

When a salt crystal is placed in water, the strongly charged ions attract the water molecules—with their weak charges—like iron filings to a magnet. A layer of water molecules surrounds each ion, insulating it from the surrounding ions (Fig. 3.5). This greatly weakens the ionic bonds that hold the salt crystal together. The ions pull apart, or **dissociate,** and the salt dissolves.

Seawater

The characteristics of seawater are due both to the nature of pure water and to the materials dissolved in it. Some substances dissolved in seawater are produced by the chemical **weathering** of rocks on land

and are carried to the sea by rivers (Fig. 3.6). Other materials come from Earth's interior. Most of these are released into the ocean at **hydrothermal vents** and fissures along the rift valley of the **mid-ocean ridges.** Some are released into the atmosphere from volcanoes and enter the ocean in rain and snow.

Salt Composition Seawater contains at least a little of almost everything, but most of the **solutes,** or dissolved materials, are made up of a surprisingly small group of ions. In fact, only six ions compose over 99% of the material dissolved in seawater (Table 3.1). Sodium and chloride account for about 85%, which is why seawater tastes like table salt.

When seawater evaporates, the ions are left behind and combine to form various salts. **Salinity** is the total amount of dissolved salt in seawater. Salinity was traditionally measured as the amount of salt left behind after seawater evaporated. If 35 grams of salt are left from evaporating 1,000 grams of seawater, for example, the seawater has a salinity of 35 parts per thousand, or 35‰.

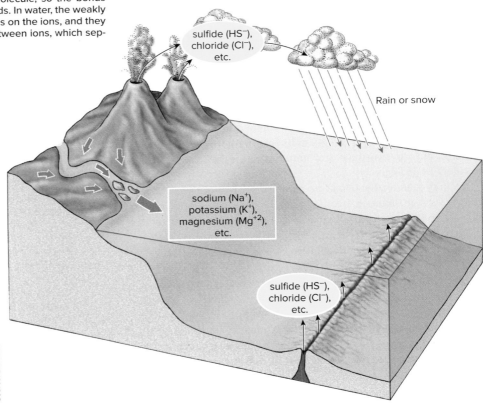

sulfide (HS^-), chloride (Cl^-), etc.

Rain or snow

sodium (Na^+), potassium (K^+), magnesium (Mg^{+2}), etc.

sulfide (HS^-), chloride (Cl^-), etc.

FIGURE 3.6 Not all ions in seawater enter the ocean at the same place. Positive ions like sodium and magnesium come mostly from the weathering of rocks and are carried to the sea by rivers. Negative ions like chloride and sulfide enter the ocean at hydrothermal vents and from volcanoes by way of precipitation. If the ocean was not thoroughly mixed, coastal water would have a relatively high proportion of sodium and magnesium. Deeper water, influenced by hydrothermal input, would be rich in chloride and sulfate, which is produced from sulfide. Actually, the proportions of ions do vary right near river mouths and hydrothermal vents, but most of the ocean is well mixed and the rule of constant proportions holds.

Hydrothermal Vents Undersea hot springs associated with mid-ocean ridges.
• 2.3, The Geological Provinces of the Ocean

Weathering The physical or chemical breakdown of rocks.
• 2.2, The Origin and Structure of the Ocean Basins

Table 3.1
The Composition of Seawater of 35‰ Salinity
Although the concentration varies slightly from place to place in the ocean, the percentage of total salinity of each ion remains constant.

Ion	Concentration‰	Percentage of Total Salinity
Chloride (Cl^-)	19.345	55.03
Sodium (Na^+)	10.752	30.59
Sulfate (SO_4^{-2})	2.701	7.68
Magnesium (Mg^{+2})	1.295	3.68
Calcium (Ca^{+2})	0.416	1.18
Potassium (K^+)	0.390	1.11
Bicarbonate (HCO_3^-)	0.145	0.41
Bromide (Br^-)	0.066	0.19
Borate ($H_2BO_3^-$)	0.027	0.08
Strontium (Sr^{+2})	0.013	0.04
Fluoride (F^-)	0.001	0.003
Other dissolved material	<0.001	<0.001

Today salinity is measured with electronic instruments. Because of their electrical charges, ions are good electrical conductors. The conductivity of seawater therefore reflects the salinity. Oceanographers express salinity determined from conductivity measurements in **practical salinity units (psu)** rather than parts per thousand, but the two units are numerically the same: 35 psu is equivalent to 35‰.

Salinity greatly affects marine organisms. Most of them die in freshwater. Even slight changes in salinity harm some. Many, especially those that live in river mouths or other places where salinity fluctuates markedly, have evolved specific mechanisms to cope with salinity changes (see "Regulation of Salt and Water Balance," in 4.3).

The chemist William Dittmar analyzed seawater samples from the *Challenger* expedition and found that the relative percentage of the major ions in seawater remained constant even though the total amount of salt varied from place to place. Chloride ion, for example, nearly always makes up 55.03% of however much salt is present. This principle is called the **rule of constant proportions.**

The rule of constant proportions states that the relative amounts of the various ions in seawater are always the same.

The proportions of different ions do in fact vary slightly, especially near the sources of different ions such as river mouths and hydrothermal vents (Fig. 3.6). In some places intense biological activity also affects ion ratios. Still, in the vast majority of the ocean the proportions remain remarkably constant. This indicates that the oceans are chemically well mixed and that ocean salinity varies almost entirely as a result of the addition or removal of pure water rather than the addition or removal of salts. If salinity varied by adding or removing any particular salt, then the relative amounts of the ions in the seawater would change. If magnesium chloride ($MgCl_2$) were added, for example, then the proportions of magnesium and chloride would go up. Although marine organisms are exposed to changes in total salinity, they rarely have to deal with changes in the ratios of the various ions. This makes it easier for them to control their internal salt and water balance.

Water is removed from the ocean primarily by evaporation and to a lesser extent by freezing. When seawater freezes, the ions are excluded from the forming ice. They are left behind in the unfrozen water, increasing its salinity, and the ice is almost pure water. That is why icebergs are not salty. Water is added by **precipitation—**rain and snow—and, on longer timescales, by melting glaciers and polar ice. Of course, rivers deliver large amounts of water to the ocean, but that is still from precipitation—on land.

The average salinity of the ocean is about 35 psu. The open ocean varies relatively little, between about 33 psu and 37 psu, depending mostly on the balance between evaporation and precipitation. Partially enclosed seas may have more extreme salinities. The Red Sea, for instance, is in a hot, dry region where evaporation predominates over precipitation, so it is very salty, about 40 psu. Near coasts or in enclosed basins, river runoff may have a strong effect. River runoff gives the Baltic Sea a typical salinity at the surface of only about 7 psu, for example.

The "other dissolved material" listed in Table 3.1 includes substances such as essential nutrients that, though only present in tiny amounts, are critically important to marine life. Compounds containing nitrogen (N), phosphorus (P), and iron (Fe) are particularly important and their availability determines the biological productivity of much of the oceans (see "The Importance of Nutrients," in 4.1 and "Nutrients," in 15.3).

Salinity, Temperature, and Density We have already seen that temperature greatly affects water's density. Salinity also influences seawater density: The saltier the water, the denser it is. The density of seawater therefore depends on both its temperature and its salinity.

The temperature and salinity of seawater determine its density: It gets denser as it gets saltier and colder.

Temperature in the open ocean varies between about −2 and +30 °C (28 and 86 °F). Temperatures below 0 °C (32 °F) are possible because saltwater freezes at a colder temperature than pure water. This is one reason that the ocean is less prone to freezing than lakes and rivers.

Temperature in the ocean varies more than salinity, so as a practical matter density is usually controlled more by temperature than salinity. There are exceptions, however, and both the temperature and salinity of ocean water need to be measured to determine the density.

Temperature and salinity can be measured by lowering specially designed bottles and thermometers on a wire to the desired depth (Fig. 3.7). Then a weight called a messenger is released to slide down the wire, triggering the bottles to snap shut and trap a water sample that can be analyzed. The thermometers are also triggered to "freeze" the temperature reading so that it doesn't change as the thermometer is retrieved.

A series of bottles can be attached to the cable to measure temperature and salinity, and therefore density, at several depths at once (Fig. 3.8). A graph showing the temperature at different depths in the ocean is called a temperature **profile.** A temperature

FIGURE 3.7 Niskin bottles are one of several types of water sampling bottles. The bottles are clamped to a cable and lowered to the desired depth with both ends open. A weight called a messenger is sent down from the surface, "tripping" the spring-loaded end caps, which then trap a sample of seawater in the bottle.

profile obtained from a given location can be thought of as showing the temperature in a vertical shaft of water, or **water column,** extending down from the surface. Profiles can also be plotted for salinity, density, or any other characteristic. In a profile the vertical axis appears "upside down," as shown in Figure 3.8.

> A profile is a plot that shows temperature, salinity, or any other characteristic of seawater at various depths in the water column.

Using bottles and thermometers is time-consuming, expensive, and only yields measurements at a few places down the water column. Today oceanographers use electronic sensors to quickly and accurately record salinity, temperature, and depth throughout the water column. Conductivity-temperature-depth meters (CTDs) are widely used in conjunction with other instruments (Fig. 3.9). Expendable bathythermographs (XBTs), which measure temperature but not salinity profiles, are even disposable.

Though temperature, salinity, and various other things can be measured electronically, many other measurements still require a water sample, so Niskin bottles, and nowadays more sophisticated devices, remain in use. These days, oceanographers usually mount all the open bottles on a single rack (Fig. 3.9) rather than stringing them along the wire. To collect samples from different depths, each bottle is closed at a different time while the rack is lowered. The rack is easier to use than a series of individual bottles.

Even with electronic instruments, measurements from ships can be made in only one place at a time. To study a large area, the ship has to steam from place to place. In the meantime, conditions might change because of currents or the weather. One alternative is to use a number of ships at once. This is expensive and not often done. Today marine scientists increasingly use automated instruments (see Box 1.1, "Observing the Ocean").

Satellites are now an indispensible way to get the big picture. With some important exceptions, they usually measure conditions only near the surface, but they give instantaneous coverage of a large area (Fig. 3.10). Furthermore, many satellites fly over the same part of the ocean at least once or twice a day, while others stay in place over a particular area taking constant measurements. This makes it possible to follow rapid changes in surface conditions.

Dissolved Gases There are gases as well as solid materials dissolved in seawater. For organisms the most important gases in the ocean are **oxygen (O_2),** **carbon dioxide (CO_2),** and **nitrogen (N_2).** All three are

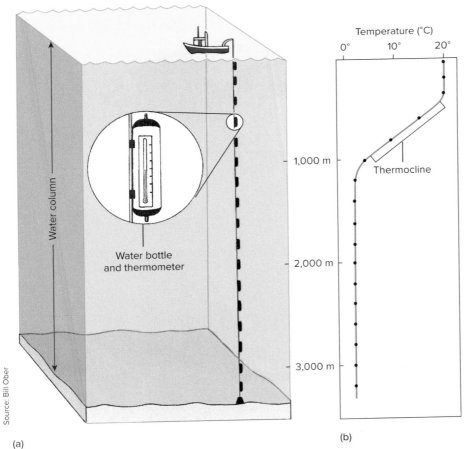

(a)

(b)

FIGURE 3.8 (*a*) Sampling bottles can be used to measure temperature and salinity at several depths at once. (*b*) The results are plotted on a graph, or profile, showing how temperature, salinity, or any other property varies with depth. This example shows a temperature profile. Temperature is measured only where the bottles are (dots) and the temperature between the bottles (red line) must be inferred. The zone in which the temperature rapidly declines with depth is called a thermocline.

> **Density** The mass of a given volume of a substance.
>
> $$density = \frac{mass}{volume}$$
>
> • 2.1, The Water Planet
>
> The *Challenger* expedition (1872–1876) marked the birth of modern oceanography.
>
> • 1.1, The Science of Marine Biology

(a)

Michael E. Huber

(b)

Michael E. Huber

FIGURE 3.9 (*a*) Instead of being hung on a wire individually, water sampling bottles (red arrow) are now usually mounted in a "rosette" to a single frame. A variety of electronic instruments (yellow arrows) that measure temperature, salinity, light, water clarity, and other factors can also be mounted on the frame, (*b*) which is then lowered through the water column. Many of the instruments provide real-time information to computers on the surface.

Mean Sea Surface Temperature (°C)

4 8 12 14 16 18 20 22 24 26 27 28 29

FIGURE 3.10 This image shows the temperature of the ocean surface derived from satellite data. The large patch of very warm (29.5 °C, 85.1 °F) water just north of the island of New Guinea (arrow) is called the Pacific Warm Pool. It contains the ocean's largest reservoir of heat and strongly influences the climate of the entire planet. During El Niño years, for example, the pool of warm water moves east to the central Pacific (see "The El Niño–Southern Oscillation," in 15.3).

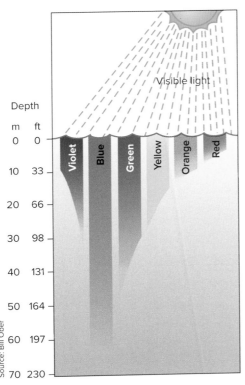

FIGURE 3.11 Different colors of light penetrate to different depths in the ocean. In clear ocean water shown here, blue light penetrates the deepest, red light the least. Coastal waters often contain materials that absorb blue light so that green penetrates deepest.

This makes the ocean critical to understanding the effects of human activities on Earth's climate (see When CO_2 dissolves in seawater, it makes the water slightly more acidic (see "Ocean Acidification: the Other CO_2 Problem," in Special Report: Our Changing Planet)).

Transparency One of the most biologically important properties of seawater is that it is relatively transparent, so sunlight can penetrate into the ocean. This is vital because photosynthetic organisms need light to grow. If seawater weren't transparent, there could be little photosynthesis in the sea, and only right at the surface.

Sunlight contains all the colors of the visible spectrum of light, which is seen in the rainbow, but not all colors penetrate seawater equally well. Clear ocean water is most transparent to blue light. Other colors are absorbed more than blue, so as depth increases more and more of these other colors are absorbed and soon only blue light remains (Fig. 3.11). Things that appear red on the surface look gray or black at depth because there is no red light to reflect off them to be seen (Fig. 3.12). At greater depths—about 1,000 m (3,300 ft) in the clearest water—even the blue light gets absorbed and there is only darkness.

The transparency of water is strongly affected by suspended and dissolved material (Fig. 3.13). Obviously, muddy water is not as clear as clean water. Rivers bring in large amounts of sediment, often making coastal waters muddy. Rivers also often bring in organic material that gives coastal waters a greenish tint and makes them less transparent. Large quantities of plankton, both near coasts and in the open ocean, also make the water green and reduce transparency.

in the atmosphere and dissolve in the ocean at the sea surface. Sometimes the reverse occurs and the sea surface releases gases to the atmosphere. This ocean–atmosphere **gas exchange** is critically important to organisms both on land and in the sea, as well as to Earth's climate, the global distribution of pollutants, and many other aspects of our planet.

Unlike solids, gases dissolve better in cold than warm water, so dissolved gas concentrations are higher in polar waters than in the tropics. Oxygen is not very soluble. The ocean contains between 0 and 8 ml of dissolved oxygen per liter of seawater, but more typically 4 to 6 ml/L. Air, by comparison, contains about 210 ml/L of oxygen, or 21% by volume. The amount of oxygen in the water is strongly affected by organisms through **photosynthesis** and **respiration.** Much of the oxygen produced by photosynthesis in the ocean is released to the atmosphere. The relatively low dissolved oxygen content makes seawater more susceptible than air to oxygen depletion by respiration (see "The Oxygen Minimum Zone," in 16.1).

CO_2 is much more soluble than oxygen because it reacts chemically when it dissolves. As a result, CO_2 makes up more than 80% of the dissolved gas in the ocean, compared to less than 0.04% of air, and the ocean stores more than 50 times as much CO_2 as the atmosphere.

(a) (b)

FIGURE 3.12 At a depth of 30 m (98 ft) only blue light remains, and under natural lighting (*a*) this sea star (*Thromidia catalai*) appears light blue, with the tips of the arms almost black. (*b*) An electronic flash reveals the sea star's true colors.

Photosynthesis
$CO_2 + H_2O$ + sun energy → organic matter + O_2
(glucose)

Respiration
organic matter + O_2 → $CO_2 + H_2O$ + energy
(glucose)

• 4.1, The Ingredients of Life

Ivan Hoermann/Shutterstock

FIGURE 3.13 Sophisticated electronic instruments like those shown in Figure 3.9 allow precise measurements of water clarity and light penetration. For surface waters, however, this simple instrument called a Secchi disk gives a surprisingly useful measurement of water clarity. The disk is slowly lowered to where it just ceases to be visible. The greater this depth, the clearer the water. In some places, Secchi disk measurements provide the longest available records of ocean clarity.

Pressure Another factor that changes dramatically with depth in the ocean is **pressure.** Organisms on land are under 1 **atmosphere** (14.7 pounds per square inch, or psi) of pressure at sea level—the weight of all the air above them. Marine organisms, however, are under the weight of water as well as the atmosphere. Since water is much denser than air, marine organisms are under much more pressure than those on land. The pressure increases dramatically with depth because the amount of water above gets greater (Fig. 3.14). With each 10 m (33 ft) of increased depth, another atmosphere of pressure is added.

As pressure increases, gases are compressed. Gas-filled structures inside organisms like air bladders, floats, and lungs shrink or collapse. This limits the depth range of many marine organisms. It also means that submarines and scientific instruments must be specially engineered to withstand pressure. This greatly increases the difficulty, expense, and sometimes the danger of studying the sea. The reverse effect also causes problems: Organisms that contain gas-filled structures are often injured when brought up from the deep (Fig. 3.15).

3.2 OCEAN CIRCULATION

The ocean never rests. Throughout its depths, currents move and mix ocean waters and transport heat, nutrients, pollutants, and organisms. Ocean circulation profoundly affects not only marine organisms and their habitats but also Earth's climate and therefore all habitats on land.

Surface Circulation

The wind drives the strongest ocean currents, which occur in the surface layer. Both wind and surface currents are ultimately driven by heat energy from the sun. Both surface currents and the wind are also influenced by what is known as the Coriolis effect.

Source: Bill Ober

Water depth	Total pressure		
	atm	bar	psi
0	1	1.0	14.7
10 m (33 ft)	2	2.0	29.4
20 m (66 ft)	3	3.0	44.1
30 m (98 ft)	4	4.1	58.8
40 m (131 ft)	5	5.1	73.5
50 m (164 ft)	6	6.1	88.2
60 m (197 ft)	7	7.1	102.9
70 m (230 ft)	8	8.1	117.6
80 m (262 ft)	9	9.1	132.3

FIGURE 3.14 The pressure at any place depends on the weight pressing down from above. At the sea surface or on land, only the atmosphere is above. Divers and marine organisms, however, are also under the weight of the water column. The deeper the diver goes, the more water presses down from above and the greater the pressure. As the pressure increases, flexible gas-filled structures like the red balloon are compressed. Pressure can be measured in atmospheres (atm), bars, pounds per square inch (psi), or other units.

The Coriolis Effect Because Earth is round and rotating, anything that moves over its surface appears to turn a little rather than moving in a straight line. This curving, or deflection, is called the **Coriolis effect** (Fig. 3.16). The Coriolis effect arises because Earth is round and rotating. Everywhere on Earth rotates once every 24 h. Earth's circumference is about 40,000 km (25,000 mi) so moves at about 1,650 km/h (1,040 mi/h) to make the rotation. A spot at, say, 2 m (6 ft) from the North Pole, only moves fraction of a kilometer per hour to make the rotation—you could easily walk around the Pole much faster than Earth turns.

When an object moves from the equator to the poles, it keeps its original momentum as it passes over Earth's surface, so viewed on a flat map it appears to curve. Imagine someone threw a ball straight at you as you drove by in a car. From their point of view, the ball would appear to go straight while you went past, but from yours, the ball would appear to curve and pass behind you.

FIGURE 3.15 Many fishes, like this longfin grouper (*Epinephelus quoyanus*), have an internal air sac called a swim bladder. If the fish is brought to the surface too quickly, the bladder blows up like a balloon because of the decreased pressure. This fish's swim bladder has expanded so much that it has pushed its stomach out of its mouth. Fish like this sometimes survive if the bladder is carefully punctured and the fish returned to the water, though there are often severe internal injuries.

The Coriolis effect is too slight to notice when you're walking along or driving a car, so we aren't usually aware of it. It is very important, however, for things like winds and ocean currents that move long distances. In the Northern Hemisphere the Coriolis effect always deflects things to the right. In the Southern Hemisphere, things are deflected to the left.

The Coriolis effect appears to deflect large-scale motions like winds and currents to the right in the Northern Hemisphere and to the left in the Southern Hemisphere.

Wind Patterns

The winds in our atmosphere are driven by heat energy from the sun. The Equator is warmer than the poles because most of the sun's energy is absorbed near the Equator. As solar energy heats the Equator, the air there becomes less dense and rises. Air from higher latitudes flows in to replace the rising equatorial air, creating wind (Fig. 3.17). The winds do not move straight toward the Equator but are bent by the Coriolis effect. These winds, called the **trade winds,** approach the Equator at an angle of about 45°. Over the ocean, where they are not affected by land, the trade winds are the steadiest winds on Earth.

Other winds are also driven by solar energy but are more variable than the trades. The **westerlies** lie at middle latitudes (Fig. 3.18) and move in the opposite direction to the trade winds. The high-latitude **polar easterlies** are the most variable winds of all.

Surface Currents

Friction on the ocean surface from the major wind fields of the atmosphere causes the sea surface to move, creating currents. All the major surface currents of the open ocean, in fact, are driven by the wind and ultimately by heat energy from the sun.

When pushed by the wind, the uppermost layer of surface water begins to move. Instead of going in the same direction as the wind, the surface current moves off at an angle of 45° because of the Coriolis effect (Fig. 3.19). This top layer pushes on the layer of water below, and again the Coriolis effect comes into play: The second layer moves not in the same direction as the top one, but slightly to the right, and slightly slower. This process passes down through the water column, each layer pushed by the layer above and pushing the one below, in a pattern called the **Ekman spiral** after the Swedish oceanographer who described it. The effect of the wind decreases with depth, so that progressively deeper layers move more and more slowly. Eventually, at a depth of a few hundred meters at most, the wind is not felt at all. The upper part of the water column that is affected by the wind is called the **Ekman layer.** Though each microlayer moves in a different direction, taken as a whole the Ekman layer moves at 90° from the wind direction. This process is called **Ekman transport.**

The Coriolis effect causes surface currents to move at 45° from the wind that drives them. Lower water layers move at progressively greater angles from the wind in a pattern called an Ekman spiral. This produces Ekman transport, in which the upper part of the water column moves perpendicular to the wind direction, to the right in the Northern Hemisphere and the left in the Southern Hemisphere.

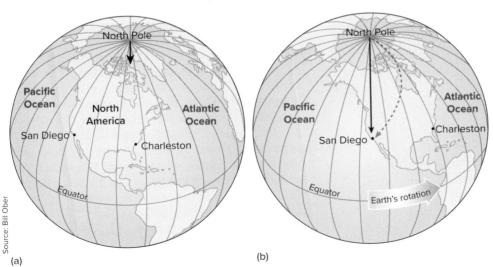

(a) (b)

FIGURE 3.16 The Coriolis effect. (*a*) Imagine someone fires a missile at Charleston, North Carolina, from the North Pole. As the missile takes 2½ h to reach Charleston (*b*) Earth rotates under the missile while it is in the air so that the missile ends up hitting San Diego, California. From space it is clear that the missile moved in a straight line (black arrows) and Earth rotated, but to an observer on Earth it looks like the missile curved (red arrow). The Coriolis effect would still apply if the missile was fired from east to west. Can you think of ways to explain this?

A comparison of wind and surface current patterns demonstrates the consequences of the Coriolis effect. While the

FIGURE 3.17 Air near the Equator is warmed by solar heating and rises. Air from higher latitudes moves in over Earth's surface to replace the rising air, creating wind. These winds, the trades, are deflected by the Coriolis effect and approach the Equator at an angle of about 45°.

Source: Bill Ober

FIGURE 3.19 When a steady wind blows over the sea surface, the uppermost layer moves at 45° from the wind direction. Each deeper layer moves farther to the right in the Northern Hemisphere, shown here, or to the left in the Southern Hemisphere. When the direction of the current at each depth is plotted, the result is a spiral, called the Ekman spiral. The net result of this process is that the affected layer of water, called the Ekman layer, is transported at right angles to the wind direction.

Source: Bill Ober

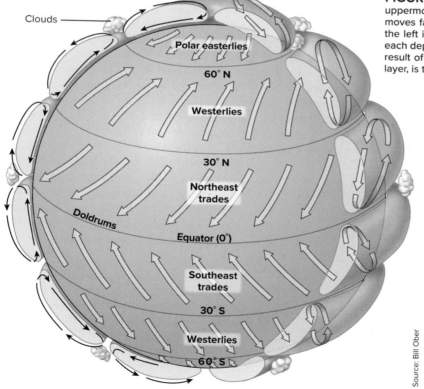

FIGURE 3.18 The major wind patterns on Earth are created by the rising of sun-warmed air and the sinking of cold air. The trade winds lie between about 30° north and south latitude and are the steadiest of all winds. The westerlies are found from about 30° to 60°, and above 60° lie the most variable winds, the polar easterlies. The transition zones or boundaries between these major wind belts have very light and changeable winds (see Box 3.1, "Tall Ships and Surface Currents"). The wind fields are pictured here as they would look on an imaginary water-covered Earth. In actuality, they are modified by the influence of the continents (see Fig. 3.20).

Source: Bill Ober

trade winds move toward the Equator, for example, the **equatorial currents** that these winds produce move parallel to the Equator (Fig. 3.20). Under the influence of the Coriolis effect, the wind-driven surface currents combine into huge, more or less circular systems called **gyres.**

Recall that water is particularly good at transporting heat because of its high heat capacity. The warm currents on the western sides of the gyres carry vast amounts of solar heat from the Equator to higher latitudes. Cold currents flow in the opposite direction on the eastern sides. Ocean currents thus act like a giant thermostat, warming the poles, cooling the tropics, and regulating the climate of our planet. Large-scale fluctuations in current patterns such as El Niño can dramatically affect weather around the world (see "The El Niño–Southern Oscillation," in 15.3).

The role of surface currents in transporting heat is reflected in sea-surface temperature (Fig. 3.21). Surface temperature is higher on the western sides of the oceans, where currents carry warm water away from the Equator, than on the eastern sides, where cold currents flow toward the Equator. Because of this, tropical organisms like corals extend into higher latitudes on the western sides (see "Conditions for Reef Growth," in 14.1 and Fig. 14.11).

Box 3.1 Tall Ships and Surface Currents

For purely practical reasons, winds and surface currents were among the first oceanic phenomena to be observed and documented. For centuries ships were at the mercy of the wind, and the names sailors gave to various areas reflected their knowledge of global wind patterns. Many of these names are still used. The trade winds got their name from the traders who relied on them during their voyages. The equatorial region where the winds are light and variable because of the rising air masses there (see Fig. 3.17) is called the doldrums. Winds are also variable at 30° north and south latitudes, where the trade winds and westerlies are moving apart (see Fig. 3.18). At these latitudes, sailors, becalmed and short of drinking water, sometimes had to throw their dying horses overboard. To this day these are known as the horse latitudes.

Sailors also knew about surface currents. A clever navigator could shorten a passage by weeks or months by riding favorable currents and avoiding unfavorable ones. In the fifteenth century, Portuguese sailors under the guidance of Prince Henry the Navigator made careful observations of currents along the west coast of Africa. Soon they were using their knowledge of these currents on their trading voyages. On the southbound journey, the ships sailed close to shore while in the Northern Hemisphere,

Outward voyage ⟶
Return voyage ⤏
Gyre currents ⟶

The route of early Portuguese ships on trading voyages to the west coast of Africa. The southbound route is shown by a solid line and the northward journey by a dotted line. The prevailing currents are indicated by red arrows.

riding the Canary Current. When they crossed the Equator they swung to the west to avoid the Benguela Current. On the voyage home, they took the opposite path, completing a figure eight.

Early mariners knew about other currents as well. Christopher Columbus noted the existence of the North Atlantic Equatorial Current on his third voyage to the Americas. While searching for the "Fountain of Youth" the Spaniard Juan Ponce de León described the Florida Current. In the Pacific, fishers recorded their knowledge of the Perú Current and the Kuroshio.

Even Ben Franklin has a place in this story. While serving as deputy colonial postmaster he noticed that mail ships routinely made the trip to Europe two weeks faster than they returned. Upon questioning seafarers he learned of the mighty Gulf Stream and asked his cousin, a sea captain, to sketch it on a nautical chart. Franklin developed the sketch into the first published chart of the Gulf Stream, which is remarkably accurate. He understood that the Gulf Stream is a vast river of warm water flowing through the cold waters of the surrounding Atlantic Ocean and instructed ships to stay in the warm water of the Gulf Stream when sailing east but to avoid it on the westward journey. Later, on voyages as emissary to England, Franklin regularly measured sea temperature and published his findings in a report about the Gulf Stream.

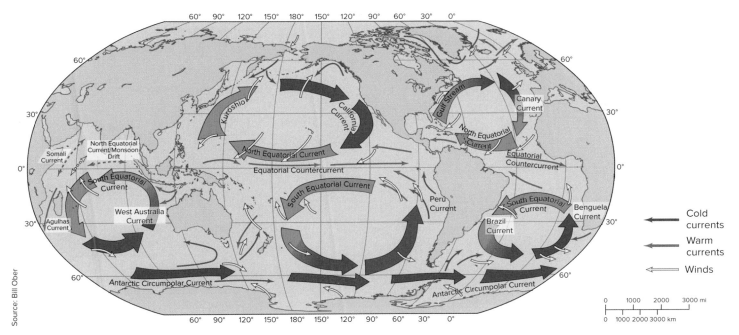

FIGURE 3.20 The major surface currents of the oceans. In the main ocean basins, the currents combine to form large circular systems called gyres.

Cold-loving organisms like kelps, on the other hand, occur closest to the Equator on the eastern sides (see "Kelp Communities," in 13.3 and Fig. 13.21).

Global wind patterns and the Coriolis effect produce gyres, large circular systems of surface currents. These currents regulate Earth's climate by transporting heat from tropical to polar regions and greatly affect the geographic distribution of organisms in the ocean.

The currents shown in Figure 3.20 are average patterns over large distances and a long time span. At a given place on a given day, the current is often different: Currents shift with the season and the weather. On the continental shelf, currents are strongly affected by the seabed, the shape of the coastline, and the tides (see 13.1).

Thermohaline Circulation and the Great Ocean Conveyor

The ocean is a three-dimensional habitat, and the major currents shown in Figure 3.20 reflect circulation only at the surface, not at greater depths. Over much of the ocean, surface waters are partially isolated from deeper waters by differences in density, which is why oceanographers painstakingly measure the two factors—temperature and salinity—that determine seawater density.

Because the densest water sinks, the ocean is usually layered, or **stratified,** with the densest water on the bottom and the least dense at the surface. This can be seen in typical profiles of salinity, temperature, and density (Fig. 3.22). Deep water is normally cold and dense, whereas the surface water is relatively warm and "light."

The water column in the ocean is usually stratified, with the least-dense water at the surface and the densest water on the bottom.

The Three-Layered Ocean Although there are actually many thin layers of water, each of slightly different density, it is not a bad approximation to view the ocean as having three principal layers (Fig. 3.22*a*). The **surface layer** is usually 100 to 200 m (330 to 660 ft) deep. The surface layer is mixed by wind, waves, and currents, so it is also known as the **mixed layer.** The surface layer is not always well mixed, however. Sometimes, usually in the spring and summer in temperate and polar latitudes, the very uppermost part of the surface layer gets heated by the sun. The warm water floats in a shallow "lens" on top, and there is a sharp transition to the cooler water below. These sudden changes in temperature over small depth intervals, called **thermoclines,** are often noticed by divers. When the weather becomes colder, wind and waves again mix the water column and these temporary, shallow thermoclines break down.

The **intermediate layer** lies below the surface layer, typically to 1,000 to 1,500 m depth (3,300 to 5,000 ft). The **main,** or **permanent, thermocline,** a transition zone between warm surface water and cold water below, defines the intermediate layer. The main thermocline should not be confused with the much shallower, seasonal thermoclines in the surface layer. The main thermocline breaks down only occasionally and then only in a few places. The main thermocline is a feature of the open ocean. The waters over the continental shelf are not deep enough to have a main thermocline; in shelf waters the mixed surface layer often extends all the way to the bottom.

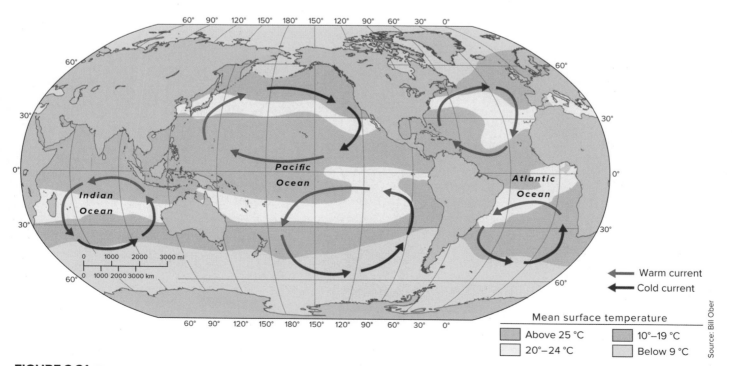

FIGURE 3.21 The average sea-surface temperature of the oceans is strongly affected by the ocean gyres.

Below about 1,500 m (5,000 ft) lie the **deep** and **bottom layers.** Technically, deep water and bottom water are different, but they are similar in being uniformly cold, typically less than 4 °C (39 °F).

The ocean has three main layers: the surface or mixed layer, the intermediate layer, and the deep layer.

Stability and Overturn Most of the time surface water, being warmer and less dense, floats on top of the denser water below unless wind or wave energy stirs up the water column. Such a water column is said to be **stable.** *How* stable the water column is depends on the density difference between the layers. If the surface layer is only slightly less dense than the layer below, less energy is required to mix the two layers and the water column has low stability. A highly stable water column, on the other hand, results from a large

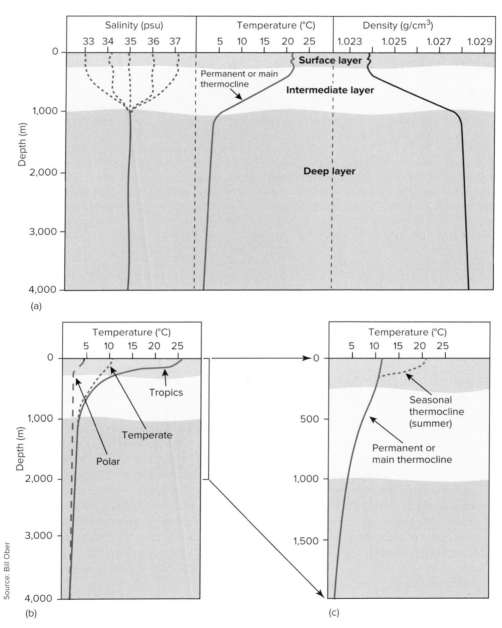

FIGURE 3.22 (*a*) Typical profiles of salinity, temperature, and density in the open ocean. Salinity profiles near the surface vary considerably because of precipitation, evaporation, and river runoff. Temperature and density profiles are usually mirror images of each other because temperature largely controls seawater density. Surface water is usually warmer and therefore less dense than the water below. (*b*) The surface temperature, as you might expect, varies with latitude, with the highest surface temperature occurring in the tropics. Deep-water temperature and salinity is much more uniform. (c) In temperate and polar waters, seasonal thermoclines may develop in the surface layer during the summer when the sun warms the uppermost part of the water column. Note that the depth scale in (c) is different from that in (*a*) and (*b*).

EYE ON SCIENCE

Box 3.2 Larval Transport Near Hydrothermal Vents

Because currents are so important to marine life, marine biologists often rely on the work of physical oceanographers in their studies. This is true not only at the scale of entire ocean basins but also at much smaller scales. Recent studies of currents in the vicinity of hydrothermal vents provide an example.

Hydrothermal vents support rich communities of worms, mussels, clams, shrimps, and other animals (see 16.4). Each vent is like a tiny oasis, however, separated from similar communities, sometimes by distances of hundreds or thousands of kilometers. Furthermore, the vent communities can be short-lived, as the vents that support them can die out or, alternatively, erupt and wipe out the community under a wave of hot lava. One of the mysteries about vent communities is how they are established when new vents appear and re-colonized after being wiped out by an eruption. The animals at vent communities can't disperse as adults, but only in their tiny larval stages, which swim only weakly and must be carried from place to place in the currents. Another question is whether some larvae from a vent community settle at the same vent to sustain the populations there, or if they are all carried away by the currents

so the community depends on importing larvae from other vents.

After a Pacific vent off the coast of Mexico was wiped out by a violent eruption, biologists found that new larvae apparently came in from more than 300 km (200 mi) away. This was a surprise, because they had thought the larvae only spend 30 to 40 days in the water column before settling to the bottom and that the prevailing currents could transport them no more than 100 km (60 mi) in that time.

So, the biologists teamed with physical oceanographers to study currents around the vents. They put current meters along the vents and in the water column above to measure current speed and direction. It isn't feasible to deploy enough current meters over a large enough area to measure the broader circulation pattern. Instead, the current measurements were used to develop a computer model of the circulation. Finally, the predictions of the model were tested by releasing a chemical tracer that can be detected in very low amounts, and taking water samples at various distances around the vent to determine where the currents carried the tracer.

The results brought more surprises. The working hypothesis had been that larvae probably rode plumes of warm water

rising from the vents several hundred meters up into the water column and were carried horizontally from there by currents. Instead, the results indicate that the fastest currents flow along the bottom at the edges of the rift zone where the vents are located. The study also showed that the current swirls around the vent in eddies, initially flowing away from the vent and then coming back to it. Thus, it seems likely that some larvae from the vent community would return to maintain the population, at least at this study site.

Even the relatively fast currents measured near the bottom did not flow fast enough to carry larvae 300 km in their 30- to 40-day larval span. Are there faster currents? Do the larvae spend longer in the water column than thought? Are there other transport mechanisms that the scientists missed? Also, the eddies observed may be due to the current swirling around some nearby seamounts. Do other vent sites have similar circulation? For marine scientists to answer these and other questions, there's only one thing to do: Head back to the deep sea!

For more information, explore the links provided in the Marine Biology *Online Learning Center.*

density difference between deep and shallow water and requires more energy to mix.

Sometimes water columns become unstable, meaning that the surface water becomes more dense than the water below. The surface water sinks, which is called **downwelling,** and displaces and mixes with deeper water. This process is known as **overturn** (Fig. 3.23). Because surface water, all with the same temperature and density, is descending through the water column, the temperature and density profiles are vertical straight lines, and oceanographers identify conditions of overturn by looking for such straight-line profiles. Overturn usually occurs in temperate and polar regions during the winter when the surface water cools.

When overturn occurs over only a small area, or when the surface water is only slightly denser than the water below, the downwelling water simply mixes with deeper water, so that the mixed layer extends deeper in the water column. This mixing is important for the productivity of temperate and polar waters (see "Patterns of Production," in 15.3). When downwelling is intense, however, a large volume of water may sink without mixing much with the surrounding water.

The processes that change salinity in the open ocean—precipitation, evaporation, and freezing—occur only at the surface. Temperature also changes primarily at the surface, through evaporative cooling, solar heating, or the exchange of heat with the atmosphere. Once surface water has sunk, therefore, its salinity and temperature don't change. From then on the volume of water, or **water mass,** has a "fingerprint," a characteristic combination of temperature and salinity. Oceanographers can use this to follow the movement, or **circulation,** of water masses over great distances. Because this form of circulation is driven by changes in density, which in turn is determined by temperature and salinity, this form of circulation is known as **thermohaline circulation.**

The Great Ocean Conveyor After water masses leave the surface they sink to a depth determined by their density. Water of intermediate density descends only part way, to a depth where it is denser than the water above but less dense than the water below. To sink all the way to the bottom of the ocean, surface water must become very dense—that is, cold and relatively salty. This occurs at only a few locations, and only intermittently. The

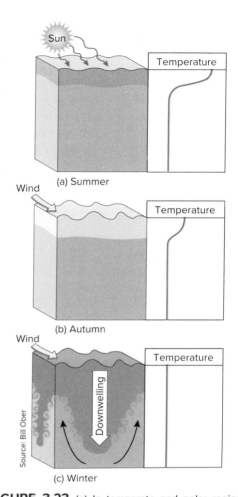

FIGURE 3.23 (*a*) In temperate and polar regions the summer sun warms the surface layer, making it much less dense than the water below. (*b*) In autumn the surface water begins to cool, and storm winds mix colder deep water to the surface. (*c*) If the surface water gets cold enough, which usually happens in winter, it becomes denser than the deeper water and sinks, which is called downwelling. The deeper water is displaced to the surface, and the entire process is known as overturn.

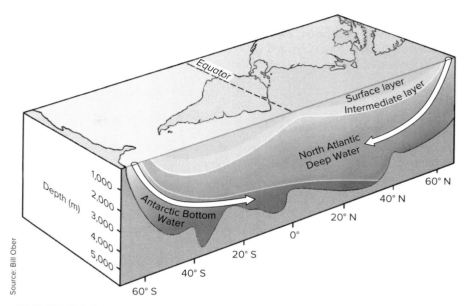

FIGURE 3.24 The deepest water in the deep and bottom layers of the Atlantic Ocean consists largely of two large water masses called North Atlantic Deep Water and Antarctic Bottom Water. These water masses originate at the surface in the extreme North and South Atlantic, respectively, then sink and spread along the bottom. Deep water originating in the Atlantic also spreads to the other ocean basins (see Fig. 3.25).

FIGURE 3.25 The deep circulation of the oceans is part of a global pattern known as the great ocean conveyor. This circulation constantly replenishes the oxygen supply to the ocean depths. Small variations in the conveyor circulation are thought to produce dramatic changes in weather patterns around the world. Larger changes may even bring on ice ages.

main places where surface overturn reaches the bottom are in the Atlantic Ocean, south of Greenland and just north of Antarctica (Fig. 3.24). After sinking, the water spreads through the Atlantic and into the other ocean basins. The water eventually rises to the surface and flows back to the Atlantic, where the cycle begins again (Fig. 3.25). This global thermohaline circulation, called the **great ocean conveyor,** mixes the oceans on a timescale of about 1,000 years. The great ocean conveyor is also critical in regulating Earth's climate, because the warm surface currents transport vast amounts of heat. Fluctuations in the conveyor have produced rapid climate changes in the past, even the onset and end of ice ages. This is concerning because there is growing evidence that global climate change is disrupting the Great Ocean Conveyor. In particular, the warming of surface water and the input of freshwater from melt-

ing ice is making the surface layer south of Greenland, one of the two main places where surface water sinks to the bottom, less dense. The consequences of this aren't completely understood but could be huge.

The conveyor also brings dissolved oxygen to the deep sea (see "Adaptations of Midwater Animals" in 16.1). This effect is enhanced because oxygen dissolves best in cold water (see "Dissolved Gases," in 3.1, above). The great ocean conveyor doesn't flow steadily and uniformly like an actual conveyor belt. Instead it constantly varies both in strength and exact position in a series of

superimposed cycles, or oscillations. The best known of these is the **El Niño–Southern Oscillation,** but many other such oscillations, operating on different timescales and in different parts of the world, are now known (see "The El Niño–Southern Oscillation," in 15.3).

3.3 WAVES AND TIDES

The great ocean currents, as important as they are, aren't apparent to the casual observer. Waves and tides, on the other hand, are among the most visible of all ocean phenomena. Anyone who has swum in, sailed on, or simply walked by the sea is familiar with waves and tides.

Waves

The wind not only drives surface currents, it also causes **waves.** The highest part of a wave is called the **crest** and the lowest part the **trough** (Fig. 3.26). The size of an ocean wave is usually expressed as the wave **height,** which is the vertical distance between the trough and the crest. Wave crests or troughs can be close together or far apart. The distance between them is called the **wavelength.** The time a wave takes to go by a given point is called the **period** of the wave.

When under a wave crest the water moves up and forward; under the troughs it moves down and back. On the whole the water particles don't go anywhere at all as the wave passes; they just move in circles (Fig. 3.27). Though waves carry energy across the sea surface, they do not actually transport water.

Waves begin to form as soon as the wind starts to blow. The faster and longer the wind blows, the larger the waves get. The size of waves generated by the wind also depends on the **fetch,** the span of open water over which the wind blows (Fig. 3.28).

While the wind is blowing it pushes the wave crests up into sharp peaks and "stretches out" the troughs (Fig. 3.29). Waves being driven by the wind like this are called **seas.** The waves move away from where they are generated slightly faster than the speed of the wind. Once away from the wind the waves settle into **swells.** With their smoothly rounded crests and troughs, swells are similar to the idealized waves shown in Figure 3.26.

When the waves approach the shore and get into shallow water, they begin to

Source: Bill Ober

FIGURE 3.26 An idealized series of waves, or wave train. The highest point of a wave is called the crest, the lowest point the trough. The wavelength is the distance between crests. The wave period refers to how long it takes the wave to go by. In this example the period is 15 s, which is how long it will take for the next crest to reach the bird.

Source: Bill Ober

FIGURE 3.27 Water particles do not move along with a wave but instead move in circles. Under the crest they move up and forward with the wave, then they are pulled back down under the trough. As wave after wave passes, the water and anything floating in or on it moves in circles.

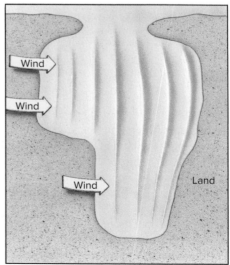

Source: Bill Ober

FIGURE 3.28 The wind is blowing at the same speed and has been blowing for the same length of time over this entire imaginary bay. On the top side of the bay, however, the wind is blowing over a much longer stretch of water. In other words, the fetch is longer on the top side, so the waves are bigger there.

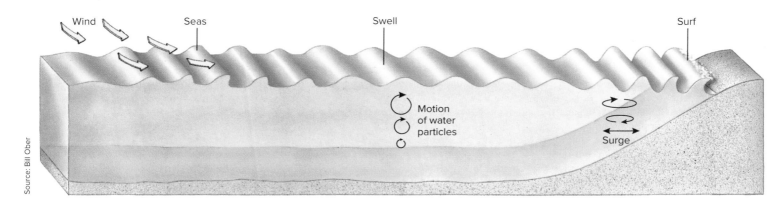

Source: Bill Ober

FIGURE 3.29 Storm winds generate seas, peaked waves with relatively flat troughs. The waves move out of the storm area, carrying energy away, and become swells, with rounded crests and troughs. When the waves reach shallow water, they get higher and shorter, that is, closer together. Eventually, they become unstable and break, expending their energy on the shoreline. Water particles under swells have the ideal circular motion shown in Figure 3.27. In shallower water, the influence of the bottom causes the particle motion to flatten out into a back-and-forth movement known as surge.

"feel" the bottom. The bottom forces the water particles to move in elongated ellipses instead of circles, which slows the wave. As the waves behind catch up, the waves get closer together, giving them a shorter wavelength. The waves "pile up," becoming higher and steeper. Eventually they become so high and so steep that they fall forward and break, creating **surf.** The energy that was put into the wave by the wind is expended on the shoreline as the wave breaks.

The sea surface is usually a confused jumble instead of a series of nice, regular waves moving in one direction. This is because the surface at any given location is affected by a mixture of waves coming from many different places, generated by winds of different speeds blowing in different directions for different lengths of time. The complex surface of the ocean results from the interactions of all these waves. **Wave cancellation** occurs when the crest of one wave meets the trough of another, and the sea surface ends up intermediate between the two. If the crests of two waves collide, however, they add together to produce a higher wave. This **wave reinforcement** occasionally produces **rogue waves** as tall as a 10-story building that seem to come up out of nowhere. Oceanographers once dismissed rogue waves as rare or even nonexistent, nothing more than sailors' myth, but have now confirmed that rogue waves do occur. They may account for a significant fraction of the 100 or so large ships lost at sea every year.

Tides

The sea surface has been rising and falling in the rhythmic pattern known as the **tides** since the ocean formed. The tides are a dominant influence on nearshore sea life. They alternately expose and submerge organisms on the shore (see Chapter 11), drive the circulation of bays and estuaries (see Chapter 12), trigger spawning (Fig. 3.30), and influence the lives of marine organisms in countless other ways.

Why Are There Tides? The tides are caused by the gravitational pull of the moon and sun and by the rotations of the Earth, moon, and sun. The moon and Earth are held together by gravitational attraction. The moon's gravity is strongest on the side of the planet closest to the moon. Here the moon's gravity pulls the water in the ocean toward the moon, so that if Earth were covered entirely by water the ocean would bulge toward the moon (Fig. 3.31). On Earth's opposite side, further away from the moon,

Mark Conlin/Alamy Stock Photo

FIGURE 3.30 These grunion (*Leuresthes tenuis*) are spawning high on a California beach. A male has wrapped around a female to fertilize her eggs as she releases them. Spawning is precisely timed to coincide with the highest tides, when the grunion can reach the uppermost parts of the beach. Hatching of the eggs, not quite a month later, also corresponds to high tides so that the fry, or juvenile fish, can swim away.

Box 3.3 Waves That Kill

Surfers and beachgoers who've been hit by a wave know how forceful they can be. Most waves are pretty harmless, but coastal storm waves cause damage, and occasionally deaths, every year, and rogue waves take an unknown toll. Sometimes, however, killer **tsunamis**, a Japanese word meaning "harbor waves," unleash all the awesome power of the sea.

Sometimes called tidal waves, tsunamis are unrelated to tides and are produced by seismic disturbances like earthquakes, landslides, and volcanoes, so they are also called seismic sea waves. Tsunamis are much longer and faster than ordinary waves. They can have wavelengths of 240 km (150 mi) and travel at over 700 km/h (435 mi/h). In the open ocean, tsunamis are typically less than 1 m (40 in) high and are hardly noticeable. They grow when they reach shore, but usually not much, and most tsunamis do little damage.

Once in a while, though, tsunamis are devastating. In 1883 the volcanic island of Krakatoa in the Indian Ocean exploded, causing tsunamis around half the globe that killed over 35,000 people. Fatal tsunamis occur every year or two on average, mostly in the Pacific because of seismic activity around the Pacific Rim. A 1946 tsunami in Hawai'i killed 159 and another in 1960, the result of a Chilean earthquake, killed 61. The U.S. west coast suffered deadly tsunamis caused by both the 1960 Chile earthquake and the great Alaskan earthquake of 1964. A 1998 tsunami in Papua New Guinea left 2,200 known dead. Many other places have been hit. Between 2001 and 2022, tsunamis killed more than a quarter-million people.

The deadliest tsunami struck in the Indian Ocean on 26 December 2004, triggered by a massive earthquake off the Indonesian island of Sumatra. Within minutes, waves at least 10 m (30 ft) high—estimates range as high as 30 m (100 ft)—smashed onto Aceh, on the Sumatran coast. In less than 8 h, tsunami waves radiated around the Indian Ocean, killing an estimated 230,000 people. Indonesia was worst affected, but people died in 12 countries. Survivors suffered the loss of their homes, businesses, farms, hospitals, schools, and water and electricity supplies.

Tsunamis continue to cause destruction. One of the worst was triggered in 2011 by an earthquake off the coast of Sendai, Japan, that was so severe it changed the orbits of satellites and knocked icebergs off Antarctica. Tsunami waves estimated at up to 39 m (130 ft) high hammered the northeast coast of the main Japanese island of Honshu, killing nearly 16,000. The waves overtopped a protective seawall around the critical backup electrical generators for a nuclear plant at Kagoshima. With the main electricity grid already down, the plant lost power to its critical cooling system, resulting in explosions and the release of radioactivity to the atmosphere and ocean in the worst nuclear accident since the Chernobyl disaster in 1986. Areas around

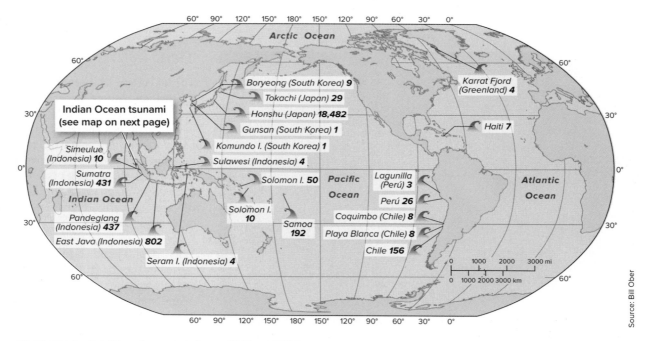

Worldwide death toll from tsunamis between 2001 and 2022.

Source: Bill Ober

the Kagoshima plant may be uninhabitable for decades, but fortunately the Kagoshima accident was much less severe than Chernobyl. Increases in radioactivity are detectible throughout the north Pacific Ocean, but not at harmful levels.

To survive a tsunami, people simply have to evacuate to higher ground—if they know the tsunami is coming. A tsunami warning system was established in the Pacific for Hawai'i and the west coast of North America in the 1960s and has probably saved at least hundreds of lives. Another system was established in the Indian Ocean after the 2004 tsunami, too late for its victims but hopefully a future life-saver. Unfortunately, this system has sometimes been plagued by malfunctions due to inadequate funding to maintain it. Many coasts have no warning systems, and even when they do word may not get out to rural areas or people who aren't tuned in to media. In Hawai'i, media and other electronic systems are supplemented by old-fashioned sirens, but this is the exception and not the rule. And when earthquakes strike right near the coast, where the carnage is often greatest, there may not be time to issue warnings. Here, education is key: People on the coast need to understand that any earthquake might bring a tsunami. Many in earthquake-prone Japan knew to evacuate after the Sendai earthquake, or there would have been many more dead. In both the 2004 Indian Ocean tsunami and one in Chile in 2010, schoolgirls were credited with saving hundreds of lives by raising the alarm. But in many places tsunami education still lags. The ocean often briefly recedes as a tsunami approaches, and people sometimes move into harm's way to look at the exposed marine life. Where small earthquakes are common people can become complacent; even when they know to move to high ground they may not respond appropriately. After a 2009 earthquake in Samoa, people could have reached the hills on foot but evacuated in their cars and were killed by the tsunami while stuck in traffic. People can also get complacent because the first tsunami warnings are often issued immediately after significant earthquakes, but such earthquakes don't always generate a tsunami so the warnings are sometimes false alarms.

We can't stop tsunamis, but coastal cities and industries need to be more resilient. In addition to warning systems and education, this means wiser choices of where to build on the coast and better engineering. Since the Kagoshima accident, for example, higher seawalls are being built around many nuclear plants. Resilience also means protecting natural habitats such as reefs, mangrove forests, and salt marshes that protect the coast. Habitat loss is thought to have worsened the impacts of the Indian Ocean tsunami, for example. Humans will never be immune from tsunamis as long as we choose to live on the coast, but we can adapt to minimize the damage.

Source: Bill Ober

● Epicenter 26 Dec 04 ● Epicenter 28 Mar 05

Waves from the Indian Ocean tsunami of 26 December 2004 and the resultant toll of dead and missing. As with many other tsunamis, there was actually a series of waves rather than a single one. Most places were hit by three waves, with the second being the most destructive.

mTaira/Shutterstock

Aftermath of the 11 March 2011 tsunami in Sendai, Japan.

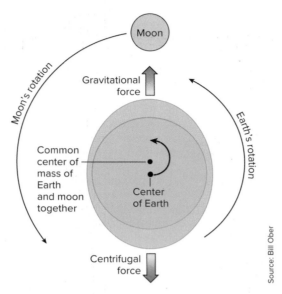

FIGURE 3.31 The moon does not exactly rotate around Earth. Instead, both the moon and Earth rotate around their common center of mass, which lies inside Earth. Thus, Earth actually "wobbles" a bit. Centrifugal force produced by the motion of the Earth–moon system causes the water to bulge outward, away from the moon. On the side of Earth closest to the moon, however, the moon's gravitational pull overcomes the centrifugal force and pulls the water into a bulge *toward* the moon.

the moon's gravitational pull is weaker, so the water does not move toward the moon. In fact, it bulges in the opposite direction, away from the moon, because of centrifugal force. This centrifugal force arises because, strictly speaking, the moon does not revolve around Earth. Instead, Earth and moon both rotate around their combined center of mass, which lies inside Earth but offset slightly from Earth's actual center (Fig. 3.31). This offset causes the Earth–moon system to wobble slightly, like an unbalanced tire, and creates a centrifugal force that pushes water away from the moon.

Thus, on a water-covered Earth, the ocean would form bulges on opposite sides of the planet, one bulge toward the moon where the moon's gravity predominates and the other bulge away from the moon where centrifugal force predominates. The water would be deep under the bulges and shallow away from the bulges.

In addition to the rotation of the Earth and moon illustrated in Figure 3.31, Earth spins like a top on its own axis. As it does so, any given point on the planet's surface will alternately lie under a bulge and then under a shallow spot (Fig. 3.32). High tide occurs when the point is under a bulge. Because Earth takes 24 h to complete a rotation, the point will have two high tides and two low tides every day. Actually, the moon advances a little in its own orbit in the course of 24 h. It takes the point on Earth an extra 50 min to catch up and come directly in line with the moon again. A full tidal cycle therefore takes 24 h and 50 min.

The sun produces tidal bulges in the same way as the moon. Though the sun is much larger than the moon, it is 400 times farther away, so the effect of the sun on the tides is only about half as strong as the moon's. When the sun and moon are in line with each other, which happens at the full and new moons (Fig. 3.33), their effects add together. At these times the **tidal range,** or difference in water level between successive high and low tides, is large. Such tides are called **spring tides** because they seem to surge up like a spring of water. The name has nothing to do with the season; spring tides occur throughout the year. The other planets in the solar system also have a minor influence on the tides, according to their mass and distance from Earth.

When the sun and moon are at right angles their effects partially cancel each other. During these **neap tides** the tidal range is small. Neap tides occur when the moon is in the first and third quarters.

> The tides are caused by a combination of the gravity of the sun and moon and the centrifugal force that results from the rotation of the Earth, moon, and sun.

FIGURE 3.32 As Earth spins on its axis, a given point like the one marked by the flag alternates between being under a bulge, making it high tide, and being between the bulges, making it low tide. Because the moon moves while Earth is rotating, a full tidal cycle takes 50 min longer than the 24 h it takes Earth to make a complete rotation.

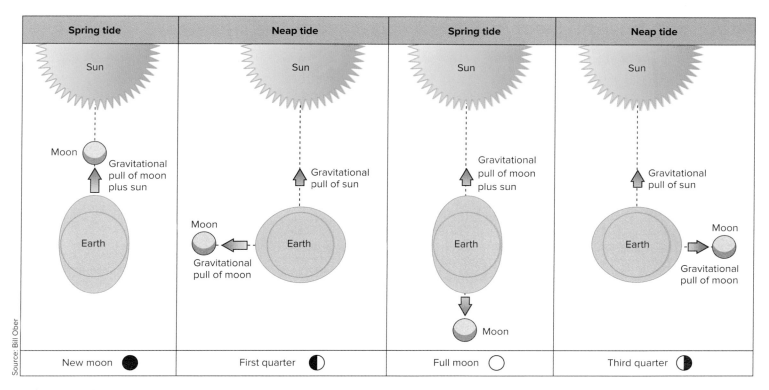

Spring tide	Neap tide	Spring tide	Neap tide
New moon ●	First quarter ◑	Full moon ○	Third quarter ◑

FIGURE 3.33 The tidal bulges are largest, and therefore the tidal range is greatest, when the moon and sun are in line and acting together. This happens at new and full moon. When the moon and sun are pulling at right angles to each other, which occurs when the moon is in quarter, the bulges and tidal range are smallest.

Tides in the Real World Fortunately for us, Earth is not completely covered with water. Because of the continents and the shape of the sea floor, tides in the real world behave differently than they would on a water-covered Earth. Most places do have **semidiurnal tides** as expected, which means there are two high tides and two low tides a day (Fig. 3.34*a* and *b*). The east coast of North America and most of Europe and Africa have semidiurnal tides (Fig. 3.35). Some places have a **mixed semidiurnal tide,** with successive high tides of different heights (Fig. 3.34*b*). Mixed semidiurnal tides are characteristic of most of the west coast of the United States and Canada. **Diurnal tides** occur when there is only one high and one low tide every day (Fig. 3.34*c*). Diurnal tides are uncommon. They occur on the coast of Antarctica and in parts of the Gulf of Mexico,

Caribbean, and Pacific (Fig. 3.35). The distinctions between the types of tide illustrated in Figure 3.34 are not absolute, and in most places the tidal pattern varies somewhat. Southern California, for example, has a predominantly mixed semidiurnal tide but on some days the tides are almost diurnal.

Tides vary from place to place and time to time because of the effects of continents, islands, and bottom topography. On a water-covered Earth with a perfectly flat sea floor, the tides would move around Earth in a smooth, symmetrical wave. In the real world, however, the continents prevent the wave from sweeping around the globe, essentially breaking the wave into several separate waves within individual basins. Islands, ridges, basins, canyons, reefs, and other features further affect the waves. The tide at a given place thus

(a)

(b)

(c)

FIGURE 3.34 Types of tides. In most places the tide is semidiurnal, with two high and two low tides per day. (*a*) In some places, successive high tides are nearly equal in height. (*b*) In many other places, one of the high tides is considerably higher than the other. This is called a mixed semidiurnal tide. (*c*) A few places have a diurnal tide, with only one high and one low tide per day.

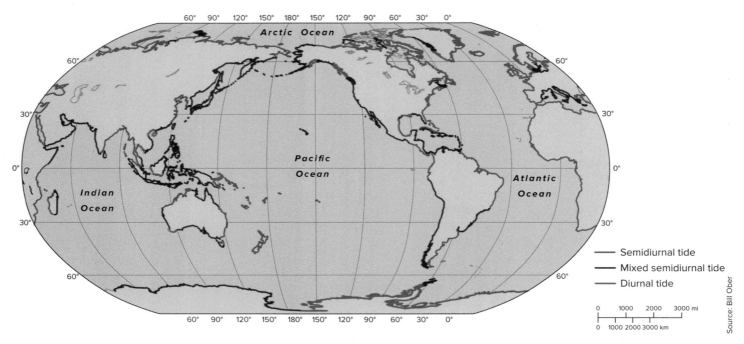

FIGURE 3.35 The worldwide distribution of semidiurnal, mixed semidiurnal, and diurnal tides. This map shows the dominant type of tide. At most places there is variation; a place that usually has, say, a mixed semidiurnal tide may occasionally experience diurnal tides.

depends on its location relative to these features. The tides are also influenced by variation in the orbits of the sun and moon relative to the Equator, and the small effects of other planets, which are also moving. Even weather affects the tides. Strong winds, for example, can pile water up on shore, causing higher tides than would otherwise occur. To predict the tides at a given place, oceanographers have to combine observations of actual tides at that place with their theoretical equations. They are then able to produce remarkably accurate **tide tables** that predict the time and height of high and low tides (Fig. 3.36). Tide tables are available for most coastal areas.

AUSTRALIA, EAST COAST – BRISBANE BAR
LAT 27° 22' S LONG 153° 10' E
Times and Heights of High and Low Waters

2022
Time Zone –1000

JANUARY				FEBRUARY				MARCH				APRIL			
Time	m	Time	m	Time	m	Time	m	Time	m	Time	m	Time	m	Time	m
1 0144 0.31 0820 2.55 SA 1459 0.54 2021 1.90		**16** 0210 0.47 0846 2.39 SU 1524 0.69 2047 1.75		**1** 0317 0.29 0949 2.71 TU 1637 0.43 ● 2204 1.96		**16** 0312 0.44 0937 2.47 WE 1613 0.60 2145 1.95		**1** 0219 0.42 0847 2.60 TU 1531 0.45 2105 2.01		**16** 0209 0.56 0829 2.39 WE 1504 0.60 2044 2.00		**1** 0339 0.44 0941 2.40 FR 1610 0.42 ● 2203 2.30		**16** 0313 0.48 0906 2.37 SA 1536 0.38 2138 2.39	
2 0234 0.26 0912 2.67 SU 1557 0.47 2118 1.88		**17** 0248 0.44 0924 2.43 MO 1601 0.66 2125 1.78		**2** 0405 0.27 1034 2.71 WE 1720 0.42 2249 2.00		**17** 0350 0.40 1012 2.50 TH 1647 0.56 ○ 2221 2.01		**2** 0310 0.35 0930 2.62 WE 1613 0.42 2148 2.10		**17** 0252 0.47 0905 2.45 TH 1540 0.53 2122 2.11		**2** 0417 0.48 1015 2.30 SA 1638 0.43 2238 2.34		**17** 0359 0.45 0945 2.32 SU 1612 0.35 ○ 2220 2.48	
3 0324 0.23 1001 2.73 MO 1651 0.43 ● 2213 1.87		**18** 0325 0.42 1000 2.46 TU 1638 0.64 ○ 2200 1.82		**3** 0449 0.30 1115 2.65 TH 1759 0.44 2332 2.02		**18** 0428 0.39 1045 2.51 FR 1720 0.53 2300 2.06		**3** 0355 0.33 1011 2.59 TH 1648 0.42 ● 2229 2.16		**18** 0333 0.42 0941 2.47 FR 1615 0.47 ○ 2201 2.20		**3** 0455 0.54 1045 2.19 SU 1704 0.45 2313 2.35		**18** 0445 0.47 1026 2.22 MO 1645 0.35 2302 2.53	
4 0412 0.24 1050 2.74 TU 1742 0.43 2304 1.87		**19** 0401 0.41 1034 2.47 WE 1713 0.63 2237 1.85		**4** 0531 0.38 1154 2.53 FR 1834 0.48		**19** 0506 0.42 1118 2.47 SA 1752 0.51 2339 2.09		**4** 0435 0.37 1047 2.51 FR 1721 0.44 2306 2.19		**19** 0415 0.41 1016 2.46 SA 1647 0.43 2241 2.27		**4** 0530 0.62 1116 2.05 MO 1729 0.49 2346 2.33		**19** 0531 0.52 1107 2.09 TU 1720 0.39 2347 2.53	
5 0459 0.29 1136 2.68 WE 1829 0.45 2353 1.86		**20** 0438 0.41 1109 2.47 TH 1746 0.62 2315 1.87		**5** 0014 2.02 0612 0.50 SA 1230 2.38 1907 0.53		**20** 0545 0.49 1152 2.39 SU 1824 0.51		**5** 0514 0.44 1121 2.39 SA 1750 0.47 2343 2.20		**20** 0455 0.43 1051 2.39 SU 1719 0.42 2320 2.32		**5** 0605 0.72 1146 1.91 TU 1755 0.56		**20** 0621 0.60 1153 1.93 WE 1757 0.47	
6 0545 0.38 1221 2.58 TH 1913 0.50		**21** 0515 0.45 1143 2.45 FR 1821 0.61 2356 1.88		**6** 0055 2.00 0653 0.65 SU 1304 2.20 1940 0.59		**21** 0020 2.10 0626 0.58 MO 1229 2.27 1857 0.53		**6** 0550 0.55 1152 2.24 SU 1816 0.51		**21** 0537 0.50 1128 2.27 MO 1750 0.44		**6** 0020 2.27 0643 0.82 WE 1218 1.76 1824 0.65		**21** 0035 2.48 0718 0.69 TH 1245 1.76 1841 0.58	
7 0042 1.84 0631 0.50 FR 1304 2.44 1956 0.56		**22** 0554 0.51 1218 2.40 SA 1857 0.61		**7** 0139 1.97 0737 0.81 MO 1341 2.01 2015 0.64		**22** 0104 2.10 0714 0.70 TU 1309 2.10 1935 0.56		**7** 0019 2.18 0627 0.68 MO 1223 2.07 1844 0.57		**22** 0001 2.33 0621 0.60 TU 1206 2.11 1823 0.49		**7** 0059 2.19 0726 0.91 TH 1257 1.62 1900 0.77		**22** 0130 2.39 0829 0.76 FR 1353 1.64 1937 0.70	

FIGURE 3.36 Part of the 2022 tide tables for Brisbane, Australia. It shows the times of high and low tide and the phases of the moon (closed circle represents new moon).

Interactive Exploration

McGraw-Hill Connect® is a great place to check your understanding of chapter material. Visit **www.mcgrawhillconnect.com** for access to interactive chapter summaries, chapter quizzing, and more! Further enhance your knowledge with video clips and weblinks to chapter-related material.

Critical Thinking

1. In unusually cold winters the northern Black Sea sometimes freezes, while the nearby Adriatic Sea usually doesn't, even if it is just as cold. Freshwater runoff gives the surface of the Black Sea a low salinity of about 18‰. What would you guess about the salinity of the Adriatic?

2. Just for the fun of it, someone in Beaufort, South Carolina, throws a message in a bottle into the sea. Some time later, someone in Perth, on the west coast of Australia, finds the bottle. Referring to Figure 3.20 and the fold-out map at the back of this book, can you trace the path the bottle probably took?

3. If you owned a seaside home and a bad storm brought heavy winds and high surf to your coastline, would you prefer it to be during a new moon or a quarter moon? Why?

4. Most tsunamis occur in the Pacific Ocean, as indicated by the map in Box 3.3, "Waves That Kill." How would you explain this?

For Further Reading

Some of the recommended reading may be available online. Look for live links on the *Marine Biology* Online Learning Center.

General Interest

Bogdanoff, A., 2016. Through the looking-glass of the ocean surface. *Oceanus*, vol. 51, no. 2, winter, pp. 106–109. Studies of the critically important exchange between ocean and atmosphere.

Catlidge, E., 2010. A drop of the weird stuff. *New Scientist*, vol. 205, no. 2746, 3 February, pp. 3235. Water's unique properties revealed.

Cromwell, D., 2000. Ocean circulation. *New Scientist*, vol. 166, no. 2239, 20 May, "Inside Science" supplement no. 130, pp. 1–4. A summary of what is known about ocean currents and current research efforts to learn more.

Dixon, C., 2018. Monster waves. *Scientific American*, vol. 319, no. 2, August, pp. 65–67. A small group of daredevil surfers use the latest science to chase epic breaks.

Eriksen, M., 2012. Tracking tsunami flotsam. *Natural History*, vol. 120. No. 7, July/Aug., pp. 18–23. Floating debris carried away by the Fukushima tsunami in Japan is tracked across the Pacific.

Harris, M., 2015. Waves of destruction. *Scientific American*, vol. 312, no. 5, May. The ice that once largely covered the Arctic Ocean is melting. The opening waters allow winds to drive increasingly destructive waves.

Kostel, K., 2012. Lessons from Fukushima. *Oceanus*, vol. 49, no. 2, Spring, pp. 34–41. The 2011 Fukushima earthquake and tsunami in Japan have provided scientists with a wealth of information on the causes and consequences of earthquakes.

Le Bras, I., 2016. Detours on the oceanic highway. *Oceanus*, vol. 51, no. 2, winter, pp. 40–43. We depict ocean currents on maps as though they were as stable as rivers on land, but there are many smaller flows that have important effects in the ocean.

Linn, A., 1983. Oh, what a spin we're in, thanks to the Coriolis effect. *Smithsonian*, vol. 13, no. 11, February, pp. 66–73. A detailed explanation of the Coriolis effect and a look at some of its consequences.

Marshall, M., 2018. From the deep. *New Scientist*, vol. 239, no. 3189, 4 Aug., pp. 24–27. Changes in the Great Ocean Conveyor will affect us all.

Moreton, M. 2019. Wicked high tides. *Science News*, vol. 196, no. 3, 17 August, pp. 16–21. The city of Boston, Massachusetts, is taking steps to deal with increased tidal inundation caused by sea level rise.

Moskovitch, K., 2014. Cryptic river: The torrents that flow on the seabed. *New Scientist*, vol. 221, no. 2957, 22 February, 42–46. Underwater "rivers" crisscross the ocean floor, carrying oxygen and nutrients.

Oreskes, N., 2022. Operational oceanography. *American Scientist*, vol. 110, no. 2, March/April, pp. 102–109. The birth of modern oceanographic field measurement techniques is rooted in World War II.

Ornes, S., 2014. High rollers. *New Scientist*, vol. 223, no. 2979, 26 July. There is no longer a question that rogue waves occur, but predicting them is a daunting task.

Riser, S. C. and M. S. Lozier, 2013. Rethinking the Gulf Stream. *Scientific American*, vol. 308, no. 2, February, pp. 50–55. Recent studies have provided evidence that don't support the long-held hypothesis that the Gulf Stream moderates European winters.

Sanderson, K., 2018. H_2Oh!. *New Scientist*, vol. 238, no. 31810, 2 June 2018, pp. 26–29. Water may be one of the most familiar things in all our lives, but on close look it is pretty strange.

Villano, M., 2010. The mysterious movements of deep-sea larvae. *Oceanus*, vol. 48, no. 1, June, pp. 24–27.

In Depth

Boers, N., 2021. Observation-based early-warning signals for a collapse of the Atlantic Meridional Overturning Circulation. *Nature Climate Change*, vol. 11, August 2021, pp. 680–688.

Cessi, P., 2019. The global overturning circulation. *Annual Review of Marine Science*, vol. 10, pp. 249–270.

Gregg, M. C., E. A. D'Asaro, J. J. Riley, and E. Kunze, 2018. Mixing efficiency in the ocean. *Annual Review of Marine Science*, vol. 10, pp. 443–473.

Løvholt, F., S. Glimsdal, C. B. Harbitz, N. Zamora, F. Nadim, P. Peduzzi, H. Dao, and H. Smebye, 2012. Tsunami hazard and exposure on the global scale. *Earth-Science Reviews*, vol. 110, pp. 58–73.

Paduan, J. D. and L. Washburn, 2013. High-frequency radar observations of ocean surface currents. *Annual Review of Marine Science*, vol. 5, pp. 115–136.

Palter, J. B., 2015. The role of the Gulf Stream in European climate. *Annual Review of Marine Science*, vol. 7, pp. 113–137.

Rippeth, T. P. and J. A. Mattias Green, 2020. Tides, the Moon and the kaleidoscope of ocean mixing. *Oceanography and Marine Biology: An Annual Review*, vol. 58, pp. 319–350.

Rossby, T., 2016. Visualizing and quantifying oceanic motion. *Annual Review of Marine Science*, vol. 8, pp. 35–57.

Stammer, D., A. Cazenave, R. M. Ponte, and M. E. Tamisiea, 2013. Causes for contemporary regional sea level changes. *Annual Review of Marine Science*, vol. 5, pp. 21–46.

Talke, S. A. and D. A. Jay, 2019. Changing tides: the role of natural and anthropogenic factors. *Annual Review of Marine Science*, vol. 12, pp. 121–151.

Design elements: chapter opener (ocean wave) ©EpicStockMedia/Shutterstock, (blue Parrotfish) ©ivvv1975/Shutterstock; Eye on Science box ©Westend61/Getty Images; Evolutionary Perspective box ©vilainecrevette/123RF; end-of-chapter (beach): ©photoaraki.com/Getty Images

CHAPTER

4

Fundamentals of Biology

Bill Ober

A shark (*Squalus acanthias*) embryo begins a new phase of the cycle of life.

Now that we have discussed the major features of the marine environment, we can turn our attention to life in the sea. Perhaps the most basic question is, What *is* life? Most people have a pretty good feel for what the word *living* means, but biologists have never been able to agree on a precise definition. The best we can do is describe the common properties of living things.

Organisms are not random collections of material but have a precise chemical and physical **organization.** They all use **energy** and have the ability to do work, maintain themselves, and grow. They do this through a vast number of chemical reactions that are collectively called **metabolism.** Living things also use energy to maintain stable internal conditions different from their surroundings, which is known as **homeostasis.** They sense and react to their external environment. Finally, all life forms reproduce to perpetuate their kind and use **nucleic acids** to record their individual characteristics and pass them on to their offspring (see "Nucleic Acids," below).

All living things are physically and chemically organized, grow, metabolize, regulate their internal environment, react to the external environment, reproduce, and use nucleic acids to store genetic information.

The basic features of living things are shared by all organisms, not just those that live in the sea. Here, however, we pay particular attention to marine organisms.

4.1 THE INGREDIENTS OF LIFE

Life requires an intricate series of interactions among an immense variety of chemicals. The most important of these is one of the simplest: **water.** As the universal solvent, water provides the medium in which all the other **molecules** dissolve and interact. Water is the base of a complex "chemical soup" inside all organisms where the chemical reactions of metabolism take place.

The Building Blocks

Besides water, most of the chemicals that make life possible are **organic compounds,** molecules that contain atoms of **carbon, hydrogen,** and usually **oxygen.** Organic compounds are high-energy molecules; that is, it takes energy to make them (Fig. 4.1). The ability to use energy to make, or **synthesize,** organic compounds is an important characteristic of living things. Organic compounds break down when left to themselves. When this happens they release the energy that went into their construction. Organisms have developed the ability to control this breakdown to harness the energy that is released.

Carbohydrates Most organic molecules that occur in organisms are in four main groups. **Carbohydrates** are composed mainly of only the basic elements of all organic molecules: carbon, hydrogen, and oxygen. The simplest carbohydrates are **glucose** and a few other **simple sugars.** More complex carbohydrates are formed by the combination of simple sugars into chains. Ordinary table sugar, for example, consists of two simple sugar molecules joined together. **Starches** and other complex carbohydrates consist of much longer chains, which may contain components other than simple sugars.

Organisms use carbohydrates in many ways. Simple sugars play a vital role in the most basic metabolic processes, as we will see. Organisms often use complex carbohydrates like starches to store energy reserves.

Some carbohydrates are **structural molecules,** which provide support and protection. For example, some animals use **chitin,** a modified carbohydrate, as a skeletal material. Plants and many algae produce a structural carbohydrate called **cellulose,** the main ingredient of wood and plant fibers (see Table 6.1). Other carbohydrates have roles in reproduction, metabolism, and cell interactions—in fact, in nearly every biological function—that scientists are only beginning to understand.

Proteins **Proteins** are another major group of organic molecules. Like complex carbohydrates, proteins are composed of chains of smaller subunits. In proteins the subunits are **amino acids,** which contain **nitrogen** as well as the carbon, hydrogen, and oxygen in all organic compounds. The world's organisms make countless different proteins, but they all are made from just 22 different amino acids.

Proteins have an equally extraordinary variety of functions. Muscles and many other structures are made largely of protein. **Enzymes** are proteins that speed up, or **catalyze,** specific chemical reactions. Without enzymes, most metabolic reactions would proceed very slowly or not at all. There are also many structural proteins, including those in the skin, hair, and skeletons of some marine animals. Some **hormones,** chemicals that act as messengers to help different parts of the body work together, are proteins. Other proteins carry oxygen in the blood and muscles. Proteins also act as poisons, send

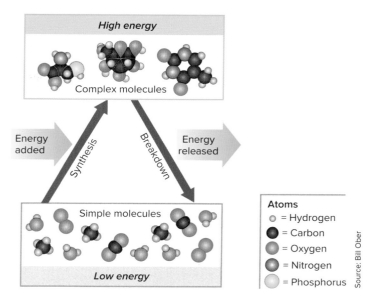

FIGURE 4.1 Chemical reactions either require energy or release it. Organisms need energy to make complex molecules from simple ones. The breakdown of energy-rich complex molecules releases energy.

chemical signals, generate light, act as antifreeze in the blood of some Antarctic fishes, and have countless other functions.

Glycoproteins are a particularly important group of proteins. Glycoproteins are protein molecules that bound with extremely complex sugars called glycans. The combination of proteins and complex sugars greatly expands the potential biological function of these molecules. Their complexity has made them hard to study, but new technologies are rapidly revealing the importance of glycoproteins.

Lipids Fats, oils, and waxes are examples of **lipids.** Lipids are often used for energy storage (Fig. 4.2). Another useful property of lipids is that they repel water: Many marine mammals and birds use a coating of oil or wax to keep their fur or feathers dry. Some marine organisms that are exposed to the air at low tide have a coating of wax to help keep from drying out. Lipids also provide buoyancy because they float, and provide insulation from the cold. Some hormones are lipids rather than proteins.

Nucleic Acids **Nucleic acids** store and transmit the basic genetic information of life. Nucleic acid molecules are chains of subunits called **nucleotides,** which consist of a simple sugar joined to molecules, called **nitrogen bases,** that contain phosphorus and nitrogen. One type of nucleic acid is **DNA (deoxyribonucleic acid).** In most organisms, DNA molecules specify the organism's "recipe"—the instructions for its construction and maintenance. An organism's complete genetic information is called its **genome.** The organism inherits this genetic information, in the form of DNA, from its parents and passes it on to its offspring. The DNA chains are often tens or hundreds of millions of nucleotides long, but the nucleotides

Water is called the **universal solvent** because it can dissolve more different substances than any other liquid.
Molecules Combinations of two or more *atoms;* most substances are composed of molecules rather than individual atoms.
• 3.1, The Waters of the Ocean

FLPA/Alamy Stock Photo

FIGURE 4.2 The thick layers of blubber on this whale are composed almost entirely of lipid. Whales can go without eating for long periods by using the energy stored in the blubber. The whale's blubber also helps protect it from the cold and gives it buoyancy. People once used the energy contained in blubber by burning oil made from it for light and heat. Most industrial whaling has ceased but traditional whaling, such as that undertaken by these Alaskan Inuit hunters, continues legally in some places.

contain only four different types of nitrogen bases: adenine, cytosine, thymine, and guanine.

A key function of DNA is to provide the instructions for the synthesis of specific proteins. The **sequence** of the different nucleotides on the DNA chain forms a code, like a four-letter alphabet. Four letters doesn't sound like much, but Morse code can record messages using only two: dots and dashes. DNA's "words" are **genes,** sequences of DNA that specify the order of amino acids in a single protein.

This coding for protein synthesis was thought to be the primary function of DNA until it was discovered that large amounts—up to 99%—of the DNA in many organisms does not code for proteins. This **non-coding DNA** was once referred to as "junk DNA," but at least some of it has important functions. Some of it regulates protein synthesis. Organisms do not need to make every protein in their genetic code all the time, but only, say, to respond to stress or disease, or during certain life stages or rapid growth. Regulatory DNA switches genes "on" and "off," that is, it initiates or terminates the synthesis of a protein from its gene. A considerable amount of non-coding DNA actually does code for something: not proteins but another important class of nucleic acids, **RNA (ribonucleic acid).** Other functions of non-coding DNA are still being found, and some of it may indeed have no function, just being a holdover from generations far in the past.

Epigenetic markers are chemical compounds that attach to the DNA molecule in response to environmental conditions. They can switch genes on and off like regulatory DNA does, or otherwise affect how the genetic information coded in DNA is expressed. Epigenetic markers provide a genetic mechanism for organisms to respond quickly to changes in their environment. It was once thought that epigenetic markers could not be inherited, but we now know that they can be passed from one generation to the next.

Like DNA, RNA consists of chains of only four types of nucleotides. Three are the same as in DNA, but the fourth nucleotide in RNA is uracil instead of thymine. Some RNA molecules act as intermediaries in assisting in the conversion of the information stored in DNA into proteins, and in some microbes RNA stores the genetic information itself. For decades these were thought to be the only roles for RNA, but we now know that RNA influences many if not most biochemical processes. Small RNAs regulate the expression of genes stored in DNA into proteins, trigger immune responses and defend against viral infections, regulate embryonic development, and catalyze reactions much as enzymes do. Discovery of the critical and widespread roles of RNA ranks among the most exciting discoveries in biology in decades and has triggered a wave of new research, including many possible applications in medicine.

Because organisms' nucleic acids define so much about them, determining their nucleotide sequences is one of the hottest topics in biology. Complete genome sequences are known for an increasing number of organisms. Partial nucleic acid sequences are available for many more organisms and contain a wealth of information. These sequences can be used as genetic "bar codes" to identify species, including ones that have never been collected, and shed light on details of their metabolism, lifestyle, and even relationships to other organisms (see Box 5.2, "Tiny Cells, Big Surprises").

Organic compounds are chemicals that contain carbon, hydrogen, and usually oxygen. The main types of organic compounds are carbohydrates, proteins, lipids, and nucleic acids.

The Fuel of Life

The molecules that make up living things interact in many complex chemical systems. The most basic of these have to do with the capture, storage, and use of energy or, more simply put, with the production and use of "food". These systems store and transfer energy using **ATP (adenosine triphosphate)** as a common "energy currency." ATP is a high-energy molecule based on adenosine, one of the nucleotides in nucleic acids. Energy is stored as chemical energy by converting a related but lower-energy molecule, **ADP (adenosine diphosphate),** into ATP by adding an atom of phosphorus. This transformation requires a lot of energy, which is released when the ATP is converted back to ADP. When the ATP is broken back down into ADP the energy is transferred to other molecules to be used in metabolism. In an average day a person cycles through 57 kg (125 lb) of ATP. Whales must use tons!

Organisms transfer energy between different molecules using ATP (adenosine triphosphate), the energy currency of life.

Microorganisms use a variety of metabolic pathways to process energy (see Table 5.1). Most other organisms, however, largely rely on only two: photosynthesis and respiration.

Photosynthesis: Making the Fuel Most organisms ultimately get their energy from the sun (Fig. 4.3). In **photosynthesis,** algae, plants, and some other organisms capture the sun's energy and use it to make glucose, a simple sugar, some of which is converted into other organic compounds. Most other organisms use these organic molecules as a source of energy. Organic material contains a tremendous amount of energy. As food it fuels our bodies and those of most other creatures. In such forms as oil, gas, and coal, it heats our homes, runs our factories, and powers our cars.

FIGURE 4.3 Seaweeds like these kelp capture sunlight to perform photosynthesis and grow. Other organisms eat the kelp, using energy that originally came from the sun.

Photosynthesis (Fig. 4.4) begins when an organism absorbs sunlight with chemicals called **photosynthetic pigments.** The most common photosynthetic pigment is **chlorophyll,** which gives plants their characteristic green color. Most algae have additional pigments that often mask the green chlorophyll (see Table 6.1). Because of these pigments, algae may be brown, red, purple, or even black instead of green.

In a long series of enzyme-controlled reactions, solar energy captured by chlorophyll and other pigments is converted into chemical energy, in the form of ATP, and then used to make glucose, with **carbon dioxide** (CO_2) and water (H_2O) as the raw materials. Carbon dioxide is one of very few carbon-containing molecules not considered to be an organic compound. Photosynthesis, then, converts carbon from an inorganic to an organic form. This is called **fixing** the carbon or **carbon fixation.** The solar energy absorbed by chlorophyll is stored as chemical energy in the form of glucose. The glucose is then used to make other organic compounds (see "Primary Production," below). ATP may be the "energy currency" of the cell, but fixed carbon—organic matter—is the "currency" in which energy flows through food webs and ecosystems.

Photosynthesis produces **oxygen gas** (O_2), as a by-product. All the oxygen gas on Earth, in the atmosphere we breathe and in the ocean, was produced by photosynthetic organisms, which constantly replenish Earth's oxygen supply. We rely on photosynthesis not only for food but also for the very air we breathe.

Photosynthesis captures light energy from the sun to produce glucose. Carbon dioxide and water are used to make the glucose, and oxygen gas is liberated as a by-product:

$$H_2O + CO_2 \xrightarrow{\text{sun energy}} \text{organic matter} + O_2$$
$$\text{(glucose)}$$

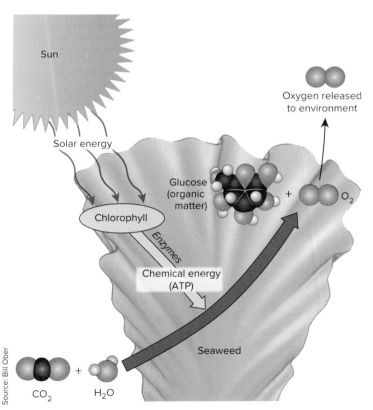

FIGURE 4.4 In photosynthesis, carbon dioxide and water are used to make glucose. The energy for this process comes from sunlight. Oxygen is given off as a by-product.

FIGURE 4.5 Respiration is basically the opposite of photosynthesis. Respiration breaks down glucose, using oxygen, and produces carbon dioxide and water. The energy that originally came from the sun is then made available to the organism.

Organisms that are capable of photosynthesis can obtain all the energy they need from sunlight and don't need to eat. They are called **autotrophs** ("self-feeders"). Plants are the most familiar autotrophs on land. In the ocean, however, bacteria and algae are the most important autotrophs.

Many organisms cannot produce their own food and must obtain energy from organic matter produced by autotrophs. These organisms, including all animals, are called **heterotrophs.**

Respiration: Burning the Fuel Both autotrophs and heterotrophs perform **respiration** to use the solar energy stored in organic chemicals by photosynthesis. The chemical reactions are different, but the net result of oxygen-dependent, or **aerobic,** respiration is essentially the reverse of photosynthesis (Fig. 4.5). Sugars are broken down using oxygen, and carbon dioxide and water are given off. This process is sometimes called cellular respiration to distinguish it from the physical act of breathing.

> Respiration, which occurs in nearly all organisms, breaks down glucose, releasing the energy it contains. Respiration consumes oxygen and produces carbon dioxide and water:
>
> $$\text{organic matter} + O_2 \longrightarrow CO_2 + H_2O$$
> $$\text{(glucose)} \quad\quad\quad \longrightarrow \text{chemical energy}$$

Cellular respiration is similar to burning wood or oil in that organic material is broken down, oxygen is consumed, and energy is released. That's why dieters talk about "burning calories." In respiration, however, the energy in organic material is not released in flames. Instead, it is stored in ATP.

If oxygen isn't available, many organisms can use a different form of respiration called **anaerobic** respiration. Anaerobic respiration does not require oxygen, but it isn't as efficient as aerobic respiration and provides less energy to the organism. Many animals temporarily switch to anaerobic respiration, however, when extreme exertion depletes the oxygen in their muscles and blood. Some organisms that live in oxygen-depleted environments, like muddy sediments or the guts of fishes, use anaerobic respiration all the time. Aerobic respiration is much more widespread than anaerobic respiration, however, and in this text the general term "respiration" refers to aerobic, or oxygen-dependent, respiration.

Primary Production The sugars produced by photosynthesis supply both raw material and energy, via respiration, for the manufacture of other organic compounds. Through elaborate chemical processes, some of the glucose formed during photosynthesis is converted into other types of organic molecules—carbohydrates, proteins, lipids, and nucleic acids (Fig. 4.6). The energy for these conversions, temporarily stored in ATP, comes from metabolizing much of the rest of the glucose. Thus, most of the glucose produced by photosynthesis is either converted to other organic compounds or respired to fuel this conversion.

When autotrophs produce more organic matter than they use in respiration, there is a net increase in organic matter. This is called **primary production.** Autotrophs use the extra organic material to grow and reproduce. In other words, the extra organic matter forms more living material, which means more food for animals and other

FIGURE 4.6 In photosynthesis, autotrophs capture energy from the sun and store it as chemical energy in simple sugars like glucose. Some of the sugars are broken down in respiration, and the energy is stored in ATP. This makes the energy available to the rest of the organism's metabolism—for example, to make other organic matter from the remaining glucose. ATP is converted to ADP when its stored energy is used. If there is no light, autotrophs can perform only respiration, like animals and other heterotrophs. The thin black arrows represent molecules moving in and out of the cell.

heterotrophs. Organisms that perform this primary production of food are called **primary producers,** or sometimes just **producers.**

> Primary production is the net gain in organic matter that occurs when autotrophs make more organic matter than they respire, usually by photosynthesis.

The Importance of Nutrients Only carbon dioxide, water, and sunlight are needed to make glucose by photosynthesis, but additional materials are needed to convert the glucose into other compounds. These raw materials, called **nutrients,** include minerals, vitamins, and other substances. Primary producers use large amounts of nitrogen, which is needed to make proteins, nucleic acids, and other compounds. **Nitrate (NO_3^{-1})** is the most important form of nitrogen in the ocean (see "Cycles of Essential Nutrients" in 10.3). Phosphorus, needed to make ATP and nucleic acids among other compounds, is another important nutrient. Its main source is **phosphate (PO_4^{-3}).** **Diatoms, radiolarians,** and **silicoflagellates** require large amounts of **silica (SiO_2)** to make their shells. Another important nutrient is **iron** in various forms. Although needed in much smaller amounts than

nitrogen, phosphorus, or silica, iron is in critically short supply in large parts of the ocean (see "Patterns of Production" in 15.3).

Primary production by photosynthesis requires nutrients as well as light. Nitrogen, phosphorus, silica, and iron are the most important nutrients in the ocean.

4.2 LIVING MACHINERY

The chemical reactions of metabolism make life possible, but chemical reactions are not living things and organisms are not just bags of chemical soup. If you ran a fish through a blender, you would have all the same molecules but the fish would definitely not be alive. The molecules in living things are *organized* into structural and functional units that work in a coordinated way. It is this living machinery that is responsible for many of the properties of living things.

Cells and Organelles

The basic structural unit of life is the **cell.** All organisms are made of one or more cells. Cells contain all the molecules needed for life packaged in a living wrapper called the **cell membrane,** or **plasma membrane.** This membrane isolates the gelatinous contents of the cell, or **cytoplasm,** from the outside world. The cell membrane allows some substances to pass in or out but prevents others from doing so.

There are a number of structures within the cytoplasm. Among the most important are membranes similar to the outer cell membrane. These interior membranes act as sites for such chemical processes as photosynthesis and respiration. Membranes may also divide the cell into compartments that enclose still more complex structures specialized for particular tasks. These membrane-bound structures are known as **organelles.**

Cells also have a complex internal framework made of protein fibers. This framework, called the **cytoskeleton,** supports the cell, allows it to move and change shape, and helps it divide.

Structurally Simple Cells: Prokaryotes Prokaryotic cells are primitive in the sense that they are the most ancient of the two major types of cells. They are also the structurally simplest and smallest cells. Prokaryotic cells lack most kinds of organelles (Fig. 4.7), though some prokaryotes do have certain organelles or organelle-like structures and a more complex cytoskeleton than was previously thought. Organisms with prokaryotic cells are called **prokaryotes. Bacteria** are the best-known group of prokaryotes. **Archaea** are the second group of prokaryotes. Most prokaryotes are microscopic, and most are tiny even by the standards of microscopic organisms, but there are a few giant bacteria that can be seen with the naked eye.

Outside the cell membrane of prokaryotes lies a supportive **cell wall.** Inside, the cell has a single, ring-like molecule of DNA. Attached to the cell membrane and scattered through the cytoplasm are small structures made of protein and RNA called **ribosomes** that make the cell's proteins. In photosynthetic prokaryotes, folds of the plasma membrane contain photosynthetic pigments. Some prokaryotes have one or more protein filaments known as **flagella** (singular,

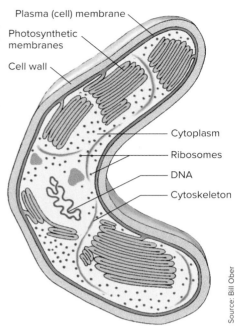

FIGURE 4.7
Prokaryotic cells have a plasma membrane inside a cell wall. The plasma membrane is where respiration occurs and may fold into the cell's interior. Membrane folding is particularly pronounced in photosynthetic bacteria like this one. The folds contain chlorophyll and are the site of photosynthesis. Prokaryotic cells also contain scattered ribosomes and a ring-like molecule of DNA. Otherwise, there is relatively little structure inside the cell.

Plasma (cell) membrane
Photosynthetic membranes
Cell wall
Cytoplasm
Ribosomes
DNA
Cytoskeleton

Source: Bill Ober

flagellum) that extend outside the cell membrane. These cells move by rotating their flagella like tiny propellers.

The structurally simplest cells are prokaryotic. They have relatively little internal structure and lack most kinds of membrane-bound organelles.

Despite this structural simplicity, various kinds of prokaryotes can carry out a vast range of metabolic reactions.

Structurally Complex Cells: Eukaryotes **Eukaryotic cells,** the second major cell type, are more organized and complex than prokaryotic cells (Fig. 4.8). Various membrane-bound organelles found only in **eukaryotes** do specialized jobs within the cell. The **nucleus** contains **chromosomes** that carry most of the cell's DNA. The nucleus thus holds most of the cell's genetic information and directs most of its activities. The nucleus can be thought of as the cell's headquarters.

The "factories" of eukaryotic cells are two structures, mostly folded membranes, called the **endoplasmic reticulum** and the **Golgi apparatus.** These organelles make, package, and transport many of the organic molecules the cell needs. Ribosomes sit in some of the endoplasmic reticulum. Organic molecules, water, and other materials are often stored in **vacuoles.**

Diatoms Single-celled algae with a shell, or test, made of silica.
• 5.3, Unicellular Algae; Figure 5.6

Radiolarians Single-celled protozoans with a test made of silica.
• 5.3, Unicellular Algae; Figure 5.12

Silicoflagellates Single-celled algae with a skeleton made of silica.
• 5.3, Unicellular Algae; Figure 5.9

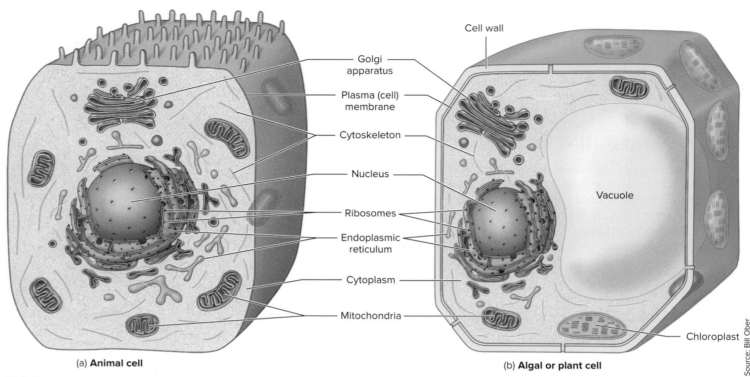

(a) **Animal cell** (b) **Algal or plant cell**

Source: Bill Ober

FIGURE 4.8 Typical cells of (*a*) animals and (*b*) algae and plants, and some of the structures they contain.

Respiration in eukaryotes takes place in **mitochondria.** Mitochondria are the cell's power plants, breaking down organic molecules to provide energy. Mitochondria also contain small amounts of DNA. Plant and algal cells have two important structures that animals don't. First, they have **chloroplasts,** chlorophyll-containing organelles where photosynthesis takes place that also contain DNA. Second, except for some single-celled algae, they have a cell wall.

Eukaryotic cells often have flagella, which are called **cilia** when they are short and numerous. Eukaryotic flagella and cilia differ from prokaryotic flagella in being enclosed in a membrane, having a more complex structure, and beating back and forth instead of rotating. Some eukaryotes use their flagella or cilia to swim, as prokaryotes do, but many eukaryotes use flagella and cilia to push water and particles through or over their bodies instead of pushing their bodies through the water. Many marine animals, for example, use cilia to push food particles to the mouth. Cilia in your lungs carry away dust and other irritants.

> The cells of eukaryotes are more structured than those of prokaryotes. They have membrane-bound organelles, including a nucleus in which the DNA is carried in chromosomes.

Levels of Organization

A cell is a self-contained unit that can carry out all the functions necessary for life. Indeed, many organisms get by just fine with only a single cell. One-celled organisms are called **unicellular.** **Multicellular** organisms have more than one cell. The human body, for instance, has around 100 trillion cells. In multicellular organisms, the cells interact and communicate, and cells become specialized for particular jobs. Nearly all prokaryotes are unicellular, but

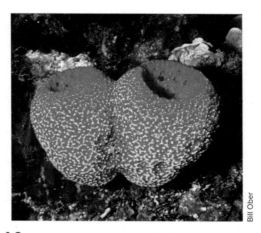

Bill Ober

FIGURE 4.9 Sponges are the only multicellular animals that are at the cellular level of organization (see 7.1). They do have specialized cells, but these cells don't form tissues.

some bacteria group together, interact, and specialize for specific functions in ways that border on multicellularity. Many eukaryotes, however, are multicellular.

In multicellular organisms, specialized cells that perform the same task may be organized into more complex structures. The extent of specialization and organization is referred to as the **level of organization** (Table 4.1).

At the **cellular** level of organization, each cell is essentially an independent, self-sufficient unit. It can perform all the functions needed to sustain itself and reproduce, and there is little or no cooperation among cells.

Only a few multicellular organisms remain at the cellular level (Fig. 4.9). In most, groups of cells act together to do a particular job. These specialized, coordinated groups of cells are called

Table 4.1 Levels of Organization of Biological Systems

Level	Description	Examples	
Biosphere	All of Earth's ecosystems interacting as a functional whole		
Ecosystem	A community or communities in a large area, together with their physical environment	Nearshore ecosystem	Multiple species
Community	All the populations in a particular habitat	Rocky shore community	
Population	A group of organisms of the same species that occur together	All the mussels on a stretch of rocky shore	One or more organisms of the same species
Individual	A single organism	One mussel	
Organ system	A group of organs that work in cooperation	Digestive system	
Organ	Tissues organized into structures	Stomach	Within individual organisms
Tissue	Groups of cells bound together and specialized for the same function	Muscle tissue	
Cell	Independent cells, the fundamental unit of living things	Muscle cell, single-celled organisms	
Organelle	A complex structure within cells, bound by a membrane	Nucleus, mitochondrion	
Molecule	Combinations of atoms that are bound together	Water, proteins	Within cells
Atom	The fundamental unit of all matter	Carbon, phosphorus	

Increasing complexity →

tissues. Cells that are specialized to contract and do work, for example, are bound together to form muscle tissue. Nervous tissue, specialized to collect, process, and transmit information, is another example.

In most animals, organization doesn't stop at the tissue level. Their tissues are further organized into **organs** that carry out specific functions. The heart is an example of an organ. There are several different tissues that make up the heart. Muscle tissue, for example, allows the heart to contract and pump blood, and nervous tissue controls the muscle.

Different organs act together in **organ systems.** The digestive system, for instance, includes many organs: mouth, stomach, intestine, and so on. Animals usually have a number of organ systems, including nervous, digestive, circulatory, and reproductive systems.

Complex organization also exists at levels above the individual organism. A **population** is a group of organisms of the same kind, or **species,** that lives in one place and shares genetic information. Mussels on a stretch of rocky shore, for example, form a population (Fig. 4.10).

Populations of different species that occur in the same place form **communities.** A community is more than just a collection of

FIGURE 4.10 These blue mussels (*Mytilus edulis*) growing on a rocky shore in New Zealand are part of a population.

Michael E. Huber

organisms that happen to use the same habitat. The characteristics of communities are determined by the way the organisms *interact*—which organisms eat each other, which compete, and which depend on each other (see "Ways That Species Interact," in 10.1). Rocky shores, for example, are home to many organisms in addition to mussels: seaweeds, crabs, barnacles, snails, and sea stars, to name a few (Fig. 4.11). The interactions among all these organisms give the rocky shore community its own unique structure.

A community, or often several communities, together with the physical, or non-living, environment, make up an **ecosystem.** The rocky shore community, for instance, along with other nearby communities, is part of a larger ecosystem that includes the tides, currents, nutrients dissolved in the water, and other physical and chemical aspects of the area.

Earth's ecosystems are not independent of each other. Ecosystems interact with and depend on each other in many critical ways that determine the nature of both the individual ecosystems and the entire planet as a whole. The inter-functioning whole of Earth's ecosystems is called the **Biosphere.**

Michael E. Huber

FIGURE 4.11 The community that lives on this rocky shore is made up of populations of blue mussels, barnacles, seaweeds, and many other species.

4.3 CHALLENGES OF LIFE IN THE SEA

Every **habitat,** the natural environment where an organism lives, has a unique set of characteristics and presents special challenges to the organisms living there. Marine organisms must cope with problems unlike those of land dwellers. Even within the marine environment there are different habitats, each of which poses specific challenges. **Planktonic** organisms—those that drift in the water—face very different conditions than **benthic** organisms—those that live on the bottom—or **nekton**—organisms that are strong swimmers (see Fig. 10.11). Organisms have evolved countless ways to adapt to the conditions of their habitats.

Many adaptations of marine organisms have to do with maintaining homeostasis. The living machinery inside most organisms is sensitive and can operate properly only within a narrow range of conditions. Living things have therefore evolved ways to keep their

internal environments within this range regardless of the external conditions.

Salinity

Many enzymes and other organic molecules are sensitive to **ion** concentrations. Marine organisms are thus immersed in a medium—seawater—with the potential to profoundly alter their metabolism. To fully understand the problems posed by **salinity,** we must know something about how dissolved ions and molecules behave.

Diffusion and Osmosis In solution, ions and molecules move around just like water molecules do. If the molecules are concentrated in one part of the solution, this random movement spreads them out until they are evenly distributed (Fig. 4.12). The overall result is that the molecules move from areas of high concentration to areas of low concentration. This process is called **diffusion.**

Whenever the internal composition of a cell differs from that on the outside, substances tend to move in or out of the cell by diffusion. If the surrounding seawater contains more sodium, say, than the cell's cytoplasm, sodium tends to diffuse into the cell. This is not good if the organism is sensitive to sodium. Similarly, substances that are concentrated inside cells tend to diffuse out. Many of the cell's most precious molecules—like ATP, amino acids, and nutrients—are much more concentrated within the cell than in seawater. Therefore, they tend to leak out of the cell.

One answer to this problem is to have a barrier that stops molecules from diffusing in and out. The cell membrane is just such a barrier. It blocks the passage of the common ions in seawater as well as many organic molecules. The membrane cannot be a complete barrier, however, because the cell needs to exchange many materials—like oxygen and carbon dioxide—with its surroundings. The cell membrane is **selectively permeable;** that is, it allows some substances to enter and leave the cell but blocks others. Water and other small molecules pass readily through the cell membrane, for example, whereas ATP and many proteins do not.

The selective permeability of the cell membrane solves the problem of diffusion of ions and organic molecules, but it creates a new problem. Like any other molecule, water diffuses from areas where it is concentrated to areas of lower concentration. If the total concentration of *solutes* inside the cell is higher than that outside, the concentration of *water* will be lower. Because water molecules are free to cross the cell membrane, they will stream into the cell, causing it to swell (Fig. 4.13). On the other hand, the cell will tend to lose water and shrivel if the

Source: Bill Ober

FIGURE 4.12 Ions and molecules dissolved in water tend to move around randomly just like water molecules do. When a crystal of salt dissolves in water, the ions start out concentrated in one part of the solution but eventually spread out because of their random movement. This process, called diffusion, results in the flow of ions from areas of high concentration to areas of low concentration.

BOX 4.1 EVOLUTIONARY PERSPECTIVE

From Snack to Servant: How Complex Cells Arose

Prokaryotes were the first life on Earth. There are fossil bacteria thought to be 3.8 *billion* years old, nearly as old as the oceans themselves. It was another billion years or more before eukaryotic cells appeared. Strangely enough, this advance in cell design, shared by all multicellular life, may have started with a simple "meal."

Mitochondria, the "powerhouses" of the cell (see Fig. 4.8), were once free-living bacteria. They are 1 to 3 microns (μm) long, about the same size as many bacteria. Respiration in both bacteria and mitochondria takes place in their membranes, and mitochondria have folded internal membranes similar to those found in many bacteria. Although most of a eukaryotic cell's DNA is in the nucleus, mitochondria have a small amount of their own DNA, in the form of a single, circular molecule like the chromosome of bacteria. When a cell needs new mitochondria, it does not make them from scratch. Instead, the cell's mitochondria divide, much as bacteria reproduce by cell division.

Biologists believe that these and other similarities show that mitochondria were originally free-living bacteria, but came to live inside other cells. A relatively large cell that had already evolved some chemical features of today's eukaryotes may have engulfed a smaller one but been unable to digest it, or a disease-causing bacterium may have invaded the larger cell but not killed it. Both phenomena have been observed in the laboratory in living cells. Either way, the small cells eventually took up permanent residence in the larger cells, using them as hosts. The living together of different kinds of organisms like this is called **symbiosis** (see "Ways That Species Interact," in 10.1).

It appears that the host cells could not use oxygen in respiration, but the symbionts could. The symbionts' ability to perform oxygen-dependent respiration gave the host cells an advantage over cells without the symbionts.

Over time, the host cells transferred most of the symbiotic bacteria's genes into their own nuclei, and thus came to control the symbionts. The symbionts and host cells became more and more dependent on each other. Eventually the symbionts became mitochondria (see Box 5.1, "The Origin of Eukaryotes").

Chloroplasts, the organelles that perform photosynthesis, are also thought to have arisen from symbiotic bacteria. Like mitochondria, they are about the right size, have a circular DNA molecule, and can reproduce themselves. Chloroplasts also contain folded membranes very similar to those of photosynthetic bacteria (see Fig. 4.7). Chloroplasts probably arose when a eukaryotic cell containing mitochondria engulfed a photosynthetic bacterium that wasn't digested and became symbiotic. The exact nature of this symbiont is debated, but it probably looked something like a

1 μm

Prochloron. This bacterium was once thought to be closely related to the symbiotic, photosynthetic bacterium that gave rise to chloroplasts, but genetic studies indicate that a slightly different group of bacteria was involved.

symbiotic bacterium called *Prochloron* that lives in some sea squirts and other invertebrates. The eukaryotic host cells gained the symbiont's photosynthetic ability and were the first algae. The algae eventually evolved different types of chloroplasts, which were later exchanged when one kind of alga engulfed another.

All multicellular organisms, including humans, carry in their very cells the legacy of these bacterial partnerships, perhaps the result of an ancient snack.

total salt concentration outside the cell is higher than inside. This diffusion of water across the cell membrane is known as **osmosis.**

Diffusion and osmosis always move molecules from high concentration to low. The selective permeability of the cell membrane can control this movement, but not reverse it, and cells often need to move materials in the opposite direction. They may need to rid themselves of excess sodium even though the seawater outside is more concentrated than inside the cell or to take up sugars and amino acids from the surrounding water even though they are already more concentrated inside the cell. In **active transport,** proteins in the cell membrane pump materials in the opposite direction to which they

would move by diffusion. This process requires energy, in the form of ATP. Active transport is so important that it represents over one-third of cells' total energy expenditure.

Ions *Atoms* or groups of atoms that have a positive or negative charge. The most common ions in seawater are chloride and sodium.
Solutes Ions, organic molecules, or anything else that is dissolved in a solution.
Salinity The total amount of *salts* dissolved in water. Salts are combinations of ions.
• 3.1, The Waters of the Ocean

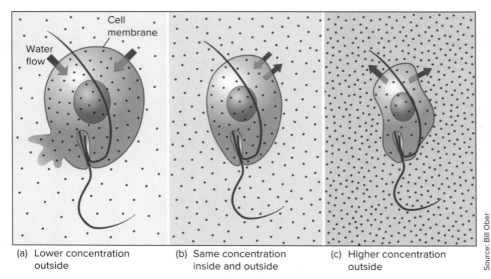

Source: Bill Ober

(a) Lower concentration outside

(b) Same concentration inside and outside

(c) Higher concentration outside

FIGURE 4.13 Osmosis. (*a*) If there is more dissolved material, and therefore less water, inside a cell then outside water will move into the cell by osmosis (a special case of diffusion). The cell will swell until it bursts. (*b*) If the internal and external concentrations are the same water moves in and out of the cell equally, and the cell stays in balance. (*c*) When the outside water is *more* concentrated, the cell loses water by osmosis and shrivels.

Diffusion is the movement of ions and molecules from areas of high concentration to areas of low concentration. Osmosis is the diffusion of water across a selectively permeable membrane. In active transport the cell uses energy to move materials in the opposite direction to diffusion.

Regulation of Salt and Water Balance Marine organisms have adapted to the problems of maintaining the proper balance of water and salts in various ways. Some don't actively maintain salt and water balance at all; their internal concentrations change as the salinity of the water changes (see Fig. 12.6). Such organisms are called **osmoconformers.** Because they don't actively maintain salt

and water balance, many osmoconformers can only live in a narrow salinity range. Others tolerate relatively large changes in the salinity of the surrounding seawater (and therefore their tissues), but even they experience osmotic problems outside their tolerance range. In areas like the open ocean, where salinity doesn't fluctuate much, osmoconformers have few difficulties.

Other marine organisms **osmoregulate,** or control their internal concentrations to avoid osmotic problems. Osmoregulators still have limits and are generally able to tolerate salinity changes better than osmoconformers. One way osmoregulators adapt to different salinities is by adjusting the concentration of solutes in their body fluids so that the overall concentration of their fluids matches that of the water outside (see Fig. 12.6). It doesn't matter if there are the same chemicals inside and out as long as the total *amount* of dissolved material is the same. Some organisms osmoregulate by changing the amount of just one particular chemical to match changes in the salinity outside. Sharks, for example, increase or decrease the amount of a chemical called **urea** in their blood (see Fig. 8.18). A single-celled marine alga called *Dunaliella* uses a different chemical, glycerol, to do the same thing. *Dunaliella* may be the champion osmoregulator. It can maintain its water balance in water ranging from nearly fresh to more than nine times saltier than normal seawater.

By contrast, many osmoregulators maintain blood concentrations that are different from that of the surrounding seawater and remain more or less constant. Most marine fishes have body fluids more dilute than seawater (Fig. 4.14*a*) and tend to lose water by osmosis. They replace the lost water by drinking seawater. They also conserve water by producing only a very small amount of urine. Some of the excess salts that are taken in with the seawater they drink are never absorbed and pass right through the gut. Marine fishes do absorb some of the salts they drink and must actively rid themselves

(a) Marine fish

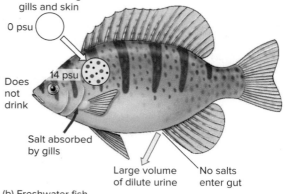

(b) Freshwater fish

Source: Bill Ober

FIGURE 4.14 Regulation of salt and water balance. (*a*) In most marine fishes, water flows by osmosis from the relatively dilute body fluids to the more concentrated seawater. To compensate and avoid dehydration, the fish drinks seawater. It excretes as little urine as possible to conserve water. Some salts pass through the gut without being absorbed. Salts that are absorbed are excreted, mostly through the gills but also in the urine. (*b*) Freshwater fishes are in the reverse situation: The outside water has a very low salinity, so they tend to gain water by osmosis. To avoid swelling up, they refrain from drinking and produce large amounts of dilute urine. Salts are absorbed by the gills to replace those lost in the urine.

Michael E. Huber

FIGURE 4.15 Sea turtles have glands near the eyes that excrete excess ions, producing salty "tears." This is a hawksbill turtle (*Eretmochelys imbricata*).

Marine birds and reptiles, and some marine plants, also have special cells or glands to rid themselves of excess salt (Fig. 4.15). Marine plants and most algae have the added advantage of a fairly rigid cell wall that helps them resist the swelling caused by osmotic water gain.

Temperature

Organisms are greatly affected by temperature. Metabolic reactions proceed faster at high temperatures and slow down as it gets colder. A general rule of thumb is that most reactions occur about twice as fast with a 10 °C (18 °F) rise in temperature. At extreme temperatures, however, most enzymes cease to function properly.

Most marine organisms are adapted to live in particular temperature ranges. Many polar species, for instance, have enzymes that work best at low temperatures, and they cannot tolerate warm water. The reverse is true of many tropical species. As a result, tempera-

of, or **excrete,** these excess salts. Some salts are excreted in the urine, but because so little urine is produced this is not enough. Most of the excess salts are excreted through the gills (see "Regulation of the Internal Environment," in 8.3).

Freshwater fishes have the reverse problem: Their blood has a higher concentration of salt than the surrounding water, and they take in water by osmosis. Their adaptations are opposite to those of marine fishes (Fig. 4.14*b*).

ture plays a major role in determining where different organisms are found in the ocean (Fig. 4.16).

Organisms are often categorized according to how their metabolism affects their body temperature. All organisms generate metabolic heat, but in most organisms this heat is quickly lost to the environment and does not raise body temperature. These organisms are known as **ectotherms,** commonly called "cold-blooded." In **endotherms,** on the other hand, metabolic heat is retained and raises

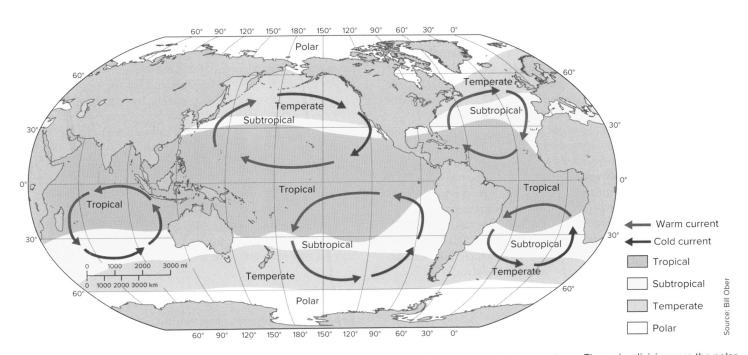

FIGURE 4.16 Marine organisms are often restricted to specific regions that correspond to average water temperatures. The major divisions are the polar, temperate, subtropical (or warm temperate), and tropical regions. The boundaries of these regions are not absolute and change slightly with the seasons and shifts in current patterns. This map refers only to surface waters; deep water is uniformly cold.

Table 4.2
Classification of Animals by Their Response to Changes in External Temperature

	Poikilotherms: Temperature varies with external temperature	Homeotherms: Regulate body temperature so it doesn't vary as much as external temperature
Ectotherms: Most metabolic heat is rapidly lost to the environment; body temperature matches external temperature	Invertebrates, most fishes, and marine reptiles	None
Endotherms: Retain significant metabolic heat; internal temperature stays warmer than external temperature	Some large sharks, tunas, and billfishes	Mammals and birds

Volume (V)	Surface area (S)	S/V ratio	
1 cm³	6 cm²	6:1	
8 cm³	48 cm²	6:1	
8 cm³	24 cm²	3:1	

Source: Bill Ober

FIGURE 4.17 A cube that is 1 cm on a side (top) has a volume of 1 cm³ and, because it has six sides, a surface area of 6 cm². Eight such cubes (middle) will, of course, have both eight times the volume and eight times the surface area, so the ratio of the surface area to the volume of the cubes, or surface-to-volume (S/V) ratio, will stay the same: 6:1. If the eight cubes are combined into a single large one (bottom), half the surfaces are hidden in the interior. The S/V ratio, like the surface area, is reduced by half, to 3:1. A large cube, therefore, has a lower S/V ratio than a small one.

the body temperature above that of the surroundings. Endotherms are often called "warm-blooded." Endotherms include mammals, birds, and some large fishes, including some tunas and sharks (see "Predators and Their Prey," in 15.2).

Another way to categorize organisms is by whether they can keep their body temperature more or less constant regardless of the temperature of the environment. The body temperature of **poikilotherms** changes along with the temperature of the surroundings. All ectotherms are also poikilotherms. As the temperature of the water rises and falls so does their body temperature and consequently their metabolic rate. This can make ectothermic animals sluggish if the water is colder than they are used to. Warm-blooded, or endothermic, tunas and sharks are also poikilotherms. They retain metabolic heat generated by their large muscles and their core temperature is warmer than the surrounding water, but it still rises and falls with the external water temperature.

Mammals and, to a lesser extent, birds are able to regulate their internal temperature so that it stays almost constant when the external temperature varies. They are called **homeotherms.** Being endotherms, they retain heat, but they also control their metabolism, producing more heat as needed by burning up fats and other energy-rich molecules. This allows them to remain highly active regardless of water temperature. It also requires a lot of energy, so homeotherms need to eat more than poikilotherms. To reduce the "heat bill"—the energy cost of maintaining their body temperature— mammals and birds are insulated with feathers, hair, or blubber. The classification of organisms according to how they respond to changes in the temperature of their environment is summarized in Table 4.2.

Surface-to-Volume Ratio

Adaptations to salinity and temperature are needed because salts and heat can flow in and out of organisms—if organisms were not affected by their environment, they would not have to adapt. Organisms also exchange nutrients, waste products, and gases with the environment. Such materials often move in and out across the surface of marine organisms, so the amount of surface area is very important. More precisely, it is the amount of surface area relative to the total volume of an organism—in other words, the **surface-to-volume ratio,** or **S/V ratio**—that determines how rapidly heat and materials flow in and out.

One thing that determines the S/V ratio is the size of the organism. As organisms grow larger, their volume increases faster than their surface area. Small organisms have a larger S/V ratio than big ones (Fig. 4.17). Small organisms, especially single-celled ones, can therefore rely on simple diffusion across their surfaces for the exchange of materials. Larger organisms must develop supplementary mechanisms, like respiratory and excretory systems.

4.4 PERPETUATING LIFE

One of the most basic characteristics of living things is the ability to reproduce—to generate offspring similar to themselves. Any life form that failed to replace itself with new individuals of its own kind would soon vanish from the planet. It is only by reproducing that a species ensures its survival.

FIGURE 4.18 Cells of a microscopic organism called a diatom (*Striatella unipunctata*). The cells were formed by the division of a single 'mother' cell. The cells may separate into individual cells, or continue to divide to form a chain.

Elif Bayraktar/Shutterstock

Organisms must do two things when they reproduce. First, they must produce new individuals to perpetuate the species. Second, they must pass on to this new generation the characteristics of the species in the form of genetic information. The transfer of genetic information from one generation to the next is called **heredity.**

Organisms achieve the first objective, the production of offspring, in many different ways. But they use relatively few ways to pass on genetic information. This similarity of hereditary mechanisms is evidence that all living things are fundamentally related.

Modes of Reproduction

Individual cells reproduce mainly by dividing to form new **daughter cells** (Fig. 4.18). In prokaryotes, where the DNA that carries the genetic information is not enclosed in a nucleus, the cell divides into two new ones by a simple process called **cell fission.** Before dividing, the cell copies, or **replicates,** its DNA. Each daughter cell gets one of the copies, as well as the rest of the cellular machinery it needs to survive.

In eukaryotes the DNA lies on several different chromosomes. Before a cell divides, each chromosome is replicated. The most common form of eukaryotic cell division, **mitosis,** is a complex process that takes place in the nucleus. Mitosis ensures that each daughter cell gets a copy of every chromosome. As in bacterial cell division, the end result is two daughter cells that are exact duplicates of the original, with the same genetic information.

Asexual Reproduction Cell division is the primary way that single-celled organisms reproduce. Because a single individual can reproduce itself without the involvement of a partner, this form of reproduction is called **asexual reproduction.** All forms of asexual reproduction are similar in that the offspring inherit all the genetic characteristics of the parent. They are, in fact, exact copies, or **clones.**

Many multicellular organisms also reproduce asexually. Some sea anemones, for example, split in half to create two smaller anemones. This process is known as **fission.** Another common form of asexual reproduction is **budding.** Instead of dividing into two new individuals, the parent develops small growths, or buds, that break away and become separate individuals (Fig. 4.19a). Many plants reproduce asexually by sending out various kinds of runners that take root and then sever their connection to the parent (Fig. 4.19b). Because it is so common in plants, asexual reproduction is sometimes called **vegetative reproduction,** even when it occurs in animals.

Asexual, or vegetative, reproduction can be performed by single individuals and produces offspring that are genetically identical to the parent.

Sexual Reproduction Most multicellular and some unicellular organisms reproduce part or all of the time by **sexual reproduction,** in which new offspring arise from the union of two separate cells called **gametes.** Usually each of the gametes comes from a different parent.

Organisms that reproduce sexually have a special kind of tissue called **germ tissue.** Whereas all the other cells in the body divide only by mitosis, germ cells are capable of a second type of cell division, **meiosis.**

In most cells of eukaryotic organisms the chromosomes occur in pairs, with each chromosome of a pair storing similar genetic information. Such cells are **diploid,** designated **2n.** Meiosis produces daughter cells that have copies of only half the parents' chromosomes—one of each pair. Cells with half the normal number of chromosomes are **haploid,** designated **n** or **1n.** The haploid daughter cells produced in meiosis are the gametes. In some seaweeds and microbes, all the gametes are the same. Sexual reproduction usually, however, involves two types of gametes: female gametes called **eggs** and male gametes called **sperm** (Fig. 4.20). In animals the germ tissue is usually contained in

James Gilmour, Australian Institute of Marine Science

(a)

Michael E. Huber

(b)

FIGURE 4.19 (*a*) Budding is a common form of reproduction in marine animals, including this mushroom coral (*Fungia fungites*). The parent coral is nearly dead, but the many buds on its surface will soon break off and become free-living adults (see Fig. 14.3a). (*b*) This seagrass (*Halodule pinifolia*) reproduces asexually by sending out rhizomes, or "runners," that take root and form new plants.

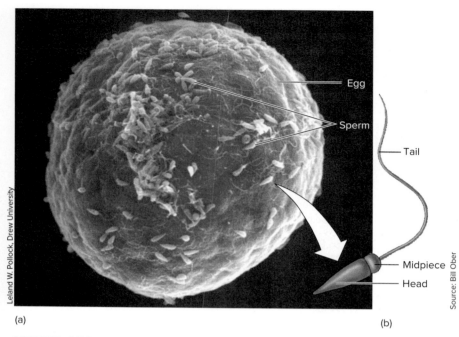

(a)

(b)

FIGURE 4.20 (*a*) The egg of the variegated sea urchin (*Lytechinus variegatus*) is many times larger than the sperm. Though many sperm surround the egg, only one will fertilize it. The egg contains a large amount of cytoplasm and the organelles characteristic of other cells. It also contains yolk to nourish the developing embryo. (*b*) The head of a sperm cell is made up almost entirely of the cell nucleus and contains the genetic material. The midpiece contains mitochondria that power the tail, or flagellum, with which the sperm swims.

gonads, the organs that produce the gametes. **Ovaries** are the female gonads, which produce eggs. In animals the male gonads, or **testes,** produce sperm. Seaweeds also have gonads that produce sperm, while in flowering plants sperm develop within pollen, which is produced by organs in the flower.

Eggs are large cells, usually an organism's largest. They contain all the cellular machinery—organelles and cytoplasm—of regular cells. The eggs of many species also contain large amounts of energy-rich yolk. Sperm, by contrast, are usually an organism's smallest cells, with almost no cytoplasm and few of the typical organelles. Sperm are little more than tiny packages of chromosomes equipped with mitochondria-powered flagella that enable the sperm to swim.

Mitosis, the most common form of cell division, produces two daughter cells that are identical to the original cell. Meiosis, on the other hand, produces daughter cells that have half the normal number of chromosomes—that is, they are haploid. These daughter cells are called gametes. Eggs and sperm are the female and male gametes, respectively.

Sperm are attracted to eggs from the same species. When egg and sperm come into contact, they fuse; in other words, **fertilization** occurs. The genetic material contained in the two gametes combines. Since both haploid gametes had $1n$ chromosomes—or half the normal number—the fertilized egg, called a **zygote,** is back to the normal diploid, or $2n$, number of chromosomes. It has DNA from *both* parents, however, and is therefore different from either. This **recombination** of genetic information to produce offspring that differ slightly from their parents is the most important feature of sexual reproduction.

In sexual reproduction two gametes, usually egg and sperm, fuse to create a genetically distinct individual.

The fertilized egg begins to divide by ordinary mitosis. Now called an **embryo,** it is nourished by the yolk. Through an extraordinarily complex process called embryological development, the embryo eventually becomes a new adult of the species. Along the way, most marine organisms pass through immature, or **larval,** stages that often look completely different from the adults (see Figs. 7.41 and 15.11).

Reproductive Strategies

Organisms reproduce in a nearly endless variety of ways (Fig. 4.21). Some species release millions of eggs and sperm into the water, where fertilization occurs, and have no further interaction with their offspring. This is called **broadcast spawning.** Others issue only a few offspring and invest a lot of time and energy in caring for them. Some species have many different larval stages, whereas others develop directly from egg to adult. Some reproduce asexually, some reproduce sexually, and some do both. In sexually reproducing species, males and females may always be separate individuals, or there may be **hermaphrodites,** individuals that have both male and female reproductive organs, either at the same time or at different times of life.

The particular combination of methods used by a given species is called its **reproductive strategy.** The strategy used by a species depends on its size, where and how it lives, and what kind of organism it is—in fact, on just about everything about it and its environment.

4.5 THE DIVERSITY OF LIFE IN THE SEA

There are so many different living things in the sea that it almost boggles the mind. From microscopic bacteria to gigantic whales, marine organisms come in all shapes, sizes, and colors. The ways in which they live are just as varied. Making sense of all this **diversity** might seem a hopeless task. Fortunately, there is a unifying concept that helps make the bewildering diversity of life comprehensible. This concept is the **theory of evolution.** Remember that scientists do not use the term "theory" lightly. Evolution, the gradual alteration of a species' genetic makeup, is supported by a vast body of evidence. The *ways* in which evolution occurs, on the other hand, never cease to fascinate biologists.

Natural Selection and Adaptation

Evolution occurs because individual organisms have genetic differences in their ability to find food and avoid being eaten, in their success at producing offspring, in their metabolism, and in countless other attributes. The best-adapted individuals, those most successful at meeting the challenges of the environment, produce more offspring on average than those that are not so well adapted. Charles Darwin, the nineteenth-century English naturalist who, along with

(a) Sea cucumber spawning (b) Male jawfish incubating eggs (c) Nursing fur seal (d) Seagrass fruit

FIGURE 4.21 Marine organisms have many different reproductive strategies, a few of which are shown here. (*a*) Many marine organisms, like this sea cucumber (*Holothuria leucospilota*) simply spawn into the water, a strategy known as broadcast spawning. Successful fertilization requires that other members of their species are spawning nearby and that currents will mix their eggs and sperm together. (*b*) Male yellowhead jawfish (*Opistognathus aurifrons*) aerate and incubate their fertilized eggs in their mouth, a relatively rare example of parental investment by the male partner. (*c*) Marine mammals like this New Zealand fur seal (*Arctocephalus forsteri*) take care of their young for much longer than most marine animals. (*d*) There are very few marine flowering plants—those that flower and produce fruit and seeds. Seagrasses are the most common. This is the fruit of the Indo-Pacific seagrass *Enhalus acoroides*, which along with being the world's largest seagrass has the largest flowers and fruit.

another English biologist, Alfred Wallace, first proposed the modern theory of evolution, called this process **natural selection.**

The best-adapted individuals not only produce more offspring, they also pass their favorable characteristics on to those offspring. The favorable traits therefore become more common, and over generations the population as a whole gradually becomes more similar to the best-adapted individuals. Thus, the result of natural selection is that the population continually adapts to its environment—that is, it evolves.

> Natural selection occurs when some members of a population survive and reproduce more successfully in their particular environment than others. Evolution is the genetic change in the population that results because these more successful individuals pass their favorable characteristics on to their young.

Every population is constantly adapting to its environment. The world is an ever-changing place, however, and organisms are continually faced with new challenges. Populations either adapt to the changes in the environment or become extinct, making way for others. Evolution is an endless process.

Classifying Living Things

The adaptation of populations to different environments has produced a fantastic variety of life forms. It is difficult to study and discuss the millions of life forms on Earth without sorting them into groups according to their similarities and differences. One of the goals of biological classification is to give a universally accepted name to different types of organisms so that scientists from all over the world can call a species by the same name.

The Biological Species Concept We have loosely defined a species as a "type" of organism, but what exactly does that mean? After all, fishes are all the same general type of animal, but a sailfish is obviously not the same species as a tuna (see Figs. 1.15 and 1.17).

No definition is perfect, but here we will define species as populations of organisms that have common characteristics and can successfully breed with each other. This definition is often referred to as the **biological species concept.**

Successful breeding means that the offspring produced are fertile and can themselves propagate the species. Dogs, to use a familiar example, are all the same species because all breeds of dog—no matter how different they may look—can interbreed to produce fertile offspring. Organisms that cannot breed with each other are not members of the same species no matter how similar they look. When two populations are unable to interbreed successfully, they are said to be **reproductively isolated.**

> A species is a population of organisms that share common characteristics, can breed with each other, and are reproductively isolated from other populations.

This definition of species seems simple, but nature is anything but simple. Dogs can breed with wolves and the offspring are fertile and can themselves breed with either parent species. Dogs and wolves are still considered different species because they *don't* actually interbreed very often. This situation is very common in marine organisms, and though the species concept is a powerful tool for marine biologists it is still a human concept imposed upon the complex reality of nature.

In fact, more and more biologists have come to understand that the traditional biological species concept doesn't reflect the reality of the biological world very well. It does serve the very useful purpose of defining categories of organisms, so that biologists working around the world can be clear about what group of organisms they are describing or studying. But another purpose of the concept has been to capture the evolutionary relationships among

> **Scientific Theory** A *hypothesis* that is accepted as "true" because it has passed test after test and is supported by a large body of evidence.
> • 1.2, The Scientific Method

EYE ON SCIENCE

Box 4.2 When Fishes Stepped on Land

Organisms evolve in tiny steps, with each change only incrementally different from before, so a key challenge in evolutionary biology is to understand how complex and radically different new structures could have evolved. Fins are great for swimming, and legs are great for walking, but how did animals get from one to the other while still being able to catch food, avoid predators, and find mates every step of the way? Recent breakthroughs have helped us understand how fishes moved onto land to become tetrapods (animals with two pairs of limbs).

Paleontologists recently discovered fossils of a fish *(Tiktaalik roseae)* that appears very close to the so-called missing link between fishes and the first land vertebrates. *Tiktaalik* lived about 375 million years ago, 10–15 million years before the earliest known fossil tetrapods. The arrangement of bones in *Tiktaalik's* fins is almost perfectly intermediate between the limbs of early tetrapods and the fins of lobe-finned fishes, the ancestors of tetrapods. In particular, *Tiktaalik's* fin bones foreshadow the elbow, wrist, and fingers

of tetrapods. *Tiktaalik* was probably unable to walk, but it could at least use its fins to do push-ups. *Tiktaalik*, had other features that would be refined in tetrapods, such as the beginnings of the first neck. Like its fins, *Tiktaalik's* skull and associated vertebrae have features in between those of fishes and tetrapods. Scientists doubt that *Tiktaalik* is the direct ancestor of tetrapods, but it is probably a very close cousin. Every summer *Tiktaalik's* discoverers return to the Canadian Arctic where they found its fossils in hope of new discoveries about the emergence of tetrapods, which 300 million years later would return to the sea as whales (see Box 9.2, "The Whales That Walked to Sea").

Meanwhile, biologists are learning the genetic basis for these changes. The key is that evolution does not have to completely reinvent the wheel—or the limb. The genome is flexible enough that the same basic system, with only minor tweaks, can control the development of a range of different structures. The earliest fishes did not have paired fins on the side, only median fins and single fins

along the midline like the dorsal fin of sharks (see "Cartilaginous Fishes," in 8.2). In today's sharks the dorsal fin and paired fins develop from different cells in different parts of the embryo, but biologists recently showed that the same genetic programs control the embryonic development of both. These genes are also involved in the development of median fins in lampreys, primitive fishes that branched off before paired fins emerged (see "Jawless Fishes," in 8.2), and the development of wings in chick embryos. Thus, the same genetic mechanism controls the development of median fins, paired fins, limbs, and wings. Paired fins and limbs did not evolve from scratch, but emerged through the application of the molecular system that was already producing median fins. The researchers are testing this hypothesis by studying lancelets, the nearest invertebrate relatives of vertebrates (see 7.10).

For more information, explore the links provided on the Marine Biology *Online Learning Center.*

**Lobe-finned Fish
380 million years ago**

Tiktaalik

**Early Tetrapod
365 million years ago**

Source: Bill Ober

different organisms and populations, and this is where the concept runs into difficulties. This is a good example of how scientists must adapt their theories to take new information into account.

For one thing, vast numbers of bacteria and microorganisms don't reproduce sexually. Thus, the biological species concept of an interbreeding population doesn't apply at all. Microbes *do* exchange genetic information, through the process of **horizontal gene transfer,** in which cells, sometimes very different types of cells, directly exchange genetic information. This is, for example, a major way in which antibiotic resistance has been transferred among very different types of bacteria.

The biological species concept doesn't necessarily work well to describe evolutionary relationships even for more complex organisms. First, all biological populations are constantly evolving to adapt to a changing environment. At some point in time, new species arise from old. The biological species concept tends to impose snapshots in time on what is really a continual process. This is reinforced by recent findings that **hybridization,** the interbreeding of what were thought to be genetically isolated populations, is much more common than had been thought. Hybridization is another powerful evolutionary mechanism to recombine genetic information and allow populations to adapt.

Throughout this text we refer to biological species, but it should be remembered that this is a human construct, and is mostly used simply as a tool to refer to a specific group of organisms.

Biological Nomenclature Species are traditionally identified by two names, the name of their **genus** and a species name or, more correctly, **species epithet.** A genus is a group of very similar species. Dogs, for example, have the scientific name *Canis familiaris.* They are closely related to other species in the genus *Canis,* like wolves, *Canis lupus,* and coyotes, *Canis latrans.* Similarly, the genus *Balaenoptera* contains several related species of whales, including the blue whale, *Balaenoptera musculus;* the fin whale, *Balaenoptera*

physalus; and the minke whale, *Balaenoptera acutorostrata.* This two-name system is called **binomial nomenclature.** It was first introduced in the eighteenth century by the Swedish biologist Carolus Linnaeus. At that time Latin was the language of scholars and Latin is still used for scientific names, along with Greek. By convention, binomial names are always underlined or italicized. The first letter of the generic name, but not the species epithet, is capitalized. When the name of the genus has been previously mentioned it may be abbreviated. Thus, the blue whale could be identified as *B. musculus.* The species epithet is never used by itself, but only in conjunction with the genus name or initial.

Students often ask why biologists have to use complicated, hard-to-pronounce Latin or Greek names rather than ordinary common names. The trouble with common names is that they are imprecise and mean different things to different people. The same common name may be applied to different species, and the same species may have different common names. The name "spiny lobster" (Fig. 4.22), for example, is applied to many different species that are not even all in the same genus. Australians call spiny lobsters "crayfish." Americans reserve the name "crayfish" for freshwater relatives of lobsters. Things get even more confusing when people speak different languages. In Spanish, spiny lobsters are called *langostas,* which can also refer to grasshoppers. Another example is the name "dolphin," which is applied not only to the lovable relatives of whales but also to a delicious game fish. Dolphin fish are called *dorado* in Latin America and *mahimahi* in Hawai'i. At the local crab shack this confusion is only a minor annoyance. To biologists, however, it is essential to precisely identify the particular individual species they are discussing. The use of scientific names, accepted worldwide, avoids confusion.

Confusion about common names can have practical implications as well. After a dive on an unfamiliar coral reef near Australia, one of the authors mentioned to his dive buddy that he'd seen a gray reef shark. Gray reef sharks, although not so dangerous as to force you out of the water, can be aggressive and merit attention and respect—in fact there are more documented attacks on humans by gray reef sharks than any other shark species. The diving partner, who was familiar with the area, replied that the shark was not a gray reef, but a "graceful whaler." "Looked like a gray reef shark to me," thought the author but, reassured, he continued diving, blissfully ignoring the "graceful whalers" that swam by. Only later did he discover that "graceful whaler" was just a local name for the gray reef shark, *Carcharhinus amblyrhynchos*!

Phylogenetics: Reconstructing Evolution The goals of biological classification include not only assigning agreed names to organisms but also grouping them according to their relatedness. Most people instinctively understand that a seal is related to a sea lion, for example, or that oysters and clams are related. They might be hard-pressed, though, to explain exactly what they mean by "related." So are biologists. Biologists have agreed that "related" means that species share a common evolutionary history, or **phylogeny.** In particular, it means that both groups evolved from a common ancestor. Closely related groups evolved

Charlie Arneson

FIGURE 4.22 *Panulirus interruptus,* the Pacific spiny lobster, is sometimes called a rock lobster or a crayfish depending on where you live.

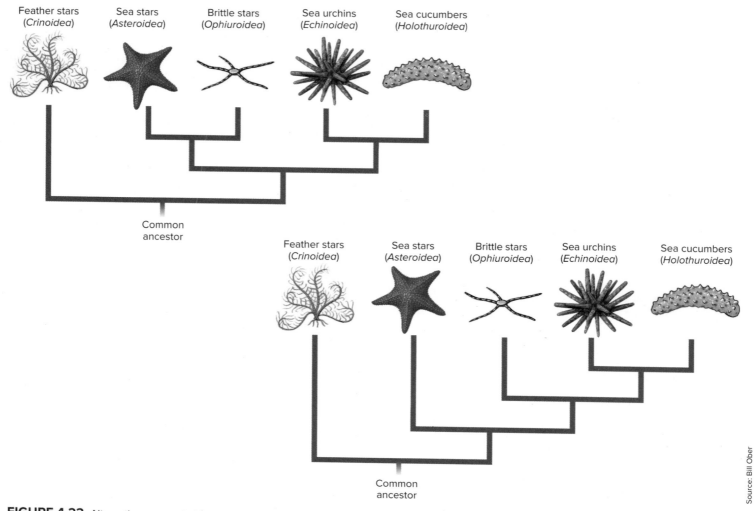

FIGURE 4.23 Alternative proposals for the phylogeny of the major groups of echinoderms. Both schemes accept that feather stars diverged early from the common ancestor of all echinoderms and that urchins and sea cucumbers are more closely related to each other than to other echinoderms. The proposals differ, however, with regard to the phylogeny of sea stars and brittle stars. Conflicting hypotheses like these are common in phylogenetics.

from common ancestors relatively recently, while the common ancestors of distantly related groups occurred further in the past. The study of such evolutionary relationships is called **phylogenetics.**

It can be difficult to determine the phylogenetic relationships among organisms. Very few groups have a good record of fossils that trace their evolutionary history.

Usually the fossil record is incomplete or nonexistent. Biologists have traditionally tried to piece together an organism's evolutionary history from other evidence, such as body structure, reproduction, embryological and larval development, and behavior. Modern technology that allows us to analyze DNA and RNA sequences, and their differences among species, have revolutionized our understanding of phylogeny, including the biological species concept. Because evolution is genetic change by definition, the study of the nucleic acids that store organisms' genetic information reveals the history of evolution. Different analyses sometimes give a different picture of phylogeny (Fig. 4.23). Classification schemes change and new arguments arise as fresh information becomes available, but our understanding of how life has evolved is increasing as never before.

As noted previously, biological classification seeks to group organisms according to their relatedness. Species that are very closely related, for example, are grouped into the same genus.

Genera with similar phylogenies can be grouped together into a larger group, called a family. This process can be continued to sort organisms into progressively larger groups. All the members of a group, or **taxon** (plural, **taxa**), have certain common characteristics and are thought to share a common ancestry. Taxa are systematically arranged in a hierarchy that extends from the most general classification, the domain, down to the species (Table 4.3).

The Tree of Life In centuries past, all organisms were classified as either plants (kingdom **Plantae**) or animals (kingdom **Animalia**). But vast numbers of organisms don't fit this ancient classification scheme. A system of five kingdoms became widely accepted. In addition to the Animalia and Plantae, this traditional system included fungi (kingdom **Fungi**), bacteria (kingdom **Monera**), and protists (kingdom **Protista**). Fungi are multicellular, heterotrophic organisms that are neither plants nor animals. Protists are an extremely varied group of organisms, some plant-like and some animal-like, that includes both unicellular eukaryotes and multicellular seaweeds. Biologists now recognize that protists are a collection of taxa with different evolutionary histories rather than a true kingdom, although for convenience they are still often grouped together under the name "protists."

Table 4.3 Biological Classification of Humans (*Homo sapiens*) and the Bottlenose Dolphin (*Tursiops truncatus*)

Taxonomic Level	Example
Human	
Domain	Eukarya
Kingdom	Animalia
Phylum	Chordata
Class	Mammalia
Order	Primates
Family	Hominidae
Genus	*Homo*
Species	*Homo sapiens*
Dolphin	
Domain	Eukarya
Kingdom	Animalia
Phylum	Chordata
Class	Mammalia
Order	Cetacea
Family	Delphinidae
Genus	*Tursiops*
Species	*Tursiops truncatus*

Tursiops truncatus, the bottlenose dolphin.

Note: The term "division" is used in place of "phylum" in the classification of plants.

In recent years, studies of the RNA and cellular chemistry of prokaryotes have led biologists to conclude that there are two main groups of prokaryotes that are as different from each other as they are from all eukaryotic organisms (see 5.2). To recognize this, some classification systems place these two groups of prokaryotes into two new kingdoms, the **Bacteria** and the **Archaea.** Other systems recognize a new taxon, the domain, that is even more general than the kingdom; in this system the Bacteria and Archaea are separate domains and each includes a number of different kingdoms. In this text, we use the three-domain system of classification (Fig. 4.24), but not all biologists agree with this system.

Viruses are not included in this system because biologists are not in agreement that they are alive or where to fit them in the tree of life (see 5.1). Viruses consist of a small number of genes, compared to cellular life forms, which encoded are in either RNA or DNA, enclosed in a capsule of proteins. Viruses are best known for causing disease in humans. Viruses also infect marine organisms, from prokaryotes to marine mammals, and even other viruses, and in doing so have been a driving force in evolution and play a major role in marine food webs.

FIGURE 4.24 The major groups of living things.

Interactive Exploration

McGraw-Hill Connect® is a great place to check your understanding of chapter material. Visit **www.mcgrawhillconnect.com** for access to interactive chapter summaries, chapter quizzing, and more! Further enhance your knowledge with video clips and weblinks to chapter-related material.

Critical Thinking

1. During the day, algae carry out both photosynthesis and respiration, but at night they can only perform respiration. Small, isolated tide pools on rocky shores often have thick growths of seaweeds, which are algae. Would you expect the amount of oxygen in the water to differ between night and day? How?

2. The cells of some marine organisms have high concentrations of ions found in minute amounts in seawater. Could these organisms accumulate the ions by diffusion? Formulate a hypothesis to explain how this accumulation is accomplished. How might this hypothesis be tested?

For Further Reading

Some of the recommended reading may be available online. Look for live links on the *Marine Biology* Online Learning Center.

General Interest

Barras, C., 2015. Adapt first, mutate later. *New Scientist*, vol. 205, no. 3004, 17 January, pp. 26–30. Biologists accept that natural selection acts to winnow out favorable genetic mutations. Now there is evidence that physiological adaption can drive such mutation.

Baum, D. A., 2015. Selection and the origin of cells. *BioScience*, vol. 65, no. 7, 1 July, pp. 678–684. How cells arose.

Bowler, P., 2016. Darwin and DNA. *New Scientist*, vol. 231, no 3088, 27 August, pp. 39–43. It took nearly 60 years for biologists to recognize that evolution by natural selection was a genetic process.

Cogdell, R., 2013. Instant Expert 30: Photosynthesis. *New Scientist*, vol. 217, no. 2902, 2 February, pp. i–viii. A summary of the process and potential applications in sustainable energy.

Costa, J. T., 2017. *Darwin's Backyard*. W.W. Norton & Co. Darwin is justly famous for his observations and collections on the *Beagle* expedition, but he developed his revolutionary ideas about the natural world through careful study and reflection in his later years.

Dance, A., 2021. The incredible diversity of viruses. *Nature*, vol. 595, no. 7865, 1 July, pp. 22–25. Viruses are everywhere and are major drivers of the biosphere.

DeSalle, R., and I. Tatersall, 2018. The name game. *Natural History*, vol. 126, no. 6, June. We humans have a need to put everything into boxes with labels—not limited to all of life, but even ourselves.

Douglas, K., 2016. Intelligent without design. *New Scientist*, vol. 229, no. 3066, 26 March, pp. 34–39. Genes don't act independently, instead they are networked with other genes. As a result, evolution has similarities to learning.

Dunker, A. K. and R. W Kriwacki, 2011. The orderly chaos of proteins. *Scientific American*, vol. 304, April, pp. 68–73. New findings about the complex functions of proteins.

Hagen, J. B., 2012. Five kingdoms, more or less: Robert Whittaker and the broad classification of organisms. *BioScience*, vol. 62, pp. 67–74. The five-kingdom system of classification, rather than the traditional two-kingdom system, became a standard in biology.

Hargreaves, A., 2018. The hunt for dark DNA. *New Scientist*, vol 237, no. 3168, pp. 29–31. The functions of DNA are much more complex than coding for protein synthesis.

Holmes, B., 2017. Before the beginning. New Scientist, vol. 236, no. 3150, 4 November, pp. 28–31. We all descend from the primordial life form that invented nucleic acids.

Laland, K., 2016. Evolution evolves. *New Scientist*, vol. 231, no. 3092, 24 September, pp. 41–45. New information challenges our traditional understanding of evolution: It's a lot more than parents passing genes to offspring.

Madhusoodanan, J., 2020. The cell's sweet side exposed. *Nature*, vol. 579, no. 7799, 19 March, pp. 459–461. New techniques are revealing the critical roles of glycans—combinations of proteins and complex sugars, in many functions of cells.

Milius, S., 2015. Strange relations. *Science News*, vol. 188, no. 3, 8 August, pp. 22–27. The struggle to understand how the vast diversity of today's life on Earth evolved is never-ending.

Multiple authors, 2020. Evolving evolution. *New Scientist*, vol. 247, no. 3301, 26 September. The theory of evolution underpins modern biology, but we are still learning about it. Twelve different authors describe new facets of our understanding.

Sarchet, P., 2016. Life, spontaneously. *New Scientist*, vol. 231, no. 3087, 20 August, pp. 26–29. Life may have spontaneously arisen multiple times and in multiple places.

van Wyhe, J., 2016. Darwin's discovery: the remarkable history of evolution. *New Scientist*, vol. 231, no., 3082, 13 July, pp. 35–39. The story of how Darwin came to understand the process of evolution by natural selection.

Williams, C., 2011. Who are you calling simple? *New Scientist*, vol. 211, no. 2821, 16 July, pp. 38–41. The rules about the supposedly simple cells of bacteria have exceptions.

In Depth

Ding, Y., Q. Zhou, and W. Wang, 2012. Origins of new genes and evolution of their novel functions. *Annual Review of Ecology, Evolution, and Systematics*, vol. 43, pp. 345–363.

Foo, S.A. and M. Byrne, 2016. Acclimatization and adaptive capacity of marine species in a changing ocean. *Advances in Marine Biology*, vol. 74, pp. 69–116.

Giesen, M., 2011. Mitochondria and the rise of eukaryotes. *BioScience*, vol. 61, pp. 594–601.

Kaji, T., A. Anker, C. S. Winker, and A. R. Palmer, 2018. Parallel evolution of ultrafast movements in snapping shrimp claws. *Current Biology*, vol. 28, no. 1, pp. 106–113.

Vermeij, G. J., 2012. The evolution of gigantism on temperate seashores. *Biological Journal of the Linnean Society*, vol. 106, pp. 776–793.

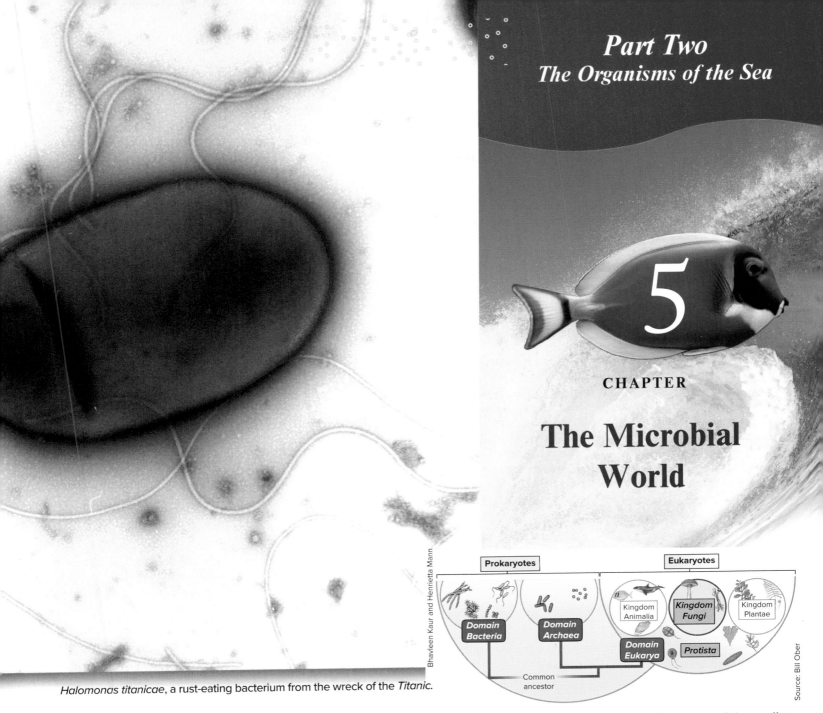

Bhavleen Kaur and Henrietta Mann

Source: Bill Ober

Halomonas titanicae, a rust-eating bacterium from the wreck of the *Titanic*.

Part Two
The Organisms of the Sea

CHAPTER

5

The Microbial World

This chapter, the first in our survey of life in the ocean, is devoted to marine **microorganisms,** which are easily the most abundant forms of marine life. Microorganisms live everywhere in the ocean, from the deepest trenches to the highest tide pools, and even below the sea floor. The microbial world includes an incredibly diverse assortment of organisms, and new microorganisms are discovered all the time. The various groups of marine microorganisms discussed in this chapter have little in common and span all three biological **domains,** the most basic divisions of life (the diagram on this page and Fig. 4.24). They do share having a small size, much smaller than most other forms of life (see Appendix A for relative size), hence the name of "microorganisms" or "microbes." The diversity of the microbial world can be bewildering even to **microbiologists,** the biologists who study microorganisms, and much of the scientific debate about how to group organisms into kingdoms within domains centers on microorganisms.

Though marine microorganisms include some of the smallest and structurally simplest organisms, they have played critical roles in the evolution of life on our planet. Indeed, without microorganisms there would be no life on Earth. Not only did life as we know it today evolve from microorganisms, but without them the planet could not support other forms of life.

Microorganisms are the most important **primary producers** in many marine environments, and directly or indirectly they feed most marine animals. Some microorganisms make essential nutrients available to primary producers, either for the first time or by recycling them. Others swim about in the water to ingest food very much as animals do and play critical roles in marine food webs.

Primary Producers Organisms that manufacture organic matter from carbon dioxide (CO_2), usually by photosynthesis.

• 4.1, The Ingredients of Life

The ecological relevance of microorganisms will unravel in upcoming chapters, which will look in more detail at the key position of microbes in the economy of the world ocean.

5.1 VIRUSES

Most biologists consider **viruses** to be non-living. Unlike living organisms, a virus is a particle not made up of a cell. Viruses consist of only a short chain of genetic material (**nucleic acid**) containing relatively few **genes** and protected by an outer protein coat, or **capsid.** They are parasites that reproduce and develop only when infecting a living cell. Nearly all viruses are minute, roughly between 20 and 200 nm, 1 nm being equal to one-billionth of a meter, or 1,000 μm (see Appendix A for relative size). They can be seen only with the most powerful electron microscopes. A giant marine virus (Fig. 5.1) is an exception, being 440 nm in diameter and thus visible through an ordinary light microscope.

Several types of viruses have been described. **Retroviruses** store their genetic information in the form of single-stranded **RNA,** in contrast to the double-stranded **DNA** of most viruses and all forms of life. Retroviruses are responsible for deadly human diseases, such as AIDS and some types of leukemia. Some viruses reproduce by attaching into a living cell and injecting their nucleic acid into the cell. The viral nucleic acid then commands the cell to produce, or replicate, copies of the virus, which are ultimately released as the infected cell bursts. The new generation of viruses then infects other cells or is released from the organism to infect new hosts. Another type, the **lysogenic** viruses, reproduce by inducing their nucleic acid to become part of the

complete genetic information contained in the DNA, or **genome,** of the host cell. The infecting virus will then, sometimes long afterward, direct the production not of host proteins but of new viruses. Many more viruses are then released as the infected cell is destroyed. Of particular importance in the ocean are the highly diverse **bacteriophages,** viruses that specifically target—and destroy—bacteria.

Until recently, marine viruses were practically ignored by marine scientists. They are nearly invisible, so it was not until the development of new techniques (see Box 5.2, "Tiny Cells, Big Surprises") that viruses were shown to be extremely common in marine environments and to play an important role in the complex cycles of life in the ocean. Though viruses are not referred to as living "organisms" in the strict sense of the word, viruses constitute the most abundant and diverse life-like particles in the ocean. Virus numbers in water samples can be determined by staining them with chemicals and observing them under a microscope, something that can be done on a research vessel. Their numbers in seawater samples can be staggering. Viruses are extremely abundant in deep-sea sediments ("Microbes in the Deep Sea," in 16.3), in polar waters, and in water polluted by sewage.

The abundance of viruses in the water is directly related to the abundance of microbial life, particularly bacteria, which they infect and destroy in order to reproduce. Viruses also infect other marine microbes that form part of the **phytoplankton,** the very important primary producers that are part of the drifting **plankton** (see 5.3). The bursting of the cells of bacteria (mostly by bacteriophages) and phytoplankton as the result of viral infections also releases into the water large amounts of organic molecules and cell debris, which make up **dissolved organic matter (DOM).** DOM cannot be utilized as such by most organisms. It is, however, readily taken in by bacteria and other microbes. These microbes are eaten by small **zooplankton,** the non-photosynthetic components of the plankton, which are then eaten by larger zooplankton, so that the energy contained in DOM, a significant part of primary production by the phytoplankton, is not lost but ultimately is available to all kinds of animals, from small fishes to whales (see "The Microbial Loop," in 15.3). The bursting of cells as a result of viral infections also releases some essential nutrients, which can then be made available to primary producers. Some viruses infecting phytoplankton "hijack" the process of photosynthesis and shift some of the captured solar energy to their own reproduction.

Viruses are also responsible for diseases affecting marine life other than microbes. Some viruses affect molluscs and crustaceans of commercial importance, while others cause serious diseases in other invertebrates, fishes, sea turtles, and marine mammals. Humans are also vulnerable. Oysters and mussels that filter hepatitis viruses from sewage-contaminated water commonly infect humans eating them raw or improperly cooked.

5.2 PROKARYOTES

Prokaryotes are the smallest and structurally simplest true living organisms and the oldest forms of life on Earth. Prokaryotes are made up of a cell that lacks a nucleus and other organelles (see Fig. 4.7), whereas the cells of **eukaryotes** have a nucleus and several types of organelles (see Fig. 4.8). Nonetheless, they carry out nearly all the chemical processes performed by supposedly more complex organisms, as well as many that are unique to prokaryotes (Table 5.1). Most of these chemical processes actually evolved first among prokaryotes.

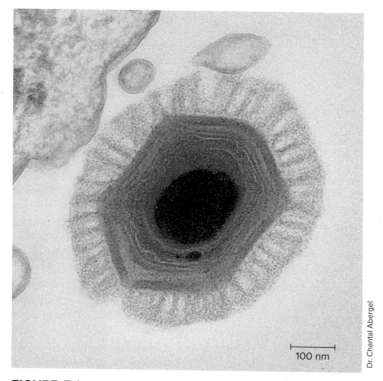

100 nm

Dr. Chantal Abergel

FIGURE 5.1 *Megavirus,* one of the largest viruses ever recorded, has a diameter of 440 nm and bigger than some bacteria, was discovered off the coast of Chile in 2010. It appears to live in marine amebas. The capsid, or outer coat, has hair-like structures. Its DNA has been estimated to have around 1,120 genes, more than some bacteria.

Table 5.1 Examples of Metabolic Reactions in Marine Prokaryotes

Name of Reaction	Energy Source	Other Raw Materials	By-product(s)	Production of Organic Carbon	Major Groups	Comments and *Examples*
Photosynthesis	Light	Carbon dioxide, water	Oxygen	Yes	Cyanobacteria	Light captured by chlorophyll, essentially the same process performed by algae and plants
	Light	Hydrogen sulfide	Sulfur or sulfate	Yes	Purple and green bacteria	Light captured by bacteriochlorophyll
Chemosynthesis						Energy supplied by a variety of inorganic molecules, of which only a few examples are included here
Sulfur oxidation	Hydrogen sulfide	Oxygen	Sulfate	Yes	Sulfur-oxidizing bacteria	*Bacteria in wetland sediments, mudflats, deep-sea hydrothermal vents*
Aerobic ammonium oxidation	Ammonium	Oxygen	Nitrite	Yes	Nitrifying bacteria and archaea	*Bacteria in wetland sediments, mudflats, deep-sea hydrothermal vents; open-water archaea*
Nitrite oxidation	Nitrite	Oxygen	Nitrate	Yes	Nitrifying bacteria	*Bacteria in wetland sediments, mudflats, deep-sea hydrothermal vents*
Iron oxidation	Reduced iron	Oxygen	Oxidized iron	Yes	Iron-oxidizing bacteria	*Bacteria in sediments, deep-sea hydrothermal vents*
Aerobic respiration	Organic matter	Oxygen	Carbon dioxide, water	No	Heterotrophic, aerobic bacteria and archaea; decay bacteria and archaea	Organic matter broken down using oxygen to release energy
Anaerobic respiration						Organic matter broken down in the absence of oxygen to release energy; less efficient than aerobic respiration
Sulfate reduction	Organic matter	Sulfate	Hydrogen sulfide	No	Sulfate-reducing bacteria and archaea	
Nitrate reduction, denitrification	Organic matter	Nitrate, nitrite	Nitrogen gas, ammonia	No	Denitrifying bacteria	
Methanogenesis	Organic matter	Hydrogen, carbon dioxide	Methane	No	Methanogens	*Archaea in many environments*
Nitrogen fixation	ATP	Nitrogen gas	Ammonium	No	Nitrogen-fixing bacteria and archaea	Ammonium and other compounds produced from ammonium can be used as nutrients by primary producers
Anaerobic ammonium oxidation	Ammonium	Nitrite	Nitrogen gas	No	Some bacteria and archaea	Ammonium converted to nitrogen in the absence of oxygen to release energy
Light-mediated ATP synthesis	Light		ATP	No	Archaeum in highly saline pools	Light captured by bacteriorhodopsin

In contrast to viruses, prokaryotes are made up of a single cell. Prokaryotic cells are enclosed by a protective **cell wall.** The **cell,** or **plasma, membrane** lies immediately inside the cell wall (see Fig. 4.7). Prokaryotes not only lack a nucleus and most other membrane-bound organelles but also differ from **eukaryotes** in the circular shape of the DNA molecules that encode their genetic information, the size of their ribosomes, and a number of other ways.

Despite their similarities, the two prokaryotic domains, **Bacteria** and **Archaea,** also have important differences, including the chemistry of their cell walls (see Table 5.2), cell membranes, and the cellular machinery that manufactures proteins. In fact, genetic analyses indicate that bacteria and archaea are as different from each other as they are from humans.

Bacteria

Bacteria (domain **Bacteria**) appear to have branched out very early on the tree of life and are genetically distant from both archaea and eukaryotes (see phylogenetic relationship in Fig. 4.24 and at the beginning of this chapter). Because they are structurally simple, bacteria (singular, **bacterium**) are classified as prokaryotes. Nevertheless, they have evolved a great range of metabolic abilities. They are abundant in all parts of the ocean.

Bacterial cells have many shapes, including spheres, spirals, rods, and rings (Fig. 5.2), depending on the species. The unique chemistry of bacterial cell walls (see Table 5.2) makes them rigid and strong. A stiff or slimy covering often surrounds the cell wall as additional protection or a means of attaching to surfaces. The cells are very small (see Appendix A for relative size), much smaller than those of single-celled eukaryotes. About 250,000 average bacterial cells would fit on the period at the end of this sentence. There are exceptions, however, such as a sediment bacterium discovered off southwest Africa (Fig. 5.3). The largest bacterium so far known is *Thiomargarita magnifica*, discovered in underwater mangrove leaves in the French West Indies. It grows as hair-like filaments that can reach 1 cm, or 0.39 in. In large numbers, marine bacteria are sometimes visible as whitish hairs on rotting seaweed or iridescent or pink patches on the surface of stagnant pools in mudflats and salt marshes.

Bacteria can grow to extremely high numbers in favorable environments such as **detritus,** particles of dead organic matter. **Decay**

FIGURE 5.2 A high-magnification photograph taken with an electron microscope showing *Cyclobacterium marinus*, a ring-forming marine bacterium.

Dr. Harkisan D. Raj

FIGURE 5.3 Three cells of *Thiomargarita namibiensis*, one of the largest known bacteria. Cells can be 0.75 mm (0.03 in) wide. The round, yellowish structures are sulfur granules. *Thiomargarita* lives in oxygen-poor water.

Heide Schulz, University of California, Davis

bacteria break down waste products and dead organic matter and release nutrients into the environment. They are vital to life on Earth because they ensure the recycling of essential nutrients, as in the recycling of dissolved organic matter in oceanic food webs (see "The Microbial Loop," in 15.3). Most organic matter is sooner or later broken down by **decomposition,** though in very deep, cold water the process is slower than elsewhere (see "Microbes in the Deep Sea," in 16.3). **Decay** bacteria (or **decomposers,** those that carry out decomposition) play another crucial role because they constitute a major part of the organic matter that feeds countless bottom-dwelling animals. Even many organic particles in the water column are composed mostly of bacteria. Some marine bacteria are also involved in degrading oil and other toxic pollutants that find their way into the environment. The same process of decomposition is unfortunately involved in the spoilage of valuable fish and shellfish (molluscs and crustaceans) catches. Other types of marine bacteria cause diseases in marine animals and humans.

Bacteria are found everywhere in the marine environment, on almost all surfaces and in the water column. In fact, the most abundant forms of life on the planet seem to be bacteria, found in surprisingly high numbers in open water. Their role, though probably highly significant due to their vast numbers, remains unknown. Bacteria have also been found in seemingly harsh environments, such as in sediment more than 3 km (1.9 mi) below the sea floor (see Box 2.1, "Life Below the Sea Floor").

> Bacteria are structurally simple microorganisms that are particularly significant as decomposers, breaking down organic compounds into nutrients that can be used by other organisms, and as primary producers. They are also an important food source.

Cyanobacteria, once known as blue-green algae, are a group of **photosynthetic** bacteria (see "Autotrophs," below). In addition to having the pigment chlorophyll *a*, as do eukaryotic photosynthetic organisms (see 6.1), most contain a bluish pigment called **phycocyanin.** Most marine cyanobacteria also have a reddish pigment, **phycoerythrin.** The visible color of the organism depends on the relative amounts of the two pigments. When phycocyanin predominates, the bacteria appear blue-green; when phycoerythrin predominates, they appear red. Two other groups of photosynthetic bacteria are the **purple** and **green bacteria** (see Table 5.1).

Cyanobacteria were among the first photosynthetic organisms on Earth. They are thought to have had an important role in the accumulation of oxygen (O_2) in our atmosphere. Fossil

stromatolites, massive **calcareous** (made of CaCO₃) mounds formed by cyanobacteria, are known to date back some 3 billion years. Stromatolites are still being formed in tropical seas (Fig. 5.4).

Cyanobacteria are widely distributed in the marine environment. *Prochlorococcus,* a minute cyanobacterium, is thought to be the most abundant photosynthetic organism in the ocean. It is particularly common in the nutrient-poor tropical and subtropical waters. Many species of cyanobacteria can tolerate wide ranges of salinity and temperature, while others are found in unexpected places, like inside the hair of polar bears! Some cyanobacteria, called **endolithic,** burrow into calcareous rocks and coral skeletons. Others form thick, dark crusts along the wave-splashed zone of rocky coasts. Some exploit oxygen-poor sediments, including polluted sites. Cyanobacteria that are members of the **plankton** can rapidly multiply and change the color of the water. Some so-called **red tides** (see Box 15.1, "Red Tides and Harmful Algal Blooms") are caused by cyanobacteria that contain a red pigment. A few species can cause skin rashes on swimmers and divers.

Some cyanobacteria live on the surface of seaweeds and seagrasses. Photosynthetic organisms that live on algae or plants are called **epiphytes.** Some biologists, however, use this term to refer to *all* organisms living on algae or plants. Other cyanobacteria live inside algae and are called **endophytes.**

> Cyanobacteria are photosynthetic bacteria. They were one of the first groups of photosynthetic organisms on Earth.

FIGURE 5.4 Stromatolites, calcareous mounds deposited by cyanobacteria, are frequently found as fossils. These, however, are living stromatolites growing in shallow water in the Exuma Cays, Bahama Islands.

Charlie Arneson

Archaea

Archaea (domain **Archaea**) are among the simplest, most primitive forms of life. Some look very similar to the oldest fossils ever found, cells estimated to be at least 3.8 billion years old. Archaea are thought to have had an important role in the early evolution of life. Like bacteria, their cells are small and can be spherical (Fig. 5.5), spiral, or rod-shaped. In fact, archaea (singular, **archaeum**) were thought to be bacteria. The origins of Archaea remain unclear. Despite being prokaryotic, however, there is evidence that archaea are more closely related to eukaryotes than to bacteria (see Box 5.1, "The Origin of Eukaryotes").

Some groups of archaea were discovered only recently, first in extreme environments on land, such as hot sulfur springs, saline lakes, and highly acidic or basic environments. Archaea were thus named "extremophiles," meaning "lovers of extremes." Archaea were subsequently found in extreme marine environments, such as in very deep water, where they survive at pressures of 300 to 800 atmospheres. Some archaea live at the high temperatures of **hydrothermal vents** (Fig. 5.5). Some of these cannot grow in temperatures less than 70 to 80 °C (158 to 176 °F), and one hydrothermal

vent archaeum can live at 121 °C (250 °F), the highest of any known organism. Other archaea depend on extremely salty environments, such as coastal salt pans and deep ocean basins.

Because the first groups of microorganisms to be classified as archaea were extremophiles, it was thought that *all* archaea were extremophiles; indeed, the two terms became almost synonymous. New techniques based on detecting **nucleic acid** sequences, however, have shown that archaea are common in many marine environments, not only in the water column (see Box 5.2, "Tiny Cells, Big Surprises") but also in sediments. Some archaea are also known to live symbiotically in sponges, sea cucumbers, and fishes. Thus, the hypothesis that archaea are restricted to extreme environments was proven false.

> Archaea are prokaryotic microorganisms once thought to be bacteria but more closely related to eukaryotes. They were first known from extreme environments, but they are now known to be common in the marine environment.

Plankton Primary producers (*phytoplankton*) and consumers (*zooplankton*) that drift with the currents.
• 10.2, Major Marine Lifestyles and Environments; Figure 10.11

Prokaryotes Organisms with cells that do not have a nucleus or most other organelles.
• 4.2, Living Machinery; Figure 4.7

Eukaryotes Organisms with cells that contain a nucleus and other organelles that are enclosed by membranes.
• 4.2, Living Machinery; Figure 4.8

Nucleic Acids DNA and RNA, complex molecules that store and transmit genetic information.
Gene A sequence of *nucleotides* in the DNA molecule that directs the production of a particular protein.
• 4.1, The Ingredients of Life

EYE ON SCIENCE

Box 5.1 The Origin of Eukaryotes

How the more complex cell structure of eukaryotes evolved from simpler prokaryotic cells has been an ongoing question in modern biology (see Box 4.1). About 2 billion years ago, a bacterium or an archaeum, most-probably marine, gave rise to a more complex eukaryotic cell, and as such the ancestors of all more complex forms of life.

A group of archaea, the so-called Asgard archaea, was first described in 2010 by a Swedish team from nucleic acid obtained from sediment dredged near hydrothermal vents in the Arctic Ocean. The discovery was made thanks to **metagenomics** by identifying particular sequences of genetic material without actually isolating any microorganisms (see Box 5.2). Asgard archaea were found to be unique because their genome includes genes that had been previously found in eukaryotes, not in any other prokaryotes. That Asgard archaea are the closest relatives of eukaryotes was confirmed by scientists at the University of Bristol in England,

who analyzed more than 3,000 genes in Archaea and eukaryotes.

The next step followed when a team from the Japan Agency for Marine-Earth Science isolated, and for the first time cultured and grew, an Asgard archaeum in the laboratory. The Japanese scientists obtained material using a deep-sea vehicle that collected sediment from a deep-sea methane seep 2,533 m (8,310 ft) deep off southern Japan. The team reconstructed an anaerobic methane seep in the laboratory by continuously pumping methane into a chamber containing artificial seawater and artificial sponges saturated with the deep-sea sediment. The microorganisms living in the sediment slowly grew in the chamber. After a wait of more than 2,000 days, the scientists were able to have enough numbers of the archaeum to test its growth under different energy sources and conditions. Antibiotics killed any bacteria contaminating the experimental setups.

An extremely slow-growing archaeum, named MK-D1 (eventually under the proper

name of *Prometheoarchaeum syntrophicum*), was finally isolated and characterized by 2018. It was the first Asgard archaeum to be observed (and photographed) under the microscope. MK-D1 consists of round cells that eventually develop tentacle-like extensions. The extensions were speculated to be capable of capturing bacteria that could have eventually develop into the symbiotic mitochondria hypothesized as being involved in the evolution of the first eukaryotic cell from an ancestral prokaryote (see Box 4.1).

Some scientists have nevertheless expressed reservations about the hypothesis that an archaeum is the closest relative to eukaryotes. They point out, for example, that the outer cell membrane of bacteria looks like the membrane of eukaryotic cells, closer than that of archaea. Most importantly, many eukaryotic genes are also found in bacteria. Perhaps both archaea and bacteria were involved, in separate occasions, in the evolution of eukaryotes.

Prokaryote Metabolism

Prokaryotes show an amazing variety of chemical reactions that are involved in the transfer of energy and in the manufacture of chemical compounds. Some actually obtain energy in more than one way. **Metabolism** is all the chemical reactions that take place in an organism.

Autotrophs Autotrophic bacteria and archaea make their own organic compounds and thus are primary producers. Energy sources vary. Some autotrophic bacteria, such as the cyanobacteria previously mentioned, are **photosynthetic** or photoautotrophic. They contain chlorophyll or other photosynthetic pigments (see Table 5.2) to trap light energy to manufacture organic compounds from carbon dioxide (CO_2); cyanobacteria release oxygen in the process (see Table 5.1). Photosynthesis takes place on folded membranes within the bacterial cell (see Fig. 4.7 and photo in Box 4.1, "From Snack to Servant: How Complex Cells Arose") rather than in chloroplasts, as in algae and plants. Photosynthetic bacteria account for much of the primary production in many open-ocean areas. Even bacteria living at depths where no surface light penetrates have been suggested as using the faint glow of hydrothermal vents to perform photosynthesis.

Though the end products can be similar, the biochemistry of bacterial photosynthesis is different from that of algae and plants. It also varies considerably among different groups of bacteria. Some

photosynthetic bacteria, for example, have a kind of chlorophyll unique to prokaryotes (**bacteriochlorophyll**) and produce sulfur (S) instead of oxygen (see Table 5.1). Some bacteria could use a pigment called proteorhodopsin to capture light energy and store it in **ATP**. They do not have chlorophyll or use the energy to manufacture organic compounds from carbon dioxide and thus are not photosynthetic. An archaeum (*Halobacterium*) similarly lacks chlorophyll but contains a pigment, bacteriorhodopsin, that converts light energy directly into ATP. Marine microbes can therefore use light as an energy source in many ways, not just in photosynthesis.

Other bacterial autotrophs, called **chemosynthetic,** or **chemoautotrophic,** derive energy not from light but from chemical compounds, including **hydrogen sulfide (H_2S)** and other sulfur, nitrogen, and iron compounds (see Table 5.1). Some chemosynthetic bacteria live in symbiotic associations with several kinds of marine animals (see Box 5.1, "Symbiotic Bacteria–The Essential Guests"). Others live wherever hydrogen sulfide accumulates, as in the low-oxygen conditions that result when large amounts of organic matter decompose. Chemosynthesis is also involved in altering some of the minerals found in sea-floor rocks (see Box 2.1, "Life Below the Sea Floor"). Some chemosynthetic archaea, the methanogens, produce methane (CH_4). One example is *Methanopyrus*, an archaeum that has been isolated from sediments near hydrothermal vents. Some deep-sea bacteria use methane instead, and produce coral-like limestone deposits.

Prokaryotes show a wide variety of metabolic processes. Many bacteria (including cyanobacteria) and some archaea are autotrophs and account for much of the oceanic primary production.

Heterotrophs Most marine bacteria, like animals, are **heterotrophs** that obtain energy from organic matter by **respiration** (see Table 5.1). Many heterotrophic bacteria and archaea are decomposers. Respiration in **aerobic** bacteria and archaea uses oxygen, as in most other groups of organisms, whereas in **anaerobic** species respiration does not require oxygen. Anaerobic bacteria do not grow when oxygen is present and thrive when it is absent, as in sediments that are devoid of oxygen, or **anoxic.** This is the case in bacteria that use sulfate (SO_4^{-2}) instead of oxygen to perform respiration, producing in the process the hydrogen sulfide (H_2S) that is to blame for the rotten-egg smell of some sediments (see Fig. 11.28).

Heterotrophic prokaryotes obtain energy from organic matter. Many are decomposers.

Nitrogen Fixation Many planktonic cyanobacteria (such as *Trichodesmium*) carry out **nitrogen fixation,** converting gaseous nitrogen (N_2), which is not available as a nitrogen source to primary producers, into ammonium (NH_4^{+1}). Most of the ammonium is then transformed into nitrates (NO^{-1}) and other nitrogen compounds (see Table 5.1) that can be finally used by primary producers as a nitrogen source for the manufacture of essential proteins and other nitrogen-containing compounds (see Fig. 10.21). Other bacteria and some archaea are also known to be nitrogen fixers. Nitrogen fixation requires energy, which is provided by ATP generated from photosynthesis or other reactions.

Some prokaryotes, particularly cyanobacteria, are nitrogen fixers. They convert gaseous nitrogen into ammonium, which is used by primary producers.

Dennis Kunkel Microscopy/Science Source

FIGURE 5.5 *Methanocaldococcus jannaschii* is a methane-producing archaeon that lives at high temperatures near deep-sea hydrothermal vents. It was the first archaeon to have its genome sequenced.

The color of algae is a result of the pigments and their concentration. In contrast to the land plants with which we are familiar, algae lack true leaves, stems, roots, and flowers. They have relatively simple reproductive structures, and their non-reproductive cells are also mostly simple and unspecialized.

Autotrophs Organisms that can use energy (usually solar energy) to make organic matter.
Heterotrophs Organisms that cannot make their own food and must use the organic matter produced by autotrophs.
• 4.1, The Ingredients of Life

ATP The molecule used to store and transfer energy in metabolic reactions.
• 4.1, The Ingredients of Life

Hydrothermal Vents Undersea hot springs associated with mid-ocean ridges and other geologically active environments.
• 2.3, The Geological Provinces of the Ocean

5.3 UNICELLULAR ALGAE

Algae (singular, **alga**) are a very diverse group of simple, mostly aquatic (that is, marine and freshwater), mostly photosynthetic organisms. Being eukaryotic, their cells contain a nucleus and other organelles enclosed by membranes. Photosynthesis takes place in **chloroplasts**—green, brown, or red organelles with layers of internal membranes that contain photosynthetic pigments (see Fig. 4.8*b*).

Box 5.2 Tiny Cells, Big Surprises

It is surprising how little biologists know about the lives of marine microbes. We know they are everywhere but we are not sure how many types there are, how common they are, and what exactly they are up to. The situation is rapidly changing as we apply new techniques and approaches to studying the private lives of marine microorganisms that call the ocean home.

Information about marine microbes (what nutrients the microbes need to grow, the type of compounds they produce, and such) has traditionally been gathered mostly from organisms collected in water samples and then grown under artificial conditions. Many organisms, unfortunately, do not grow in the lab, and their presence in samples goes undetected. At least some of this information has been used by marine ecologists to deduce the role of microbes in the big ocean world—the role of decay bacteria in releasing nutrients, for example, and of bacteria that convert free nitrogen into nitrates or make dissolved organic matter (DOM) available to larger forms of life. Still, bacteria and other marine microbes are poorly understood. Some groups of microbes remained undiscovered for a long time. Most archaea, for instance, have been known only since the 1970s.

Viruses and the minute prokaryotic cells of bacteria and archaea and the smallest eukaryotic cells of some algae and other organisms seem to be everywhere, but are very difficult to collect and characterize by the microscopic examination of cells. Instead of culturing or filtering out these cells, fragments of nucleic acid (see "Nucleic Acids," in 4.1) are collected from the water and chemically analyzed. The presence of organisms can be detected by identifying characteristic sequences of nucleotides, the subunits of DNA and RNA, a research approach called **metagenomics,** a technique where the genomes of unknown organisms are recovered from

the environment, not from laboratory cultures as is traditionally done. Furthermore, the partial sequences can yield information about the unique characteristics of these microbes, even if whole cells or whole nucleic acid molecules are not collected.

The presence of RNA sequences characteristic of archaea in seawater and sediment samples has shown archaea to be abundant. In 2001 two groups of archaea were found to be extremely abundant in water samples collected from depths below the photic zone— that is, where light does not penetrate (see Fig. 16.1). The samples, collected from the Pacific Ocean south of Hawai'i, showed that archaea were rare at the surface but sharply increased in abundance below depths of 250 m (720 ft). Below 1,000 m (3,280 ft) archaea were as common as bacteria. Judging from their numbers and the huge volume of the ocean in question, these archaea are among the ocean's most abundant forms of life. DNA sequences in samples from the Sargasso Sea have demonstrated the presence of at least 1,800, and possibly as many as 50,000, new species of microbes.

Similar techniques based on the detection of characteristic nucleic acid sequences have been used to identify previously unknown eukaryotic microorganisms. These eukaryotes are larger than prokaryotes but still minute (smaller than 2 to 3 μm), making them difficult to collect and study. This sharply contrasts with other unicellular but larger eukaryotes

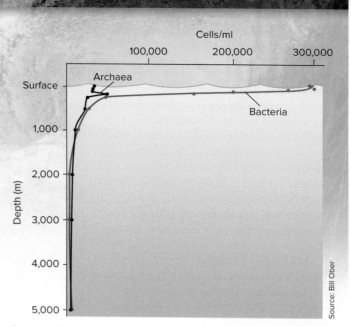

Depth distribution of bacteria and archaea in the subtropical North Pacific.

Source: Bill Ober

in the plankton, which are relatively easy to collect using plankton nets (see "The Plankton: A New Understanding," in 15.1). In 2001 two new groups related to dinoflagellates were discovered at depths of 250 to 3,000 m (720 to 9,840 ft) near Antarctica. Similar but unique groups of eukaryotic microorganisms (including yet another new group related to dinoflagellates) were reported at the same time by another team working at depths of 75 m (246 ft) in the tropical Pacific. The fact that some of these microorganisms, collected in relatively shallow water where light still penetrates, are photosynthetic, adds a new dimension to the discovery. They represent a previously unknown source of primary production in typically unproductive tropical waters. Other groups of minute algae have been discovered in recent years, including three groups that are related to dinoflagellates. Others remain to be found.

Biologists used to refer to algae as plants. Many of the unicellular algae, however, show animal-like characteristics. Some swim by moving their flagella, and distinguishing these free-swimming algae from some of the structurally simpler animals can be difficult at first glance. Some species carry out photosynthesis as plants do, and very similar species move and eat food particles as animals do. Some species do both and are claimed by both botanists (plant

biologists) and zoologists (animal biologists). These unicellular organisms are collectively called **protists,** the traditional "kingdom" **Protista,** even if the various groups of protists have different evolutionary histories. Multicellular seaweeds are also considered to be protists, mostly because they lack the specialized tissues of plants. Seaweeds, together with other multicellular primary producers, the marine plants, are discussed in Chapter 6.

BOX 5.3 EVOLUTIONARY PERSPECTIVE

Symbiotic Bacteria—The Essential Guests

Some bacteria have evolved to live in close, or **symbiotic,** associations with other marine organisms. Some symbiotic bacteria are **parasites** that can cause diseases. Others, on the other hand, benefit their hosts. These symbiotic bacteria began their association by increasing the chances of survival of the host and evolved to become essential—hosts could not survive without them. In many cases, the symbiotic bacteria are even sheltered in special tissues or organs that evolved in the host, an example of **coevolution,** in which two species evolve in response to each other.

All eukaryotic organisms, including humans, shelter bacteria without which they could not live. The chloroplasts and mitochondria of eukaryotic cells evolved from symbiotic bacteria (see Box 4.1, "From Snack to Servant: How Complex Cells Arose"). These bacteria have become an integral part of all complex cells.

There are many cases of symbiotic bacteria among marine organisms. Symbiotic bacteria, for example, are involved in digesting the wood that is ingested by shipworms (*Teredo*), which happen to be bivalve molluscs, not worms. Like all wood-eating animals, shipworms lack cellulase, the enzyme needed to digest **cellulose,** the main component of wood. Wood is a surprisingly common habitat in many marine environments, so everything from driftwood to boat bottoms is exploited by shipworms, thanks to their symbiotic bacteria.

Symbiotic bacteria are also responsible for the light, or **bioluminescence,** that is produced by some fishes, squids, octopuses, and other mostly deep-sea animals (see "Bioluminescence," in 16.1). The bacteria are usually sheltered in special light-producing organs, or **photophores.** These deep-sea animals, which live in darkness, use light to communicate with other members of their species, lure prey, blend with the light that filters from the surface, and perform other functions. The symbiosis between a bioluminescent bacterium (*Vibrio*) living in the photophores of a small, shallow-water squid (*Euprymna scolopes*) has provided fascinating details of the coevolution between the two

partners. The partners use a "secret language" in the form of particular molecules used by the squid to properly select and maintain the bacterium. The squid controls the downwards-directed light produced by the bacterium in order to hide from predators when viewed from below the surface at night, thus matching the light coming from the night sky above the surface (see Fig. 16.15).

Flashlight fishes (*Anomalops*), which live in shallow tropical waters, lodge their symbiotic bacteria in an organ beneath each eye. A shutter mechanism controls the emission of light, so that the fish can "blink" at night. Groups of fish blink in synchrony, a behavior that is involved in attracting prey.

Chemosynthetic bacteria symbiotic with mussels, clams, and tubeworms that live around deep-sea hydrothermal vents have a very particular role: manufacturing organic matter from CO_2 and the abundant hydrogen sulfide (H_2S) from the vents. The symbiotic bacteria live in a special organ, the **feeding body,** of the giant hydrothermal-vent tubeworm *Riftia* (see Fig. 16.29).

Marine symbiotic bacteria can also affect human health. Pufferfishes store a toxin that is deadly to any predators (including humans) that eat them. The fish, or *fugu*, is a delicacy in Japan. Licensed chefs must prepare the fish; otherwise, the toxin **(tetrodotoxin)** will kill anyone feasting on fish that has been improperly prepared. Tetrodotoxin is a deadly neurotoxin (that is, it affects the nervous system). In fact, it is one of the most powerful poisons known, and there is no antidote. The deadly toxin is stored mostly in the liver and gonads of the fish, so the internal organs must be expertly removed. Mistakes do happen and numerous deaths (including the suicides of disgraced cooks) take place every year in Japan. Cooks could still be guilty, but not the puffers: the toxin is not produced by puffers but apparently by symbiotic bacteria. The fish are actually resistant to tetrodotoxin as a result of a genetic mutation that changes the site where the toxin binds to nerve cells.

Tetrodotoxin and very similar toxins have also been found in a variety of marine organisms, including flatworms, snails,

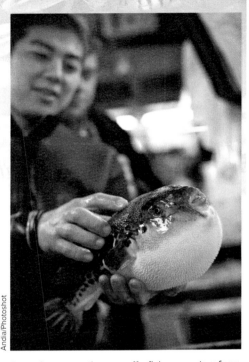

A poisonous tiger pufferfish, or *torafugu* (*Takifugu rubripes*), Tokyo fish market. It is valued as a delicacy in Japan even if highly toxic.

crabs, sea stars, and several species of fishes. It is also found in the blue-ringed octopuses, notoriously toxic animals. Tetrodotoxin of an unknown source has also been found in dead sea urchins and is suspected as their cause of death. We are not yet sure if in all of these animals the toxin is produced by symbiotic bacteria or if it is accumulated from their food. In arrow worms (see Fig. 7.17), however, symbiotic bacteria in the mouth do produce tetrodotoxin that is used to paralyze prey.

Being a neurotoxin, tetrodotoxin blocks pain signals in humans. A derivative being tested as a pain reliever for cancer and other diseases would have the advantage of not being addictive, as are morphine and similar drugs.

The production of powerful toxins that are used by other organisms is just one example of the amazing abilities of bacteria—invisible to the eye but powerful giants when it comes to their role in the environment.

Algae are protists. They are mostly aquatic primary producers that lack the specialized tissues of plants. They range in size and complexity from single cells to large, multicellular seaweeds.

Diatoms

Diatoms (division, or phylum, **Bacillariophyta**) are unicellular, though many species aggregate into chains or star-like groups. Diatom cells are enclosed by cell walls made largely of **silica (SiO₂)**, a glass-like material. This glassy shell, or **frustule,** consists of two tightly fitting halves often resembling a flat, round, or elongated box (Fig. 5.6). The frustule typically has intricate perforations and ornaments such as spines or ribs, making diatoms strikingly beautiful when seen under a microscope. The frustule allows light to pass through, so that the conspicuous golden brown chloroplasts can capture light energy for photosynthesis. The minute perforations allow dissolved gases and nutrients to enter and exit. The sinking of open-ocean diatoms below the well-lit surface layer is often slowed by oil droplets in their cells and spines on the frustules (see "Staying Afloat," in 15.2).

The characteristic color of diatoms is due to yellow and brown **carotenoid** pigments, in addition to two types of chlorophyll, *a* and *c* (see Table 5.2). Diatoms are efficient photosynthetic factories, producing much-needed food (the food being the diatoms themselves), as well as oxygen, for other forms of life. They are a potential source of biofuels as alternatives to fossil fuels (see Box 6.2, "Marine Algae as Biofuels"). Diatoms are very important open-water primary producers in temperate and polar regions (see Table 15.1 and 15.3, Epipelagic Food Webs). In fact, the huge number of diatom cells in the ocean account for a hefty share of the organic carbon and oxygen produced on planet Earth.

Around half the estimated 12,000 living species of diatoms are marine. Most are planktonic, but many produce a stalk-like structure for attachment to rocks and other surfaces in shallow water, where they contribute significantly to primary production. The brownish scum sometimes seen on mudflats or glass aquaria often consists of millions of diatom cells. Some are able to glide slowly on surfaces. A few are colorless, having no chlorophyll, and live as heterotrophs on the surfaces of seaweeds. Some planktonic diatoms produce a potent toxin, **domoic acid,** which accumulates in shellfish (clams, oysters, mussels) and plankton-feeding fishes that eat the diatoms. The toxin causes a serious, sometimes fatal, illness of the nervous system in humans and marine mammals that eat contaminated shellfish or fish.

Diatoms are unicellular organisms that live mostly as part of the plankton. A silica shell, or frustule, is their most distinctive feature. They are important open-water primary producers in cold waters.

Diatoms reproduce mostly by cell division, a type of **asexual reproduction** (see Fig. 4.18). The overlapping halves of the frustule separate, and each secretes a new, smaller half. The smaller, lower frustule of the parent cell becomes the larger frustule of a daughter cell, which then secretes a new, smaller frustule (Fig. 5.7). Full size is regained by the development of specialized stages known as **auxospores.** Auxospores then re-establish the normal cell size that display the frustule characteristic of the species.

Favorable environmental conditions, such as abundant nutrients and light, trigger periods of rapid reproduction called **blooms.** Such blooms may even occur under Arctic and Antarctic ice. This is a general phenomenon that also occurs in other algae. During blooms most diatoms get progressively smaller, not only because of asexual reproduction but also as a result of depletion of silicate from the water by the growing population.

The glassy frustules of dead diatoms eventually settle to the bottom of the sea floor, where they can form thick deposits of siliceous material that cover large portions of the ocean floor. Such **biogenous sediments** are known as **diatomaceous ooze,** a type of **siliceous ooze.** Huge fossil deposits of these sediments can be found inland in various parts of the world. The siliceous material, or **diatomaceous earth,** is mined and used in products such as filters for swimming pools, for clarifying beer, as temperature and sound insulators, and as mild abrasives in toothpaste.

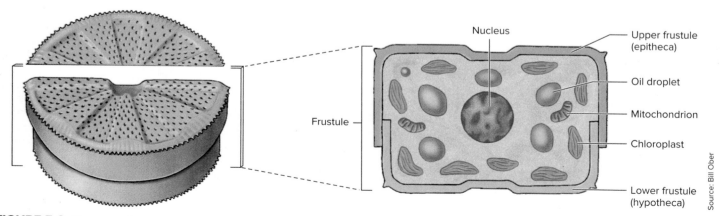

Nucleus

Upper frustule (epitheca)

Oil droplet

Mitochondrion

Chloroplast

Frustule

Lower frustule (hypotheca)

Source: Bill Ober

FIGURE 5.6 Diagrammatic representation of a diatom cell (also see Fig. 15.3).

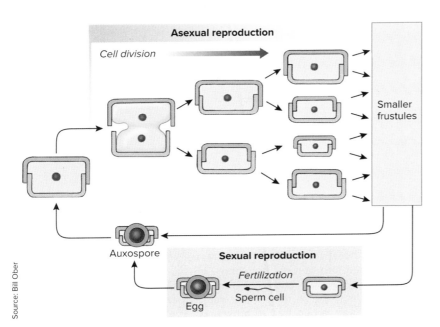

Asexual reproduction

Cell division

Smaller frustules

Auxospore

Sexual reproduction

Fertilization

Sperm cell

Egg

Source: Bill Ober

FIGURE 5.7 The usual method of reproduction in diatoms is by cell division. Most, but not all, frustules get smaller after each successive division. Resistant cells called auxospores are produced two ways: directly from the expansion of a smaller frustule or by sexual reproduction when an egg is fertilized by a sperm cell, both of which are liberated from separate frustules.

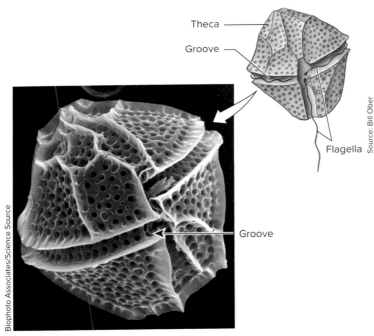

Theca

Groove

Flagella

Source: Bill Ober

Groove

Biophoto Associates/Science Source

FIGURE 5.8 Dinoflagellates like *Gonyaulax polyedra* have a cell wall, or theca, which consists of cellulose plates. The theca is marked by grooves for the flagella; only one groove is visible here (arrow). This species is bioluminescent and it produces red tides.

Dinoflagellates

The **dinoflagellates** (division **Dinophyta,** or phylum **Dinoflagellata**) make up another large group of planktonic, unicellular organisms. Their most outstanding characteristic is the possession of two flagella, one wrapped around a groove along the middle of the

cell and one trailing free (Fig. 5.8). These flagella direct movement in any direction. Most dinoflagellates have a cell wall armored with plates made of **cellulose,** the characteristic component of the cell walls of seaweeds and land plants. The plates have spines, pores, or other ornaments.

Though most dinoflagellates photosynthesize, many can also ingest food particles. A few have a light-sensitive pigment spot that acts as a crude "eye." It has been suggested that during their evolution dinoflagellates gained the ability to function as primary producers by capturing and using chloroplasts from other algae. Almost all known dinoflagellates, around 2,000 living species, are marine. Dinoflagellates are important planktonic primary producers, especially in warm water (see Table 15.1).

Dinoflagellates reproduce almost exclusively by simple cell division. They sometimes form blooms that color the water red, reddish-brown, yellow, or other unusual shades (see Box 15.1, "Red Tides and Harmful Algal Blooms"). Some of these dinoflagellates release toxic substances, and seafood collected during red tide periods can be poisonous, as in the case of ciguatera, a tropical fish poisoning (see Box 14.4, "Must Have Been Something I Ate"). Other dinoflagellates are noted for the production of light, or bioluminescence (see Box 5.4, "The Bay of Fire"). Though bioluminescence has also been observed in some bacteria and many types of animals, dinoflagellates are generally responsible for the diffuse bioluminescence sometimes seen on the sea surface. This effect is, of course, seen only at night. It is especially bright if the water is disturbed by a boat or when a wave crashes on the shore.

A group of round, golden brown dinoflagellates called **zooxanthellae** live in close association with a variety of animals. Animals harboring zooxanthellae range from sponges and sea anemones to giant clams. It is perhaps in reef-building corals where zooxanthellae are most significant (see Fig. 14.1). They fix carbon dioxide by photosynthesis, release organic matter used by the coral, and help in the formation of the coral skeleton (see "Coral Nutrition," in 14.1).

Types of reproduction:
Asexual (or *vegetative*) The production of new individuals by simple division (or other means) without involving *gametes*, so that the offspring are genetically identical to the parents.
Sexual The production of new individuals by the formation of *gametes* (sperm and eggs), so that the offspring are genetically different from the parents.
• 4.4, Perpetuating Life

Biogenous Sediments Sediments made of the skeletons and shells of marine organisms; *siliceous ooze* is made of silica, *calcareous ooze* of calcium carbonate.
• 2.2, The Origin and Structure of the Ocean Basins

Cellulose A complex carbohydrate characteristic of plants and other primary producers.
• 4.1, The Ingredients of Life

BOX 5.4 The Bay of Fire

Imagine entering a quiet tropical bay at night. There are no lights on shore, and on a moonless night the spectacle is unforgettable. As the propeller of your boat churns the black water, an intense blue-green light is left behind, like an eerie trail of cool fire. Outside the bay you see a few sparks of light as you approach, but inside the bay things are very different. Long streaks of light shoot like fireworks beneath the boat. They are created by fleeing fish. A swim in the bay is even more spectacular. Your dive into the water is accompanied by a blinding flood of light, and sparks scatter out as you wave your arms.

Such light effects result from an unusual concentration of bioluminescent dinoflagellates, a natural and permanent phenomenon in a few selected locations such as Bahía Fosforescente, or Phosphorescent Bay, in southwestern Puerto Rico.

"Bioluminescent Bay" is a more apt name because the light is produced by living organisms. The bay's most important source of bioluminescence is *Pyrodinium bahamense*, a unicellular, photosynthetic dinoflagellate about 40 microns (μm) (0.004 cm, or 0.0015 in) in diameter. As

many as 720,000 individuals can be found in a gallon of water, many more than outside the bay. The bay is small, about 90 acres, fan-shaped, and it does not exceed 4.5 m (15 ft) in depth. The main reason that the dinoflagellates are concentrated there is that the bay is connected to the open sea by a narrow, shallow channel. As water containing the dinoflagellates flows into the bay, evaporation in the shallow water causes the surface water to sink because of the increase in salinity and therefore density. Evaporation is enhanced by the dry and sunny days. *Pyrodinium* cells stay near the surface and are therefore not carried out as the denser water flows out along the bottom of the shallow entrance. The tidal range is only about a foot at the most, so water exchange with the outside is limited. The bay thus acts as a trap that keeps the dinoflagellates from leaving.

Of all the planktonic organisms that enter the bay, why is *Pyrodinium* favored? A key factor seems to be the thick mangrove trees bordering the bay. They grow along the muddy shores, together with all

Bahía Fosforescente, Puerto Rico.

Paul A. Zahl, Ph.D./NGS Image Collection

kinds of organisms living attached to their roots. Mangrove leaves fall into the water, where intense bacterial decomposition increases the organic nutrient levels in the water. Some nutrients essential to the growth of *Pyrodinium*, perhaps vitamins, could be released by bacteria or other microorganisms.

Bahía Fosforescente is protected to keep the critical natural balance intact, but bioluminescence has noticeably decreased during recent years. A few other bays, termed "bio bays," in Puerto Rico fortunately show even more spectacular bioluminescence, Laguna Grande on the northeastern tip of the island and Puerto Mosquito on the island of Vieques.

A few highly modified dinoflagellates are parasites of seaweeds and some marine animals. Like zooxanthellae, these specialized forms reveal their true nature by having life cycles that include free-swimming stages resembling typical dinoflagellates.

One such dinoflagellate is *Pfiesteria*, sometimes called the "phantom dinoflagellate" because it spends most of its life as a harmless resting stage, or **cyst,** in the sediment. It has been suggested that coastal pollution in the form of excessive nutrients can trigger blooms of *Pfiesteria*. *Pfiesteria* and *Pfiesteria*-like microorganisms are responsible for deadly open sores on fishes. *Pfiesteria* causes the sores by producing a toxin, not by actively feeding on the fishes' tissues as first thought. These parasites are also known to be harmful to crabs, oysters, and clams and have been implicated in sores and in symptoms such as temporary memory loss in humans.

FIGURE 5.9 Skeleton of *Dictyocha speculum*, a silicoflagellate.

Gustaff M. Hallegraeff

Dinoflagellates are unicellular organisms that have two unequal flagella. Some are noted for their emission of light. Zooxanthellae are dinoflagellates that are symbiotic with marine animals, especially reef corals.

Other Unicellular Algae

Three additional groups can be abundant in some areas and thus very significant primary producers in the plankton (see Table 15.1). **Silicoflagellates** (division, or phylum, **Chrysophyta**) are characterized by a star-shaped internal skeleton made of silica (Fig. 5.9) and two flagella of different lengths. Fossil silicoflagellates are common in marine sediments and can be used to date the sediments. Typical **coccolithophorids** (division, or phylum, **Haptophyta**) are flagellated, spherical cells covered with button-like, ornamented structures called **coccoliths** made of

Gustaff M. Hallegraeff

FIGURE 5.10 Coccolithophorids, such as *Umbilicosphaera sibogae* from Australia, are tiny, single-celled phytoplankton that can be significant primary producers in the open ocean. The plates that cover the cell are made of calcium carbonate.

calcium carbonate (Fig. 5.10). Coccoliths can be found as fossils in chalk sediments that were uplifted from the ocean floor such as the white cliffs of Dover in England. **Cryptophytes** (division, or phylum, **Cryptophyta**) have two flagella and lack a skeleton. Like other eukaryotes, cryptophytes have a chloroplast derived from a prokaryote (see Box 4.1, "From Snack to Servant: How Complex Cells Arose"), but the chloroplast is contained within a reduced eukaryotic cell that lives symbiotically inside the cryptophyte cell. Members of these three groups of algae are so small that hundreds could fit into a large diatom or dinoflagellate cell.

5.4 PROTOZOANS: THE ANIMAL-LIKE PROTISTS

Protozoans are structurally simple and very diverse eukaryotic organisms that are traditionally considered to be animal-like. Most biologists agree that protozoans (meaning "first animals") actually comprise several groups of unrelated origins. Having a single cell is about the only thing that protozoans—which show an enormous diversity in structure, function, and lifestyle—have in common. Though a few form colonies, most protozoans are single-celled, unlike true animals, and are visible only under a microscope. Like animals, protozoans are heterotrophs and ingest food. Some, however, also contain chlorophyll and photosynthesize.

There is considerable disagreement as to how to classify the estimated 50,000 species of protozoans, though they are generally considered to be protists along with unicellular algae and seaweeds.

Protozoans are the most animal-like of the protists. They are eukaryotic and unicellular. They are essentially heterotrophic and ingest food, as animals do.

The minute size and apparent simplicity of protozoans disguise a complex nature. As in all unicellular organisms, each cell might be described as a "super cell" because it can perform many of the same functions carried out by the multitude of cells in structurally more complex organisms.

Protozoans inhabit water everywhere, living not only in marine and freshwater environments but even inside other organisms. Many kinds of marine protozoans can be readily collected from sediments rich in organic debris, the surface of seaweeds, the guts of animals, and plankton samples.

Foraminiferans

Foraminiferans (phylum **Foraminifera,** or **Granuloreticulosa**), often called **forams,** are marine protozoans that usually have a shell, or **test,** made of **calcium carbonate (CaCO$_3$).** The test is usually microscopic and can have several chambers (Fig. 5.11*a*), which increase in size as the foram grows. Foraminiferans have long, thin, retractable **pseudopodia**—extensions of the **cytoplasm.** The pseudopodia protrude through pores in the test and form a network used to trap diatoms and other organisms suspended in the water (see Fig. 15.5). Food is then moved into the interior of the cell as if on a conveyor belt.

Most of the more than 4,000 known species of foraminiferans are **benthic,** and thus live on the bottom, either free or attached. Attached forams develop into conspicuous growths as much as 5 cm (2 in) in diameter (Fig. 5.11*b*). Each growth consists of a single cell that forms a test, though some can be covered with sand grains or other materials instead. The tests of bottom-living foraminiferans can be important contributors of calcareous material on coral reefs and sandy beaches. Relatively few species are planktonic, but these can be very abundant. Their tests are smaller and thinner than those that live on the bottom and can have delicate spines that aid in flotation. The tests of planktonic foraminiferans eventually sink to the bottom in such high numbers that large stretches of the ocean floor are covered by **foraminiferan ooze,** a type of calcareous ooze. Many limestone beds around the world are products of foraminiferan sediments that were uplifted from the ocean floor.

Foraminiferans (forams) are protozoans characterized by a test usually made of calcium carbonate. Most live on the bottom. The tests of planktonic species are important components of marine sediments.

Most species of forams are known only as **microfossils** (see Fig. 2.18). The distribution of these microfossils in sediments is important to geologists. Tests of warm-water species are slightly larger and more porous than those from colder water. Past water temperatures and levels of glacial ice at the poles can be determined from the distribution of certain marker species as well as chemical analyses of foram tests. Their distribution is a good indicator of the right type of environment for the formation of oil, as well as the age of sediments.

(a) (b)

Emmanuel G. Reynaud

Charlie Arneson

FIGURE 5.11 Foraminiferans. (*a*) Foraminiferans, such as *Globigerina*, typically have calcareous tests that consist of a spiral arrangement of chambers. The thin, long strands are thin spines with pseudopodia running along them, which are used to capture food. (*b*) *Homotrema rubrum* is a foraminiferan that forms bright red calcareous growths several millimeters in diameter at the base of corals in the tropics. It is so common in Bermuda that its skeletons are responsible for the island's famous pink beaches.

Radiolarians

Radiolarians (phylum **Radiolaria**) are planktonic marine protozoans that secrete elaborate and delicate skeletons made of glass (silica) and other materials. The typical skeleton is spherical with radiating spines (Fig. 5.12), though the structure varies. Thin pseudopodia capture food, as in foraminiferans. There are about 2,500 known species.

Most radiolarians are microscopic, but some form sausage-shaped colonies that reach 3 m (9 ft) in length, making them true giants among protozoans. Radiolarians inhabit open water throughout the oceans. When abundant, the remains of their skeleton settle to the bottom and form a siliceous ooze known as **radiolarian ooze.** This ooze is more extensive in deep water because the radiolarian skeleton is more resistant to dissolving under pressure than those of forams.

> The skeleton of radiolarians is made primarily of silica (glass). Skeletons form siliceous sediments that cover large areas of the ocean floor.

Ciliates

Ciliates (phylum **Ciliophora,** or **Ciliata**) are protozoans that have many hair-like **cilia,** which are used in locomotion and feeding. The

most familiar ciliates are freshwater forms, such as *Paramecium.* Biologists recognize more than 10,000 species. Many marine ciliates are found creeping over seaweeds and in bottom sediments. Some live on the gills of clams, in the intestines of sea urchins, on the skin of fishes, and in other unusual places. Other ciliates live attached to surfaces, even forming branched colonies of tiny individuals. **Tintinnids** are common ciliates that drift in the water and build vase-like cases, or **loricas,** loosely fitting tests that drift in the water (Fig. 5.13). The cases can be transparent or made of bits of particles. Planktonic ciliates are important in the so-called microbial loop of open-water food webs, which facilitates the flow of energy from dissolved organic matter to the larger plankton (see Fig. 15.25).

5.5 FUNGI

Fungi (kingdom **Fungi**) are eukaryotic and mostly multicellular, though some, such as molds and yeasts, are unicellular. Multicellular fungi typically form long filaments called **hyphae.** Fungi are heterotrophs that lack chloroplasts and chlorophyll and cannot perform photosynthesis. As in plants, however, fungi have cell walls. The cell wall of fungi is made of **chitin,** a highly resistant carbohydrate found in the skeleton of many animals, whereas it is made of cellulose in plants.

There are at least 2,000 known species of marine fungi, mostly microscopic. Microscopic fungi can be found in practically all marine environments from the tropics to polar regions, including brackish water, salt marshes, mangrove forests, and high-salinity ponds. Many are found in the plankton. Fungi absorb nutrients from their environment by secreting digestive enzymes, and many, as in

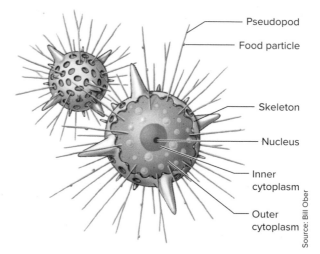

Pseudopod

Food particle

Skeleton

Nucleus

Inner cytoplasm

Outer cytoplasm

Source: Bill Ober

FIGURE 5.12 A typical radiolarian cell consists of a dense central portion surrounded by a less dense zone that is involved in the capture of food particles and in buoyancy.

FIGURE 5.13
Tintinnopsis is a marine tintinnid that forms a vase-like lorica made of sand grains. Specialized cilia on one end are used in feeding.

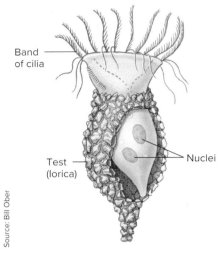

Band of cilia

Test (lorica)

Nuclei

Source: Bill Ober

as the result of plankton blooms and pollution. Some marine fungi are parasites of planktonic diatoms, seaweeds, and seagrasses or borers in mollusc shells. Others are parasites that cause diseases of economically important seaweeds, oysters, lobsters, and fishes, as well as sponges, corals, and marine mammals. Some marine fungi are being investigated as a source of antibiotics for use in medicine (see Box 17.3, "Take Two Sponges and Call Me in the Morning"), or to help breakdown oil and other pollutants.

Many fungi live in symbiotic associations, mostly with green algae or cyanobacteria, to form unique entities, the **lichens.** In lichens the long hyphae of the fungi provide support, whereas the algae or cyanobacteria provide food from photosynthesis. Marine lichens can be typically found as thick, dark brown or black patches in the wave-splashed zone of exposed rocky shores (Fig. 5.14), often mistaken as polluting oil. They are tolerant to exposure to air for long periods of time.

By comparison with the multitude of lichens on land, there are very few types of marine lichens. Their role on the ecology of rocky shores is largely unknown. The cyanobacteria of some marine lichens are known to be nitrogen-fixers. Some lichens are able to loosen bits of the rocks where they live by growing into the rock. A few types live on the shells of rocky shore barnacles and molluscs.

Molecular techniques similar to those used in identifying viruses and marine microbes (see Box 5.2, "Tiny Cells, Big Surprises") are being applied to the sampling of fungi in places such as deep-sea sediments and anoxic environments. These are fungi that are often difficult to culture in the lab. The number of species of marine fungi will undoubtedly increase with time.

bacteria, decompose detritus. They can decompose the cellulose in the cell walls of seaweeds and plants. Cellulose, which is abundant in driftwood and the dropped leaves of seagrasses and salt-marsh plants, is not digested by most bacteria. Fungi are the most important decomposers of dropped mangrove leaves and thus contribute to the recycling of nutrients in mangrove forests (see "Mangrove Forests," in 12.3). A similar process occurs with dropped seagrass leaves, drift seaweed, and in the driftwood that accumulates in deep water along tropical rain forests. Marine fungi are also important in the breakdown of detritus and other organic matter that accumulates

Peter Castro

FIGURE 5.14 Encrusting marine lichens, cyanobacteria, and some microscopic algae are often visible as a black band on wave-splashed rocky shores, as in this exposed rocky point south of Monterey Bay, California.

Table 5.2 Most Important Characteristics of Marine Microbes

Group	Distinguishing Features	Photosynthetic and Accessory Pigments	Major Food Reserves	Major Cell-Wall or Cell-Membrane Components	Ecology
Viruses	Non-cellular, parasites of all organisms	None	None	Capsid of protein, sometimes lipids	Infect all marine organisms, release dissolved organic matter (DOM) from destroyed cells
Bacteria	Prokaryotic, unicellular, some form colonies	Chlorophyll *a*, phycocyanin, phycoerythrin, carotenoids in cyanobacteria; bacteriochlorophyll in other photosynthetic bacteria	Variety of types	Cell wall of peptidoglycan containing muramic acid, chains of amino sugars, and amino acids in cyanobacteria	Essential role in nutrient cycles; autotrophs (especially cyanobacteria) and heterotrophs (including decomposers), nitrogen fixers; components of detritus, some cause diseases, symbiotic in many organisms, some produce blooms
Archaea	Prokaryotic, unicellular	Bacteriorhodopsin in light-capturing archaea	Variety of types	Cell wall made up of variety of compounds but no muramic acid	Autotrophs and heterotrophs, nitrogen fixers
Diatoms	Eukaryotic, unicellular, some form chains, mostly planktonic	Chlorophyll *a*, *c*, carotenoids	Chrysolaminarin, oil	Cell membrane secretes frustule of silica, pectin	Important primary producers, frustules are components of siliceous sediments
Dinoflagellates	Eukaryotic, unicellular, two flagella, mostly planktonic, some bottom-dwelling	Chlorophyll *a*, *c*, carotenoids	Starch, oil	Cell membrane secretes cellulose plates (thecae)	Primary producers, symbiotic with other organisms as zooxanthellae, red tides, many are bioluminescent, some cause diseases (*Pfiesteria*)
Silicoflagellates	Eukaryotic, unicellular, two flagella, planktonic	Chlorophyll *a*, *c*, fucoxanthin	Starch	Cell membrane secretes silica skeleton	Primary producers, skeletons are components of siliceous sediments, some produce blooms
Coccolithophorids	Eukaryotic, unicellular, one or two flagella, planktonic	Chlorophyll *a*, *c*, carotenoids	Starch	Cell membrane secretes calcium carbonate plates	Important primary producers, plates are components of calcareous sediments, some produce blooms
Cryptophytes	Eukaryotic, unicellular, usually two flagella, planktonic	Chlorophyll *a*, *c*, carotenoids, phycobilins	Variety of types	Cell membrane made up mostly of protein	Important primary producers
Foraminiferans	Eukaryotic, unicellular, bottom-dwelling and planktonic	None	Variety of types	Cell membrane secretes calcium carbonate shell (test)	Heterotrophs, tests are components of calcareous sediments
Radiolarians	Eukaryotic, unicellular, some colonial, mostly planktonic	None	Variety of types	Cell membrane secretes silica skeleton	Heterotrophs, skeletons are components of siliceous sediments
Ciliates	Eukaryotic, unicellular, planktonic and bottom-dwelling	None	Variety of types	Cell membrane made up mostly of lipids	Heterotrophs, some associated with marine animals
Fungi	Eukaryotic, unicellular or multicellular, mostly bottom-dwelling	None	Variety of types	Cell wall of chitin and other compounds	Decomposers, many cause diseases, symbiotic with algae or cyanobacteria in lichens

Source: Bill Ober

Interactive
Exploration

McGraw-Hill Connect® is a great place to check your understanding of chapter material. Visit **www.mcgrawhillconnect.com** for access to interactive chapter summaries, chapter quizzing, and more! Further enhance your knowledge with video clips and weblinks to chapter-related material.

Critical Thinking

1. Scientists use the particular structure of nucleic acids and other chemical differences to separate the archaea from the bacteria. Can you think of other characteristics that could be used to distinguish not only between these two domains but also between them and protists?

2. What might be the adaptive significance of bioluminescence in a dinoflagellate? Are there any disadvantages of bioluminescence in a planktonic organism?

3. An autotrophic protist, such as a diatom or a dinoflagellate, can evolve into a heterotrophic protist (and therefore a protozoan) simply by losing its chloroplasts. Under what conditions might this take place?

4. What would be the long-term effects of a toxic spill that caused severe harm to the populations of marine microbes on a particular beach?

5. Propose some hypotheses that could explain how the fungi and the algae (or cyanobacteria) that form marine lichens are able to find each other.

For Further Reading

Some of the recommended reading may be available online. Look for live links on the *Marine Biology* Online Learning Center.

General Interest

Frazer, J., 2021. Real living fossils. *Scientific American*, vol. 324, no. 6, June, pp. 76–79. Microbes buried for 100 million years in deep-water sediments in the middle of the Pacific come alive and reproduce.

Higgs, N., 2015. Alternative lifestyle. *New Scientist*, vol. 226, no. 3015, 4 April, pp. 41–43. Symbiotic chemosynthetic bacteria are found in association with a wide range of shallow-water animals.

Marshall, M., 2019. Life's dark ages. *New Scientist*, vol. 242, no. 3212, 12 January, pp. 28–32. Prokaryotes had a crucial role not only in the evolution of life on Earth but in the shaping of a life-supporting atmosphere.

Martin, R. and A. Quigg, 2013. Tiny plants that once ruled the seas. *Scientific American*, vol. 308, no. 6, June, pp. 4–45. An increase in the biodiversity and complexity of phytoplankton may have promoted the rise of some marine animal groups.

Mitra, A., 2018. The perfect beast. *Scientific American*, vol. 318, no. 4, April, pp. 26–33. Protists that use both photosynthesis and ingestion of food play an important role in the ocean.

Ogasa, N., 2022. Live wires. *Science News*, vol. 202, no. 2, pp. 24–28. Long filamentous bacteria living in sediments could help clean up coastal environments.

Samoray, C., 2016. Floating fortress of microbes. *Science News*, vol. 189, no. 4, February 20, pp. 20–23. Diatoms and bacteria thrive on microplastic debris that pollutes the ocean.

Stone, S., 2022. Healing waters. *Scientific American*, vol. 327, no.2, August, pp. 56–74. Chemicals from marine microbes are investigated as sources of crucial medicines.

In Depth

Arzul, I., S. Corbeil, B. Morga, and T. Renault, 2017. Viruses infecting marine molluscs. *Journal of Invertebrate Pathology*, vol. 147, pp. 118–135.

Baker, B. J., K. E. Appler, and X. Gong, 2021. New microbial biodiversity in marine sediments. *Annual Review of Marine Science*, vol. 13, pp. 161–175.

Coutinho, F., G. Gregoracci, J. Walter, M. Juline, C. Thompson, and F. Thompson, 2018. Metagenomics sheds light on the ecology of marine microbes and their viruses. *Trends in Microbiology*, vol. 26, pp. 955–965.

de Carvalho, C. 2018. Marine biofilms: A successful microbial strategy with economic implications. *Frontiers in Marine Science* [https://doi.org/10.3389/fmars.2018.00126].

DeLong, E. F., 2021. Genome-enabled exploration of microbial ecology and evolution in the sea: a rising tide lifts all boats. *Environmental Microbiology*, vol. 23, pp. 1301–1321.

Laffy, P., E. Wood-Charlson, D. Turaev, S. Jutz, C. Pascelli, E. Botté, S. Bell, T. Peirce, K. Weynberg, M. van Oppen, T. Rattei, and N. Webster, 2018. Reef invertebrate viromics: diversity, host specificity and functional capacity. *Environmental Microbiology*, vol. 20, pp. 2125–2141.

Liu, L., C. Wu, H., and P. Qian, 2020. Marine natural products as antifouling molecules – a mini-review (2014-2020). *Biofouling*, vol. 36, pp. 1210–1226.

Pelusi, A., P. De Luca, F. Manfellotto, K. Thamatrakoln, K., Bidle, and M. Montresor, 2021. Virus-induced spore formation as a defense mechanism in marine diatoms. *New Phytologist*, vol. 229, pp. 2251–2259.

Record, N. R., Talmy, D., and Våge. S. 2016. Quantifying tradeoffs for marine viruses. *Frontiers in Marine Science* [https://doi.org/10.3389/fmars.2016.00251].

Ryabov, A., O. Kerimoglu, E. Litchman, I. Olenina, L. Roselli, A. Basset, E. Stanca, and B. Blasius, 2021. Shape matters: the relationship between cell geometry and diversity in phytoplankton. *Ecology Letters*, vol. 24, pp. 847–861.

Santoro, A. E., R. A. Richter, and C. L. Dupont, 2019. Planktonic marine archaea. *Annual Review of Marine Science*, vol. 11, pp. 131–158.

Wiese, J. and J. F. Imhoff, 2019. Marine bacteria and fungi as promising source for new antibiotics. *Drug Development Research*, vol. 80, pp. 24–27.

Young, J.N. and K. Schmidt, 2020. It's what's inside that matters: physiological adaptations of high-latitude marine microalgae to environmental change. *New Phytologist*, vol. 227, pp. 1307–1318.

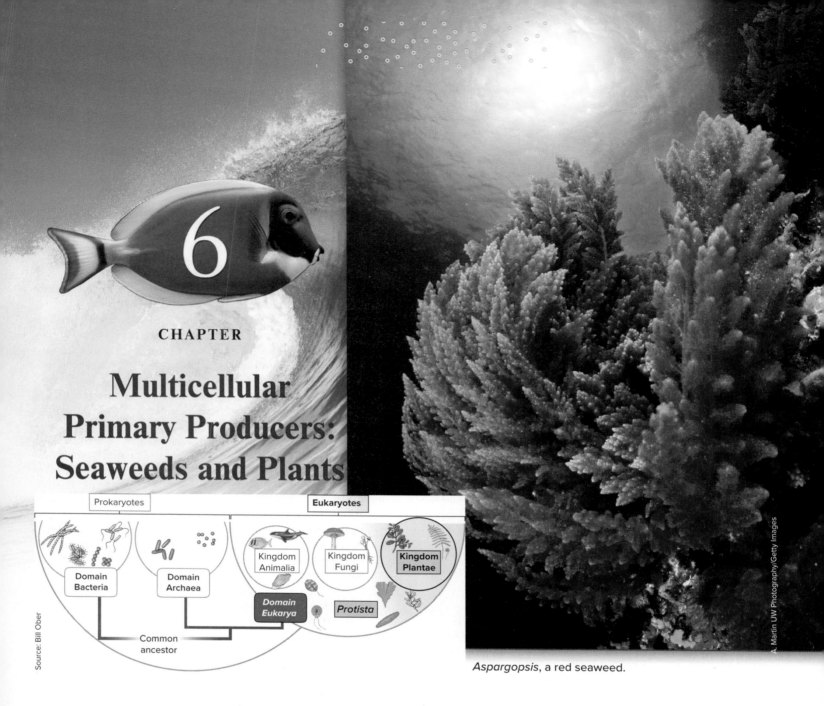

Source: Bill Ober

6

CHAPTER

Multicellular Primary Producers: Seaweeds and Plants

Aspargopsis, a red seaweed.

A. Martin UW Photography/Getty Images

As inhabitants of land, our perception of the world of photosynthetic organisms is based mostly on plants such as trees, ferns, and mosses. Many fascinating photosynthetic organisms populate the oceans, but for the most part they are very different from land plants. Unlike terrestrial plants, most marine photosynthetic organisms are not considered true plants at all and therefore are not members of the kingdom Plantae. Non-plant photosynthetic organisms include photosynthetic bacteria and unicellular **algae** (both described in Chapter 5) and the **seaweeds** covered here. We refer as **phycology** the scientific study of algae and seaweeds. Some biologists, however, consider some or all seaweeds to be plants. The true marine plants, including **seagrasses, salt-marsh grasses,** and **mangroves,** are also covered in this chapter.

Seaweeds and true marine plants are both **primary producers** capable of using light energy to perform photosynthesis. In other words, these organisms are **autotrophs.** As such, marine primary producers not only release oxygen (O_2), but absorb carbon dioxide (CO_2) and thus help reduce the effect of this greenhouse gas on global climate change (see Special Report: Climate Change).

6.1 MULTICELLULAR ALGAE: THE SEAWEEDS

The most familiar types of marine algae are those popularly known as **seaweeds.** "Algae" (singular "**alga**") and "seaweeds" are interchangeably used, except that, to complicate our lives, unicellular "algae" are not seaweeds but all seaweeds are algae. Just remember that "red algae" and "red seaweeds" mean the same thing! "Seaweed" is a rather unfortunate name. First of all, the word "weeds" does not do justice to these conspicuous and often elegant inhabitants of rocky shores and other marine environments. Some biologists opt for the

more formal name of **macroalgae.** On the other hand, the term "seaweeds" is useful in distinguishing them from the unicellular algae surveyed in Chapter 5 and the true marine plants described later in this chapter. By definition, seaweeds are all multicellular; unicellular green and red algae are therefore not considered seaweeds. All seaweeds and unicellular green and red algae are nevertheless considered **protists** (formerly kingdom Protista) whereas seagrasses, salt-marsh grasses, and mangroves are true plants (kingdom Plantae).

Like unicellular algae, seaweeds are eukaryotic. The structures of seaweeds, however, are far more complex than those of unicellular algae. Reproduction is also more elaborate. Though more complex than unicellular algae, seaweeds lack the highly specialized structures and reproductive mechanisms of most terrestrial true plants, especially the flowering plants.

The range of variation observed among seaweeds is spectacular. Those we see on rocky shores at low tide are usually small and sturdy as an adaptation to withstand waves. Some small, delicate ones live on other seaweeds. Kelps found offshore in cold waters are true giants that form dense underwater forests (see Fig. 6.8*b*). The multicellular condition of seaweeds allows many adaptations not available to unicellular forms. The ability of seaweeds to grow tall and rise off the bottom provides new opportunities as well as challenges, particularly that of wave action.

Seaweeds are autotrophs that play an important role in many coastal environments. They transform solar energy into chemical energy in the form of organic matter and make it available to a long list of hungry creatures, which can include humans. There are always exceptions, and there are a few seaweeds that are not primary producers but parasites of other seaweeds. Other organisms live on or even within the tissues of seaweeds, and more importantly, seaweeds also take carbon dioxide from their environment and release oxygen to be used by organisms both in the ocean and on land. It has been estimated that seaweeds, together with the unicellular algae in the water, produce 90% of all the oxygen in the atmosphere.

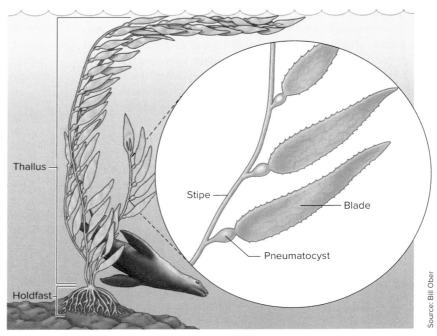

FIGURE 6.1 The giant kelp (*Macrocystis*), indicating the general structure of seaweeds.

Source: Bill Ober

General Structure

Seaweeds show a wide range of growth forms and complexity of structures. Nevertheless, several unifying features are worth mentioning. Seaweeds lack the true leaves, stems, and roots of plants. The complete body is known as the **thallus** (plural, **thalli**) whether it is a filament, a thin leafy sheet, or a giant kelp (Fig. 6.1).

The leaf-like, flattened portions of the thallus of many seaweeds are known as **blades** (Fig. 6.1). They have a large surface area and are the main photosynthetic regions, though all portions of the thallus are able to photosynthesize in light as long as they have chlorophyll. Blades are technically not true leaves because they have no veins or specialized transport tissue like those found in land plants. Another difference is that, in contrast to true leaves, the upper and lower surfaces of blades are identical to each other. Gas-filled bladders known as **pneumatocysts** (Fig. 6.1) sometimes keep the blades close to the sea surface, thereby maximizing their exposure to sunlight.

Some seaweeds have a distinct, stem-like structure to provide support, the **stipe** (Fig. 6.1), from which blades originate. It is long and tough in the large kelps. A structure that looks like roots, the **holdfast,** attaches the thallus to the bottom. Holdfasts are particularly well developed in the kelps (Fig. 6.1). They are not involved in any significant absorption of water and nutrients and do not penetrate through the sand or mud, as true roots do. Most seaweeds cannot anchor in soft sediments and are therefore restricted to hard bottoms. Water and nutrients, which bathe the entire thallus, are picked up directly across the surface without the need of roots. Also, in contrast to the leaves and stems of plants, the stipe and holdfast usually lack tissues specialized for water and nutrient transport.

> Seaweeds consist of a thallus, which is sometimes provided with leaf-like blades, and a root-like holdfast. They lack true leaves, stems, or roots.

Photosynthetic Pigments

Chlorophyll is the essential photosynthetic pigment in practically all photosynthetic organisms, including unicellular algae, seaweeds, and true-plants. Because of its chemical structure, chlorophyll captures solar energy (see Fig. 4.4). There are three main types of chlorophyll: *a*, *b*, and *c*. Chlorophyll *a* is the primary pigment found in photosynthetic organisms, with the exception of some bacteria and archaea (see Tables 5.2 and 6.1).

> **Primary Producers** Organisms that manufacture organic matter from carbon dioxide (CO_2), usually by photosynthesis.
> **Autotrophs** Organisms that can use energy (usually solar energy) to make organic matter.
> • 4.1, The Ingredients of Life

Accessory photosynthetic pigments, such as **carotenoids,** are chemical compounds that also capture solar energy but can only pass it on to chlorophyll *a*. Chlorophyll *a* and accessory pigments absorb particular wavelengths of the visible light spectrum (see Fig. 3.11) so that by working together they broaden the range of wavelengths, or **absorption spectrum,** used in photosynthesis. Chlorophyll *a* is more efficient in absorbing violet-blue and red light, not green light, which is reflected and makes chlorophyll appear green. Carotenoids, in contrast, reflect the red to yellow portions of the visible light spectrum. Chlorophyll *b*, which is only found in some groups of seaweeds (see Table 6.1), is an accessory pigment that absorbs somewhat similar wavelengths as does chlorophyll *a*. Chlorophyll *c*, also an accessory pigment, is characteristic of some unicellular protists (see Table 5.2) as well as brown seaweeds (see Table 6.1). Still other types of chlorophylls are found among bacteria and archaea (see Table 5.1).

Types of Seaweeds

The classification of seaweeds takes into consideration not only structure but also the types of photosynthetic pigments and the food products they store (see Table 6.1). There are three types of seaweeds: green, brown, and red algae. It is not always easy to recognize these groups by their color because the relative proportion of chlorophyll and other pigments (see Table 6.1) can vary depending on factors such as water depth and age. Chemical analysis, however, reveals the characteristic pigments of each group.

Green Algae Most **green algae** (division, or phylum, **Chlorophyta**) live in freshwater and terrestrial environments. Only around 10% of the more than 7,000 species are marine; many of these marine species are unicellular and only about 1,800 are multicellular. This, however, does not mean that multicellular green algae are uncommon in the sea. Certain species dominate in environments with variations in salinity such as bays and estuaries and isolated tide pools on rocky coasts.

Most multicellular green algae have a simple thallus compared to the other two groups of seaweeds. Their photosynthetic

pigments and food reserve are the same as those in plants (see Table 6.1), so it is thought that land plants evolved from green algae. Chlorophyll in both green algae and plants is not normally masked by any accessory pigments, and green algae typically have a bright green thallus.

> Multicellular green algae are common in some marine environments. They are typically bright green because chlorophyll is not masked by other pigments.

Filamentous green algae commonly grow on other seaweeds and on rocks in shallow water, including rocky shore tide pools. The filaments of these species can be branched or unbranched. Species of *Enteromorpha* have a thin thallus in the form of a hollow tube. They sometimes flourish in polluted areas. Sea lettuce (*Ulva;* Fig. 6.2) forms paper-thin sheets whose shape varies depending on environmental factors. Different species of *Ulva* are widespread, from polar to tropical waters. *Valonia* forms large spheres or clusters of spheres in the tropics and subtropics.

Several other green algae consist of thin filaments or tubes (siphons) formed by a single giant cell with many nuclei. Such is the case in *Caulerpa,* which is restricted to the tropics and subtropics. Its many species show a great variety of shapes. Dead man's fingers (*Codium;* Fig. 6.3) is a green alga that extends from tropical to temperate waters, including both coasts of North America. It consists of multinucleated filaments woven into a spongy, often branching thallus. The thallus of *Halimeda,* a **calcareous green alga,** consists of numerous segments with deposits of calcium carbonate (see Fig. 14.10). The shedding and accumulation of its dead, calcified segments plays an important role in reef building (see "Other Reef Builders," in 14.1).

Brown Algae The color of the **brown algae** (division, or phylum, **Phaeophyta**), which actually varies from olive green to dark brown, is due to a preponderance of yellow-brown accessory pigments, particularly **fucoxanthin,** over chlorophyll (see Table 6.1). Almost all the approximately 1,800 known species are marine.

FIGURE 6.2 *Ulva,* or sea lettuce, is a green alga that is common on rocks where fresh water, often containing high amounts of nutrients, reaches the sea.

Bob Barnes/Alamy Stock Photo

FIGURE 6.3 The dead man's fingers (*Codium fragile*) form branched clumps on rocky shores. Its chloroplasts remain alive, and still photosynthesize, in sea slugs (shell-less relatives of snails) that feed on the seaweed.

sciencepics/Shutterstock

Brown algae are often the dominant primary producers on temperate and polar rocky coasts and include the largest and most complex seaweeds.

The brown algae have yellow-brown accessory pigments in addition to chlorophyll. They include the largest and structurally most complex seaweeds.

The simplest brown algae have a finely filamentous thallus, as in the widely distributed *Ectocarpus*. The thallus is flat and branched in *Dictyota* and fan-shaped and lightly calcified in *Padina* (Fig. 6.4). Both are tropical and subtropical. The thallus of most species of *Desmarestia* is branched in many ways. *Desmarestia* is found in cold waters. It ranges from the Antarctic, where it is one of the dominant species, to temperate shores elsewhere.

Some of the most conspicuous of all brown algae are those exposed at low tides at the middle and upper levels of rocky shores. Their thick, leathery thalli can withstand exposure to air (see "Exposure at Low Tide," in 11.1). Many species have gas-filled floats. Known locally as **rockweeds,** or **wracks,** *Fucus* (Fig. 6.5) is found on the Atlantic and Pacific coasts of North America and other temperate shores. The knotted rockweed (*Ascophyllum;* Fig. 6.6) is found along temperate Atlantic coasts. In warm waters, including the Gulfs of Mexico and California, these temperate species are replaced by sargasso weed (*Sargassum*). Sargasso weed has spherical air bladders that keep the small, leaf-like blades afloat at the sea surface. Most species grow on rocks, but at least two float offshore in huge masses. The **Sargasso Sea,** an area in the Atlantic north of the West Indies (see Fig. 8.24), takes its name from sargasso weed. The seaweed drifts in other regions of the world as well. Washed ashore, the bad-smelling masses of sargasso weed have become a major problem in beaches in Florida and many Caribbean islands, threatening the tourist industry. Pollution by fertilizers that make their way to the open ocean and global climate change have been pointed out as possible culprits of these recent outbreaks.

The **kelps** are the most complex and largest of all brown algae. Most kelps are found below the low tide level in temperate and subpolar latitudes. In these environments they can occur in great abundance, providing food and shelter for many other organisms.

Some kelps consist of a single large blade, up to 3 m (almost 10 ft) in length, as in the many species of *Laminaria* (see Figs. 13.21

Peter Castro

FIGURE 6.4 *Padina*, a brown alga, consists of clusters of flat blades that are rolled into circles. This species is from the Hawaiian Islands.

Peter Castro

FIGURE 6.5 The spiral rockweed (*Fucus spiralis*) is common on rocky shores on the Atlantic coasts of temperate North America and Europe. Its thallus lacks the air bladders that characterize a similar species, the bladder rockweed (*Fucus vesiculosus*).

and 13.26). Their blades are harvested for food in several parts of the world (see Box 6.1, "Seaweeds for Gourmets"). Several blades can grow from a single holdfast. In some species of *Laminaria* the blade is split or branched. In *Agarum* and *Alaria* (see Fig. 13.21), a conspicuous rib runs along the middle of the single blade. The blade of *Alaria* can be as long as 25 m (82 ft). *Postelsia*, commonly known as the sea palm because of its appearance (Fig. 6.7), grows on intertidal rocks exposed to heavy waves. It occurs in thick clusters from central California to British Columbia. Two branched

FIGURE 6.6 The knotted rockweed (*Ascophyllum nodosum*) occurs on the North American and European coasts of the North Atlantic.

Bill Ober

FIGURE 6.7 Stands of the sea palm (*Postelsia palmaeformis*) are common on rocky shores exposed to heavy wave action on the Pacific coast of North America (also see Figs. 11.12 and 11.16).

Charlie Arneson

forms, the feather-boa kelp (*Egregia;* see Fig. 13.26) and the southern sea palm (*Eisenia;* see Fig. 11.12), are also common on Pacific rocky shores.

In the Pacific, the largest kelps are found in deeper water just below the lowest tide level. The bull kelp, *Nereocystis*, consists of a floating whip-like stipe up to 30 m (almost 100 ft) long with a large, spherical pneumatocyst at the upper end (see Fig. 13.26). Another large kelp is *Pelagophycus* (see Figs. 13.23 and 13.26). It is similar to the bull kelp, but it has impressive antler-like branches.

Macrocystis (see Fig. 6.1), the giant kelp, is the largest of the kelps and the world's largest bottom-dwelling organism. Its massive holdfast is attached to hard bottoms from the intertidal to depths of 25 m (83 ft) or more. Several long stipes grow from the holdfast, from which elongated blades develop (Fig. 6.8*a*). At the base of each blade, a gas-filled pneumatocyst eventually develops, which helps keep the blades close to the surface. Individuals as long as 100 m (330 ft) have been recorded. It has been estimated that such kelps can grow as much as 14 cm (5.5 in) per day in optimal conditions. Many individuals, each with many fast-growing and intertwined stipes, form dense and very productive **kelp beds,** or **forests** (Fig. 6.8*b*),

in the colder waters of the North and South Pacific (see the map in Fig. 13.22). Kelp beds are harvested by chopping off the tops for the extraction of several natural products (see "Economic Importance," below). Kelp beds are among the richest, most productive environments in the marine realm. They show very high **primary production,** the rate of production of organic matter. The ecological significance and other aspects of the biology of kelp beds will be discussed under "Kelp Communities" (in 13.3).

Red Algae There are more species of marine **red algae** (division, or phylum, **Rhodophyta**) than of marine green and brown algae combined. Among other features, they have red accessory pigments called **phycobilins** (phycocyanin and phycoerythrin), which mask chlorophyll (see Table 6.1). Most species appear red, though some have different colors depending on their daily exposure to light. The group is essentially marine; only a few of the approximately 10,000 species live in fresh water or soil. Red algae inhabit most shallow-water marine environments. Some are harvested for food and for the extraction of various products (see "Economic Importance" below).

The red algae are the largest group of seaweeds. Their chlorophyll is typically masked by red accessory pigments.

The structure of the thallus of red algae does not show the wide variation in complexity and size seen in brown algae. Some reds have become greatly simplified, at least in their structure, by becoming parasites of

(a)

Charlie Arneson

(b)

Charlie Arneson

FIGURE 6.8 (*a*) The growing end of a stipe of the giant kelp (*Macrocystis pyrifera*). (*b*) A kelp forest in California (also see Figs. 13.24 and 13.26).

FIGURE 6.9 Many species of *Porphyra*, a red alga, inhabit temperate, polar, and tropical rocky shores around the world. Some are of economic importance.

Peter Castro

other seaweeds. A few have lost all trace of chlorophyll and have become heterotrophs, depending entirely on their host for nutrition. Most red algae are filamentous, but the thickness, width, and arrangement of the filaments vary a great deal. Dense clumps are more common on the upper levels of rocky shores that are exposed at low tide; longer and flatter branches predominate in areas less exposed to air and in deeper water. These variations are observed among the many species of *Gelidium* and *Gracilaria* that are found worldwide. *Endocladia* forms wiry clumps on rocky shores from Alaska to Southern California.

Some species of *Gigartina* have large blades as long as 2 m (6 ft). These are among the most massive of the red algae. Numerous species of *Porphyra* are common on rocky shores above the lowest tide marks from polar to tropical coasts (Fig. 6.9). The most common growth form is a thallus with thin, large blades. *Rhodymenia* is common in the North Atlantic. Its blades can reach 1 m (3 ft) in length. Irish moss (*Chondrus*) is another North Atlantic red alga. It can tolerate wide ranges of temperature, salinity, and light, and its shape varies greatly in response to these physical factors.

The **coralline algae** are red algae that deposit calcium carbonate within their cell walls. They are important in several marine environments. The calcified thallus takes a variety of shapes: thin disks growing over other seaweeds, branches with many joints (*Corallina;* Fig. 6.10), and smooth or rough **encrusting** growths on rocks. Warm-water coralline algae are actively involved in the formation and development of coral reefs (see "Other Reef Builders," in 14.1). Other species thrive in temperate and polar waters, often attaining a large size.

Life History

Reproduction is a complex affair in seaweeds. **Asexual,** or vegetative, reproduction is common. It can be more important than **sexual** reproduction in most species. Fragments of the thallus can often grow into new individuals, as occurs in the floating masses of sargasso weed in the Sargasso Sea in the Atlantic Ocean. Some seaweeds produce **spores,** which are cells specialized for dispersing to new locations or persisting through unfavorable conditions. Some spores are protected by resistant cell walls; others have flagella for movement and are known as **zoospores.**

The production of **gametes** is a key event in sexual reproduction. Gametes from two different individuals fuse, so that the new generation contains genetic information from both parents. Genetic variation is thus ensured generation after generation. Gametes produced by all members of a seaweed species can be similar in appearance or can consist of larger, non-motile eggs and smaller sperm that can swim by means of flagella. Male gametes in the red algae lack flagella and are non-motile. They can be released in strands of slime. Male and female gametes can be formed in the same thallus, but the chances are good that fusing gametes will be from separate thalli.

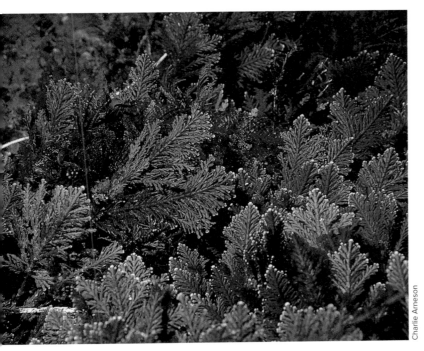

Charlie Arneson

FIGURE 6.10 *Corallina*, a coralline alga. The color of live coralline algae typically varies from light to intense reddish-pink; dead ones are white.

> **Primary Production** The conversion of carbon from an inorganic form, carbon dioxide, into organic matter by autotrophs—that is, the production of food.
> • 4.1, The Ingredients of Life

Cells of seaweeds (and of all organisms—clam, fish, or human) divide and produce identical cells by **mitosis.** Seaweeds can also produce haploid spores or gametes by **meiosis.** The existence of diploid and haploid cells is fundamental in understanding the often complex life histories of seaweeds. Their life histories can be divided into two basic types.

The first basic type (Fig. 6.11c) is the most common among all three groups of seaweeds, and it involves two types of thalli. The first is a diploid (2n) **sporophyte** generation that through meiosis produces not gametes but haploid (n, or 1n) spores. Except in the red algae, these spores are typically motile. They divide and develop into the second kind of thallus, a haploid (n) **gametophyte** generation. The gametophyte is the one that produces haploid gametes. In some species there are separate male (sperm-producing) and female (egg-producing) thalli; in others, both types of gametes are produced by every thallus. The gametes are released and, on fertilization, produce a diploid (2n) zygote that develops into the diploid sporophyte. A life history with two generations, a sporophyte and

a gametophyte, is an example of the phenomenon of **alternation of generations.** In some algae, such as sea lettuce (*Ulva*) and the brown *Dictyota*, the sporophyte and gametophyte are structurally identical, or **isomorphic.** On the other hand, in kelps (*Laminaria, Macrocystis,* and others) the large plant we see is the sporophyte, whereas the gametophyte is minute and barely visible (see Fig. 13.25), thus being **polymorphic** because there are at least two different-looking generations. A similar type of alternation of generations takes place in flowering plants, when a sporophyte dominates over a minute gametophyte.

The second basic type of life history (Fig. 6.11a) is the easiest to understand because it is similar to that of animals, including humans. There is no alternation of generations. Thus, there is only one thallus, and it is diploid. The thallus produces haploid gametes by meiosis. After fertilization, the resulting zygote develops into a new diploid thallus. This type of life history is observed in some brown algae (*Fucus* and other rockweeds) and in some green algae (*Codium, Halimeda*). A variation of the first type of life history,

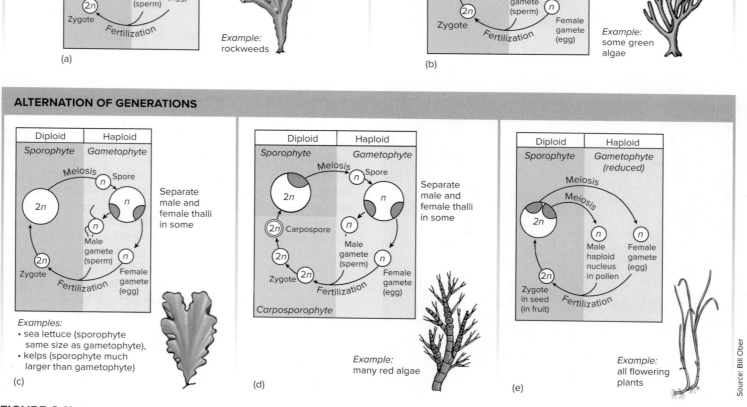

FIGURE 6.11 Generalized patterns of sexual reproduction in the life histories of seaweeds and marine flowering plants. These patterns are not absolute, and many modifications have been described. In some groups, certain reproductive stages have different names.

unique to the red algae, is more complex, involving alternation of three generations (Fig. 6.11*d*).

A variation of this second basic type of life history, which occurs in some green algae (Fig. 6.11*b*), the dominant thallus is haploid and produces haploid gametes.

> Reproduction in seaweeds is by asexual and sexual means. Sexual reproduction can involve an alternation of a haploid (or gametophyte) and a diploid (or sporophyte) generation.

There are many known variations of these life history schemes, and probably others waiting to be discovered. Other aspects of the life history of seaweeds are also noteworthy. For example, the development of gametes or spores can be influenced by the amounts of nutrients in the water, by temperature, or by day length. High levels of nitrogen in the water cause the development of asexual spores in sea lettuce, but low levels stimulate the development of gametes instead. The release of gametes and spores can be triggered by an incoming tide (and therefore by the cycles of the moon) or by chemical messengers received from cells of the opposite sex. In some seaweeds, the release of male and female gametes is timed to take place at about the same time. An isopod, a small crustacean, transfers male gametes to female gametes in a red alga!

Economic Importance

People have used seaweeds since time immemorial. Samples from the oldest human settlement in the Western Hemisphere, in southern Chile, show that the first Americans probably used seaweeds as food and medicine. People around the world still harvest seaweeds to be used in many ways. The most obvious use is as a food source. People from different cultures have discovered that many seaweeds are edible, especially some of the red and brown algae. They are consumed in a variety of ways (see Box 6.1, "Seaweeds for Gourmets"). The farming, or **aquaculture,** of seaweed is big business in China, Japan, Korea, and many other nations (see Table 17.3). Seaweeds are grown sustainably on weighted ropes attached to buoys floating just below the surface, providing a source of income for an increasing number of fishers worldwide, particularly females. Seaweed farming has become popular and successful in many places. No need to feed or use fertilizers or pesticides!

Seaweeds produce several types of gelatinous chemicals, called **phycocolloids,** that are used in food processing and in the manufacture of different products. These phycocolloids are valuable because of their ability to form viscous suspensions or gels even at low concentrations.

One important phycocolloid, **algin** (which comprises alginic acid and its salts, the alginates), is used extensively as a stabilizer and emulsifier in the manufacture of dairy products such as ice cream and cheese, which need to be smooth and not likely to separate. Algin is also used in the baking industry to prevent frostings and pies from becoming dry. As a thickener and emulsifier, it is used in the pharmaceutical and chemical industries and in the manufacture of various products, from shampoo and shaving cream to plastics and pesticides. Algin also has uses in the making of rubber products, paper, paints, and cosmetics. One of its biggest applications is in the textile industry, where algin thickens the printing paste to provide sharper prints. Major sources of algin for commercial uses are the kelps (*Laminaria, Macrocystis*) and other species of brown algae.

Another phycocolloid, **carrageenan,** is obtained from red algae such as Irish moss (*Chondrus*) in the North Atlantic and *Eucheuma* in the tropics. Several species are farmed in Asia. Carrageenan is especially valued as an emulsifier. It is used to give body to dairy products and an amazing variety of processed foods, including instant puddings.

Another phycocolloid extracted for its ability to form jellies is **agar.** Agar is used to protect ham, fish, and meats during canning, in low-calorie foods (because it is not digestible by humans), and as a thickener. It is also used in laxatives and other pharmaceuticals and in cosmetics. Biologists use agar as a medium in which to grow bacteria and molds. It is also widely used in research involving the analysis of proteins and DNA. Agar is obtained commercially from several red algae, especially from species of *Gelidium, Gelidiella*, and *Pterocladiella.*

Seaweed can also be used for fertilizer, food additives in animal feeds, wound dressings in hospitals, and in the manufacture of plastic substitutes, or **bioplastics.** Coralline algae are sometimes used in Europe to reduce the acidity of soils, and some red seaweeds are marketed as nutritional supplements. Farmed seaweeds are also being investigated for removing polluting excess nutrients from the water, decreasing carbon dioxide to combat acidification and global climate change, increasing oxygen in the water, and as a source of **biofuels** (see Box 6.2, "Marine Algae as Biofuels"). A red seaweed, *Asparagopsis* (see photo at the beginning of this chapter), is known to inhibit the production of methane by cattle. Methane is a powerful greenhouse gas, and using this seaweed as a cattle-feed additive is very promising.

There is evidence that feeding cattle with seaweeds reduces the amount of **methane**, a greenhouse gas abundantly produced by the cattle. Greenhouse gases, such as CO_2, trap heat in the atmosphere and warm Earth (see Special Report: Climate Change).

6.2 FLOWERING PLANTS

The approximately 350,000 species of **flowering plants,** or **angiosperms** (variously classified as division, or phylum, **Anthophyta** or **Magnoliophyta**), are the dominant plants on land, but a few do live in the ocean. Like other land plants (ferns, conifers, and other non-flowering plants), and in sharp contrast to algae (which are protists), flowering plants have true leaves, stems, and roots, all provided with specialized **vascular tissues** to transport water, nutrients, and the food manufactured by photosynthesis (Fig. 6.12). As such, they are grouped in the kingdom Plantae.

Few of these "higher" plants are successful in the oceans. Marine flowering plants are nevertheless highly productive and diverse. Of all flowering plants, only the **seagrasses** are truly marine.

> **Types of cell division:**
> **Mitosis** The resulting cells are identical to the original cell, having their chromosomes in pairs (diploid cells, or 2*n*).
> **Meiosis** The resulting cells are haploid (*n*, or 1*n*), as in gametes (spores in seaweeds), because they contain half the number of the parent's chromosomes.
> • 4.4, Perpetuating Life

Box 6.1 Seaweeds for Gourmets

Seaweeds, raw, cooked, or dried, are used as food in many cultures. Seaweeds are good sources of some vitamins (particularly B12), minerals, fiber, and antioxidants. Seaweeds can add variety and taste to bland foods and can be used to wrap such foods as *sushi*. Mariculture of edible seaweed is a growing business in many parts of the world (see Table 17.3). Seaweeds are harvested by hand, dried on lines, and sold at health food stores or on the Internet. Connoisseurs use seaweed, all of which are low in calories, in salads, soups, omelettes, casseroles, and sandwiches. The increased popularity of vegan food has further increased the demand for seaweed products, including substitutes for animal-based ingredients such as gelatin. Seaweed teas, jerky, instant salads, and even chocolate seaweed candy are nowadays available. Cookbooks and websites containing seaweed recipes are available to whet the appetites of the most demanding gourmets.

Ulva is not called sea lettuce for nothing. It can be eaten fresh in salads. Seaweeds (or *limu*) are an important part of Hawaiian traditional cuisine. Purple laver (a species of *Porphyra*, a red alga) is washed and boiled and in Wales eaten as a hot vegetable, fried with bacon, or as laverbread, formed into flat cakes, rolled in oatmeal, and fried. Irish moss (*Chondrus*, a red alga and a source of carrageenan) is dried and used in preparing *blancmange* and other desserts in eastern Canada, New England, and parts of northern Europe. *Rhodymenia*, another red alga, is dried and eaten, mostly by those living along the coasts of the North Atlantic. Called *dulse*, it is sometimes still used in making bread and several types of desserts. For those on a diet, dulse can also be chewed like nicotine-free tobacco.

Pickled bull kelp (*Nereocystis*) tastes like pickled cucumbers, and another type of bull kelp (*Durvillea*) is widely used in salads and other dishes in Chile. Chilean cuisine also includes dried sea lettuce in soups and stews. Sea palm (*Postelsia*), also known as "sea noodles," is reported to be excellent when sautéed in honey or stir-fried in sesame-seed oil and soy sauce. Coastal North

Harvesting kelp (*Laminaria japonica*) in Japan.

American Indians in the Pacific cook it in ovens and made it into cakes. Its indiscriminate collection is unfortunately endangering its survival, which is also true for other edible seaweeds.

It is in Japan, Korea, and other nations in Asia, however, that eating seaweed has reached the level of an art. Several species are carefully cultivated, supporting multimillion-dollar operations. Seaweed culture is a very old tradition in Japan, and Japanese cuisine uses seaweed extensively. Species of *Laminaria* and *Alaria* are dried and shredded, then prepared in various ways. *Laminaria japonica* is heavily cultivated in Japan and when processed is known as *kombu*. Seaweeds are even used to prepare kelp martinis! *Undaria*, or *wakame*, is another edible kelp that is best when fresh or cooked for a very short time. *Porphyra*, is used to make thin sheets of *nori*, widely used in soups and to wrap *sushi* (see Fig. 17.7). Are you ready for feather-boa burgers, French-fried sea palm, and *wakame* shakes?

Seaweed Cake*

1 1/2 cups salad oil
2 cups sugar

3 eggs
2 cups grated or chopped seaweed: bull kelp (*Nereocystis*), *ogo* (*Gracilaria coronopifolia*), *Eucheuma* (local species from Hawai'i), or local equivalent
2 cups grated carrots
1 cup crushed, drained pineapple (or 1 cup grated coconut, preferably fresh)
2 1/2 cups flour
1 teaspoon baking soda
1 teaspoon salt
1 teaspoon cinnamon
1 cup chopped walnuts (optional)

Mix sugar and salad oil. Add eggs, one at a time, beating well after each egg is added. Add seaweed, carrots, and pineapple (or coconut). Sift together flour, baking soda, salt, and cinnamon and add to mixture; mix well. Add chopped walnuts if desired. Bake in oblong or bread-loaf pan at 160 °C (350 °F) for 45 to 50 min. Cake can be covered with buttercream frosting. Enjoy.

*Adapted from I. A. Abbot, *Limu, An Ethnobotanical Study of Some Hawaiian Seaweeds*, 4th edition, National Tropical Botanical Garden, Lawa'i, Kauai'i, Hawai'i, 1996.

They often live submerged by seawater, rarely exposed at low tide. **Salt-marsh plants** and **mangroves** inhabit estuaries and shores protected from wave action. They are not completely at home in the ocean, and usually only their roots are covered by water at high tide. There are also many flowering plants adapted to colonize coastal areas exposed to salt-laden winds and occasional sea spray, though they do not tolerate immersion in seawater. Such plants can be found on sand dunes or living along the edges of salt marshes.

Reproduction in flowering plants involves alternation of generations between a dominant sporophyte and minute

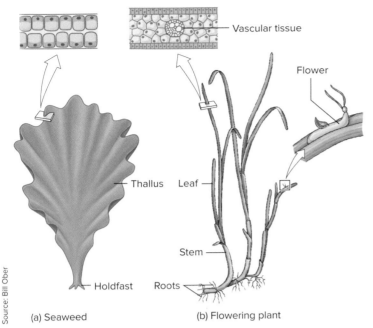

FIGURE 6.12 In contrast to algae (*a*), flowering plants, illustrated here by a seagrass (*b*), have true leaves, stems, roots, and vascular tissues.

gametophytes (Fig. 6.11*e*). The gametophytes develop in the sporophyte's flowers and are thus dependent on the sporophyte. The male gametophyte, which produces the haploid male gametes, is contained within the **pollen grain.** The female gametophyte is the **embryo sac,** which produces the haploid egg cells. Both gametocytes develop either within a single flower or in separate male and female flowers (Fig. 6.13*a*).

The most important species, distribution, adaptations, and ecological importance of salt-marsh plants and mangroves, as well as the threats to their existence because of human activities, are discussed in detail in Chapter 12 ("Salt Marshes" and "Mangrove Forests," in 12.3, and in "Human Impact on Estuaries Communities," in 12.4). Various aspects of the ecology of seagrasses and threats to seagrass meadows are similarly discussed in Chapter 13 ("Seagrass Meadows," in 13.2).

Seagrasses

Seagrasses superficially resemble grass but actually are not grasses at all. The closest relatives of certain seagrasses seem to be members of the lily family, so we know that seagrasses evolved from land plants.

Seagrasses have adapted to life in the marine environment. They have horizontal stems called **rhizomes** that commonly grow beneath the sediment (Fig. 6.13*a*). Roots and erect leaves grow from the rhizomes.

The sexual reproduction of seagrasses involves tiny flowers. The pollen grains, which contain the sperm, are produced by male flowers that typically develop in plants that are separate from plants producing female flowers (Fig. 6.11*e*). Some seagrasses produce long, thread-like pollen grains instead of the minute and round pollen of land flowering plants. Pollen, which is often produced in sticky strands, is carried to female flowers for fertilization, or **pollination,** of the egg. Water currents are involved in the dispersal of pollen, but marine animals, such as small crustaceans, could also be involved. It has been suggested that seagrass flowers are inconspicuous because insects are not needed for pollination, as in most land plants.

Tiny seeds, which in some species develop inside small fruit (Fig. 4.21*d*) within the flower or in floating fruit, result from successful fertilization. Seeds and fruit are dispersed by water currents and perhaps in the feces of the sea turtles, fishes, ducks, and other animals that graze on the plants. Seagrasses readily reproduce asexually by extending rhizomes under the substrate (Figs. 6.13 and 4.19*b*). Some seagrass meadows actually consist of a single gigantic, long-living, genetically identical **clone.**

About 70 species of seagrasses are known. Most are tropical and subtropical, but several species are common in colder waters. Most seagrasses are restricted to muddy and sandy areas in shallow water, but some, like surf grass (Fig. 6.13*e*), live on rocky shores. Different species of seagrasses vary in their maximum depth, but all are limited by the penetration of light through the water.

Most species of seagrasses are found in the tropical Pacific and Indian oceans. Typical seagrass meadows in this region consist

(a) Manatee grass (*Syringodium*) (b) Eelgrass (*Zostera*) (c) Paddle grass (*Halophila*) (d) Turtle grass (*Thalassia*) (e) Surf grass (*Phyllospadix scouleri*)

FIGURE 6.13 Some common seagrasses.

EYE ON SCIENCE

Box 6.2 Marine Algae as Biofuels

Land plants such as corn and soybeans are currently used as sources of **biofuels**, alternatives to oil, the increasingly scarce—and polluting—fossil fuel. Biofuels help offset the effects of **global climate change** because the plants used to produce biofuels take up carbon dioxide (CO_2) from the atmosphere (see Special Report, Rolling the Dice: Climate Change). Biofuels still release CO_2 when burned but they return back to the atmosphere at best the same amount of CO_2 without any long-term increase in CO_2 as in fossil fuels. Most importantly, biofuels, unlike fossil fuels, are renewable resources that can be naturally replaced.

Marine unicellular algae are some of the most promising sources of biofuels. Fast-growing microalgae are among the most efficient primary producers, typically more efficient than land plants. Instead of transforming solar energy into organic matter that is fermented into ethanol, the biofuel most commonly obtained from land plants, many marine algae transform the glucose produced by photosynthesis (see Fig. 4.6) into lipids, which are stored as energy-rich oils that can be used as biofuels. The algae can be grown in arid or desert areas along the coast, thus avoiding the use of valuable agricultural land in competition with food crops. The use of seawater rather than freshwater, already a scant resource in many parts of the world, is another advantage of marine algae over

land plants or freshwater algae. Some microalgae are heterotrophs so they can be grown in the dark and thus are able to grow around the clock. Furthermore, in contrast to land-based biofuels, marine biofuels do not increase food prices, as has happened with corn and soybeans. Nutrients from treated wastewater can be used as fertilizer, the use of nitrogen fertilizers to grow land plants is a major cause of eutrophication in marine environments (see Special Report, Overwhelming the Nitrogen Cycle). Organic waste obtained after the extraction of lipids can be fermented to obtain ethanol.

CO_2, a **greenhouse gas** that makes up roughly 10% of emissions from fossil-fuel power plants, helps the growth of algae. CO_2 can be separated from other gases by the use of chemicals, "captured," and buried on land or under the sea floor, an expensive process. Pumping this CO_2 into ponds or tanks used to grow the algae is therefore another advantage of marine biofuels, that of **carbon capture.**

There are nevertheless some drawbacks in the production of marine biofuels. The algae must be grown in quantities large enough to make the process economically feasible. The right algae must be grown under very particular conditions, and they should not be affected by toxic substances and pollutants that might accumulate in the water where the algae are grown, or even eaten by contaminating grazers. Extractions of lipids

must be efficient enough in order to not get other chemical components in the process. Production cost is also high, so far higher than costs for producing gasoline and other fuels.

Numerous pilot plants around the world are at work aiming to produce marine biofuels in a sustainable way. One such project is OMEGA (Offshore Membrane Enclosures for Growing Algae), which was developed by NASA's space program in the United States and envisioned for long space flights. OMEGA uses freshwater algae that are grown in treated wastewater contained in flexible plastic tubes that float offshore. The fast-growing unicellular algae produce oil that could be used as a source of biofuels, fertilizer, and animal food. Sources include oils from marine unicellular green algae (such as some species of *Chlorella* and *Dunaliella*) and marine diatoms (species of *Navicula*). Biofuels from genetically engineered algae are already added to jet fuel used by several airlines. Fast-growing seaweeds such as kelps and some of the red algae are also being considered as producers of biofuels in the form of ethanol. Floating "seaweed farms" for biofuel production have been envisioned in Japan, Europe, and elsewhere, which together with other marine biofuels could help power the road vehicles and planes of the future.

For more information, explore the links provided on the Marine Biology *Online Learning Center.*

of several species of seagrasses living together. Among the most common are turtle grass (*Thalassia*; Fig. 6.13*d*), paddle grass (*Halophila*; Fig. 6.13*c*), strapweed (*Amphibolis*), and ribbon weed (*Posidonia*). Turtle grass is the most common seagrass in the tropical and subtropical Atlantic. Extensive meadows are found to depths of about 10 m (33 ft), deeper in clear water. Manatee grass (*Syringodium*; Fig. 6.13*a*) is often found together with turtle grass.

Eelgrass (*Zostera*) is the most widely distributed of the seagrasses. It is found in many temperate and tropical regions of the world, where it inhabits shallow, well-protected coastal waters such as bays and estuaries (see Fig. 13.15). It has distinctively flat, ribbon-like leaves (see Figs. 6.13*b* and 13.17). It is common in oxygen-poor sediments. Like tropical seagrasses, thick *Zostera* meadows, or beds, are highly productive and provide shelter and food to a variety of animals, some of considerable economic importance. Several species of *Posidonia*, which are found in the Mediterranean and along the southern coast of Australia, also play an important role in shallow coastal waters. The Mediterranean *Posidonia* meadows, known as Neptune grass, are threatened by pollution and fishing trawls.

Surf grass (*Phyllospadix;* Fig. 6.13*e*) is an unusual seagrass because it is an inhabitant of rocky coasts exposed to wave action, as its common name implies. Some species can become exposed at low tides. It is found on the Pacific coast of North America.

Seagrasses form extensive meadows that have a most important ecological role in shallow-water environments. They provide shelter to a variety of organisms including some of considerable economic importance, their roots and leaves decrease water turbulence that helps stabilize soft bottoms, and are highly productive, providing a rich source of **detritus** that directly or indirectly feeds many animals. The ecological importance of seagrass meadows and the threats to their existence because of human intrusion are discussed in detail in Chapter 13 ("Seagrass Meadows," in 13.2).

Salt-Marsh Plants

Cordgrasses (*Spartina;* Fig. 6.14) are true members of the grass family. At least 14 species are known. They are not really marine species but, rather, land plants tolerant of salt. Unlike seagrasses, which are

true marine species, cordgrasses do not tolerate total submergence by seawater. They live in salt marshes and other soft-bottom coastal areas throughout temperate regions worldwide (see Fig. 6.15). Cordgrass salt marshes have high primary production and provide habitat and breeding grounds for many species important to fisheries. They also offer protection against erosion, the result of the network of horizontal rhizomes that extends under the sediment, and provide natural water purification systems (see Fig. 18.7). Flowers, and to a much lesser extent leaves, provide food to insects and other grazers. Most organic matter is made available to other organisms in the form of detritus (see Fig. 12.24).

Plants have an extensive network of rhizomes that stretch out underground. The leaves and roots develop from the stems. Rhizomes spread horizontally, developing extensive clones. Roots just below the soil also take oxygen from the air, a crucial adaptation for living in oxygen-poor sediments. **Aerenchyma**, soft tissue with air spaces, help transport oxygen from the air to the submerged parts of the plants.

Cordgrasses inhabit the zone above mudflats that becomes submerged by seawater only at high tide, so their leaves are always partly exposed to air. Salt glands in the leaves excrete excess salt. Other salt-tolerant plants, or **halophytes,** such as pickleweed (*Salicornia;* see Fig. 12.8), salt grasses (*Distichlis*), and rushes (*Juncus*) can be found at higher levels on the marsh.

The ecological significance of salt-marsh plants as a result of their high productivity, a source of detritus, shelter for many marine and terrestrial species, and protection against erosion is highly significant. Salt marshes are nevertheless rapidly disappearing as victims of coastal development. These and other issues related to the ecology of salt marshes are discussed in Chapter 12 (12.3 and 12.4).

Mangroves

Mangroves are trees and shrubs adapted to live along tropical and subtropical shores around the world (Fig. 6.15). They are essen-

FIGURE 6.14 Cordgrass (*Spartina*) is a flowering plant that dominates the seaward margin of salt marshes in temperate and subarctic regions around the world. Salt marshes develop in soft-bottoms that are protected from wave action and are partially flooded at high tide.

tially land plants that can tolerate salt to varying degrees. Luxuriant and very productive mangrove forests, or **mangals,** flourish along muddy or sandy shores protected from wave action (Fig. 6.16).

Mangroves include around 70 mostly unrelated species of flowering plants. They are adapted in various ways to survive in a salty environment where water loss from leaves is high and sediments are soft and poor in oxygen. Adaptations become more crucial in mangroves living right on the shore, such as species of the red mangrove (*Rhizophora;* Figs. 6.16 and 6.17), which are found throughout the tropics

Detritus Particles of dead organic matter.
• 10.3, The Flow of Energy and Materials

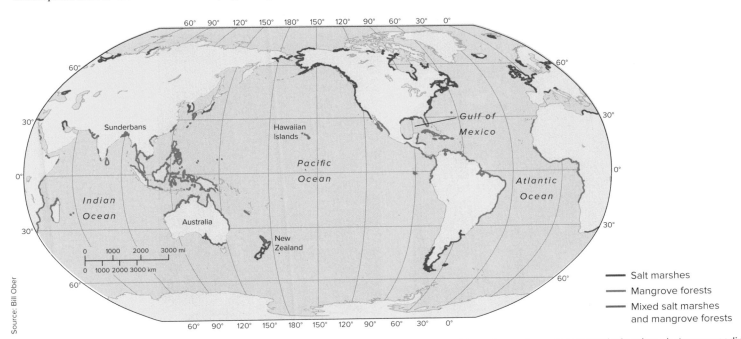

FIGURE 6.15 The world distribution of salt marshes and mangrove forests. Mangroves tend to replace salt marshes in tropical regions, but are spreading in some temperate regions as temperatures rise because of climate change. The two overlap in such areas as the Gulf of Mexico, southern Australia, and New Zealand. Mangroves were introduced by humans to the Hawaiian Islands.

Peter Castro

FIGURE 6.16 The red mangrove (*Rhizophora mangle*) forms lush forests along shores in Florida, the Caribbean, the Gulf of California, and other tropical regions of the Western Hemisphere and West Africa. Notice the long aerial roots extending into the mud, exposed here at low tide. Other species of mangroves can be found farther inland (see Fig. 12.17).

and subtropics. The extreme northern and southern limits of the red mangrove are those areas in which killing frosts begin (Fig. 6.15). Salt marshes replace red mangrove forests in areas exposed to frosts.

The **Indo-West Pacific** region has the world's most extensive mangrove forests with by far the highest number of mangrove species, which include species of *Aegiceras, Avicennia, Ceriops, Rhizophora,* and *Sonneratia.* Indo-West Pacific mangrove forests extend as far as 320 km (200 mi) inland in southern New Guinea and

some islands in Indonesia. The world's largest mangrove forest is the Sunderbans, some 10,000 km² (3,860 mi²) along the coast of Bangladesh and western India. Mangroves are nevertheless abundant in the tropical Atlantic Ocean and the Gulf of Mexico.

Atlantic and eastern Pacific mangrove forests, although not as extensive and diverse as those in the Indo-West Pacific region, are nevertheless of great ecological significance. The most common species of mangroves along the shores of southern Florida,

Charlie Arneson

(a)

Charlie Arneson

(b)

FIGURE 6.17 A seedling of the red mangrove (*Rhizophora mangle*) (*a*) as it appears in the tree and (*b*) one that has taken root in the soft sediment.

the Caribbean, and the gulfs of California and Mexico is the red mangrove (*Rhizophora mangle*). It lives right on the shore (see Fig. 12.17) and is easily identified by its peculiar prop roots, which support the trees very much like stilts (Fig. 6.16). Flexible **aerial roots** drop down from the higher branches, helping extend the tree laterally. The trees can be as tall as 9 m (30 ft). Under optimal conditions, they form dense forests noted for their high primary production as a result of such high plant biomass. Other species of *Rhizophora* are found on tropical coasts around the world.

The black mangrove (*Avicennia germinans*) and the white mangrove (*Laguncularia racemosa*) live inland from the red mangrove along the Atlantic and Pacific coasts of the Western Hemisphere and the Atlantic coast of Africa (see Fig. 12.17). Black mangrove seedlings can survive the high salinity of the water that remains standing after high-tide flooding. Seedlings of the white mangrove do not easily tolerate flooding by seawater, and as a result, this species is found only along the landward edge of the mangrove forest.

The leaves of many mangroves are thick, an adaptation to reduce water loss. Mangrove flowers are typically conspicuous (see Fig. 12.18), and insects are involved in pollination. As in several other mangroves, seeds of the red mangrove germinate while still attached to the parent tree (Fig. 6.17*a*). They develop into elongated, pencil-shaped seedlings as long as 30 cm (1 ft) before falling from the parent. Successful seedlings stick in the soft, muddy sediment like a knife thrown into a lawn (Fig. 6.17*b*), or float in the water to be carried by currents to new locations.

Economic Importance

The economic value of seagrasses, salt-marsh plants, and mangroves is mostly indirect, the result of all three groups being crucial nurseries for many species of commercial and recreational values

(see "Human Impact on Estuarine communities," in 12.3). Mangrove forests, particularly, have an incalculable value to humans. They contribute significant portions of the economy of many developing nations, not only in terms of fishery resources (many coral reef fishes use mangroves as nurseries), as revenue from the tourist industry (snorkeling trips to mangrove forests), and as a source of timber and charcoal. More importantly, mangrove forests as well as salt marshes improve water quality by removing pollutants and particulate matter and help protect coasts from erosion by wave action, especially during storms, and increasing sea levels as well as runoff from land. There is evidence that damage by recent tsunamis and hurricanes would have not been as severe if mangroves had not been cleared in some of these areas.

Many species of marine and terrestrial organisms live among the roots or branches of mangroves. Like seagrasses and salt-marsh plants, mangroves have high primary production, but relatively few animals graze on the hard-to-digest leaves, with most organic matter being consumed as detritus (see Fig. 12.24). The ecological significance of mangrove forests and human impacts are discussed in detail in Chapter 12 (12.3 and 12.4).

Flowering plants, dominant on land, have few marine representatives. Seagrasses, which are true marine species, and salt-tolerant plants like salt-marsh plants and mangroves are exceptions. They have successfully adapted to soft-bottom coastal regions, developing as highly productive meadows and, in the case of mangroves, forests along the shore.

Indo-West Pacific Region The tropical Indian and western and central Pacific oceans.
• 14.2 Kinds of Coral Reefs

Table 6.1 Most Important Characteristics of Seaweeds and Marine Plants

Group	Distinguishing Features	Photosynthetic and Accessory Pigments	Major Food Reserves	Major Cell Wall Components	Ecology
Green algae	Eukaryotic protists, unicellular and multicellular; mostly bottom-dwelling, some planktonic; alternation of generations in many	Chlorophyll *a, b*, carotenoids	Starch	Cellulose, calcium carbonate in calcareous algae	Primary producers; calcareous algae are important sources of calcareous deposits in coral reefs
Brown algae	Eukaryotic protists, multicellular; bottom-dwelling; alternation of generations present in some	Chlorophyll *a, c*, carotenoids (fucoxanthin and others)	Laminarin, oil	Cellulose, alginates	Primary producers; dominant components of kelp forests
Red algae	Eukaryotic protists, multicellular; bottom-dwelling; alternation of three generations	Chlorophyll *a*, phycobilins (phycocyanin, phycoerythrin), carotenoids	Starch	Agar, carageenan, cellulose, calcium carbonate in coralline algae	Primary producers; coralline algae are important sources of calcareous deposits in coral reefs
Flowering plants (seagrasses, salt-marsh plants, mangroves)	Eukaryotic plants, multicellular; bottom-dwelling; alternation of dominant sporophyte and minute male and female gametophytes	Chlorophyll *a, b*, carotenoids	Starch	Cellulose	Dominant primary producers in seagrass meadows, salt marshes, and mangrove forests; nursery grounds for many species; help stabilize soft bottoms, protect coast from turbulence; food for many species in the form of detritus

Source: Bill Ober

McGraw-Hill Connect® is a great place to check your understanding of chapter material. Visit **www.mcgrawhillconnect.com** for access to interactive chapter summaries, chapter quizzing, and more! Further enhance your knowledge with video clips and web links to chapter-related material.

Critical Thinking

1. Some biologists place the seaweeds in the kingdom Plantae; others consider seaweeds to be protists. Assume that a better arrangement is to group the green, brown, and red algae in their own kingdom, which we will call Macrophyta. Characterize the new kingdom by first giving its unique characteristics and then differentiate it from the protists and the true plants. Be sure to consider major exceptions or overlaps.

2. The actual color can vary among some species of red and brown algae. A particular species is collected and is described as "dark red-brown." How could we tell if this alga is a member of the Rhodophyta or of the Phaeophyta?

3. Only very few flowering plants have invaded the oceans, but those that have are very successful. What are some possible reasons for the small number of species of marine flowering plants? How do those that have taken the step manage to thrive in some environments?

4. While some flowering plants have become marine, no seaweeds are known to have become adapted to live permanently on land. Could you propose some possible explanations to the absence of land seaweeds?

5. An accidentally introduced brown seaweed has become a pest on some Pacific and Atlantic rocky shores. What kind of negative effects can be predicted as a result of this invasive species?

For Further Reading

Some of the recommended reading may be available online. Look for live links on the *Marine Biology* Online Learning Center.

General Interest

Ceurstemont, S., 2014. Kelp wanted! *New Scientist*, vol. 223, no. 2978, 19 July, pp. 44–47. Seaweed farming is taking hold around the world.

Kassinger, R., 2019. *Slime: How algae created us, plague us, and just might save us*. Houghton Mifflin Harcourt, New York, NY. Algae, from unicellular prokaryotes to multicellular seaweeds, have helped shape our atmosphere and are a source of many valuable products.

Marshall, M., 2020. Kelp is on the way. *New Scientist*, vol. 246, no. 3282, 16 May, pp. 36–39. The farming of kelp and other seaweeds is envisioned, among other potential benefits, as a way to reduce CO_2 in the atmosphere.

Mouritsen, O. G., 2013. The science of seaweeds. *American Scientist*, vol. 101, no. 6, Nov./Dec., pp. 458–465. Humans use seaweeds as a source of food and other resources.

Orth, R. J., T. J. B. Carruthers, W. C. Dennison, C. M. Duarte, J. W. Fourqurean, K. L. Heck, A. R. Hughes, G. A. Kendrick, W. J. Kenworthy, S. Olyarnik, F. T. Short, M. Waycott, and S. L. Williams, 2006. A global crisis for seagrass ecosystems. *BioScience*, vol. 56, no. 12, December, pp. 987–996.

Popkin, G., 2015. Breaking the waves. *Science*, vol. 350, 13 November, pp. 756–759. Salt marsh plants can be used as a defense against rising sea levels.

Prosek, J., 2019. The weed that feeds the North Atlantic. *National Geographic*, vol. 235, no. 6, June, pp. 126–141. The masses of sargasso weed that drift in the Sargasso Sea is the home of a large variety of organisms, many uniquely adapted to this habitat.

Shetterly, S. H., 2018. *Seaweed chronicles: A world at the water's edge*. Algonquin Books, Chapel Hill, NC. An informative account of the biology and role of seaweeds, particularly their impact on the animals living around then, including humans.

In Depth

Bringloe, T. T., S. Starko, R. M. Wade, C. Vieira, H. Kawai, O. De Clerck, M. Cock, S. M. Coelho, C. Destombe, M. Valero, J. Neiva, G. A. Pearson, S. Faugeron, E. A. Serrão, and H. Verbruggen, 2020. Phylogeny and evolution of the brown algae. *Critical Reviews in Plant Sciences*, vol. 39, pp. 281–321.

Cragg, S. M., D. A. Friess, L. G. Gillis, S. M. Trevathan-Tackett, O. M. Terrett, J. E.M. Watts, D. L. Distel, and P. Dupree, 2020. Vascular plants are globally significant contributors to marine carbon fluxes and sinks. *Annual Review of Marine Science*, vol. 12, pp. 469–497.

Dybas, C. L., 2015. Forests between the tides: Conserving Earth's vanishing mangrove ecosystems. *BioScience*, vol. 65, pp. 1039–1045.

Engelen, A. H., A. Serebryakova, P. Ang, K. Britton-Simmons, F. Mineur, M. F. Pedersen, F. Arenas, C. Fernández, H. Steen, R. Svenson, H. Pavia, G. Toth, F. Viard, and R. Santos, 2015. Circumglobal invasion by the brown seaweed *Sargassum muticum*. *Oceanography and Marine Biology: An Annual Review*, vol. 53, pp. 81–126.

Hafting, J. T., J. S. Craigie, D. B. Stengel, R. R. Loureiro, A. H. Buschmann, C. Yarish, M. D. Edwards, and A. T. Critchley, 2015. Prospects and challenges for industrial production of seaweed bioactives. *Journal of Phycology*, vol. 51, pp. 821–837.

Hurd, C. L., P. J. Harrison, K. Bischof, and C. S. Lobban, 2014. *Seaweed ecology and physiology*. Cambridge University Press, Cambridge, UK.

Koch, M., G. Bowes, C. Ross, and X. H. Zhang, 2013. Climate change and ocean acidification effects on seagrasses and marine macroalgae. *Global Change Biology*, vol. 19, pp. 103–132.

Marcelino, V. R. and H. Verbruggen, 2015. Ecological niche models of invasive seaweeds. *Journal of Phycology*, vol. 51, pp. 606–620.

Marois, M., 2015. Coastal protection from tsunamis and cyclones provided by mangrove wetlands: A review. *International Journal of Biodiversity Science, Ecosystem Services & Management*, vol. 11, pp. 71–83.

Van der Stocken, T., A. K. S. Wee, D. J. R. De Ryck, B. Vanschoenwinkel, D. A. Friess, F. Dahdouh-Guebas, M. Simard, N. Koedam, and E. L. Webb, 2019. A general framework for propagule dispersal in mangroves. *Biological Reviews*, vol. 94, pp. 1547–1575.

CHAPTER

Marine Animals Without a Backbone

ImageQuest Marine

The crab *Trapezia flavopunctata* and its coral host, *Pocillopora*.

Prokaryotes | Eukaryotes

Kingdom Animalia

Domain Bacteria

Domain Archaea

Domain Eukarya

Kingdom Fungi

Kingdom Plantae

Protista

Common ancestor

Source: Bill Ober

Most species of multicellular organisms inhabiting our planet are **animals** (kingdom **Animalia**). In contrast to photosynthetic organisms like algae and plants, we animals cannot manufacture our own food and must therefore obtain it from others. The need to eat has resulted in the evolution of myriad ways of obtaining and processing food, as well as equally diverse ways of avoiding being eaten.

The colorful crab above is a good example. It inhabits reef-building corals, relying on them for food and shelter. The crabs feed on mucus, which the coral produces to keep its surface free from debris. The coral is also an animal, though it may not look like one. It gets some of its food from **zooxanthellae** that live in its tissues. The coral also eats small planktonic organisms that it captures by using stinging structures in its tentacles. Though a crab is occasionally captured by a fish or an octopus, crabs are usually

safe among the coral branches. They repay the favor by using their claws to drive away other animals that have a taste for coral tissue.

Our survey of the marine animals follows the traditional classification into two major groups: the **vertebrates,** which have a **backbone** (a row of bones called **vertebrae**), and the **invertebrates,** animals without a backbone.

At least 97% of all species of animals are invertebrates, the subject of this chapter. All major groups, or **phyla,** of invertebrates have marine representatives, and many are exclusively marine. Only a few groups have successfully invaded land. Were it not for one of these

Zooxanthellae Dinoflagellates (single-celled algae) that live within animal tissues.

• 5.3, Unicellular Algae; Figure 14.1

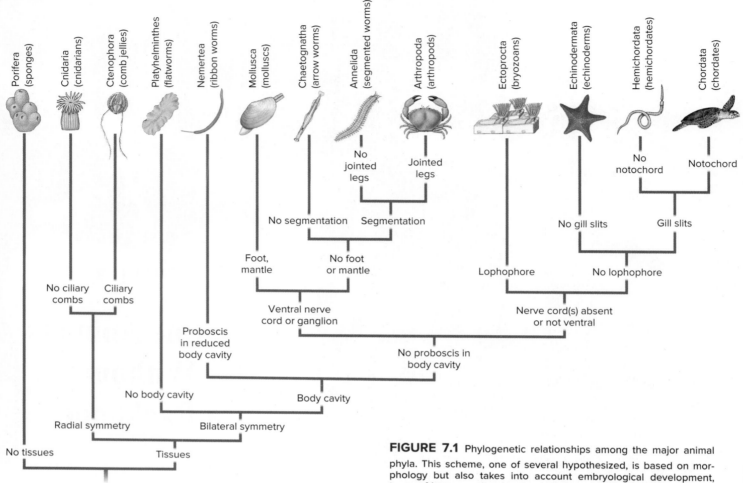

FIGURE 7.1 Phylogenetic relationships among the major animal phyla. This scheme, one of several hypothesized, is based on morphology but also takes into account embryological development, types of larvae, and molecular data. Recent molecular investigations suggest that ctenophores (comb jellies) are closer to the base of the tree than previously established.

Source: Bill Ober

groups, the insects, we could boast that most invertebrate species, and therefore most animals, are marine. Different interpretations explain the relationships between the major groups of invertebrates. The scheme given here (Fig. 7.1) will serve as a guide to our survey.

7.1 SPONGES

Sponges are best described as aggregations of specialized cells. Sponges have a cellular level of organization, meaning that the cells are largely independent of each other and do not form true **tissues** and **organs** (see Table 7.1). They are among the structurally simplest multicellular animals (Fig. 7.1).

Nearly all sponges are marine. All are **sessile,** living permanently attached to the bottom or some other hard surface. They show an amazing variety of shapes, sizes, and colors but share a relatively simple body plan. Numerous tiny pores, or **ostia,** on the surface allow water to enter and circulate through a series of canals where oxygen is made available to cells and **plankton** and organic particles are filtered out and eaten (Fig. 7.2*a*). This network of canals and a relatively flexible skeletal framework give most sponges a characteristic spongy texture. Because of this unique body plan, sponges are classified as the phylum **Porifera,** or "pore bearers."

Sponges could be similar to the first multicellular animals, which were probably simple colonies in which some cells became specialized for such functions as feeding and protection. Sponge cells are very plastic and easily change from one type to another. If experimentally separated, the cells can even regroup and form a new sponge (Fig. 7.3).

The architecture of sponges is best understood by examining the simplest kind of sponge (Fig. 7.2*a*). The outer surface is covered with flat cells called **pinacocytes** and occasional tube-like **pore cells,** or **porocytes,** through which a microscopic canal allows water to enter. Water is pumped into a larger feeding chamber lined with **collar cells,** or **choanocytes.** Each choanocyte has a flagellum that creates currents and a thin collar that traps food particles, which are then ingested by the body of the cell. Water then leaves through the **osculum,** a large opening on top of the sponge.

Sponges are an example of **suspension feeders,** animals that eat food particles suspended in the water. Because sponges actively filter the food particles, they are a type of suspension feeder known as **filter feeders** (Fig. 7.4). By contrast, other animals are **deposit feeders** that eat **detritus** settling on the bottom.

Most marine sponges show a more complex arrangement in which the collar cells are restricted to chambers connected to the outer pores by a network of canals (Fig. 7.2*b*). Water exits not through a single osculum but through several oscula, each of which serves as the exit

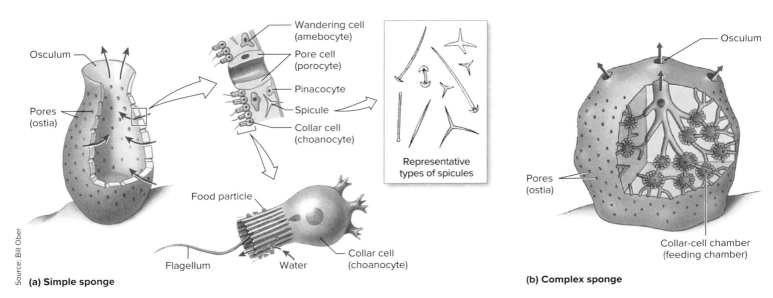

(a) Simple sponge

(b) Complex sponge

FIGURE 7.2 Sponges consist of complex aggregations of cells that carry out specific functions. Collar cells trap food particles in both (*a*) simple and (*b*) complex sponges.

for many canals. This increased complexity is associated with increased size, which demands higher water flow through the sponge and therefore a larger surface area of collar cells.

> Sponges are among the structurally simplest multicellular animals, lacking true tissues and organs. They are mostly marine, living as attached filter feeders.

As sponges get larger, they need structural support. Most have **spicules,** transparent **siliceous** or **calcareous** structures of different shapes and sizes (Fig. 7.2*a*). Many also have a skeleton of tough, elastic fibers made of a protein called **spongin.** Spongin can be the only means of support, or it can be found together with spicules. When present, spongin and spicules are mostly between the outer and inner layers of cells. Wandering cells, or **amebocytes,** secrete the spicules and spongin. Some of these wandering cells also transport and store food particles, and some can even transform themselves into other types of cells, quickly repairing any damage to the sponge.

Many sponges reproduce **asexually** when branches or buds break off and grow into separate sponges identical to the original one. Sponges also reproduce **sexually** by producing **gametes.** Unlike most animals, sponge gametes are not produced by **gonads.** Instead, specialized collar cells or amebocytes develop into gametes (Fig. 7.5). The gametes are like those of other animals: large, nutrient-rich eggs and smaller sperm cells with a flagellum. Most sponges are **hermaphrodites** that produce both eggs and sperm. Some species, however, have separate males and females. Sponges typically release sperm into the water. The release of gametes into the water is called **broadcast spawning.** The eggs, however, are usually retained inside the body and fertilization takes place internally after sperm enter the sponge.

FIGURE 7.3 Some sponges form new individuals after their cells are separated from one another. The cells can be separated by squeezing pieces through a very fine sieve (*a*). In a matter of hours, the cells begin to aggregate and reorganize in seawater (*b*) and eventually form new sponges (*c*). When cells of different species are mixed, they generally reaggregate into their individual species.

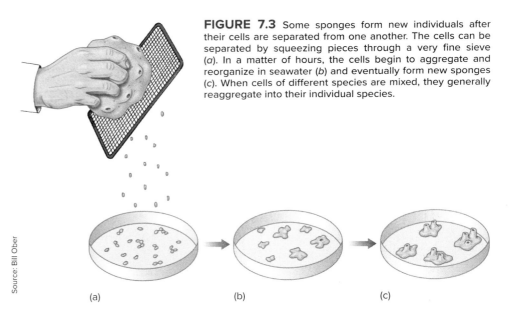

(a) (b) (c)

Tissues Specialized, coordinated groups of cells.
Organs Structures consisting of several types of tissues grouped together to carry out particular functions.
• 4.2, Living Machinery; Table 4.1

Plankton Organisms that drift with the currents.
• 10.2, Major Marine Lifestyles and Environments; Figure 10.11

Detritus Particles of dead organic matter.
• 10.3, The Flow of Energy and Materials

Siliceous Made of silica (SiO_2).
Calcareous Made of calcium carbonate ($CaCo_3$).
• 2.2, The Origin and Structure of the Ocean Basins

Gametes Specialized reproductive cells with half the genetic complement of each parent, usually produced by organs called *gonads: sperm* (male gametes produced by the *testes*) and *eggs* (female gametes produced by the *ovaries*).
• 4.4, Perpetuating Life

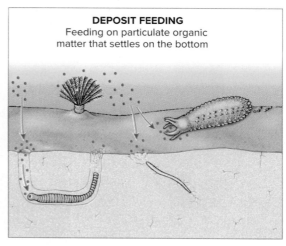

FIGURE 7.4 Feeding on particulate organic matter can be classified as suspension or deposit feeding. The difference between these two types of feeding is not always well defined. Fanworms, for instance, are tube-dwelling polychaetes that switch back and forth between suspension and deposit feeding, depending on the strength of the water current.

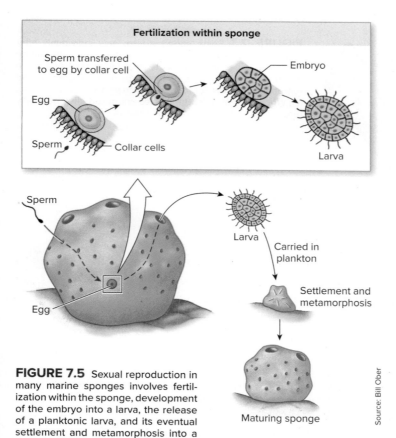

FIGURE 7.5 Sexual reproduction in many marine sponges involves fertilization within the sponge, development of the embryo into a larva, the release of a planktonic larva, and its eventual settlement and metamorphosis into a new sponge on the bottom.

The early stages of development take place inside the sponge. A tiny, flagellated sphere of cells is eventually released into the water (Fig. 7.5). This planktonic **larva,** called the **parenchymula larva** in most sponges, is carried by currents until it settles on the bottom and develops into a minute sponge. Most marine invertebrates have characteristic larvae that eventually change into juveniles that resemble adults. This drastic change from the larva to a juvenile is called **metamorphosis** (Fig. 7.5).

Sponges live from polar regions to the tropics, but the largest number of species inhabits shallow tropical waters. Sponges grow into branching, tubular (Fig. 7.6*a*), round, or volcano-like masses that sometimes reach a huge size. These giant sponges filter huge volumes of water. **Encrusting** sponges, by contrast, form thin, sometimes brightly colored growths on rocks or dead coral (Fig. 7.6*b*).

Glass sponges, such as the Venus flower basket sponge (*Euplectella*), live anchored in deep-water sediments and have a lace-like skeleton of fused siliceous spicules. **Boring sponges** (*Cliona*) bore thin channels through calcium carbonate, such as oyster shells and corals. In the **sclerosponges,** or **coralline sponges** (*Ceratoporella;* Fig. 7.6*c*), a calcium carbonate skeleton forms beneath the body of the sponge, which also contains siliceous spicules and spongin. Sclerosponges were first known as fossils, but living specimens were discovered in underwater caves and on steep coral reef slopes after the advent of scuba diving.

Some marine sponges are of commercial importance. Bath sponges, not to be confused with synthetic sponges, consist of the spongin fibers remaining after cells and debris are washed away. Some marine sponges produce potentially useful chemicals (see Box 17.3, "Take Two Sponges and Call Me in the Morning").

7.2 CNIDARIANS: RADIAL SYMMETRY

The next level of complexity among animals after the sponges involves quite a big step: the evolution of multicellular animals with tissues that perform specific functions. This development makes possible swimming, responding to external stimuli, and engulfing prey, among other things. **Cnidarians,** sometimes called **coelenterates** (phylum **Cnidaria**), include the sea anemones, jellyfishes, corals, and their relatives.

Besides having a tissue level of organization, cnidarians display **radial symmetry,** where similar parts of the body are arranged and repeated around a central axis (Figs. 7.7 and 7.14*a*). If a radially symmetrical animal were cut like a pizza, all the resulting slices would be similar. Animals with radial symmetry look the same from all sides and have no head, front, or back. They do, however, have an **oral surface,** where the mouth is, and an **aboral surface** on the opposite side (Fig. 7.7).

(a) (b) (c)

FIGURE 7.6 (*a*) *Aplysina archeri*, a tubular sponge from the Caribbean. (*b*) An encrusting sponge growing on the dead base of a coral in the Hawaiian Islands. (*c*) *Ceratoporella nicholsoni*, a coralline sponge, or sclerosponge, photographed at a depth of 52 m (170 ft) in Puerto Rico. Also see Figure 4.9. A species of giant sponge in the Caribbean has been estimated to live as long as 2,300 years, one of the oldest living animals on Earth.

FIGURE 7.7 The flower-like appearance of many cnidarians is a consequence of their radial symmetry. In both the medusa and the polyp, tentacles are arranged and repeated around a central axis that runs through the mouth.

Cnidarians have a centrally located mouth surrounded by **tentacles,** slender, finger-like extensions used to capture and handle food. The mouth opens into a **gut,** where food is digested. The cnidarian gut is a blind cavity with only one opening, the mouth. Cnidarians capture small prey by discharging their **nematocysts** (or cnidae), unique stinging structures found within **cnidocytes,** specialized cells in the tentacles (see Fig. 7.10).

Cnidarians occur in two basic forms (Fig. 7.7): a **polyp,** a sac-like attached stage with the mouth and tentacles oriented upward, and a bell-like **medusa** (commonly known as jellyfish, or sea jelly), which is like an upside-down polyp adapted for swimming. The life history of some cnidarians includes both polyp and medusa stages. Others spend their entire lives as either polyp or medusa.

The characteristic larva of most cnidarians is the **planula,** a cylindrical, ciliated stage consisting of two layers of cells. After a time in the plankton, the planula settles on the bottom and metamorphoses into a polyp or develops into a medusa.

The radially symmetrical cnidarians have unique stinging structures, nematocysts, that are used to capture prey. Cnidarians exist as either polyps or medusae, or both in alternation. Most have a planula larva.

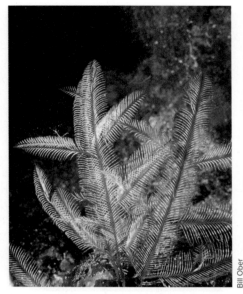

FIGURE 7.8 Colonial hydrozoans include this feather-like colony of the hydroid *Macrorhynchia phillipina*. It is a common species in warm and some temperate waters around the world.

Bill Ober

Two layers of cells form the body wall of cnidarians. One of these, the **epidermis** (see Figs. 7.7 and 7.10), is external, whereas the other, the **gastrodermis,** lines the gut. There is also a narrow, gelatinous middle layer, or **mesoglea,** that typically does not contain cells. In medusae this layer is expanded to form a gelatinous, domed bell, hence their common name of jellyfish.

The presence of tissues allows cnidarians to perform more complex functions than sponges can. Their basic body plan, though structurally simple, has been very successful.

Types of Cnidarians

Hydrozoans The **hydrozoans** (class **Hydrozoa**) have a wide range of forms and life histories. Many consist of feathery or bushy colonies of tiny polyps. They attach to pilings, shells, seaweeds, and other surfaces (Fig. 7.8). The polyps can be specialized for feeding, defense, or reproduction.

Reproductive polyps produce minute, transparent medusae (Fig. 7.9). These medusae, usually planktonic, release gametes into the water. The fertilized eggs develop into free-swimming planula larvae. Each planula settles on the bottom and develops into a polyp. This first polyp divides repeatedly and develops into a colony of many interconnected polyps. There are, however, several variations of this life cycle. Some hydrozoans lack a polyp stage, and instead their planula develops into a medusa.

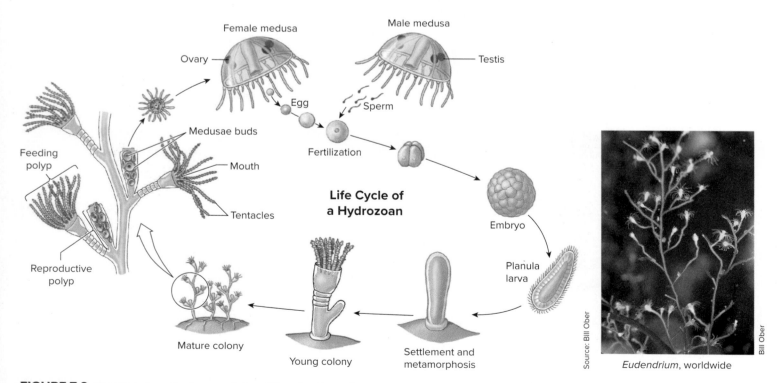

FIGURE 7.9 The life cycles of hydrozoans follow different patterns. A common one involves a sessile, asexually reproducing colony of polyps that releases planktonic, sexually reproducing medusae.

Although they look like medusae, **siphonophores** are drifting colonies of hydrozoan polyps. Some polyps in the colony are specialized as floats, which can be gas-filled, as in the Portuguese man-of-war (*Physalia physalis;* Fig. 7.10), or contain droplets of oil. Other polyps in the same animal form long tentacles used to capture prey. Toxins from the nematocysts can produce painful reactions in swimmers or divers (see Box 7.1, "The Case of the Killer Cnidarians").

Scyphozoans The larger jellyfishes, or sea jellies, are quite different from the often tiny hydrozoan medusae. These large medusae (Fig. 7.11) are the dominant stage of the life cycle of **scyphozoans** (class **Scyphozoa**). Scyphozoan polyps are very small and release juvenile medusae. A few species lack a polyp stage altogether. The rounded body, or **bell,** of some scyphozoan medusae can reach a diameter of 3 m (10 ft) across in some deep-water species. Scyphozoans swim with rhythmic contractions of the bell, but their swimming ability is limited and they are easily carried by currents. Some can sting swimmers. Jellyfishes in general have become more common and widespread worldwide in recent years, an indication of the declining health of the oceans due to pollution or perhaps a natural fluctuation in numbers.

Cubomedusae The **cubomedusae,** or box jellyfishes (class **Cubozoa**), are cnidarians that have a small, mostly transparent, cube-shaped medusa with at least four tentacles (see photo in Box 7.1). The life cycle includes a minute polyp as in scyphozoans. Box jellyfishes, particularly the sea wasp, are among the most dangerous marine animals known, giving extremely painful and sometimes fatal stings (see Box 7.1, "The Case of the Killer Cnidarians").

Anthozoans Most cnidarian species, more than 6,200, are **anthozoans** (class **Anthozoa**), solitary or colonial polyps that lack a medusa stage. The anthozoan polyp is more complex than hydrozoan or scyphozoan polyps. The gut, for instance, contains several thin partitions, or **septa** (see Fig. 14.2), which provide additional surface area for the digestion of large prey. Septa also provide support, which allows the polyp to be larger than the polyps of other cnidarians. **Sea anemones** are common and colorful anthozoans that often have large polyps (see Fig. 11.25). Colonial anthozoans occur in an almost infinite variety of shapes. **Corals** include various groups of mostly colonial anthozoans (see Table 14.1). Many of these have calcium carbonate skeletons and, though such corals occur in cold waters, they often form **coral reefs** in tropical waters. **Gorgonians,** such as sea fans (Fig. 7.12), are colonial anthozoans that secrete a tough, branching skeleton made in part of protein. **Precious corals** are gorgonians with fused red or pink calcareous spicules in addition to the protein skeleton. **Black corals,** which are neither gorgonians nor stony corals, secrete a hard, black, protein skeleton. Precious and black corals are carved into jewelry, but are being brought to near extinction in the process. Some anthozoans form fleshy colonies with large polyps and no hard skeletons. Examples of these are the **soft corals** (see Fig. 14.28), **sea pens** (see Fig. 13.13), and **sea pansies.**

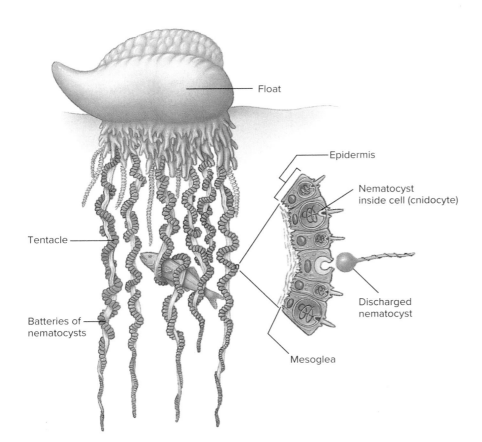

Float

Epidermis

Nematocyst inside cell (cnidocyte)

Tentacle

Batteries of nematocysts

Discharged nematocyst

Mesoglea

FIGURE 7.10 A diagrammatic representation of the Portuguese man-of-war (*Physalia physalis*). It consists of a colony of specialized polyps, one of which forms a gas-filled float that can reach 30 cm (12 in) in length. The long tentacles, here contracted, are armed with nematocysts notorious for their ability to sting swimmers.

Charlie Arneson

FIGURE 7.11 Scyphozoan medusae are larger and more complex than hydrozoan medusae. This example is the sea nettle (*Chrysaora quinquecirrha*), which is found from Cape Cod to the Gulf of Mexico. It is especially common in the Chesapeake Bay.

Box 7.1 The Case of the Killer Cnidarians

The stings of most cnidarians are harmless to humans, but some cnidarians are among the most dangerous marine animals. The sinister side of these creatures is due to the potent toxins released by their nematocysts.

The Portuguese man-of-war (*Physalia*), a siphonophore, is found in warm waters around the world. Though its blue, sail-like float can be seen fairly easily, its long tentacles are nearly invisible. These tentacles, armed with batteries of nematocysts, can reach 50 m (165 ft) in length. *Physalia* can occur by the thousands, sometimes forcing the closure of beaches. Pieces of tentacle that wash ashore can be as nasty as the whole animal.

Physalia stings are very painful, like being repeatedly burned with a hot charcoal. The pain can last for hours, especially if sensitive areas of the body are affected. Red lines appear wherever tentacles have touched the skin, and welts usually follow. One of the authors of this text saw someone get stung on the hand. When the wave of intense pain reached the armpit, the person passed out. There can be nausea and difficulty in breathing. Contact of tentacles with the eye can damage the cornea. Allergic reactions to the toxin can cause shock and even death, and swimmers can drown because of pain or shock.

It's best not to panic if you are stung. Carefully wash the area with seawater, but don't rub the area or wash with fresh water because this stimulates firing of the nematocysts. Alcohol will inactivate the nematocysts. Urine may be useful if nothing else is available. The toxin is a protein, and some recommend papain, a protein-digesting enzyme found in meat tenderizer. The meat tenderizer is of little help, however, because the poison is injected into the skin while the meat tenderizer remains on the surface. The use of vinegar as first aid has been questioned, but a cream containing copper gluconate has been found to inhibit the toxin. Severe reactions must be treated in a hospital.

A group of medusae, the cubomedusae, releases even more powerful toxins. The sea wasp, *Chironex fleckeri*, of northern Australia and Southeast Asia has been responsible for many deaths. Its stings cause extreme pain. Death due to heart failure can follow within minutes, especially in children. Skin that touches the tentacles swells up, and the purple or dark brown lines that are left are slow to heal. An antivenin ("antivenom") has been developed.

There are other tropical cubomedusae that give severe stings, particularly in

Chironex fleckeri, the sea wasp, is a cubomedusa potentially deadly to humans.

Australia and the West Indies. The irukandji (*Carukia barnesi*) of northern Australia have caused several deaths in recent years. Unlike the sea wasp, irukandji normally live offshore but currents occasionally sweep them into shallow water.

Cubomedusae are more common along the shore during summer. Their transparent bells are difficult to see in the water and, unlike other medusae, are quite mobile and do not simply drift with currents. Most are small, but in the sea wasp the bell can reach 25 cm (almost 10 in) in diameter, and the tentacles can stretch to 4.5 m (15 ft). Irukandji have a bell only 2.5 cm (1 in) in diameter and four tentacles of about the same length.

Biology of Cnidarians

Feeding and Digestion Practically all cnidarians are **carnivores,** animals that prey on other animals. Many capture and digest prey much bigger than that of filter feeders such as sponges. Cnidarians use their nematocysts primarily to capture prey. Each nematocyst consists of a fluid-filled capsule containing a thread that can be quickly ejected (see Fig. 7.10). The thread can be sticky or armed with spines, or it can be a long tube that wraps around parts of the prey. Some nematocysts contain toxins.

After ingestion, food passes into the gut, where it is digested. The initial phase of digestion is said to be **extracellular** because it takes place outside cells. **Intracellular digestion** within cells lining the gut completes the breakdown of food.

FIGURE 7.12 Sea fans are gorgonians with branches that grow in only one plane and have many cross-connections.

Behavior Though cnidarians lack a brain or true nerves, they do have specialized **nerve cells,** or **neurons.** These cells interconnect to form a **nerve net** that transmits impulses in all directions. This simple nervous system can produce some relatively sophisticated behaviors. Some anemones can tell whether other members of the same species are also members of the same **clone,** a group of genetically identical individuals, by using special nematocysts. They are known to attack and even kill anemones from other clones using special nematocysts. Some scyphozoan medusae have simple eyes that can only detect light, but the eyes of cubomedusae are known to form images. Medusae also have **statocysts,** small, calcareous bodies in fluid-filled chambers surrounded by sensitive hairs. Statocysts give medusae a sense of balance.

7.3 COMB JELLIES: RADIAL SYMMETRY REVISITED

The **comb jellies,** or **ctenophores** (phylum **Ctenophora**), are an exclusively marine group of at least 150 species. Their radially symmetrical and gelatinous body resembles that of a medusa, but a closer look reveals some unique traits. Ctenophores swim with eight rows of **ciliary combs,** long cilia fused at the base, like combs, that beat in waves. They are the largest animals that swim using cilia. The continuous beating of the ciliary combs refracts light, creating a prism-like, multicolor effect (Fig. 7.13). Body length varies from a few millimeters in the sea gooseberry (*Pleurobrachia*) to 2 m (6.6 ft) in the elongated Venus's girdle (*Cestum;* see Fig. 15.12*c*).

Comb jellies, or ctenophores, are radially symmetrical and similar in appearance to cnidarians but possess eight rows of ciliary combs.

Comb jellies are carnivores common worldwide. Swarms of comb jellies consume large numbers of fish larvae and other plankton (see Box 18.2, "Biological Invasions: The Uninvited Guests"), capturing their prey using long tentacles armed with sticky cells called **colloblasts.** Practically all comb jellies spend their complete lives in the plankton, never having a sessile stage as cnidarians do.

FIGURE 7.13 This comb jelly (*Mnemiopsis leidyi*) displays the rows of ciliary combs characteristic of the group. Four rows are visible, the middle ones appearing as multicolored bands. This species is common along the Atlantic coast of North America but it has been accidentally introduced into other locations.

7.4 BILATERALLY SYMMETRICAL WORMS

Radial symmetry works fairly well in animals that attach to surfaces or drift in currents, but animals that crawl or swim in one direction have different needs. Most animals show **bilateral symmetry,** the arrangement of body parts in such a way that there is only one way to cut the body and get two identical halves (Fig. 7.14*b*). Bilaterally symmetrical animals, including humans, have a front, or **anterior,** end and a rear, or **posterior,** end. At the anterior end is a head with a brain, or at least an accumulation of nerve cells, and sensory organs such as eyes. Bilaterally symmetrical animals also have a back, or **dorsal** surface, that is different from the belly, or **ventral** surface. Bilateral symmetry allows animals to be more active in the pursuit of prey and to develop more sophisticated behaviors than those of radially symmetrical animals.

Flatworms

The structurally simplest bilaterally symmetrical body plan is seen in the **flatworms** (phylum **Platyhelminthes**), so called because they are dorsoventrally flattened having flat backs and bellies. Flatworms also are the simplest animals in which tissues are organized into real organs and organ systems.

The presence of a **central nervous system** in which information is stored and processed is of special significance. In flatworms it

typically consists of a simple **brain,** which is simply an aggregation of nerve cells in the head. There are also several nerve cords running from the brain through the length of the worm. The nervous system coordinates the movements of a well-developed muscular system. The gut is similar to those of cnidarians and ctenophores in having only one opening to the outside, the mouth. The space between the outer and inner tissue layers, however, is no longer thin or gelatinous as in cnidarians and ctenophores but is filled with tissue. In developing embryos this middle layer of tissue, the **mesoderm,** gives rise to muscles, the reproductive system, and other organs—not only in flatworms but also in structurally more complex animals. The gut and other internal organs are surrounded by tissue, since there is no body cavity, a feature of more specialized animals.

Flatworms are bilaterally symmetrical invertebrates typically flattened in appearance. They have true organs and organ systems, including a central nervous system.

The most commonly seen marine flatworms are the **turbellarians,** a group that consists mostly of free-living carnivores. Most are small, but some are obvious because of their striking color patterns (Fig. 7.15). Some turbellarians live inside or on the surface of oysters, crabs, and other invertebrates.

Flukes, or **trematodes,** are the largest group of flatworms, with roughly 12,000 species, many of which are marine. All flukes are **parasites,** living in close association with other animals and feeding on

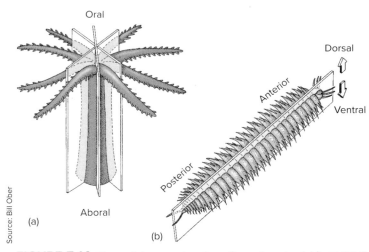

FIGURE 7.14 The radial symmetry of a soft coral's polyp (*a*) in contrast to the bilateral symmetry of a worm (*b*). Bilateral symmetry implies the development of an anterior end with a head, a brain, eyes, and all the other features demanded by more complex behaviors.

(a)

(b)

FIGURE 7.15 (*a*) A turbellarian flatworm (*Pseudobiceros gratus*) from Australia's Great Barrier Reef. (*b*) Turbellarian flatworms (*Pseudoceros bifurcus*) joust in a mating ritual known as penis fencing. The worms are hermaphrodites, and each tries to penetrate the skin of the other with its needle-like penis to inject its sperm. The first to succeed acts as the male and avoids the costs of healing the wound and developing eggs.

FIGURE 7.16 Ribbon, or nemertean, worms use a proboscis to entangle prey. The proboscis secretes toxins and can be armed at the tip with a spine. The proboscis is pulled back and the captured prey is eaten.

their tissues, blood, or intestinal contents. Like most parasites, flukes have complex life histories with amazing reproductive abilities, a key to their success. Adult flukes always live in a vertebrate. The larvae inhabit invertebrates like snails or clams or vertebrates like fishes. The larva must then be eaten by the vertebrate destined to harbor the adult. Flukes are common in fishes, seabirds, and whales.

Tapeworms, or **cestodes,** are parasitic flatworms that, with a few exceptions, have a long body consisting of repeated units. These unique worms live inside the intestine of most species of vertebrates, including marine ones. The head of the worm attaches to the walls of the gut by suckers, hooks, or other structures. Tapeworms lack a gut or mouth. They absorb nutrients from their host's intestinal contents directly across the body wall. Their larvae are found in invertebrates or vertebrates. Tapeworms can reach a prodigious length. The record appears to be a species found in whales known to reach 40 m (130 ft), which makes it among the longest invertebrates!

Ribbon Worms

Though they look like long flatworms, **ribbon, or nemertean, worms** (phylum **Nemertea**) show several features that indicate a more complex degree of organization. Their digestive tract is complete, with a gut that includes a mouth and an anus to get rid of undigested material. They also have a reduced **body cavity** and a **circulatory system,** by which blood transports nutrients and oxygen to tissues. The most distinctive feature of ribbon worms, however, is their **proboscis** (Fig. 7.16), a long, fleshy tube used to entangle prey. It is everted from a cavity above the mouth like the finger of a glove. All ribbon worms are predators that feed on worms and crustaceans.

Most ribbon worms are marine. They are found in all oceans but are most common in shallow temperate waters. Some are nocturnal and not easily seen; others are brightly colored and found under rocks at low tide. Ribbon worms are incredibly elastic, and the proboscis can extend a meter or more beyond the body. One species reaches 30 m (100 ft) long.

Nematodes

Nematodes (phylum **Nematoda**), commonly known as **roundworms,** are hardly ever seen, but their numbers in sediments, particularly those rich in organic matter, can be staggering. Many species are parasitic, and most groups of marine organisms have nematode parasites. Nematodes are perfectly adapted to live in sediments or in other organisms. They are mostly small, with slender and cylindrical bodies that are typically pointed at both ends (see the figure in Box 13.2, "Life in Mud and Sand"). Nematodes that inhabit sediments feed mostly on bacteria and organic matter. The gut, which ends in an anus, lies within a well-developed body cavity filled with fluid that transports nutrients. A layer of muscles in the tough but flexible body wall pushes and squeezes against the fluid, which acts as a **hydrostatic skeleton** that provides support and aids in locomotion.

Nematodes are very common inhabitants of marine sediments and some are widespread parasites of most groups of marine animals.

The actual number of species of nematodes is debatable. It is estimated that there are at least 61,000 marine species alone.

The adults of *Anisakis* and a few related nematodes inhabit the intestine of seals and dolphins. Their larvae, however, are found in the flesh of many types of fishes and can infect humans who eat raw or poorly cooked marine fish. Often these larvae are vomited or coughed up without further complications. Sometimes, however, larvae penetrate into the walls of the stomach or intestine, causing symptoms similar to those of ulcers. It is a risk that lovers of raw-fish dishes such as *sashimi* and *ceviche* must take.

Arrow Worms

In terms of number of species, the **arrow worms,** or **chaetognaths** (phylum **Chaetognatha**), rank among the smallest animal phyla. About 190 species, all marine, are known. They are nevertheless one of the most common and important members of the plankton. They are almost transparent, streamlined, with fish-like fins and tail (Fig. 7.17). The head has eyes, grasping spines, and teeth. Total length ranges from a few millimeters to 10 cm (up to 4 in).

Arrow worms are voracious carnivores with efficient sensory structures to detect their prey. They prey on small crustaceans, the eggs and larvae of fishes and other animals, other arrow worms, and practically anything else that is small. They spend most of their time motionless in the water but will swim in rapid, darting movements to grab their prey.

Segmented Worms

A large group of perhaps as many as 23,000 species, the **segmented worms,** or **annelids** (phylum **Annelida**), includes many marine worms

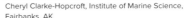

Cheryl Clarke-Hopcroft, Institute of Marine Science, Fairbanks, AK

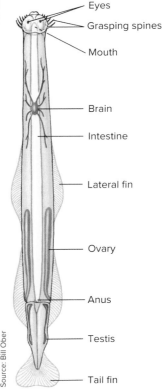

FIGURE 7.17 Arrow worms, or chaetognaths, have a transparent, fish-like body, an adaptation to living as planktonic predators. *Sagitta elegans* ("elegant arrow"), illustrated here, is widely distributed. Notice that individuals have both testes and ovaries. A copepod, a favorite prey, clearly shows in the intestine of the arrow worm shown above.

Source: Bill Ober

as well as the earthworm. The body consists of a series of similar compartments, or **segments,** a condition known as **segmentation.** Segmentation can be clearly seen in the rings of the familiar earthworm. Some annelids, however, have lost external segmentation. The gut extends through all the segments and lies in a cavity known as a **coelom** (Fig. 7.18c). The coelom is entirely surrounded by tissue that develops from mesoderm in contrast to the simpler body cavity of nematodes. It is present in all of the rest of the structurally complex phyla. The coelom of segmented worms is filled with fluid and divided by partitions that correspond to the external segments. The importance of the coelom and segments is that they act as a hydrostatic skeleton and can be contracted in sequence by means of muscles in the body wall. When **longitudinal muscles** (Fig. 7.18c) contract they shorten the segments, lengthening them when the muscles relax, whereas contraction and relaxation of **circular muscles** reduces and increases segment diameter, respectively. These movements, plus the flexibility given by segmentation, make annelids efficient crawlers and burrowers.

Polychaetes Almost all marine annelids are **polychaetes**, a term now seen as a convenient way of grouping marine segmented worms of diverse origins, all of which were traditionally placed in class **Polychaeta.** Each of the body segments of most polychaetes has a pair of flattened extensions, or **parapodia,** which are provided with stiff and sometimes sharp bristles, or **setae** (Fig. 7.18).

Annelids have a body consisting of similar segments and a coelom. Most marine annelids are polychaetes, segmented worms that have parapodia.

Labels for Figure 7.17: Eyes, Grasping spines, Mouth, Brain, Intestine, Lateral fin, Ovary, Anus, Testis, Tail fin

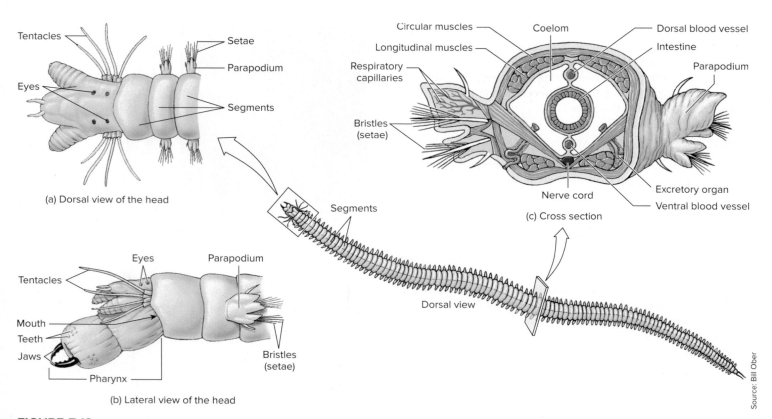

FIGURE 7.18 and labels: Tentacles, Setae, Parapodium, Eyes, Segments, (a) Dorsal view of the head. Circular muscles, Coelom, Dorsal blood vessel, Longitudinal muscles, Intestine, Respiratory capillaries, Parapodium, Bristles (setae), Nerve cord, Excretory organ, Ventral blood vessel, (c) Cross section. Segments, Dorsal view. Eyes, Parapodium, Tentacles, Mouth, Teeth, Jaws, Pharynx, Bristles (setae), (b) Lateral view of the head.

Source: Bill Ober

FIGURE 7.18 This sandworm (*Nereis*) illustrates the meaning of the name polychaetes—"many setae, or bristles." (*a*) Dorsal view of the head, with the pharynx retracted, showing the sensory tentacles and eyes. (*b*) Side view of the head, showing the large pharynx in an extended position. (*c*) Section across a segment.

Like all annelids, polychaetes have a circulatory system that transports nutrients, oxygen, and carbon dioxide. Circulating blood always remains within distinct blood vessels (Fig. 7.18*c*), making it a **closed circulatory system.** Muscular contraction of vessels helps in the circulation of blood. Wastes from the coelom are removed by a pair of **excretory organs** in each segment (Fig. 7.18*c*).

In small animals, oxygen—essential in the release of energy through **respiration**—can easily move from the water across the body wall to all the tissues. In the larger and relatively more active polychaetes, however, obtaining enough oxygen from the water is a potential problem. Polychaetes have solved this problem by evolving **gills** on the parapodia or elsewhere. The gills are thin-walled extensions of the body wall that have many blood vessels called **capillaries,** which allow for the easy absorption of oxygen. Capillaries are also found on the walls of the parapodia (Fig. 7.18*c*). This absorption of oxygen, along with the elimination of carbon dioxide, is known as **gas,** or **respiratory, exchange.**

The life history of many polychaetes involves a planktonic larval stage known as the **trochophore,** which has a band of cilia around the body (see Fig. 15.11*d*). The trochophore is of considerable interest because it is also one of the larval stages in some other groups of invertebrates. The types of larvae, among other characters, are used by biologists to deduce evolutionary relationships among different groups of invertebrates.

The approximately 10,000 species of polychaetes are almost entirely marine. Length varies a great deal but is typically 5 to 10 cm (2 to 4 in). Many polychaetes crawl on the bottom, hiding under rocks

or coral. These crawling worms, such as most sandworms (*Nereis*), are mostly carnivores. They feature heads provided with several pairs of eyes and other sense organs (see Fig. 7.18) used to search for small invertebrates. A proboscis, often armed with jaws, is used to capture prey. The parapodia are well developed and are used in locomotion.

Other polychaetes burrow in mud or sand (see Fig. 11.30). Many, like bloodworms (*Glycera*), capture small prey. Others, like lugworms (*Arenicola*), are deposit feeders (see Fig. 7.4).

Many polychaetes live in temporary or permanent tubes, either singly or in aggregations (Figs. 7.19*b* and 13.6). The tubes are made of mucus, protein, bits of seaweed, cemented sand or mud particles, or tiny fragments of shells. Tube-dwelling polychaetes usually have reduced parapodia. Some, such as *Terebella* and related forms, are suspension feeders. Their tentacles have cilia and mucus that catch organic particles in the water and move them to the mouth (see Fig. 7.4). Fanworms, or feather-duster worms (*Sabella;* Fig. 7.19*b*), use feathery tentacles covered with cilia to capture, sort, and transport particles. Serpulids (*Serpula*) and spirorbids (*Spirorbis*), also suspension feeders, extend feather-like tentacles from calcium carbonate tubes they build on rocks and other surfaces (see Fig. 13.17).

Polychaetes are also successful at other lifestyles. Species of *Tomopteris* are planktonic throughout life. Their parapodia are flat and expanded to help in swimming (see Fig. 15.12*d*). In the tropical Pacific the bodies of the Palolo worm (*Eunice*) periodically break off, and the posterior half swims up to the surface to spawn. This behavior, known as **swarming,** is timed in some areas with the

(a)

(b)

FIGURE 7.19 Polychaetes are common inhabitants of most marine bottoms. (*a*) The anterior end of a free-living polychaete (*Hermodice carunculata*), a fireworm that feeds on corals. The bright red structures are gills. (*b*) *Sabella melanostigma*, a feather-duster worm, inhabits leathery tubes.

phases of the moon, reaching its peak just after full moon. This bit of information is useful because in some places people gather the worms for food.

Beard worms, also known as **pogonophorans,** and **vestimentiferans** are highly specialized polychaetes. They lack a mouth and gut. Except for sponges and tapeworms, this phenomenon is uncommon in animals. A tuft of one to many thousand long tentacles characterize beard worms (Fig. 7.20), the tentacles being responsible for the group's common name. The tentacles appear to be involved in absorbing nutrients dissolved in the water. Some beard worms have **symbiotic** bacteria that use the nutrients to manufacture food, which in turn is used by the worms.

About 130 species of beard worms are known. They are mostly restricted to deep water, which helps explain why they remained unknown until 1900. Beard worms and vestimentiferans were once grouped as separate phyla. The total length of beard worms ranges from 10 cm to 2 m (4 in to 7 ft).

(a) Retracted worm

(b) Protruding worm

(c) Adult worm removed from tube

FIGURE 7.20 Diagrammatic representation of a beard worm, or pogonophoran. (*a*) Most secrete and live in tubes buried in the soft sediment. (*b*) Only the upper end of the tube protrudes, with the tentacle or tentacles extending from it. (*c*) Worm removed from its tube.

Large numbers of nearly 20 species of vestimentiferans are found at hydrothermal vents, deep-sea whale remains, and methane seeps. These tubeworms depend on symbiotic bacteria to obtain nutrients, the organic food manufactured by the bacteria (see 16.4).

Echiurans Long regarded as a separate phylum, echiurans are now considered annelids (class Echiura). They look like soft, externally unsegmented sausages buried in the mud or in coral. They have a non-retractable, spoon-like or forked proboscis (see Fig. 13.9). All of the approximately 200 species are marine. Echiurans are deposit feeders that use the proboscis to gather organic matter. The "fat innkeeper" (*Urechis caupo*) of the Pacific coast of North America lives in U-shaped tubes in mud (see Fig. 12.11).

Sipunculans Often called **peanut worms,** the **sipunculans** (class **Sipuncula**) have soft, unsegmented bodies. They were once grouped as a separate phylum. Peanut worms are deposit feeders that burrow in muddy bottoms, rocks, and corals or hide in empty shells. All are marine, living mostly in shallow water. The long and retractable anterior portion contains a mouth and a set of small lobes or branching tentacles (Fig. 7.21). These can be pulled into the remaining portion of the body, and the worm then becomes a compact bundle that looks like a large peanut. Peanut worms are 1 to 35 cm (0.4 to 14 in) long. Approximately 150 species are known, all deposit feeders.

Respiration
organic matter + $O_2 \rightarrow CO_2 + H_2O$ + energy (glucose)
• 4.1, The Ingredients of Life

FIGURE 7.21 _Antillesoma antillarum_, a peanut worm (or sipunculan), burrows in coral and rocks in the Caribbean. The anterior portion, which is extended in this specimen, can be retracted.

7.5 MOLLUSCS: THE SUCCESSFUL SOFT BODY

Snails, clams, octopuses, and other familiar forms are members of the phylum **Mollusca. Molluscs** have been very successful: there are more species of molluscs in the ocean than of any other animal group. They exhibit an immense diversity of structures and habits, thrive on practically every conceivable type of diet, and occupy all marine environments, from the wave-splashed zone of rocky shores to hydrothermal vents in the deep sea. There are nearly 117,000 known living species of molluscs, of which at least 46,000 are marine. Many remain to be discovered, and molluscs could be surpassed only by the arthropods (and perhaps nematodes) as the largest phylum of animals.

Most molluscs have a soft body enclosed in a calcium carbonate shell (Fig. 7.22). The body is covered by a **mantle,** a thin layer of tissue that secretes the shell. The unsegmented body is typically bilaterally symmetrical. There is a ventral, muscular **foot,** usually used in locomotion. Most molluscs have a head that normally includes eyes and other sensory organs. A feature unique to molluscs is the **radula,** a ribbon of small teeth that is used to feed, usually by rasping food from surfaces (Fig. 7.22). The radula is modified in carnivorous molluscs (Figs. 7.23 and 7.24c). It is made largely of **chitin,** a highly resistant carbohydrate also found in other invertebrates. Gas exchange is through paired gills. The body cavity, a coelom, is much reduced, being restricted to small cavities around the heart and a few other organs.

All molluscs have this basic body plan, but it is often greatly modified. The shell, for example, is internal in squids and absent in octopuses and a few other groups. Portions of the body are coiled and asymmetrical in snails, and in some molluscs the radula is modified or even absent.

Molluscs with a shell face the problem of thinner shells with increased acidification of the water, the result of rising CO_2 levels (see Special Report, Ocean Acidification: The Other CO_2 Problem).

The molluscs constitute the largest group of marine animals. Their body is soft with a muscular foot. They usually have a shell and a radula, a rasping "tongue" unique to the group.

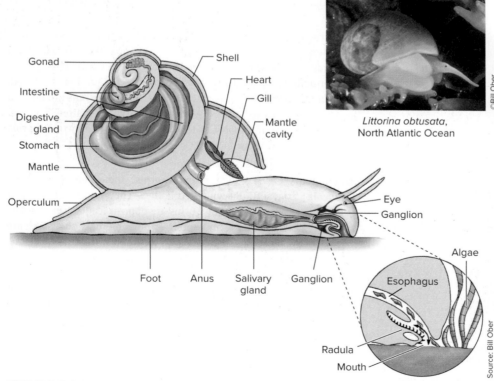

Gonad — Shell — Heart — Gill — Mantle cavity
Intestine
Digestive gland
Stomach
Mantle
Operculum
Eye — Ganglion
Foot — Anus — Salivary gland — Ganglion
Algae
Esophagus
Radula
Mouth

Littorina obtusata, North Atlantic Ocean

FIGURE 7.22 The general body plan of a gastropod, indicating the most important internal structures. In many species the head and foot can be retracted into the shell, leaving a tough operculum blocking the shell opening.

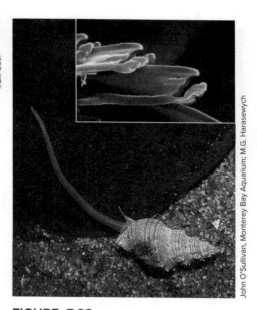

FIGURE 7.23 The Cooper's nutmeg snail (_Cancellaria cooperi_) seeks out electric rays, which rest partially buried in sand. The snail then extends its long proboscis, makes a tiny cut in the ray's skin with the radula at the end of the proboscis, and then sucks the ray's blood. A high-magnification photo (inset) shows the teeth of the radula.

(a)

(b)

(c)

(d)

FIGURE 7.24 Gastropods come in all shapes, colors, and habits. (*a*) The giant keyhole limpet (*Megathura crenulata*), from the Pacific coast of North America. (*b*) The red abalone (*Haliotis rufescens*) is much sought after for food and is now rare in many areas. (*c*) Cone shells, such as *Conus geographus*, are carnivorous snails that bury themselves in sand, waiting for prey such as small fishes. Their radula is modified into a dart-like tooth that is shot—together with a poison—into the unsuspecting prey, which is eaten whole, very much as in snakes (see Fig. 10.7). The poison is now used as a painkiller in humans. (*d*) A flashy nudibranch (*Hermissenda crassicornis*). The colorful body projections serve for gas exchange and also contain extensions of the gut.

Types of Molluscs

Gastropods The **gastropods** (class **Gastropoda**) comprise the largest, most common, and most varied group of molluscs. Snails are the most familiar gastropods, but the group includes other forms such as limpets, abalones, and nudibranchs (Fig. 7.24). There may be as many as 70,000 species, mostly marine. A typical gastropod can best be described as a coiled mass of vital organs enclosed by a dorsal shell (Fig. 7.22). The shell rests on a ventral creeping foot (the term "gastropod" means "stomach footed") and is usually coiled.

Most gastropods use their radula to scrape algae from rocks, as in periwinkles (*Littorina;* see Fig. 11.2), limpets (*Fissurella, Megathura;* Fig. 7.24*a*), and abalones (*Haliotis;* Fig. 7.24*b*). Some, like mud snails (*Hydrobia*), are deposit feeders on soft bottoms. Whelks (*Nucella, Buccinum;* see Fig. 11.20), oyster drills (*Murex, Urosalpinx*), and cone shells (*Conus;* Fig. 7.24*c*), are carnivores. They prey on

clams, oysters, worms, and even small fishes (see Fig. 10.7). The violet snail *Janthina* has a thin shell and produces a bubble raft out of mucus to float on the surface, looking for siphonophores, its prey (see Fig. 15.15). Sea hares (*Aplysia*), whose shells are small, thin, and buried in tissue, graze on seaweeds.

Nudibranchs, or **sea slugs,** are gastropods that have lost the shell altogether. Colorful branches of the gut or exposed gills make nudibranchs among the most beautiful of all marine animals (Fig. 7.24*d*). They prey on sponges, hydroids, and other invertebrates. As a defensive mechanism, nudibranchs often produce noxious chemicals or retain undischarged nematocysts taken undigested from their prey.

Bivalves Bivalves (class **Bivalvia**) include clams, mussels, oysters, and similar molluscs. Approximately 9,200 living species are known. The bivalve body is laterally compressed (that is, flattened sideways) and enclosed in a shell with two parts, or **valves** (Fig. 7.25). The **umbo,** the upper hump near the hinge of each shell, is the oldest part of the shell. Growth from the umbo proceeds in the form of concentric growth lines. There is no head to speak of, and no radula. The gills, expanded and folded, are used not only to obtain oxygen but also to filter and sort small food particles from the water. The inner surface of the shell is lined by the mantle, so that the whole body lies in the **mantle cavity,** a large space between the two halves of the mantle. Strong muscles, the **adductor muscles,** are used to close the valves.

Clams (*Macoma, Mercenaria*) use their shovel-shaped foot to burrow in sand or mud (see Figs. 11.29 and 12.11). When the clam is buried, water is drawn in and out of the mantle cavity through **siphons** formed by the fusion of the edge of the mantle (Fig. 7.25*a* and *d*). This allows clams to feed and obtain oxygen while buried in sediment.

Not all bivalves are burrowers. Mussels (*Mytilus;* see Fig. 11.15) for instance, secrete strong **byssal threads** that attach them to rocks and other hard surfaces. Oysters (*Ostrea, Crassostrea;* Fig. 7.26*a*) cement their left shell to a hard surface, often the shell of another oyster. Aphrodisiac or not, they have been swallowed by food lovers for thousands of years. Pearl oysters (*Pinctada*) are the source of most commercially valuable pearls. Pearls are formed when the oyster secretes shiny layers of calcium carbonate to coat irritating particles or parasites lodged between the mantle and the iridescent inner surface of the shell, which is called mother-of-pearl. Cultured pearls are obtained by carefully inserting a tiny bit of shell or plastic

Symbiosis The living together in close association of two different species.

• 10.1, The Organization of Communities

Box 7.2 How to Discover a New Phylum

It is not difficult to discover a new marine invertebrate species. Small animals living in sediments, among rocky shore seaweeds, in crevices or holes in coral, or in deep water are good candidates. Discovering a new phylum of invertebrates, however, is a different story. The founding species of three new phyla escaped description until relatively recently. All three are exclusively marine.

The first species of what eventually became the new phylum **Gnathostomulida** was not officially described until 1956. Gnathostomulids are a group of at least 100 species of minute worms living among sediment particles around the world. They are similar to flatworms but possess unique features, including a set of toothed jaws to scrape bacteria, diatoms, and other organisms from sand grains.

The next of the new phyla has a short but turbulent history. In 1961 Robert Higgins, then at the Smithsonian Institution in the United States, predicted the existence of a group living in the spaces between coarse sediment particles in deep water. He actually found a specimen in 1974 but, unfortunately, did not realize it was something new.

A year later Reinhardt Kristensen of the University of Copenhagen, Denmark, collected a specimen, but it was destroyed while being prepared for microscopic examination. Kristensen later found larvae of the elusive animal in coarse sediments from western Greenland and the Coral Sea. In 1982 he was working with a large sample off the coast of Brittany in France. It was his last day at the Roscoff Biological Station, and to save time he washed the sample with fresh water instead of following a more time-consuming method. It happened to loosen the grip of the animals on the sediment particles, and Kristensen got a complete series of larval and adult specimens.

The microscopic animals Kristensen found have a body encased by six plates. The head, which can be retracted, bears a set of spines and a mouth at the end of a cone. Kristensen got together with Higgins, and they concluded that the specimens Higgins examined in 1974 and those subsequently found by Kristensen were members of a new phylum. They found additional adults in eastern Florida, which further confirmed the new status of the group.

The new phylum **Loricifera** (meaning "armor bearer") was officially born in 1983 when Kristensen published a paper in a German scientific journal. The first species was named *Nanaloricus mysticus* ("mystic, or enigmatic, dwarf armor"), and the larva was baptized the Higgins larva in honor of Higgins—a nice consolation prize! Some 38 species have so far been described, but many more are known but not yet officially described.

Another recently identified new phylum comes from another unexpected location: the hairs around a Norway lobster's mouth. Though first observed in the 1960s, the phylum **Cycliophora** was not described until 1995. It originally consisted of just one species, *Symbion pandora*, a tiny, bottle-shaped sac with a disk-like mouth. Cilia around the mouth sweep food particles that come off the lobster's mouth at mealtime.

This strange lifestyle coincides with a bizarre life cycle. The minute but multicellular animal—hundreds often live on a lobster—alternates sexual and asexual generations. Dwarf males, which live attached to females, exist only to produce sperm. Females also reproduce asexually, but they produce only females that develop inside box-like structures within their mothers. The new generation of females is set free from the boxes as it bursts out from the mothers. The Greek myth of a box that Pandora (and hence the name of the first cycliophoran) opened to allow all human ills to escape is thus re-created around a lobster's mouth.

Close to 40 species of loriciferans have so far been recognized from around the world.

Gnathostomulid

Loriciferan

Cycliophoran

Source: Bill Ober

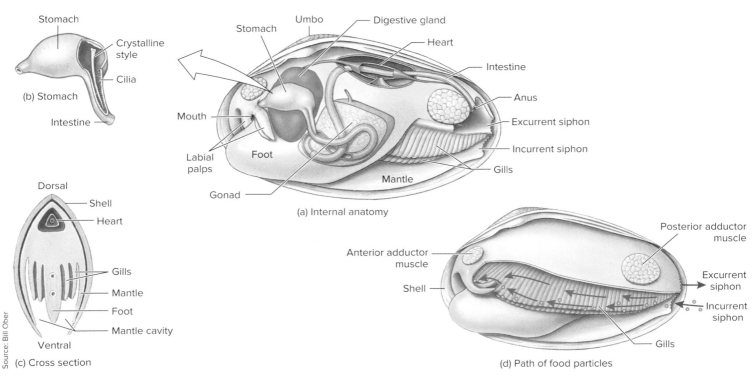

(b) Stomach

(c) Cross section

(a) Internal anatomy

Source: Bill Ober

(d) Path of food particles

FIGURE 7.25 A laterally compressed body is the most distinctive feature of bivalves, illustrated here by a clam. The gills, which hang on both sides of the body (*a, c*), sort out food particles and transport them to the mouth with the help of cilia and mucus. The palps then push the food into the mouth. Food is digested in the stomach with the help of the crystalline style (*b*). The path of the particles from the incurrent siphon to the mouth is indicated by arrows (*d*).

into the mantle. Some scallops (*Pecten, Chlamys;* Fig. 7.26*b*) live unattached and can swim for short distances by rapidly ejecting water from the mantle cavity and clapping the valves. The largest bivalve is the giant clam (*Tridacna;* see Fig. 14.34), which grows to more than 1 m (3 ft) in length.

Many bivalves bore in coral, rock, or wood. The shipworm (*Teredo*) bores in mangrove roots, driftwood, and wooden structures such as boats and pilings. They use their small valves to excavate the wood, which is eaten. Symbiotic bacteria in the shipworm's gut digest the wood. The rasping valves lie at the inner end of a tunnel lined with calcium carbonate, and a tiny siphon protrudes from the entrance at the other end. Shipworms are an example of **biofouling,** the undesirable accumulation of organisms that settle on the bottoms of boats, pilings, and other submerged structures.

Cephalopods The **cephalopods** (class **Cephalopoda**) include the octopuses, squids, cuttlefishes, and other fascinating creatures. Cephalopods are predators that adapt the molluscan body plan to an active way of life. Nearly all are agile swimmers with a complex nervous system and a reduction or loss of the shell. All known

Gilbert S. Grant/Shutterstock

(a)

Bill Ober

(b)

FIGURE 7.26 Oysters such as *Crassostrea virginica* (*a*) are harvested commercially around the world. Some bivalves, like scallops and the file clam *Lima scabra* (*b*), live free on the bottom and can swim by clapping their shells. Others bury themselves in sand or mud.

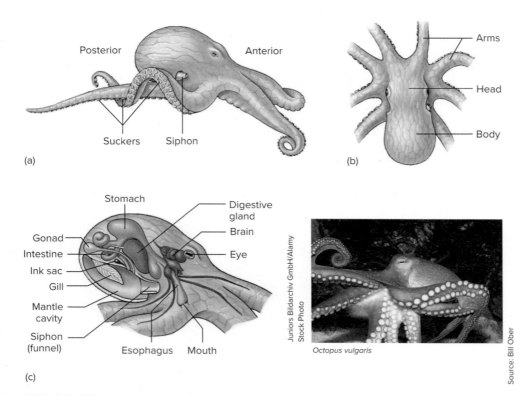

(a)

(b)

(c)

Labels in figure: Posterior, Anterior, Suckers, Siphon, Arms, Head, Body; Stomach, Digestive gland, Brain, Eye, Gonad, Intestine, Ink sac, Gill, Mantle cavity, Siphon (funnel), Esophagus, Mouth

Octopus vulgaris

Juniors Bildarchiv GmbH/Alamy Stock Photo

Source: Bill Ober

FIGURE 7.27 External (*a* and *b*) and internal (*c*) structure of the octopus. The tip of the third right arm is modified in males to transfer packets of sperm from his siphon into the mantle cavity of the female. Copulation is preceded by courtship behavior that includes intricate color changes.

through the **siphon,** or **funnel,** a muscular tube formed by what remains of the foot, which projects under the head. Cephalopods swim by forcing water out of the mantle cavity through the siphon. The flexible siphon can be moved around, allowing the animal to move in practically any direction, an example of jet propulsion in nature.

Octopuses (*Octopus*)—not "octopi"—have eight long arms and lack a shell (Fig. 7.27). They are common bottom dwellers. Including arms, the size varies from 5 cm (2 in) in the dwarf octopus (*Octopus joubini*) to a record of 9 m (30 ft) in the Pacific giant octopus (Fig. 7.28*a*).

Octopuses are efficient hunters, with crabs, lobsters, and shrimps among their favorite dishes. They bite their prey with a pair of beak-like jaws, and the radula rasps away flesh. Some octopuses may also secrete a paralyzing substance, and some have a highly toxic bite. Most, however, are harmless. They use crevices in rocks, and even discarded bottles and cans, as homes. Their shelters are identified by the presence of rocks, which they move around, and by the remains of crabs. Like most other cephalopods, they can distract potential predators by emitting a cloud of dark fluid produced by the **ink sac** (Fig. 7.29).

700 living species are marine. The foot of cephalopods (the name means "head-footed") is modified into arms and tentacles, usually equipped with suckers that are used to capture prey (Fig. 7.27). The large eyes, usually set on the sides of the head, are remarkably like ours. The body, rounded in octopuses and elongated in squids, is protected by a thick and muscular mantle. The mantle forms a mantle cavity behind the head that encloses two or four gills. Water enters through the free edge of the mantle and leaves

Squids (*Loligo;* Figs. 7.28*b* and 7.29) are better adapted for swimming than octopuses are. The body is covered by the mantle, which has two triangular fins (Fig. 7.29). The arrangement of the internal organs is similar to that of the octopus (Fig. 7.27*c*), except that the squid's body is elongated. Squids can remain motionless in one place or move backward or forward just by changing the direction of the

(a)

Mauricio Handler/Getty Images

(b)

Mark Conlin/Getty Images

FIGURE 7.28 (*a*) The Pacific giant octopus (*Enteroctopus dofleini*). (*b*) Mating in squids such as the market squid (*Doryteuthis opalescens*) of the Pacific coast of North America involves males seizing females and depositing sperm packets (spermatophores) into the females' mantle cavity. Adults of this species migrate to shallow water to breed, dying after mating and laying their white, gelatinous eggs. This squid is harvested for food and bait.

EYE ON SCIENCE

Box 7.3 The Complex Eyes of Mantis Shrimps

Mantis shrimps, or **stomatopods,** are extraordinary in many ways. About 500 species of these relatively large and colorful shrimps are found worldwide, but are most common in tropical and subtropical waters. They live in burrows excavated in soft sediments or in crevices in coral and other hard bottoms. Mantis shrimps are carnivores, preying on molluscs and other bottom animals, which are typically captured by the shrimps darting out from their burrows and stunning or killing their prey using unique, powerful claws. The claws are also used in ritualized combats over mates or territories. Some of the species, called "smashers," use their claws to smash their prey by using a hammer-like structure. The claws are powerful enough to break gastropod shells and even aquarium glass! Others are called "spearers" because they use a spear-like structure in each claw to stab the prey.

Most amazing, however, are the truly remarkable eyes of mantis shrimps, part of what is considered the most complex visual system among all animals. The large eyes, almost always in continuous motion, are each mounted on a stalk that moves independent of one another, allowing the scanning of a large field of view. The eyes, as in most other arthropods, are compound eyes that consist of many thousands of separate units, the ommatidia. Each ommatidium consists of a group of many light-sensitive cells, or photoreceptors, with mantis shrimps having the highest number and types of photoreceptors than any other animal known. Mantis shrimps not only have color vision (unlike octopuses!) and thus able to see the

human visible spectrum, but also detect UV light and at least six different channels of polarized light, which allows them to tell apart the different ways in which light waves bounce off objects.

The typical mantis shrimp eye is divided into three regions, a mid-band and two side regions, which results in a unique "trinocular" vision. The mid-band is further subdivided into bands, each specialized in particular wavelengths of the visible light spectrum as well as UV light. Tiny hairs on the ommatidia of some of the rows are thought to detect polarized light. A researcher has described the mid-band as looking more like a set of satellite sensors and video cameras than to the eye of an animal!

We are just beginning to understand how the mantis shrimps eyes work by using new techniques and approaches. Researchers in many parts of the world are searching for answers to challenging questions. How does the complex mid-band work? How is this complexity put into action when searching for prey or a mate, and can shrimp communicate with each other visually? How is this information actually processed? Could we apply such information to human-built instruments and systems?

It has been discovered, for example, that mantis shrimps independently rotate their eyes to boost their ability to see polarized light, aligning particular photoreceptors

The peacock mantis shrimp, *Odontodactylus scyllarus.*

to the angle of polarization of light. This ability increases contrast between objects and the background, a feature applied by a University of Illinois Urbana-Champaign research team to design an underwater video camera that incorporates miniaturized polarized lenses. Surprisingly, mantis shrimps also appear to use polarized light as a navigational compass.

Each of the two eyes has a separate nerve pathway with information processed in the photoreceptors themselves, not in the brain as in us and most other animals. The interactions between these two separate but interrelated connections could have applications in the development of the multi-camera systems used in robotics. Such eye interconnections and coordination could also be applied to satellite technology, with multiple channels arranged in a strip to scan the planet.

siphon. Eight arms and two tentacles, all with suckers, circle the mouth. The tentacles are long and retractable and have suckers only at the broadened tips. They can be swiftly shot out to catch prey. The shell is reduced to a stiff **pen** embedded in the upper surface of the mantle. Adult size varies from tiny individuals of a few centimeters in length to the largest living invertebrate, the deep-sea colossal squid (*Mesonychoteuthis hamiltoni*). Very few specimens of this squid have been caught, but the largest had a total length of about 10 m (33 ft). The giant squids (*Architeuthis*) are also found in deep water. One species supposedly grows to 20 m (66 ft) in length but weighs less than the colossal squid. Although not as large, the Humboldt, or jumbo, squid (*Dosidicus gigas*) can reach 1.8 m (6 ft). Once found from

Mexico to southern South America, it has been gradually extending its range as far north as Alaska. A voracious predator, the invading squid could threat northern Pacific fisheries.

Cuttlefishes (*Sepia*) resemble squids in having eight arms and two tentacles, but the body is flattened and has a fin running along the sides. Cuttlefishes, which are not fish at all, have a calcified internal shell that aids in buoyancy. This shell is the "cuttlebone" sold as a source of calcium for cage birds.

The chambered nautilus (*Nautilus;* see Box 16.1, "The Chambered Nautilus") has a coiled external shell containing a series of gas-filled chambers that serve as a buoyancy organ. The shell can be up to 25 cm (10 in) in diameter. The body, which occupies the

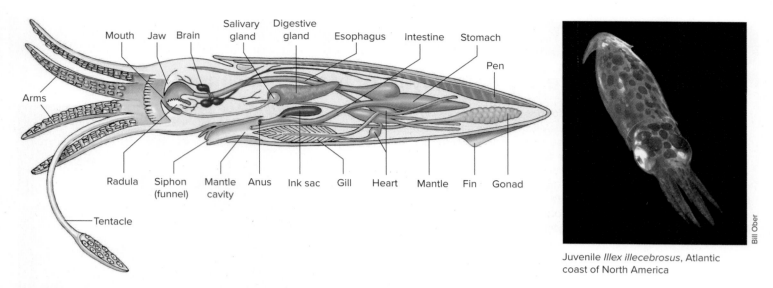

Juvenile *Illex illecebrosus*, Atlantic coast of North America

FIGURE 7.29 Section across a squid, showing its internal anatomy and only half the number of arms and tentacles.

FIGURE 7.30 Chitons use their strong foot and the flexibility provided by the eight articulated shells to fit tightly to the irregular surface of rocky shores. Hundreds of tiny eyes are embedded in the shells.

outer, largest chamber, has 60 to 90 short, suckerless tentacles used to capture prey.

Other Molluscs Close to 850 species of **chitons** (class **Polyplacophora**) are known, all marine. They can be readily identified by the eight overlapping shell plates that cover their slightly arched dorsal surface (Fig. 7.30). Their internal organs are not coiled as in snails.

Most chitons live on shallow, hard bottoms where they use a rasping radula to feed on algae. Many of them return to a homesite after feeding.

The more than 500 species of **tusk shells,** or **scaphopods** (class **Scaphopoda**), have an elongated shell, open at the top and tapered like an elephant tusk. They live in sandy or muddy bottoms. The narrow top end of the shell protrudes from the bottom, while the foot projects from the wide end. Many species have thin tentacles with adhesive tips. They are used to capture young bivalves and other small animals from the sediment. Tusk shells are most common in deep water, but empty shells sometimes wash ashore.

Biology of Molluscs

Feeding and Digestion The molluscan gut has a separate mouth and anus. Digestion involves **salivary** and **digestive glands** (see Figs. 7.22 and 7.29) that release digestive **enzymes,** which break down food into simpler molecules.

Grazers such as chitons, limpets, and many snails have a rasping radula that removes minute algae from surfaces or cuts through large seaweeds. Their relatively simple digestive system can efficiently process large amounts of hard-to-digest plant material. Digestion is partly extracellular in the gut cavity and partly intracellular in the digestive glands. Some shell-less gastropods that feed on seaweeds keep the seaweeds' **chloroplasts** intact. The chloroplasts are kept in the digestive gland, where they can photosynthesize and provide nourishment for the gastropod.

Carnivorous snails have a radula modified to drill, cut, or even capture prey. The radula and mouth are contained in a proboscis that can be protruded to strike the prey (see Fig. 10.7). Jaws can even be present. In these snails, digestion is extracellular and takes place in the stomach.

Bivalves ingest food particles that are filtered and sorted out by the cilia on the gills. The radula is absent, and food enters the mouth trapped in long strings of mucus. An enzyme-secreting rod in the stomach, the **crystalline style** (see Fig. 7.25b), continually rotates the food to help in its digestion. The stomach contents eventually pass into a large digestive gland for intracellular digestion. Giant clams not only filter food but also obtain nutrients from zooxanthellae living in tiny branches of the gut that extend into the clam's expanded mantle (see Fig. 14.34). Specialized cells focus light to zooxanthellae that live below the mantle. This extra nourishment probably allows the clams to attain their giant size.

All cephalopods are carnivores that have to digest large prey. The stomach is sometimes connected to a sac in which digestion is rapidly and efficiently completed. It is entirely extracellular.

Molluscs have a circulatory system that transports nutrients and oxygen. A dorsal, muscular heart pumps blood to all tissues. Most molluscs have an **open circulatory system** in which blood flows out of vessels into open blood spaces. Cephalopods, by contrast, have a closed circulatory system in which the blood always remains in vessels and can be more effectively directed to oxygen-demanding organs such as the brain.

Nervous System and Behavior The nervous system of molluscs varies in complexity. Gastropods and bivalves do not have a single brain but, rather, several sets of **ganglia,** or "local brains," clusters of nerve cells located in different parts of the body (see Fig. 7.22).

Cephalopods have the most complex nervous system not just of molluscs but of all invertebrates. Some of the separate local brains of other molluscs are fused into a single, large brain (see Figs. 7.27c and 7.29) that coordinates and stores information. Different functions and behaviors of cephalopods are controlled by particular regions of the brain, as in humans. Giant nerve fibers rapidly conduct impulses, allowing cephalopods to capture prey or escape at amazing speeds. The arms of some octopuses have cells that "taste" and "smell" potential prey. The strikingly complex eyes of cephalopods reflect the development of their nervous system. Octopuses and cuttlefishes have a remarkable capacity for learning. Most cephalopods display color changes correlated with particular behaviors and moods, from intricate sexual displays to camouflage. Some cuttlefishes flash two large, black spots resembling eyes, perhaps to fool potential predators. Octopuses are known to use tools and even show play behavior. Some species change color and behavior to mimic, or imitate, poisonous fishes and sea snakes to deceive predators!

Reproduction and Life History Most molluscs have separate sexes, but some species have both male and female gonads. In bivalves, chitons, tusk shells, and some gastropods, sperm and eggs are released into the water and fertilization is external (see Fig. 4.21a). Fertilization is internal in cephalopods and most gastropods. When cephalopods mate, the male uses a modified arm to transfer **spermatophores,** elongated packets of sperm, to the female (Fig. 7.28b). Males of gastropods that copulate have a long, flexible penis.

Some molluscs have a trochophore larva like polychaetes, a characteristic often used as evidence for close affinities between molluscs, the segmented worms, and other groups. In gastropods and bivalves the trochophore usually develops into a **veliger,** a planktonic larva that has a tiny shell (see Fig. 15.11a). In many gastropods, however, part or all of development takes place within strings or capsules of eggs. Cephalopods lack larvae, and the young develop from large, yolk-filled eggs. Female octopuses protect their eggs, sometimes for years in deep-water species, which are often attached to crevices or holes in rocks until they hatch. The female usually dies afterward because she eats little or nothing while guarding the eggs.

7.6 ARTHROPODS: THE ARMORED ACHIEVERS

Arthropods (phylum **Arthropoda**) make up the largest phylum of animals, with more than a million known species, with many remaining to be discovered. Perhaps as many as 85% of all animal species on Earth are arthropods. The largest group of arthropods by far, however, are the insects, which, though the dominant arthropods on land, are rare in the sea. The overwhelming majority of marine arthropods are **crustaceans** (subphylum **Crustacea**), a group that includes barnacles, shrimps, lobsters, crabs, and a huge variety of less familiar animals.

The arthropod body is segmented and bilaterally symmetrical. In addition to a flexible, segmented body, arthropods have jointed appendages, the legs and mouthparts that are moved by sets of attached muscles. Another characteristic of arthropods is a tough, non-living external skeleton, or **exoskeleton,** composed of chitin and secreted by the underlying layer of tissue. The exoskeleton and jointed appendages provide protection, flexibility, and increased surface area for muscle attachment.

Arthropods must **molt,** or shed their exoskeleton to grow (Fig. 7.31). A new shell develops under the old one prior to molting, then hardens after the old skeleton is discarded and the animal takes in water to expand itself. Most arthropods are small because the rigid exoskeleton imposes limitations on size. We will never see arthropods as big as giant squids or whales, but the legs of a giant spider crab (*Macrocheira*) can reach 3 m (10 ft) long.

> More species belong to the arthropods than to any other animal group. Most arthropods on land are insects, but crustaceans are the dominant arthropods in the sea. Arthropods have a segmented and bilaterally symmetrical body. Their success in adapting to all types of environments is due in part to a protective exoskeleton and jointed appendages.

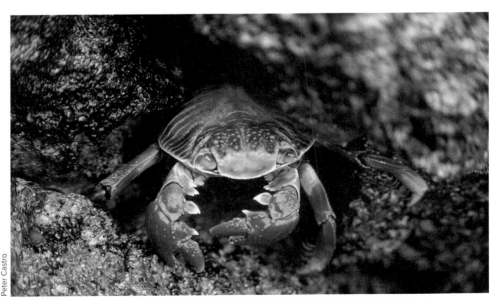

Peter Castro

FIGURE 7.31 This is not really a live Galápagos shore crab (*Grapsus grapsus*) but its exoskeleton, or molt. The old exoskeleton covered the entire external surface of the crab, even its mouthparts and eyes. After molting, which is regulated by hormones, the soft, helpless crab must find shelter for a few days until its new, larger skeleton hardens.

Chloroplasts Cell organelles in plants and other primary producers in which the process of photosynthesis takes place.
• 4.2, Living Machinery; Figure 4.8b

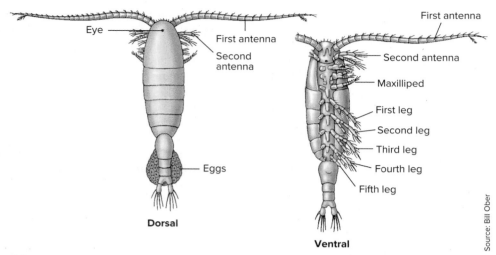

FIGURE 7.32 The structurally simplest crustaceans, like this planktonic copepod, tend to be small and have appendages that are similar to each other. One exception here is the first antenna, which is specialized for swimming (also see Figs. 15.6 and 15.7). All appendages are paired, but the ventral view shows only those on one side.

Source: Bill Ober

Crustaceans

There are approximately 70,000 known species of crustaceans. Most are marine.

Crustaceans are specialized for life in water, and most possess gills to obtain oxygen. Their chitinous skeleton is usually hardened by calcium carbonate. The appendages are specialized for swimming, crawling, attaching to other animals, mating, and feeding. Crustaceans possess two pairs of **antennae** (Figs. 7.32, 7.34, and 7.36) in contrast to insects, which have only one pair. Antennae are usually involved in sensing the surroundings. The crustacean body plan is repeated in myriad forms, from the familiar to the not-so-familiar.

Crustaceans are arthropods adapted for life in water. They have two pairs of antennae, gills, and a calcified exoskeleton.

The Small Crustaceans Small crustaceans are everywhere: in the plankton, on the bottom, among seaweeds, and on and in other animals.

Copepods are extremely abundant and most important in the plankton (see "Copepods" in 15.1). They use their mouthparts to filter out or capture food. Some species are so common that they are among the most abundant animals on Earth. Many planktonic species keep from sinking by using their enlarged first pair of antennae (Fig. 7.32) to swim. Many species are parasitic, some being so simplified that they look like little more than small bags of tissue.

Barnacles are filter feeders that usually live attached to surfaces, including living surfaces like whales and crabs. Many are very particular about the type of surface on which they live. Some are among the most important types of fouling organisms.

Common barnacles look almost like molluscs because their bodies are enclosed by heavy, calcareous plates (Fig. 7.33). The plates on the upper surface open to allow the feathery filtering appendages **(cirri),** which are actually the legs, to sweep the water. Some barnacles have become highly modified parasites and lack

plates. All barnacles, however, have typical crustacean larvae, which swim and attach to surfaces before metamorphosing into adults (see Fig. 7.41).

Amphipods are small crustaceans with a curved body that is flattened sideways (Fig. 7.34). Most amphipods are under 2 cm (3/4 in) in length, but some deep-water species are much larger (see Fig. 16.26). The head and tail typically curve downward, and the appendages are specialized according to function. Beach hoppers, common in shore debris, are strong jumpers that spring about by briskly stretching their curved bodies. Other amphipods crawl among seaweeds. Burrowing in the skin of whales (as whale lice; see Fig. 10.9) and living as part of the plankton (see Fig. 15.19*a*) are some other lifestyles of this large, mostly marine group of about 11,000 species.

Isopods are found in many of the same environments as amphipods. They are about the same size as amphipods, but isopods are easily identifiable because the main part of the body has legs that are similar to each other and the body is dorsoventrally flattened and thus has a flat back (Fig. 7.35). Pill bugs are common land isopods that are similar to many marine species. **Fish lice** (no relation to lice of birds and land mammals, which are insects) and other isopods are parasites of fishes (see Fig. 10.10) and other crustaceans.

Krill, or **euphausiids,** are planktonic, shrimp-like crustaceans up to 6 cm (2.5 in) long. The head is fused with some of the body segments to form a distinctive **carapace** that covers the anterior half of the body like armor (see Fig. 17.12). Most krill are filter feeders that feed on diatoms and other plankton. Krill are extremely common in polar waters, aggregating in gigantic schools of billions of individuals. They are an almost exclusive food source for many Antarctic whales, penguins, and fishes (see Fig. 10.14). Other species of krill live in the deep sea (see Fig. 16.2).

Shrimps, Lobsters, and Crabs With around 18,000 living species, the **decapods** (meaning "10 legs") are the largest group of crustaceans. They include the shrimps, lobsters, and crabs. Decapods are also the largest crustaceans in size. Many are prized as food and are of great commercial importance.

Decapods feature five pairs of legs, or **pereopods,** the first of which is heavier and usually has claws used for feeding and defense (Fig. 7.36). Decapods also have three pairs of **maxillipeds,** which are closer to the mouth, turned forward, and specialized to sort out food and push it toward the mouth. Maxillipeds are used as filtering devices in decapods that eat small food particles. The carapace is well developed and encloses the part of the body known as the **cephalothorax.** The rest of the body is called the **abdomen.**

Shrimps and **lobsters** tend to have laterally compressed bodies with distinct and elongated abdomens, the "tails" we like to eat. Shrimps are typically **scavengers,** specialists in feeding on bits of detritus on the bottom. Many colorful shrimps, particularly in the tropics, live on the surface of other invertebrates (Fig. 7.37) or remove parasites from the skin of fish (see Box 10.2, "Cleaning

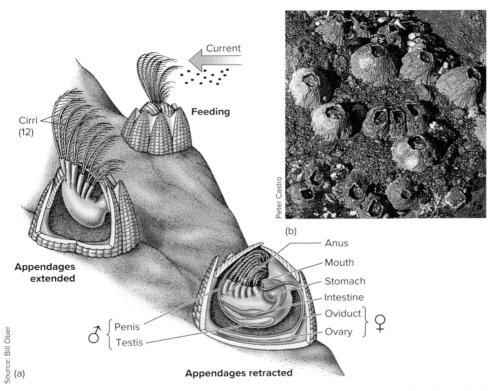

Current

Feeding

Cirri (12)

Appendages extended

Source: Bill Ober

(a)

Anus
Mouth
Stomach
Intestine
Oviduct
Ovary ♀

♂ { Penis
Testis

Appendages retracted

Peter Castro

(b)

FIGURE 7.33 (*a*) Barnacles conceal a crustacean body beneath thick plates. They lie on their backs and use their legs to filter feed. Note that barnacles are hermaphrodites. Individuals, however, mate with each other, alternatively taking different sex roles. One individual acts as "male" by inserting its extended penis into a nearby "female." It can then turn into a "female" by accepting the penis of a neighbor. Barnacles also use sperm transported by water. (*b*) The thatched barnacle (*Tetraclita squamosa*) from the Pacific coast of North America.

First antenna
Second antenna
Maxilliped

FIGURE 7.34 Most amphipods, like this beach hopper (*Orchestoidea*), can be recognized by a body that is curved and flattened sideways. The skeleton shrimps common among seaweeds and hydroids, however, are amphipods with bizarre skinny bodies. A giant deep-sea amphipod is illustrated in Figure 16.24.

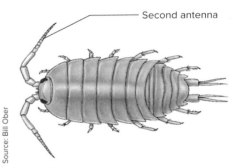

Second antenna

Source: Bill Ober

FIGURE 7.35 The sea louse, or sea roach (*Ligia oceanica*), is neither a louse nor a roach but an isopod. It feeds mainly on decaying seaweeds. Some isopods live as parasites on fishes (see Fig. 10.10).

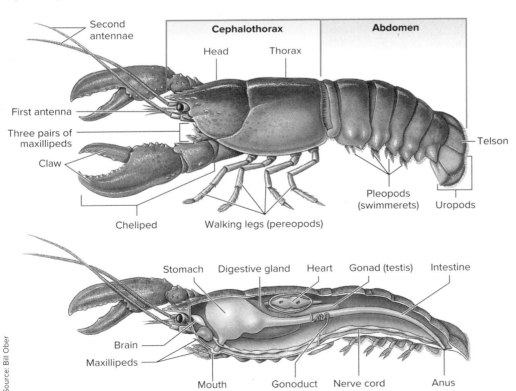

Second antennae

Cephalothorax
Head Thorax

Abdomen

First antenna
Three pairs of maxillipeds
Claw

Telson

Pleopods (swimmerets) Uropods

Cheliped Walking legs (pereopods)

Stomach Digestive gland Heart Gonad (testis) Intestine

Brain
Maxillipeds

Mouth Gonoduct Nerve cord Anus

Source: Bill Ober

FIGURE 7.36 The American lobster (*Homarus americanus*) illustrates the basic body plan of decapod crustaceans. One significant omission from this drawing is the feathery gills, which lie in a chamber on each side of the cephalothorax. The ducts from the gonads, the gonoducts, open at the base of the last pair of walking legs in males and at the base of the second pair in females. Be sure to check next time you eat a lobster.

Associations"). Other shrimps live in deep water (see Fig. 16.2). Ghost and mud shrimps burrow in muddy bottoms (see Fig. 12.11). Lobsters, such as the American, or Maine, lobster (*Homarus;* Fig. 7.36) and the clawless spiny lobster (*Panulirus;* see Fig. 4.22) are mostly nocturnal and hide during the day in rock or coral crevices. They are scavengers and predators that crush molluscs and sea urchins. **Hermit crabs,** which are not true crabs, are also scavengers. They hide their long, soft abdomens in empty gastropod shells (see Fig. 10.5). Some hermit crabs cover their shells with sea anemones (Fig. 7.38) or sponges for added protection and camouflage. One type, however, doesn't hide its abdomen (Fig. 7.39).

In the **true crabs,** or **brachyurans,** the abdomen is small and tucked under the compact and typically broad cephalothorax. The abdomen is visible as a flat, V-shaped plate in males; in females it is expanded and U-shaped for carrying eggs (Fig. 7.40). Crabs can be highly mobile, and most can easily move sideways when in a hurry. They make

FIGURE 7.37 This shrimp (*Dasycaris zanzibarica*) is camouflaged to live on the branching arms of crinoids (see Fig. 7.51) in the tropical Indian and Pacific oceans.

FIGURE 7.38 Hermit crab (*Dardanus*) with sea anemones living on its shell. The hermit crab is protected by the nematocysts on the sea anemone's tentacles, and the sea anemones get to eat food particles that are let loose when the hermit crab feeds.

FIGURE 7.39 The coconut crab (*Birgus latro*) is a large, land-dwelling hermit crab that does not use a shell as an adult. Females return to sea only to release larvae from their eggs. After a planktonic existence, the young settle on the bottom and use shells or any objects they can find for a home as they crawl out of the sea to begin life on land. Coconut crabs, like other land crabs, are air breathers. Their gills are reduced and chambers lined with blood vessels take oxygen from the air. Coconut crabs, so called because they often eat coconuts by tearing them with the powerful claws, are found in the tropical Indian and Pacific oceans. They have been known to reach 13.5 kg (30 lb) in weight and are thus the largest and heaviest of all land arthropods.

up the largest and most diverse group of decapods, more than 7,000 species. Most are scavengers or predators, but some have specialized diets such as seaweeds, organic matter in mud, or even coral mucus (see Fig. 14.25). Many crabs live along rocky shores or sandy beaches, exposed to air much of the time. Land crabs, which are found in the tropics, spend most of their lives on land, returning to the sea only to release their eggs.

Biology of Crustaceans

Feeding and Digestion Filter feeding is very common in copepods and many of the small planktonic crustaceans (see Fig. 15.7). Stiff, hair-like **setae** on some appendages are used to catch food particles in the water. Particles are carried to the setae by currents induced by the beating of other appendages. Still other specialized appendages move food from the setae to the mouth. Appendages are adapted for piercing and sucking in parasitic copepods and isopods.

Food passes to a stomach that typically has chitinous teeth or ridges for grinding and bristles for sifting. The stomach, two-chambered in decapods, is connected to digestive glands that secrete

FIGURE 7.40 The abdomen is V-shaped in male crabs (top) and larger and U-shaped in females (bottom). This is the European, or shore, crab (*Carcinus maenas*), an introduced pest on the Atlantic and Pacific coasts of North America and other regions around the world.

digestive enzymes and absorb nutrients. Digestion is essentially extracellular. The intestine ends in an anus.

As in molluscs, absorbed nutrients are distributed by an open circulatory system. Gas exchange is typically carried out by gills attached to some of the appendages. In most decapods the gills lie in a chamber under the carapace, where they are constantly bathed by water. In land crabs, however, the gill chamber, though moistened, is filled with air and acts almost as our lungs do.

Nervous System and Behavior The nervous system of the structurally simplest crustaceans is ladder-like, but it is more centralized in decapods. Crustaceans have a small, relatively simple brain (see Fig. 7.36) but well-developed sensory organs. Most have **compound eyes,** which consist of a bundle of up to 14,000 light-sensitive units, the **ommatidia,** grouped in a mosaic (see Box 7.3, "The Complex Eyes of Mantis Shrimps"). The compound eyes of decapods are at the end of movable stalks and can be used as periscopes. Crustaceans have a keen sense of "smell," being very sensitive to chemicals in the water. Many crustaceans have a pair of statocysts for balance.

Crustaceans are among the most behaviorally complex invertebrates. They use a variety of signals to communicate with each other. Many of these signals involve special body postures or movements of the legs and antennae, which are often distinctively marked or colored to make the signals more conspicuous. This type of communication has been shown to be very important in settling disputes between neighbors and in courtship. Courtship behavior can be especially elaborate (see Box 12.1, "Fiddler on the Mud").

Reproduction and Life History The sexes are separate in most crustaceans. Gametes are rarely shed into the water. Instead, males use specialized appendages to transfer sperm directly into the female. Even hermaphroditic species transfer sperm between individuals. Barnacles, for instance, have a penis that can stretch to reach other barnacles in the neighborhood (see Fig. 7.33*a*). Mating in decapods usually takes place immediately after the female molts, while the exoskeleton is still soft. Females of many species can store sperm for long periods and use it to fertilize separate batches of eggs. In amphipods and isopods, eggs are brooded in a chamber formed by lateral extensions of the body. In decapods and other groups, females carry their eggs using **pleopods,** or swimmerets, specialized appendages beneath the body (see Fig. 7.36).

Most crustaceans have planktonic larvae that look nothing like the adult. Probably the most characteristic crustacean larva is the **nauplius,** but the type and number of larval stages vary widely from group to group (Fig. 7.41).

Other Marine Arthropods

Horseshoe Crabs The **horseshoe crabs** are the only surviving members of a group (class **Merostomata**) that is widely represented in the fossil record. The four living species of horseshoe crabs are not true crabs but "living fossils" not unlike forms that became extinct long ago. Horseshoe crabs live on soft bottoms in shallow water on the Atlantic and Gulf coasts of North America (*Limulus;* Fig. 7.42) and South and Southeast Asia. Their most distinctive feature is a horseshoe-shaped carapace that encloses a body with five pairs of legs. They emerge on beaches to reproduce.

Sea Spiders Sea spiders (class **Pycnogonida**) only superficially resemble true spiders. Four or more pairs of jointed legs stretch from a small body (Fig. 7.43). A large proboscis with the mouth at the tip is used to feed on soft invertebrates such as sea anemones and hydrozoans. Sea spiders are most common in cold waters, but they occur throughout the oceans. Approximately 1,300 species are known.

Insects Insects (class **Insecta**) are distinguished from other arthropods by having only three pairs of legs as adults. They are the most diverse group of animals on Earth but are rare in the sea. Most marine insects live at the water's edge, where they scavenge among seaweeds, barnacles, and rocks. Many inhabit the decaying seaweed at the high-tide mark. One marine insect that is found far from shore is the marine water strider (*Halobates;* see Fig. 15.17).

7.7 BRYOZOANS

Bryozoans, or **moss animals** (phylum **Ectoprocta**), feature a unique feeding structure, the **lophophore** (see Fig. 13.11), which consists of a set of ciliated tentacles arranged in a horseshoe-shaped, circular, or coiled fashion. Bryozoans are suspension feeders using the cilia of the lophophore to create feeding currents. Almost all bryozoans are marine. They form colonies on seaweeds, rocks, and other surfaces. Colonies consist of minute interconnected individuals, or **zooids,** that secrete skeletons of a variety of shapes. The colonies can be encrusting or take an upright form that looks like tufts of crusty lace (Fig. 7.44). A close look reveals the rectangular, round, or vase-like compartments occupied by zooids (see Fig. 13.17). The lophophore is retractable. The U-shaped gut ends in an anus outside the edge of the lophophore.

7.8 ECHINODERMS: FIVE-WAY SYMMETRY

Sea stars, sea urchins, sea cucumbers, and several other forms make up the **echinoderms** (phylum **Echinodermata**). Echinoderms are radially symmetrical, like cnidarians and comb jellies. The radial symmetry of echinoderms, however, is only a secondary development. Their planktonic larvae are bilaterally symmetrical (see Fig. 15.11*c*), and only the adults develop radial symmetry. Unlike cnidarians and comb jellies, echinoderms have **pentamerous** radial symmetry, a symmetry based on five parts (Fig. 7.45). As might be expected in a radially symmetrical animal, echinoderms lack a head. They have no anterior or posterior end or dorsal or ventral side. It is useful instead to refer to one surface of echinoderms as oral, because that is where the mouth is located, and the opposite surface as aboral (Fig. 7.45*a* and *b*). Most echinoderms have an anus unlike cnidarians and comb jellies.

Echinoderms typically have a complete digestive tract, a well-developed coelom, and an **endoskeleton,** a skeleton that is internal just like ours. It is secreted within the tissues, rather than externally, like the exoskeleton of arthropods. Though sometimes it looks external, as in the spines of sea urchins, the endoskeleton is covered by a thin layer of ciliated tissue. Spines and pointed bumps give many echinoderms a spiny appearance, hence the name Echinodermata, meaning "spiny-skinned."

Copepods	Nauplius	Copepodite	Adult copepod
Barnacles	Nauplius	Cypris	Adult barnacle
Spiny lobsters	Phyllosoma		Adult lobster
Most shrimps	Zoea		Adult shrimp
Crabs	Zoea	Megalopa	Adult crab

Source: Bill Ober

FIGURE 7.41 The eggs of marine crustaceans hatch into planktonic larvae that undergo consecutive molts. Each molt adds a new pair of appendages, with the ones already present becoming more specialized. The last larval stage eventually metamorphoses into a juvenile (see Fig. 13.5). The larvae and adults shown here are not drawn to scale, and each arrow may represents several molts. Other crustacean larvae are shown in Figure 15.13.

Unique to echinoderms is the **water vascular system,** a network of water-filled canals (Fig. 7.45*c*). **Tube feet** are muscular extensions of these canals. They are extended when filled with water, sometimes by the action of muscular sacs, the **ampullae,** that extend inside the body opposite the tube feet. Tube feet often end in a sucker and are used for attachment, locomotion, and the reception of chemical and mechanical stimuli. In sea stars and sea urchins (see Fig. 7.49) the system connects to the outside through the **madreporite,** a porous plate on the aboral surface.

Echinoderms are radially symmetrical as adults. They are characterized by an endoskeleton and a unique water vascular system.

Types of Echinoderms

The echinoderms constitute a large and diverse group of around 7,300 species, all marine. They are important members of bottom

FIGURE 7.42 *Limulus polyphemus* is a horseshoe crab reaching 60 cm (2 ft), including the tail. It feeds on clams and other small, soft-bottom invertebrates. The numbers of horseshoe crabs are in decline. Their eggs are an important food for shorebirds, and their blood, which is blueish, is used to test the purity of vaccines.

U.S. Fish & Wildlife Service/Greg Breese

FIGURE 7.44
Canda simplex and many other bryozoans form crusty, lace-like colonies.

Bill Ober

Bill Curtsinger/National Geographic/Getty Images

FIGURE 7.43 Most shallow-water sea spiders are small, with body length rarely more than 1 cm (about ½ in). Some deep-sea sea spiders are bigger, as are species in Arctic and Antarctic waters like the one shown here.

communities worldwide. Radial symmetry is associated with sedentary lifestyles, and with the exception of limited swimming in some feather stars and some deep-water sea cucumbers, adult echinoderms are relatively slow bottom crawlers.

Sea Stars Sea stars (class **Asteroidea**), sometimes called starfishes, clearly display the distinctive echinoderm body plan (Fig. 7.45). Most species have five arms that radiate from a central disk, though some have more than five (Fig. 7.46*a*), sometimes close to 50. Hundreds of tube feet protrude from the oral surface along radiating channels on each arm called **ambulacral grooves** (Fig. 7.45*b*). Sea stars can move in any direction, though usually slowly, by reaching out their tube feet and pulling themselves along.

The endoskeleton of sea stars consists of interconnected calcium carbonate plates that form a relatively flexible framework. This allows their arms to be somewhat flexible. The aboral surface of many sea stars is often covered with spines modified into minute, pincer-like organs called **pedicellariae** (Fig. 7.45*c*). They help keep the surface clean.

Most of the over 1,900 known species of sea stars are predators of bivalves, snails, barnacles, and other attached or slow-moving animals. Typical examples include *Asterias* (Fig. 7.45), common on rocky shores from the North Atlantic to the Gulf of Mexico, and *Pisaster* (see Fig. 11.25), its counterpart on the North Pacific.

Brittle Stars Brittle stars (class **Ophiuroidea**) also have a star-shaped body architecture. The five arms, however, are long, very flexible, and sharply demarcated from the central disk (Fig. 7.47). The swift, snake-like movements of the arms are used in locomotion, sometimes to capture food. The tube feet, which lack suckers, are used in feeding. Unlike sea stars, the gonads and other internal organs of brittle stars are contained within the central disk and do not extend into the arms.

Most brittle stars eat detritus and small animals they pick up from the bottom. Particles are collected by the tube feet and passed from foot to foot to the mouth. There are more species of brittle stars, some 2,000, than of any other group of echinoderms. Brittle stars are widely distributed but not always visible, often hiding under rocks and corals or covering themselves with mud or sand.

Sea Urchins In sea urchins (class **Echinoidea**) the endoskeleton forms a round, rigid, shell-like test with movable spines and pedicellariae (Figs. 7.48 and 7.49). Locomotion is achieved by the movable spines, jointed to sockets in the test, and the sucker-tipped tube feet. The flat and radiating body plan of sea stars can be transformed into a sea urchin by dropping the arms to form a sphere. The five rows of ambulacral grooves with their tube feet now extend along the outer surface of the sphere (Fig. 7.49). The mouth is on the bottom and the anus on top. The plates that make up the test can be seen in a sea urchin cleaned of spines and tissue. Bands of pores along the ambulacral grooves correspond to the bands of tube feet.

Sea urchins graze on attached or drifting seaweeds and seagrasses. They also ingest detritus and encrusting animals such as sponges and bryozoans. The mouth has an intricate system of jaws and muscles called **Aristotle's lantern** (Fig. 7.49), which is used to bite off algae and other bits of food from the bottom.

Sea urchins are a common sight on rocky shores throughout the world. Examples are species of *Arbacia* from the Atlantic Ocean and Gulf of Mexico and *Strongylocentrotus* from most North Atlantic and Pacific coasts (Figs. 7.48*a* and 13.19). Sea urchins in the tropics show an even richer variety of shapes and sizes, particularly on coral reefs (*Echinometra, Diadema;* see Fig. 14.33).

Not all of the estimated 1,000 species in the class Echinoidea have round tests with prominent spines. **Heart urchins** (see Fig. 13.7) and **sand dollars** (Figs. 7.48*b* and 13.8) are adapted to live in soft bottoms by having flattened bodies and short spines. They are deposit feeders that use their tube feet and sometimes strands of mucus to pick up organic particles.

FIGURE 7.45 (*a*) Aboral and (*b*) oral surfaces of a sea star (*Asterias vulgaris*) common on the Atlantic and Gulf coasts of North America. (*c*) Internal structure, with an arm cut across to show the relationship between tube feet, the internal sacs (ampullae), and the canals that make up the water vascular system. This and other carnivorous sea stars evert their thin-walled stomach and begin digesting prey externally without having to eat it.

FIGURE 7.46 (*a*) The sunflower sea star (*Pycnopodia helianthoides*) from the Pacific coast of North America is one of the largest sea stars. It feeds on sea urchins, snails, and other invertebrates. (*b*) *Linckia guildingi*, from the Caribbean, shows a remarkable ability for regeneration; here the larger arm regenerated the central disk and four small arms to form a complete individual.

Sea Cucumbers In yet another modification of the echinoderm body plan, the 1,690 known species of **sea cucumbers** (class **Holothuroidea**) are superficially worm-like (Fig. 7.50). They do not have spines and appear to lack radial symmetry. The basic body plan of sea cucumbers is elongated along the oral-aboral axis, as if they were pulled from the mouth and anus and stretched. The animal lies on one side, where the five rows of tube feet, extending from mouth to anus, are concentrated. The oral and aboral surfaces are at the ends. The endoskeleton consists of microscopic, calcareous spicules scattered throughout the warty, often tough skin.

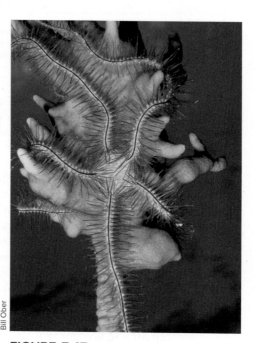

FIGURE 7.47 *Ophiothrix oerstedii* is a brittle star typically found on sponges and other habitats in the Caribbean.

Many sea cucumbers are deposit feeders. The tube feet around the mouth are modified into branched tentacles that are used to pick up organic matter from the bottom or scoop sediment into the mouth (see Fig. 7.4). Some sea cucumbers burrow or hide and extend only their tentacles to obtain food directly from the water.

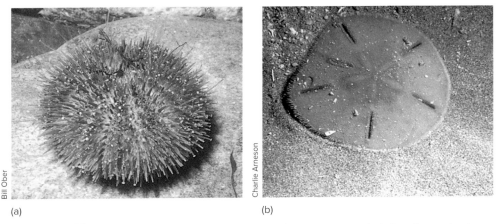

(a)

(b)

FIGURE 7.48 (*a*) The green sea urchin (*Strongylocentrotus droebachiensis*) is found on rocky shores and kelp forests on the Atlantic, Arctic, and Pacific coasts of North America. (*b*) *Mellita sexiesperforata*, the six-hole sand dollar from sandy bottoms along the southern United States and the Caribbean. The five-part pattern characteristic of all echinoderms can be seen in the star pattern in the center of the test.

Many sea cucumbers have evolved novel defensive mechanisms that compensate for the lack of a test and spines. Some secrete toxic substances. When disturbed, some species discharge sticky, sometimes toxic filaments through the anus to discourage potential predators. Others resort to a startling response, the sudden expulsion of the gut and other internal organs through the mouth or anus, a response known as **evisceration**. It is assumed that evisceration distracts the offender while the sea cucumber, which will eventually grow back the lost organs, escapes—messy, perhaps, but effective.

Crinoids Crinoids (class **Crinoidea**) are suspension feeders that use outstretched, feathery arms to obtain food from

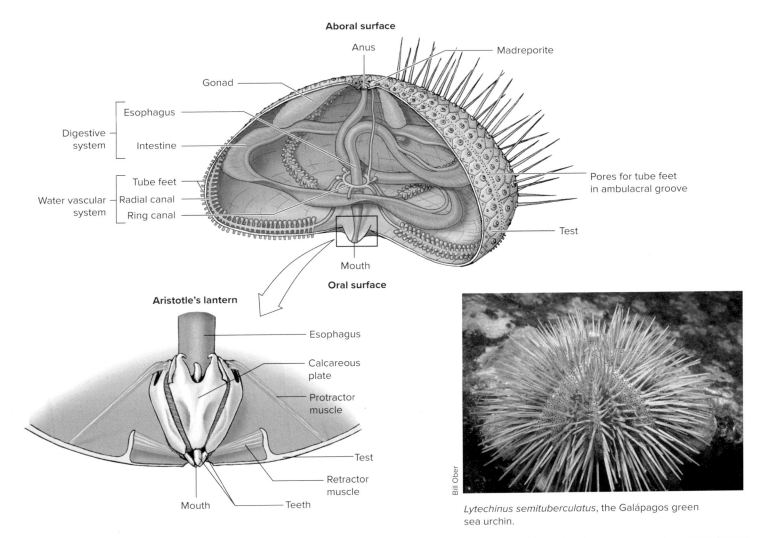

Lytechinus semituberculatus, the Galápagos green sea urchin.

FIGURE 7.49 Internal structure of a typical sea urchin, with a simplified diagram of the Aristotle's lantern. Five pairs of protractor muscles pull the lantern down, exposing the teeth; five pairs of retractor muscles move the lantern and teeth in. Additional muscles are responsible for grasping and other movements of the teeth.

FIGURE 7.50 A sea cucumber (*Stichopus horrens*) from the tropical Indian and Pacific oceans, together with some slate pencil urchins (*Eucidaris thouarsii*). Sea cucumbers in general are among the largest echinoderms, reaching 2 m (6.6 ft) in length in some species.

FIGURE 7.51 A feather star, or crinoid, photographed at night in the Marshall Islands. The outstretched arms of feeding individuals can reach a diameter of 70 cm (more than 2 ft).

The coelomic fluid also transports oxygen because most echinoderms lack a distinct circulatory system. In sea stars and sea urchins gas exchange takes place across small, branched projections of the body wall connected at the base to the coelomic cavity. Gas exchange in sea cucumbers occurs by drawing water through the anus into a pair of thin, branched tubes called **respiratory trees.** The respiratory trees are extensions of the gut and are suspended in the body cavity, surrounded by coelomic fluid. They provide a large surface area in close proximity to the coelomic fluid, thus allowing considerable gas exchange.

the water. Crinoids are represented by around 625 living species of **feather stars** (Fig. 7.51) and **sea lilies.** More than 5,000 species are only known as fossils. Sea lilies are restricted to deep water. They attach permanently to the bottom, but some are known to crawl on hard bottoms. Feather stars perch and crawl in both shallow and deep waters, especially in the tropical Indian and Pacific oceans. They are also capable of graceful swimming.

The body plan of crinoids is best described as an upside-down brittle star with the ambulacral grooves and mouth directed upward. The mouth and larger organs are restricted to a small, cup-shaped body from which the arms radiate. Some crinoids have only five arms but most have many—up to 200—because of branching of the initial five. The arms also have small side branches. Tiny tube feet along these side branches secrete mucus, which aids in catching food particles. Food makes its way into the mouth by way of ciliated ambulacral grooves. These appendages tilt the body, so that the extended arms orient to currents for efficient suspension feeding (Fig. 7.51).

Biology of Echinoderms

Feeding and Digestion The digestive system of echinoderms is relatively simple. Most sea stars are carnivores that feed by extending, or everting, part of their stomach inside out through the mouth to envelop the food. The stomach then secretes digestive enzymes produced by large digestive glands that extend into the arms (Fig. 7.45c). The digested food is carried into the glands for absorption and the stomach pulled back inside the body. The intestine is short or missing. Brittle stars and crinoids also have simple, short guts. Brittle stars lack an anus.

The gut of sea urchins and sea cucumbers is long and coiled (Fig. 7.49). In sea urchins this is an adaptation for the lengthier digestion needed for the breakdown of seaweed and plant material. A long gut also is advantageous to sea cucumbers because they need to process large amounts of sediment to obtain enough organic matter.

In all echinoderms nutrients are transported in the fluid that fills the extensive body cavity. The fluid is called **coelomic fluid** because the body cavity of echinoderms is a coelom.

Nervous System and Behavior The presence of a nerve net in echinoderms is reminiscent of cnidarians. The nervous system coordinates movements of tube feet and spines in the absence of a brain. Nevertheless, the righting of the body after being turned over, light-sensitive organs that allow some sea stars to recognize their home reef, the detection of light by brittle stars even when true eyes are absent, and camouflaging with bits of debris by sea urchins, are evidence that the nervous system not as simple as it looks.

Reproduction and Life History The sexes are separate in most echinoderms. The gonads, 5, 10, or more in number, are usually located in the body cavity and open to the outside by way of a duct (see Figs. 7.45c and 7.49). They shed sperm or eggs directly into the water. Gametes do not survive long, so individuals of many species spawn all at once to ensure fertilization.

Development of the fertilized egg proceeds in the plankton and typically results in a ciliated larva characteristic of each group (see Fig. 15.11b and c). Echinoderm larvae are bilaterally symmetrical and it is not until metamorphosis that radial symmetry develops. Some echinoderms do not have planktonic larvae and brood their offspring in special pouches or under the body.

Some sea stars, brittle stars, and sea cucumbers regularly reproduce asexually by the separation of the central disk or body into two pieces. The resulting halves then grow into complete individuals. **Regeneration,** the ability to grow lost or damaged body parts, is highly developed in echinoderms. Sea stars, brittle stars, and crinoids regenerate lost arms. In some species of sea stars a severed arm can grow into a new individual (see Fig. 7.46b). Efforts to control sea stars that prey on oyster beds or corals by cutting them up and throwing the pieces back into the water have failed miserably. In most sea stars, however, only arms that include portions of the central disk can regenerate.

7.9 HEMICHORDATES: A "MISSING LINK"?

The search for links between the chordates—our own phylum—and other groups of animals (see Fig. 7.1) has been a provocative challenge and several explanations have been proposed. As strange as

it may seem, echinoderms and chordates share several features related to the development of our embryos. The wide evolutionary gap between echinoderms and chordates, however, could be filled by a small and infrequently seen group of worms, the **hemichordates** (phylum **Hemichordata**). Hemichordates share the same basic developmental characteristics of chordates and echinoderms. Some also have a larva similar to that of some echinoderms. Hemichordates share with us chordates some of the features used to define our phylum. These characteristics—a dorsal, hollow nerve cord, and openings along the anterior part of the gut—will be discussed in the following section.

The hemichordates include 140 known species. Most are **acorn worms,** or **enteropneusts,** worm-like deposit feeders that live free or in U-shaped tubes. Some acorn worms are found around hydrothermal vents, often in large numbers. They generally range in length from about 8 to 45 cm (3 to 18 in) but some reach 2.5 m (more than 8 ft). Like sea cucumbers, practically all acorn worms ingest sediment, using a thick, mucus-secreting proboscis to collect organic material, which is then swept toward the mouth.

7.10 CHORDATES WITHOUT A BACKBONE

The **chordates** (phylum **Chordata**) are divided into three major groups, or subphyla. Two of these lack a backbone and one of these two is discussed here with the invertebrates. These invertebrate chordates are collectively called **protochordates.** The third and by far the largest chordate subphylum comprises the **vertebrates,** the subject of Chapters 8 and 9.

The estimated 61,000 living species of chordates share many characteristics, but four stand out. During at least part of their development, all chordates, including humans, have (1) a single, hollow **nerve cord** that runs along the dorsal length of the animal, (2) **gill** (or **pharyngeal**) **slits,** small openings along the anterior part of the gut (or **pharynx**), (3) a **notochord,** a flexible rod for support that lies between the nerve cord and the gut, and (4) a **post-anal tail** that extends beyond the anus (Fig. 7.52*b*). The notochord originally served for muscle attachment but in vertebrates it became surrounded or replaced by a series of articulating bones, the **backbone.** All chordates also have a ventral heart.

All chordates possess—at least during part of their lives—a dorsal nerve cord, gill slits, a notochord, and a post-anal tail. Vertebrate chordates also have a backbone.

Tunicates

Tunicates (subphylum **Urochordata** or **Tunicata**) make up the largest group of protochordates. All 3,000 known species are marine. Those we are most apt to see are the **sea squirts,** or **ascidians** (class **Ascidiacea**). Their sac-like bodies are attached to hard surfaces, often as fouling animals (Fig. 7.53*a*), or anchored in soft sediments. They are the only sessile, or permanently attached, chordates. Some sea squirts can be confused with sponges because of their general appearance. The body of the sea squirt, however, is protected by a **tunic,** a leathery or gelatinous outer covering different from that of sponges, and the internal structure is completely different (Fig. 7.53*b*).

Sea squirts are filter feeders. Water typically flows through the mouth, or **incurrent siphon,** and is filtered by a ciliated, sieve-like sac. This sac represents the pharynx, and the openings are derived from the gill slits. Food is filtered from the water and passed into a U-shaped or coiled gut. Filtered water is expelled through a second opening, the **excurrent siphon.** When disturbed or expelling debris, ascidians force a jet of water out of both siphons, giving them their common name of sea squirts. Some sea squirts are colonial, some consisting of clumps of separate individuals (Fig. 7.52*a*) and others of a circular, flower-like arrangement of individuals having a common tunic and excurrent siphon (Figs. 7.53*a* and 13.17).

Were it not for their planktonic larvae, the headless, attached sea squirts could easily pass as anything but chordates. The adults possess neither a notochord nor a dorsal nerve cord (Fig. 7.53*b*). Ascidian larvae are known as **tadpole larvae** because of their resemblance to the tadpoles of frogs (Fig. 7.52*b*). Tadpole larvae clearly display the fundamental chordate traits. They have gill slits, a dorsal nerve cord, a notochord, and a well-developed post-anal tail. They also have an eye. Tadpole larvae do not feed; their only purpose is to find a suitable surface on which to settle. During metamorphosis of a tadpole larva into a juvenile ascidian, the notochord and tail are reabsorbed and free existence is no more.

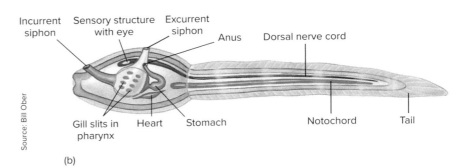

FIGURE 7.52 (*a*) *Clavelina picta* is a colonial sea squirt, or ascidian. Its outer covering, the tunic, contains cellulose, a substance typical of plants. (*b*) The tadpole larva of ascidians exhibits all the distinguishing characteristics of chordates. Some of these characteristics, however, are missing in the adults.

Table 7.1 Some of the Most Important Characteristics of the Major Animal Phyla

Phylum	Representative Groups	Distinguishing Features	General Habitat	Ecology	Number of Species
Porifera (sponges)	Sponges	Collar cells (choanocytes)	Benthic	Filter feeders	9,000
Cnidaria (cnidarians)	Jellyfishes (sea jellies), sea anemones, corals	Nematocysts	Benthic, pelagic	Predators, passive suspension feeders; corals are important reef builders	13,300
Ctenophora (comb jellies)	Comb jellies	Ciliary combs, colloblasts	Mostly pelagic	Predators	150
Platyhelminthes (flatworms)	Turbellarians, flukes, tapeworms	Flattened body	Mostly benthic, many parasitic	Predators, many parasitic	26,500
Nemertea (ribbon worms)	Ribbon worms	Long proboscis	Mostly benthic	Predators	1,300
Nematoda (nematodes)	Nematodes, roundworms	Body round in cross section	Mostly benthic, many parasitic	Many parasitic, deposit feeders	+80,000
Chaetognatha (arrow worms)	Arrow worms	Transparent body with fins	Mostly pelagic	Predators	190
Annelida (segmented worms)	Polychaetes, oligochaetes, leeches, echiurans, peanut worms	Segmentation	Mostly benthic	Predators, deposit feeders, passive suspension feeders	23,000
Mollusca (molluscs)	Snails, clams, oysters, octopuses, chitons	Foot, mantle, radula (absent in some groups)	Benthic, pelagic	Predators, grazers, filter feeders, some parasitic	117,000
Arthropoda (arthropods)	Crustaceans (crabs, shrimps), insects	Exoskeleton, jointed legs	Benthic, pelagic, some parasitic	Predators, grazers, filter feeders, some parasitic	++1,000,000
Ectoprocta (bryozoans)	Bryozoans	Lophophore, colonial	Benthic	Filter feeders	6,300
Echinodermata (echinoderms)	Sea stars, brittle stars, sea urchins, sea cucumbers	Tube feet, five-way radial symmetry, water vascular system	Mostly benthic	Predators, deposit feeders, passive suspension feeders	7,300
Hemichordata (hemichordates)	Acorn worms	Dorsal, hollow nerve cord, gill slits	Mostly benthic	Deposit feeders	140
Chordata (chordates)	Tunicates, vertebrates (fishes, reptiles, birds, mammals)	Dorsal, hollow nerve cord, gill slits, notochord	Benthic, pelagic	Predators, grazers, filter feeders	61,000

Source: Bill Ober

	Level of Organization	Symmetry	Segmentation	Body Cavity	Digestive Tract	Respiratory Exchange	Circulatory System
	Cellular	Asymmetrical	No	None	None	↑ Body surface ↓	None
	Tissue	Radial	No	None	Incomplete		None
	Tissue	Radial	No	None	Incomplete		None
	↕ Organ system	↕ Bilateral	No	None	Incomplete or absent	Body surface	None
			No	Reduced (proboscis cavity)	↕ Complete		Closed
			No	Present, not true coelom			None
			No	↕ Coelom			None
			No				None
			Yes			Gills (in many crustaceans)	Open
			Yes			Body surface	None
			No			Body surface	Closed
		Radial (adults) Bilateral (larvae)	No			Body surface	None
		Bilateral	No			Body surface	Part closed, part open
		Bilateral	Yes			Gills, lungs	Closed

Cliona intestinalis and *Botryllus schlosseri* (a)

Labels (a): *Cliona intestinalis*; *Botryllus schlosseri*; Bill Ober

Labels (b): Incurrent siphon; Excurrent siphon; Tunic; Genital duct; Pharynx; Anus; Intestine; Heart; Gonad (ovary and testes); Stomach; (b); Source: Bill Ober

FIGURE 7.53 *Cliona intestinalis* is a shallow-water sea squirt that has become a common fouling animal in many parts of the world. A colonial sea squirt (*Botryllus schlosseri*) can be seen on the outer covering, or tunic, of *Cliona* (*a*).

Some tunicates lead a planktonic existence throughout their lives. **Salps** (class **Thaliacea**) have a transparent, barrel-shaped body with muscle bands for locomotion (see Fig. 15.8). Water enters through the anterior mouth, or incurrent siphon, and is forced out through the excurrent siphon on the posterior end. Salps can be very abundant, particularly in warm water. Some are colonial, much like floating colonies of sea squirts, and can reach several meters in length. **Larvaceans,** or **appendicularians** (class **Larvacea**), comprise another group of planktonic tunicates. They retain the body of a tadpole larva through life. Each tiny individual secretes a complex but delicate gelatinous "house" for protection and to filter water for food (see Fig. 15.9).

Interactive
Exploration

McGraw-Hill Connect® is a great place to check your understanding of chapter material. Visit **www.mcgrawhillconnect.com** for access to interactive chapter summaries, chapter quizzing, and more! Further enhance your knowledge with videoclips and weblinks to chapter-related material.

Critical Thinking

1. If bilateral symmetry were to evolve among cnidarians, in which group or groups would you expect it to occur? Why?

2. Cephalopods, the squids, octopuses, and allies, show a much higher degree of structural and behavioral complexity than the other groups of molluscs. What factors triggered the evolution of these changes? A rich fossil record among cephalopods shows that once they were very common and even dominant in some marine environments. Now there are only about 650 living species of cephalopods, far fewer than gastropods. In the end, were cephalopods successful? What do you think happened along the way?

3. A new group of echinoderms, the sea daisies, or concentricycloids, was discovered in 1986. They are deep-water animals living on sunken wood. They are flat and round, looking very much like a small sea star without arms. They also lack a gut. Without ever having seen them, why do you think they were classified as echinoderms, not as members of a new phylum? Do you have any hypotheses as to how they feed or move around?

4. There has been a tendency among invertebrates to evolve extracellular digestion from intracellular digestion. What are the advantages (and disadvantages) of intracellular digestion?

5. Many groups of marine invertebrates have distinctive free-living larvae, but some species in these groups never release larvae. How would you characterize the species that do not reproduce by means of larval development? Can you predict any particular adaptations these species must have evolved to compensate for the absence of larvae?

6. Larval development is common among marine crustaceans but very rare among freshwater ones. Can you hypothesize why?

For Further Reading

Some of the recommended readings may be available online. Look for live links on the *Marine Biology* Online Learning Center.

General Interest

Barras, C., 2017. Out of breath. *New Scientist*, vol. 233, no. 3109, 21 January, pp. 32–35. Some marine invertebrates live in water containing no oxygen.

Bennett, H., 2018. Sight unseeing. *New Scientist*, vol. 240, no. 3198, 6 October, pp. 39–41. Octopuses and squids are color-blind and yet display an amazing color-changing ability.

Bernwald, J., 2017. The immortal jellyfish. *Discover*, vol. 38, no. 10, December, pp. 58–63. Jellyfishes could hold the secret of the genetic control of tissue regeneration.

Hanlon, R., M. Vecchione, and L. Alcock, 2018. *Octopus, squid and cuttlefish.* University of Chicago Press, Chicago, IL. A comprehensive yet readable general account of the biology of cephalopods.

Judson, O., 2016. The power of eight. *National Geographic*, vol. 230, no. 5, November, pp. 62–81. Octopuses never fail to amaze us, most especially because of the complexity of their nervous system and intelligence.

Kolbert, E., 2018. Scary, squishy, brainless, beautiful. *National Geographic*, vol. 234, no. 4, October, pp. 72–91. The name "jellyfish" is unfortunately used to refer to an assortment of marine animals many of which are not closely related to each other.

Milius, S., 2016. Strange visions. *Science News*, vol. 189, no. 11, May 28, pp. 22–25. The eyes of many marine invertebrates show an amazing variety of shapes and the way they function.

Moulton, D. E., A. Goriely, and R. Chirat, 2018. How seashells take shape. *Scientific American*, vol. 318, no. 4, April, pp. 68–75. Mathematical models help explain the often intricate shape of mollusc shells.

Quammen, D., 2018. When life got complicated. *National Geographic*, vol. 233, no. 3, March, pp. 88–107. Fossils help elucidate the evolution of animals from single-cell forms to large, complex ones.

Tennenhouse, E., 2017. It's a no-brainer. *New Scientist*, vol. 235, no. 3134, pp. 32–35. Some of the "simplest" marine invertebrates can learn, even when they have very simple nervous systems.

In Depth

Costello, J. H., S. P. Colin, J. O. Dabiri, B. J. Gemmell, K. N. Lucas, and K. R. Sutherland, 2021. The hydrodynamics of jellyfish swimming. *Annual Review of Marine Science,* vol. 13, pp. 375–396.

Helm, R. R., 2018. Evolution and development of scyphozoan jellyfish. *Biological Reviews,* vol. 93, pp. 1228–1250.

Hewson, I., B. Sullivan, E. W. Jackson, Q. Xu, H. Long, C. Lin, E. M. Quijano, J. Seymour, N. Siboni, M. R. L. Jones, and M. A. Sewell, 2019. Something old, something new? Review of wasting and other mortality in Asteroidea (Echinodermata). *Frontiers in Marine Biology* [https://doi.org/10.3389/fmars.2019.00406].

Martin, D. and T. A. Britayev, 2018. Symbiotic polychaetes revisited: an update of the known species and relationships (1998–2017). *Oceanography and Marine Biology: An Annual Review,* vol. 56, pp. 371–448.

Melzner, M., F. C. Mark, B. A. Seibel, and L. Tomanek, 2020. Ocean acidification and coastal marine invertebrates: Tracking CO_2 effects from seawater to the cell. *Annual Review of Marine Science,* vol. 12, pp. 499–523.

Morton, B. and F. M. Machado, 2019. Predatory marine bivalves: A review. *Advances in Marine Biology,* vol. 84, pp. 1–98.

Pitt, K. A., C. H. Lucas, R. H. Condon, C. M. Duarte, and B. Stewart-Koster, 2018. Claims that anthropogenic stressors facilitate jellyfish blooms have been amplified beyond the available evidence: A systematic review. *Frontiers in Marine Biology* [https://doi.org/10.3389/fmars.2018.00451].

Schnell, A. K., P. Amodio, M. Boeckle, and N. S. Clayton, 2020. How intelligent is a cephalopod? Lessons from comparative cognition. *Biological Reviews,* vol. 96, pp. 162–178.

Steinberg, R. K., K. A. Dafforn, T. Ainsworth, and E. L. Johnston, 2020. Know thy anemone: A review of threats to octocorals and anemones and opportunities for their restoration. *Frontiers in Marine Biology* [https://doi.org/10.3389/fmars.2020.00590].

Wanninger, A. and T. Wollesen, 2019. The evolution of molluscs. *Biological Reviews,* vol. 94, pp. 102–115.

CHAPTER 8

Marine Fishes

Source: Bill Ober

fratiseKhojdysz/Shutterstock

Fishes of many colors and shapes inhabit tropical coral reefs.

ishes were the first vertebrates, appearing more than 500 million years ago. The first fishes probably evolved from an invertebrate chordate not much different from the lancelets or the tadpole larvae of sea squirts that still inhabit the oceans.

Fishes soon made their presence felt and have had a tremendous impact on the marine environment. They feed on nearly all types of marine organisms. Some of the organisms discussed in Chapters 5 through 7, from bacteria to crustaceans, use fishes as their home. Many other animals eat them.

Fishes are the most economically important marine organisms, and are a vital source of protein for millions of people. Some are ground up for fertilizer or chicken feed. Leather, glue, vitamins, and other products are obtained from them. Many marine fishes

are chased by sportfishing enthusiasts. Others are kept as pets and have brought the wonders of ocean life into many homes.

8.1 VERTEBRATES: AN INTRODUCTION

Vertebrates (subphylum **Vertebrata**) share four fundamental characteristics of the phylum Chordata with **protochordates,** the invertebrate chordates like lancelets and sea squirts. Vertebrates differ from these other chordates in having a **backbone,** also called the **vertebral column** or **spine,** which is a dorsal row of hollow skeletal elements, usually bone, called **vertebrae.** The vertebrae enclose

and protect the **nerve cord,** also called the **spinal cord,** which ends in a brain that is protected by a **skull** made of cartilage or bone. Vertebrates also are characterized by a bilaterally symmetrical body and the presence of an internal skeleton, or **endoskeleton.**

Vertebrates are chordates with a backbone that encloses a nerve cord, or spinal cord.

8.2 TYPES OF FISHES

Fishes are the oldest and structurally the simplest of all living vertebrates. They also are the most abundant vertebrates in terms of both species and individuals. It is estimated that there are as many as 33,000 species of fishes. They make up about half of all species of vertebrates on Earth. Most species of fishes, about 58%, are marine. Many new species are being discovered every year, but

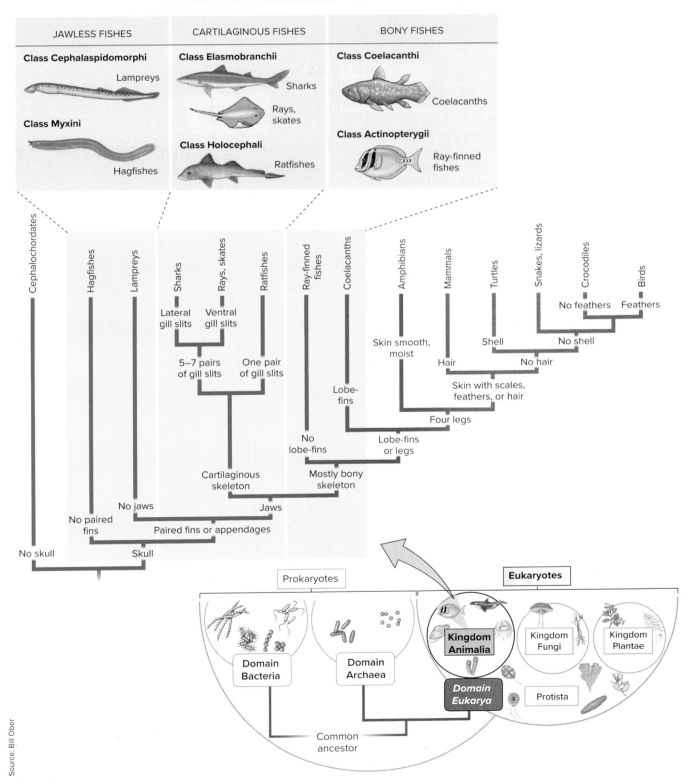

Source: Bill Ober

FIGURE 8.1 Classification scheme of fishes.

many, like numerous species of sharks and rays, are on the brink of extinction.

There is some disagreement as to how to classify the major groups of fishes. Three main groups are generally recognized (Fig. 8.1).

Jawless Fishes

The most primitive fishes living today are the **jawless fishes** (superclass **Agnatha**). Because they lack jaws, they feed by suction with the aid of a round, muscular mouth and rows of teeth. The body is cylindrical and elongated like that of eels or snakes (Fig. 8.2). They lack the paired fins and scales of most fishes, but, like fishes and other vertebrates, the brain is protected by a skull. Some biologists do not even consider jawless fishes to be vertebrates because they lack true vertebrae.

Hagfishes, or **slime eels** (*Myxine, Eptatretus;* Fig. 8.2), are jawless fishes that feed mostly on dead or dying fishes (see Table 8.1). They sometimes bore into their prey and eat them from the inside out. Hagfishes live in burrows they dig in muddy bottoms, mostly at moderate depths in cold waters. More than 70 species are known. They reach a maximum length of approximately 80 cm (2.6 ft). Their skin is used in the manufacture of leather goods, but they are mostly known for attacking bait or fishes on fishing lines, nets, and traps.

Lampreys (*Petromyzon*), found in most temperate regions, are primarily freshwater fishes. They breed in rivers and lakes, but some move to the sea as adults. They attach to other fishes and suck their blood or feed on bottom invertebrates. There are an estimated 30 species of lampreys.

Hagfishes and lampreys lack jaws and are the most primitive living fishes.

Cartilaginous Fishes

The **cartilaginous fishes** (traditionally grouped as "Chondrichthyes") are a fascinating and ancient group that includes the sharks, rays, skates, and ratfishes. Cartilaginous fishes have a skeleton made of **cartilage,** a material that is lighter and more flexible than bone. Though the skeleton of jawless fishes is also cartilaginous, sharks and related fishes feature some significant advances. They possess movable jaws that are usually armed with well-developed teeth (Fig. 8.3). The mouth is almost always ventral—that is, underneath the head. Another important development is the presence of paired lateral fins for efficient swimming. Cartilaginous fishes have rough, sandpaper-like skin because of the presence of tiny **placoid scales.** These consist of a pointed tip that is directed backward (Fig. 8.4a) and have the same composition as teeth. Placoid scales reduce drag, or water resistance, and could account for the fast acceleration of sharks.

Sharks, rays, skates, and ratfishes are characterized by a cartilaginous skeleton and a rough skin covered by minute placoid scales. They also have movable jaws and paired fins.

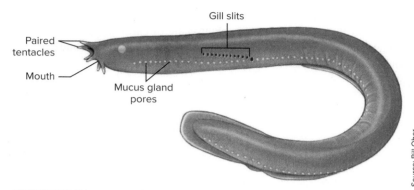

FIGURE 8.2 The Pacific hagfish (*Eptatretus stoutii*) has four pairs of sensory tentacles around the mouth and 12 pairs of gill slits. Hagfishes are also known as slime eels because of the abundant mucus produced by glands on the skin. The mucus is used by hagfishes to protect themselves from predators while feeding with their heads buried in dead fishes and whales. Notice the absence of paired fins.

FIGURE 8.3 Shark jaws have several rows of triangular teeth. Individual teeth often have even smaller serrations, or denticles, along their edges. A tiger shark (*Galeocerdo cuvier*) can grow and discard 24,000 teeth in a 10-year period. These are the jaws of a sand tiger shark (*Carcharias taurus*). The small holes in the skin between the eye and the nostrils are the ampullae of Lorenzini (see Fig. 8.19b).

Sharks **Sharks** (class **Elasmobranchii**) are adapted for fast swimming and predatory feeding. They are often described as "mysterious," "evil," or "formidable," evidence of our fascination with sharks.

Sharks are sometimes referred to as "living fossils" because many of them are similar to species that swam the seas more than 100 million years ago. Their typically fusiform, or spindle-shaped, bodies, tapering from the rounded middle toward each end, slip easily through the water. The tail, or **caudal fin,** is well developed and powerful. The tail is usually **heterocercal,** meaning that the upper lobe is longer than the lower lobe (Fig. 8.4a). The upper surface of the body typically features two **dorsal fins,** the first of which is typically larger and nearly triangular. The paired **pectoral fins** are large and pointed in most species. Five to seven gill slits are located behind the head (Fig. 8.4) and are present on each side of the body.

The powerful jaws of sharks have rows of numerous sharp, often triangular teeth (Fig. 8.3). The teeth are embedded in a tough, fibrous membrane that covers the jaws. A lost or broken tooth is replaced by another, which slowly shifts forward from the row behind it as if on a conveyor belt.

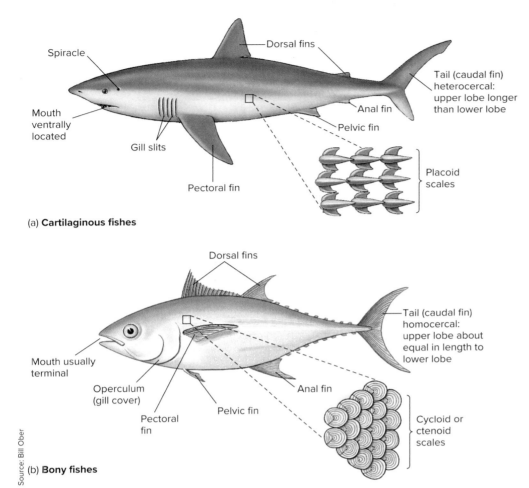

(a) **Cartilaginous fishes**

(b) **Bony fishes**

Source: Bill Ober

FIGURE 8.4 The most important external differences between (*a*) cartilaginous and (*b*) bony fishes. Also see Figure 8.12.

which is considered the most dangerous to humans, can exceed 6 m (20 ft) in length. An even larger predatory shark is the now extinct megalodon, *Otodus megalodon*, which prowled the seas as recently as 8 million years ago. The cartilaginous skeletons of sharks do not leave fossil records, but teeth do. Fossilized teeth of magalodons have been used to estimate a maximum total length of 18 m (59 ft)!

Sharks are found throughout the oceans at practically all depths, but they are more prevalent in tropical coastal waters. Sharks are primarily marine, but a few species travel far up rivers. The bull shark (*Carcharhinus leucas;* Fig. 8.5*d*) can be permanently established in some rivers and lakes in the tropics. Several sharks are found mostly in deep water (Fig. 8.6*b*).

Shark meat is eaten around the world, often illegally sold as "regular" fish or scallops. Sharks are also fished for their oil and skin, which is processed into a leather called shagreen. Shark cartilage is sold on the deceptive belief that it is a "joint nutrient" for treating arthritis. They are also discarded as by-catch in longline fishing and in sport fishing. But the most valuable shark fishery is the booming international trade in shark fins, which are used for soup, a symbol of wealth and respect among the Chinese and other Asian cultures. Sharks are caught, their fins cut off (a practice known as shark finning), and the wounded, less valuable, animals sometimes dumped in the sea to die. Global fin sales alone are estimated to account for more than the official shark catches.

So many sharks are being caught that the number of these slow-growing and slow-reproducing fishes has sharply declined around the world. Most of the open-water species of sharks are now at a risk of extinction, and coastal species are declining as well. Even deep-water sharks have not escaped. Overfishing has led to a global call for the conservation of sharks and a more stringent management of their fisheries (see Box 8.1, "Shark!").

Rays and Skates The approximately 600 species of **rays and skates** have dorsoventrally flattened bodies and for the most part

Not all of the more than 500 living species of sharks conform to this body plan. Hammerhead sharks (*Sphyrna*), for example, have flattened heads with eyes and nostrils at the tip of bizarre lateral extensions (Fig. 8.5*a* and photo in Box 8.1, "Shark!"). The head serves as a sort of rudder and separates the eyes and nostrils, which gives the shark binocular vision and sensory perception in practically all directions. The head of sawsharks (*Pristiophorus*) extends in a long, dorsoventrally flattened blade armed with teeth along the edges. The upper lobe of the tail is very long in the thresher sharks (*Alopias;* Fig. 8.5*k*). They use the tail to herd and stun schooling fishes, which they then eat.

The size of fully grown adults also varies. The spined pygmy shark (*Squaliolus laticaudus;* Fig. 8.5*l*) grows to no longer than 25 cm (almost 10 in). At the other extreme, the whale shark (*Rhincodon typus;* Figs. 8.5*i* and 10.6) is the largest of all fishes. This huge animal, found in tropical waters around the world, can be as long as 18 m (60 ft), though specimens longer than 12 m (40 ft) are rare. Whale sharks pose no danger to swimmers because they are **filter feeders** that feed on plankton. They appear to be long lived, and a dead specimen was estimated to be at least 50 years old. Another giant, second in size only to the whale shark, is the basking shark (*Cetorhinus maximus;* Fig. 8.5*h*), also a filter feeder. There are reports of basking sharks 15 m (50 ft) long, but most do not exceed 10 m (33 ft). The great white shark (*Carcharodon carcharias;* Figs. 8.5*g* and 8.6*a*),

Four basic characteristics of chordates:
1. A single, dorsal, hollow nerve cord
2. Gill, or pharyngeal, slits
3. A notochord
4. A post-anal tail
• 7.10, Chordates Without a Backbone

The term "fish" is used for a single individual or for more than one individual of the same species.

The term "fishes" is used to refer to more than one species of fish.

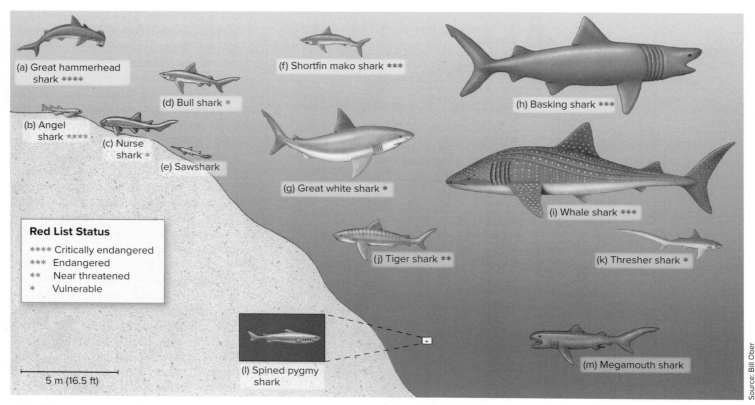

FIGURE 8.5 Sharks live practically everywhere in the ocean. Their numbers, however, have declined dramatically. The status of some species follows IUCN (International Union for Conservation of Nature and Natural Resources) Red List classification. Unclassified species are still common or there is not enough data. Some sharks mentioned in the text include (*a*) great hammerhead shark (*Sphyrna mokarran*), (*b*) angel shark (*Squatina squatina*), (c) Atlantic nurse shark (*Ginglymostoma cirratum*), (*d*) bull shark (*Carcharhinus leucas*), (*e*) sawshark (*Pristiophorus cirratus*), (*f*) shortfin mako shark (*Isurus oxyrinchus*), (*g*) great white shark (*Carcharodon carcharias*), (*h*) basking shark (*Cetorhinus maximus*), (*i*) whale shark (*Rhincodon typus*), (*j*) tiger shark (*Galeocerdo cuvier*), (*k*) thresher shark (*Alopias vulpinus*), (*l*) spined pygmy shark (*Squaliolus laticaudus*) (not drawn to same scale), and (*m*) megamouth shark (*Megachasma pelagios*).

(a) Great white shark

(b) Goblin shark

FIGURE 8.6 (*a*) The great white shark (*Carcharodon carcharias*) is found along most coasts and in open water around the world. (*b*) The bizarre goblin shark (*Mitsukurina owstoni*) is typically found in water deeper than 100 m (330 ft) in many coastal regions worldwide. Another deep-water shark, the Greenland shark (*Somniosus microcephalus*), has been estimated to live at least 400 years, the oldest living vertebrate.

live on the bottom (Fig. 8.7). Fishes that live on the bottom are called **demersal**. Some sharks, like angel sharks (*Squatina*) and sawsharks (*Pristiophorus*), also have flattened bodies (Fig. 8.5*b* and *e*). To complicate things, some true rays, like the guitarfishes (*Rhinobatos*), have a body that looks very much like a shark's. Only rays, skates, and related fishes, however, have their gill slits (always five pairs) on the underside of the body—that is, located ventrally (Fig. 8.7*b*)—rather than on the sides. The pectoral fins

are flat and greatly expanded, looking almost like wings. They are typically fused with the head. The eyes are usually on top of the head.

The tropical sawfishes (*Pristis*) look very much like sawsharks but have ventral gill slits and are therefore grouped with the rays and skates. They feed by swimming through schools of fish and swinging their blades back and forth to disable their prey. They are known to grow up to 11 m (36 ft) long.

Charlie Arneson

(a) Yellow stingray (*Urolophus jamaicensis*)

Source: Bill Ober

Spiracle

Gill slits

Dorsal view

Ventral view

(b) Manta ray (*Manta birostris*)

FIGURE 8.7 Rays and skates have a flattened body and ventral gill slits. Examples are (*a*) the yellow stingray (*Urolophus jamaicensis*) and (*b*) the manta ray (*Manta birostris*).

Many species of **stingrays** (Fig. 8.7*a*) and their relatives—the eagle, bat, and cow-nosed rays—have a whip-like tail usually equipped with stinging spines at the base for defense. Poison glands produce venom that can cause serious wounds to anyone who steps or falls on them. Abdominal wounds from stingrays, which often occur when handling rays caught in nets, can result in death. Many stingrays cover themselves with sand, becoming nearly invisible. They feed on clams, crabs, small fishes, and other small animals that live in sediment. Stingrays have been known to damage valuable shellfish beds. They expose their food by excavating sediment with their pectoral fins. Their teeth are modified into grinding plates that crush their prey.

Electric rays (*Torpedo*) have special organs that produce electricity on each side of the head. They can deliver shocks of up to 200 V that stun the fishes they eat as well as discouraging predators. The ancient Greeks and Romans used the shocks of electric rays to cure headaches and other ailments, the original shock treatment.

Not all rays spend their lives on the bottom. Eagle rays (*Aetobatus*) and the spectacular manta and devil rays (*Manta, Mobula*) "fly" through the water, using their pectoral fins like wings. Eagle rays return to the bottom to feed, whereas mantas feed in midwater on plankton. Both leap out of the water. The manta ray (*Manta birostris;* Fig. 8.7*b*) grows into a majestic giant. One individual was found to be almost 7 m (23 ft) wide.

Skates (*Raja*) are similar to rays in appearance and feeding habits, but they lack a whip-like tail and stinging spines. Some have electric organs. Skates lay egg cases (similar to that shown in Fig. 8.29), whereas rays give birth to live young. Skates can be abundant, and the larger species are fished for food in some parts of the world.

Ratfishes (class **Holocephali**) About 30 species of strange-looking, mostly deep-water, cartilaginous fishes are grouped separately because of their unique features. The **ratfishes,** or **chimaeras** (Fig. 8.8), for instance, have only one pair of gill slits covered by a flap of skin. Some have a long, rat-like tail. They feed on bottom-dwelling crustaceans and molluscs.

Source: Bill Ober

FIGURE 8.8 The elephant fish (*Callorhinchus*), an example of a ratfish, or chimaera. The elephant fish, which is caught commercially for food in the Southern Hemisphere, receives its name because of a snout that hangs down like an elephant's trunk.

Bony Fishes

The great majority of fishes are **bony fishes,** traditionally classified under "Osteichthyes." Practically all bony fishes are included in the Class **Actinopterygii** (see scheme of classification in Fig. 8.1). As the name implies, they have a skeleton made at least partially of bone. There are more than 31,000 species of bony fishes—about half of all vertebrates. Roughly 200 new species are described every year. A little more than half of all bony fishes live all or part of their lives in the ocean, where they are by far the dominant vertebrates. Bony fishes provide most of the food humans get from the oceans, a resource that is increasingly being overexploited (see "Food from the Sea," in 17.1).

The composition of the skeleton is not the only distinguishing feature of bony fishes. In contrast to the tiny, pointed placoid scales of cartilaginous fishes, bony fishes usually have **cycloid** or **ctenoid scales,** which are thin, flexible, and overlapping (see Fig. 8.4*b*). Cycloid scales are smooth, whereas ctenoid scales have many tiny spines along their exposed borders. The scales are made of bone and are covered by a thin layer of skin (see Fig. 8.19) as well as protective mucous. Some bony fishes, however, lack scales altogether. Another characteristic of bony fishes is the presence of an **operculum,** or **gill cover,** a flap of bony plates and tissue that protects the gills.

Box 8.1 Shark!

Most sharks are harmless—at least to humans. Nevertheless, 25 species of sharks are known to have attacked humans, and at least 12 more are suspected of doing so. Three are particularly dangerous: the great white, tiger, and bull sharks (see Fig. 8.5). The number of unprovoked attacks around the world was 73 (9 fatal) in 2021, 57 (10 fatal) in 2020, 64 (five fatal) in 2019, and 66 (four fatal) in 2018. The annual average for 2016–2020 was 80 attacks. Attacks are becoming less common, but fatalities have been increasing. Even when more tourists are visiting less spoiled areas, shark attacks are rare. The chances of being attacked by a shark are lower than those of being hit by lightning.

The great white shark (Fig. 8.6a) typically launches at its prey (such as fat-rich seals and sea lions) from below, inflicts massive wounds, and releases it to let it bleed before returning to feed. The sharks wait until the bleeding prey is too weak to resist, then move in for the kill. Great white attacks on humans wearing wet suits could be cases of mistaken identity. Sometimes people are able to escape when sharks release them after the first bite. Before attacking, sharks can display distinctive aggressive behaviors—pointing downward of the pectoral fins, pointing upward of the nose with back hunched, or the shivering of the body. Displaying sharks can attack if someone approaches.

How can you decrease the risk of an attack? First, do not swim, dive, or surf in an area known to be frequented by dangerous sharks. Seal and sea lion colonies and coastal garbage dumps attract them. Blood,

Although fierce-looking, the great hammerhead shark (*Sphyrna mokarran*) is considered as only potentially dangerous to humans. It is a critically endangered species.

Ken Kiefer 2/Cultura/Image Source

urine, and feces also attract sharks. Avoid murky water. Many sharks are more active at night, so avoid night swims. Sharks should not be provoked in any way. Even resting nurse sharks can turn and bite. Leave the water if fish suddenly appear in large numbers and behave erratically, which can be an indication that sharks are around. If you see a large shark, get out of the water with as little splashing as possible. If attacked, hit the shark's nose or gills with any object on hand, a spear or camera, but not with your bare hands! Do not panic. So far there is no absolutely guaranteed shark repellent that works on all species. For someone like a downed flyer or shipwrecked sailor, perhaps the best protection is a black plastic bag large enough to float inside.

We threaten sharks more than they threaten us. Sharks are been drastically reduced by overfishing. The drop in the number of sharks in the wild has been staggering. Around 100 million sharks are taken annually by commercial fisheries, mostly for their fins.

A negative attitude toward sharks is shortsighted because they play a most important role in marine communities. Overfishing of sharks in coral reefs, for example, has triggered an increase in the number of groupers and other small predators, which prey on parrotfishes and other algal feeders. Algae then thrive, growing over and killing reef-building corals.

Conservation efforts are slowly but surely being implemented. A shark sanctuary of nearly 2 million km² (750,000 mi²) was established in the Marshall Islands, central Pacific, and 126 countries agreed in 2017 to protect migratory sharks. There is also evidence of a decrease in the demand for shark fins in China, the leading consumer. Some fear that many sharks, the magnificent predators, could be exterminated by humans, the fiercest predators of all, if no additional measures are taken.

Drying shark fins, Hong Kong.

Anthony Dickson/AFP/Getty Images

The upper and lower lobes of the tail, the caudal fin, are generally the same size, or **homocercal** (see Fig. 8.4b). The fins of bony fishes generally consist of thin membranes that are supported by bony spines, or **fin rays,** in contrast to the stiff, fleshy fins of cartilaginous fishes. Fin rays can consist of rigid spines that act as rudders or are used for protection, sometimes associated with venom glands (see Fig. 8.10a, c). Some are flexible and used for propulsion and added maneuverability.

Whereas cartilaginous fishes have a ventral mouth, the mouth of most bony fishes is terminal—that is, located at the anterior end. Bony fishes have jaws with much more freedom of movement than

those of sharks. The jaws of bony fishes are said to be protrusible because they can be projected outward from the mouth. The teeth are generally attached to the jawbones. Though they are usually replaced, the new teeth do not move forward in rows as do those in sharks.

Another important characteristic is the presence in many bony fishes of a **swim bladder,** a gas-filled sac just above the stomach and intestine (see Fig. 8.12b). It allows the fish to adjust its buoyancy to keep from sinking or rising (see "Increased Buoyancy," in 15.2). This is a significant development that compensates for the relatively heavy bony skeleton.

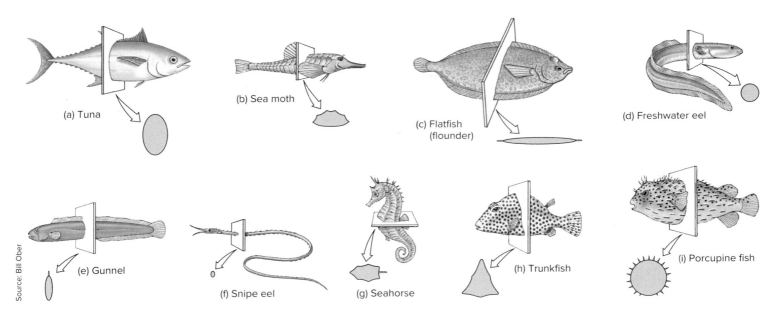

Source: Bill Ober

FIGURE 8.9 Body shape among bony fishes varies as an adaptation to habitat. It is streamlined for fast swimming in (*a*) tunas (*Thunnus*); dorsoventrally flattened in bottom-dwellers such as (*b*) the sea moth (*Pegasus*); or laterally flattened in bottom-dwellers such as (*c*) the flounder (*Platichthys*). Fishes living among vegetation or rocks have eel-like bodies, as in (*d*) the freshwater eel (*Anguilla*); ribbon-shaped, as in (*e*) the gunnel (*Pholis*); or thread-like, as in (*f*) the snipe eel (*Nemichthys*). Slow swimmers feature bodies that are elongated on a vertical plane, as in (*g*) the seahorse (*Hippocampus*); triangular, as in (*h*) the trunkfish (*Ostracion*); or round, as in (*i*) the porcupine fish (*Diodon*).

Bony fishes are the largest group of living vertebrates. In addition to their bony skeleton, they typically have gills covered by opercula, highly maneuverable fins, protrusible jaws, and usually a swim bladder.

As we shall see in "Biology of Fishes" (below), bony fishes are extraordinarily diverse in shape, size, color, feeding habits, reproductive patterns, and behavior. They have adapted to nearly every type of marine environment. All land four-legged vertebrates, or **tetrapods,** evolved from early bony fishes.

8.3 BIOLOGY OF FISHES

Discovering how fishes, cartilaginous and bony alike, have adapted to their environment so successfully is one of the objectives of **ichthyology,** the scientific study of fishes.

Body Shape

The body shape of a fish is directly related to its lifestyle. Fast swimmers like sharks, tunas (*Thunnus, Euthynnus*), mackerels (*Scomber, Scomberomorus*), and marlins (*Makaira*) have a streamlined body shape that helps them move through the water (Figs. 8.4 and 8.9*a;* also see Box 15.2, "Swimming Machines"). Laterally compressed bodies are good for leisurely swimming around coral reefs, kelp beds, or rocky reefs but are still efficient enough to allow for bursts of speed to escape from enemies or capture food. This body form is seen in many inshore fishes like snappers (*Lutjanus*), wrasses (*Labroides, Thalassoma*), damselfishes (*Amphiprion, Chromis;* see Fig. 8.20), and butterflyfishes (*Chaetodon;* see Fig. 8.27). Many demersal fishes, like rays, skates, and sea moths (*Pegasus;*

Fig. 8.9*b*), are dorsoventrally flattened. Flatfishes such as flounders (*Platichthys*), soles (*Solea*), and halibuts (*Hippoglossus*) are flat and adapted to live on the bottom, but their bodies are actually laterally compressed (Fig. 8.9*c*). They lie on one side, with both eyes on top. They begin life with one eye on each side like other fishes, but one eye migrates up to lie next to the other one. Moray eels (*Gymnothorax*), trumpetfishes (*Aulostomus*), and pipefishes (*Syngnathus*), among others have elongated bodies. Eel-like fishes often live in narrow spaces in rocks or coral reefs, or among vegetation (Fig. 8.9*d–f*). Many bony fishes, like seahorses (*Hippocampus;* Fig. 8.9*g*) depart from these generalized shapes. Trunkfishes (*Ostracion*) have truncate, or relatively short, bodies (Fig. 8.9*h*).

Body shapes can be especially useful for camouflage. For example, some pipefishes live among the eelgrass they resemble. The long, thin trumpetfishes often hang vertically among gorgonian corals or tube-like sponges, or even sneak behind other fish when approaching prey. An irregular shape is often an excellent means of concealment. Bottom fishes such as blennies (*Blennius*) and sculpins (*Oligocottus*) have their outline broken up with irregular growths, particularly on the head, that resemble seaweeds. The body of the stonefish (*Synanceia verrucosa;* Fig. 8.10*a*) resembles a rock so closely that it is almost invisible to both potential prey and humans. Unfortunately for humans, this shallow-water fish from the tropical Indian and Pacific oceans possesses the most potent venom known in fishes. Stepping on a stonefish is excruciatingly painful and potentially fatal.

Coloration

Some bony fishes use color for camouflage, but others, particularly those living in the tropics, are among the most brightly colored animals in the sea. The colored pigments in bony fishes are mostly found in special cells in the skin called **chromatophores.** These cells

(a)

(b)

(c)

Gerard Soury/Getty Images

Charlie Arneson

Charlie Arneson

FIGURE 8.10 The variety of forms and habits among marine bony fishes is spectacular. (*a*) The stonefish (*Synanceia verrucosa*) does look like a stone, thus concealing its deadly venom. (*b*) The queen parrotfish (*Scarus vetula*) and other parrotfishes, so called because of their beak-like mouths, sleep at night by secreting a loose mucus envelope that surrounds the body, apparently as a protection against blood-sucking parasites. (*c*) A colorful bar-tailed lionfish (*Pterois radiata*) advertises spines that contain a powerful venom that sometimes kills humans. A species of lionfish was accidentally introduced in the tropical Atlantic with potentially serious consequences (see Box 18.2, "Biological Invasions: The Uninvited Guests").

iridophores. The iridescent, shiny quality of many fishes is produced by structural colors in combination with pigments (Fig. 8.10*b*).

Colors can tell us a lot about fishes. Some change color with their mood or reproductive condition. They can also use color to advertise the fact that they are dangerous, are poisonous, or taste bad—a phenomenon known as **warning coloration** (Fig. 8.10*c*). **Cryptic coloration,** blending with the environment to deceive predators or prey, is a common adaptation (Fig. 8.10*a*). Flatfishes and some blennies, sculpins, rockfishes (*Sebastes*), and others can change color to match their surroundings. Another use of color is **disruptive coloration,** the presence of color stripes, bars, or spots that help break up the outline of a fish. These and other uses of color are especially common among coral reef fishes (see Figs. 8.27 and 14.30 and the photo at the beginning of this chapter).

Open-water fishes and many shallow-water predators, on the other hand, are rarely as colorful. Most of them have silver or white bellies in sharp contrast to dark backs (see Fig. 8.4). This distinctive color pattern, known as **countershading,** is a form of disguise in open water (see "Coloration and Camouflage," in 15.2). Deep-water fishes also use color for concealment. They tend to be black or red, both of which are hard to see in the ocean depths (see "Coloration and Body Shape," in 16.1).

Locomotion

Swimming is obviously a major part of the life of fishes. Fishes swim to obtain food, escape from predators, and find mates. Many cartilaginous and some bony fishes must also swim to flush their gills with water to obtain oxygen.

Most fishes are **body and caudal-fin swimmers** that move with side-to-side motions of the body and tail (Fig. 8.11*a, b*).

are irregular in shape and have branches radiating from the center. The amazing variety of colors and hues observed among marine fishes results from combinations of chromatophores with varying amounts of different pigments. Many fishes can rapidly change color by contracting and expanding the pigment within the chromatophores. Fishes can also have **structural colors** that result when a special surface reflects only certain colors of light. Most structural colors in fishes are the consequence of crystals that act as tiny mirrors. The crystals are contained in special chromatophores called

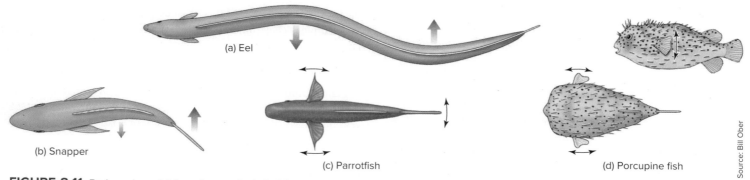

(a) Eel

(b) Snapper

(c) Parrotfish

(d) Porcupine fish

Source: Bill Ober

FIGURE 8.11 Body and caudal-fin swimmers include (*a*) eels, (*b*) snappers, and other groups of streamlined fishes (see Fig. 8.9*a,d*) that move primarily by undulating their bodies in lateral waves. The waves travel from head to tail in eels, but in tunas (and many open-sea sharks) the waves begin at the base of the tail. Other body and caudal-fin swimmers start the waves at different intermediate positions along their bodies. Median and paired-fin swimmers are very diverse. Wrasses, (*c*) parrotfishes, and butterflyfishes "fly" through the water using primarily their pectoral fins. Others, like the heavy and rigid-bodied trunkfishes and (*d*) porcupine fishes (see Fig. 8.9*h,i*), swim using their pectoral fins in various combinations with their dorsal and anal fins while the rest of their bodies remain straight. These median and paired-fin swimmers use their tails primarily for steering and rapid escapes from predators.

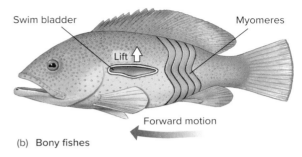

FIGURE 8.12 Cartilaginous and bony fishes use different adaptations to maintain their position in the water. (*a*) Sharks use their fins and an enlarged, oil-rich liver for lift. (*b*) Many bony fishes have evolved a gas-filled swim bladder to compensate for their heavier bony skeleton. This frees their fins for maneuverability, resulting in a much greater diversity of swimming styles (see Fig. 8.11).

These fishes typically have streamlined bodies that vary in shape. A second major group consists of **median and paired-fin swimmers,** which move mostly by fin movements, without involving their usually straight and stiff bodies. Their tails are primarily used for steering (Fig. 8.11*c,d*).

The rhythmic contractions are produced by bands of muscle called **myomeres,** which run along the sides of the body (Fig. 8.12). The distinctive bands of muscle are easily seen in fish fillets. Myomeres are attached to the backbone for support. Muscles make up a large percentage of the body weight of a fish—as much as 75% in tunas and other active swimmers.

Sharks tend to sink because they lack the buoyant swim bladder of most bony fishes. To compensate, they have large, stiff pectoral fins that provide lift somewhat like the wings of a plane (Fig. 8.12*a*). The longer upper lobe of the tail tends to tilt the body upward, also generating some lift. The large amount of oil in the huge liver also provides buoyancy because it is less dense than water. In rays and skates the tail is greatly reduced and the pectoral fins are the main source of both thrust and lift, as in bird wings.

Because most bony fishes have a swim bladder, they do not have to rely on their pectoral fins to provide lift. The pectorals are thus free to serve other purposes. This gives bony fishes great maneuverability. Some can hover in the water or even swim backward, things that sharks cannot do. The other fins of bony fishes also help provide maneuverability. The dorsal and **anal fins** (see Fig. 8.4*b*) are used as rudders, at least part of the time, to steer and provide stability. The paired **pelvic fins** (see Fig. 8.4*b*) also help the fish turn, balance, and "brake."

The flexibility of their fins has allowed many bony fishes to depart from the standard undulating style of swimming. Some open-water fishes, such as tunas, emphasize speed (see Box 15.2, "Swimming Machines"). Because muscles work best at warm temperatures, some of these high-speed swimmers have evolved the remarkable ability to keep their internal temperature higher than that of the water (see "Swimming: The Need for Speed," in 15.2). These fishes are therefore considered "warm-blooded" in contrast to the great majority of fishes, which are "cold-blooded" (see Table 4.2). A similar mechanism has also evolved in sharks such as the great white shark. Many fishes, particularly those living around coral reefs, rocks, or kelp beds, swim mainly by moving their fins rather than their bodies, especially for the precise movements needed in feeding. Their tails are used almost solely as rudders. Wrasses, surgeonfishes (*Acanthurus*), and parrotfishes (*Scarus, Sparisoma*), which all live on coral reefs, and the California sheephead (*Semicossyphus pulcher*), common in kelp beds, swim mainly with their pectoral fins. Triggerfishes (*Balistes*) undulate their dorsal and anal fins to swim. This style is perfect for hovering over the bottom while hunting for crabs and sea urchins. Flying fishes (*Cypselurus*) have greatly expanded pectoral fins, which they use to glide through the air (see Fig. 15.21). A large variety of bottom fishes (gobies, sculpins, and many others) crawl or rest on the bottom on their pectoral and/or pelvic fins (see Fig. 8.9*b*). Clingfishes (*Gobiesox*) are small fishes that have their pelvic fins modified into part of a sucker that allows them to attach to rocks. Remoras, or sharksuckers (*Echeneis*), attach to sharks, whales, turtles, and many types of large fishes, using a large sucker on top of their heads. This sucker is derived from part of the dorsal fin.

Fishes usually swim with sideways undulations of the body and tail. The pectoral fins and tail of sharks have an important role in buoyancy control. The fins and tail of bony fishes are generally not used to control buoyancy and instead have become highly maneuverable and important in swimming.

Feeding

Most sharks are carnivores, but in contrast to typical carnivores, which capture smaller prey, some sharks feed by taking bites from prey larger than themselves. For this they use their formidable jaws coupled with shaking of the head. A few sharks are not particular; almost anything can be found in a shark's stomach. A tiger shark (see Fig. 8.5*j*) that was caught off South Africa was found to contain the front half of a crocodile, the hind leg of a sheep, three gulls, and two cans of peas. Nurse sharks feed mostly on bottom invertebrates, including lobsters and sea urchins. Some deep-water sharks subsist mainly on squids. Cookie-cutter sharks (*Isistius*) are small, slow-moving, deep-water sharks that attack larger fishes and dolphins and cut out chunks of flesh with their razor-sharp teeth and sucking lips. They also eat whole squids. Scientists have suggested that they use bioluminescence to lure their prey (see "Bioluminescence," in 16.1). Even the rubber sonar domes of nuclear submarines have not escaped their bites.

Several species of cartilaginous fishes are filter feeders: the whale shark, the basking shark, the manta and devil rays, and the megamouth shark (*Megachasma pelagios;* see Fig. 8.5*m*), a gigantic deep-water shark discovered off Hawai'i in 1976 and soon after in Southern California and several other locations around the world. Like other filter-feeding fishes, basking sharks filter the water with their **gill rakers,** slender projections on the inner surface of the **gill arches** (see Fig. 8.17*b*). Whale sharks have filter plates made of modified placoid scales. The large mouths (see Fig. 10.6) of the three filter-feeding sharks have many small teeth and, excluding the megamouth, very long gill slits. The width of the spaces between the gill rakers or filter plates determines the size of the food captured. Water is strained through the gill rakers, and the shark swallows the food that is left behind. Whale sharks feed in warm water on small schooling fishes, squids, and planktonic crustaceans. Basking sharks, which live in colder water, feed on plankton by opening their mouths and slowly swimming through the water (see Fig. 8.5*h*).

Mantas feed on plankton and small fishes, filtering them from the water with their gill rakers. Two fleshy, horn-shaped projections on the sides of the manta's mouth help channel food into the cavernous mouth (see Fig. 8.7*b*).

Bony fishes are very diverse in the ways they feed. Their protrusible jaws allow them much more flexibility in feeding habits than sharks and rays have. Most bony fishes are carnivores; most groups of animals in the ocean are subject to being eaten by some bony fish. Bony fishes capture their prey from sediments, the water column, the surface of rocks, or other organisms, including other fishes, or combinations of these. Some chase their prey; others sit and wait.

Carnivorous bony fishes typically have well-developed teeth for catching, grasping, and holding their prey (Fig. 8.13*a*), which is usually swallowed whole. The roof of the mouth, gill rakers, and pharynx can also have teeth to help hold the prey. Deep-water fishes often have huge mouths and teeth (see Fig. 16.10), and a few capture and swallow prey larger than themselves.

Unusual food preferences have evolved in fishes. Some prefer sponges, infrequently touched by other carnivores. Others prefer sea urchins, sea squirts, or other seemingly tough-to-eat food items. Reef corals, skeleton, and all are eaten by several types of fishes including some butterflyfishes and parrotfishes, though only the living tissue is digested (Figs. 8.13*b* and 8.27). Many species, however, are non-specialists and capture a wide variety of prey. Some feed on small invertebrates and dead animal material from the bottom. These bottom feeders have a downward-oriented mouth adapted to suck food from the bottom. Frogfishes (*Antennarius*) and anglerfishes (*Gigantactis;* see Fig. 16.21) use a modified spine on the head to lure small fishes.

Fishes that feed primarily on seaweeds and plants are known as **grazers.** Parrotfishes, for example, graze on small algae growing on hard surfaces. Their front teeth are fused to form a beak-like structure (Fig. 8.13*d*). Some species use the beak to scrape off bits of live coral.

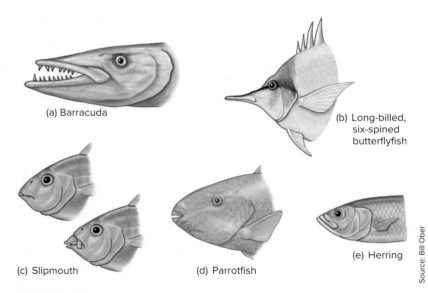

(a) Barracuda

(b) Long-billed, six-spined butterflyfish

(c) Slipmouth

(d) Parrotfish

(e) Herring

Source: Bill Ober

FIGURE 8.13 The shape of the mouth of bony fishes tells much about their diets. (*a*) The barracuda (*Sphyraena*) uses its large mouth to tear off chunks of prey. Most bony fishes, however, swallow their prey whole. (*b*) Many butterflyfishes (*Chaetodon*) use a long snout and small mouth to feed on very small prey. (*c*) The extremely protrusible mouth of the slipmouth (*Leiognathus*) is used for feeding on relatively small prey. (*d*) Parrotfishes (*Scarus*) use their beak-like mouths to graze on small algae and coral (see Fig. 8.10*b*). (*e*) Herrings (*Clupea*) and other filter feeders typically have large mouths.

Fishes such as herrings (*Clupea*), sardines (*Sardinops*), anchovies (*Engraulis*), and menhadens (*Brevoortia*) filter plankton with their gill rakers. They typically strain their food by swimming with their large mouths (Fig. 8.13*e*) open. These plankton feeders are small, in contrast to the huge plankton-feeding sharks. They usually occur in large, often immense, schools. Plankton feeders are the most abundant fishes in the ocean, and they are an important food source for many types of carnivores. They also account for a large share of the world's fish catch (see "Major Food Species," in 17.1).

Digestion

After being swallowed, food passes through the pharynx and a short tube called the **esophagus** into the **stomach** (Fig. 8.14). The stomach is where the process of digestion usually begins. It is typically J-curved or elongated, but can be modified into a grinding structure. The food passes from the stomach into the **intestine.** In most bony fishes the anterior portion of the intestine has many slender, blind tubes, the **pyloric caeca,** which secrete digestive enzymes. Other digestive enzymes are secreted by the inner walls of the intestine and the **pancreas.** Another organ important in digestion is the **liver,** which secretes **bile** needed for the breakdown of fats. The liver is particularly large and oil-rich in sharks, sometimes making up as much as 20% of their body weight, an adaptation to increase buoyancy (see above).

A few fishes lack a stomach and tend to have a portion of the intestine expanded for the digestion of food. Carnivorous fishes have short, straight intestines. Fishes that eat seaweeds, which are more difficult to digest, have coiled intestines, which can be much longer than the fish itself. The intestines of cartilaginous fishes and a few primitive bony fishes contain a spiraling portion called

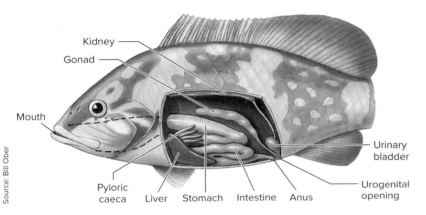

(a) **Cartilaginous fishes**

(b) **Bony fishes**

Source: Bill Ober

FIGURE 8.14 The digestive systems of (*a*) cartilaginous and (*b*) bony fishes display many of the basic features found in all vertebrates.

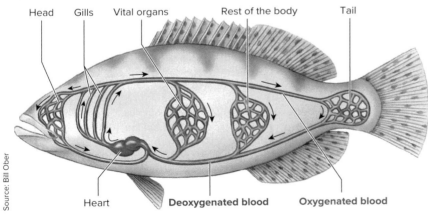

Source: Bill Ober

FIGURE 8.15 The circulatory system of fishes consists of veins that carry deoxygenated blood (in blue) from the body, a two-chambered heart that pumps blood to the gills for oxygenation, and arteries that carry oxygenated blood (in red) to the rest of the body.

digestive, excretory, and reproductive systems in cartilaginous fishes (Fig. 8.14*a*).

Circulatory System

All fishes have a two-chambered **heart** located below the gills (Fig. 8.15). Deoxygenated blood enters the first chamber of the heart from the body. The blood is then pumped to the second chamber, which then pumps it to the gills, where **gas exchange** takes place. The oxygenated blood is then carried back to the body by blood vessels called **arteries.** The arteries branch out into thin-walled **capillaries,** which allow oxygen and nutrients to reach every cell. Other capillaries then collect into larger blood vessels, **veins,** which carry deoxygenated blood, along with dissolved carbon dioxide, back to the heart to complete the cycle.

Respiratory System

Fishes obtain oxygen dissolved in water and release carbon dioxide from their blood through paired gills. The gills lie in the pharynx, a chamber just behind the mouth that represents the front part of the gut.

Irrigation of the Gills Fishes get the oxygen they need by extracting it from the water. To do this, they must make sure that water flows over the gills—that is, they must irrigate, or ventilate, the gills.

Most sharks swim continuously. Swimming, plus the opening and closing of the mouth, forces water through the mouth, over the gills, and out through the gill slits (Fig. 8.16*a*). When caught in fishing nets, sharks cannot swim to force the water in and therefore "drown." Not all sharks need to swim, however. Nurse sharks (*Ginglymostoma*) and several other sharks rest on the bottom during the day (see Fig. 8.5*c*). They force water over the gills by opening and closing the mouth.

Expansion and contraction of the walls of the pharynx and the gill slits assist in the irrigation of gills in sharks. Every gill lies in its own chamber, and each gill chamber opens to the outside by a separate gill slit. The first pair of gill slits of cartilaginous fishes is modified into **spiracles,** a pair of round openings just behind each eye. The spiracles are located on the dorsal surface of rays and skates (see Fig. 8.7*b*). They allow these fishes, many of which live on the bottom, to take in water even when the ventral mouth is buried in the sediment. When lampreys and other jawless fishes feed by sucking on other fishes, the passage of water through their mouth is blocked and they pump water in as well as out through the gill slits.

Most bony fishes have a more efficient mechanism to bring in water to the gills. The gills on each side share a gill chamber, which

the **spiral valve,** which increases the internal surface area of the intestine (Fig. 8.14*a*). The intestine is responsible for absorbing the nutrients resulting from digestion. These nutrients pass into the blood to be distributed through the body. Undigested material exits through the anus, or the **cloaca,** the common passage for the

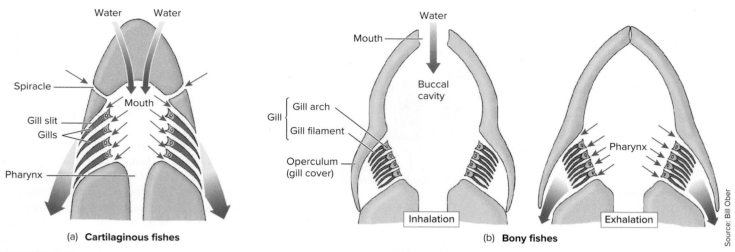

FIGURE 8.16 The mechanism behind the irrigation of the gills. (*a*) Cartilaginous fishes like sharks allow water in (path of water indicated by arrows) by opening the mouth, which is then closed. The rising of the floor of the mouth causes water to be pumped through the gills and out by way of the separate gill slits. The spiracles also allow water to move in; in rays and skates these play a crucial role. (*b*) Bony fishes are more efficient because of the presence of opercula, which close as the pharynx expands, sucking the water in. The closing of the mouth and the opening of the opercula force water through the gills and out.

opens to the outside through an opening on each side of the head. Each opening is covered by an operculum (Fig. 8.16*b*). When the mouth opens, the opercula close and the pharynx expands, sucking water in. The fish does the reverse to pump water out: the mouth closes, the pharynx contracts, and the opercula open. Some fast swimmers simplify things by just opening their mouths to force water into the gills.

Structure of the Gills Fish gills are supported by cartilaginous or bony structures, the gill arches (Fig. 8.17*b*). Each gill arch bears two rows of slender, fleshy projections called **gill filaments.** Gill rakers project along the inner surface of the gill arch. They prevent food particles from entering and injuring the gill filaments or can be specialized for filtering the water in filter-feeding fishes.

The gill filaments have a rich supply of capillaries (Fig. 8.17*c*), the oxygenated blood of which gives them a bright red color. Each gill filament contains many rows of thin plates or disks called **lamellae,** which contain capillaries. The lamellae greatly increase the surface area through which gas exchange can take place. The number of lamellae is greater in active swimmers, which need large supplies of oxygen.

Gas Exchange Oxygen dissolved in the water diffuses into the capillaries of the gill filaments to oxygenate the blood. **Diffusion** will take place only if oxygen is more concentrated in the water than in the blood. This is usually true because the blood coming to the gills has already traveled through the rest of the body and is depleted of oxygen (Fig. 8.15). As oxygen diffuses from the water to blood in the capillaries, the amount of oxygen in the water decreases and that in the blood increases. This can reduce the efficiency of gas exchange, which depends on the water having more oxygen than the blood. Fishes, however, have evolved a clever adaptation called a **countercurrent system of flow** to increase

efficiency. The blood in the gills flows in the *opposite* direction to the water passing over them (Fig. 8.17*d*). When the water has passed over the gill and given up much of its oxygen, it meets blood that has just come from the body and is "hungry" for what oxygen remains in the water (Fig. 8.17*e*). By the time the blood has flowed most of the way through the gill, picking up oxygen, it encounters water that is just entering the gill chamber and is rich in oxygen. Thus, the oxygen content of the water is always higher than that of the blood. This system makes the gills very efficient at extracting oxygen. Without this countercurrent system, blood returning to the body would have less oxygen.

The blood disposes of its carbon dioxide using the same mechanism. Blood flowing into the gills from the body has a high concentration of carbon dioxide, a product of respiration. It easily diffuses out into the water.

Gas exchange in the gills of fishes is highly efficient. The surface area of gills is greatly increased by lamellae, and the flow of water through them is in a direction opposite to that of blood.

Once oxygen enters the blood it is carried through the body by **hemoglobin,** a red protein that gives blood its characteristic color. Hemoglobin is contained in specialized cells called **erythrocytes,** or **red blood cells.** The hemoglobin releases oxygen to the tissues as it is needed. After it gives off its oxygen, the hemoglobin picks up carbon dioxide from the body and carries it to the gills, where it diffuses into the water.

Muscles use a lot of oxygen during exertion. They have a protein, called **myoglobin,** similar to hemoglobin, that can store oxygen. Hard-working muscles tend to have a lot of myoglobin, which makes them dark red. Strong swimmers, such as open-water sharks and tunas, have a high proportion of red muscle, as opposed to white muscle (see "Swimming: The Need for Speed,"

Cut edge of
operculum
(gill cover)

Gill raker

Gill arch

Gill filament

Lamellae

(a)

(b)

Capillaries

Lamella

(c)

Direction of
water movement

Oxygenated
blood to body

Capillary
blood flow

Deoxygenated
blood from body

(d)

Water

Oxygenated
blood to body

Oxygen

Diffusion

Diffusion

Capillary
in lamella

Flows out of
operculum

Deoxygenated
blood from body

(e)

Source: Bill Ober

FIGURE 8.17 The gills of fishes are very efficient structures for gas exchange. Bony fishes have four pairs of gills (*a*), each containing two rows of numerous gill filaments (*b*). Lamellae in the gill filaments (*c*) increase the surface area of the gill filaments. (*d*) Diffusion of oxygen from seawater into the blood gets a boost because the water flows across the lamellae in the opposite direction to that of the blood. (*e*) The concentration of oxygen (indicated by dots) is always higher in the water than in the blood. If circulation were not reversed, blood to the body would have less oxygen.

Cartilaginous fishes use a different approach to salt balance (Fig. 8.18*a*). They reduce osmosis by increasing the amount of dissolved molecules, or **solutes,** in their blood, making the blood concentration closer to that of seawater. They do this by retaining a chemical called **urea,** a waste product that results from the breakdown of proteins. The amount of urea in the blood is controlled by the kidneys. In most animals urea is toxic and is excreted, but sharks and other cartilaginous fishes excrete only small amounts. Urea and related compounds are less toxic to cartilaginous fishes. They retain most of the urea in their blood; their gills help in this process by blocking the loss of urea.

Cartilaginous fishes also absorb water to prevent dehydration, mostly through the gills and from food. Excess salts are excreted by the kidneys, intestine, and a special gland near the anus called the **rectal gland** (Fig. 8.18*a*).

Marine fishes keep a constant internal environment and control water loss through the osmoregulatory activities of the kidneys, gills, and other mechanisms.

Nervous System and Sensory Organs

Vertebrates have the most complex and advanced nervous systems of any animal group. At the heart of the system is the **central nervous system,** consisting of the brain and spinal cord. The central nervous system coordinates and integrates all body activities and stores information. The brain is divided into several regions known to serve as centers for particular functions such as olfaction and vision. The region that controls vision is

in 15.2). Many other fishes have concentrations of red muscles at the base of heavily used fins.

Regulation of the Internal Environment

In contrast to most marine organisms, the blood of marine bony fishes is less salty than seawater (see Fig. 4.14). As a result, they lose water by **osmosis.** Marine bony fishes therefore need to **osmoregulate** to prevent dehydration. To replace lost water, they swallow seawater (Fig. 8.18*b*). Seawater contains excess salts, some of which pass straight through the gut without being absorbed. Salts that are absorbed are excreted by the **kidneys,** the most important excretory organs of vertebrates, and specialized **chloride cells** in the gills. The kidneys conserve water by producing only small amounts of urine.

Gas Exchange The absorption of oxygen to be used in respiration (the breakdown of glucose to release energy) and the elimination of carbon dioxide that results from the same process.
• 7.4, Bilaterally Symmetrical Worms

Diffusion The movement of molecules from areas of high concentration to areas of low concentration.
• 4.3, Challenges of Life in the Sea

Osmosis The diffusion of water across a selectively permeable membrane, such as a cell membrane.

Osmoregulation The active control by an organism of its internal *solute* concentration to avoid osmotic problems.
• 4.3, Challenges of Life in the Sea

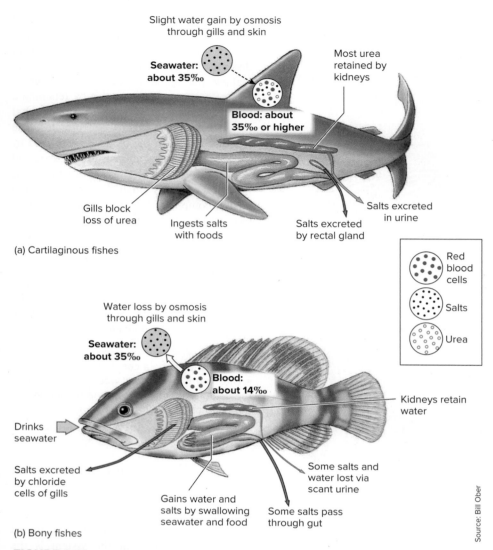

(a) Cartilaginous fishes

(b) Bony fishes

Red blood cells

Salts

Urea

Source: Bill Ober

FIGURE 8.18 Marine fishes live in water that is saltier than their body fluids. For this reason, water tends to diffuse out of the body. (*a*) To prevent dehydration, sharks and other cartilaginous fishes concentrate urea, absorb seawater through their gills and skin, and excrete excess salts by way of the urine and feces. A special gland, the rectal gland, also excretes excess salts. Their blood ends up with a solute concentration almost equal to or even higher than that of seawater. (*b*) Marine bony fishes do not concentrate urea, which is toxic to them. Instead, their kidneys conserve water, and they drink seawater, excreting excess salts, as do cartilaginous fishes, but using different organs. Compare with Figure 4.14. Salt concentrations in water and blood are expressed in psu, practical salinity units.

The sense of smell is particularly well developed in sharks. They can detect blood and other substances in concentrations as low as fractions of one part per million. Salmon (*Oncorhynchus*), which live as adults at sea but reproduce in fresh water, use olfaction to find the stream where they were born years earlier (see "Migrations," below). They accomplish part of this remarkable feat by memorizing the sequence of smells on their way out to sea.

Fishes detect other chemical stimuli with **taste buds** located in the mouth and on the lips, fins, and skin. Taste buds also are found on **barbels,** whisker-like organs near the mouth of many bottom feeders such as marine catfishes (*Plotosus*). Fishes that have barbels use them to detect food on the bottom.

Fish eyes are not very different from those of vertebrates that live on land. One important difference, though, is the way they focus. Whereas the eyes of most land vertebrates focus by changing the shape of the lens, the round lens of the fish eye focuses by moving closer to or farther away from the subject. This is partially why fish eyes tend to bulge. Bony fishes appear to rely on vision more than most cartilaginous fishes. Many bony fishes—particularly shallow-water species—have color vision, but most cartilaginous fishes have little or none. Some sharks have a distinct **nictitating membrane** that can be drawn across the eye to reduce brightness and to protect the eye during feeding.

Fishes have a unique sense organ called the **lateral line** that enables them to detect vibrations in the water. The lateral line consists of a system of small canals that run along the head and body (Fig. 8.19a). The canals lie in the skin and in the bone or cartilage of the head. They are lined with clusters of sensory cells, or **neuromasts,** that are sensitive to vibration. The canals usually open to the surface through pores that are quite visible.

The lateral line system picks up vibrations resulting from the swimming of other animals as well as water displacements caused by sound waves. It allows fishes to avoid obstacles and predators, detect prey, orient to currents, and keep their position in a school.

Cartilaginous fishes also have sense organs in the head called the **ampullae of Lorenzini** (see Figs. 8.3 and 8.19b) that can detect weak electrical fields. This system helps them locate prey. It can also help in navigation as a sort of electromagnetic compass or perhaps a detector of currents. The use of Earth's magnetic field in navigation has been confirmed in some sharks.

Fishes can also perceive sound waves with their **inner ears,** paired hearing organs located to the sides of the brain just behind

enlarged in solitary hunters such as the great white shark, whereas the frontal lobes controlling social behavior is enlarged in hammerheads, which gather for reproduction. The brain is protected by a cartilaginous or bony skull. Nerves connect the central nervous system with various organs of the body and with sense organs that receive information from the surroundings. This information is sent to the brain in the form of nerve impulses.

Most fishes have a highly developed sense of smell, which they use to detect food, mates, and predators, and sometimes to find their way home. Fishes do this with special sensory cells located in **olfactory sacs** on both sides of the head. Each sac opens to the outside through one or two openings, the nostrils, or **nares.**

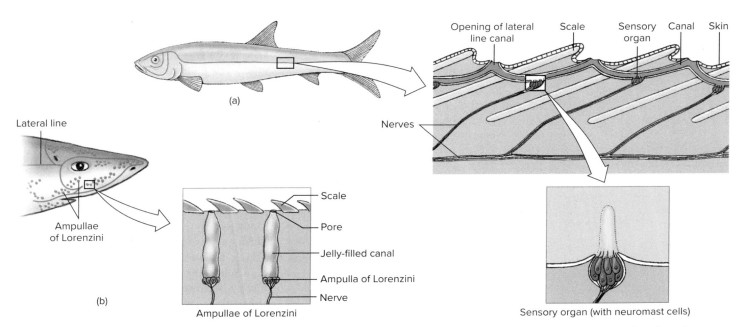

FIGURE 8.19 (*a*) Cross section through the skin of a fish, showing the lateral line sensory system. The nerves collect nerve impulses from the sensory organs and transmit the information to the brain. (*b*) In addition to the lateral line, cartilaginous fishes have ampullae of Lorenzini, a network of jelly-filled canals capable of detecting electrical fields in the water.

the eyes. The inner ears are a set of fluid-filled canals that contain sensory cells similar to those in the lateral line canals. In some fishes the swim bladder amplifies sound by vibrating and transmitting sound waves to the inner ear. The inner ear is also involved in equilibrium and balance. Many fishes detect changes in body position from the movement of calcareous **ear stones,** or **otoliths,** that rest on sensory hairs, a mechanism similar to the **statocysts** of invertebrates.

> The sense organs of fishes include eyes, olfactory sacs, taste buds, and inner ears, as well as a lateral line and other specialized organs that pick up vibrations or electrical stimuli from the water.

Behavior

Nearly all aspects of the lives of fishes involve complex behavior to adapt to light and currents, to find food and shelter, and to avoid predators. Behavior is also an important part of fish courtship and reproduction, which are described in the next section. This section provides only a glimpse of some aspects of fish behavior; some other highlights are discussed in other chapters.

Territoriality Many marine fishes, particularly open-water species, do not reside in any particular area. Others, however, are known to establish **territories,** home areas that they defend against intruders. Some fishes defend territories only during reproduction. Many others have more or less permanent territories that they use for feeding and resting or as shelter. It is thought that fishes often guard territories to ensure that they have enough food and other resources. Territoriality is therefore most common in crowded environments

like kelp beds and coral reefs, where resources are most likely to be in short supply. Coral reef damselfishes are famous for fiercely defending their territories, often attacking fishes many times their size or even divers.

Fishes use a variety of **aggressive behaviors** to defend their territories. Actual fights are surprisingly rare. Instead, fishes usually prefer to avoid risking injury by bluffing. Raised fins, an open mouth, and rapid darting about are examples of such threatening postures. Territorial defense can also involve sound production. Marine bony fishes are able to make sound by grinding their teeth or rubbing bones or fin spines on another bone. Some fishes "drum" by pulling muscles on the swim bladder, and this sound is amplified by the air-filled bladder.

Sometimes a solitary individual defends a territory. In other species, like some butterflyfishes, territories are established by a male-female pair. Territories can also be inhabited by groups that belong to the same species. This is the case in many damselfishes, which inhabit spaces between the branches of corals (Fig. 8.20), and anemonefishes, or clownfishes (*Amphiprion;* see Fig. 14.35). Members of such groups often divide the territory into subterritories.

Schooling Many fishes form well-defined groups, or **schools.** Some, including herrings, sardines, mullets, and some mackerels, school throughout their lives. Others are part-time schoolers,

> **Statocysts** Sense organs of many invertebrates consisting of one or more grains or hard bodies surrounded by sensitive hairs and used to orient the animal with gravity.
>
> • 7.2, Cnidarians: Radial Symmetry

FIGURE 8.20 Some damselfishes live among corals. They dash into spaces between the coral whenever danger approaches. Many species actually cultivate gardens of algae on dead coral, and many aggressively guard "nests" of eggs laid on coral or other surfaces (see Fig. 8.28).

Georgette Douwma/Getty Images

especially as juveniles or during feeding. Most cartilaginous fishes are solitary, but a few, such as hammerhead sharks, mantas, and other rays, sometimes travel in schools. At least 4,000 species, including marine and freshwater species, school as adults. Schools can be huge, as large as 4,580 million m³ (161,720 ft³) in the Atlantic herring (*Clupea harengus*). The members of a school are typically all about the same size. The stationary schools that are common around coral reefs, kelp beds, rocks, and shipwrecks, however, can include members of different sizes or even different species.

Schools function as well-coordinated units, though they appear to have no leaders (Fig. 8.21). The individual fishes tend to keep a constant distance between themselves, turning, stopping, and starting in near perfect unison. Vision plays an important role in the orientation of individuals within a school. In some species,

though, blinded fish can school in a coordinated way. These fish probably use the lateral line, olfaction, and sound they emit to keep track of each other. The tight coordination of schooling fishes can break down when they are feeding or attacked by a predator.

Why do fishes school? One explanation is that schooling offers protection against predation. Predators can be confused if, for instance, the school circles a predator (Fig. 8.21c) or splits into several groups. It is also difficult for a predator to aim for just one fish in a cloud of shifting, darting individuals (Fig. 8.21d). On the other hand, some predators, such as jacks (*Caranx*), are more efficient when they attack schools of prey rather than individuals. Schooling could increase swimming efficiency because the fish in front form an eddy that reduces water resistance for those behind. There is experimental evidence, however, that this is not always the case and that fish do not always align in a hydrodynamically efficient way. In at least some fishes, schooling is advantageous in feeding or mating. There is probably no single reason that fishes school, and the reasons probably vary among species.

Migrations Migration is the regular mass movements from one place to another once a day, once a year, or once in a lifetime. Schools of parrotfishes and other fishes migrate daily onshore and offshore to feed. Many open-water fishes migrate several hundred meters up and down the water column every day (see "Vertical Migration," in 15.2). The most spectacular migrations, however, are the transoceanic journeys made by tunas, salmon, and other fishes. We still know little about why fishes migrate, but most migrations seem to be related to feeding or reproduction.

(a) Traveling (b) Feeding on plankton (c) Encirclement of predator (d) Streaming to avoid predator

Source: Bill Ober

FIGURE 8.21 Some of the common patterns that fishes follow when schooling.

EYE ON SCIENCE

Box 8.2 Great White Shark Migrations

It was long thought that great white sharks (*Carcharodon carcharias*; Fig. 8.6*a*) spend a good part of their lives prowling along coasts hunting sea lions, seals, and large fishes. Current research in several parts of the world has nevertheless shown a new insight: great white sharks surprisingly travel long distances in regular, frequent migrations across the open ocean using Earth's magnetic field to navigate.

Electronic tags and satellite technology (see Box 1.1, "Observing the Oceans") have permitted recording the long-term movements of large marine animals such as the great white shark. Individual sharks are tagged by using a long pole while they swim along a boat, and photos of the dorsal fin are taken to record notches and other markings for individual identification. Photos are also taken to determine size and sex. The use of "pop-up" tags is a major advantage. They remain attached to a shark before being released at a pre-programmed time and float to the surface to transmit data on location, depth, and water temperature at previously determined intervals along the route. The data are sent to ARGOS (Advanced Research and Global Observation Satellite), a satellite-based system that supplies positions around the globe, which then relays the information to a laboratory on land.

Great whites tagged with pop-up tags off the central California coast were tracked to an area 2,400 km (1,500 mi) east of Hawai'i. The migratory route from California to the central Pacific followed a similar route during five years of tracking. The start of the migration was timed with a decrease in the abundance of sea lions and seals along the coast, suggesting that food was a factor in triggering migrations. Individual sharks remained in the central Pacific for as long as four months before returning to California. It is speculated that sharks gather in the area to feed on marine mammals such as sperm whales and large fishes; some suggested sharks feed on deep-water squids. A different study tracked great whites from off northern Baja California, Mexico, to the same central Pacific location where the California sharks gathered. Sharks returned to the same areas in California and Mexico, thus showing homing behavior (see "Migrations," below). Long-lived batteries allowed the tracking of females along the same route, suggesting that they give birth to their young upon returning to Mexico after an 18-month gestation period spent traveling to the central Pacific. Males, on the other hand, return to Mexico every year.

A similar study recorded the transoceanic migration of a shark from South Africa to western Australia and back, a total of about 20,000 km (nearly 12,500 mi), a trip that took under nine months to complete. The estimated minimum speed of this migration was 4.7 km/h (2.9 mi/h), not much different from the fastest tunas. Tagging has also shown that great whites undertake long migrations along the coasts of Australia as well as patrolling along the coast.

One promising technique for investigating shark migrations is testing water samples for the "genetic signature" of particular species of sharks. This technique involves detecting traces of **environmental DNA (eDNA)** derived from mucus, feces, or tissues of sharks. eDNA from great whites and of other sharks can supplement information obtained from tagging or drones for mapping long-distance migrations.

One unanswered question is the role of long-distance migrations in the reproduction of great whites. So far there does not seem to be a connection with reproduction, but DNA analysis should help identify the genetic makeup of great white populations in different continents for determining the genetic parentage of individuals. How great whites orient during their transoceanic migrations without any clues from landmasses or islands is another provocative question. The long-distance migrations of the great white shark, which is listed as vulnerable in the IUCN Red List of threatened species (see Table 18.1), are menaced while away from coasts, where it is legally protected.

For more information, explore the links provided on the Marine Biology *Online Learning Center.*

Feeding is one reason behind the migration of open-water species like tunas. Recaptures of tagged fish have provided much information on how far, how fast, and when tunas migrate (see "Swimming: The Need for Speed," in 15.2). Though essentially tropical, some species migrate long distances to feed in temperate waters. Such is the case in the skipjack tuna (*Katsuwonus pelamis;* Fig. 8.22) and other tunas. Some sharks are now known to undertake long migrations (see Box 8.2, "Great White Shark Migrations," above).

Also amazing are the migrations between the sea and fresh water undertaken by some fishes that are dependent on fresh water for reproduction. **Anadromous** fishes spend most of their lives at sea but migrate to fresh water to breed. Sturgeons (*Acipenser*), whose eggs are eaten as caviar, some lampreys, and smelts (*Osmerus*) are examples. By far the best-known anadromous fish, however, is the salmon.

There are seven species of salmon in the Pacific, each known by several common names. They spend their adult lives in the North Pacific, traveling thousands of miles in vast sweeps along the coast, the Aleutian Islands, and the open sea (Fig. 8.22). Some even venture into the Bering Sea and the Arctic Ocean. How they navigate at sea is not known. They could use land features at least part of the way. Currents, salinity, temperature, and other water characteristics might provide clues. Other possibilities include orientation to polarized light, the sun, or, as now shown in the great white and in the bonnethead shark (*Sphyraena tiburo*), Earth's magnetic field.

After several years at sea, salmon mature sexually and start migrating into rivers probably guided by Earth's magnetic field. They do not feed once they enter fresh water, living instead on stored fat. Their kidneys must adjust to the change from salt to fresh water. Eventually, they reach the exact stream of their birth, sometimes far

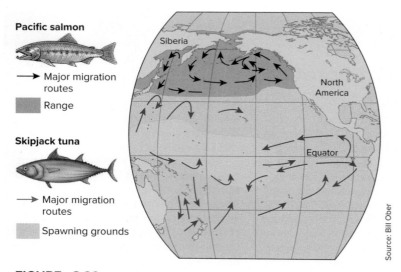

Pacific salmon

→ Major migration routes

▇ Range

Skipjack tuna

→ Major migration routes

▇ Spawning grounds

Source: Bill Ober

FIGURE 8.22 The skipjack tuna (*Katsuwonus pelamis*), the leading commercial catch among tunas, undertakes extensive migrations that every year take it almost halfway across the globe. The Pacific salmon (*Oncorhynchus*) migrates to spawn only once in a lifetime. Approximate limits of distribution and migration routes indicated are for all seven species of salmon.

upstream. The king, or chinook, salmon (*Oncorhynchus tshawytscha*) and chum, or dog, salmon (*Oncorhynchus keta*) reach as far inland as Idaho and the headwaters of the Yukon River.

Salmon find their home streams with remarkable accuracy, using a type of chemical memory. They recognize not only the "smell" of their own stream but also those of other streams they pass along the way. There also is evidence that they respond to chemicals released by other members of their own species. The timing of migration, at least in the chinook salmon, is influenced by genes. The ability of an animal to find its way back to a home area is known as **homing behavior.**

Most salmon undergo dramatic changes before spawning. Both sexes of the sockeye salmon (*Oncorhynchus nerka*) turn from silver

to bright red, giving rise to one of its common names, the red salmon. The jaws grow into vicious looking hooks in male sockeye and pink, or humpback, salmon (*Oncorhynchus gorbuscha*). Males of the latter species also develop a large hump.

Salmon spawn on beds of clean gravel in the shallows. The female digs out a shallow nest, or "redd," into which she deposits her eggs. The eggs are fertilized by the male and covered with gravel. After defending the nest for a while, the salmon die.

After hatching, the young salmon, or smolt, can return to sea immediately, as in the pink salmon. The young of other species remain in fresh water for a time, as long as five years for the sockeye salmon. The kokanee salmon, a race of this last species, is landlocked and does not migrate to sea at all. This is also the case of the rainbow trout, the landlocked variety of the steelhead salmon (*Oncorhynchus mykiss*). Unlike other salmon, the steelhead and rainbow trout can spawn many times before dying.

One of the biggest hazards Pacific salmon endure is the destruction of their natural environment by humans. Migration routes have been blocked by dams, spawning grounds filled with silt as a result of logging and cattle grazing, and rivers polluted by pesticides (which, among other toxic effects, are suspected of disrupting salmon's sense of smell), fertilizers, and animal waste. Around 11 to 15 million salmon once spawned in the Columbia River system in the northwestern United States. The number has now decreased by 90%, and most of the returning adults were born in hatcheries. Some species, like the sockeye, king, and chum salmon, have been declared endangered in some rivers. As a result, sharp restrictions have been imposed on the harvest of salmon along the Pacific coast. Calls to remove dams have strong support, especially from indigenous groups.

The Atlantic salmon (*Salmo salar*) breeds on both sides of the North Atlantic. It migrates across the ocean, mostly off Greenland, before returning to rivers from New England to Portugal. Atlantic salmon sometimes survive after spawning and return to the ocean. Some females have made as many as four round trips. Populations of Atlantic salmon in the wild are in serious decline, though they are farmed for food in some temperate regions besides the Atlantic (see Table 17.3).

Catadromous fishes have a migratory pattern opposite that of salmon. They breed at sea and migrate into rivers to grow and mature. Several catadromous fishes are known, but the longest migration of any of them is that of freshwater eels (*Anguilla*). There are at least 16 species, including the American (*Anguilla rostrata*) and European (*Anguilla anguilla*) eels, which were once thought to belong to the same species, but DNA analysis has shown they are distinct.

Both American and European eels spawn in the **Sargasso Sea** north of the West Indies at depths of at least 400 to 700 m (1,300 to 2,300 ft) and then die (Fig. 8.23). They spawn at different, though

Leptocephalus larva

Adult eel

North America

Europe

Sargasso Sea

Africa

South America

American eel	**Prevailing ocean currents**	**European eel**
→ Larva	→	→ Larva
⇒ Adult		⇒ Adult

Source: Bill Ober

FIGURE 8.23 Two species of freshwater eels, the American (*Anguilla rostrata*) and European (*A. anguilla*) eels, breed in the Sargasso Sea and migrate to rivers in North America and Europe. The return trip of larvae is not precisely known, so the arrows indicate only the most likely routes. Both species, once very abundant, are now endangered, the European eel critically so.

overlapping, periods and locations in the sea. The eggs hatch into tiny, transparent larvae that gradually develop into leaf-shaped **leptocephalus larvae.** American eel larvae drift in the plankton for at least a year. The juveniles, "glass eels" when transparent, then move into rivers along the Atlantic coast of North America. The leptocephalus larvae of the European eel are believed to spend at least an extra two or three years drifting in the Gulf Stream to reach rivers throughout western Europe. Adults of both species eventually grow to more than 1 m (40 in) in length. Both juveniles and adults are highly valued as food, particularly in Europe. The European eel is now critically endangered, and live glass eels are illegally brought from China. After 10 to 15 years in fresh water, adults turn silver and their eyes become larger. Soon after this, they head out to sea.

The migration of eels back to the Sargasso Sea is not completely understood. There is experimental evidence that they use Earth's magnetic field as a cue for navigation.

Reproduction and Life History

Reproduction in fishes involves a number of adaptations of the reproductive system and the behavior that brings the two sexes together to ensure successful reproduction.

Reproductive System The reproductive system of fishes is relatively simple. Both sexes have paired gonads located in the body cavity (see Fig. 8.14). In cartilaginous fishes, ducts lead from the ovaries and testes into the cloaca, which opens to the outside (see Fig. 8.14*a*). Jawless and bony fishes have a separate opening for urine and gametes, the **urogenital opening,** which is located just behind the anus (see Fig. 8.14*b*).

In many marine fishes the gonads produce gametes only at certain times. The timing of gamete production is crucial. Both sexes must be ready to spawn at the same time. Spawning, as well as larval development, must take place during the period with the most favorable conditions. The exact timing of reproduction is especially critical for fishes that make long migrations to breed.

The timing of reproduction is controlled for the most part by **sex hormones.** Sex hormones are produced in the gonads and released in small amounts into the blood. They stimulate the maturation of gametes and can cause changes in color, shape, and behavior before breeding. The release of sex hormones is triggered by environmental factors such as day length, temperature, and the availability of food. Fishes can be artificially induced to spawn when these environmental factors are controlled or when hormones are injected. This technique is used to increase reproduction in fishes grown for food (see "Aquaculture," in 17.1).

A few marine fishes are **hermaphrodites.** Some, like the hamlet (*Hypoplectrus*), are called **simultaneous hermaphrodites** because they can produce sperm and eggs at the same time. Though able to fertilize their own eggs, simultaneous hermaphrodites usually breed with one or more other individuals, ensuring cross-fertilization. One member of a pair of mating hamlets, for example, acts as a male and its sperm fertilizes the eggs released by the other individual. Roles are reversed after fertilization, and the "female" releases sperm to fertilize eggs released by the "male." Hermaphroditism

also is found among several deep-water fishes, including a few sharks, an adaptation to the depths of the ocean where it can be difficult to find members of the opposite sex (see "Sex in the Deep Sea," in 16.2).

A variation of hermaphroditism among fishes is **sex reversal,** or **sequential hermaphroditism,** in which individuals begin life as males but change into females **(protandry)** or females change into males **(protogyny).** These changes are controlled by sex hormones but triggered by social cues such as the absence of a dominant male. Sex reversal occurs in several groups of marine fishes as an adaptation to maximize the number of offspring, but it is most prevalent among sea basses and groupers (*Serranus, Epinephelus*), parrotfishes, and wrasses. Some rather complicated reproductive strategies have been discovered among these fishes. Sex reversal is known in about 450 species of marine and freshwater fishes.

In at least some species of anemone-fishes (*Amphiprion*), all individuals begin as males. Each sea anemone is inhabited by a single, large female that mates only with a large, dominant male. All the other fishes that live on the anemone are small, non-breeding males. If the female disappears or is experimentally removed, her mate changes into a female and the largest of the non-breeding males becomes the new dominant male. The new female can start spawning as soon as 26 days after her sex change. Males of some wrasses form harems of many females. If the male disappears, the largest, dominant female immediately begins to act as a male and within a relatively short period of time changes color and transforms into one that is capable of producing sperm.

Reproductive Behavior Potential mates must get together at the right time to breed. Many species migrate and congregate in specific breeding grounds, as in the salmon and freshwater eels previously discussed. Sharks are usually loners but come together during the breeding season. Some of them appear to stop feeding at spawning time.

Many bony fishes change color to advertise their readiness to breed, as in the dramatic case of salmon (see above). Color changes also can be observed in tropical fishes. Many male wrasses, colorful all the time, appear even more spectacular before breeding.

The first step in reproduction is **courtship,** a series of behaviors that attract mates. These behaviors involve an exchange of active displays such as "dances," special postures that display colors, and upside down swimming (Fig. 8.24). Each species has a unique courtship behavior. This is thought to help keep fishes from mistakenly mating with members of the wrong species.

> Reproduction in fishes involves many adaptations that help individuals get together for mating. These include migrations, the display of particular colors as sex signals, and courtship behavior.

Some fishes have **internal fertilization** of the eggs, in which the sperm is directly transferred from males to females through the act

Hormones Molecules that act as chemical messengers within the body.
• 4.1, The Ingredients of Life

BOX 8.3 EVOLUTIONARY PERSPECTIVE

A Fish Called *Latimeria*

In December 1938, the skipper of a fishing trawler operating in deep water off the Chalumna River in South Africa found a very strange fish in his catch. He took it to Marjorie Courtenay-Latimer, a young curator at the local museum, who recognized the fish as something special. She sent a sketch of the 1.5 m (5 ft) specimen to Dr. J. L. B. Smith at nearby Rhodes University, and history was made.

The fish was a big catch, indeed. It was a **coelacanth**, a type of fish thought to have become extinct 60 million years ago. Extinction is not a rare event in evolution, and coelacanths were previously known only from fossils, some at least 400 million years old. They belong to the crossopterygian fishes, a group of fishes that might have given rise to the first land vertebrates, or tetrapods. About 375 million years ago a crossopterygian fish with **lobed fins,** paddle-like bony fins, crawled out of the water and changed life on Earth forever. There is ample evidence that all present-day tetrapods evolved from crossopterygian fishes (see Box 4.2, "When Fishes Stepped on Land").

Dr. Smith officially described the fish and named it *Latimeria chalumnae* in honor of its discoverer and the river near which it was caught. Unfortunately, the internal organs of the fish had been discarded by the time Dr. Smith got to it, so nothing was known of its internal structure. A reward was offered for more specimens of the incredible "living fossil," so called because it is similar to no known species other than fossils. It was not until 1952 that a second specimen was caught near the Comoro Islands, between Madagascar and mainland Africa. Ironically, the fish is well known to the inhabitants of the islands. They eat its oily flesh after drying and salting it, and they use its rough skin for sandpaper.

The fish, which is nocturnal in habits, is still very rare. None of the captured specimens has survived more than 20 hours, so little is known about its habits.

The coelacanth (*Latimeria chalumnae*), a living fossil.

A small submersible was used for the first time in 1987 to film and observe a live *Latimeria* in its natural environment at depths of 117 to 200 m (386 to 660 ft). Divers have filmed live *Latimeria* off the northeastern coast of South Africa from depths of only 104 m (320 ft) since 2000.

Latimeria is a large fish, up to 1.8 m (6 ft) in length and weighing as much as 98 kg (216 lb). The body is covered by large scales. This living fossil is unique in many ways. It has heavy, stalked fins that have bones as tetrapods do. The fish appears to stand on the fins, but not to crawl over the bottom with them, as once thought. The pectoral fins can rotate nearly 180° allowing the fish to swim slowly over the bottom, sometimes standing on its head or with its belly up. The fish is neutrally buoyant because of oils in its tissues and a fat-filled swim bladder. Jelly-filled organs on the head could be used to detect electrical fields and thus help in the location of food: fishes, squids, and octopuses.

Little is known about its reproduction. Females bear live young, as many as 26, and the huge eggs (about 9 cm, or 3.5 in in diameter) develop in the reproductive tract, apparently for at least a year. The scales of fetuses suggest that the young develop for at least five years. DNA tests showed that each of the two clutches analyzed were fathered by only one male. Studying the annual growth rigs in the scales has provided estimates of the age of *Latimeria*. Surprisingly, individuals can live, as in humans, up to 60–80 years!

Scientists published the complete set of genetic information in the DNA, or genome, of an African coelacanth in 2013. Coelacanths were found to be genetically closer to mammals, including humans, than to fishes. Evidence suggests that lungfishes, freshwater fishes with lobe fins and lungs, are closer to tetrapods than coelacanths are. In fact, coelacanths, lungfishes, and tetrapods are grouped together in a recent classification scheme. Although truly "living fossils," the coelacanth genes have not remained unchanged. They have evolved but at a slower rate than in other vertebrates. There is perhaps no pressure to change much to adapt to changes in their very stable deep-water environment. The close similarity of *Latimeria* to their fossil ancestors is perhaps best explained by this slow genetic change.

Latimeria remains a priceless catch, and several aquaria around the world would like very much to capture live specimens. As their value in dollars soars, so do the concerns about the 200 individuals that could still survive in the Comoros. International trade has now been officially outlawed. Catches along the Indian Ocean coast of East Africa as far north as Kenya, however, indicate a wider distribution than originally thought. The South and East African specimens are genetically similar, so they are members of the same species.

In 1997 *Latimeria* surprised everybody by turning up in a fish market on the island of Sulawesi, Indonesia, almost 10,000 km (6,200 mi) from the Comoros! A live specimen was taken off the same island in 1998. Though very similar in appearance to the Indian Ocean specimens, DNA evidence showed that the Indonesian coelacanth belonged to a species different from that in the Indian Ocean. The Indonesian coelacanth was described as *Latimeria menadoensis*. Additional Indonesian coelacanths were filmed in deep water in 2006.

Are there other coelacanths waiting to be discovered somewhere else?

of **copulation. External fertilization,** the release of gametes into the water, or **broadcast spawning,** is more common in fishes, however.

Internal fertilization occurs mainly in cartilaginous fishes. Unfortunately, not much is known about their sex life. Male sharks, rays, and skates have a pair of copulatory organs, called **claspers,**

located along the inner edge of the pelvic fins (Fig. 8.25). The typical approach of an amorous male shark consists of biting his potential mate on the back. The male copulates by inserting his claspers into the female's cloaca. He bites and hangs from her or partly coils around her middle. Some skates mate after the male bites the

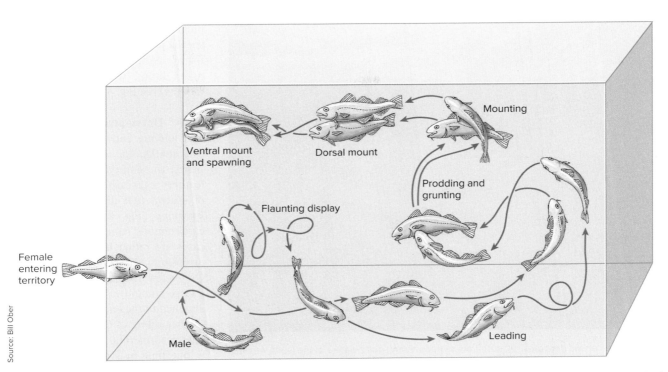

Source: Bill Ober

FIGURE 8.24 The Atlantic cod (*Gadus morhua*) spawns in large aggregations in the North Atlantic. The two sexes follow a strictly choreographed series of behaviors. The male establishes a territory, and the action starts after an interested female enters his territory. Most of the display is made by the male, which uses fully spread fins, grunting sounds, and a series of swimming behaviors. If the female does not follow the male, he has to start all over again to try to attract another female. The spawning of gametes into the water thus climaxes a series of behaviors that includes visual, sound, and tactile signals.

Michael E. Huber

Yann hubert/Shutterstock

FIGURE 8.25 Fertilization in cartilaginous fishes is internal, so males must possess some type of copulatory organ. This is the function of the claspers, which are located on the inner edge of the pelvic fins. They are provided with a groove for the passage of sperm. Only one clasper is inserted into the female at a time. The photo shows a male whitetip shark (*Triaenodon obesus*); the claspers of a scalloped hammerhead shark (*Sphyrna lewini*) are shown in the inset.

female's pectoral fins. He presses his ventral surface against hers and inserts the claspers.

Open-water fishes (sardines, tunas, jacks, and others) and those living around coral reefs and other inshore environments (such as surgeonfishes, parrotfishes, wrasses, and the capelin)

spawn directly into the water after courtship (Fig. 8.26). Females typically release many eggs. In the Atlantic cod (*Gadus morhua*), for example, a female 1 m (40 in) long can release up to 5 million eggs. The Atlantic tarpon (*Megalops atlanticus*) releases more than 100 million eggs every time it spawns.

Some fishes, like butterflyfishes, spawn in pairs (Fig. 8.27), others in groups. Individual males can establish territories or aggregate into groups. Groups of males can be approached by single females or by females in groups. Usually, males seek out the females and entice them to spawn via courtship. Two individuals can pair only during spawning time, as in butterflyfishes, or can establish long-lasting bonds.

Eggs fertilized in the water column drift in currents and develop as part of the plankton. Most eggs contain oil droplets and are buoyant. Other eggs sink to the bottom. Herrings deposit their eggs on the surface of seagrasses, seaweeds, and rocks. Lampreys and salmon bury their eggs after spawning. The California grunion (*Leuresthes tenuis*) buries its eggs on sandy beaches during high tides; they don't hatch until the next high tide (see Fig. 3.30).

Most of the eggs that are released into the plankton don't survive. Fishes and other marine animals that spawn into the plankton are broadcast spawners that release as many eggs as possible to ensure that at least some hatch and make it to adulthood. Eggs require a lot of energy to produce because they must contain enough yolk to nourish the young until they hatch and can feed.

Fishes that spawn fewer and larger eggs have evolved ways to take care of them. In many damselfishes males establish and defend breeding sites or nests (Fig. 8.28) on rocks or coral, empty mollusc shells, and other shelters—even discarded tires. After spawning, the

FIGURE 8.26 The capelin (*Mallotus villosus*), from temperate and polar waters of the North Atlantic, comes inshore to spawn in swarms. It typically spawns on gravel beaches.

eggs are retained in the nest and guarded by the males; the females leave after spawning. Males are promiscuous and will guard eggs they have fertilized from different females. Nests also are guarded by males in some gobies, blennies, and sculpins. In the Antarctic plunderfish (*Harpagifer bispinis*), the female prepares a breeding site and guards it for four to five months after spawning. If she disappears or is removed, her job is taken over by another plunderfish, usually a male.

Some fishes go even further and physically carry the eggs after they have been fertilized. Male pipefishes carry the eggs attached in neat rows to their bellies. A male seahorse literally becomes pregnant after the female deposits eggs in a special pouch on his belly. In some cardinalfishes, marine catfishes, and other groups, males brood the fertilized eggs in their mouths (see Fig. 4.21*b*).

Early Development Most fishes spawn eggs and are known as **oviparous.** In oviparous sharks, skates, and other cartilaginous fishes, the embryo is enclosed by a large, leathery egg case (the "mermaid's purse" of skates) that drops to the bottom after spawning (Fig. 8.29). About 43% of all cartilaginous fishes are oviparous. The egg cases are rather large and often have thin extensions that attach them to surfaces. Only a few are laid at a time. The eggs have a large amount of yolk in a **yolk sac** that is attached to the embryo's belly (see photo at the beginning of Chapter 4). Yolk provides energy for several months of development, a long time by fish standards. As a result, the pup is well developed when it finally hatches.

Development of the embryo proceeds rather quickly in most bony fishes. The transparent outer envelope of the eggs, the **chorion,** is thin, allowing oxygen to diffuse through. The eggs are usually spherical.

The embryo is supplied with nutrient-rich yolk. After one or more days of development, the eggs hatch into free-swimming larvae, or fry. When they first hatch, the larvae still carry the yolk in a yolk sac. The yolk is eventually consumed, and the larvae begin feeding. Many larvae, like the leptocephalus larvae of eels (see Fig. 8.23), do not resemble their parents at all and undergo metamorphosis to a juvenile stage that resembles the adult.

(a)

(b)

FIGURE 8.27 Butterflyfishes are among the most colorful of coral reef fishes. Some species use their tiny mouths (see Fig. 8.13*b*) to feed on coral. Adults of some species occur in male and female pairs as in the oval butterflyfish (*Chaetodon trifasciatus*) (*a*), which establish territories around coral colonies. (*b*) Experiments using transparent plastic cages provide valuable information on their behavior. Here, a caged oval butterflyfish elicits an aggressive response from an individual chevron butterflyfish (*Chaetodon trifascialis*), an indication that the caged fish has intruded in the territory of the latter. This technique can be used to map the boundaries of territories. Territorial butterflyfishes that live in pairs fight with other pairs, but fighting occurs only between individuals of the same sex in each pair. Researchers can therefore determine the sex of the fish, which is normally impossible in the field.

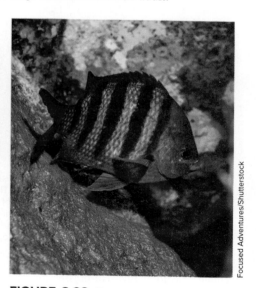

FIGURE 8.28 The sergeant major (*Abudefduf saxatilis*), like many other damselfishes, establishes and actively defends breeding sites where females lay their eggs, here shown as a red film.

FIGURE 8.29 An egg of the swell shark (*Cephaloscyllium ventriosum*) containing a one-month-old embryo. The large, white structure is the yolk sac. The egg case has been cut open to show the embryo. The complete egg case of another shark is shown in the inset.

two branches of its mother's uterus by eating its siblings. When that source of food is gone, they consume unfertilized eggs produced by their mother's ovaries.

Some sharks and rays have embryos that absorb nutrients from the walls of the mother's uterus. These sharks are said to be **viviparous.** The surfperches (*Embiotoca*) are viviparous bony fishes. Their young have large fins that absorb nutrients from the walls of the mother's uterus. Some sharks go further and have evolved to possess what some call a **placenta,** tissue that provides nourishment to the embryo. It is not a true placenta, however, because it develops from the walls of the mother's uterus rather than from the embryo as in the case of the true placenta of practically all mammals, including humans. All viviparous fishes are therefore said to show **aplacental viviparity.**

There is yet another method of reproduction among fishes. A female bonnethead shark gave birth to a pup after three years in an aquarium together with two females of the same species but no males. Though it was possible that the female had stored sperm as the result of sex with a male shark prior to capture, the DNA of the pup matched the DNA of one of the three females with no evidence of DNA from a male. Though very rare among vertebrates, **parthenogenesis,** the development of an egg into a normal female embryo without fertilization by sperm, has also been reported in a few other sharks and bony fishes. A female whitespotted bamboo shark (*Chiloscyllium plagiosum*) born in captivity by parthenogensis went on to give birth to a second generation of parthenogenetic pups, all females.

In some cartilaginous fishes the female retains the eggs within her reproductive tract, in the **uterus,** for additional protection. The eggs develop inside the female, which gives birth to live young. The young are larger than in oviparous species. Such fishes are known as **ovoviviparous.** Most ovoviviparous fishes are cartilaginous. A total of 300 embryos, still in egg cases, were found ready to emerge in the uterus of a female whale shark. Some rockfishes are among the few marine bony fishes that are ovoviviparous. Most bony fishes are oviparous and spawn their eggs for external fertilization.

The embryos of some ovoviviparous sharks rely on other sources of nutrition once they have consumed the yolk. In the sand tiger shark (*Carcharias taurus*) only two pups, which are large (up to 1 m or 3.3 ft) and active, are born. Each survived in one of the

Most marine fishes are oviparous and release eggs into the water. Internal fertilization leads to ovoviviparous or viviparous conditions in some, especially cartilaginous fishes.

Table 8.1 Most Important Characteristics of Marine Fishes

Group	Distinguishing Features	Skeleton	Feeding	Reproduction	Ecology
Hagfishes	No paired fins, no scales, exposed gill slits, marine	Cartilaginous skull, no vertebrae, no jaws	Suction by round, muscular mouth with teeth	Oviparous	Predators of dead or dying fishes and bottom invertebrates
Lampreys	Two dorsal fins only, no scales, exposed gill slits, freshwater or anadromous	Cartilaginous skull, no vertebrae, no jaws	Suction by round, muscular mouth with teeth	Oviparous	Suckers of fish blood or predators of bottom invertebrates
Rays, skates	Paired fins, placoid scales, pectoral fins greatly expanded, five ventral gill slits, mostly marine	Cartilaginous	Grinding plates to feed on bottom animals or gill rakers to filter plankton	Oviparous, viviparous	Predators of bottom animals or filter feeders of plankton and small fishes
Sharks	Paired fins, placoid scales, 5 to 7 exposed and lateral gill slits, mostly marine	Cartilaginous	Teeth in jaws to capture prey or gill rakers to filter plankton	Oviparous, ovoviviparous, viviparous	Predators or filter feeders of plankton and small fishes
Ratfishes	Paired fins, placoid scales, one pair of gill slits covered by flap of tissue, deep water	Cartilaginous	Grinding plates to feed on bottom invertebrates	Oviparous	Predators of bottom invertebrates
Bony fishes	Paired fins, cycloid or ctenoid scales (absent in some), gills covered by operculum, marine and freshwater	Bony	Teeth in jaws to capture prey or graze or gill rakers to filter plankton	Oviparous, ovoviviparous, viviparous	Predators, grazers, or filter feeders
Coelacanths	Paired lobed fins, large scales, gills covered by operculum, deep water	Bony	Teeth in jaws to capture prey	Ovoviviparous	Predators of deep-water fishes, squids, and octopuses

Interactive Exploration

McGraw-Hill Connect® is a great place to check your understanding of chapter material. Visit **www.mcgrawhillconnect.com** for access to interactive chapter summaries, chapter quizzing, and more! Further enhance your knowledge with video clips and weblinks to chapter-related material.

Critical Thinking

1. Hagfishes and lampreys are the only living representatives of a very ancient group. Why do you suppose there are still species of these jawless fishes around?

2. A deep-water shark, new to science, is collected for the first time. The specimen is studied in detail, but its stomach is empty. How can you get a rough idea of its feeding habits? The specimen is a female, and its reproductive tract is found to contain 20 eggs. Can you tell the type of development characteristic of this species?

3. Individuals of some species of bony fishes change sex, some to maintain more males than females, others more females than males. What are the advantages and disadvantages of each situation? Are there any advantages and disadvantages in having an equal number of males and females?

4. Recent research has shown that bamboo sharks kept in captivity showed the ability to distinguish among different numbers of objects. How do you think researchers reached such a conclusion? What kind of experimental setup they could have used?

5. Other than feeding and reproduction, could you suggest other possible reasons why marine fishes migrate?

For Further Reading

Some of the recommended reading may be available online. Look for live links on the *Marine Biology* Online Learning Center.

General Interest

Balcombe, J., 2017. *What a fish knows: The inner lives of our underwater cousins.* Scientific American, New York. The author explores the many facets of the life of fishes.

Ballesta, L. 2018. Frenzy. *National Geographic*, vol. 233, no. 5, May, pp. 126–143. Sharks prey on spawning groupers.

Betz, E., 2017. The vanishing eels. *Discover*, vol. 38, no. 8, October, pp. 22–24. Researchers use satellite tagging to track migrations of the American freshwater eel.

Castañón, L., 2019. Sharks take 'tunnels' into the depths. *Oceans*, vol. 54, Spring, pp. 26–29. Sharks use spiraling eddies to find food in open water.

Dance, A., 2017. A sea of hurt. *Science News*, vol. 191, no 8, April 29, pp. 28–33. The ability to produce venoms, many of which affect humans, has evolved in many groups of fishes.

Dixson, D., 2017. Lost at sea. *Scientific American*, vol. 316, no. 6, June, pp. 42–45. There is evidence that ocean acidification can alter the behavior of fishes.

Hodges, G., 2016. Swimming with tigers. *National Geographic*, vol. 229, no. 6, June, pp. 84–99. The tiger shark is an impressive predator that plays an important role in the health of tropical shallow waters.

Hodges, G., 2016. The shipwreck shark. *National Geographic*, vol. 230, no. 2, August, pp. 112–125. The whitetip shark, once common in open waters, is now becoming rare.

Hodges, G., 2017. Bolt from the blue. *National Geographic*, vol. 232, no. 2, August, pp. 120–139. The shortfin mako, among the fasted sharks, has a wide range because key parts of the body maintain a warm temperature.

Joel, L., 2019. Jaws: The never-ending story. *New Scientist*, vol. 242, no. 3236, 29 June, pp. 43–45. Sharks are successful survivors of a long history on Earth, which includes several periods of mass extinctions.

Shiffman, D., 2021. Thoughts from a brain collector. *Discover*, vol. 42, November/December, pp. 56–60. A researcher discusses the significance of the organization of shark brains and how such organization affects shark behavior.

Shiffman, D., 2022. *Why sharks matter.* John Hopkins University Press, Baltimore. An exploration of how and why we need to protect sharks.

Vance, E., 2016. Great white mystery. *National Geographic*, vol. 230, no. 1, July, pp. 84–101. Relatively little is known about the great white, perhaps the most famous of all sharks.

In Depth

Cresci, A., 2020. A comprehensive hypothesis on the migration of European glass eels (*Anguilla anguilla*). *Biological Reviews,* vol. 95, pp. 1273–1286.

Daichi, G. S. and S. Grillner, 2018. The stepwise development of the lamprey visual system and its evolutionary implications. *Biological Reviews,* vol. 93, pp. 1461–1477.

Hammerschlag, N., R. A. Skubel, H. Calich, E. R. Nelson, D. S. Shiffman, J. Wester, C. C. Macdonald, S. Cain, L. Jennings, A. Enchelmaier, and A. J. Gallagher, 2017. Nocturnal and crepuscular behavior in elasmobranchs: a review of movement, habitat use, foraging, and reproduction in the dark. *Bulletin of Marine Science,* vol. 93, pp. 355–374.

Newton, K. C., A. B. Gill, and S. M. Kajiura, 2019. Electroreception in marine fishes: chondrichthyans. *Journal of Fish Biology,* vol. 95, pp. 135–154.

Olds, A. D., E. Vargas-Fonseca, R. M. Connolly, B. L. Gilby, C. M. Huijbers, G. A. Hyndes, C. A. Layman, A. K. Whitfield, and T. A. Schlacher, 2018. The ecology of fish in the surf zones of ocean beaches: A global review. *Fish and Fisheries,* vol. 19, pp. 78–89.

Shiffman, D. S. and N. Hammerschlag, 2016. Shark conservation and management policy: a review and primer for non-specialists. *Animal Conservation,* vol. 19, pp. 401–412.

Tiralongo, F., G. Messina, B. M. Lombardo, L. Longhitano, G. Li Volti, and D. Tibullo, 2020. Skin mucus of marine fish as a source for the development of antimicrobial agents. *Frontiers in Marine Biology* [https://doi.org/10.3389/fmars.2020.541853].

Watanabe, Y. Y. and Y. P. Papastamatiou, 2019. Distribution, body size and biology of the megamouth shark *Megachasma pelagios. Journal of Fish Biology,* vol. 95, pp. 992–998.

Williamson, M. J., E. J. Tebbs, T. P. Dawson, and D. M. P. Jacoby, 2019. Satellite remote sensing in shark and ray ecology, conservation and management. *Frontiers in Marine Biology* [https://doi.org/10.3389/fmars.2019.00135].

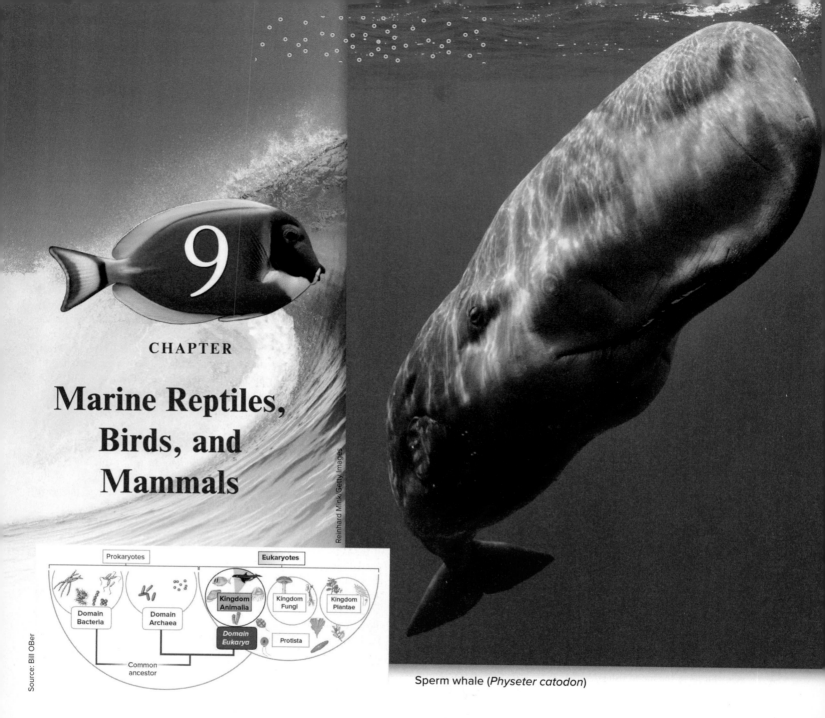

9

CHAPTER

Marine Reptiles, Birds, and Mammals

Prokaryotes Eukaryotes

Kingdom Animalia Kingdom Fungi Kingdom Plantae

Domain Bacteria Domain Archaea

Domain Eukarya Protista

Common ancestor

Sperm whale (*Physeter catodon*)

Vertebrates originated in the ocean and have thrived there ever since. Roughly 350 million years ago, vertebrates invaded the land as well, an event that changed life on Earth forever. Descended from bony fishes, land vertebrates had to adapt to the harsher conditions ashore. They lost the structural support that water provides and had to develop ways of crawling or walking to get around. They evolved from fish-like vertebrates with two pairs of limbs as an adaptation for "walking" on the bottom or on land between pools of water (see Box 4.2, "When Fishes Stepped on Land"). Because of this, land-dwelling vertebrates—even snakes— are called **tetrapods,** meaning "four-footed."

Living on land also means having to breathe air. Tetrapods evolved from fishes that had **lungs,** internal air sacs that allow absorption of oxygen directly from air. Tetrapods had to evolve ways to keep from drying out. The delicate egg is especially vulnerable, and the first land tetrapods, the **amphibians** (class **Amphibia**), never really solved this problem. Represented today by frogs, salamanders, and their relatives, amphibians must keep themselves moist, and, with a few exceptions, most lay their eggs in water. None of them are strictly marine.

Other groups of tetrapods solved the problem of water loss and truly adapted to life on land. **Reptiles** (class **Reptilia;** Fig. 9.1) evolved from now-extinct species of amphibians and for a long time were the dominant land vertebrates. The **birds** (class **Aves**) and **mammals** (class **Mammalia**) both evolved from now-extinct species of reptiles.

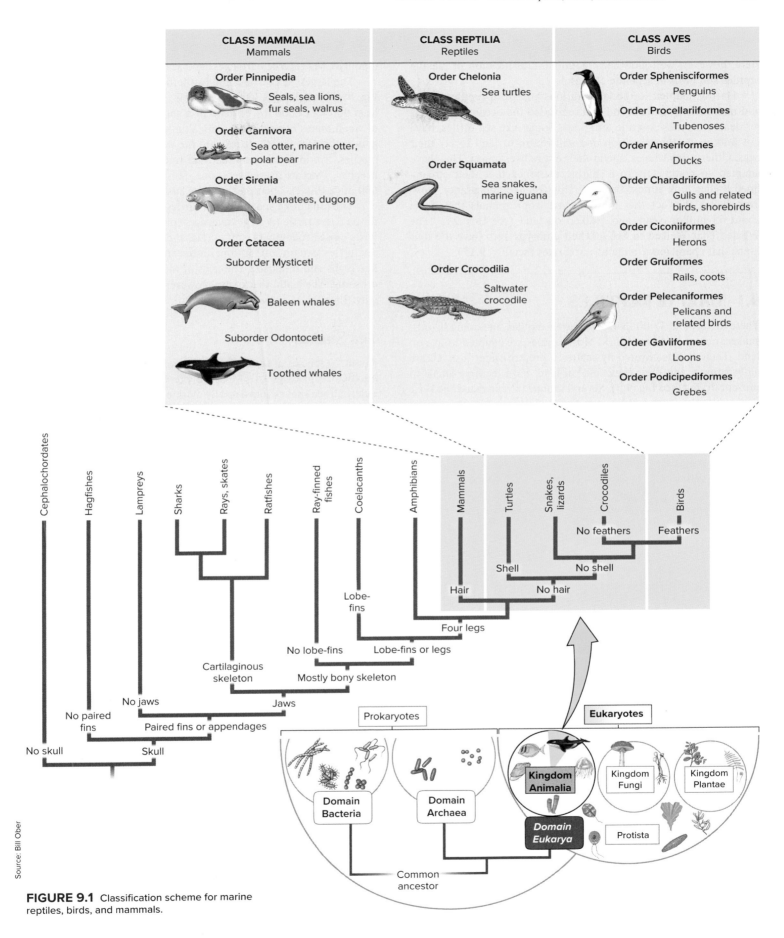

FIGURE 9.1 Classification scheme for marine reptiles, birds, and mammals.

Source: Bill Ober

Most biologists agree that birds are actually reptiles, having evolved from the same line that includes dinosaurs and crocodiles. Here, however, we follow the traditional classification of placing reptiles and birds in separate classes.

Having adapted to the land, various groups of reptiles, birds, and mammals turned around and reinvaded the ocean. This chapter deals with these marine tetrapods. Some, like sea turtles, have not fully made the transition and still return to land to lay their eggs. Others, like whales, spend their entire lives at sea. They have adapted so completely to a marine existence that their streamlined bodies look almost fish-like. This fish-like appearance, however, belies the fact that they evolved from animals that once, about 55 million years ago, walked on land (see Box 9.2, "The Whales That Walked to Sea"). Their embryos even have the four limbs that characterize all land vertebrates (see Fig. 9.17).

9.1 MARINE REPTILES

There are around 7,000 living species of reptiles, including lizards, snakes, turtles, and crocodiles. Most reptiles are adapted to live on land. Their skin is covered by scales to prevent water loss, all are air-breathing, and their eggs, laid on land, have leathery shells to prevent drying (see Fig. 9.3). Several groups have invaded the seas. Some, like the ichthyosaurs (see Fig. 9.15) thrived in the oceans during the so-called Age of Reptiles. Only a few reptiles still roam the seas.

> Reptiles are air-breathing vertebrates. Their skin is covered with dry scales, and they typically lay their eggs on land.

Sea Turtles

Sea turtles belong to an ancient group of reptiles. Their bodies are enclosed by an armor-like **shell,** or **carapace,** that is fused to the backbone (see Table 9.3). Unlike land tortoises and turtles, sea turtles cannot retract their heads into the shell. Their legs, particularly the larger forelimbs, are modified into flippers for swimming (see "Biology of Marine Reptiles," below).

There are only seven species of sea turtles (some biologists recognize eight), which live primarily in warm waters. Green turtles (*Chelonia mydas*, see photo in Box 9.1, "The Endangered Sea Turtle") were once common in coastal waters throughout the tropics, but like all species of sea turtles, their numbers have drastically declined due to overexploitation and increased mortality (see Box 9.1, "The Endangered Sea Turtle"). Their shells can grow to 1 m (40 in) in length. They feed mostly on seagrasses and seaweeds. Like all turtles, green turtles have strong biting, toothless jaws. The hawksbill turtle (*Eretmochelys imbricata;* Fig. 9.2*a*) is

smaller, and the shell is reddish brown with yellow streaks. It uses its beak-like mouth (see Fig. 4.15) to feed on encrusting animals (sponges, sea squirts, barnacles) and seaweeds.

The largest sea turtle is the leatherback (*Dermochelys coriacea;* Fig. 9.2*b*), attaining a length of nearly 3 m (9 ft) and weighing at least 900 kg (2,000 lb). Instead of a solid shell, they have a series of small bones buried in the dark skin, forming seven distinct longitudinal ridges. Leatherbacks are the widest ranging of all marine reptiles, live in open water, and are rarely seen except on nesting beaches. They are deep divers—one individual was tracked diving to 640 m (2,100 ft). Their diet consists largely of jellyfishes.

The remaining species of sea turtles have diverse diets, like the flatback sea turtle (*Natator depressus*) of northern Australia, which feeds on sea cucumbers, soft corals, and other invertebrates. Other sea turtles feed on soft, bottom invertebrates as well as hardier ones like crabs and molluscs. The jaws of most species are adapted for crushing. The leatherback jaws, however, are scissor-like to capture jellyfishes.

Sea Snakes

About 70 species of **sea snakes** are found in the tropical Indian and Pacific oceans (Fig. 9.4). Most are 1 to 1.3 m (3 to 4 ft) long. Practically all sea snakes lead a totally marine existence, lacking the belly scales that allow land snakes to move. Like all snakes, sea snakes are carnivores. Most feed on eels and other bottom fishes, but a few specialize on fish eggs, one species on bottom invertebrates. They are closely related to cobras and their allies, the most venomous of all snakes. Sea snake bites can be fatal to humans. Fortunately, they are rarely aggressive, and the mouth is too small to get a good bite. Most casualties are swimmers accidentally stepping on them and fishers removing them from nets. Sea snakes are also victims of overexploitation. They are hunted for their skins and meat, and some species have become rare in certain areas.

Other Marine Reptiles

An unusual lizard is among the unique inhabitants of the Galápagos Islands off the Pacific coast of South America. The **marine iguana** (*Amblyrhynchus cristatus;* Fig. 9.5) spends most of its time

(a) (b)

FIGURE 9.2 (*a*) The hawksbill turtle (*Eretmochelys imbricata*) takes its name from the shape of its jaw (see Fig. 4.15). (*b*) The leatherback turtle (*Dermochelys coriacea*) is found in the tropics worldwide but sometimes ventures into cold waters as far north as Newfoundland and Alaska.

Bill Ober

Brian Skerry/Bancroft Media/Getty Images

Box 9.1 The Endangered Sea Turtles

Humans are by far the most formidable and destructive enemies of sea turtles. Exploitation for food is one of the reasons. The green turtle is especially esteemed for its meat, and its cartilage is used to make turtle soup. Some people consider the oily leatherback meat a delicacy. Sea turtles can live for months without food or water, and sailors kept them alive aboard ship as a source of fresh meat in the days before refrigeration, storing them on their backs for months. Coming ashore by the thousands, females were an easy catch. They were, and still are, immobilized by turning them on their backs to be gathered later without giving them a chance to lay their eggs. Thousands of sea turtles are illegally killed every year for meat in coastal regions of Latin America, Southeast Asia, and India (see Fig. 18.16).

The polished shell of the hawksbill is the source of tortoiseshell used to make jewelry, combs, and other articles. Baby sea turtles are stuffed and sold as souvenirs, and sea turtle leather, which is soft and durable, is much prized for shoes, handbags, and wallets. Sea turtle oil is also used in cosmetics.

More harmful is that many nesting areas have been turned into resorts or public beaches. Females searching for nesting beaches avoid lights because dark areas along the horizon indicate land, and lights along a beach could look like a starry horizon. Nests are also destroyed by the more frequent storms. Sea turtle eggs, particularly those of leatherbacks, are said to be an aphrodisiac, a myth that probably arose because adult turtles can be seen copulating for long periods at sea. There is still a flourishing, though technically illegal, market for sea turtle eggs in many coastal regions, particularly in Latin America and Southeast Asia. The eggs are located by pushing a stick into the sand until it comes out yellow and then the eggs are taken by the bucketful. Eggs are fed to pigs or cattle and eaten by birds, dogs, wild pigs, and other animals. Artificial lighting also disorients baby turtles after hatching, so they do not head to sea and therefore die, often eaten by seabirds and other predators.

Sea turtles also become entangled in gill and drift fishing nets, including abandoned ones, and die asphyxiated because they cannot swim to the surface to breathe. Others, like the loggerhead (*Caretta caretta*) in the Pacific, get snagged in pelagic longlines and end up part of the discarded by-catch. Many choke to death after swallowing plastic bags they think are jellyfishes. Shrimp nets are estimated to kill thousands of sea turtles a year in Southeast Asia and elsewhere. They have been especially deadly to the Kemp's (or Atlantic) ridley turtle (*Lepidochelys kempii*), the smallest of all sea turtles, in the Gulf of Mexico, once very common but now so rare that only a few thousand breeding females remain. It is the most endangered sea turtle.

All seven species of sea turtles are classified by the International Union for Conservation of Nature and Natural Resources (IUCN) as **threatened** worldwide because their numbers are low (see Table 18.1). IUCN's Red List places two of the species as **critically endangered,** one as **endangered,** and as such in great danger of disappearing. The number of leatherbacks has decreased by 95% since the early 1980s, mostly victims of fishing nets, and only a few thousand nesting leatherbacks remain in the Pacific. The six species of sea turtles found in United States waters are protected

Green turtle (*Chelonia mydas*).

Bill Ober

under the Endangered Species Act of 1973. Three of these species are officially classified as endangered: the leatherback, hawksbill, and Kemp's ridley. The numbers of green turtles, once very common, have been increasing in some areas because of protection, and loggerheads increased by 154% from 1973 to 2009 in a protected area off South Africa.

Shrimp nets in the United States have been required since 1989 to be fitted with turtle exclusion devices, or TEDs, to allow sea turtles to escape once caught in the nets. But sea turtles are not protected at all in many countries and, in those where they are, enforcement is difficult because it is impossible to protect all coasts and nesting grounds from fishers and egg hunters. Stricter worldwide enforcement of conservation practices, the establishment of reserves and national parks to protect nesting beaches, the control of pollution and fishing practices, the restocking of former nesting areas, and the regulation of trade in sea turtle products might help save them.

basking in large groups on rocks along the coast, warming up after swimming in the cold water. It eats seaweeds, diving as deep as 10 m (33 ft) to graze.

Another marine reptile is the **saltwater crocodile** (*Crocodylus porosus*), which inhabits mangrove forests and estuaries in the eastern Indian Ocean, Australia, and some of the western Pacific islands. Saltwater crocodiles are also found in rivers but are known to venture into the open sea. There is a record of an individual 10 m (33 ft) long, but they are rarely more than 6 m (20 ft). They are among the most aggressive of all marine animals and do attack and eat humans. They are more feared than sharks.

The **American crocodile** (*Crocodylus acutus*) is also considered a marine species. Although it lives mostly in freshwater, it tolerates seawater and can be found in coastal areas in Florida, the West Indies, and Central America and northern South America. It has also been recorded in the open ocean.

Marine reptiles include the sea turtles, sea snakes, the marine iguana, and the saltwater and the American crocodiles. Almost all lay their eggs on land.

FIGURE 9.3 Egg laying in the olive ridley turtle (*Lepidochelys olivacea*) culminates a long and hazardous trip by females. It is at this time that they are most vulnerable.

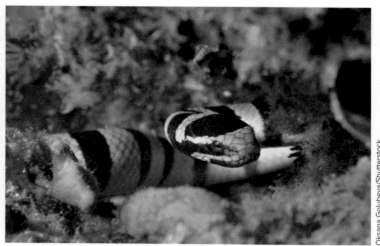

FIGURE 9.4 Sea snakes are found across the Indian Ocean to the Pacific coast from the Gulf of California to Ecuador. The conspicuous patterns of sea snakes, like in the yellow-lipped, or banded, sea krait (*Laticauda colubrina*) from the western Pacific shown here, could be a warning to potential predators because many fishes learn to associate such ornamentation with danger. There are no sea snakes in the Atlantic, but a sea-level canal across Central America could allow their dispersal into the Caribbean. Notice the flattened tip of the body (just under the head here), an adaptation for swimming.

Biology of Marine Reptiles

Swimming and Diving Like most fishes and all land reptiles, marine reptiles are **poikilotherms,** or "cold blooded," because their body temperature varies with that of the environment. With the exception of the leatherback turtle (see below), marine reptiles are **ectotherms** because they lose most of their metabolic heat to the environment to match their body temperature with the external temperature (see "Temperature," in 4.3; Table 4.2). Like other poikilotherms, their metabolic rate—and therefore activity level—varies with temperature so they get sluggish in the cold. This tends to keep reptiles out of cold regions.

A remarkable exception is the leatherback turtle, which can venture into cold water because of its ability to keep body temperature higher than that of the surrounding water, which makes it an **endotherm.** Heat loss is reduced by transferring body heat back to the body by means of a network of blood vessels in the flippers as in the muscles of tunas and other fishes (see Fig. 15.22), by being large with a comparatively small surface area, and by storing fat for insulation.

> Reptiles are poikilotherms and ectotherms, generally limiting their distribution to warm water. One exception is the leatherback turtle, which is an endotherm.

Sea turtles, although slow on land, are fast swimmers in water. They use their flattened, flipper-like forelimbs to propel them through the water, while the smaller, paddle-shaped back limbs are mostly used for steering. The heavy shell is streamlined and flattened, but bones are spongy and the accumulation of fat further helps in buoyancy. While most sea turtles are shallow divers, leatherbacks have been tracked diving more than 1,000 m (3,300 ft).

The bodies of sea snakes, which are not particularly fast swimmers, are laterally flattened and the tail paddle-shaped for

FIGURE 9.5 Though seemingly awkward on land, the marine iguana of the Galápagos Islands (*Amblyrhynchus cristatus*) is an elegant swimmer under water. It swims by undulating the body and the laterally flattened tail, the tip of which is shown on the bottom left.

swimming. A similar adaptation is seen in the marine iguana, a strong swimmer, where the tail is laterally flattened.

Reproduction All sea turtles must return to land to reproduce. They typically migrate long distances to lay their eggs on remote sandy beaches, and they have been doing so millions of years before humans appeared on the scene. Green turtles still gather to nest on beaches on the Caribbean coast of Central America, Northern

Australia, Southeast Asia, Ascension Island (in the middle of the South Atlantic), and a few other locations.

Marine biologists have tagged adult sea turtles at Ascension and have found that the turtles regularly cross 2,200 km (1,360 mi) of open water from their feeding grounds along the coast of Brazil (see map of the world in Appendix C), a journey that takes a little more than two months. Loggerhead turtles travel as much as 14,500 km (9,000 mi) between feeding and nesting grounds, and leatherbacks have been tracked as traveling as much as 17,614 km (10,945 mi). Researchers now use satellite tracking tags attached to shells to investigate migrations. There is evidence that they do it by sensing Earth's magnetic field.

Green turtles return to their nesting areas every two to four years, often against prevailing currents. Copulating pairs of sea turtles are often seen offshore, but only females venture ashore, usually at night. Biologists have mostly tagged females because turtles can be tagged most easily on land. Evidence that females return to the beaches where they were born has been obtained by analyzing the **DNA** of breeding populations at sites around the world. The DNA of turtles breeding in one area differs from the DNA of turtles breeding at other sites. It thus appears that turtles keep returning to the same place generation after generation. Females congregate on the beach, and each excavates a hole in the sand using both pairs of flippers. They lay between 100 and 200 large, leathery eggs in each nest (see Fig. 9.3). Molecular studies have demonstrated the multiple paternities of offspring in single clutches of eggs in green and other sea turtles. The female covers the eggs with sand before she returns to sea. She can make several trips ashore during the breeding season, laying eggs each time.

The eggs hatch after about 60 days of incubation in the sand. The baby turtles must then dig themselves out of the sand and crawl all the way back to the water, protected by darkness if lucky. The hatchlings are easy prey for land crabs and birds, especially during the day. Young turtles are also taken by fishes and seabirds.

Sea turtles, as in many other reptiles, show **temperature-dependent sex determination.** Almost all eggs incubated at lower temperatures, as in nests covered by vegetation or nests built in light-colored sand, hatch as males; most of those incubated at higher temperatures hatch as females. There are concerns that a global temperature rise (see Special Report: Climate Change) could seriously affect sex ratios in sea turtles and other marine reptiles, increasing pressure on already threatened or endangered species. The proportion of female green turtles has already sharply increased in the northern Great Barrier Reef, Australia.

Sea turtles return to nesting areas to lay their eggs, often after swimming long distances. Sex determination is temperature-dependent.

Some sea snakes form large groups, a behavior perhaps related to reproduction. They mate in the ocean. Males have two copulatory organs, so fertilization is internal. Sea snakes are **ovoviviparous,** and the eggs develop inside the mother, who then gives birth to live young. A few species, however, still come ashore to lay their eggs. In contrast to other marine reptiles, the offspring in each sea snake brood share the same father. Female marine iguanas burrow their

eggs in sand, as many as six in the larger females and, like sea turtles, abandon their nests after a short time.

9.2 SEABIRDS

Most living birds have the ability to fly, and in contrast to living reptiles, their bodies are covered with waterproof feathers that help conserve body heat. Waterproofing is provided by oil from a gland above the base of the tail, and birds rub the oil into their feathers with their beaks during preening. Flight is made easier by their light, hollow bones. Their eggs have hard shells that are more resistant to water loss than those of reptiles.

Birds are vertebrates that have feathers and light bones as adaptations for flight.

Seabirds are birds that spend a significant part of their lives at sea, feeding on marine life. Most breed in large colonies on land and often build their nests on the ground, sometimes traveling long distances to get food.

Seabirds are birds that nest on land but feed entirely or partially at sea.

Though comprising only about 3% of the estimated 9,700 species of birds, seabirds are distributed worldwide, and their impact on marine life is significant. Most are predators of fishes, squids, and bottom invertebrates, but some feed on plankton. Seabirds have amazing appetites, needing a lot of food to supply the energy required to maintain their body temperature.

Seabirds have evolved from several different groups of land birds. As a result, they differ widely in their flying skills, feeding habits, and ability to live away from land.

Penguins

Of all seabirds, **penguins** (Fig. 9.6*a*) are the most radically adapted to live at sea. They are flightless, with wings modified into stubby "flippers" that allow them to "fly" underwater (see "Biology of Seabirds," below). All but one of the 18 species of penguins live primarily in Antarctica and other cold temperate regions of the Southern Hemisphere. The exception is the Galápagos penguin (*Spheniscus mendiculus*), which lives right on the Equator. Even so, this penguin is confined to regions in the Galápagos that are bathed by cold currents.

The larger penguins, like the imposing emperor penguin (*Aptenodytes forsteri;* Fig. 9.6*a*), hunt for fish and squid. The Adélie (*Pygoscelis adeliae*) and other small penguins feed mostly on **krill.**

Ovoviviparous Animals Live-bearing animals in which the eggs develop and hatch in the reproductive tract of females.
• 8.3, Biology of Fishes

Krill Planktonic, shrimp-like crustaceans.
• 7.6, Arthropods: The Armored Achievers; Figure 17.12

(a)

(b)

(c)

(d)

(e)

FIGURE 9.6 (*a*) An emperor penguin (*Aptenodytes forsteri*) and chick. The emperor is the largest living penguin, with a height of up to 115 cm (45 in). (*b*) The brown booby (*Sula leucogaster*) nests in the Caribbean and Gulf of California. It is a regular visitor to the Gulf of Mexico. (*c*) The gannet (*Morus bassanus*) is the largest seabird in the North Atlantic. It nests in large colonies on offshore islands like Bonaventure Island, Québec, Canada, where around 50,000 birds breed every year. (*d*) The black-browed albatross (*Thalassarche melanophrys*) breeds mostly on islands bordering the Southern Ocean. The large wings allow albatrosses to cover long distances with a minimum exertion. (*e*) Male frigatebirds (*Fregata*) display to females by inflating a bright-red throat pouch.

Penguins have strong beaks, a characteristic of seabirds that feed on fish and large plankton like krill (Fig. 9.7*b*). Some species migrate seasonally between feeding grounds at sea and nesting areas on land or ice. They establish breeding colonies, which in Adélies, the most widely distributed of penguin species, can number more than a million pairs. Emperor and Adélies are the only penguins that breed on the Antarctic continent rather than on subantarctic islands or elsewhere.

Tubenoses

The **tubenoses** comprise a large group of seabirds with distinctive tube-like nostrils and heavy beaks that are usually curved at the tip (Fig. 9.7*a*). They spend months and even years on the open sea. Like other seabirds and sea turtles, they have **salt glands** that empty into the nostrils and get rid of excess salts. Tubenoses include the albatrosses (*Diomedea, Thalassarche;* Fig. 9.6*d*), shearwaters (*Puffinus*), and petrels (*Pterodroma*; Figs. 9.7*a* and 9.8*d, e*).

Tubenoses are very skillful fliers, often seen flying low over the water. Most catch fish at the sea surface (Fig. 9.7*a*), though some, like the giant petrel (*Macronectes*), scavenge on dead birds or whales. The whalebirds, or prions (*Pachyptila*), feed on krill and other plankton. Albatrosses are magnificent gliders with huge wings that hardly

ever seem to flap. They are among the most efficient fliers in the world, allowing them to fly very long distances in search of food. The wandering albatross (*Diomedea exulans*) has wingspans of up to 3.4 m (11 ft), the largest of any bird alive. Most species of albatrosses are threatened or endangered as a consequence of increased mortality resulting from longline fishing coupled with their slow reproductive rate. Pairs breed every two years because it takes almost a year to rear a single chick.

Tubenoses make some of the most spectacular migrations of any animal. Many breed on islands around Antarctica, then migrate across the open ocean to summer feeding grounds near the Arctic. The wandering albatross gets its name from the fact that it spends two years or more traveling, taking advantage of the strong winds that blow across the Southern Ocean, before returning to nesting sites near Antarctica. Some non-breeding individuals wander off and pay visits as far away as California and the Mediterranean.

Pelicans and Related Seabirds

Pelicans (*Pelecanus*) have a unique pouch below their large beaks that are used as nets for fishing. Some species, like the brown pelican (*P. occidentalis;* see Fig. 18.11), feed by plunging into the water and catching fish in the pouch (Fig. 9.8*a*). The brown pelican

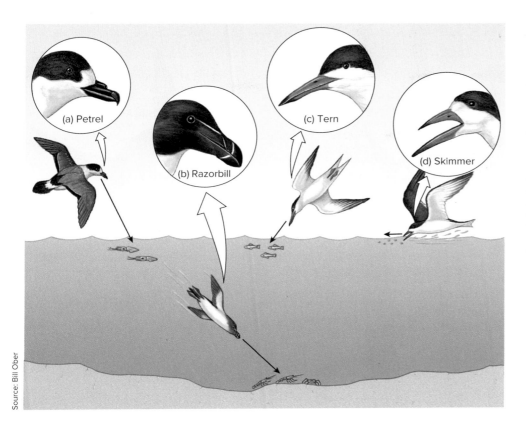

Source: Bill Ober

FIGURE 9.7 The shape of a seabird's beak is related to the bird's food and its feeding style. (*a*) In tubenoses like petrels (*Pterodroma*) the beak is relatively short, heavy, and hooked—an ideal shape for holding and tearing prey that is too big to be swallowed whole. Such a beak is best suited for shallow feeding because its size and shape interfere with fast pursuit under water. (*b*) The beak is heavy but more streamlined in the razorbill (*Alca*), penguins (*Aptenodytes*), and other seabirds that dive deeper to feed on crustaceans and other prey. (*c*) Terns (*Sterna*), boobies (*Sula*), and other plunge divers have a straight and narrow beak for feeding on fish that are swallowed whole. (*d*) Skimmers (*Rynchops*) are the only birds with a lower beak that is longer than the upper, which permits feeding while flying. Shorebirds that feed on mudflats have a long, thin beak that allows them to get to prey buried in mud (see Fig. 12.12).

was decimated by pesticide pollution (see "Persistent Toxic Substances," in 18.2). It has made a comeback as a result of restrictions on the manufacture and use of the pesticide DDT.

Cormorants (*Phalacrocorax;* Fig. 9.8*e*) are long-necked, usually black, seabirds that dive and pursue their prey. About 40 species are recognized, some known as **shags.** Cormorants can be easily identified by their low flights over water and that they float low in the water, with only the neck above the surface. The Galápagos cormorant (*P. harrisi*), however, is flightless. Cormorants are generally seen ashore in a spread-wing resting position, allegedly to dry their feathers.

Frigatebirds (*Fregata*) have narrow wings and a long, forked tail. They soar majestically along the coast, forcing other seabirds to regurgitate fish in midair or catching prey, such as flying fish chased out of the water by tuna or dolphinfish, from the surface (Fig. 9.8*b*). These agile pirates rarely, if ever, enter the water, not even to rest, because their feathers are not very waterproof. They can fly for days, recorded as long as 63 days, without rest! They soar with the air that rises under cumulus clouds and glide downward to feed, hardly moving their wings. They do manage to sleep while flying, with one or both sides of their brains asleep for short intervals.

Gulls and Related Seabirds

Gulls (*Larus*) and their relatives make up the largest group of seabirds. Common and widespread, gulls are predators and scavengers happy to eat just about anything (Fig. 9.8*c*). They are very successful in the company of humans and congregate near piers, garbage dumps. Jaegers and skuas (*Stercorarius*) are gull-like predators that

steal fish from other birds (Fig. 9.8*b*). They nest near the rookeries of penguins and other seabirds and eat their eggs and young.

Terns (*Sterna*) are graceful flyers that hover over their fish prey before plunging for it (Fig. 9.7*c*). The Arctic tern (*S. paradisaea*) is another amazing wanderer. It breeds in the Arctic during the northern summer and can travel an average of 70,800 km (44,000 mi), to Antarctica for the southern summer, and then returns before returning to the Arctic.

Also related to gulls are several cold-water diving seabirds. Puffins (*Fratercula;* Fig. 9.6*e*) have heavy beaks similar to those of parrots. The related razorbill (*Alca torda*) is a black and white bird reminiscent of penguins (Fig. 9.7*b*). Razor bills could fill the role of penguins, which are absent in the Northern Hemisphere. Like penguins, they use their wings to swim under water. Their extinct cousin, the great auk (*Pinguinus impennis*), looked and acted like a penguin. Great auks once lived in great numbers in the North Atlantic but were slaughtered for their eggs, meat, and feathers. The last great auk died in 1844.

Shorebirds

Usually included among the seabirds are many species of wading **shorebirds,** most of which do not have webbed feet. Because they do not swim much, they are not seabirds in the strict sense. Many live in inland waters as well as the sea. Some are common in estuaries and coastal marshes. Plovers, sandpipers, and similar birds are related to gulls (see Fig. 9.1). Many other shorebirds live on the coast: rails, coots, herons, egrets, and ducks. The distribution and significance of shorebirds is discussed in Chapter 12.

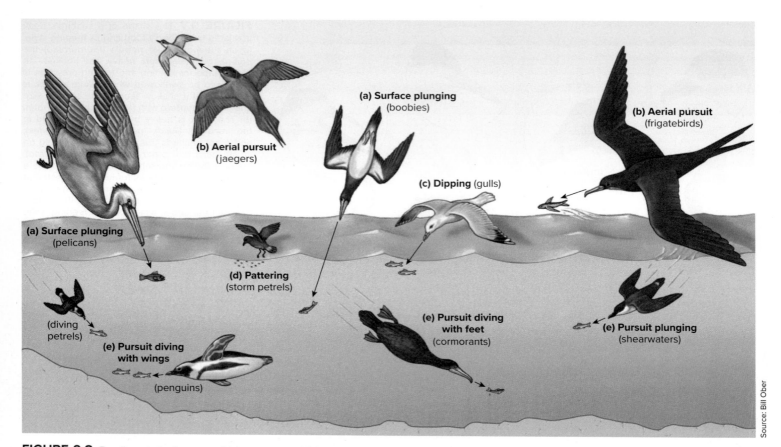

FIGURE 9.8 Feeding strategies vary widely among seabirds. (a) Pelicans (_Pelecanus_) and boobies (_Sula_) plunge from the air into the water, (b) jaegers (_Stercorarius_) pursue other seabirds and force them to regurgitate food, and (b) frigatebirds (_Fregata_) take fish from the surface and steal fish from other seabirds. (c) Gulls (_Larus_) rarely plunge from the air, and (d) storm petrels (_Oceanodroma_) simply flutter over the waves. (e) Divers like cormorants (_Phalacrocorax_) pursue prey under water, swimming with their wings or feet. Mudflat shorebirds also follow various strategies (see Fig. 12.13).

Biology of Seabirds

Swimming and Diving. Birds are **homeotherms,** commonly referred to as "warm-blooded." They are also endotherms. This has allowed seabirds, in contrast to marine reptiles, to swim and dive in a wide variety of marine environments, mostly along coasts.

Seabirds are endotherms and homeotherms and are thus able to live across practically all oceans.

Penguins are spectacular swimmers, propelling their streamlined bodies with powerful strokes of the wings (see Fig. 9.8e). Like all true seabirds, penguins have webbed feet for swimming. Their bones are denser than those of other birds to reduce buoyancy to make diving easier. The upper part of their bodies is black, their bellies white, an example of **countershading** as in many open-water fishes (Fig. 9.15; see "Coloration and Camouflage," in 15.2), and they are adapted to cold temperatures by having a layer of fat under the skin and closely packed feathers. The waterproof feathers trap air that, warmed by body heat, protects against the cold like a down coat. They can also jump out of the water and sometimes cover long distances by alternately swimming and jumping. They breathe air while jumping out of the water, with the efficiency of oxygen intake increased by air continuously flowing, in addition to the lungs,

through air sacs characteristic of all birds. Antarctic penguins do not freeze when out of the water because water within the feathers is squeezed out rather than staying in and freezing. Oil from the oil glands helps repel water. Emperor penguins have been known to dive more than 200 m (650 ft) deep. As in marine mammals (see "Diving," below), penguins have a high number of **erythrocytes,** or red blood cells, which have a high concentration of **hemoglobin,** their muscles contain high amounts of **myoglobin** to store additional oxygen, and their heart rate is reduced to cut down oxygen consumption while diving. On land it is another story. They are clumsy, awkward, and nearsighted, having eyes that are adapted for underwater vision.

Penguins are adapted to fast swimming and diving in cold water by having a streamlined body, flipper-like wings, a layer of fat, closely packed feathers, a high number of erythrocytes with a high concentration of hemoglobin, and myoglobin in muscles.

Reproduction Seabirds typically mate for life. Courtship to selection of the "perfect" partner and recognition by the mated pairs involves elaborate display behaviors, which include calls.

The male emperor penguin incubates a single large egg during the dark Antarctic winter. The female leaves to feed as soon as she lays the egg. The male, standing on ice, must keep the egg warm by holding it on top of his feet and against his body for 64 days. Males huddle

together in huge groups to protect themselves from the cold and winter storms. Emperors lay their eggs at the coldest time of the year so that the egg hatches during the productive Antarctic summer, when food is most plentiful. When the single egg hatches, the female finally returns and regurgitates food for the fuzzy chick. Both parents take turns feeding the chick. While the parents feed, the fast-growing young are herded into groups guarded by a few adult "baby sitters." Returning parents identify their chick among thousands by its voice and appearance. The parents continue to feed the chick for five-and-a-half months, until it is strong enough to feed itself at sea (Fig. 9.6a). In contrast, Adélies and other Antarctic penguins lay their eggs, typically two, during summer.

A threat to penguins is the reduction of Antarctic sea ice, a result of **global climate change** (see Special Report: Climate Change). Emperor penguins depend on the ice to breed and escape from predators. There has also been a drop in the populations of some species of penguins correlated with a decline in their food, krill, which depend in part on minute algae that grow under ice. Satellite images, however, have revealed previously unknown colonies of emperor penguins.

Albatrosses and other tubenoses take a long time to reach sexual maturity, around five years in albatrosses. They live for a long time, however, 50 years or more in albatrosses. Most return to nest on the same wind-swept, remote islands that are inaccessible to predators. Male and female remain faithful to each other and perform particularly elaborate courtship and greeting behaviors. Incubation of the egg in large nests and care of the single chick takes eight months or more. Incubation in the albatrosses lasts from 70 to 80 days, even longer in the large-size species. They feed the young regurgitated food and energy-rich oil produced by the parents' stomachs. The overall investment in reproduction is great, so they typically do not lay eggs in successive years.

> Seabirds typically nest in dense colonies on land, mate for life, have elaborate mating behaviors, and lay few, usually large eggs.

Pelicans nest in large colonies along the coast, where space, as in gannets (see Fig. 9.6c), can be limited. As in many other seabirds, they typically lay fewer eggs than land birds do, and their broods are reduced when less food is available. The nests are made of twigs and anything else they can find. The excrement of millions of pelicans, boobies, cormorants, and other seabirds accumulates as **guano.** Guano deposits are particularly thick in dry coastal regions and islands near very productive waters like the coasts along western South America and southwestern Africa. These deposits are mined for fertilizer (see Box 17.1, "Of Fish and Seabirds, Fishers and Chickens").

9.3 MARINE MAMMALS

About 200 million years ago another major group of air-breathing vertebrates, the mammals (class Mammalia), evolved from now-extinct reptiles. Mammals were overshadowed by the dinosaurs, which were reptiles. About 65 million years ago, however, the dominant dinosaurs became extinct. It was then that mammals thrived, taking the place of the dinosaurs. There are now roughly 4,600 species of mammals, including humans, but fishes, reptiles, and birds each outnumber mammals in number of species.

Like birds, mammals have the advantage of being endotherms and homeotherms. The skin of mammals, however, has hair instead of feathers to retain body heat. With few exceptions, mammals are **viviparous.** The embryo receives nutrients and oxygen through the **placenta,** or afterbirth, a membrane that connects it to the womb, thus an instance of **placental viviparity.** The newborn is fed by milk secreted by the mother's **mammary glands.** Instead of releasing millions of eggs, mammals produce few—but well-cared-for—young.

And then there is the brain. It is larger in relation to body size and far more complex than that of other vertebrates, allowing the storage and processing of more information. This accounts in part for the amazing adaptability of mammals. They live anywhere there is air to breathe and food to eat. This, of course, includes the ocean.

At least five different groups of land mammals succeeded in invading the oceans. They have followed different paths in adapting to the marine environment. Some are so fish-like that we have to remind ourselves that they have hair and bear live young nourished by their mother's milk.

Seals, Sea Lions, and the Walrus

Seals, sea lions, and the walrus are marine mammals that have paddle-shaped flippers for swimming but still need to rest and breed on land. They make up one of the 19 or 20 major groups, or orders, of mammals, the **pinnipeds** (order **Pinnipedia;** see Fig. 9.1). Pinnipeds evolved from an early form of terrestrial carnivore (order Carnivora), which includes cats, dogs, and bears. The similarities are so close that many biologists classify them with the carnivores. Pinnipeds are predators, feeding mostly on fish and squid. Their streamlined bodies are adapted for swimming (Fig. 9.9).

Most pinnipeds live in cold water. To keep warm they have a thick layer of fat, called **blubber,** under their skin. Besides acting as insulation, it serves as a food reserve and helps provide buoyancy. Some pinnipeds also have bristly hair for added protection against the cold. Many of them are quite large, which also helps conserve body heat because large animals have less surface area for their size than small animals and therefore lose less body heat (see Fig. 4.17).

> Pinnipeds, which include seals and their relatives, are marine mammals, with flippers and blubber, that need to breed on land.

The largest group of pinnipeds, some 19 species, is the **seals.** Seals are distinguished by having rear flippers that cannot be moved forward (Fig. 9.9b). On land they must move by pulling themselves along with their front flippers. They swim with powerful strokes of the rear flippers.

Homeotherms Organisms able to keep their body temperature more or less constant regardless of the temperature of the environment.
• 4.3, Challenges of Life in the Sea; Table 4.2

Hemoglobin A blood protein that transports oxygen in many animals; it is contained in *erythrocytes*, or red blood cells, in vertebrates.
Myoglobin A muscle protein in many animals that stores oxygen.
• 8.3, Biology of Fishes

Viviparous Animals Live-bearing animals whose embryos develop within their mothers' bodies and are nourished by the maternal bloodstream.
• 8.3, Biology of Fishes

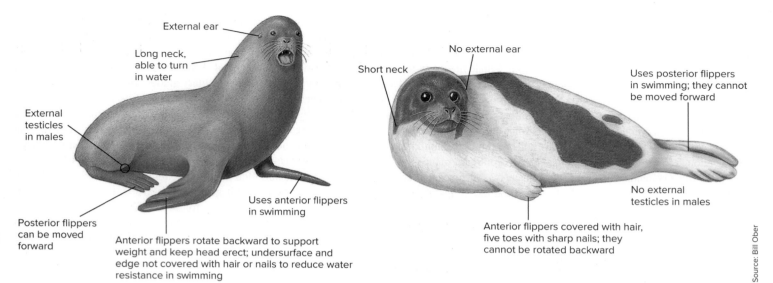

External ear

Long neck, able to turn in water

External testicles in males

Posterior flippers can be moved forward

Anterior flippers rotate backward to support weight and keep head erect; undersurface and edge not covered with hair or nails to reduce water resistance in swimming

Uses anterior flippers in swimming

(a) **Sea lions and fur seals**

No external ear

Short neck

Uses posterior flippers in swimming; they cannot be moved forward

No external testicles in males

Anterior flippers covered with hair, five toes with sharp nails; they cannot be rotated backward

(b) **Seals**

Source: Bill Ober

FIGURE 9.9 Though they differ in some structural features and the ways in which they swim and move on land, (*a*) sea lions and fur seals and (*b*) seals are now thought to have evolved from the same group of land carnivores.

(a)

John Heine

(c)

slowmotiongli/Shutterstock

(b)

Peter Castro

FIGURE 9.10 Seals. (*a*) The northern elephant seal (*Mirounga angustirostris*), so called because of the huge proboscis of the male, was almost exterminated for its blubber. By 1890 only about 100 remained, but because of protection and a drop in the use of its blubber, it rapidly recovered, and there are now around 110,000 of them along the Pacific coast of North America. (*b*) The New Zealand fur seal (*Arctocephalus forsteri*), like the other fur seals, has a thick underfur. (*c*) Female harp seals (*Phoca groenlandica*), give birth to white, furry pups on the floating Arctic ice. Pups must grow fast and shed their white coats before the drifting ice melts. The clubbing of young pups for their white fur in eastern Canada provoked worldwide protests, and it was banned in 1987. Unemployment caused by the collapse of fisheries and higher demand for the fur, however, prompted the hunt of older harp seals. Some 335,000 seals were killed in 2006 during the commercial seal hunt, about 26,000 in 2001. Decreased ice because of global climate change is now a major threat.

Harbor seals (*Phoca vitulina;* Fig. 9.9*b*) are common in the North Atlantic and North Pacific. They feed mostly on fish, using their whiskers to detect the currents produced by fish gills. Elephant seals (*Mirounga;* Fig. 9.10*a*) are the largest pinnipeds. Males, or bulls, reach 6 m (20 ft) in length and can weigh as much as 3,600 kg (4 tons). One unusual seal is the crabeater seal (*Lobodon carcinophagus*), which feeds on Antarctic krill. These seals strain krill from the water with their intricately cusped, sieve-like teeth. Unlike most seals, monk seals (*Monachus*) live in warm regions. The Mediterranean (*M. monachus*) and Hawaiian (*M. schauinslandi*) monk seals are now endangered. A third species, the Caribbean monk seal (*M. tropicalis*), was last seen in 1952.

Seals are hunted for their skin and meat and for the oil extracted from their blubber. The Marine Mammal Protection Act of 1972 extends protection to all marine mammals and restricts the sale of their products in the United States. For some seals, however, this protection has not been enough (see Table 18.1).

Sea lions, or eared seals, and the related **fur seals** have external ears, and can move their rear flippers forward so they can use all four limbs to walk or run on land. The front flippers can be rotated backward to support the body, permitting the animal to sit on land with its neck and head raised (Fig. 9.9a). Sea lions are graceful and agile swimmers, relying mostly on their broad front flippers. Adult males are much bigger than females, or cows, and have a massive head with a hairy mane (see Fig. 9.34a).

There are six species of sea lions and nine of fur seals. The most familiar is the California sea lion (*Zalophus californianus;* see Fig. 9.35) of the Pacific coast of North America. These sea lions are the trained barking circus "seals" that do tricks for a fish or two. Fur seals (Fig. 9.10b), like the northern fur seal (*Callorhinus ursinus*), were once almost exterminated for their fur. Now most are protected around the world, though some species are still hunted. Sea lions are luckier because they lack the underfur of their cousins. Still, both sea lions and fur seals can run afoul of fishers. They sometimes drown in nets or are shot because of their notorious ability to steal fish. Populations of the Steller sea lion (*Eumetopias jubatus*) in Alaska have decreased by 80% since the 1970s, probably because of a decline in the fish they eat as a result of an increase in commercial fishing.

The **walrus** (*Odobenus rosmarus;* Fig. 9.11) is a large pinniped with a pair of distinctive tusks protruding from the mouth in both sexes. It feeds mostly on bottom invertebrates, particularly clams. It was once thought that the walrus used its tusks to dig up food, but there is no evidence for this. Instead, they apparently suck up their food as they move along the bottom. The stiff whiskers of the snout probably act as feelers. The tusks are used for defense and to hold or anchor to ice.

The walrus is restricted to the Arctic Ocean and adjacent waters. Two populations isolated from each other can be identified, one along the Arctic coasts of Russia and Alaska extending to the North Pacific, and a second in northern Canada, Greenland, and the North Atlantic. Each population is considered as belonging to a geographically isolated race, or **subspecies.**

Sea Otter, Marine Otter, and Polar Bear

The **sea otter** (*Enhydra lutris;* Fig. 9.12) is a member of the order **Carnivora.** The sea otter is the smallest truly marine mammal; an average male weighs 25 to 35 kg (60 to 80 lb). It also differs from other marine mammals in lacking a layer of blubber. Insulation from the cold is provided by air trapped in its dense fur. This splendid, dark brown fur, unfortunately, attracted hunters. Sea otters were slaughtered to near extinction until they became protected by an international agreement in 1911. Sea otters in California then slowly expanded from the few individuals that had managed to survive in remote locations. Their numbers, however, have been declining in recent years. They have slightly declined in California since peaking in 2004, mostly as a result of disease (see "Kelp Communities," in 13.3, and Box 13.3, "*Toxoplasma*: From Cats to Sea Otters"). The sea otter is still a threatened species (see Table 18.1).

Three subspecies of sea otters are recognized. The Asian sea otter is found from northern Japan to Siberia, the Alaskan sea otter from the Aleutian Islands to the northwestern United States, and the California, or southern, sea otter in central California. They differ from one another in having slightly different sizes, in the amount of time they spend on land, and a few other characters.

Sea otters are playful and intelligent animals. They spend most or all of their time in the water, including breeding and giving birth. The furry pup is constantly groomed and nursed by its mother. Sea otters need to eat 25 to 30% of their body weight per day, so they spend a lot of time looking for food. They satisfy their appetites with sea urchins, abalone, mussels, crabs, other invertebrates, and

U.S. Fish & Wildlife Service

FIGURE 9.11 The walrus (*Odobenus rosmarus*) lives at the edge of pack ice in the Arctic. They also crowd onto beaches on isolated islands and coasts, but a reduction of coastal sea ice has limited these resting areas. The walrus is still hunted legally by indigenous people of Alaska and Siberia.

steve bly/Alamy Stock Photo

FIGURE 9.12 California sea otters (*Enhydra lutris*) are remarkable for their use of a tool—a rock for crushing sea urchins and molluscs. They carry a flat rock in side "pockets" of loose skin and fur. The sea otter floats on its back at the surface, places the rock on its chest, and crushes its toughest prey against it. Some have been observed carrying and using beer bottles as tools!

FIGURE 9.13 The polar bear (*Ursus maritimus*) is beautifully adapted to live in the Arctic drifting ice, a habitat that is rapidly shrinking. Males have been reported to weigh as much as 700 kg (1,540 lbs). The legs, tail, and ears of polar bears are proportionally shorter than in other bears, adaptations to minimize heat loss in low temperatures.

FIGURE 9.14 An estimated 6,300 West Indian manatees (*Trichechus manatus*) remain along the coasts and rivers of Florida. Some concentrate in the warm-water effluents of power plants. They are strictly protected, but collisions with boats take their toll. An alarming increase in mortality in Florida has been linked to nutrient pollutants triggering light-blocking algal blooms that affect seagrasses, the main food of manatees.

even fishes. Sea otters help protect kelp beds from sea urchins (see "Kelp Communities," in 13.3).

The rare marine otter, or sea cat (*Lontra felina*), is a small (up to 6 kg, or 13 lb) otter that inhabits the Pacific coast of temperate South America. It feeds mostly on small invertebrates, but, unlike the sea otter, it spends most of the time on rocky shores. The marine otter is endangered (see Table 18.1) because of hunting and habitat loss.

The **polar bear** (*Ursus maritimus;* Fig. 9.13) is the second member of the order Carnivora that inhabits the marine environment. Polar bears are semiaquatic animals that spend a good part of their lives on drifting ice in the Arctic. They are threatened by the decrease in Arctic ice. They feed primarily on seals, which they stalk and capture as the seals surface to breathe or rest. As the ice retreats, however, polar bears are venturing inland in search of alternative land-based food such as snow geese eggs and caribou. Attacks on humans have also increased.

Manatees and Dugong

It is hard to believe that relatives of the elephant, **manatees** and the **dugong,** live at sea. They are also known as **sea cows,** or **sirenians** (order **Sirenia**). Both have a pair of front flippers but no rear limbs (Fig. 9.14). They swim with up-and-down strokes of their horizontal tail. Manatees have a rounded, paddle-shaped tail, whereas the dugong's tail has pointed tips like the tails of whales and dolphins (see Fig. 9.25). The round, tapered body is well padded with blubber. They have wrinkled skin with a few scattered hairs. The group is named after the mythical mermaids or sirens whose songs lured lonely sailors!

Sirenians are gentle creatures usually living in groups. They are the only strict vegetarians among marine mammals. Their large and prehensile lips are used to feed on seagrasses and other aquatic vegetation. All sirenians are large. Dugongs can reach 3 m (10 ft) and 420 kg (930 lb), manatees 4.5 m (almost 15 ft) and 600 kg (1,320 lb).

The largest sirenian of all was the now-extinct Steller's sea cow, which supposedly grew to 7.5 m (25 ft) long (see Fig. 18.15). It was hunted to extinction.

Humans have exploited sirenians for their meat (which supposedly tastes like veal), skin, and oil-rich blubber. Like elephants and other large mammals, they reproduce slowly, typically one calf every three years. All four species of sirenians are in danger of extinction (see Table 18.1). Three species of manatee (*Trichechus*) live in the Atlantic Ocean; one is restricted to the Amazon and the other two inhabit shallow coastal waters and rivers from Florida to West Africa. The dugong (*Dugong dugon*) is strictly marine and survives from East Africa to some of the western Pacific islands. Its numbers are critically low throughout most of its range.

Whales, Dolphins, and Porpoises

The largest group of marine mammals is the **cetaceans** (order **Cetacea**)—the **whales, dolphins,** and **porpoises.** No group of marine animals has captured our imaginations like the dolphins and whales, perhaps because they are mammals like us. The heated controversy surrounding the treatment of cetaceans, particularly of orcas (killer whales) in marine parks is a good example of our emotional involvement with cetaceans.

Of all marine mammals, the cetaceans, together with the sirenians, have made the most complete transition to aquatic life. Whereas most other marine mammals return to land at least part of the time, these two groups spend their entire lives in the water. The bodies of cetaceans are streamlined and look remarkably fishlike (Fig. 9.15). This is a dramatic example of **convergent evolution,** in which different species develop similar structures because they have similar lifestyles. Though they superficially resemble fishes, cetaceans breathe air and will drown if trapped below the surface. They are endotherms, have hair (though scanty), and produce milk for their young.

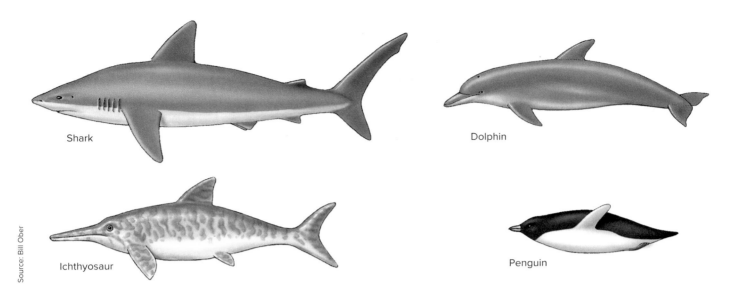

Source: Bill Ober

FIGURE 9.15 Streamlining to reduce water resistance evolved independently in different groups of fast-swimming marine animals: sharks, ichthyosaurs (reptiles that became extinct about 65 million years ago), dolphins, and penguins. Notice that dolphins lack posterior fins and that their flukes are horizontal, not vertical like the tail (caudal fin) of fishes (see Fig. 9.25).

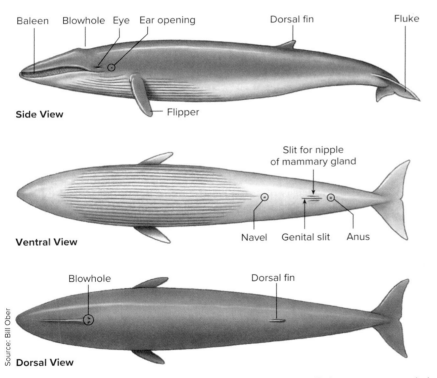

Source: Bill Ober

FIGURE 9.16 External morphology of a female blue whale (*Balaenoptera musculus*). Males have a genital slit halfway between the anus and navel, and they lack mammary slits.

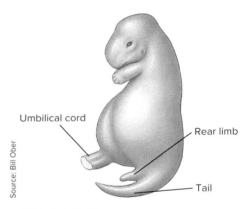

Source: Bill Ober

FIGURE 9.17 The fetus of a white-sided dolphin (*Lagenorhynchus*) shows two distinct pairs of limbs; the rear pair will eventually disappear. The umbilical cord connects the fetus with the placenta.

Cetaceans have a pair of front flippers (Fig. 9.16), but the rear pair of limbs has disappeared, though present in the embryo but failing to develop (Fig. 9.17). In adults they remain only as small, useless bones. Like fishes, many cetaceans have a dorsal fin, another example of convergent evolution. The muscular tail ends in a pair of fin-like, horizontal **flukes.** Blubber (see Fig. 4.2) provides insulation and buoyancy; body hair is practically absent. Cetacean nostrils differ from those of other mammals. Rather than being on the front of the head, they are on top, forming a single or double opening called the **blowhole** (Fig. 9.16). **Barnacles,** attached crustaceans, are often found living on the tough skin of whales (see Fig. 10.9).

There are some 90 living species of cetaceans. They are all marine except for five species of river dolphins in Asia and South America. Cetaceans are divided into two groups: the toothless, filter-feeding whales and the toothed, carnivorous whales, a group that includes the dolphins and porpoises.

Baleen Whales The toothless whales are better known as the **baleen whales.** Instead of teeth they have rows of flexible plates, named **baleen,** which hang from the upper jaws (Fig. 9.18). Baleen is made of keratin, the same material as our hair and nails. The inner edge of each plate consists of hair-like bristles that overlap

BALEEN WHALE	BALEEN PLATE	MOUTH OPEN, WATER IN	MOUTH CLOSED, WATER OUT

FIGURE 9.18 Filtering in whales involves vertical baleen plates. The number of plates varies with species, up to an average of 360 on each side in the sei whale (*Balaenoptera borealis*). The plates are up to 3 m (almost 10 ft) in the northern right whale (*Eubalaena glacialis*) but only 1 m (around 3 ft) in the blue whale (*Balaenoptera musculus*). The baleen, also called whalebone, was once used to make corset stays and whips. Water is filtered as the mouth closes and the tongue (yellow arrow) pushes up, forcing the water out through the baleen. Cetaceans, however, don't drink water.

and form a dense mat in the roof of the mouth. The whale filter-feeds by taking a big mouthful of water and squeezing it out through the bristles by pushing up the tongue.

Baleen whales are cetaceans that filter-feed with baleen plates.

Baleen whales are not only the largest whales but also are among the largest animals that have ever lived on Earth. Baleen whales feed on plankton and small fishes, and large size is an adaptation for increasing filter-feeding efficiency, a condition that has also evolved in the largest sharks (see Fig. 8.5), which are filter feeders. Furthermore, large size is not a constraint in water as it is for land animals because of gravity. They were once common in all the oceans, but overhunting has brought many species to the brink of extinction. There are 14 recognized species of baleen whales. The blue whale (*Balaenoptera musculus*), which is actually blue-gray, is the largest of all (Figs. 9.19*g* and 9.24). Males average 25 m (80 ft), and there is a record of a female 33.5 m (110 ft) long. How do you weigh a blue whale? Very carefully. They average 80,000 to 130,000 kg (90 to 140 tons), but the record is an estimated 178,000 kg (200 tons).

The blue, the fin (*Balaenoptera physalus;* Fig. 9.19*f*), and the minke whales (now recognized as two different species, the common minke, *Balaenoptera acutorostrata*, and the Antarctic minke,

Balaenoptera bonaerensis; Fig. 9.19*b*), together with four other related species, are known as the **rorquals.** The rorquals and the humpback whale (*Megaptera novaeangliae;* see Figs. 9.19*c* and 9.30), which is often included among the rorquals, feed by gulping up schools of fish and swarms of krill (see Box 9.3, "Feeding in the Blue Whale"). The lower part of the anterior half of the body expands when feeding, hence the distinctive, accordion-like grooves on the underside of these whales (Fig. 9.16). Krill is the most important part of the rorqual diet, especially in the Southern Hemisphere. Humpback whales often herd fishes like herring and mackerel by blowing curtains of bubbles around them and then surfacing after feeding with their mouths wide open (Fig. 9.20).

The right (*Eubalaena, Caperaea;* Fig. 9.19*a*) and the bowhead whales (*Balaena mysticetus;* Fig. 9.19*e*) feed by swimming along the surface with their huge mouths open. They have the largest baleen plates but the finest bristles (Fig. 9.18). This allows them to filter small plankton like copepods and some krill (Table 9.1).

Gray whales (*Eschrichtius robustus*) feed mostly on amphipods, small crustaceans that inhabit soft bottoms (Table 9.1). Grays stir up the bottom with their pointed snouts and then filter the sediment (Fig. 9.19*h*), leaving characteristic pits on the bottom. Most appear to feed on their right side because the baleen on this side is more worn. Some, however, are "left-handed" and feed on the left side. A 10-week-old female kept in captivity was fed 815 kg (1,800 lb) of squid every day, gaining weight at the rate of 1 kg (2.2 lb) an hour.

Source: Bill Ober

BOX 9.2 EVOLUTIONARY PERSPECTIVE

The Whales That Walked to Sea

It should be obvious that cetaceans are mammals. Their streamlined bodies and the absence of hind legs cannot disguise their affinities with land-dwelling mammals. Unlike the sea otter and pinnipeds, however, it is not easy to suggest what the first whales looked like and how they evolved into modern cetaceans. Extinct but already fully marine cetaceans are known from the fossil record. Missing were fossils clearly intermediate, or transitional, filling the gap between walking land mammals and swimming cetaceans.

An exciting discovery was made in Pakistan in 1979 when scientists found what proved to be the oldest known fossil whale. The fossil, officially described as *Pakicetus*, was found embedded in rocks formed from river deposits 52 million years old. The river was actually not far from the shores of the former Tethys Sea (see "Earth Geological History," in 2.2.

The fossil consists of a complete skull of an **archeocyte,** an extinct group of ancestors of modern cetaceans. Though limited to a skull, the fossil provides precious details on the origin of cetaceans. The skull is cetacean-like but its jawbones lack the enlarged space that is filled with fat or oil used for receiving underwater sound in modern whales (see "Echolocation," below). *Pakicetus* probably detected sound through the ear opening as in land mammals. The skull also lacks a blowhole, another adaptation for diving in cetaceans. Other features, however, show that

Pakicetus is a transitional form between a group of extinct flesh-eating mammals, the mesonychids, and cetaceans. It has been suggested that *Pakicetus* fed on fish in shallow water and was not yet adapted for life in the open ocean. It probably bred and gave birth on land.

Several skeletons of another early whale, *Basilosaurus*, were found in 1989 in sediments left by the Tethys Sea and now exposed in the Sahara Desert in Egypt. This whale lived around 40 million years ago, 12 million years after *Pakicetus*. Many incomplete skeletons were found but they included, for the first time in an archeocyte, a complete hind leg that features feet with three tiny toes. The legs are small, far too small to have supported the 50-foot-long *Basilosaurus* on land. *Basilosaurus* was undoubtedly a fully marine whale with possibly non-functional, or **vestigial,** hind legs.

Another remarkable find was reported in 1994, also from Pakistan. The now-extinct *Ambulocetus natans* ("the walking whale that swam") lived in the Tethys Sea 49 million years ago, 3 million years after *Pakicetus* but 9 million years before *Basilosaurus*. The fossil includes a good portion of the hind legs. The legs were strong and ended in long feet very much like those of a modern pinniped. The legs were certainly functional both on land and sea. The whale still retained a tail and lacked a fluke. The structure of the backbone shows, however, that *Ambulocetus* swam as modern whales do, by moving the rear portion of its body up and down,

Ambulocetus natans, "the walking whale that swam."

even if a fluke was missing. The large hind legs were used for propulsion in water. On land, where it probably bred and gave birth, *Ambulocetus* could have moved as a sea lion does. It was undoubtedly a whale that linked life on land with life at sea.

The skeleton of a 36-million-year-old whale from Perú, *Mystacodon,* appears to be the oldest known baleen whale. It shows the first steps in the transition from a toothed to a baleen whale. The skull is pointed and has teeth, but is flattened as in the modern baleen whales. Surprisingly, it shows evidence of tiny hind legs. There is no evidence of baleen, however, which is difficult to fossilize. It has been hypothesized that *Mystacodon* was a suction feeder, a possible first step in the evolution of filter feeding.

The Rice's whale (*Balaenoptera ricei*), which is restricted to the northeastern Gulf of Mexico, was officially established as a new species of baleen whale in 2021. It is estimated that there are less than 100 individuals, and as such one of the most endangered cetaceans in the world.

Toothed Whales The roughly 80 remaining species of cetaceans are toothed whales. Their teeth are adapted for a diet of fish, squid, and other prey. They use the teeth only to catch and hold prey, not to chew it, so food is swallowed whole. As in all cetaceans, food is ground up in one of the three compartments of the stomach. The blowhole has one opening, as opposed to two in the baleen whales.

The largest toothed whale is the sperm whale (*Physeter catodon*), the blunt-nosed giant of *Moby Dick* fame (Fig. 9.19s; also see photo at the beginning of the chapter and Fig. 1.18). Together, the sperm

and baleen whales are often called the **great whales.** The sperm whale is now the most numerous of the great whales, even though it was the mainstay of the whaling industry for centuries (Table 9.2). The largest on record weighed 38,000 kg (42 tons).

The toothed whales, which include the dolphins and porpoises, lack baleen and feed mostly on fish and squid.

Sperm whales are fond of squid, including the giant deep-sea ones. Undigested squid beaks and other debris accumulate in the gut as large globs of sticky material known as **ambergris,** a rare and prized material used to preserve the fragrance of fine perfumes. Evidence of the high value of ambergris is the finding by

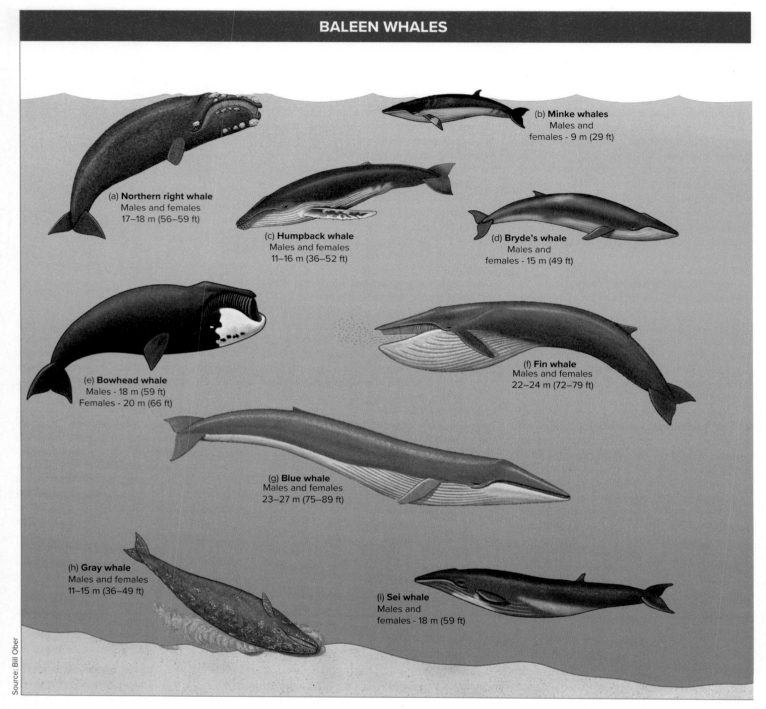

FIGURE 9.19 Representative baleen and toothed whales.

Yemeni fishers of $1.5 million worth of the material in the belly of the carcass of a sperm whale in 2021. Sperm whales also eat a wide variety of fishes (including sharks) and other marine animals (Table 9.1).

The other toothed whales are much smaller than the great whales. One is the orca, or killer whale (*Orcinus orca;* Fig. 9.19*p*), a predator of seals, penguins, fishes, and even other whales. They appear to use their white bellies to flash and frighten herring schools and their flukes to stun the fish. Orcas are most common

in cold water but are found around the world. They have a nasty reputation, but there are very few confirmed cases of their attacking humans in the wild, although there have been cases of individuals aggressively ramming boats. DNA analysis has confirmed that there are several different types, probably different species, of orcas, each with a distinct appearance, hunting habit, and diet. Orcas are quick to learn new tricks to catch their prey, and these behaviors are communicated to other members of the same population. Orcas in Antarctica have learned to make waves to knock

TOOTHED WHALES

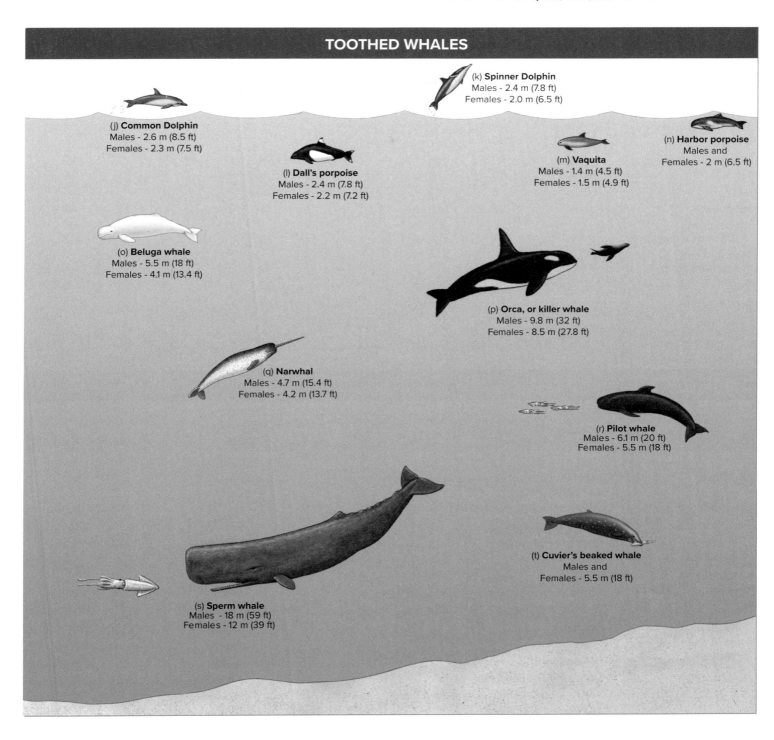

(k) **Spinner Dolphin**
Males - 2.4 m (7.8 ft)
Females - 2.0 m (6.5 ft)

(j) **Common Dolphin**
Males - 2.6 m (8.5 ft)
Females - 2.3 m (7.5 ft)

(n) **Harbor porpoise**
Males and
Females - 2 m (6.5 ft)

(l) **Dall's porpoise**
Males - 2.4 m (7.8 ft)
Females - 2.2 m (7.2 ft)

(m) **Vaquita**
Males - 1.4 m (4.5 ft)
Females - 1.5 m (4.9 ft)

(o) **Beluga whale**
Males - 5.5 m (18 ft)
Females - 4.1 m (13.4 ft)

(p) **Orca, or killer whale**
Males - 9.8 m (32 ft)
Females - 8.5 m (27.8 ft)

(q) **Narwhal**
Males - 4.7 m (15.4 ft)
Females - 4.2 m (13.7 ft)

(r) **Pilot whale**
Males - 6.1 m (20 ft)
Females - 5.5 m (18 ft)

(t) **Cuvier's beaked whale**
Males and
Females - 5.5 m (18 ft)

(s) **Sperm whale**
Males - 18 m (59 ft)
Females - 12 m (39 ft)

seals off floating ice and others in Patagonia climb ashore on beaches to catch resting sea lions. Orcas of other pods work as teams to herd and ambush dolphins; others herd schools of herring into tight balls and push them to the surface to feast on them.

One of the most enigmatic of whales is the narwhal (*Monodon monoceros;* Fig. 9.19*q*), a small Arctic whale having a long, spiral tusk that can be as long as 2.7 m (9 ft). Narwhal tusks washed ashore presumably gave rise to the legend of the unicorn. The tusk, a modified tooth found only in males, appears to be related to the

establishment of a hierarchy of dominance. Narwhals have been recorded with drones using the tusk to hit and stun fish.

Most of the small toothed whales are called dolphins or porpoises. The six species of porpoises are blunt-nosed whales (Fig. 9.19*m*, *n*) and have flattened teeth in contrast to the conical teeth of dolphins. In some places, however, the name "porpoise" is given to some of the dolphins.

The many species of dolphins typically possess a distinctive snout, or **beak,** and a perpetual "smile." Playful, highly social, and

Table 9.1 Diet of Great Whales

Whale Species	Bottom Invertebrates (%)	Large Zooplankton (%)	Small Squids (%)	Large Squids (%)	Small Pelagic Fishes (%)	Mesopelagic Fishes* (%)	Miscellaneous Fishes (%)
Blue	—	100	—	—	—	—	—
Bowhead	20	80	—	—	—	—	—
Bryde's	—	40	—	—	20	20	20
Fin	—	80	5	—	5	5	5
Gray	90	5	—	—	—	5	—
Humpback	—	55	—	—	15	—	30
Common and Antarctic minkes	—	65	—	—	30	—	5
Northern and southern rights	—	100	—	—	—	—	—
Sei	—	80	5	—	5	5	5
Sperm	5	—	10	60	5	5	15

*Fishes found at depths of around 200 to 1,000 m (660 to 3,300 ft; see Fig. 16.1).

Table 9.2 Status and Estimated Numbers of Great Whales

Whale Species	Status (Red List[1])	Estimated Pre-exploitation Number	Current Estimated Numbers
Blue	Endangered	160,000–240,000	5,000–15,000
Bowhead	Least concern but some populations endangered; aboriginal whaling	52,000–60,000	24,000
Bryde's	Least concern; Japanese and aboriginal whaling	100,000	21,000–90,000
Fin	Vulnerable; hunted	300,000	100,000
Gray (eastern Pacific)	Least concern	15,000–22,000	22,000–26,000
Gray (western Pacific)	Endangered	1,500–10,000	140
Gray (Atlantic)	Extinct	Unknown	0
Humpback	Recovering populations; aboriginal whaling	150,000	90,000
Common minke	Hunted, including aboriginal whaling	265,000	205,000
Antarctic minke	Hunted	670,000	460,000–690,000
North Pacific right	Endangered	Unknown	430–450
North Atlantic right	Facing extinction; aboriginal whaling	Unknown	400–450
Southern right	Recovering populations	100,000	16,000
Sei	Endangered; Japanese whaling	100,000	8,000
Sperm	Recovering populations	>2,000,000	300,000–500,000

[1]Compiled by the International Union for Conservation of Nature and Natural Resources (IUCN). Classified as "Least Concern," "Near Threatened," "Vulnerable," "Endangered," and "Critically Endangered."

easily trained, dolphins win people's hearts. They often travel in large groups called **pods,** herds, or schools. They like to catch rides along the bows of boats (Fig. 9.21) or around great whales. The bottlenose dolphin (*Tursiops truncatus*) is the dolphin seen in marine parks around the world.

Conservation of Cetaceans Whale hunting, or **whaling,** is an old tradition with a rich history. Stone Age people hunted whales as early as 6000 BCE Native Americans hunted gray whales in prehistoric times; the aboriginal peoples of the Arctic still legally hunt them. It was not until the 1600s, however, that Europeans started to substantially exploit the great whales in the North Atlantic. Whales were harpooned from small, open boats (Fig. 9.22), a technique whalers learned from the Native Americans. It was a rewarding fishery, though not one exploited primarily for food. Blubber provided "train oil," which was used to make soap and used as lamp oil.

FIGURE 9.20 Humpback whales (*Megaptera novaeangliae*) often hunt in groups by surrounding schools of small fish with bubbles before lunging to the surface with open mouths and swallowing hundreds of fish in one gulp. Some of the whales help others by diving below the school to force the fish to the surface; others are known to flap the surface to herd the fish with their flukes before forming the bubbles.

FIGURE 9.21 Dolphins like the Atlantic spotted dolphin (*Stenella frontalis*) often ride the bow wave of boats or even that of whales. They ride without beating their tails, obtaining thrust from the pressure wave in front of the ship.

Baleen, meat, and other valuable products also were obtained. Whaling efforts rapidly increased after fast steamships and the devastating explosive harpoon were introduced in the 1800s. The largest and fastest, like the blue and fin whales, were then at the mercy of whalers.

Whales are long-lived mammals with a low reproductive rate. Females usually don't become pregnant for one or two years after giving birth. As a result of this low reproductive potential, whale populations could not stand the intense whaling pressure, and many of the fisheries collapsed.

The first to be seriously depleted was the slow-swimming North Atlantic right whale (*Eubalaena glacialis;* Fig. 9.19a), the "right" species to be killed, according to whalers, because it floated after being harpooned. By the early 1900s whaling had moved to the rich feeding grounds around Antarctica, where other species could be hunted. This location proved to be a bonanza. Whaling nations developed factory ships able to process whole carcasses. The Antarctic fishery reached its peak in the 1930s. It is estimated that more than a million whales were taken from Antarctica alone.

Blue whales, the largest of them all, were especially sought. A large specimen yielded more than 9,000 gallons of oil. It has been estimated that more than 200,000 blue whales were taken worldwide between 1924 and 1971, close to 30,000 during the 1930–1931 whaling season alone. Catch per whaler-day's effort declined every year after 1936. As many as 80% of all blue whales caught by 1963 were sexually immature, so that there were even fewer individuals able to perpetuate the species.

Fin whales, the second largest of all whales, became the next major target as blue whales became more and more scarce. The 1950s and early 1960s saw annual catches of 20,000 to 32,000 fin whales per year, mostly from Antarctica. As catches dwindled, whalers shifted their target again in the mid-1960s, this time to the smaller sei whale (*Balaenoptera borealis;* Fig. 9.19i).

The disappearance of the more commercially valuable whales meant lower profits for the whaling industry. Twenty whaling nations established the **International Whaling Commission (IWC)** in 1946 in an attempt to regulate whale hunting to stop overfishing. It collected data on the number of whales and set annual quotas for the number of whales to be caught each year, quotas that were non-binding and could not be enforced. Furthermore, some whaling nations did not belong to the IWC. The blue whale was not protected by the IWC until the 1965–1966 season, long after its numbers had been drastically reduced. By then blue whales were so hard to find that it's fishery was no longer profitable. Even under the protection of the IWC, blue whales were hunted at least until 1971 by countries that did not belong to the IWC.

Intense whaling has led to the near extermination of most species of great whales. Practically all species are now endangered.

Under mounting pressure from conservationists, the IWC gradually banned the hunting of other whales. Demand for whale products, mostly oil used in the manufacture of margarine and lubricants, was reduced because substitutes had been found for most of them. Whale meat, however, continued to be used as pet food and as human food, mostly in Japan. The lower quotas of the IWC were, unfortunately, not always accepted by all nations.

The United States Congress passed the **Marine Mammal Protection Act of 1972,** which bans the hunting of all marine mammals in U.S. waters (except in the traditional fisheries of the indigenous people of Alaska; see Fig. 4.2) and the importation of marine mammal products. By 1974 the IWC had protected the blue, gray, humpback, and right whales worldwide, but only after their catches were no longer economically viable. Sperm, minke, fin, and sei whales were still hunted, but catches began to dwindle. Catches of these whales fell from 64,418 in 1965 to 38,892 in 1975 and 6,623

FIGURE 9.22 Long-boat crew harpooning a right whale in the 1800s.

North Wind Picture Archives/Alamy Stock Photo

in 1985. A moratorium on all commercial whaling was declared by the IWC in 1985. The former Soviet Union halted all whaling in 1987. Japan, Iceland, and Norway, however, opted in 1988 to continue catching minke, fin, and sei whales, as allowed by the IWC under the controversial title of "scientific whaling."

In 1994 the IWC created a vast sanctuary for all whales in the waters around Antarctica, the main feeding ground for 80% of the surviving great whales. Japan, however, decided to continue hunting whales in Antarctica. Starting with the 1997–1998 season, Japan took 440 minkes from Antarctica and 100 from the North Pacific each season until 2002, when it expanded its North Pacific catch to include 150 minke, 50 Bryde's (*Balaenoptera edeni;* Fig. 9.19*d*), 10 sperm, and, for the first time since 1987, 50 sei whales. Disruptions from anti-whaling activists and low demand at home were responsible for the low Japanese catches, almost all minkes, in Antarctica.

In 2006 the 70-nation IWC abandoned its conservationist policies on the belief that the populations of many of the whale species were large enough to support sustainable whaling. Norway had already resumed commercial whaling in 2005 by setting itself an annual quota of 796 North Sea minkes (Fig. 9.23). Iceland, which had not hunted whales since 1989, joined Norway in 2006 to further break the 1985 ban.

Since 2005 and under the provisions of "scientific" whaling, about 3,600 minkes were taken in Antarctica, a high of 680 during the 2005–2006 season to 251 in 2013–2014. The IWC approved stricter criteria for nations applying to undertake whaling for research purposes. Japan nevertheless restarted whaling under a new "scientific" program during the 2015–2016 season, when 333 minkes were caught. The same number was taken during the 2016–2017 season before Japan withdrew from IWC and abandoned Antarctic whaling in 2018. It nevertheless resumed, after a 31-year absence, commercial whaling in its own coastal waters in the northwestern Pacific, catching 187 Bryde's, 91 minke, and 25 sei whales, an endangered species (see Table 9.2), in 2021.

Small-scale whaling, or **aboriginal subsistence whaling,** remains part of the traditional fisheries of the indigenous inhabitants of the Arctic region from Greenland to Siberia and in the Lesser Antilles in the Caribbean. One of the whales hunted in the Arctic, the bowhead, and another in the Lesser Antilles, the humpback, are endangered. Other smaller whales, the orca, narwhal, and beluga (*Delphinapterus leucas;* see Figs. 9.19*o* and 9.29), are also hunted in the Arctic and North Atlantic.

The current status of the great whale species according to population estimates varies from "vulnerable" to "critically endangered" or facing extinction depending on the classification of particular agencies or countries (see Tables 9.2 and 18.1). The status may also vary among different populations of the same species. Collision with ships, entanglement in fishing nets, noise pollution, and illegal hunting remain as threats now that pressure from commercial whaling has almost disappeared. The North Atlantic right whale, which is facing extinction, has been hit by entanglement in ropes connecting lobster traps with buoys. Eighteen of them died in 2017, a tragedy considering that only 100 breeding females are left and that no calves were born during the 2017-2018 breeding season.

Nobody knows when the great whales will again roam the oceans in numbers approaching those before the start of large-scale whaling. Some experts are afraid that a few critically endangered species will never recover completely. Recovery is nevertheless underway in some species. The California gray whale, protected since 1947, has made a comeback. It was removed from the

FIGURE 9.23
Harpooned Antarctic minke whales (*Balaenoptera bonaerensis*) being hauled on board a Japanese whaling ship in the Southern Ocean in 2005. Japan abandoned whaling in Antarctica in 2018, but still hunts minkes in the North Pacific.

jeremy sutton-hibbit/Alamy Stock Photo

endangered species list in 1994. It is estimated that 78,000 to 117,000 grays lived before exploitation, much higher than most estimates (see Table 9.2). In 1997 the IWC allowed the catching of 600 gray whales by indigenous hunters in Siberia and 20 by the Makah native Americans in Washington State. The Makah only took a single whale, in 1999. Hundreds of dead grays have nevertheless been washing up along North American beaches since 2019. These unusual mortality events appear to be caused by malnutrition resulting from the lack of prey, perhaps the consequence of warming Arctic waters. Some of the whales, however, were probably struck by ships or entangled by fishing gear.

Even the blue whale, whose reproduction is severely limited by its restriction to small populations scattered around the world, is making a comeback. It has returned to the Arctic Ocean north of Norway, a region where they flourished before their near extermination by whalers. Sightings off the Pacific coast of North America have increased sharply (Fig. 9.24), and they were recently seen off Sydney Harbor, Australia for the first time in 100 years. Their numbers in Antarctica, however, are even lower than first estimates: around 500 individuals, or only about 1% of those feeding there before whaling began. Increased sightings of blue and other baleen whales in Arctic waters appear to be an unexpected benefit of the rapid melting of Arctic sea ice. Increased penetration of light could be triggering increases in the amount of the plankton used as food.

A decrease in Arctic sea ice, however, is negatively impacting cetaceans such as the narwhal, beluga, and bowhead whales, all of which are closely associated with sea ice. Decreasing ice is also allowing orcas, an important predator to these cetaceans, to enter areas otherwise not accessed by the orcas. The noise of increased shipping traffic has also been reported as affecting whales.

Dolphins and other small cetaceans are also at great risk (see Table 18.1), having replaced the larger whales as the most threatened of all cetaceans. Small cetaceans are not under IWC regulation, and as many as 28 species are in immediate danger of extinction.

The vaquita, or "little cow" (*Phocoena sinus;* see Figs. 9.19*m* and 18.13), is Earth's most endangered marine cetacean. Scientists estimated that as few as eight vaquitas remained in 2022. This small, shovel-nosed porpoise is found only in a small area in the northern end of the Gulf of California, Mexico, where it remained unknown to science until 1958. It is the smallest of all porpoises, and it is restricted to the smallest geographical range of any marine mammal. Their numbers have undergone a catastrophic decline in recent years, with half of the surviving vaquitas vanishing between 2015 and 2016. The culprit is legal and illegal gill-net fishing, mostly for totoaba (*Totoaba macdonald*), a fish found nowhere else and also threatened with extinction. The fish's swim bladders are illegally traded for thousands of dollars in China, where they are believed to have medicinal powers. Although vaquitas are now protected by the Mexican government, some drastic measures must be taken to save them. One proposed, but risky, scheme is to use dolphins to herd the remaining vaquitas to a marine sanctuary.

Everywhere, fishers are depleting stocks of fish and squid on which dolphins feed. Dolphins themselves are being hunted for human food. Most of the five species of river dolphins are critically endangered. China's Yangtze River dolphin, or *báijìtún* (*Lipotes vexillifer*), a freshwater dolphin found only in that Chinese river was declared extinct in 2006, the first cetacean to become extinct as a

Francois Gohier/VWPics/Alamy Stock Photo

FIGURE 9.24 The blue whale (*Balaenoptera musculus*) has made a remarkable, and unexpected, comeback along the Pacific coast of North America. It is estimated that 1,750 to 2,500 individuals now live in the northeastern Pacific, which is nearly the same population living in the same region when commercial whaling for this species began here at the beginning of the twentieth century. Nearly 10,000 blue whales were caught in the North Pacific between 1905 and 1971. These two individuals were photographed in the Gulf of California, Mexico.

result of human activity. A second freshwater cetacean, the Yangtze finless porpoise (*Neophocaena phocaenenoides asiaorientalis*), is in danger of also becoming extinct.

Tuna fishers using giant purse seine nets (see Fig. 17.6*b*) sometimes trap and drown the many dolphins that often swim above schools of tuna, mostly yellowfin tuna (*Thunnus albacares*) in the eastern Pacific. An estimated 200,000 dolphins died annually during the early 1970s, mostly at the hands of American fishing fleets. The slaughter induced such public outrage that the United States, through the Marine Mammal Protection Act of 1972, called for a reduction in the accidental deaths of dolphins. It imposed a quota of 20,500 for the number of dolphins that could be killed by American fleets. The use of special nets was enforced, and observers were placed on board vessels to verify compliance with the ruling. By 1990 it was estimated that the number of dolphins killed by the American tuna fleet, by then operating in western Pacific waters, had reached zero. The same year the three biggest tuna packers in the United States pledged not to buy or sell fish that was caught using methods that injure or kill dolphins. Tuna cans began to display "dolphin-safe" labels, and imported tuna caught without the use of dolphin-safe methods were banned from sale in the United States.

Dolphins have also been entangled and killed in **drift nets** (see Fig. 17.6*a*), which also threaten sharks, sea turtles, seabirds, and other marine life. The nets, some as large as 60 km (37 mi) long and 15 m (50 ft) deep, have been used to catch fish and squid, but they actually catch practically anything that tries to swim by. Not only do they deplete valuable commercial fisheries like albacore tuna and salmon, but they also trap many noncommercial species. Hundreds of fishing boats outfitted for drift netting were used to catch tuna in the South Pacific. The United Nations called for a moratorium on drift-net fishing in 1992, and Japan and Taiwan, with the largest fleets of drift-net boats in the Pacific, ended the practice in 1993. Still drift-net fishing, some of it illegal, continues in some areas.

Keeping dolphins and orcas captive in marine parks is a much-debated issue. Attendance has sharply declined at some parks, and others have been forced to close. In response, some parks have canceled breeding programs or have released the cetaceans after teaching them how to live in the wild. Unfortunately, some cannot adapt to freedom.

Biology of Marine Mammals

It is surprising how little we know about marine mammals. Most are difficult or impossible to keep in captivity or even to observe for long periods at sea. Some whales and dolphins are rarely seen, so what little we know about them comes from captive or stranded individuals and information gathered over the years by whalers.

Swimming Streamlining of the body for swimming is a hallmark of marine mammals. Seals, sea lions, and the walrus swim mostly by moving their flippers. Sea otters swim by using their hind feet, which are broad and webbed (see Fig. 9.12). Polar bears are strong swimmers and can cover long distances using all four legs for swimming, very much like a dog. Sirenians and cetaceans, in contrast, move their tails and flukes up and down (Fig. 9.25), in contrast to fishes, who move their tails from side to side (see Fig. 8.11). Sea lions have been timed at speeds of 35 kph (22 mph), orcas and blue whales at 50 kph (30 mph). A group of common dolphins (*Delphinus delphis;* Fig. 9.19*j*) was recorded bowriding at a speed of 64 kph (40 mph).

Cetaceans have the advantage of having the blowhole on top of the head. This allows them to breathe even though most of the body is under water, though many pinnipeds and dolphins jump clear out of the water to take a breath when they are swimming fast (see Fig. 9.21). It also means that cetaceans can eat and swallow without drowning. The blowhole is absent in all other marine mammals and therefore must use their frontally located nostrils to breathe air just like us. To avoid inhaling water, all marine mammals take very quick breaths. A fin whale can empty and refill its lungs in less than 2 s, half the time we take, even though the whale breathes in 3,000 times more air!

In the large whales, the moisture in their warm breath condenses when it hits the air. Together with a little mucus and seawater, this water vapor forms the characteristic **spout,** or **blow.** The spout can be seen at great distances, and its height and angle can be used to identify the whale (Fig. 9.26). The blue whale, for instance, has a spout some 6 to 12 m (20 to 40 ft) high.

To keep warm in cold water, the great whales depend on a thick layer of blubber (see Fig. 4.2). Feeding, however, leaves their huge mouths exposed to low temperatures, a major problem in the very cold polar waters where they normally feed. A network of blood vessels in their tongues reduces heat loss by transferring heat from warm blood into vessels that carry it back to the body core.

Diving Marine mammals have mastered the art of diving, and most make prolonged dives to considerable depths for food. There is a wide range in diving ability. Sea otters can dive for only 4 or 5 min, to depths of perhaps 55 m (180 ft). Pinnipeds normally dive for up to 30 min at maximum depths of 150 to 250 m (490 to 820 ft). Female northern elephant seals (*Mirounga angustirostris*), however, are capable of continuous deep dives of up to 400 m (1,300 ft). One individual was recorded diving to a depth of 1,500 m (5,000 ft). The Weddell seal (*Leptonychotes weddellii*) has been recorded diving for as long as 1 h 13 min and as deep as 575 m (1,900 ft).

Sirenians spend most of their time in relatively shallow water, but a dugong was recorded diving to 20 m (65 ft). Polar bears have been estimated capable of diving as deep as 6 m (20 ft).

The plankton-feeding habits of baleen whales do not require them to dive too deeply for their food, and they seldom venture below 100 m (300 ft). Toothed whales, by contrast, are excellent divers. Dolphins are known to dive as deep as 300 m (990 ft). Though sperm whales are known to dive to 2,250 m (7,380 ft) for at least an hour. The Cuvier's beaked whale (*Ziphius cavirostris;* Fig. 9.19*t*), one of the 23 known species of beaked whales, regularly dives to more than 1,000 m (3,300 ft) to catch the deep-water squids that make up most of its diet. Beaked whales dive deeper and stay under longer than any other marine mammal. The deepest recorded dive of a beaked whale was close to 3,000 m (about 9,800 ft); another was recorded diving for 3 hr, 42 min without surfacing for air. Different species of toothed whales have evolved different hunting strategies. Short-finned pilot whales (*Globicephala;* Fig. 9.19*r*), for instance, sprint as fast as 9 m (30 ft) per second after single or several prey as deep as 1,000 m (3,300 ft), very much like large wildcats do.

The long, deep dives of marine mammals require several crucial adaptations because they must be able to go a long time without breathing. This involves more than just holding their breath, for they must keep their vital organs supplied with oxygen. Being homeotherms means that marine mammals must use energy to keep their temperature constant—and the release of energy by **aerobic respiration** requires oxygen. To get as much oxygen as possible before dives, most marine mammals take several deep breaths, then rapidly exhale, a behavior known as **apneustic breathing** (Fig. 9.27). As much as 90% of the oxygen contained in the lungs is exchanged during each breath, in contrast to 20% in humans. Many marine

FIGURE 9.25 Cetaceans swim with strong up-and-down movements of the tail and flukes.

Source: Bill Ober

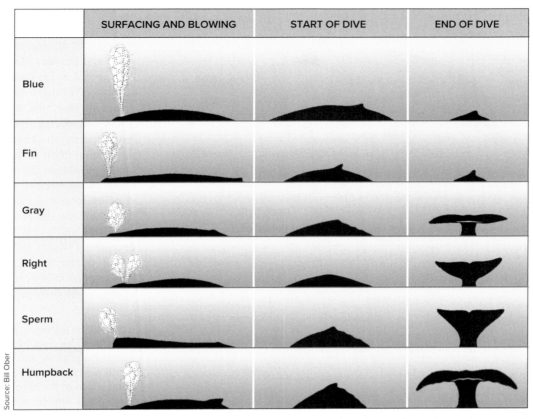

	SURFACING AND BLOWING	START OF DIVE	END OF DIVE
Blue			
Fin			
Gray			
Right			
Sperm			
Humpback			

Source: Bill Ober

FIGURE 9.26 Great whales can be identified from a distance by their blowing pattern, their outline on the surface, and the way they dive.

mammals have elastic tissues in their lungs and diaphragms, which helps lungs fill and empty rapidly and efficiently.

Marine mammals are also better than other mammals at absorbing the oxygen from the air and storing it in their blood, having relatively more blood than non-diving mammals. As in seabirds (see "Biology of Seabirds," above), their blood also contains a higher concentration of erythrocytes, and these blood cells carry more hemoglobin. Furthermore, their muscles are extra-rich in myoglobin, which means that the muscles themselves can store a lot of oxygen.

Marine mammals have adaptations that reduce oxygen consumption in addition to increasing supply. When they dive, the heart rate slows dramatically, an automatic reflex known as **bradycardia.** Diving bradycardia has been recorded in many diving vertebrates, including humans. It is thought to have evolved as an oxygen-conserving mechanism. In the northern elephant seal, for example, the heart rate decreases from about 85 beats per minute to about 12. Blood flow to non-essential parts of the body, like the extremities and the intestine, is reduced, but it is maintained to vital organs like the brain and heart. Oxygen is thus made available where it is needed most when oxygen supply is cut off during a dive.

The reduction or absence of oxygen triggers the muscle cells of many animals (including humans during exercise) to carry out **anaerobic respiration,** an "emergency" **aerobic respiration** that releases, though inefficiently, some energy without the need of oxygen. Fermentation, a type of anaerobic respiration, is the way yeasts and many bacteria release their energy. A product of anaerobic

respiration is **lactic acid,** a chemical that produces cramps. The tissues of marine mammals, however, have evolved a high tolerance to the accumulation of lactic acid, another adaptation to increase diving efficiency.

Another potential problem faced by air-breathing, diving animals (including human divers) results from the presence of large amounts of nitrogen (70% of total volume) in the air. Nitrogen dissolves much better at high pressures, like those experienced at depth. The blood of scuba divers picks up nitrogen while they are below the surface. If the pressure is suddenly released, some of the nitrogen will not stay dissolved and forms tiny bubbles in the bloodstream. As in a bottle of soda water, carbonation (carbon dioxide gas) remains dissolved as long as the bottle is kept under pressure. When the bottle is opened, the pressure is released and bubbles form. When nitrogen bubbles form in the blood after diving, they can lodge in the joints or block the flow of blood to the

Aerobic Respiration
in all cells
organic matter + O_2 → CO_2 + H_2O + energy
(glucose)

Anaerobic Respiration
in muscles
organic matter → energy + lactic acid
(glucose)

• 4.1, The Ingredients of Life

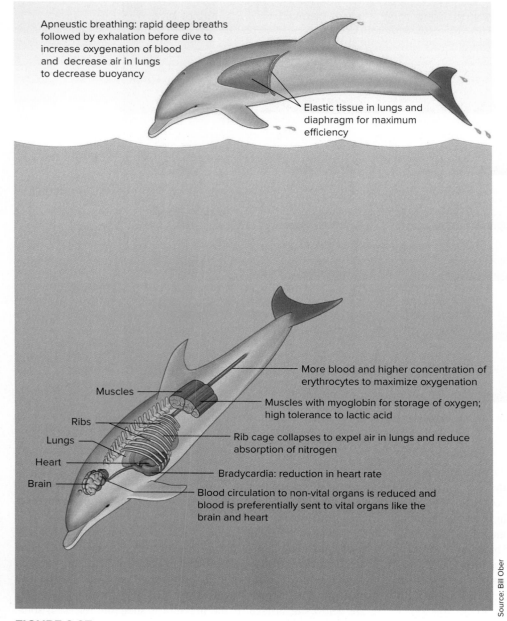

Apneustic breathing: rapid deep breaths followed by exhalation before dive to increase oxygenation of blood and decrease air in lungs to decrease buoyancy

Elastic tissue in lungs and diaphragm for maximum efficiency

More blood and higher concentration of erythrocytes to maximize oxygenation

Muscles

Muscles with myoglobin for storage of oxygen; high tolerance to lactic acid

Ribs

Lungs

Rib cage collapses to expel air in lungs and reduce absorption of nitrogen

Heart

Bradycardia: reduction in heart rate

Brain

Blood circulation to non-vital organs is reduced and blood is preferentially sent to vital organs like the brain and heart

Source: Bill Ober

FIGURE 9.27 Marine mammals have evolved a series of adaptations that allow them to undertake long, deep dives.

nitrogen is absorbed. High concentrations of hemoglobin and myoglobin store the oxygen that marine mammals need in the blood and muscles during dives. Less air is thus needed in the lungs, which reduces the amount of nitrogen that can be absorbed. Apneustic breathing, exhaling before a dive, further reduces the amount of air (and therefore nitrogen) in the lungs. A reduction in the amount of air in the lungs has the additional advantage of decreasing buoyancy, which makes descents to deep water easier.

The long-held view that marine mammals don't get the bends may not be accurate after all. It has been suggested that deep-diving whales suffer from some of the effects of the bends, as evidenced by the degeneration of bone and cartilage in sperm whales, possibly caused by nitrogen bubbles.

Adaptations for deep, prolonged dives in marine mammals include the efficient exchange of air on the surface, the storage of more oxygen in the blood and muscles, a reduction of the blood supply to the extremities, and collapsible lungs to help prevent the bends.

Echolocation Marine mammals depend little on the sense of smell, so important to many land mammals. Their vision is excellent, but some have developed **echolocation,** another sensory system based on hearing. Echolocation is nature's version of sonar. Most if not all toothed whales, including dolphins and porpoises, and some pinnipeds are known to echolocate. There is no evidence of echolocation among baleen whales or in sirenians, who use their sensitive whiskers when grazing. Echolocation is not exclusive to marine mammals. Bats, for example, use it to find insects and other prey while flying at night.

Marine mammals echolocate by emitting sound waves, which travel about five times faster in water than in air, and listening for the echoes reflected back from surrounding objects (Fig. 9.28). The brain then analyzes the echoes. The time it takes the echoes to return tells the animals how far away the object is.

Many marine mammals echolocate by analyzing the echo of sound waves they emit. Echolocation is used to find prey and orient to the surroundings.

brain and other organs. This produces a painful condition known as the **bends,** or decompression sickness. To avoid the bends, human divers must be very careful about how deep they go, how long they stay under water, and how fast they come up.

Marine mammals dive deeper and stay down longer than human divers, so do they get the bends? Marine mammals do have adaptations that prevent nitrogen from dissolving in the blood. Human lungs work pretty much the same while scuba diving under water as on land. When marine mammals dive, however, their lungs actually collapse. They have a flexible rib cage that gets pushed in by the pressure of the water (Fig. 9.27). This, and increased water pressure with the increased depth, squeezes the air out of outlying areas of the lungs where it readily dissolves into the blood. Air is moved instead into the central spaces of the lungs, where little

The sounds used in echolocation consist of short bursts of sharp clicks that are repeated at different frequencies. Low-frequency clicks have a high penetrating power and can travel long distances.

EYE ON SCIENCE

Box 9.3 Feeding in the Blue Whale

How blue whales (*Balaenoptera musculus*), the largest animals that have ever lived, maintain such a large size while having to dive for food, migrate long distances, keep body temperature in cold water, and reproduce—all on a diet of krill—is a challenging question. Blue whales and other rorquals feed by lunging at high speeds, huge mouths open, into swarms of krill. They then filter and swallow the krill in the large volumes of water contained in their greatly inflated oral cavities by closing their mouths (see Figs. 9.18 and 9.19*f*). A unique adaptation in rorquals (from the French *rorqual*, originally from *röyrkval*, Norwegian for "furrow whale") is the presence of longitudinal grooves along a good part of the lower surface of the body (see Fig. 9.16). The blubber along this area consists of tough ridges divided by deep channels of elastic tissue to allow the oral cavity to expand. The volume of the oral cavity is further increased by the retraction of the tongue along the floor of the mouth.

We know that blue whales should get enough energy from plankton (see Fig. 10.16), but it was thought that they burn lots of energy by having to accelerate their huge bodies, lunge, and feed, together with the increased drag of the expanded oral cavity, so it was believed that they had to limit the time spent diving for food. Figuring out how blue whales cope requires estimating the energetic efficiency, or cost, of feeding, in other words, how much energy they obtain after subtracting the energy they burn while feeding. Measuring energy inputs and outputs in such large animals at sea clearly seemed an impossible task.

A team from the University of British Columbia, Canada, nevertheless solved the problem after tracking as many as 265 blue whales along the Pacific coast with several types of electronic sensors. Whales were found to lunge to feed as many as six times during a dive, with each dive lasting from 3.1 to 15.2 min. The speed of whales as they lunged was calculated by correlating speed with the noise of water rushing by the animal as measured by hydrophones attached to individual whales. Since the oral cavity inflates very much like a parachute, a parachute aerodynamics expert helped develop a mathematical model that allowed calculating the energy needed in each lunge, a value found to vary from 3,226 to 8,071 kilojoules (770–1,930 kilocalories; 1 kilocalorie equivalent to 1,000 calories). They estimated the volume of the oral cavity from the size of jaw bones in museums and the density of krill in the water from data in the scientific literature. It was estimated from these values that each mouthful of krill contained from 34,726 to 1,912,680 kilojoules (8,310–457,130 kilocalories), which is 240 times as much energy spent in each lunge! Even including the cost of diving, each dive could provide 90 times as much energy as whales use while diving. Blue whales certainly obtain more than enough energy from their food, and such extraordinary feeding efficiency helps explain their ability to survive despite their gigantic size.

For more information, explore the links provided on the Marine Biology *Online Learning Center.*

Source: Bill Ober

They reflect from large features and are used to obtain information on the surroundings. Low-frequency sound waves can also be used by some toothed whales to stun their prey. It seems that sperm whales catch squids, including giant squids, without using their teeth, even if the teeth are actually of little help because they are present only in the lower jaw. Live squids have been known to come out alive from the stomachs of freshly caught whales! To discriminate more detail and locate nearby prey, cetaceans use high-frequency clicks that are inaudible to humans. Experiments have shown that blindfolded bottlenose dolphins can discriminate between objects of slightly different size or made of different types of materials and can even detect wires.

Cetaceans produce clicks, squeaks, and whistles as air is forced through the air passages and several associated air sacs while the blowhole is closed (Fig. 9.28). The frequency of the clicks is changed, or modulated, by contracting and relaxing muscles along the air passages and sacs. A fatty structure on the forehead of toothed whales, the **melon,** appears to focus and direct the outgoing sound waves.

The melon gives these whales their characteristic rounded foreheads. To accommodate the melon, the skull is modified to form a pointed, dish-shaped face. The skull is also asymmetric, the right side being slightly different from the left side. Belugas (Fig. 9.29) have a bulging forehead that changes shape as the melon focuses the sound. The huge forehead of the sperm whale is filled in part with a massive melon called the **spermaceti organ.** Whalers originally thought this was the sperm sac of the whale, hence their name. This organ is filled with a waxy oil, **spermaceti,** once much sought after for making candles and still used as a lubricant for precision instruments. It has been suggested that the deep-diving sperm whale might also use the spermaceti organ to regulate buoyancy or to absorb excess nitrogen, keeping it out of the bloodstream.

Incoming sound waves are received primarily by the lower jaw in toothed whales (Fig. 9.28). The ear canal that connects the outside with the inner ear is reduced or blocked in most cetaceans. The jawbones, filled with fat or oil, transmit sound to the two, very sensitive inner ears. Each ear receives sound independently. The ears are protected by a bony case and embedded

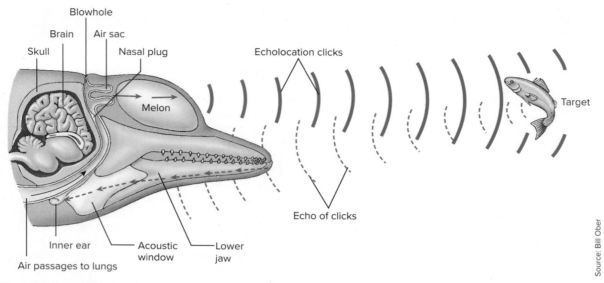

Source: Bill Ober

FIGURE 9.28 Dolphins echolocate by emitting bursts of sound waves, or clicks, as air is pushed through internal air passages. Two muscular nasal plugs act as valves, closing and opening the passages. Flaps of tissue on the plugs probably also produce sound by vibrating in the moving air. The clicks are focused into a beam by the melon. To cover a wider area, the dolphin moves its head from side to side. The melon is also known to receive the echoes and transmit them to the ears, but most are received by the lower jaw.

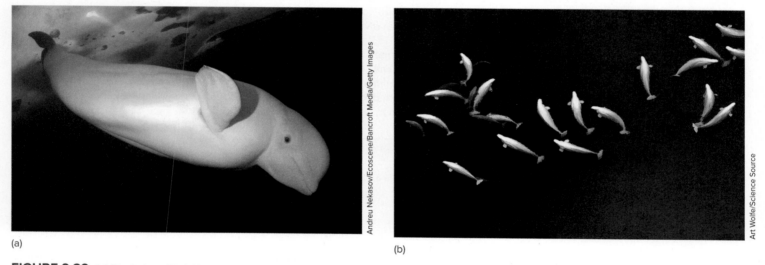

Andreu Nekasov/Ecoscene/Bancroft Media/Getty Images

Art Wolfe/Science Source

(a)

(b)

FIGURE 9.29 (*a*) The beluga (*Delphinapterus leucas*) is a white Arctic whale (*beluga* means "white one" in Russian) with a conspicuous melon. This individual was photographed under the ice in the White Sea, Russia. (*b*) In their natural environment belugas live in small groups.

in an oily mixture that insulates the ear but allows sound waves to pass from the jaws. Sound information is sent to the brain, which forms a mental "picture" of the target or surroundings. Sight and sound information seems to be handled similarly by the brain. Captive dolphins can recognize by echolocation objects they have seen and recognize by sight those they have previously echolocated.

Behavior The mammalian brain has evolved as an association center for complex behaviors in which learning, not instinct, dominates. In contrast to fishes, birds, and other vertebrates, mammals rely mostly on past experience, stored and processed by the brain, to respond to changes in the environment. Cetacean brains are as complex as those of humans as far as their anatomy is concerned.

Their brains even have the same type of brain cell that is associated with abstract reasoning in humans.

Most marine mammals are highly social, living in groups at least part of the time. The polar bear is a notable exception. Many pinnipeds live in large colonies during the breeding season. Most cetaceans spend their entire lives in highly organized pods of a few (Fig. 9.29*b*) to thousands of individuals. Some pods include smaller subgroups organized by age and sex. To keep in contact, many of their highly complex and sophisticated behaviors are directed toward members of their own species. Like humans, some cetaceans have complex cultures that vary from group to group.

Sounds, or **vocalizations,** play a prominent role in communication. Sea lions and fur seals communicate by loud barks and whimpers; seals use more sedate grunts, whistles, and chirps.

Box 9.4 How Intelligent Are Cetaceans?

We often hear that dolphins and other cetaceans are as intelligent as humans, maybe even more so. Are they really that smart?

There is no question that cetaceans are among the most intelligent of animals. Dolphins, orcas, and pilot whales in captivity quickly learn tricks. Bottlenose dolphins have been trained to detect underwater mines in murky water.

This type of learning is called **conditioning**. The animal simply learns that when it performs a particular behavior it gets a reward, usually a fish. Many animals, including rats, birds, and even some invertebrates, can be conditioned to perform tricks. We certainly don't think of these animals as our mental rivals.

Unlike most other animals, however, dolphins quickly learn by observing other dolphins, and can spontaneously imitate human activities. One captive dolphin watched a diver cleaning an underwater viewing window, seized a feather in its beak, and began imitating the diver—complete with sound effects! Dolphins have also been seen imitating seals, turtles, and even water-skiers.

Observations of cetaceans in the wild have provided some insights into their learning abilities. Bottlenose dolphins off Western Australia, for instance, have been observed carrying large, cone-shaped sponges over their beaks, tools that they could use for protection against stingrays and other hazards on the bottom as they search for fish. The use of sponges is shown mostly by females, and it appears that this behavior is passed on by mothers to offspring. This is the first record of tool use and of its cultural transmission in a marine mammal in the wild.

Given the obvious intelligence of cetaceans, people are always tempted to compare them with humans and other animals. Studies on discrimination and problem-solving skills in the bottlenose dolphin, for instance, have concluded that its intelligence lies "somewhere between that of a dog and a chimpanzee." Individuals have even been shown to recognize their own reflections in a mirror.

Such comparisons are unfair because intelligence is a very human concept and that we evaluate it in human terms. You wouldn't consider yourself stupid because you couldn't locate and identify a fish by its echo, so why should we judge cetaceans by their ability to solve human problems?

Both humans and cetaceans have large brains with an expanded and distinctively folded surface, the cortex. The cortex is the dominant association center of the brain, where abilities like memory and sensory perception are centered. Cetaceans have larger brains than ours, but the ratio of brain to body weight is higher in humans. Again, direct comparisons are misleading. In cetaceans, it is mainly the portions of the brain associated with hearing and the processing of sound information that are expanded. The enlarged portions of our brain deal largely with vision and hand-eye coordination. Cetaceans and humans almost certainly perceive the world in very different ways. Their world is largely one of sounds, ours one of sights.

Contrary to what is depicted in the media, the notion of "talking" to dolphins is also misleading. Though they produce a rich repertoire of complex sounds, they lack vocal cords and their brains probably process sound differently than ours do. Bottlenose dolphins have been trained to make sounds through the blowhole that sound something like human sounds, but this is a far cry from human speech. Nevertheless, cetaceans do not have a real language like ours. Unlike humans, dolphins probably cannot convey very complex messages. By the same token, humans cannot make whale sounds. We will probably never be able to carry on an unaided conversation with cetaceans.

As in chimps, captive bottlenose dolphins have been taught American Sign

Curious bottlenose dolphins (*Tursiops truncatus*)

Language. These dolphins have learned to communicate with trainers who use sign language to ask simple questions. Dolphins answer back by pushing a "yes" or "no" paddle. They have even been known to give spontaneous responses not taught by the trainers. Evidence also indicates that these dolphins can distinguish between commands that differ from each other only by their word order, a truly remarkable achievement. Captive orcas have shown remarkable abilities to imitate human sounds. Orcas in the wild certainly learn sounds that are used to communicate with other orcas.

Instead of "intelligence," some prefer to speak of "awareness." Cetaceans probably have a different awareness and perception of their environment than do humans. Maybe one day we will come to understand cetaceans on their terms instead of ours, and perhaps we will discover a mental sophistication rivaling our own.

The vocalizations of pinnipeds are especially important in maintaining territories during reproduction (see "Reproduction," below). Females and their pups or calves recognize each other partly by their sounds, partly by smell. Sea otters use body contact and several vocalizations to communicate with each other. Sirenians similarly use "chirps" and "squeaks" for communication.

Cetaceans produce a rich variety of vocalizations that are different from the sounds used for echolocation. Both types of sounds can be produced simultaneously, providing further evidence of the complexity of their sound production. Social vocalizations are low-frequency sounds that humans can hear. The variety of sounds is amazing and includes grunts, squeaks, chirps, and even "moos."

Different sounds are associated with various moods and are used in social and sexual signaling. Whistles, emitted in many variations and tones, are characteristic of each species. Some of these sounds serve as a "signature," allowing individuals of the same species to recognize one another. Bottlenose dolphins use signature sounds to address each other. Male fin whales use high-intensity songs to attract females. Among the more than 70 calls that have been identified among orcas, some are present in all individuals, whereas others are "dialects" that identify certain pods.

Sounds are also used to maintain the distance between individuals and have an important role in the structure of the pod. Particular sounds are emitted during breeding, feeding, alarms, and birth. Mother gray whales grunt to stay in contact with their calves. Right whales have at least six distinct calls, each related to a specific function, and they can even call louder as background noise gets louder.

The humpback whale is renowned for its soulful songs. They are sung by breeding males to attract females by advertising their readiness to mate. The songs consist of phrases and themes repeated in a regular pattern for a half hour or longer. They may be repeated over for days, and the songs often change over time. Males also start each breeding season with the song they were singing at the end of the previous breeding season. New songs learned from immigrants have been shown to gain instant popularity among native whales. Researchers record and catalog songs to help track whales in their annual migrations.

Communication among cetaceans is not restricted to vocalizations. Researchers have described a variety of postures and movements that can also indicate the animal's mood. Dolphins clap their jaws or turn around with their mouths open as a threat. The loud cracking sound made when some marine mammals slap their flukes or flippers on the surface is thought to be a way of communicating with other individuals.

Cetaceans are noted for their **play behavior,** seemingly pleasurable activities with no serious goal. Dolphins and orcas play with food or floating objects like kelp and feathers, throwing them up in the air or holding and pushing them with their snouts. Individuals can swim head down or on their backs apparently just for the fun of it. Captive dolphins and belugas play with rings of air bubbles they create. Dolphins also like to surf, and pilot and right whales go "sailing" with their flukes out of the water to catch the wind. Sex play, the rubbing and touching of the genital opening, is also common.

The sight of a great whale **breaching,** leaping up in the air and loudly crashing on the surface, is breathtaking (Fig. 9.30). Breaching has been variously interpreted as a warning signal, for scanning the surface or the shoreline, for getting rid of external parasites or an ardent lover, and simply for fun. There is evidence that humpbacks use breaching as a way of signaling distant groups of other humpbacks. After a deep dive, sperm whales can breach, fall on their backs, and make a splash that can be heard 4 km (2.5 mi) and seen 28 km (17.4 mi) away! Many whales stick their heads out of the water to spy on their surroundings (Fig. 9.31b).

The complex behavior of cetaceans is evident in other ways (see Box 9.4, "How Intelligent *Are* Cetaceans?"). When one individual is in trouble, others can come to assist (Fig. 9.31a). Members of a pod refuse to leave a wounded or dying comrade. Whalers knew that a harpooned whale was a lure for others, which are drawn from miles around. Dolphins will carry injured individuals to the surface to breathe (Fig. 9.31c), and there are records of females carrying the body of a stillborn calf until it rots. Interaction between dolphins even crosses the species barrier. Bottlenose and spotted dolphins have been reported playing and hunting together, and seemingly guarding each other's calves.

Many toothed whales work together when they hunt, some in coordinated pairs or groups. Sometimes whales take turns feeding while their partners herd a school of fish. An individual may investigate something strange lying ahead while the rest of the group waits for the "report" of the scout. Some humpback whales work in groups by producing bubbles to herd fish (see Fig. 9.20). Studies of dolphins in the wild have shown that they belong to a complex society, one in which long-term partnerships of members of the same sex play an important role in sexual behavior, parental care, and other aspects of daily life. Social behavior in cetaceans could ultimately show many parallels with social behavior in large-brained mammals like apes and humans.

One of the mysteries of the behavior of cetaceans is the **stranding,** or **beaching,** of individuals, sometimes dozens, on beaches (Fig. 9.32). Efforts to move them into deeper water usually fail. Even if they are pulled out to sea, they often beach themselves again.

FIGURE 9.30 A humpback whale (*Megaptera novaeangliae*) performing a full spinning breach.

Source: Bill Ober

FIGURE 9.31 Whale watchers can be rewarded with examples of the complex behavior of whales: (*a*) sperm whales (*Physeter macrocephalus*) surrounding an injured member of a pod, (*b*) "spying" behavior in orcas (*Orcinus orca*) in the wild, (c) two bottlenose dolphins (*Tursiops truncatus*) carrying a stunned companion to the surface to breathe.

The whales die because their internal organs collapse without the support of the water. Stranding has been described in many species, but some, like pilot and sperm whales, strand themselves more often than others. It appears that whales become stranded when they follow one or more members of their group that have become disoriented by a storm, illness, or injury. This indicates the strong cohesiveness and herd instinct of the group.

Marine mammals, particularly cetaceans, use a rich variety of vocalizations and tactile and visual signals to communicate with each other. Play behavior and mutual assistance in cetaceans are additional evidence of the complexity of their behavior.

Stranding of whales has been linked to high-intensity sonar that uses bursts of intense sound waves used by the navies of several nations to detect enemy submarines. Whales stranding after naval exercises where the sonar was used showed hemorrhages in the brain and inner ears, which cause disorientation and death. Tissue injury can also be caused by the formation of nitrogen bubbles, or the bends. The United States Navy limited the use of sonar in specified areas of the Pacific. Noise from ship propellers, depth sounders, and sonar used for scientific purposes has also been suggested as disturbing to whales. Dolphins spend more time on the surface and rest less, and orcas calls last longer, when whale-watching boats are close by. There was a noticeable increase in the sightings of cetaceans (and other marine mammals) in coastal waters worldwide as a result of the sharp decrease in shipping and other maritime traffic during the COVID-19 pandemic.

The relationship between dolphins and humans is a controversial one. Though exaggerations abound, there are authenticated cases of dolphins approaching human swimmers who appeared to be in trouble. Fishers in southern Brazil have established a unique partnership with dolphins that detect fish and deliver them to fishers waiting with nets. Some people swear of "spiritual inspiration" while swimming among dolphins during the "dolphin encounters"

offered by some resorts. Some even advocate "dolphin-assisted" deliveries of babies, and dolphins are being used to treat children suffering from behavioral disorders. Other people see this as exploitation of the captive animals, and interactions with humans could after all be harmful to dolphins.

Migrations Many pinnipeds make seasonal migrations, often traveling thousands of miles from feeding grounds to breeding areas. Male southern elephant seals (*Mirounga leonine*) are known to travel as far as 8,000 km (almost 5,000 mi) to mate. The walrus migrates following the coastal pack ice, and some migrate long distances to group in large numbers on isolated rocky beaches when the ice melts in the summer. Most toothed whales, the sea otter, and sirenians do not migrate at all, though they can move about in search of food.

The migrations of the great whales are by far the most remarkable. Many baleen whales congregate to feed during the summer

Tony Ashby/AFP/Getty Images

FIGURE 9.32 These pilot whales (*Globicephala melas*) stranded themselves on a beach in Western Australia. About 80 pilot whales and bottlenose dolphins (*Tursiops truncatus*) were stranded. Most perished, but 17 whales were saved by volunteer rescue workers.

FIGURE 9.33 Migration routes of humpback (*Megaptera novaeangliae*) and gray whales (*Eschrichtius robustus*). Both species tend to migrate and breed close to shore, where they were easily hunted. Gray whales used to live in the North Atlantic until exterminated in the nineteenth century. Gray whales were spotted in the Mediterranean Sea in 2010 and 2021, apparently swimming there along the ice-free Northwest Passage in northern Canada. Another individual was spotted off the coast of Namibia, southern Africa, in 2013.

Source: Bill Ober

in the productive waters of the polar regions of both hemispheres, where huge concentrations of diatoms and krill thrive in the long days. During the winter they migrate to warmer waters to breed. The seasons are reversed in the Northern and Southern hemispheres, so, when some humpback whales are wintering in the Hawaiian Islands or the West Indies, other humpbacks living in the Southern Hemisphere are feeding around Antarctica during the southern summer (Fig. 9.33).

Most pinnipeds and the polar bear undertake seasonal migrations. Most baleen whales migrate from winter breeding areas in the tropics to summer feeding areas in colder waters.

The migratory route of the gray whale is the best known of any of the great whales (Fig. 9.33). From the end of May to late September, the whales feed in shallow water in the northern Bering, Beaufort, and East Siberian seas. They begin moving south in late September when ice begins to form and by November begin crossing through the eastern Aleutian Islands. They eat less while on

the move, burning off close to a quarter of their body weight, covering about 185 km (115 mi) per day. They travel alone or in small groups along the coast of the Gulf of Alaska and down the western coast of North America en route to the Baja California Peninsula, Mexico. Migrating individuals often show spying behavior, pushing their heads out of the water. This raises the possibility that they navigate by using memorized landmarks. They reach Oregon around late November or early December and San Francisco by mid-December. Females generally migrate earlier. In late February pregnant females are the first to appear in shallow, quiet lagoons in southern Baja California and the southern mainland coast of the Gulf of California. It is here that females give birth and males mate with non-pregnant females.

The northbound migration begins by March, after the birth of the 700- to 1,400-kg (1,500- to 3,000-lb) calves. Females mate every two years, and the first to migrate north are the newly pregnant females that did not give birth. They will return 12 months later to give birth. Mothers with calves leave last. On the way north the whales tend to stay farther from the coast and move slower than on their southward migration, an average of 80 km (50 mi) per day

(a)

(b)

FIGURE 9.34 (*a*) A male Steller sea lion (*Eumetopias jubatus*) guarding his harem on a rocky island off the coast of Alaska. Steller sea lions are the largest of the eared seals; males can weigh nearly 900 kg (1 ton). (*b*) A harem of female California sea lions (*Zalophus californianus*) on Santa Barbara Island, Southern California. The harem (center) is being guarded by a large, darker bull (top left). Large female elephant seals (*Mirounga angustirostris*) rest near the harem, oblivious to the occasional fights between the bull and rival males around the harem.

because of the unfavorable currents (see Fig. 3.20) and the new-born calves. They can slow down their migration by taking shelter in kelp forests to avoid orcas. The last whales leave the coast off Washington State by early May. They start reaching their feeding areas by late May, completing an amazing eight-month trip of up to 18,000 km (11,200 mi), the longest migration of any mammal.

There is still much to be learned about the migrations of the gray and other whales. One vexing question is how whales navigate. It has been suggested that they use Earth's magnetic field, a possibility that implies that they carry some type of internal compass to orient themselves.

Attaching small radio transmitters to whales and tracking their movements by satellite promises to uncover intriguing details. Some isolated groups of gray whales along the migratory route do not migrate at all. One group resides off the coast of British Columbia. Analysis of the DNA of humpback whale populations in the Hawaiian Islands suggests that, as in the green turtle, individuals always return to the feeding grounds of their mothers.

Reproduction The reproductive system of marine mammals, though similar to that of land mammals, shows some unique adaptations to life in the water. To keep the body streamlined, male cetaceans and most other marine mammals have an internal penis and testes. The penis, which in blue whales can be more than 3 m (10 ft) long, is kept rigid by a bone called the **baculum.** It is extruded just before copulation through the **genital slit,** an opening anterior to the anus (see Fig. 9.16).

Pinnipeds breed on land or ice, some migrating long distances to isolated islands to do so. In most species of seals, each adult male breeds with only one female. In sea lions, fur seals, and elephant seals, however, a male breeds with many females. During the breeding season the males of these species, which are much bigger and heavier than females, come ashore and establish breeding territories. They stop eating and defend their territories by constant, violent fighting. They herd **harems** of as many as 50 females onto their territories and keep other males away (Fig. 9.34). Only the

strongest males can hold territories and breed. The others gather into **bachelor groups** and spend much of their time trying to sneak into harems for a quick copulation. Defending the harem is exhausting work, and dominant males "burn out" after a year or two, making way for newcomers. It nevertheless pays off in the huge number of offspring they leave, compared with the males that never reach dominance, even though subordinate males live longer.

Female pinnipeds give birth to their pups on shore. They seem to be indifferent to the birth process but soon establish a close relationship with the pup (Figs. 9.10*c* and 9.35). Because females continue to go to sea to feed, they must learn to recognize their own pups out of all the others by sound and smell. The pups generally cannot swim at birth. They are nursed from four days to two years, depending on the species. Most pinnipeds have two pairs of mammary glands that produce a fat-rich milk ideal for the rapid development of the pup's blubber.

A female pinniped can become pregnant only during a brief period after **ovulation,** the release of an egg by her ovaries. This occurs just days or weeks after the birth of her pup. Females of most species return to the breeding grounds only once a year. By contrast, **gestation,** the length of time it takes the embryo to develop, is less than a year. This difference would cause the pup to be born too early, before the mother returns to the breeding ground. To prevent this, the newly formed embryo stops developing and remains dormant in the female's womb, the **uterus.** After a delay of as long as four months, the embryo finally attaches to the inner wall of the uterus and continues its normal development. This phenomenon, known as **delayed implantation,** allows pinnipeds to prolong the embryo's development so that the timing of birth coincides with the female's arrival at the safety of shore.

The walrus also shows delayed implantation as in other pinnipeds. Females give birth to one pup during the summer migration after a long gestation period of 15 to 16 months. They give birth every two years, the lowest reproductive rate among pinnipeds. Walruses mate both on land and in the water; nursing takes place in the water.

FIGURE 9.35 A California sea lion (*Zalophus californianus*) with pup.

Delayed implantation allows pinnipeds to time the birth of pups with the arrival of pregnant females in breeding areas.

Sea otters reproduce year round, and males mate with multiple females. Mating takes place in the water, with males violently biting females on the nose. The gestation period, which includes delayed implantation, is of four to six months. Birth takes place in the water, sometimes on land. Females are notoriously devoted to their pups, carrying and nursing them on their chests.

Polar bears are solitary except during the mating season in late spring or early summer. Mating induces females to ovulate, so successive copulations are necessary to guarantee fertilization. Males can mate with several females, and DNA tests have shown that twins can be fathered by different males. Pregnant females build a den in the snow or ice in the fall and hibernate, giving birth to one or two cubs after a gestation period of around eight months. Delayed implantation guarantees that the cub is born at the ideal time after winter. Cubs typically nurse for approximately two years.

Manatees reproduce slowly, becoming mature after about five years and giving birth to a single calf every two to five years after a gestation period of about a year. Dugong females mature after at least six years and give birth to a calf every 2.5 to six years; gestation is from 13 to 15 months. Female sirenians, however, can mate any time of the year, typically with several males. They nurse their calves for a year or more from two mammary glands, each located behind a flipper.

We know relatively little about cetacean reproductive behavior. We do know that cetaceans are intensely sexual animals. Sex play is an important component of the behavior of captive dolphins. Like humans, they appear to use sex not only for procreation but also for pleasure. The genital opening of female bottlenose dolphins has spongy tissue rich in sensory nerves, suggesting that physical stimulation could provide sexual pleasure. Cetaceans reach sexual maturity relatively early, at age 5 to 10 in great whales. Sexual behavior appears to have a role in the establishment and maintenance of bonds among all individuals, not just potential mates. The sexes are typically segregated within the pod, and males perform elaborate courtship displays to catch the attention of potentially receptive females. Fights among rival males are common, but cooperation also occurs sometimes. Gray whales are known to copulate with the help of a third party, another male that helps support the female (Fig. 9.36*a*). Group matings have been observed in humpbacks and belugas. Considerable touching and rubbing is known to precede copulation (Fig. 9.36*b*). Actual copulation lasts less than a minute

FIGURE 9.36 Mating behavior in great whales. (*a*) Gray whales (*Eschrichtius robustus*) often mate with the help of a third party, another male that props the female against the mating male. Actual copulation is reported to last for just 30 to 60 s. (*b*) Courtship in humpback whales (*Megaptera novaeangliae*) includes rolling, slapping of the flukes, and pairs surfacing vertically face to face.

(a)

(b)

but is repeated frequently. The vaginas of the bottlenose dolphin and the harbor porpoise (*Phocoena phocoena;* see Fig. 9.19*n*) have folds that appear to block penis entry, probably giving females the ability to control paternity.

Gestation lasts for 11 or 12 months in most cetaceans. An exception is the sperm whale, which has a gestation period of 16 months. Development in most species of large baleen whales is relatively fast for a mammal of their size. It is synchronized with the annual migration to warm waters. It is remarkable that it takes nine months for a 3-kg (7-lb) human baby to develop, but a 2,700-kg (3-ton) blue whale calf needs only about 11 months.

Cetacean calves are born tail-first (Fig. 9.37). This allows them to remain attached to the placenta, which provides oxygenated blood from the mother, for as long as possible to prevent oxygen deprivation. The calf immediately swims to the surface. In captive dolphins, the mother or an attending female can help the calf to the surface. Fat-rich milk is responsible for the rapid growth of calves, particularly in the great whales. They are born without their full complement of blubber and must gain weight before migrating with their mothers to feeding grounds in polar waters. It has been estimated that a blue whale calf gains 90 kg (200 lb) in weight and 4 cm (1.5 in) in length every day for the first seven months of its life. The mother's milk is produced by two mammary glands with nipples located on both sides of the genital slit (see Fig. 9.16). The milk is squirted into the calf's mouth, which allows the calf to drink under water. In at least some of the great whales, females do not seem to feed much while they are nursing, but the calves are not weaned until they arrive at the feeding grounds. In some species, they continue to nurse for more than a year after birth.

The relationship between mother and calf during the nursing period is close. Frequent contact and vocalizations are used in communication. Dolphin mothers modify their swimming behavior to allow calves to glide alongside. Mothers are known to defend

Augusto Leandro Stanzani/ardea.com/Mary Evans Picture Library Ltd/agefotostock

FIGURE 9.37 A bottlenose dolphin (*Tursiops truncatus*) giving birth in captivity. The gestation period lasted for about a year.

their calves when there is danger. Sperm whale calves are watched by "babysitting" adults when mothers deep-dive for food. There is a report of a female gray whale lifting her calf onto her flipper to save it from the attacks of orcas. The bond between mother and calf probably lasts for several years. Captive young dolphins are known to return to their mothers for comfort in times of danger or stress.

Average estimated life expectancy in the wild is about 15 to 20 years in the polar bear, 40 to 45 years in the bottlenose dolphin, 40 to 50 years in manatees, and 20 to 30 years in male orcas, 30 to 90 in females. Female orcas living beyond their reproductive years have been suggested as providers of information about food, predators, and other aspects important for the survival of the pod. Great whales live at least 30 to 40 years, humpbacks at least 50 years, and bowheads 150 years or more.

Table 9.3 Most Important Characteristics of the Marine Reptiles, Seabirds, and Marine Mammals

Group	Distinguishing Features	Temperature Regulation	Feeding	Reproduction	Ecology
Sea turtles	Body covered by shell, scales on exposed parts of body, legs modified as flippers, found mostly in tropical waters	Poikilotherms, ectotherms	Toothless jaws adapted for crushing or grazing	Oviparous, laying eggs on sandy beaches	Predators of jellyfishes and bottom invertebrates, grazers of seagrasses and seaweeds
Sea snakes	Skin with scales, no legs, laterally flattened for swimming, venomous, found only in tropical Indian and Pacific oceans	Poikilotherms, ectotherms	Small teeth adapted for capturing small prey	Ovoviviparous, giving birth at sea, or oviparous, laying eggs on land	Predators of bottom fishes; some feed mostly on fish eggs
Marine iguana	Skin with scales, tail laterally flattened for swimming, found only in the Galápagos Islands	Poikilotherms, ectotherms	Three-cusped teeth adapted for grazing	Oviparous, laying eggs in nest on land	Grazer of seaweeds
Saltwater crocodile	Skin with scales, massive jaws and tail, found in coastal regions in Australia, Southeast Asia, and some western Pacific islands	Poikilotherms, ectotherms	Heavily toothed jaws for capturing prey	Oviparous, laying eggs in nest of mud and vegetation on land	Predator of wide variety of coastal animals, including fishes, seabirds and sea turtles
Seabirds	Feathers for insulation, webbed feet, light bones as adaptation for flight, found in all coastal regions	Homeotherms, endotherms	Beaks adapted for capturing wide range of prey, including filtering	Oviparous, laying eggs in nest on land	Predators of fishes and many groups of surface-dwelling and shallow-water invertebrates, including plankton
Pinnipeds	Seals, sea lions, walrus: blubber, flippers, reduced hair (fur in some), found mostly in temperate and polar waters	Homeotherms, endotherms	Teeth for capturing and eating prey	Viviparous, giving birth on land	Predators of mostly fishes, crab-eater seal filters water for krill, leopard seal hunts mostly seabirds, walrus feeds on clams and bottom invertebrates
Sea otter	Dense, dark fur, dorsoventrally flattened tail, flattened hind feet, found only in northern and northeastern Pacific Ocean	Homeotherms, endotherms	Flattened teeth for capturing and crushing prey	Viviparous, giving birth at sea; sometimes on land	Predator of sea urchins and wide range of bottom invertebrates and fishes in kelp forest; keeps population of sea urchins on check (see Fig. 13.27)
Polar bear	Dense, white fur, relatively short legs, tail, and ears; found in Arctic region, mostly on drifting ice	Homeotherms, endotherms	Powerful jaws and teeth for capturing and eating prey	Viviparous, giving birth on land	Primarily predator of ring seals, other prey (birds, caribou) if available
Sirenians	Manatees, dugong: blubber, reduced hair, front flippers, paddle-shaped tail, tropical seas (one species only in fresh water)	Homeotherms, endotherms	Teeth as thick ridge pads for crushing vegetation	Viviparous, giving birth at sea	Grazers of seagrasses and other coastal vegetation
Baleen whales	Blubber, streamlined body, reduced hair, front flippers, tail fluke, blowhole, found in all seas	Homeotherms, endotherms	Baleen on upper jaw for filtering small plankton	Viviparous, giving birth at sea in warm waters	Filter feeders of plankton and small fishes, mostly in polar waters; gray whale feeds on small animals (mostly amphipods) in soft bottoms
Toothed whales	Blubber, streamlined body, reduced hair, front flippers, tail fluke, blowhole, found in all seas (some dolphins live in freshwater)	Homeotherms, endotherms	Conical teeth for capturing prey	Viviparous, giving birth at sea	Predators of fishes, squids, other marine mammals, and some large bottom invertebrates like lobsters

Source: Bill Ober

Interactive Exploration

McGraw-Hill Connect® is a great place to check your understanding of chapter material. Visit **www.mcgrawhillconnect.com** for access to interactive chapter summaries, chapter quizzing, and more! Further enhance your knowledge with videoclips and weblinks to chapter-related material.

Critical Thinking

1. Sea turtles have disappeared from many regions, and one way of trying to save them is to reintroduce them to areas where they have been wiped out. This is done by reburying eggs or by releasing newborn baby turtles on beaches. Why are eggs reburied or baby turtles released instead of fully grown individuals?

2. Most seabirds are specialists that feed on particular types of fish and other prey. In some cases, this may reduce the chances of competing with other species of seabirds for limited resources. Sometimes, however, two or more species of seabirds feed on the same type of fish. What type of mechanisms might have evolved to prevent direct competition?

3. Cetaceans give birth to few well-developed calves at well-spaced intervals. They also feed and protect the calves for long periods. This is in sharp contrast to most fishes, in which many eggs are spawned and the parents spend no time feeding and protecting the offspring. What do you think is the best strategy? Has this strategy paid off in the great whales?

4. Transporting polar bears to Antarctica could be a way to ensure the survival of this species threatened by disappearing Arctic ice. Could you think reasons why this is not a good idea after all?

5. Sperm whales are by far the largest of the toothed whales, being considered one of the "great whales." What could be the adaptive significance of evolving such a large size? Are there any disadvantages, in comparison with the rest of the toothed whales, of being a large-size whale?

For Further Reading

Some of the recommended reading here may be available online. Look for live links on the *Marine Biology* Online Learning Center.

General Interest

Ainsworth, C., 2018. Penguin archeology. *New Scientist*, vol. 240, no. 3209, 22 December, pp. 54–56. The examination of waste in a penguin's colony in Antarctica reveals much about their biology.

Bessesen, B., 2019. *Vaquita: Science, politics, and crime in the Sea of Cortez.* Island Press, Washington, DC. The sad story of the most endangered marine cetacean and of the efforts to save the species from extinction.

Franzen, J., 2018. Lost at sea. *National Geographic*, vol. 234, no. 1, July, pp. 110–143. Many seabird populations are suffering staggering declines worldwide as a result of habitat destruction, climate change, pollution, and commercial fishing.

Frood, A., 2018. Creatures of war. *New Scientist*, vol. 233, no. 3184, 30 June, pp. 41–43. The military provided valuable pioneering research on the biology of dolphins and other small cetaceans.

Holland, J. S., 2017. The turtle trackers. *Nature Conservancy*, Spring, pp. 42–51. Marine biologists use tags and satellite transmitters to track migrations of hawksbill turtles.

Jaakkola, K., 2021. The riddle of dolphin handedness. *Scientific American*, vol. 324, no. 5, May, pp. 62–65. Human's perception influences the study of spinning behavior in dolphins.

King, B. J., 2019. The orca's sorrow. *Scientific American*, vol. 320, no. 3, March, pp. 30–35. Orcas, like a growing number of other animals, show distress over death.

Osborn, N., 2021. The ice is calling. *Smithsonian*, vol. 51, no. 1, March, pp. 26–37. The melting of ice in the Arctic is threatening the polar bear.

Pyenson, N., 2018. *Spying on whales: The past, present, and future of Earth's most awesome creatures.* Viking/Penguin Books, New York, NY. A cetacean researcher provides a highly readable account of the fascinating, and sometimes perilous, life of whales.

Scales, H., 2020. Marching toward extinction. *National Geographic*, vol. 237, no. 6, June, pp. 94–107. The emperor penguin faces extinction as the Antarctic ice melts.

Vance, E., 2017. Requiem for the vaquita. *Scientific American*, vol. 317, no. 2, August, pp. 36–45. Illegal fishing threatens a rare porpoise with extinction.

Ward, A., 2022. A pod's bonds. *Discover*, vol. 46, no. 5, pp. 48–55. The behavior of sperm whales is more sophisticated than once thought.

Welch, C., 2019. Surviving despite us. *National Geographic*, vol. 239, no. 45, May, pp. 40–79. Many species of cetaceans have evolved amazing adaptations, including the capacity to develop cultural differences, very much like humans.

Welch, C., 2021. Secret of the whales. *National Geographic*, vol. 236, no. 4, October, pp. 62–89. Some groups of cetaceans of the same species share unique songs, diets, and other traits, a character once thought to be found only in human cultures.

In Depth

Brakes, P. and S. R. X. Dall, 2016. Marine mammal behavior: A review of conservation implications. *Frontiers in Marine Science* [https://doi.org/10.3389/fmars.2016.00087].

Erbe, C., S. A. Marley, R. P. Schoeman, J. N. Smith, L. E. Trigg, and C. B. Embling, 2019. The effects of ship noise on marine mammals—A review. *Frontiers in Marine Science,* [https://doi.org/10.3389/fmars.2019.00606].

Lee, P. L.M., G. Schofield, R. I. Haughey, A. D. Mazaris, and G. C. Hays, 2018. A review of patterns of multiple paternity across sea turtle rookeries. *Advances in Marine Biology,* vol. 79, pp. 1–31.

Moore1, M. J., G. H. Mitchell, T. K. Rowles, and G. Earront, 2020. Dead cetacean? Beach, bloat, float, sink. *Frontiers in Marine Science* [https://doi.org/10.3389/fmars.2020.00333].

Nagelkerken, I., S. C. Doney, and P. L. Munday, 2019. Consequences of anthropogenic changes in the sensory landscape of marine animals. *Oceanography and Marine Biology: An Annual Review,* vol. 57, pp. 229–264.

Santora, J. A., M A. LaRue, and D. G. Ainley, 2020. Geographic structuring of Antarctic penguin populations. *Global Ecology & Biogeography,* vol. 29, pp. 1716–1728.

Schoeman, R. P., C. Patterson-Abrolat, and S. Plön, 2020. A global review of vessel collisions with marine animals. *Frontiers in Marine Science* [https://doi.org/10.3389/fmars.2020.00292].

Stimmelmayr, R. and F. M. D. Gulland, 2020. Gray whale (*Eschrichtius robustus*) health and disease: Review and future directions. *Frontiers in Marine Science* [https://doi.org/10.3389/fmars.2020.588820].

Themudo, G. E., L. Q. Alves, A. M. Machado, M. Lopes-Marques, R. R. da Fonseca, M. Fonseca, R. Ruivo, and L. F. C. Castro, 2020. Losing genes: The evolutionary remodeling of Cetacea skin. *Frontiers in Marine Science* [https://doi.org/10.3389/fmars.2020.592375].

Mike Johnson

10
CHAPTER

An Introduction to Marine Ecology

Juvenile halfmoon fish (*Medialuna californiensis*) pick parasites from the skin of an ocean sunfish (*Mola mola*) sheltering under floating kelp fronds.

Everywhere you look in the ocean there is life. How many and what kind of organisms there are depend on where you go—that is, on the specific **habitat,** the natural environment where an organism lives. Every habitat has distinct characteristics that help determine which organisms live there and which do not. The amount of light, for example, determines whether algae and plants can grow. The type of bottom, the temperature and salinity of the water, waves, tides, currents, and many other aspects of the environment profoundly affect marine life. Some of these physical and chemical features were introduced in Chapters 2 and 3.

Equally important are the ways that organisms affect each other. They eat each other, crowd each other out, provide habitat for other organisms, and even cooperate. Living things interact in

complex and fascinating ways. Part Two of this book, Chapters 5 through 9, introduced the organisms that live in the sea. This part, Part Three, looks at how these organisms live and interact. We will explore the different habitats that make up the ocean world, from the water's edge to the darkest depths. We will consider the special physical and chemical features of each habitat, how the organisms have adapted to each environment, and how they affect each other.

Here in Chapter 10 we first introduce some basic principles that apply to all habitats. No matter where you go, for instance, algae and plants need light and animals need food. These are just two examples of the interactions among organisms and their environment. The study of these interactions and how they affect the abundance and distribution of organisms is called **ecology.** It is

important to realize that ecology is a science, the branch of biology that studies how and why organisms interact with each other and with their environment. Contrary to the way the term is often used in the media, ecology is not the same as protecting the environment, as important as that may be.

10.1 THE ORGANIZATION OF COMMUNITIES

The nature of life in a particular habitat is determined to a large extent by the non-living, or **abiotic,** environment, that is, the environment's physical and chemical features such as salinity or bottom type. Each environment has different characteristics that present both challenges and opportunities for the organisms living there.

Organisms are also affected by other organisms—the living, or **biotic,** environment. Biological **populations** interact in complex ways that make the organisms in a **community** dependent on each other.

> The nature of a community is determined by both biotic, or living, and abiotic, or non-living, factors.

Organisms must adapt to both the biotic and abiotic features of their environment. Individual organisms can adapt to varying degrees by changes in behavior, metabolism, or other characteristics. Individual seagrasses, for example, adapt to low light levels by an increase in **chlorophyll** content, making them more efficient at capturing what little light *is* available, while corals often adapt through their growth form (Fig. 10.1). In these **physiological adaptations** the organism's genes are unchanged, and the adaptation is generally not passed on to its offspring. In some cases, adaptation occurs by the attachment of **epigenetic markers** to the organism's genes that sometimes are passed from one generation to the next.

By contrast, genetic differences that make some individuals better adapted to the environment *are* passed on to these individuals' offspring. Those individuals whose traits are best suited to their abiotic and biotic environments are more successful at reproducing than less well-adapted individuals. The best-adapted individuals produce more offspring and pass on the adaptive traits to the next generation. Because of this **natural selection,** the best-adapted individuals are better represented in each successive generation, and the population as a whole becomes more like the most successful individuals. In other words, the population **evolves.** Adaptations that result from natural selection and are passed on genetically are known as **evolutionary adaptations.**

How Populations Grow

Organisms can produce many more offspring than it takes simply to replace themselves. If every individual has more than one offspring—or each pair has more than two—the total number of offspring increases every generation (Fig. 10.2). The population grows faster and faster, and there is a population "explosion." Were its reproduction left unchecked, any species could grow to cover the Earth in a relatively short time. This rapid, unchecked population growth is known as **exponential growth.** Exponential growth sometimes occurs when conditions are just right for a population. Dinoflagellates and other algae, for example, sometimes form massive blooms known as red tides (see Box 15.1, "Red Tides and Harmful Algal Blooms"). Other organisms also occasionally undergo dramatic population explosions (Fig. 10.3).

Fortunately, we aren't up to our necks in dinoflagellates or sea urchins, because exponential growth cannot continue forever. Many factors can control, or regulate, the growth of populations. For one thing, explosive growth can occur only under favorable conditions. When the abiotic environment changes, the population may stop growing or decline. Some environmental fluctuations, like the seasons, are regular and predictable. Algal growth in temperate and polar regions, for example, often slows dramatically in winter because there is less light for photosynthesis. Other changes, like a sudden storm or a drifting log that smashes organisms on a rocky shore, are not so predictable. Predictable or not, large or small, changes in the environment can slow the growth of or even wipe out populations. Of course, conditions that wipe out one species might be just right for another.

(a)

(b)

Photograph courtesy of Dr. J. Veron, /it/ Corals of the World/xit/ (Veron 2000)

Photograph courtesy of Dr. J. Veron, /it/ Corals of the World/xit/ (Veron 2000)

FIGURE 10.1 These two corals belong to the same species, *Turbinaria mesenterina.* (*a*) The "normal" growth form occurs in relatively shallow water, where there is plenty of light. (*b*) In deeper water, with less light, the coral grows in a flattened shape. This flat shape, like that of a solar panel, is an adaptation that increases the coral's ability to capture the sunlight it needs to grow (see "Conditions for Reef Growth," in 14.1). This variation in form reflects an individual colony's response to light, and not genetic differences among colonies: The offspring of both colonies will be able to grow in either form depending on light level.

> **Population** A group of individuals of the same species that live together.
> **Community** All the different populations of organisms that live in the same place.
> • 4.2, Living Machinery; Table 4.1
>
> **Chlorophyll** A green pigment that absorbs light energy for photosynthesis.
> **Epigenetic markers** Small chemicals that attach to DNA and alter gene expression.
> **Natural Selection** The production of more offspring by those individuals in a population that are genetically best-adapted to the environment.

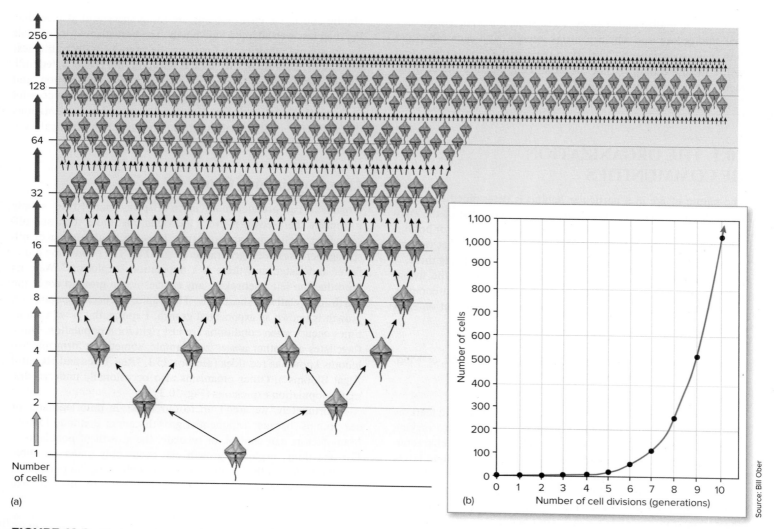

(a)

(b) Number of cell divisions (generations)

Source: Bill Ober

FIGURE 10.2 All species are capable of undergoing population explosions. (*a*) When a single-celled dinoflagellate divides, for example, it leaves two daughter cells. Each daughter cell produces two new daughter cells, which also divide, and so on. At each generation the number of cells doubles, and the population grows at an ever-increasing rate. If this population growth were to continue unchecked, the combined weight of the dinoflagellates would soon exceed the weight of the universe! Imagine the growth potential of organisms that can produce thousands of young instead of just two. (*b*) A graph of the number of cells at each generation shows a J-shaped curve, which is typical of populations undergoing unrestrained growth.

There are also mechanisms that limit population growth even if the non-living environment doesn't fluctuate. Some animals slow down or stop reproduction when their habitat becomes too crowded. Others fight among themselves or even cannibalize each other. Natural enemies may be attracted when the population gets large, or diseases may spread faster under crowded conditions. Large populations can pollute the environment with their own wastes.

As more and more individuals join the population, they use up their **resources,** the things they need to live and reproduce, like food, **nutrients,** and living space. Eventually there are just not enough resources to support any more individuals and the population levels off (Fig. 10.4). This type of population growth is called **logistic growth.** The largest population size that can be sustained by the available resources is called the **carrying capacity.**

Organisms use many different resources. A lack of any one of these will slow or prevent population growth. A dinoflagellate living in the open ocean, for example, can be limited by a lack of nitrogen,

even if it has plenty of light, water, carbon dioxide (CO_2), and other nutrients. During the winter in polar regions, there may be plenty of nutrients but not enough light. Seaweeds on a rocky shore, on the other hand, might have plenty of light and nutrients but be unable to grow because there isn't enough space. A **limiting resource** is one whose short supply restricts the growth of a population.

Because of a drain on resources or other effects of crowding, populations do not grow forever. As the population becomes more crowded, its *growth rate* goes down. In this sense the population is **self-regulating;** that is, its growth rate depends on its own numbers. Whereas non-living factors such as the weather can affect populations of any size, self-regulation acts only when the population is large.

Populations are capable of explosive growth. Population growth is usually limited, however, by either the non-living environment or by the activities of the organisms themselves.

Liquidlibrary/Getty Images

FIGURE 10.3 The purple sea urchin (*Strongylocentrotus purpuratus*) from the Pacific coast of North America sometimes undergoes dramatic population explosions, as do many other urchin species. The outbreaks can have major effects on the rest of the community.

As resources are depleted, there are not enough to go around. Each individual has to vie with other organisms for what resources remain. **Competition** is the interaction that results when a resource is in short supply and one organism uses the resource at the expense of another (Fig. 10.5). When members of the same species compete it is called **intraspecific competition.**

Ways That Species Interact

Species do not live in a vacuum, isolated from other species. Members of different species often have strong effects on each other. Species can interact in many ways, all of which influence the organization of communities. Most of these interactions in most marine communities are not well understood. In some cases, species don't interact at all but simply happen to live in the same place; such groups of species are said to form **assemblages** rather than true ecological communities. Working out if and how the species that live in the same habitat interact is a core feature of marine ecology.

Competition Organisms must compete for resources not only with members of their own species, but with other species. Competition between species is known as **interspecific competition.**

When two species use the same resource and the resource is scarce, the species must compete just as if they were members of the same population. One of the two species usually turns out to be a better competitor. If two species eat exactly the same food, for example, one of the two will be better at catching it. Unless something interferes, the inferior competitor loses out and the

Nutrients Raw materials other than carbon dioxide and water that are needed by primary producers for primary production.

• 4.1, The Ingredients of Life

Evolution A change in the genetic makeup of a population, usually resulting when natural selection favors some individual characteristics over others.

• 4.5, The Diversity of Life in the Sea

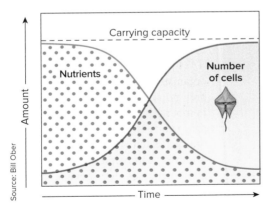

Source: Bill Ober

FIGURE 10.4 The kind of explosive population growth shown in Figure 10.2 would never go on forever. As the dinoflagellates get more and more numerous, they use up nutrients and other resources they need. The maximum number of cells that the nutrient supply can support is called the carrying capacity of the system. Curves like this are often observed in laboratory experiments, but in the real world they are rarely so smooth. In particular, fast-growing populations often overshoot the carrying capacity, severely depleting resources, and then crash.

Millard H. Sharp/Science Source

FIGURE 10.5 The short supply of any resource can lead to competition. Hermit crabs rely on abandoned snail shells for protection. When they grow out of their old shell or it wears out they must move into a new shell, and sometimes there aren't enough shells to go around. These thinstripe hermit crabs (*Clibanarius vittatus*) are fighting over a shell they both want. One of them has lost a leg.

competitively superior species takes over. When one species eliminates another by outcompeting it, it is called **competitive exclusion.**

> Competition between species results when both species use a scarce resource. In competitive exclusion, one species wins the competition and eliminates the other from the community.

Sometimes a competitively superior species is prevented from excluding poorer competitors. Periodic disturbances such as severe storms, battering by drifting logs, or underwater landslides can reduce the population of a dominant competitor and give other species a chance (see Fig. 11.23). Furthermore, which species is competitively superior sometimes depends on the conditions. On rocky shores in tropical Hong Kong, for example, foliose (leaf-like) algae (*Dermonema, Pterocladia*) are the dominant seaweeds during the relatively cool winter. In the summer heat these forms die out and are replaced by more resistant encrusting algae (*Ralfsia*). Seasonal variation thus prevents either group from excluding the other and there is a shifting balance between the competing species.

Species can also avoid excluding each other if they share the limiting resource, with each species specializing on just part of the resource. For example, two species of fish that eat seaweeds might divide the resource by specializing on different kinds of seaweed. Animals that eat exactly the same thing might live in different places or feed at different times, staying out of each other's way. Ecologists call this sharing of a resource by specialization **resource partitioning.**

> Species that might otherwise competitively exclude each other sometimes coexist by resource partitioning, or dividing the resource.

FIGURE 10.6 The whale shark (*Rhincodon typus*) feeds by straining plankton and small fish from huge mouthfuls of water. It probably evolved its huge mouth and lost the large teeth of most other sharks not to avoid competition with other sharks but as adaptations for efficient plankton feeding.

Resource partitioning allows species to coexist when they might otherwise exclude each other, but it does have its price. By specializing, each species gives up some of the resource. The fish that specializes on just one kind of seaweed, for example, will have less food available than if it ate all types. With fewer resources available, the population size tends to be smaller. On the other hand, the species might be able to use the resource more efficiently by being a specialist than if it were a "jack-of-all-trades." Different species of shorebirds, for example, have specialized bill shapes that make them more efficient at feeding on particular types of mudflat animals (see Fig. 12.12) and may also reduce competition. Not all specializations, however, are a result of interspecific competition (Fig. 10.6).

To be successful in the long run, a species must find the right balance between specialization and generalization. There is no one best answer to the problem—just look at all the different kinds of organisms. Each species has its own special role, or **ecological niche,** in the community. A species' niche is defined by the combination of virtually every aspect of its lifestyle: what it eats, where it lives, when and how it reproduces, how it behaves, and so on.

> The role a species plays in the community is called its ecological niche. The niche includes feeding habits, habitat use, and all the other aspects of the species' lifestyle.

Predator–Prey Interactions Species don't always compete for resources. Sometimes they use each other as the resource. In other words, they eat each other (Fig. 10.7). **Predation** is the act of one organism eating another. The organism that does the eating is the **predator,** and the organism that gets eaten is the **prey.** The term "predator" is often reserved for **carnivores,** animals that eat other animals. When organisms eat algae or plants, it is usually called **herbivory** rather than predation, and the organism doing the eating is called a **herbivore.** No matter what you call it, the alga or plant gets eaten just the same.

Predation obviously affects the individual organism that gets eaten, but it also affects the prey population as a whole by reducing prey numbers. If the predators don't eat too much, prey can reproduce to replace the individuals that get eaten. Predation that is too intense, however, can wipe out a prey population. In some cases, this occurs when predators are artificially introduced into new places, and the indigenous species have no natural defenses against the introduced predator (see Box 18.2, "Biological Invasions: The Uninvited Guests").

The interaction between predator and prey is not a one-way street. After all, the predator depends on the prey for its food supply.

Box 10.1 Biodiversity: All Creatures Great and Small

From bacteria to baleen whales, our planet is home to tens of millions of life forms at least; biologists can only guess at the true number of species. This richness and variety of life is referred to as **biological diversity,** or just **biodiversity.** But Earth's biodiversity is in crisis. Species are going extinct at an alarming rate. There have been mass extinctions in the geological past. But the current rate of species extinction is probably unprecedented in the history of life. Past mass extinction events were caused by geological events such as asteroid impacts, massive volcanic eruptions, or sudden changes in the atmosphere. It is the impact of humanity—pollution, habitat destruction, over exploitation, climate change, and other human folly—that is driving the current biodiversity crisis. At the rate things are going, most species will soon be gone forever, many before we even know they exist. The extinction rate of marine species is thought to be lower than terrestrial and freshwater species, in part, because many marine species are very widely distributed. There is a lot of uncertainty about this, however, because little or nothing is known about most marine species. Most marine biologists consider marine biodiversity to be under dire threat.

Our survival depends on biodiversity. Natural systems produce the oxygen we breath, purify our water, regulate our climate, maintain our soil, and provide many other benefits we can't live without. They are also a treasure trove of pharmaceuticals, new and improved crops, sustainable energy and materials, and many other benefits to society. There are so many species that scientists have not even discovered most of them, much less evaluated their usefulness. The next one to go extinct might hold the cure for cancer, a solution to hunger, or maybe just the makings of an elegant new perfume—a secret that will be lost forever.

Conservation has often focused on organisms we find beautiful or emotionally compelling. Whales and sea turtles evoke strong positive reactions in many people. Worms, seaweeds, fungi, and millions of other seemingly insignificant species aren't as popular, but are at least as vital to Earth's—and our own—survival as the larger organisms we find attractive. There is an urgent need to reverse or at least slow the rate of mass extinction of all species, not just particular ones.

Why should we worry about how many species there are, as long as the ones we care about are still around? For one thing, species are bound together in complex food webs, nutrient cycles, symbioses, and other ecological interactions. The loss of even the "lowliest" species could profoundly affect many others, including "flagship species" like whales and sea turtles. Biologists simply do not understand ecosystems well enough to predict these effects.

Diverse communities—those with many species—use resources more efficiently, produce more food and oxygen, and break down waste faster than those with few species. They are also more resilient to natural disasters, disease outbreaks, and human pressures. Maintaining biodiversity is critical to sustaining our rapidly changing planet (see Special Report).

The biodiversity crisis has caught the attention of governments as well as scientists. Since 1992, world leaders have established a series of international agreements targeting the biodiversity crisis. In 2002, governments agreed to "significantly reduce" the rate of biodiversity loss by 2010. Since we didn't (and still don't) know the number of species or their rate of extinction, this target didn't mean much. In 2010, governments established more meaningful and measurable targets for reducing biodiversity loss. Unfortunately, we have not even come close to meeting those targets.

Broad international agreements and targets, however, don't actually prevent species from going extinct—for that, specific actions are needed. Ways must be found for low-income countries to develop economically without destroying their natural biodiversity, a concept called "sustainable development." Developed countries need to support developing countries in this effort and become more sustainable themselves. Important steps have already been taken. More and more marine protected areas are being established; in 2016 the United States created the world's largest marine reserve, twice the size of Texas, northwest of Hawai'i. In 2021, a group of 50 countries launched a campaign to protect 30% of the ocean (and land) by 2030, but there is little evidence of progress. Governments have agreed to require measures in the shipping industry to reduce the spread of invasive species, a major threat to marine biodiversity, in ships' ballast water. Ballast water treatment systems have already been developed and fitted to new ships. The United Nations has been working for decades on an international treaty to protect the "high seas," the two-thirds of the world ocean beyond the control of any one country and where there is little control of environmentally harmful activities. Only a tiny fraction of the high seas is currently protected.

Marine biologists are at work too, for example developing new technologies to measure marine biodiversity, to determine the factors that maintain ecosystem health, and to identify key habitats that are not only refuges for biodiversity but also act as nurseries and larval sources to maintain biodiversity more broadly, and to protect and restore individual habitats and species.

Much more needs to be done—there is no evidence that the biodiversity crisis is slowing and most marine biologists fear it is getting worse. Without strong, swift action to prevent a catastrophic loss of marine biodiversity, the oceans may be heading for tragedy.

If bad weather or disease decimates the prey, the predators suffer as well. And, when predators consume too many prey they deplete their own food supply and start to decline themselves.

Predation, which occurs when an animal eats another organism, affects the numbers of both predator and prey.

Predators often affect species other than their prey. On temperate rocky shores, for example, sea stars that selectively prey on mussels make space for the mussels' competitors, which would otherwise be crowded out (see Fig. 11.21). Feeding, or **trophic,** interactions such as this, in which the effects of one species on another go on to affect a third species, are called **indirect interactions.** Indirect interactions sometimes result in unexpected relationships

FIGURE 10.7 Predation. A purple cone shell (*Conus purpurascens*) engulfs its prey, a redhead goby (*Elacatinus puncticulatus*). It paralyzed the fish by injecting powerful venom through a hollow, harpoon-like "tooth" derived from the radula.

FIGURE 10.8 The frond-like projections of the leafy seadragon (*Phycodurus eques*) make these fish look like a bit of drifting seaweed. Not only does this hide them from predators, it also allows them to sneak up on their own prey, tiny shrimps. They also have sharp, protective spines in case a predator isn't fooled by the camouflage.

among species. On Caribbean coral reefs, for example, a grazing chiton (*Choneplax lata*) actually *increases* the abundance of its primary prey, a coralline alga (*Porolithon pachydermum*). The chiton only scrapes a thin surface layer off the alga, which leaves most of the alga behind and actually stimulates its growth. The chiton also removes competitively superior algae that grow faster than the coralline alga. Furthermore, these fast-growing algae attract parrotfish grazers, whose deep bites do completely remove the coralline alga. There is often a web of indirect interactions, which means that an effect on one species may flow through an ecosystem in what is called a **trophic cascade.** In the northwest Pacific, for example, the effects of depleting fishes that are the prey of seals and sea lions flow through to killer whales, otters, sea urchins, and entire kelp beds (see "Kelp Communities," in 13.3 and Fig. 13.27).

Predator–prey interactions can also cause the effects of physical factors to cascade through a community. For example, a mud snail (*Hydrobia ulvae*) is the main grazer on seagrass **epiphytes** in North Sea seagrass beds. Epiphytes compete with the seagrass for light and nutrients, slowing seagrass growth. Where snail grazing keeps the seagrass leaves clean, the beds grow thick and lush. At exposed sites, however, currents wash the snails away, epiphytes grow in profusion, and the seagrass beds are sparser.

Predators don't necessarily even have to eat their prey to affect the community. Some herbivorous coral reef fishes, for example, reduce their grazing when predatory fishes are around, benefiting the algae they graze on. Fear of predators may have widespread effects on marine communities.

A tremendous variety of predatory strategies have evolved. Sharks and tunas are highly efficient killing machines, swift and powerful. Other predators sneak up on their prey, catching them unaware. Predators such as anglerfishes go a step further and lure their prey. Many snails can drill through their prey's shell, and many sea stars evert their stomachs to digest prey outside their bodies (see "Biology of Molluscs," in 7.5). Many predators eat only part of the prey, leaving the rest alive to continue growing. In the following chapters, we will examine some of the many ways that predators catch their prey, and that prey use to avoid being eaten.

The most successful individual predators catch more food and thus tend to survive longer, grow faster, and produce more offspring. Natural selection, therefore, favors the most efficient

predators in the population. This doesn't necessarily mean that predators always get bigger, stronger, and faster with each generation, because there are trade-offs. Getting bigger, for example, means needing to eat more, and perhaps getting slower or being more exposed to your own predators. In some situations, selection acts to weed out individuals that are too far from the optimal balance. This type of selection is called **stabilizing selection.** When conditions change—including not only the physical environment but the adaptations of competitors, predators, and prey—the optimal balance also changes, and selection drives evolution toward a new optimum. This form of selection is called **directional selection.**

Natural selection also favors prey that are most successful at getting away. Organisms have evolved at least as many ways to escape from predators as there are predators. Some are fast and elusive; others use camouflage (Fig. 10.8). Many organisms have protective spines, shells, or other defensive structures. Many seaweeds and animals protect themselves with distasteful or even poisonous chemicals.

Organisms may also take advantage of the defenses of other species. Many sea slugs, or **nudibranchs,** for example, protect themselves from predators with noxious chemicals or stinging cells that they obtain from their prey (see "Types of Molluscs," in 7.5). In North Carolina, a brown alga (*Sargassum filipendula*) competes with a red alga (*Hypnea musciformis*) and slows its growth when the two occur together. Nonetheless, the red alga *only* occurs together with the brown one when grazing fishes are abundant, because the brown alga is unpalatable and helps deter the fishes from eating the red one, which they relish.

Some organisms use their defenses only when they need them. The barnacle *Chthamalus anisopoma* from the Gulf of California, for example, normally grows upright, but when predatory snails are abundant it grows bent over. This makes it more difficult for the snails to get through the covering plates on the barnacles' upper

Box 10.2 Cleaning Associations

Some small fishes and shrimps form **cleaning associations** with larger "clients" in which the cleaner makes a living by picking parasites and dead or diseased tissue off its clients. Cleaner fishes include wrasses, butterflyfishes, and gobies, while the banded coral shrimp (*Stenopus hispidus*) is the best-known cleaner shrimp. Usually the clients are fishes, but some octopuses also take advantage of the service. Cleaning behavior can be a full- or part-time job. Some species are cleaners all their lives, others only as juveniles. Cleaning associations are especially common in coral reef, kelp bed, and other shallow, hard-bottom communities.

Bill Ober

A cleaning wrasse (*Labroides*) doing its job on a moray eel (*Gymnothorax*).

To attract clients, cleaners set up a "cleaning station," usually marked by a prominent feature like a large sponge or conspicuous rock. Cleaners often have distinctive coloration to advertise their services, which are popular: Clients sometimes have to wait in line. Clients remember where the stations are and continue to visit even after a cleaner is experimentally removed.

Some clients are carnivores that could easily swallow a cleaner in one gulp. Perhaps to signal their good intentions, many clients swim abnormally or change color. Cleaner fishes swim close to inspect the client. Some "dance" as part of the ritual, perhaps to remind the host that they are cleaners and not food. Cleaner shrimps use their antennae,

tapping the host, and perform specialized "dances" for predatory fish that they don't do for non-predators.

Once the cleaning starts, the hosts stay still to allow the cleaners to pick at their skin and fins. They often open their gill covers to allow the cleaner to inspect and clean their gills. Cleaners even swim into the client's mouth without mishap.

Cleaning associations benefit both sides. The cleaners get reliable "home delivery," although they are occasionally infected by the very parasites they are trying to eat. Cleaners effectively control their clients' parasites.

Clients do sometimes cheat the system and eat a cleaner. Cleaners also cheat

occasionally, biting off a scale or some protective mucus from a client. Cheating is rare, however, and both sides have strategies to keep the other side honest. Clients punish cleaners who try to cheat, attacking them or taking their business to a different cleaning station. They may move on if the cleaner keeps them waiting. They even watch how cleaners treat other clients and select cooperative cleaners; cleaners behave better when being watched.

For their part, cleaners learn to recognize individual clients and may reject ones that didn't behave during a previous encounter. They even give preferential treatment to clients that have access to a choice of cleaning stations and might seek better service elsewhere.

Cleaning associations have widespread effects on fish communities. Fishes grow slower and smaller on coral reefs that lack cleaner wrasses. Reefs with cleaners have more abundant and diverse fish communities than those without. There is also more recruitment of juvenile damselfishes, which are themselves important in reef community structure (see "Coral Reef Communities," in 14.3) on reefs with cleaners than those without. This is another example of how interactions among individual species can flow through entire communities.

surface. Some algae that use chemical defenses only produce the nasty chemicals after they have been damaged. Thus, they don't waste energy making the chemicals until they are needed. Blue mussels (*Mytilus galloprovincialis*) in southern New England can sense the presence of an introduced predator, the Asian shore crab (*Hemigrapsus sanguineus*), using an unknown cue, and grow thicker shells when the crabs are around. Defense mechanisms that are used only in response to predators are called **inducible defenses.**

Thus, there is a continual "arms race" between predators and their prey. The predator keeps getting better at catching the prey and overcoming its defenses. In response, the prey becomes more adept at escaping or develops better defenses. This interplay, with each species evolving in response to the other, is known as **coevolution.**

Symbiosis Coevolution becomes even more important when species interact more intimately. Members of different species may live in very close association, even with one inside another (see Box 4.1, "From Snack to Servant: How Complex Cells Arose"). Such close relationships are examples of **symbiosis,** which literally means "living

Chitons Molluscs whose shells consist of eight overlapping plates on their upper, or dorsal, surface.
• 7.5, Molluscs: The Successful Soft Body

Epiphytes Photosynthetic organisms that live on the surface of algae or plants.
• 13.2, Soft-Bottom Subtidal Communities

together." The smaller partner in the symbiosis is usually called the **symbiont** and the larger one the **host,** though sometimes the distinction is unclear.

Biologists traditionally categorize symbiosis according to whether the organisms involved benefit or suffer from the relationship. In **commensal** relationships, one species obtains shelter, food, or some other benefit without affecting the other species one way or the other. For example, certain barnacles live only on whales (Fig. 10.9). The barnacles get a place to live and a free ride. They feed by filtering the water, and as far as we can tell the whale is neither harmed nor helped by the barnacles. There are many other examples of symbiotic organisms that live on, or even in, a host without apparently either hurting or helping it.

On the other hand, sometimes the symbiont benefits at the expense of the host (Fig. 10.10). This is called **parasitism.** The giant tapeworms that derive food and shelter by living in the guts of whales (see "Flatworms," in 7.4) are generally considered parasites because they may weaken their whale hosts.

Marine parasites are very common. In fact, few marine species escape having at least one kind of parasite, and parasites strongly affect marine communities. They may help control population sizes, for example, as parasites spread more readily in dense host populations. Parasites sometimes make their hosts more vulnerable to predation, or they may be a mechanism for indirect interactions, for example when parasitized prey species pass the parasite on to their predator.

Not all symbiotic relationships are one-sided. In **mutualism,** both partners benefit from the relationship. In many places, small cleaner fishes and shrimps have mutualistic relationships with larger fishes known as **cleaning associations** (see Box 10.2, "Cleaning Associations").

In some cases of symbiosis, both partners can get by without the other if they have to, which is called **facultative symbiosis.** In **obligate symbiosis**, one or both partners depend on the other. In the symbiosis that forms lichens (see 5.5 for example, both the fungus and the alga are obligate symbionts that cannot live without the other.

> In symbiosis, members of different species live in close association. Symbiosis includes parasitism, in which the symbiont harms the host, commensalism, in which the host is not affected, and mutualism, in which both partners benefit.

Like other interactions among species, symbiosis can have indirect effects. In exchange for shelter and food, in the form of mucus, the colorful crab shown at the beginning of Chapter 7 drives away the sea star predators of its coral host. This can protect

FIGURE 10.9 Some barnacles live only on the skin of whales. Because they do not appear to affect their host at all, most such barnacles are considered to be commensals.

FIGURE 10.10 The isopod (*Anilocra*) just below the eye of this coney (*Cephalopholis fulva*) is a blood-sucking fish parasite.

nearby corals as well as the host coral, because the sea stars avoid crawling over the host to get to the other corals.

Larval Ecology Interactions among species and their environment occur over the organisms' entire lifetimes. Most marine animals have larval stages (see Fig. 15.12), and seaweeds have spores. What happens to the larvae and spores can be as important as interactions later in life—for many species more so.

Many factors can affect how many larvae survive. Some larvae are sensitive to temperature, salinity, and other factors, so larval survival may depend on oceanographic conditions. Larvae may also have a critical period during which they must obtain the right food. The survival of haddock larvae off the coast of Nova Scotia, for example, is closely linked to the availability of particular plankton during a few critical weeks in early spring. In years

when weather and oceanographic conditions favor an abundance of plankton during this period, the larvae survive particularly well and there are more adults of these fish in later years. Predators, pollution, and many other factors can also have a strong influence on larval survival.

If the larvae do survive, they still must reach their adult habitat for successful **recruitment,** the addition of new members to a population. Some larvae remain near their parents, but the drifting larvae of many marine species depend on favorable currents to carry them to the right habitat. It was long assumed that currents scatter most larvae far and wide, but the larvae of at least some species are able to stay fairly close to the habitats where their parents produced them, making it easier for them to get back. The larvae of some coral reef fishes, for example, are surprisingly strong swimmers and are able to stay near their home reef, recognizing the reef by sound or perhaps smell. The larvae of other species tend to stay in water layers where there isn't much current, so they aren't carried far.

On the other hand, currents do transport the larvae of some species far from the adult population. The larvae have to find a suitable habitat to settle in, and in the process they "seed" the habitat with new recruits. These larval linkages mean that many marine populations depend on distant sources of larvae, and the decline of a population in one place can have profound flow-on effects through the broader ecosystem.

If larvae do reach the right habitat, they have to recognize it and settle in the right place. The larvae of many bottom-dwelling species test the bottom before they settle. Others are attracted to chemicals produced by their hosts or adults of their own species (see Fig. 13.5).

In many marine communities it is unclear whether the abundance of organisms is determined primarily by the supply of larvae to settle in the habitat (this has been dubbed "supply-side ecology") or by competition, predation, and other interactions after the larvae settle. Both processes are important, to varying degrees depending on the species and their habitats.

10.2 MAJOR MARINE LIFESTYLES AND ENVIRONMENTS

It has already been noted that, because physical and chemical conditions change from place to place, different parts of the ocean harbor very distinct communities. Marine biologists therefore categorize communities according to where and how the organisms live. Perhaps the simplest classification relates to the lifestyle of the organism: whether it lives on the bottom or up in the water column. **Benthic organisms,** or the **benthos,** are those that live on or buried in the bottom (Fig. 10.11). Some benthic organisms are **sessile,** or attached to one place; others move around. **Pelagic** organisms live up in the water column, away from the bottom.

Pelagic organisms are further subdivided according to how well they can swim. Some marine organisms swim only weakly or not at all. These organisms, called **plankton,** are carried from place to place at the mercy of the currents. The term "plankton" comes from the Greek word for "drifters." Planktonic algae and other autotrophs are collectively called the **phytoplankton** and are the most important primary producers in many marine ecosystems. The heterotrophic plankton are called the **zooplankton.** The plankton can also be subdivided according to size, whether they live right at the sea surface or further below, or whether they spend all or only part of their lives in the plankton (see 15.1 and "Staying Afloat," in 15.2).

Animals that swim well enough to oppose the currents are called **nekton.** Most nektonic animals are vertebrates, mainly fishes and marine mammals. There are a few nektonic invertebrates, however, such as squids. Not all nekton are pelagic. The ray in Figure 10.11, for example, is part of the nekton because it can swim. It is not considered pelagic, however, because it spends most of its time on or just above the bottom rather than up in the water column.

Another way to classify marine communities is by where they live. Zonation in benthic organisms, for example, relates to depth and position on the continental shelf (Fig. 10.12). Right at the boundary between land and sea is the shallowest part of the shelf,

Nudibranchs (sea slugs) Gastropods, or close relatives of snails, that lack a shell and have exposed gills.

• 7.5, Molluscs: The Successful Soft Body; Figure 7.24*d*

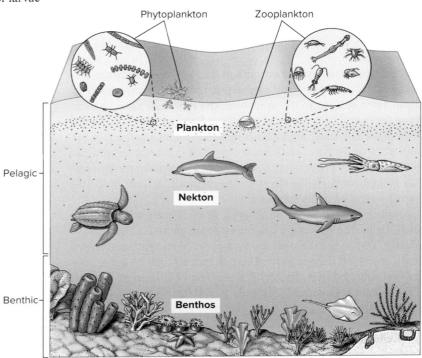

Source: Bill Ober

FIGURE 10.11 There are three basic lifestyle groups of marine organisms: the benthos, nekton, and plankton.

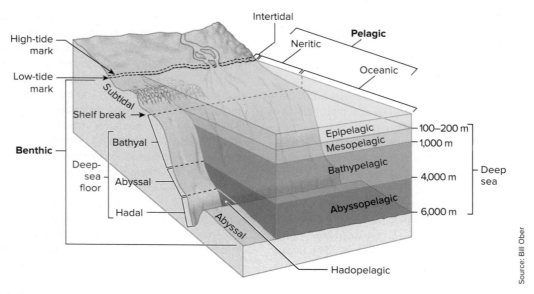

Source: Bill Ober

FIGURE 10.12 The major subdivisions of the marine environment are based on distance from land, water depth, and whether the organisms are benthic or pelagic.

the **intertidal zone,** sometimes called the **littoral zone.** This is the area between the tides that is exposed to the air when the tide is out but underwater at high tide. The intertidal zone makes up only a small fraction of the continental shelf. Most of the shelf is never exposed to the air, even at the lowest of low tides. Benthic organisms that inhabit the continental shelf below the intertidal live in the **subtidal zone,** sometimes called the **sublittoral zone.** Away from the shelf the benthic environment is subdivided by depth into the **bathyal, abyssal,** and **hadal** zones. For the sake of simplicity, we lump these different zones together and call them the "deep-sea floor."

The pelagic environment, too, is divided with respect to the continental shelf. The pelagic environment over the shelf is called the **neritic zone.** Pelagic waters beyond the **shelf break** are the **oceanic zone.**

Besides being divided into the neritic and oceanic zones, the pelagic is divided vertically into depth zones that correspond to the amount of light. In the shallowest, the **epipelagic zone,** there is plenty of light for photosynthesis, at least for part of the year. Given a supply of nutrients, phytoplankton thrive, producing food for the rest of the ecosystem. Definitions vary, but this book defines the epipelagic zone as extending to a depth of 200 m (650 ft). Because this is approximately the depth of the continental shelf, nearly all neritic waters lie in the epipelagic.

Other pelagic zones lie in deep oceanic waters beyond the shelf. Below the epipelagic lies the **mesopelagic zone.** There is not enough light in the mesopelagic to support photosynthesis, so primary producers cannot grow. There is enough light to see by, but on even the brightest day, the mesopelagic is an area of twilight. This twilight zone typically extends to a depth of around 1,000 m (3,300 ft).

No sunlight at all penetrates to the deepest parts of the ocean, the **bathypelagic, abyssopelagic,** and **hadopelagic** zones. Although each of these zones supports a different community of animals, they share many similarities. We refer to all these zones together as the "deep-sea" environment.

In virtually every marine environment, prokaryotes—bacteria and archaea—are by far the most abundant organisms. These organisms are so tiny that they were once almost ignored, but the more we learn about them the clearer it is that they are profoundly important to flow of energy and materials, and interactions among species at multiple levels. Prokaryotes drive the very nature of marine ecosystems.

10.3 THE FLOW OF ENERGY AND MATERIALS

All living things use energy to make and maintain the complex chemicals necessary for life. **Autotrophs** get this energy from the non-living environment, usually in the form of sunlight. They use the energy to make their own food from simple molecules like carbon dioxide, water, and nutrients. As the autotrophs grow and reproduce they become food for **heterotrophs** (Fig. 10.13). When one organism eats another, both the organic material and the energy stored in it are passed from one to the other. Thus, energy and chemical substances flow from the non-living part of the ecosystem to organisms, and from organism to organism. The pathways taken by energy and materials tell us a lot about how an ecosystem works.

Trophic Structure

The flow of energy and matter through an ecosystem can be traced by observing the trophic relationships among its organisms: who makes the food and who eats it. The organisms can be divided into two broad components: **primary producers,** the autotrophs that make the food, and **consumers,** the heterotrophs that eat it. Not all consumers feed directly on producers. Many animals eat other consumers rather than primary producers. Thus, the transfer of energy through the system usually takes place in several steps known as a **food chain.** Each of the steps in the food chain is known as a **trophic level.**

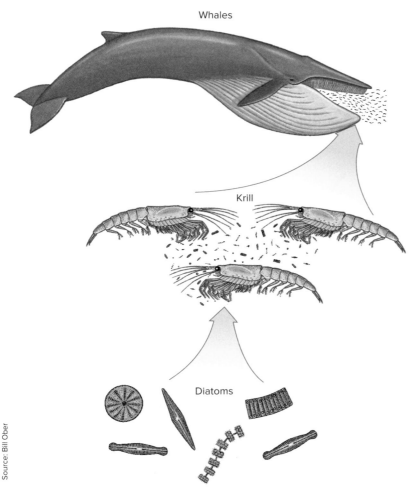

Whales

Krill

Diatoms

Source: Bill Ober

FIGURE 10.13 This three-step food chain is typical of Antarctic waters. Diatoms are primary producers that capture sunlight to fix carbon. Planktonic diatoms are the main primary producers during summer, but in winter diatoms and other algae growing in sea ice are more important. The energy is transferred from the diatoms to the krill that eat them, and then to blue whales that eat the krill. Though only part of a complex food web (see Fig. 10.14), this simple food chain accounted for a great deal of the total productivity of Antarctic waters until whales were hunted nearly to extinction.

Most ecosystems have a number of different primary producers. Furthermore, many animals eat more than just one kind of food, and many change their diet as they get older and larger (see Fig. 15.25). For these reasons, an ecosystem's trophic structure is usually a complex, interwoven **food web** (Fig. 10.14) instead of a simple, straight-line food chain. Such food webs are difficult for biologists to unravel and understand, but their complexity is one reason for the tremendous diversity of life.

Energy and materials are passed from one trophic level to another along a food chain or food web. The first level is occupied by primary producers, the other levels by consumers.

Trophic Levels Food chains and food webs are a little easier to understand if we consider the number of steps, or trophic levels, through which the energy passes (Fig. 10.15). The first step in

the flow of energy, and therefore the first trophic level, is occupied by the primary producers that originally capture the energy and store it in organic compounds. Diatoms are the main primary producers in the food web illustrated in Figures 10.14 and 10.15. Consumers that feed directly on primary producers are called **first-level,** or **primary, consumers** and occupy the next trophic level. At the level above that are **second-level,** or **secondary, consumers,** predators that eat the primary consumers. Feeding on the secondary consumers are the **third-level,** or **tertiary, consumers,** and so on. Each trophic level relies on the level below for sustenance. At the end of the food web are **top predators** such as killer whales.

The concept of trophic levels helps us understand how energy flows through ecosystems, but the organisms themselves are not concerned about which level they feed at. Predators often feed on prey from different trophic levels, for example.

The Trophic Pyramid Instead of being passed on to the next higher level, much of the energy contained in a particular trophic level is used up by the activities of the organisms. Energy and organic matter are also lost as waste. Depending on the ecosystem, only about 5 to 20% of the energy in one trophic level is passed on to the next, on average about 10%. Suppose, for example, that the diatoms in the Antarctic food chain illustrated in Figure 10.13 contain a total of 10 million calories of energy. According to the 10% rule, only about 1 million calories will make it to the primary consumers, the krill, and the whales will get only about 100,000 calories. The trophic structure of ecosystems can be represented by a **pyramid of energy** (Fig. 10.16), with less energy contained in each succeeding level.

Because there is less energy available at each level, there are also fewer individual organisms. Thus, there are fewer primary consumers than producers, and fewer secondary than primary consumers. Often, though not always, the **trophic pyramid** can be pictured in terms of numbers of individuals as well as energy and is then called the **pyramid of numbers** (see "Standing Stock," below). The pyramid can also be expressed in terms of the total weight of tissue, or **biomass,** produced by the organisms at each level. In this case, the trophic pyramid is called the **pyramid of biomass.** To support a given biomass of primary consumers, primary producers must make about 10 times as much living tissue. To support 1,000 g of copepods, for example, the copepods need to eat about 10,000 g of phytoplankton. In turn, only about one-tenth of the primary consumer's biomass will make it to the secondary consumers.

Shelf Break The increase in steepness that marks the outer edge of the continental shelf.
• 2.3, The Geological Provinces of the Ocean

Autotrophs Organisms that can use energy (usually solar energy) to make organic matter.
Heterotrophs Organisms that cannot make their own food and must eat the organic matter produced by autotrophs.
• 4.1 The Ingredients of Life

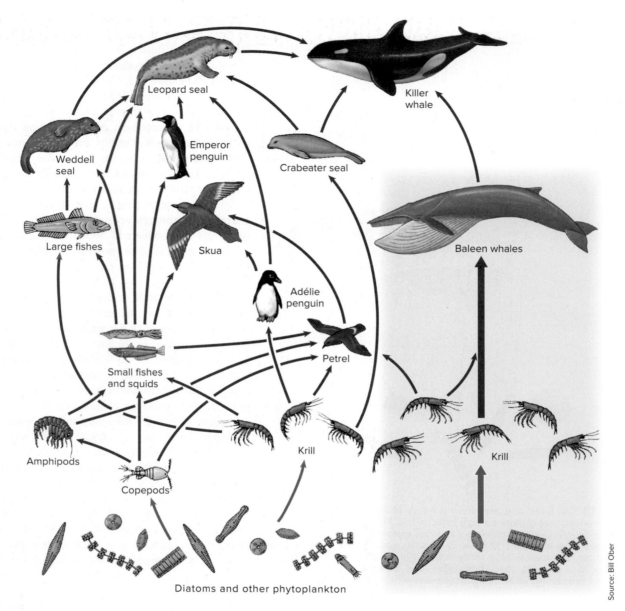

FIGURE 10.14 A simplified Antarctic food web. The simple diatom-krill-whale food chain illustrated in Figure 10.13 (blue shading) is an important part of this food web.

> On average, only about 10% of the energy and organic matter in one trophic level is passed to the next higher level.

At each step in the food web some organic matter is lost rather than being eaten by higher-level consumers. This material is not lost to the ecosystem, however. Decay bacteria, fungi, and other **decomposers** break down this non-living organic matter into its original components: carbon dioxide, water, and nutrients. Some of the organic matter is excreted as waste, is spilled during feeding, or leaks out of cells by diffusion. This material dissolves in the water, so it is known as **dissolved organic matter (DOM).** There is also a lot of dead organic matter in solid form, such as decaying seaweed, cast-off seagrass and mangrove leaves, discarded exoskeletons, fecal pellets, and dead bodies. This material is called **detritus.** Detritus is

an important energy pathway in marine ecosystems because many marine organisms feed on it. Large populations of microscopic decomposers live in association with detritus, and detritus feeders often derive as much or more nutrition from the decomposers as from the detritus itself. Similarly, many organisms eat the microorganisms that decompose DOM. Thus, decomposers play a vital role in the ocean by channeling the energy in dead organic matter back into the food web.

> Waste organic matter that is dissolved in the water is called dissolved organic matter (DOM). Detritus consists of non-living organic matter in solid form. Decomposers help channel DOM and detritus back into the food web.

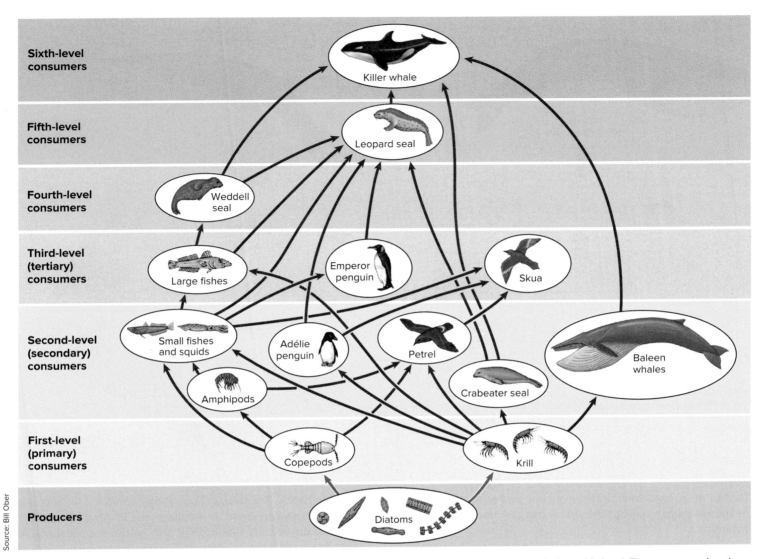

FIGURE 10.15 The organisms in the food web in Figure 10.14 can be grouped into categories according to their trophic level. The same organism, however, may feed at different levels. Petrels, for example, act as second-level consumers when they eat copepods but as third-level consumers when they eat amphipods. In this simplified diagram, they are shown as second-level consumers. The food web shown here is longer than most; three or four levels are more common.

If it were not for decomposers, waste products and dead bodies would accumulate instead of rotting away. Not only would this make quite a mess, but nutrients would remain locked up in the organic matter. When decomposers break down organic matter, the nutrients incorporated into the organic matter during primary production are released, making the nutrients available again to photosynthetic organisms. This process is known as **nutrient regeneration.** Without it, nutrients would not be recycled and made available to autotrophs, and primary production would be greatly reduced.

Parasites are not shown in Figures 10.14 and 10.15, but the total biomass of parasites in a food web can be as great as the biomass of top predators. Thus, parasites probably play an important role in the trophic structure of marine communities, but how they affect marine food webs is poorly studied and not well understood.

Measuring Primary Productivity Because primary production supplies the food at the base of the trophic pyramid, it is useful to know how much production occurs in a given area. The rate of primary production, or **productivity,** is often expressed as the amount of carbon fixed under a square meter of sea surface in a day or in a year (Fig. 10.17). It includes the production of both phytoplankton in the water column and producers that live on the bottom.

The total amount of organic carbon manufactured by primary producers is called the **gross primary production.** Primary producers immediately respire some of the organic matter they make to meet their own energy needs, however, so it is not available as

Primary Production The conversion of carbon dioxide into organic matter by autotrophs, that is, the production of food.

• 4.1, The Ingredients of Life

Source: Bill Ober

Source: Bill Ober

FIGURE 10.16 (*a*) Although the figure varies, an average of 90% of the energy that primary producers capture in photosynthesis is lost at each step up the food chain. (*b*) This relationship is often depicted as a pyramid representing the amount of energy, the numbers of individuals, or the biomass at each trophic level. Regardless of its form, the idea remains the same: It takes a lot of energy, numbers, and biomass at the bottom to support just a little at the top.

(b)

food to other organisms. It is the organic matter that is left over, or the **net primary production,** that forms the base of the trophic pyramid.

Gross primary production by **photosynthesis** can be estimated by measuring either the amount of raw material used up or the amount of end products given off by photosynthetic organisms in the sunlight. This was traditionally done by measuring the amount of oxygen (O_2) produced (Fig. 10.18) but now it is more common to measure the amount of carbon dioxide (CO_2) consumed. This method uses an **isotope** of carbon (^{14}C) that can be measured very accurately. To measure net primary production, **respiration** by the primary producers can be estimated by keeping them in the dark where no photosynthesis can occur. Other methods to estimate primary production include measuring the amount of light absorbed by the producers and measuring the glow, or fluorescence, that chlorophyll emits when it absorbs sunlight.

In the ocean the amount of primary production varies dramatically from one environment to the other (Table 10.1). Some marine environments are as productive as any on Earth. Others are biological deserts, with productivity as low as any desert on land. Productivity in the ocean depends largely on the physical characteristics of the environment, in particular on the amount of light and nutrients available. These characteristics will be explored in subsequent chapters.

Standing Stock The total amount of phytoplankton in the water, called the **standing stock** or **standing crop** of phytoplankton, is related to the primary productivity, but the two are not the same thing. The standing stock refers to how much phytoplankton is in the water. Primary productivity refers to the amount of new organic material being created. In a lawn, for example, the standing stock would correspond to the length of the grass. The primary productivity would be how fast the grass is growing, which could be measured by the amount of clippings produced if the lawn was mowed every day to keep it the same length.

This difference between primary productivity and standing stock explains why the trophic pyramid is not always reflected in a pyramid of numbers. A lawn that is growing very fast will produce a lot of clippings even if it is kept short. In other words, it can have high productivity but low standing stock. In the ocean, it often happens that when primary producers are growing very fast they are also eaten very fast. With lots of food available, the herbivore population grows, keeping the number of primary producers low. As a result, the pyramid of numbers may be turned upside down, with more herbivores than primary producers. The pyramid of biomass refers to the productivity, not the standing stock, so like the pyramid of energy the pyramid of biomass always holds true.

Phytoplankton contain chlorophyll, so the amount of chlorophyll in the water is a good indication of phytoplankton abundance.

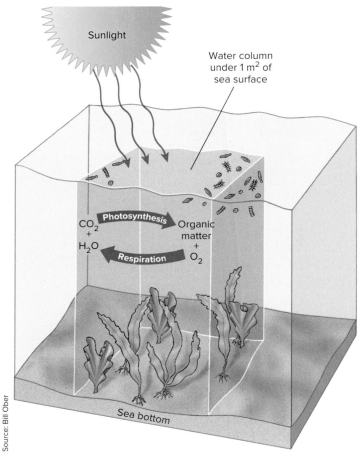

Source: Bill Ober

FIGURE 10.17 To describe primary productivity, marine biologists determine how much carbon ends up being fixed, or converted from carbon dioxide to organic material, in the water column under 1 m² of sea surface in a given time. Gross primary production refers to the total amount of organic matter produced; net primary production is the amount left over after the respiration of the primary producers themselves. Primary productivity is expressed in units of grams of carbon per square meter per day or year (gC/m²/d or gC/m²/y).

Table 10.1 Typical Rates of Primary Production in Various Marine Environments

Environment	Rate of Production (Grams of carbon fixed/m²/y)
PELAGIC ENVIRONMENTS	
Arctic Ocean	<1–100
Southern Ocean (Antarctica)	40–260
Subpolar seas	50–110
Temperate seas (oceanic)	70–180
Temperate seas (coastal)	110–220
Central ocean gyres*	4–40
Equatorial upwelling areas*	70–180
Coastal upwelling areas*	110–370
BENTHIC ENVIRONMENTS	
Salt marshes	250–2,000
Mangrove forests	370–450
Seagrass beds	550–1,100
Kelp beds	640–1,800
Coral reefs	1,500–3,700
TERRESTRIAL ENVIRONMENTS	
Extreme deserts	0–4
Temperate farmlands	550–700
Tropical rain forests	460–1,600

Notes: Production rates can be much higher at certain times or in specific locations, especially at high latitudes. Values for some selected terrestrial environments are given for comparison.

*See "Patterns of Production," in 15.3.

Indeed, the most common way to measure phytoplankton standing stock is to measure the concentration of chlorophyll in the water.

The standing stock of phytoplankton is the total amount of phytoplankton in the water column. Standing stock is usually determined by measuring the chlorophyll concentration.

Chlorophyll can be measured by chemically extracting it from the water, but that is time-consuming and expensive. Instead, an instrument called a fluorometer is usually used to determine the amount of chlorophyll present from fluorescence it emits.

Phytoplankton standing stock is now most commonly measured from space using color images taken by satellites. Phytoplankton standing stock can be estimated over large areas of the sea surface (Fig. 10.19) by applying various correction factors,

taking account of the weather at the time the photo was taken, and relating the results to actual chlorophyll measurements made from ships. Satellites are the only means for assessing the large-scale distribution of phytoplankton; ships can measure standing stock at only one place at a time.

Photosynthesis
CO₂ + H₂O + sun energy → organic matter + O₂
(glucose)
Respiration
Organic matter + O₂ → CO₂ + H₂O + energy
(glucose)
• 4.1, The Ingredients of Life

Isotopes Different atomic forms of an element.
• 2.2, The Origin and Structure of the Ocean Basins

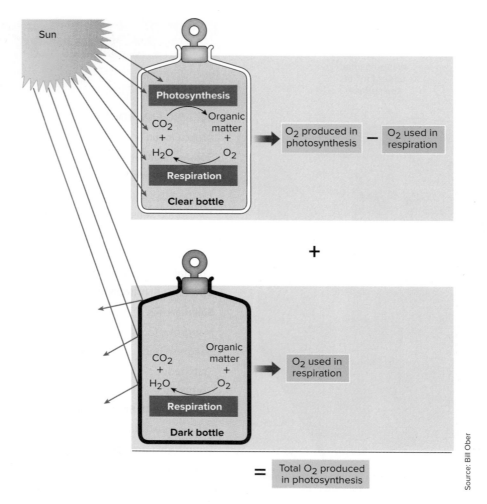

Source: Bill Ober

FIGURE 10.18 The classical way to measure primary production is to put seawater samples in both clear and dark bottles. The clear bottle allows light to enter, so both photosynthesis and respiration take place. The amount of oxygen produced reflects the balance of photosynthesis over respiration, or the net primary production. To calculate the total production of organic matter by photosynthesis the amount of respiration must be known. This can be measured from the amount of oxygen used up in the dark bottle, where only respiration occurs.

Chlorophyll *a* Concentration (mg/m³)

0.01 0.1 1.0 10 60

NASA/SeaWiFS Project

FIGURE 10.19 Global distribution of primary producer abundance based on multiple satellite measurements of chlorophyll concentration.

Cycles of Essential Nutrients

Once the energy stored in organic compounds is used in metabolism or given off as heat, it is lost to the system forever. Unlike energy, the *materials* that make up organic matter can be used over and over in a repeating cycle. These materials, like carbon, nitrogen, and phosphorus, originally come from the atmosphere, the Earth's interior, or the **weathering** of rocks. Starting out as simple inorganic molecules, they are converted into other forms and incorporated into the tissues of autotrophs. When this organic material is broken down by digestion, respiration, and decomposition, the raw materials are released back to the environment, and the cycle begins again. Human alteration

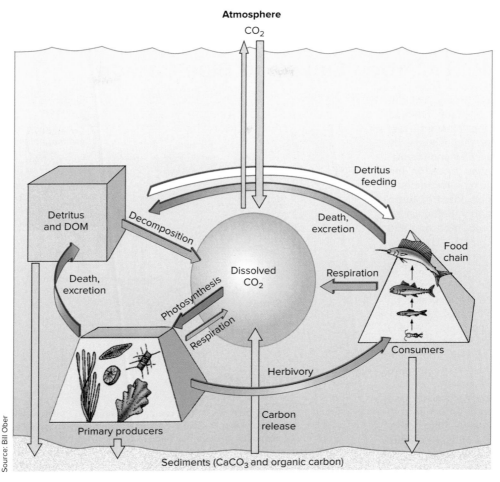

Atmosphere

CO_2

Detritus and DOM

Decomposition

Death, excretion

Detritus feeding

Death, excretion

Food chain

Dissolved CO_2

Respiration

Photosynthesis

Respiration

Consumers

Primary producers

Herbivory

Carbon release

Sediments (CaCO$_3$ and organic carbon)

Source: Bill Ober

FIGURE 10.20 The carbon cycle in the ocean. Carbon dioxide (CO_2) from the atmosphere dissolves in the ocean. In photosynthesis, primary producers convert carbon dioxide into organic matter, which is then passed to animals and other consumers in the food chain. Both producers and consumers release carbon dioxide as a product of their respiration. The rest of the carbon fixed by autotrophs eventually is excreted as waste or ends up in the form of dead bodies. This non-living organic matter forms detritus and dissolved organic matter (DOM). Bacteria and other decomposers break down this organic matter, releasing carbon dioxide and starting the cycle anew.

of these natural global cycles could have profound impacts on life on Earth that we are not yet able to predict.

The **carbon cycle** provides a good example of this process (Fig. 10.20). The carbon that forms the backbone of all organic molecules starts in the atmosphere as carbon dioxide, then dissolves in the ocean. CO_2 is highly soluble in seawater, so the ocean holds more than 50 times as much carbon as the atmosphere. This inorganic carbon is converted into organic compounds by photosynthesis. Respiration by consumers, decomposers, and the producers themselves breaks down the organic compounds and makes the carbon dioxide available to producers again. Some carbon is also deposited as calcium carbonate in **biogenous sediments** and coral reefs. Sediments contain 25 times again as much carbon as the ocean water. Under certain conditions, some of this calcium carbonate dissolves back into the water. Humans have greatly affected the global carbon cycle by burning fossil fuels and increasing the amount of CO_2 in the atmosphere (see Special Report, Climate Change).

Nitrogen, like carbon dioxide, is present in the atmosphere. Atmospheric nitrogen, however, is almost all in the form of

nitrogen gas (N_2), which most organisms are unable to use. Some cyanobacteria, other bacteria, and archaea can perform **nitrogen fixation,** and lightning also fixes atmospheric nitrogen. Without fixed nitrogen, algae and plants would not be able to get the nitrogen they need. In addition to nitrogen fixation that takes place in the ocean itself, fixed nitrogen enters the ocean from rivers and from the atmosphere in rain. Human activities, however, now produce more fixed nitrogen than natural sources, and most fixed nitrogen entering the ocean comes from agricultural fertilizers (either directly or as animal and human waste), cultivation of nitrogen-fixing crops, and fossil-fuel burning.

Biogenous Sediment Sediment made of the skeletons and shells of marine organisms.
• 2.2, The Origin and Structure of the Ocean Basins

Nitrogen Fixation Conversion of nitrogen gas (N_2) into nitrogen compounds that can be used by primary producers as nutrients.
• 5.2, Prokaryotes; Table 5.1

EYE ON SCIENCE

Box 10.3 Carbon Sinks and Blue Carbon

The seriousness and urgency of the threat of global climate change, caused mostly by the release of vast amounts of CO_2 into the atmosphere by humans, is now scientifically undeniable. This has brought increased focus on the importance of **carbon sinks,** environments where large amounts of carbon are stored out of the atmosphere, and in particular on **blue carbon,** carbon stored in coastal and marine environments.

Huge amounts of carbon are stored in ocean water itself. In fact, about 30% of all anthropogenic carbon emissions have been removed from the atmosphere by dissolving in seawater. This has the worrying impact of changing the oceans' acidity (see Special Report, Ocean Acidification: the Other CO_2 Problem), and there are signs that the ocean's ability to continue to absorb our emissions is declining.

Significant amounts of carbon are also removed to and stored in deep ocean sediments. Increasingly, however, the potential of blue carbon to help mitigate climate change has focused on coastal ecosystems including mangroves, seagrass beds, salt marshes, kelp beds, and coral reefs.

Coastal ecosystems **sequester,** or store out of the atmosphere, huge amounts of carbon. As noted in the main text, ocean sediments store about 25 times as much carbon as is dissolved in seawater. About *half* of this is stored in coastal blue carbon sinks that cover only about 2% of the total ocean sea floor. Seagrasses, for example, store about 10% of carbon sequestered in marine sediments despite covering only 0.2% of the sea floor. Clearly, coastal habitats are heavy hitters when it comes to sequestering carbon.

Source: Bill Ober

Mature coastal communities, in this example a mangrove forest, store large amounts of carbon in biomass and detritus that is rapidly exchanged with the atmosphere. Though this stores carbon out of the atmosphere, it does not remove it on a net basis. Some carbon, however, does get stored more or less permanently to the sediments, so even though much of the carbon is continually cycled, there is still important long-term carbon removal and storage.

Healthy blue carbon sinks store much of the carbon in the form of biomass and detritus in the sediments. In mature habitats, though large amounts of carbon are stored at any given time, much of this carbon is constantly consumed, broken down, and released back into the atmosphere. These rapidly recycled components of the carbon pool do not remove carbon from the atmosphere on a net basis in mature communities. Significant amounts of carbon, however, *are* sequestered over the long term—decades, centuries, millennia or even more, as some of the organic carbon is buried deep in the sediments and in some situations is converted to mineral form. Thus, mature blue carbon sinks store carbon both in forms that are rapidly recycled with the atmosphere, and over longer periods deep in the sediments.

Unfortunately, many of these critical blue carbon sinks around the world have been severely degraded or destroyed (see 18.1). When this happens, essentially all of the organic carbon formerly stored gets released into the atmosphere. This applies

Nitrogen fixation is the conversion of atmospheric nitrogen gas into a form that organisms can use. It is performed naturally by certain cyanobacteria, other bacteria, and archaea, but human activities now account for the majority of fixed nitrogen in the ocean.

Once nitrogen has been fixed, it cycles within the ecosystem as part of the **nitrogen cycle** (Fig. 10.21). There are several nutrient forms of nitrogen, the most important of which is **nitrate (NO_3^{-1}).**

Nitrate and other nitrogen compounds are taken up during primary production and regenerated by decomposition. Most of the nitrogen-containing nutrients used in primary production come from this recycling of nitrogen compounds, not the original fixation of nitrogen. Until recent times natural nitrogen fixation was balanced by **denitrification,** which converts fixed nitrogen back to N_2, so the amount of fixed nitrogen in the global environment was more or less constant. Natural denitrification can no longer keep up with human activities, however, and fixed nitrogen is building

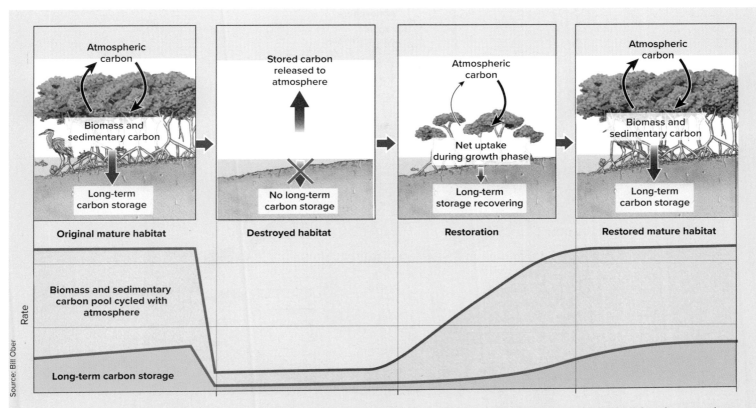

When mature coastal habitats like this mangrove forest are degraded or destroyed, nearly all of the stored carbon gets released back into the atmosphere. Restoration of such coastal communities can make them carbon sinks again. In the first years or decades of their recovery, even the biomass and detritus components, which are normally in steady state with the atmosphere, are important net carbon sinks as carbon is pulled from the atmosphere into branches, leaves, roots, and detritus. The long-term carbon sequestration functions of the community also begin to recover, until, in the best outcome, the original functions of the mature community are restored.

not only to the living carbon and detritus that is normally exchanged with the atmosphere via the food web, but also much of the carbon in long-term storage. Such degraded habitats become major sources of CO_2 emissions to the atmosphere, contributing to climate change, instead of climate-mitigating sinks.

Not surprisingly, there are important global initiatives to restore coastal blue carbon sinks. This has tremendous potential to put off the worst effects of climate change until the more fundamental changes to

society and our economy that are needed can be accomplished. Coastal habitats are particularly important in this regard because they can sequester large amounts of carbon very quickly, on time scales of years or decades. Mangroves and salt marshes, for example, can remove carbon from the atmosphere 10 times faster than tropical forests. This potential for rapidly pulling CO_2 out of the atmosphere, buying humanity time for other climate solutions, is magnified by the other benefits provided by coastal communities. Mangrove

forests, seagrass beds, salt marshes, coral reefs, and other coastal marine communities detoxify pollutants, support fisheries, protect coasts from storm erosion, provide tourism and recreational opportunities, and perform countless other functions that benefit humanity to the tune of trillions of dollars every year. There is no way to overstate the benefits of protecting and restoring our planet's blue carbon sinks.

up, with potentially catastrophic consequences (see Special Report, Overwhelming the Nitrogen Cycle).

Most of the phosphorus entering the ocean is brought in by rivers in the form of **phosphate (PO_4^{-3})**, although a small amount is deposited from the atmosphere. Much of this phosphate is derived naturally from the **weathering** of rocks and bird guano on land, but a great deal comes from fertilizers and other human sources as well. On the other hand, humans sometimes reduce phosphate input to the ocean because phosphate gets trapped in sediment that builds

up behind dams. After primary producers take up the phosphate and incorporate it into organic matter, the phosphorus cycles in

Metabolism The complex set of chemical reactions that occurs inside cells.
• 4.1 The Ingredients of Life

Weathering The physical or chemical breakdown of rocks.
• 2.2, The Origin and Structure of the Ocean Basins

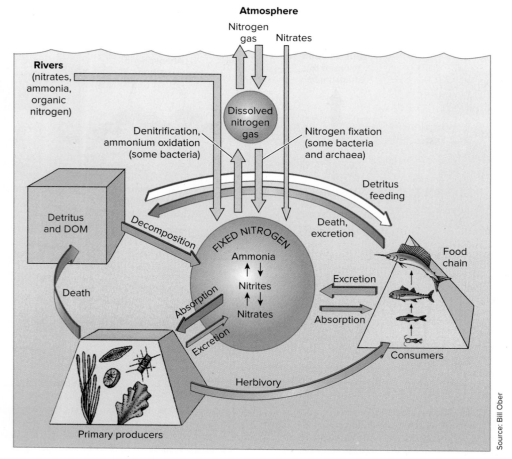

FIGURE 10.21 The nitrogen cycle in the ocean. The atmosphere is rich in nitrogen gas (N$_2$), which cannot be used by most organisms. Some cyanobacteria, other bacteria, and archaea convert N$_2$ into a usable form of nitrogen by the process of nitrogen fixation. There are several different forms of usable nitrogen; various bacteria and archaea convert nitrogen from one usable form to another (see Table 5.1). Primary producers take up the usable nitrogen to produce organic matter. The nitrogen is then passed on to animals and other consumers when they eat the organic matter. Usable nitrogen may be excreted as waste by producers and consumers or regenerated by decomposing bacteria.

organic form through the food web (Fig. 10.22). Phosphorus is deposited in ocean sediments either in biogenous sediments or through **chemical precipitation,** in which chemical reactions convert phosphate into insoluble forms that settle on the sea floor. Some phosphorus is transported from the ocean back to land by seabirds and deposited as guano (see Box 17.1, "Of Fish and Seabirds, Fishers and Chickens") but the flow of phosphorus through the ocean to the sediments is mostly a one-way street. Over millions of years, however, the phosphorus is recycled by geological processes such as the uplift of marine sediments onto land.

Other raw materials needed by organisms, like silicon and iron, undergo similar cycles. The tremendous abundance and diversity of living things depend on this recycling. Without it, the living world would soon run out of raw materials, and life on Earth would be scarce indeed.

The living world depends on the recycling of materials such as carbon, nitrogen, and phosphorus. Decomposition is a vital part of this cycle.

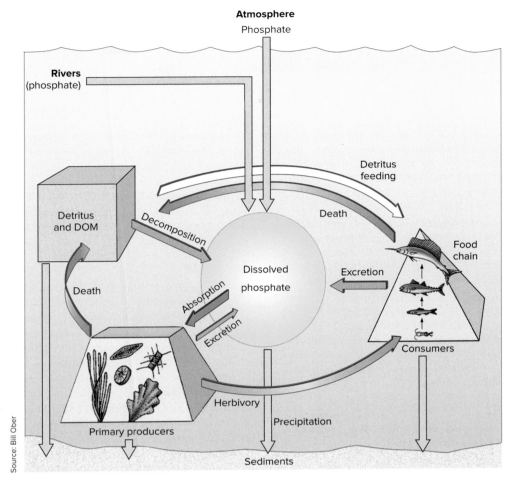

FIGURE 10.22 The phosphorus cycle in the ocean. Most phosphorus enters the ocean as phosphate in rivers. Primary producers incorporate the phosphate into organic matter, which is passed on up the food chain or becomes detritus or dissolved organic matter. The phosphorus in organisms and detritus is deposited in biogenic sediments. Dissolved phosphate is also deposited when chemical reactions convert it into insoluble forms that precipitate to the sediments.

Interactive
Exploration

McGraw-Hill Connect® is a great place to check your understanding of chapter material. Visit **www.mcgrawhillconnect.com** for access to interactive chapter summaries, chapter quizzing, and more! Further enhance your knowledge with video clips and weblinks to chapter-related material.

Critical Thinking

1. Two species of sea urchins live practically side by side on sandy bottoms. The two species appear to have the same diet: drift seaweeds and other bits of organic matter. They are able to live in the same environment with minimal competition. How might they be able to share their habitat and food resources?

2. It is not always easy to categorize a particular case of symbiosis. Suppose a certain species of snail is always found living on a certain coral. No one has found evidence that the snail harms the coral, so the relationship is classified as an example of commensalism. How would you go about testing this hypothesis? What kinds of observations might lead to the conclusion that the snail is a parasite, or that it has a mutualistic relationship with the coral?

For Further Reading

Some of the recommended reading may be available online. Look for live links on the *Marine Biology* Online Learning Center.

General Interest

Jones, G. P., M. Srinivasan, and G. R. Almany, 2007. Population connectivity and conservation of marine biodiversity. *Oceanography,* vol. 20, no. 3, September, pp. 100–111. The larval and other interlinkages between populations of marine organisms are essential to maintaining biodiversity.

Kolbert, E., 2014. *The sixth extinction: an unnatural history.* Henry Holt, New York, NY. The author argues that the current mass extinction caused by human activities is of a similar magnitude to mass extinctions in the geological past, and predicts that 2 to 50% of all species will go extinct by the end of the 21st century.

Luiz, O. J., E. M. P. Madin, J. S. Madin, A. H. Baird, and A. S. Grutter, 2016. A tropical cleaner wrasse finds new clients at the frontier. *Frontiers in Ecology and the Environment,* vol. 14, no. 2, 1 March, pp. 110–111. A tropical cleaning fish finds new species to clean as its range expands.

Nuwer, R., 2022. Parasites lost. *Scientific American*, vol. 326, no. 5, pp. 62–69. Studies of fish parasites reveal that parasites deserve more respect than we usually give them.

O'Leary, J. K., F. Micheli, L. Airoldi, C. Boch, G. De Leo, R. Elahi, F. Ferretti, N. A. J. Graham, S. Y. Litvin, and N. H. Low, 2017. The resilience of marine ecosystems to climatic disturbances. *BioScience,* vol. 67, no. 3, March, pp. 208–220. Marine ecosystems can withstand the worst effects of climate change if we manage them to protect the factors that make them resilient.

Pajares, S. and R. Ramo, 2019. Processes and microorganisms involved in the marine nitrogen cycle: knowledge and gaps. *Frontiers in Marine Science* [https://doi.org/10.3389/fmars.2019.00739]. There is still much to learn about the marine nitrogen cycle.

Palumbi, S. R. and A. R. Palumbi, 2015. *The extreme life of the sea.* Princeton University Press. A fascinating exploration of how marine organisms adapt to extreme environments, from the depths of the ocean to flying fish escaping predators at the surface.

Townsend, A. R. and R. W. Howarth, 2010. Fixing the global nitrogen problem. *Scientific American,* vol. 302, no. 2, February, pp. 64–71. Society can use a lot less fertilizer and still grow more food.

Young, E., 2008. Depths of ignorance. *New Scientist,* vol. 198, no. 2651, 12 April 2008, pp. 34–37, 40–43. Identifying hot spots of diversity in the world's oceans.

In Depth

Bauman, A. G., J. C. Seah, F. A. Januchowski-Hartley, et al., 2019. Fear effects associated with predator presence and habitat structure interact to alter herbivory on coral reefs. *Biology Letters,* vol. 15:20190409.

Casciotti, K. L., 2016. Nitrogen and oxygen isotopic studies of the marine nitrogen cycle *Annual Review of Marine Science,* vol. 8, pp. 379–407.

Caves, E. M., C. Chen, and S. Johnsen, 2019. The cleaner shrimp *Lysmata amboinensis* adjusts its behaviour towards predatory versus nonpredatory clients. *Biology Letters,* vol. 15:2019.534.

Costello, M. J. and C. Chaudhary, 2017. Marine biodiversity, biogeography, deep-sea gradients, and conservation. *Current Biology,* vol. 27, pp. R511–R527.

Díaz, S., J. Settele, E. W. Brondízio, et al., 2019. Summary for policymakers of the global assessment report on biodiversity and ecosystem services of the Intergovernmental Science-Policy Platform on Biodiversity and Ecosystem Services. IPBES Secretariat, Bonn, Germany, 56 pp.

Duffy, J. E., L. A. Amaral-Zettler, D. G. Fautin, G. Paulay, T. A. Rynearson, H. M. Soskik, and J. J. Stachowicz, 2013. Envisioning a marine biodiversity observation network. *BioScience,* vol. 63, pp. 350–361.

Gruber, N., D. Clement, B. R. Carter, et al., 2019. The oceanic carbon sink for anthropogenic CO_2 from 1994 to 2007. *Science,* vol. 363, no. 6432, 15 March, pp. 1193–1199.

Lafferty, K. D., 2017. Marine infectious disease ecology. *Annual Review of Ecology, Evolution, and Systematics,* vol. 48, pp. 473–96.

Leray, M. and N. Knowlton, 2015. DNA barcoding and metabarcoding of standardized samples reveal patterns of marine benthic diversity. *Proceedings of the National Academy of Sciences,* vol. 112, no. 7, pp. 2076–2081.

Padilla, D. K. and M. M. Savedo, 2013. A systematic review of phenotypic plasticity in marine invertebrate and plant systems. *Advances in Marine Biology,* vol. 65, pp. 67–94.

Payne, J. L., A. M. Bush, N. A. Heim, M. L. Knope, and D. J. McCauley, 2016. Ecological selectivity of the emerging mass extinction in the oceans. *Science,* vol. 353, no. 6305, pp. 1284–1286.

Thamdrup, B., 2012. New pathways and processes in the global nitrogen cycle. *Annual Review of Ecology, Evolution, and Systematics,* vol. 43, pp. 407–428.

Tilman, D., F. Isbell, and J. M. Cowles, 2014. Biodiversity and ecosystem functioning. *Annual Review of Ecology, Evolution, and Systematics,* vol. 45, pp. 471–493.

One thing is shared by all of humanity: planet Earth. With the birth and destruction of continents and oceans, the coming and going of ice ages and geological periods of steaming heat, mass extinctions, and bursts of evolution, Earth continuously changes on geological time scales. But humanity is changing "spaceship Earth" in ways and at speeds that are unprecedented in geological history. By continuing our activities unabated, humanity has been gambling that the fundamental processes that provide our most basic needs—air, food, water, and shelter—will continue to support us no matter what we do to our only home. But the facts are now inescapable: Humans are changing the planet in ways that threaten our well-being and possibly human society as we know it.

Climate Change

Earth is clearly getting warmer: global temperatures have been steadily rising since recording began (Fig. 1). Perhaps worse, warming is accelerating. As of 2021, 19 of the 20 warmest years on record were since 2001. The seven warmest years were all since 2015.

We know that Earth has warm and cool cycles on the order of centuries. For example, history records a "Medieval Warm Period" during a period of high solar activity (approximately 850–1250 CE), and later a "Little Ice Age" from roughly 1500 to 1850 when Europe experienced bitterly cold weather compared to today. Both the Medieval Warm Period and Little Ice Age were regional, not global, phenomena, restricted to Europe or at least the Northern Hemisphere. Global ice ages come and go on time scales of tens or hundreds of thousands of years. Could the pronounced warming in recent decades, though global, be just another natural fluctuation? Overwhelming evidence says "no."

It is important to understand the difference between climate and weather. "Climate" means average conditions over decades or longer, whereas "weather" refers to short-term conditions over days, months, or maybe a year or two. A frost in Miami doesn't mean Miami has a cold climate. A snap of cold weather for a few weeks, or even an unusually cold winter, doesn't tell us anything about how climate might be changing, nor is one heat wave proof of global warming. To judge Earth's recent temperature rise we need to know how climate fluctuated in the past.

Reliable, widespread measurements with thermometers only go back to about 1850, and the measurements aren't considered sufficiently reliable until about 1880. There are, however, many natural records of past temperatures, including ocean sediments (see "The Record in the Sediments," in 2.2), corals, ice cores (Fig. 2), tree rings, pollen, the elevation of ancient tree lines on mountains, boreholes in continental rock, and historical records such as the extent of Arctic sea ice or how far north grapes could be grown. Combining such varied, independent data produces a "hockey stick" graph (Fig. 3) showing a slight, steady cooling from the ninth to the nineteenth centuries (the "handle"), followed by a rapid temperature rise in the twentieth century (the "blade"). There were vehement attacks on the science behind the hockey stick, and personal attacks on the scientists themselves. Much of the criticism came from people with ties to the fossil-fuel industry, but little background in climate science. So science did its thing. Teams of researchers around the world independently tested the conclusions of the hockey stick, using different sources of data and different approaches to analyze the data. They also pushed the temperature record further back into the past.

Not surprisingly, given their varying data sets and analytical methods, different research teams varied somewhat in their results, especially further back in the past (Fig. 4). But over and over the reconstructions show the same overall trend:

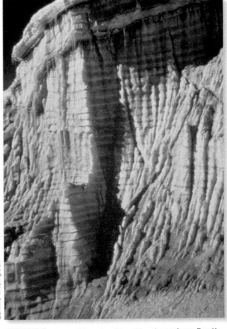

FIGURE 2 Annual bands of ice, like these from Perú's Quelccaya ice cap in the Andes, are one-way scientists can tell what past climates were like. Many of the world's glaciers and ice caps are receding, and this ice face has long since melted away.

gradual cooling before sharp warming in recent decades, with the 2000s the warmest decade in at least 1,800 years and each decade since warmer still. The warming is not evenly distributed: The Arctic and Antarctica are warming faster than the rest of the globe, and 2020 saw record high temperatures recorded in both regions.

Sea temperatures change more slowly than the atmosphere, but the ocean is also warming (Fig. 5). An estimated 84% of the total heating of the planet between 1955 and 2003 went into warming the ocean—otherwise we would be experiencing much higher air temperatures.

The evidence is so indisputable that the United States National Research Council, National Oceanic and Atmospheric Administration, and United States Geological Survey, international bodies such as the Intergovernmental Panel on Climate Change (IPCC), and virtually every credible scientific study this century agree that Earth's climate is warming, as a direct result of human activities that intensify a natural phenomenon known as the **greenhouse effect.**

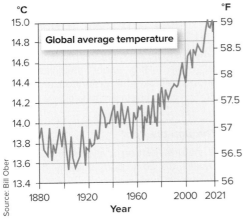

FIGURE 1 Global average temperature, 1886–2021.

Source: Bill Ober

FIGURE 5 If the North Atlantic hadn't warmed or cooled since 1960 there would be no temperature change ("warming signal") at any depth, represented here as a vertical line at 0.0 °C. The shading shows the range of natural variation. Models predict that natural factors like solar and volcanic activity should result in a slight cooling—not warming—at some depths (blue dots). Actual measurements (red dots), however, show significant warming to a depth of more than 700 m (2,300 ft). Other ocean basins show a similar trend.

Source: Bill Ober

FIGURE 3 Recent thermometer measurements and past temperatures estimated from tree rings, ice cores, corals, and historical records for the Northern Hemisphere. The light-brown shading indicates the range of uncertainty.

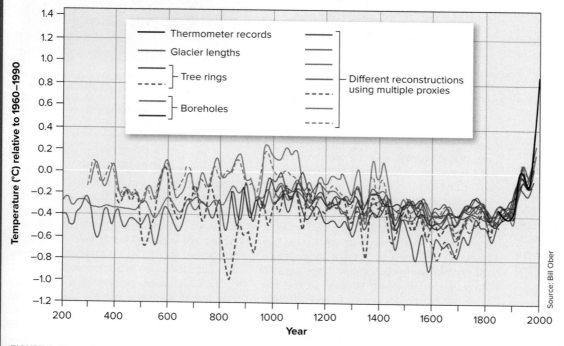

Source: Bill Ober

FIGURE 4 Many subsequent studies have confirmed the rapid twentieth-century warming shown in Figure 3. The reconstructions using multiple proxies are independent analyses of different sets of data from tree rings, glaciers, boreholes, sediments, chemical composition of ice cores and fossils, and other natural temperature records.

The Greenhouse: Too Much of a Good Thing?

Our climate is ultimately controlled by light energy from the sun. Some reflects back into space, but most is absorbed by Earth's atmosphere and surface (including the ocean) and converted from light to heat. Like the glass of a greenhouse, trace amounts of **greenhouse gases** in the atmosphere are transparent to light energy but block heat transmission back to space. The heat is retained and warms the Earth (Fig. 6). Without this greenhouse effect, Earth's surface would average about −19 °C (2 °F), some 33 °C (59 °F) colder than it is, and would be inhospitable to life as we know it—or certainly at least we humans!

The most important greenhouse gases are ordinary water vapor (H_2O), carbon dioxide (CO_2), methane (CH_4), and nitrous oxide (NO_2), but there are many other greenhouse gases with lesser effects. H_2O isn't a very potent greenhouse gas, but there is so much in the atmosphere that it accounts for most of the greenhouse effect. Atmospheric H_2O content, however, is a product, not a driver, of the greenhouse effect, just as the volume of an electric guitar comes from the amplifier and not the strings. If other greenhouse gases didn't warm the planet in the first place, Earth's water would be locked up in ice. Other greenhouse gases do raise Earth's temperature enough to allow liquid water, which evaporates into the atmosphere and warms the planet. Water vapor, however, drops out of the atmosphere as precipitation within days, so if other gases didn't maintain the warming the planet would freeze. While water vapor amplifies the greenhouse effect, other greenhouse gases drive it. The most important of these is CO_2.

CO_2 Through the Roof

In the natural carbon cycle, atmospheric CO_2 levels are controlled primarily by air-sea exchange and biological activity (see Fig. 10.20), except on timescales of hundreds of millions of years, where massive geological events can dramatically alter CO_2

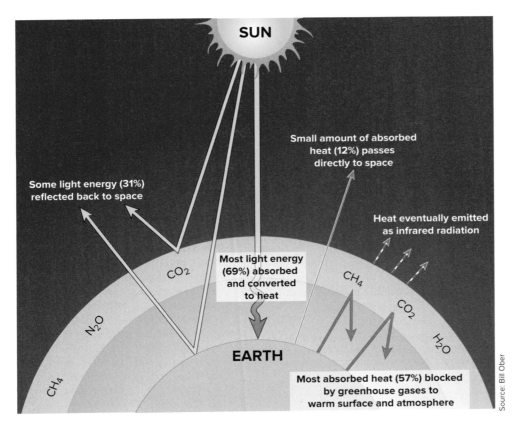

FIGURE 6 The greenhouse effect.

atmosphere, where they increase the reflection of sunlight and slightly cool the planet. Thus, for hundreds of thousands of years greenhouse gas concentrations have fluctuated in concert with other natural cycles.

Since about 1750, and particularly since the expansion of the industrial revolution in the about 1850, human activity has disrupted these natural cycles. Atmospheric CO_2 levels have gone through the roof (Fig. 7).

The first direct measurements of CO_2 in the atmosphere began in 1958, on Mauna Loa, Hawai'i. Since then, atmospheric CO_2 has increased on average about 1.5 ppm per year (Fig. 8). CO_2 levels are rising ever faster, however. Atmospheric CO_2 concentration has risen about 3 ppm per year in recent years, breaking the 400 ppm mark in 2015 and reaching new record highs every year since. The current rate of increase is 200 times faster than in the last 800,000 years. The parts of the carbon cycle that remove CO_2 from the atmosphere—dissolving in the ocean, photosynthesis, and deposition in sediments—cannot keep up. Other greenhouse gases have also risen dramatically: Atmospheric methane, for example, has more than doubled, also reaching record highs year after year and now almost triple pre-industrial levels. The combined effect of all greenhouse gases is now equivalent to about 500 ppm CO_2.

The increase in atmospheric CO_2 is the direct result of human activities: In recent decades about three-quarters of the increase is a result of burning fossil fuels and most of the rest has come from intensified land use, particularly the burning of forests and other biomass. The main human sources of methane are the fossil-fuel industry (about half of all human emissions),

levels. As for temperature, there are natural records of past CO_2 levels. Tiny bubbles of air trapped in polar ice, for example, record what the atmosphere was like when the ice formed. The temperature at the time can be determined from isotope ratios in the ice itself, so ancient atmospheric composition and air temperatures can be directly compared. Antarctic ice cores show that over the last 800,000 years, atmospheric CO_2 fluctuated between about 180 and 300 parts per million (ppm, equivalent to 0.018 to 0.030%; Fig. 7). Other greenhouse gases have also fluctuated within a relatively narrow band. These fluctuations aren't enough to produce ice ages, which are mostly driven by small variations in Earth's orbit around the sun. Volcanoes sometimes have a minor, short-term impact, mainly by injecting aerosols, microscopic particles, into the upper

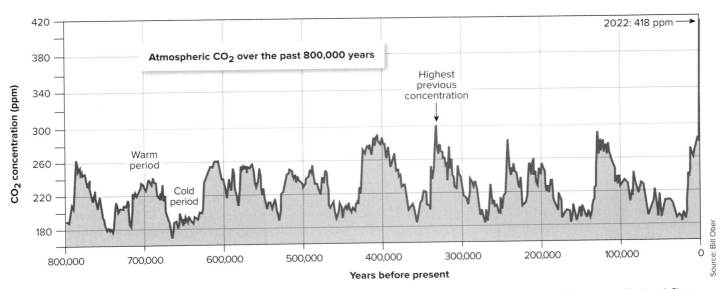

FIGURE 7 The atmospheric concentration of CO_2 has fluctuated throughout Earth's history, but for the last 800,00 years never rose above 300 parts per million (ppm). Since 1950 it has skyrocketed to over 400 ppm.

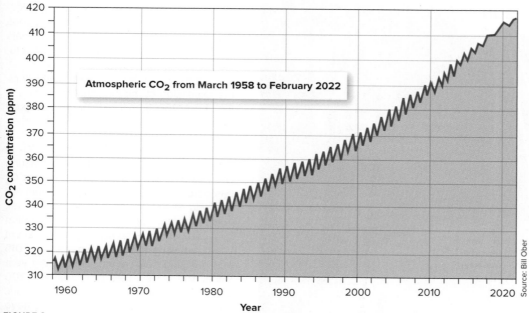

Source: Bill Ober

FIGURE 8 Atmospheric CO_2 measurements from Mauna Loa, Hawai'i. The sawtooth pattern reflects the seasonal effect of trees in the Northern Hemisphere: New growth and the emergence of leaves in spring draws down CO_2, but the leaves fall and rot in autumn, releasing the CO_2 back to the atmosphere. This is a classic example of a short-term pattern (the seasons) superimposed on a long-term trend (climate).

Source: Bill Ober

FIGURE 9 Models that consider only solar and volcanic activity but leave out the effects of greenhouse gas increases (green line shows average and shading shows variability) indicate that global temperatures should have remained stable over the last century. The model results only match actual temperature observations (black line) if the effects of greenhouse gases are included (red).

the digestive systems of cattle and sheep, rice paddies, marshes, and landfills. Human emissions of greenhouse gases are the only thing that can explain the rapid global warming in recent decades (Fig. 9). The IPCC considers 450 ppm CO_2 to be the highest concentration that will keep global warming below 2 °C (3.6 °F), at which point global warming would be catastrophic. A safer target for warming is 1.5 °C (2.7 °F), though this will be hard to reach and still have major impacts.

What's Happening Now?

We are already seeing many adverse consequences of global warming. Sea level is rising faster and faster because of the expansion of surface waters as they warm and the melting of glaciers and icecaps. This is already threatening some low-lying islands and coastal areas. Particularly worrying is that the great ice sheets covering Greenland and Antarctica are losing ice to the oceans. A few decades ago, scientists didn't expect the ice sheets to start melting until next century. Antarctic sea-ice shelves are shrinking, or even collapsing. Large parts of the Larsen B ice shelf broke away in 2002, and again in subsequent years, and the entire shelf collapsed in early 2022. The collapse of ice shelves doesn't directly affect sea level because the ice is already floating, but the shelves block the flow of glaciers from the continent into the ocean. When the shelves are gone this flow accelerates. The glaciers themselves are melting faster, and in some cases also collapsing. The Thwaites Glacier, for example, blocks 10% of Antarctic sea ice from entering the ocean, but not only is melting fast, it appears to be collapsing. The collapse of this glacier alone would raise sea level by 65 cm (25.6 in), more than triple the entire rise of 19 cm (7.5 in) in the whole twentieth century. The release of ice into the ocean caused by the collapse of the Thwaites Glacier would raise sea level by an estimated 3.3 m (10.8 ft) within a few hundred years.

Sea ice in the Arctic Ocean has been shrinking and getting thinner for at least 30 years. In particular, the area of sea ice in summer is steadily getting smaller. The 15 years to 2021 were the lowest 15 years on record, and the extent of summer sea ice in the Arctic reached an unprecedented low in 2022. The overall trend is a decline of over 13% per decade. Like the Antarctic ice shelves, melting Arctic sea ice doesn't directly raise sea level because the ice is already floating, but the melting does accelerate global warming because bright white ice reflects solar energy back to space, while open water absorbs the heat.

Marine heatwaves, extended periods of much warmer than normal seawater temperatures over a wide region, are becoming more frequent in many parts of the ocean. Climate change-driven shifts in ocean circulation, rainfall, and storms have also occurred.

Global warming is also affecting the biosphere, including marine organisms. Adélie and emperor penguins (*Pygoscelis adeliae* and *Aptenodytes forsteri*) have steadily moved closer to the South Pole, following the disappearing sea ice on which they depend, while open-water-feeding chinstrap (*P. antarctica*) and gentoo (*P. papua*) penguins followed in their wake into the newly ice-free waters. Krill have declined in large parts of the Antarctic, as their winter food, sea-ice algae, have gone along with the ice; this could affect the entire food web.

Sea turtles provide another example of the wide-ranging effects of warming on marine life. The sex of turtle hatchlings is determined by temperature—cool conditions result in male turtles and warm conditions females (see "Biology of Marine Reptiles" in 9.1). By 2100, up to 93% of newly hatched green turtles could be females.

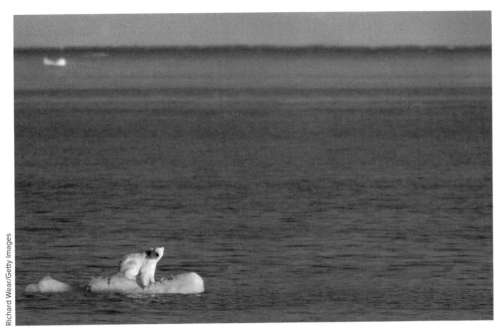

FIGURE 10 Polar bears (*Ursus maritimus*) depend on year-round sea ice to hunt seals, but summer ice in the Arctic is steadily decreasing. Arctic observers report increasing numbers of starving and dead bears. The United States Geological survey ranks climate change as the number one threat to polar bear populations.

FIGURE 11 Abundance of three warm-water planktonic foraminiferan in sediment cores from the Santa Barbara Basin, California, extending back 300 and 1,400 years (red and black lines, respectively; *G. bulloides* was not counted in the earliest samples). These species were occasionally abundant in the past, but their sustained abundance during the twentieth century marks a significant change to warmer conditions.

Declining sea ice is also altering marine ecology in the Arctic (see Box 13.1, "Under the Polar Ice,"). Polar bears (*Ursus maritimus*), for example, are in decline because the receding ice limits their ability to venture from land to hunt. In 2008 the United States Fish and Wildlife Service officially listed polar bears as threatened, the first time a U.S. government agency acknowledged climate change as a threat to any species (Fig. 10).

Climate-driven changes in marine ecosystems are not limited to polar regions. Climate change is a particular threat to coral reefs: Mass coral bleaching and mortality in response to locally high surface temperatures are becoming more frequent, more intense, and more widespread (see "Coral Bleaching," in 14.3). In temperate regions, the distributions of many intertidal, plankton, and fish species have shifted toward the poles along with their preferred temperature ranges and other climate-related factors. Two-thirds of North Sea fish species moved either northward or deeper, that is, into cooler waters, between 1977 and 2001. And estimated 60% of fish species will be unable to persist in their current ranges under current scenarios. The northern limit of the blue mussel (*Mytilus edulis*) in Norway moved north by more than 1,000 km (600 mi) to the Svalbard Islands in the Arctic, where the mussel had not been recorded for 1,000 years. Phytoplankton communities in the California Current system have shifted toward warmer-water species (Fig. 11). A venomous tropical sea snake has washed up on Southern California beaches for the first time on record. Similar changes are occurring all over the world.

Climate change appears to be affecting entire food webs as well as species distributions. The abundance of phytoplankton, the base of many of the ocean's food webs (see 15.3), has declined over much of the ocean. The recruitment of larval cod (*Gadus morhua*) in the North Sea may have declined because warm-water species of zooplankton are less suitable food for young cod than the cold-water species they are replacing. There may also be mismatches in life history. Reproduction of many zooplankton species is timed to coincide with the spring bloom of phytoplankton. Whereas the phytoplankton bloom is triggered by increased day length and light availability, temperature is the reproductive cue for many zooplankton. Warmer temperatures are occurring earlier in the spring, but day length and light levels are unchanged. Zooplankton may therefore be reproducing before the peak in their phytoplankton food, with effects that could move up the rest of the food web.

What Lies Ahead?

The Earth system takes time to balance out. Even if all human emissions ceased immediately, global temperature would rise by 0.6 °C (1.1 °F) in the twenty-first century on top of the warming that already occurred to the year 2000. This is a "warming commitment" we have already made that cannot be reversed. Global CO_2 emissions continue to rise; though there was a slight dip in 2020 due to the COVID-19 pandemic, emissions quickly rebounded. Emissions cuts of 40–70% by 2050 are needed to keep global warming below the catastrophic level of 2 °C (3.6 °F), and ultimately it is essential to reach net-zero carbon emissions. On our current path (Fig. 12), rising CO_2 levels will result in dangerous global warming. Feedbacks in the system could make our planet warm even more, or faster, than these projections (see "Will There Be a Last Straw?" below).

So What?

Temperatures a few degrees warmer might not sound like much, but a 3 °C (5.4 °F) temperature rise would make Earth its warmest in 3 million years, far beyond the 10,000-year experience of human civilization. One

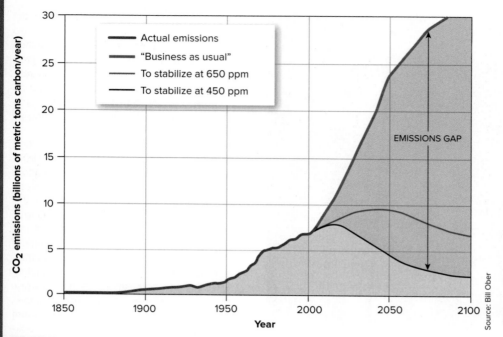

FIGURE 12 So far, global CO_2 emissions are following a path predicted by a fossil-fuel-intensive, business-as-usual model, which by 2100 would produce CO_2 levels of 750 to 1250 ppm and rising. This can be compared with emissions pathways we need to be on to stabilize atmospheric CO_2 concentrations at 450 or 650 ppm.

Source: Bill Ober

of the main effects will be to speed up the water cycle. The higher temperatures will promote evaporation, and rainfall will increase globally. The increase will not, however, be evenly distributed. Climate change is expected to intensify existing patterns. Places that are wet now will have more frequent and severe floods, while drought and forest fires will be worse in arid regions. People who depend on melting snow and glaciers for their summer water supplies, for example in the western United States, western Europe, and western China, will suffer increasing late-summer water shortages as the snow season shortens, the snow melts earlier in the year, and glaciers shrink and disappear. Globally, an estimated 1 to 4 billion people face increasing water shortage. Although increased atmospheric CO_2 may have a slight "fertilizing" effect on some crops, overall agricultural yields are expected to decline, mostly in developing countries. Declining wheat yields in a number of countries may already reflect the early impacts of climate change. Fisheries, already faced with drastic overfishing, are further threatened by climate change. Hundreds of millions more people will be at risk of hunger and malnutrition.

Sea level rise will increasingly threaten coastal areas, home to more than 40% of the world's population and most of its largest cities, including New York, Los Angeles, London, Shanghai, Cairo, and Rio de Janeiro. Recent studies predict that northeastern North America will initially be most affected by sea level rise. Coastal erosion will steadily

increase, requiring ever more expensive seawalls and other protective measures. An alternative is "strategic retreat": gradually abandoning buildings, refineries, dockyards, and other shoreline infrastructure. Saltwater intrusion will cause increasing problems with stormwater drainage, water supply, and sewage systems. Saltwater intrusion is also threatening, for example, the Florida Everglades and coastal forests in the southeastern United States. Coastal areas will be more vulnerable to storms, floods, and other disasters—not just because of the rising seas but also because storms and floods are expected to become more extreme, and possibly more frequent and more widespread. Increasing coastal vulnerability combined with more extreme weather will mean more catastrophes like Hurricane Katrina.

Human health will also suffer. Drought, floods, extreme storms, and malnutrition will inflict increasing casualties. Crippling heat waves will claim more lives, though partly offset by fewer deaths from extreme cold in northern climes. Damage to sanitation systems by floods, storms, and seawater intrusion, and increasing shortages of safe drinking water, are expected to raise the toll from dysentery, cholera, and other diseases. As mosquitoes, ticks, and other hosts spread into areas once too cold for them they will spread diseases like malaria, West Nile virus, dengue fever, and encephalitis. The World Health Organization estimates that climate change is already killing 150,000 people a year, and another 1 °C (1.8 °F) increase will double that. Independent health experts state that climate

change—and the delayed response to combat it—has already had unequivocal effects on human health, but combating climate change is the single greatest opportunity to improve public health globally.

Climate change is already affecting people in every region of the planet. Every inhabited continent is experiencing more extreme and more frequent heatwaves, many resulting in hundreds of human deaths. Associated droughts and wildfires are also increasing. Tropical storms—called hurricanes, cyclones, typhoons, or other names depending on where you are—are becoming more intense and occurring more frequently and over longer seasons. While some areas are experiencing major droughts, parts of Africa, Asia, Australia, and North and South Americas—again, every inhabited continent—have instead seen unprecedented rainfall, leading to major floods and landslides. The IPCC concludes that these increases in extreme events are a direct result of human greenhouse gas emissions. All have had major adverse impacts on society, including loss of life, disease, shortages of food and water, and economic losses running to trillions of dollars. The global economic impact of climate change is expected to be at least on the scale of the world wars and Great Depression of the twentieth century, and possibly much greater.

Ocean Acidification: The Other CO_2 Problem

Rising CO_2 levels will profoundly affect the ocean even without rising temperatures. About half the CO_2 we pump into the atmosphere dissolves in the ocean. That slows climate change, but it also changes ocean chemistry. When CO_2 dissolves in seawater it increases the ocean's acidity or, more properly, lowers its pH. Seawater is naturally slightly alkaline (pH 8.0–8.3). The dissolved CO_2 increase from human emissions has already lowered the ocean's pH by about 0.1 pH units. This which may not sound like much but because the pH scale is logarithmic it represents a 26% increase in acidity (or conversely a 26% decrease in alkalinity). The ocean's pH could drop by 0.4 units by 2100 if CO_2 emissions continue as they are now. The declining ocean pH is widely called **ocean acidification,** but the ocean is not expected to actually become acidic, only less alkaline. That doesn't mean there isn't a problem.

The organisms most at risk from ocean acidification are those with shells, skeletons, or other structures made of calcium carbonate ($CaCO_3$). Lower pH makes calcium carbonate dissolve more easily, and harder for marine species to deposit their $CaCO_3$ shells.

Healthy shell (normal pH)

Clear shell

Smooth ridges

Damaged shell (lower pH)

Ragged, dissolving ridges

Cloudy shell

Severe abrasions

National Oceanic and Atmospheric Administration

FIGURE 13 Pteropods (*Limacina helicina*) grown in more acidic water than normal develop ragged, weakened shells.

The ecological consequences of ocean acidification are profound. Corals and certain groups of plankton, like pteropod molluscs (Fig. 13; also see Fig. 15.10) are most vulnerable because of the particular type of calcium carbonate mineral they make (Fig. 13). This could be the death knell for coral reefs, already stressed by warming-induced bleaching, pollution, and overfishing (see 14.4). Plankton communities are likely to be radically altered, especially in the Southern Ocean where pteropods are an indicator of ecosystem health. As acidification becomes more severe it will affect other important plankton, like foraminiferans and coccolithophores.

Acidification will affect mussels, clams, snails, sea urchins, coralline algae, barnacles, and a host of other organisms with calcified structures, in addition to plankton. Researchers have already observed pH-related changes in intertidal communities on the coast of Washington State, with mussels, barnacles, and coralline algae declining with lower pH in favor of non-calcified competitors.

Not all the effects of ocean acidification are related to calcification. Reduced pH affects the ocean chemistry of silicon as well as $CaCO_3$, and may make it more difficult for diatoms, critically important primary producers, to get the silicon they need. Reduced pH makes squids more sluggish, probably making them less effective predators and more vulnerable to their own predators. Similar effects could apply to many other invertebrates. Surprisingly, acidification makes underwater sound go farther, potentially affecting whales and other organisms that use sound to communicate or are disturbed by ship noise or other artificial sounds. Studies of the effects of acidification are relatively new, and no doubt other effects will be discovered. We know the oceans are acidifying, and though we don't fully understand the consequences we do know they are potentially huge.

Overwhelming the Nitrogen Cycle

Humanity is gambling with the nitrogen cycle as well as the carbon cycle. Earth has lots of nitrogen—more, in fact, than the other major essential elements (carbon, oxygen, phosphorus, and sulfur) put together. Nearly all of it, however, is in the form of dinitrogen gas (N_2). N_2 is practically inert and most organisms can't use it, so nitrogen is the element least available to life despite its abundance.

Before humans came along only lightning and a few microbes could convert N_2 into more reactive forms, including forms that primary producers can use as nutrients. The formation of these **reactive nitrogen** compounds was balanced by their conversion back to N_2 by microbes in the process of denitrification, limiting the pool of reactive nitrogen. Pre-industrial humans added to reactive nitrogen formation by cultivating legumes, rice, and other crops that boost the fixation of N_2 into nutrients the plants can use. By and large, denitrification was able to keep up with this increased formation of reactive nitrogen from agriculture.

Since the mid-1800s, however, human production of reactive nitrogen has increased more than 10-fold. The industrial revolution brought mass burning of fossil fuels, which produces reactive nitrogen oxides (NO_x). Cultivation of nitrogen-fixing crops also intensified: It more than doubled between 1860 and 2000. Human production of reactive nitrogen really took off in 1913 when the invention of the Haber-Bosch process, a method to convert N_2 into ammonia (NH_3), led to industrial-scale production of nitrogen fertilizers (Fig. 14).

Without these fertilizers global food production could never have kept up with our exploding population, and about 40% of today's population would go hungry. An estimated 80% of the nitrogen in the average person comes from artificial fertilizer. Poor soils and lack of fertilizer still mean hunger and malnutrition for some people, and they need more reactive nitrogen, not less. But for the planet as a whole there is too much. Our production and use of reactive nitrogen is grossly inefficient. Creating reactive nitrogen by burning fossil fuels has no benefit at all, and only

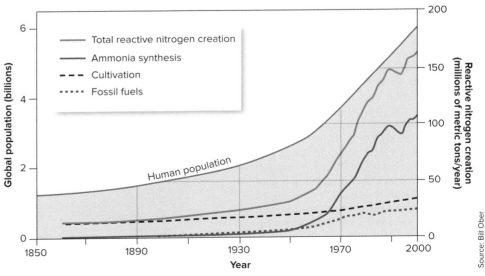

Source: Bill Ober

FIGURE 14 Reactive nitrogen creation by Haber-Bosch ammonia synthesis, the cultivation of nitrogen-fixing crops, and fossil fuel burning, 1860 to 2000.

12% of the nitrogen fertilizer applied to crops ends up in food. Most of the rest simply evaporates into the atmosphere or washes away into rivers, lakes, and the ocean.

As much as 70% of the reactive nitrogen in the environment now comes from human activities. Natural denitrification can't convert it back to N_2 fast enough, so reactive nitrogen is building up. The stuff is everywhere, flowing through the environment again and again in what has been called the **nitrogen cascade,** and overwhelming the natural nitrogen cycle. In the air, NO_x compounds cause smog, leading to eye irritation, lung and heart disease, and cancer. Nitrous oxide (N_2O) is a greenhouse gas and contributes to the destruction of the ozone layer. Reactive nitrogen compounds in the atmosphere fall as acid rain, damaging lakes, rivers, and forests. In addition to acid rain damage, excess nitrogen falling onto forests, grasslands, and other terrestrial systems causes a decline in primary productivity and the loss of biodiversity. Soil acidification also reduces agricultural production. Nitrates get into drinking water supplies, causing headache, fatigue, respiratory problems, and occasionally even death.

The nitrogen cascade is also harming the ocean. In many marine waters, phytoplankton and other primary producers are limited by a shortage of nitrogen nutrients like nitrate (NO_3^{-1}), and adding extra reactive nitrogen can produce excessive algal growth, or **eutrophication.** Although phytoplankton populations have declined on the scale of whole ocean basins, many coastal areas and shallow seas, especially those with limited water circulation, are suffering from eutrophication. Many coral reefs, for example, are threatened by the overgrowth of seaweeds, caused at least in part by excessive nitrogen fertilization. Excess nitrogen input is also a major factor in a global increase in harmful algal blooms (Fig. 15), leading to ecosystem declines, lost fisheries revenue, and human health problems. Eutrophication is also linked to seasonal or permanent oxygen-depleted zones, or **hypoxic zones.** Hypoxic zones form when large amounts of phytoplankton and the organic matter they produce sink and decay in deeper water, using up the oxygen. Hypoxic zones are often called "dead zones," which is technically incorrect because some microbes and invertebrates prosper in the low oxygen levels. Nevertheless, fish and other organisms vacate the area—eels, lobsters, crabs, and other animals have even been known to crawl up on land to escape—and most animals that can't move away die. Hypoxic zones occur naturally, but are an increasing problem. They have increased in number every decade since the 1960s (Fig. 16), and many are growing larger. The Gulf of Mexico

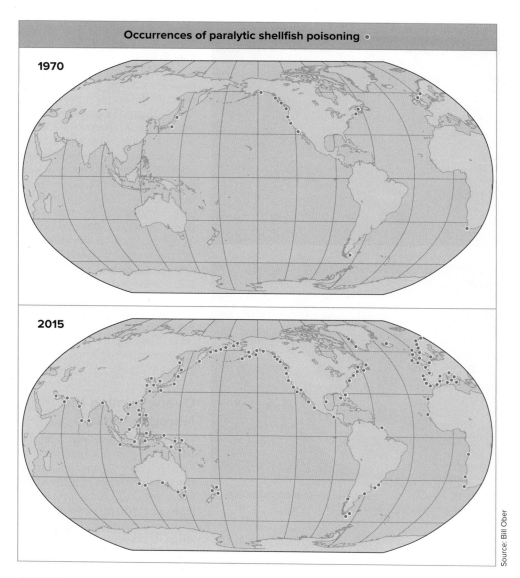

Occurrences of paralytic shellfish poisoning

1970

2015

FIGURE 15 Increasing global occurrence of paralytic shellfish poisoning, one form of seafood poisoning caused by harmful algal blooms.

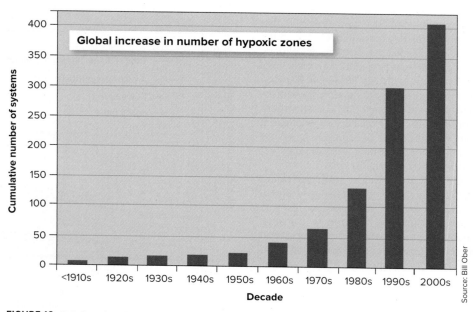

Global increase in number of hypoxic zones

FIGURE 16 Global number of hypoxic zones by decade. Data for the 2010s extend only through 2017.

Will There Be a Last Straw?

We tend to expect that the climate system works like a thermostat: add some CO_2 and the temperature goes up, add a little more and the temperature goes up a little more. As long as the system behaves like that we can always hope that before things get too bad—next year, next decade, or next century—humanity can reduce its CO_2 emissions and things will cool down again. There is, in fact, a direct correlation between CO_2 and warming, but the rest of the climate system doesn't work like that. There are a number of positive feedbacks whereby slight increases in temperature intensify warming, which intensifies the feedback effect, in a vicious cycle. Some of these positive feedbacks are understood well enough to be included in current predictions, but others are "wild cards" in the global change game. There may be a "last straw" that breaks the camel's back of the global climate system. Such effects, where the system reaches a point of sudden, largely irreversible change, are called **tipping points.** Here are some candidates—that we know about:

A Less Absorbent Sponge The ocean acts like a sponge for CO_2, absorbing about half our emissions. Because CO_2 is more soluble in colder water, warming seas will absorb less CO_2 and more will remain in the atmosphere.

Getting Steamed Water is the dominant greenhouse gas but it amplifies rather than drives greenhouse warming (see "The Greenhouse: Too Much of a Good Thing?"). Higher temperatures mean more evaporation and more water in the atmosphere, creating a feedback loop. Recent measurements indicate a 6% increase in water vapor in the upper troposphere since 1982, pretty much as predicted by climate models.

Losing That Shine Almost a third of the solar energy striking Earth is reflected back into space rather than being absorbed as heat (see Fig. 6)—creating "earthshine." Different aspects of global change are expected to affect Earth's reflectivity, or albedo, in different ways, but overall the albedo is expected to decrease, in particular as shiny white sea ice in polar regions gives way to relatively dark, heat-absorbing open water. Arctic ice loss is particularly important and likely to affect us the soonest.

Clouding the Issue Higher moisture levels are likely to make the atmosphere more cloudy, especially if ocean acidification favors plankton that release cloud-promoting gases. Some scientists predict that the clouds will increase Earth's albedo, reflecting more heat into space to partially offset the greenhouse effect. Others argue that the greenhouse effect of the clouds themselves will be more important than the albedo change.

Disrupting the Conveyor The Great Ocean Conveyor circulation (see Fig. 3.25) that transports vast amounts of heat from tropical to polar regions is driven by temperature and salinity differences between surface and deeper water. Greatly increased freshwater input in the far north Atlantic, caused by melting ice, is causing the conveyor to slow, and could ultimately shut it down. Ironically, that would bring much colder temperatures to Europe. Other regions, however, would warm even faster and the Asian monsoons could fail, bringing famine and hardship to millions. There are worrying indications that the conveyor is already starting to waver.

Greenland Melting The accumulation of ice from high-elevation snowfall maintains Greenland's ice cap, replacing ice that melts at a lower altitude. Once melting lowers the ice cap's elevation, snowfall will diminish and melting will accelerate because more of the ice cap will lie at lower, warmer altitudes. Only a new ice age could reverse this runaway process. The ice cap is 2 km (1.2 mi) thick, and if it melts entirely sea level would rise by about 7 m (23 ft). That would probably take a few thousand years, but in the meantime the flood of freshwater into the North Atlantic could shut down the conveyor circulation.

The Ocean Burps Ocean sediments hold more carbon, in the form of methane, than all the world's reserves of coal, oil, and natural gas. The methane, combined with water, is locked up in crystalline forms known as gas hydrates or clathrates. Warmer temperatures could destabilize the clathrates and suddenly release vast amounts of methane into the atmosphere. That would greatly intensify greenhouse warming, probably catastrophically.

Breaking the Soil Bank Soils are the second-largest of Earth's carbon reservoirs and absorb about a quarter of human CO_2 emissions. At the moment, soil absorption of CO_2 is increasing because higher atmospheric CO_2 levels stimulate plant growth. For now this helps slow greenhouse warming, but when temperatures rise high enough an increase in respiration by soil microbes and plants will overcome this effect and soils will release CO_2 instead of absorbing it. Furthermore, if peat bogs and wetlands dry out, and Arctic permafrost melts, they will release huge amounts of CO_2 and methane currently locked up in these soils. Methane release from the Arctic is already on the rise.

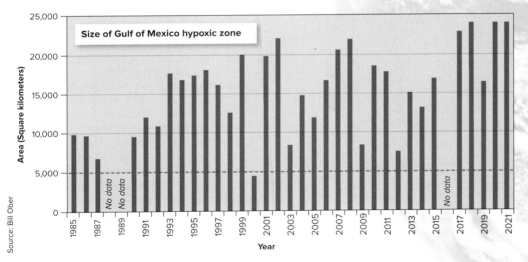

FIGURE 17 Maximum size of the hypoxic zone in the northern Gulf of Mexico by year.

hypoxic zone forms in summer when the warming of the sea surface blocks mixing of oxygen into deeper water (Figure 18.5). The zone has roughly doubled in size since the mid-1980s, though it fluctuates from year to year (Fig. 17). In particular, it is smaller in years where there are major storms that help mix the water column. Rising temperatures add to the problem of hypoxia, because oxygen is less soluble in warmer water.

Barring a major change in human emissions, nitrogen input to the open ocean from the atmosphere is predicted to increase dramatically by 2050. We're not sure what will happen next. If we're really lucky, enhanced phytoplankton growth from the increased nitrogen supply might give a boost to fisheries and pull some CO_2 out of the atmosphere to reduce the greenhouse effect. The drawdown in CO_2, unfortunately, is largely offset by the re-release of nitrogen as the potent greenhouse gas N_2O. By adding more and more reactive nitrogen to the open ocean, we could create the mother of all dead zones.

The No-Zone

Ozone (O_3) is a reactive form of oxygen, much different from the ordinary molecular oxygen (O_2) we breathe. Ozone in the lower atmosphere is a health hazard and damages plants and buildings. High in the stratosphere, however, a natural layer of ozone shields life from ultraviolet radiation (UV), which causes skin cancer and eye damage in humans and may harm crops. UV is also suspected of biological impacts ranging from damage to phytoplankton and fish eggs to blindness in polar bears.

In the late 1970s scientists found that ozone levels in the stratosphere were declining, and in 1985 they discovered a huge "hole" in the ozone layer over Antarctica. From then on the Antarctic ozone hole has formed every year in September and October, and it steadily increased in size for more than a decade (Fig. 18). Much of the Southern Hemisphere is experiencing higher UV levels as a result. Less severe, but still

245

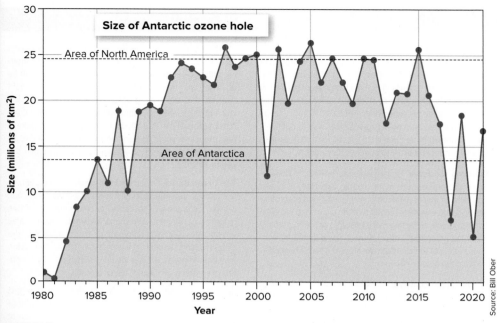

FIGURE 18 Average size of the Antarctic ozone hole between September 7 and October 13, when the seasonal ozone hole is at its peak.

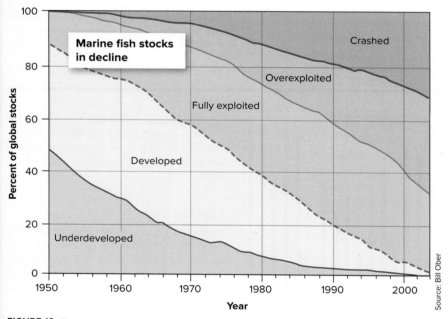

FIGURE 19 Trends in the status of global fishery stocks since 1950.

worrying, ozone depletion has also occurred over the Arctic and at middle latitudes.

Chlorofluorocarbons (CFCs), synthetic gases that were widely used in spray cans and air conditioners, caused most of the ozone depletion. CFCs released at Earth's surface gradually move up to the stratosphere, where they destroy the ozone. Nitrous oxide and other gases involved in the nitrogen cascade also contribute to ozone depletion. Ozone depletion is often confused with global warming because ozone, CFCs, and nitrous oxide are greenhouse gases, but the real issue regarding ozone is not rising temperature but a dangerous increase in UV levels.

CFCs have been largely phased out under a 1987 international agreement, the Montreal Protocol. CFC emissions have been slashed, but CFCs released in the past are still making their way into the stratosphere and it appears that some CFCs are still being manufactured, though in greatly reduced amounts. The Antarctic ozone hole reached a record size in 2006, but the Montreal Protocol appears to be working. The size of the ozone hole varies from year to year depending on Antarctic weather, but the overall trend is down (Fig. 18). The Montreal Protocol demonstrates that concerted international action can reverse negative global change.

Stripping the Sea Bare

Humans are changing the global ocean not just by putting things in, but also by taking things out—especially fish and other seafood. World fishing fleets expanded rapidly in the last half of the twentieth century, driven by government subsidies and humanity's insatiable desire for fish for human consumption and livestock feed. For a time the expansion in fishing effort resulted in growing global catches but, despite fishing harder and harder, the global catch has been declining since the 1980s. As global fishing fleets grew, one stock after another was fished to depletion, often until it crashed. Government regulators routinely ignored their own scientists and allowed greater catches than stocks could sustain. Insanity has been defined as doing the same thing over and over expecting a different result—sound familiar?

In spite of the repeated decimation of fishery stocks, the decline in global catch has so far been relatively small. That is only because the fleets could always move on to new targets farther afield or deeper in the ocean. But we are running out of new stocks: Almost every place in the ocean is fished, and nothing edible—whether by humans or livestock—is safe. Some 70% of global stocks have crashed or are overexploited—meaning headed for a crash (Fig. 19). Almost all the rest are "fully exploited," which means that fleets are taking every last bit that can be taken, supposedly without leading to overexploitation. Historically, though, "fully exploited" stocks almost always end up on the wrong side of the line. There are hardly any fisheries where there is room to catch more (see "Optimal Yields and Overfishing," in 17.1). Without new fisheries to move on to once the fleets have decimated current stocks, the global catch is headed for disaster.

The dire state of global fisheries will reduce the supply and increase the cost of seafood, an important source of healthy protein. Ironically, fishing harder and harder has meant producing less and less seafood. But marine biologists have realized that, in addition to reducing seafood supplies, overfishing is fundamentally changing the ecology of the seas. The collateral damage is huge. Bottom trawls, for example, are destroying tropical coral reefs, deep-sea coral communities, seamount communities, and many other ecosystems. Even on soft bottoms, where the physical damage is not quite so bad, in some places

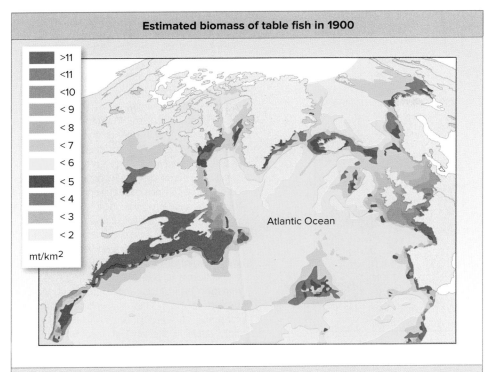

Estimated biomass of table fish in 1900

	mt/km²
	>11
	<11
	<10
	<9
	<8
	<7
	<6
	<5
	<4
	<3
	<2

Atlantic Ocean

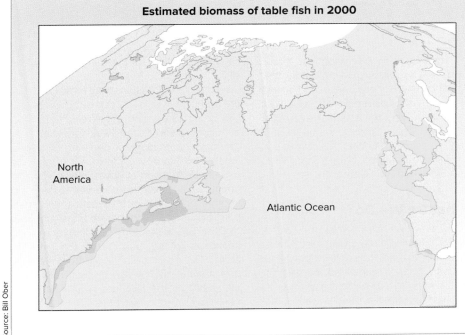

Estimated biomass of table fish in 2000

North America

Atlantic Ocean

Source: Bill Ober

FIGURE 20 The depletion of biomass in the North Atlantic Ocean during the twentieth century. Fish stocks were already depleted even in 1900 compared to 1850. Humanity has essentially "mined" the stocks—the biomass, like mineral resources, is no longer renewable, it was just stripped away.

the same bit of bottom may be trawled every few days or weeks, eliminating any possibility of a normal, productive ecosystem recovering. Many species are threatened because of their mortality as by-catch, where they are unintentionally caught, killed, and discarded.

Overfishing is having even more fundamental effects. It has stripped the sea bare, leaving almost nothing behind (Fig. 20). Removing that much biomass from the oceans can't help but radically alter them. Many species of seals, sea lions, seabirds, and other animals are suffering because populations of high-quality fish have been wiped out, forcing the animals to switch to less-nutritious "junk foods." Fisheries are systematically deconstructing food webs. People have traditionally favored large, tasty fishes like tuna, cod, and salmon near the top of the food chain. As these large predators have been wiped out, attention has steadily shifted to smaller, less palatable species lower on the food chain (Fig. 21). By **"fishing down the food chain,"** we are now depleting vast schools of baitfish, making recovery even harder for the large predators that we prefer to eat. Perhaps more importantly, these large predators often help structure entire ecosystems, and their removal can have cascading effects both up and down the food chain. The depletion of salmon stocks in the Pacific Northwest of North America, for example, threatens killer whale (*Orcinus orca*) populations, including both whales that feed directly on salmon and those that eat seals and sea lions that eat salmon. In an even more complex **trophic cascade,** overfishing of pollock may have led to a decline in their predators, seals and sea lions, forcing killer whales to eat otters. Reduced sea otter predation on sea urchins led to shrinking kelp forests (see Fig. 13.27). The depletion of coral reef sharks, largely for their fins, may produce another trophic cascade resulting in the overgrowth of reefs by algae (see "Grazing," in 14.3). Similarly, overfishing of large sharks on the east coast of the United States led to a boom in their prey of skates, rays, and small sharks, which eat scallops. The scallop fishery crashed as a result.

Especially worrisome is what appears to be a marked increase in the numbers and size of jellyfish (sea jelly) species worldwide. Among the reasons for this are the depletion of large predators like tunas and swordfish that eat jellyfishes, and of smaller fishes that compete with jellyfishes for their zooplankton food. Climate change and nutrient pollution may also be contributing to jellyfish blooms, because many jellyfishes are "weed species" that are highly adaptable to changing conditions. Once jellyfishes get the upper hand, their predation on fish larvae and juveniles can prevent fish populations from recovering. Marine biologists fear that overfishing may be more or less permanently transforming an ocean full of fish into a sea of jellyfish—yummm!

Disappearing Habitats

On top of everything else, humanity is changing the planet by destroying habitats—the places organisms live—altogether. Marine habitats, especially near the coast, are disappearing worldwide, to be replaced by artificial shorelines or degraded wastelands (see 18.1). Over half the estuaries and coastal wetlands in the United States have been degraded, in California over 90%. Southeast Asian countries have lost 46 to 100% of their coastal salt marshes and swamps. In countries with data, more than 35% of mangrove

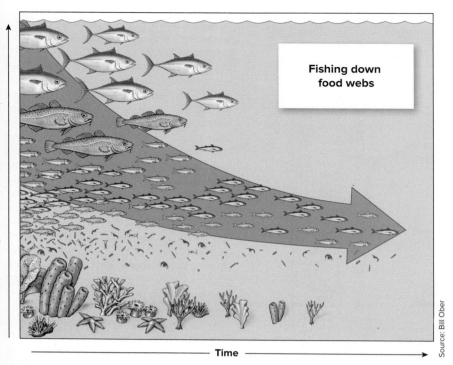

Source: Bill Ober

Time

FIGURE 21 Fishing down the food chain. After the large top predators are removed, fishing effort systematically shifts down the food chain to smaller, less palatable species, with effects on the entire ecosystem.

forests have been lost, and the situation may be worse in countries that haven't monitored their mangroves. An estimated 20% of the world's coral reefs have already been destroyed, with another 20% nearing the brink and possibly beyond hope. Intertidal habitats, seagrass beds, kelp forests, and other coastal habitats are in similar situations. Some of the losses result from indirect effects of pollution, overfishing, or the introduction of invading alien species. Many losses are more direct, for example, the clearing of mangroves, draining of coastal wetlands, and filling in of estuaries.

The loss of key marine habitats makes the world more vulnerable to other aspects of global change because these habitats absorb and store carbon, protect shorelines, remove nutrients, and provide essential breeding and nursery habitats for fisheries species. These and many other **ecosystem services** provided by intact marine habitats have enormous, tangible benefits to society. The problem is that they can't be bought and sold, and therefore they don't have a price in the market or factor into economic decisions. When we have to pay for expensive sea walls and other shoreline defenses, or for repairing storm damage, however, we pay the cost of losing mangroves, reefs, salt marshes, and other habitats that protect the shoreline. We pay for losing habitats that remove nutrients and pollution in the costs of building treatment plants and in human health costs. And we pay for lost breeding

habitat when seafood becomes less available and more expensive. Unfortunately, the people who have to pay these and many other costs are often different from those who gain from destroying habitats. But everyone loses when the carbon sequestration function of coastal habitats is lost, intensifying climate change (see Box 10.3, "Carbon Sinks and Blue Carbon")

So What Do We Do?

The only way we can avoid the worst impacts of global climate change is to take strong action immediately. We could have started with smaller steps had we started a few decades ago, but climate change is already having negative effects around the world and there is no longer time for gradual action.

The critical first step is obvious: humanity has to wean itself from fossil fuels. A 2021 analysis shows that the only possible way to limit warming to 1.5 °C (2.7 °F) by 2050 is to leave nearly 90% of existing coal reserves, and 60% of oil and gas reserves, in the ground. This, of course, means exploration for new reserves must stop. To achieve the necessary cuts, society needs to find ways to get by without the vast amount of energy we generate from fossil fuels. The contributions of alternative energy sources, particularly solar and wind, are increasing faster than predicted even a decade ago, as these sources become more efficient and cost

competitive. There is major global interest in using hydrogen as an alternative fuel. It takes energy to make hydrogen, however, so the benefits are reduced if the energy comes from burning fossil fuels, but "green" hydrogen produced from renewable energy sources could become a major piece in solving the climate puzzle.

Globally, the fossil fuel industry receives nearly a half-trillion dollars a year in government subsidies—phasing these out would make alternative energy even more competitive. This is politically difficult, however, as subsidies keep fossil fuel prices artificially low and support jobs, not to mention the political clout of the fossil fuel industry.

Cutting CO_2 emissions from fossil fuels would directly slow ocean acidification as well as global warming. Reduced fossil fuel extraction and use would also cut reactive nitrogen emissions, and methane emissions by up to half. This is important because methane, a very potent greenhouse gas, only stays in the atmosphere for around a decade, compared to an average of hundreds of years for CO_2. This means that reducing methane will slow warming much faster than cutting CO_2. Reducing other sources of methane, for example by covering landfills and improvements in agriculture, can help buy time for the transition from fossil fuels.

To reduce emissions from fossil fuels that are burnt, the CO_2 produced by power plants can be captured before it is released to the atmosphere and stored away, for example in geological formations or depleted oil or gas fields. This "carbon capture and storage" is already being used at power plants in some countries, and has the potential to be used in other industries, such as steel and cement manufacturing, that generate large amounts of CO_2. The technology is still in its relative infancy, however, and carries the risk that stored CO_2 could be released from the storage reservoirs. The risk of such release is increased by the fact that in at least some cases microbes convert the stored CO_2 into methane.

An increasing number of scientists consider that simply capturing CO_2 generated by industry will not be enough, and CO_2 will need to be captured directly from the atmosphere and stored away. Some proposals involve capturing and storing the CO_2 in similar ways to carbon capture and storage from industrial plants. Others involve **geoengineering,** or making large-scale changes to the environment to capture and store carbon. Certain minerals, for example, absorb CO_2 during their natural weathering process, and spreading large amounts of such minerals on land, or adding them to seawater, has the potential to draw down large amounts of CO_2 from the atmosphere. Adding minerals to make

ocean waters more alkaline would increase CO_2 absorption by seawater. Other geoengineering proposals involve removing CO_2 from the atmosphere in the form of biomass. These include artificially fertilizing the oceans to increase phytoplankton growth, so that the phytoplankton absorb CO_2 in photosynthesis and then sink into the deep ocean, or farming vast amounts of seaweed and then sinking that. There are even proposals to sink crop wastes from land onto the sea floor. These and other geoengineering proposals have many unresolved technical, environmental, economic, and legal issues and are unlikely to play a significant role in climate mitigation for decades to come.

There are important actions to slow global warming that can be taken now, and will have almost immediate effects. Perhaps the most important is to improve energy efficiency, which not only reduces emissions but saves money. More efficient power generation and other industrial technologies should be fast-tracked. The same goes for better insulation and more efficient heating and cooling of homes and commercial buildings. The shift from fuel-powered vehicles to electric ones that is already underway in developed countries is a welcome sign. Even if the electricity to charge the vehicles comes from burning fossil fuels, electric vehicles are more carbon-efficient that fuel-power ones, and if the electricity comes from renewable sources electric vehicles are emissions-free.

Another important measure to address climate change would be to protect and restore biological carbon sinks. Efforts to halt and reverse deforestation on land have met with only limited success to date, and should be intensified. In the ocean, blue carbon sinks including mangroves, seagrass beds, salt marshes, kelp beds, and coral reefs should be protected from further loss and where possible degraded habitats restored (see Box 10.3 "Carbon Sinks and Blue Carbon"). Not only do such habitats absorb large amounts of CO_2 from the atmosphere, when degraded ones are restored they start doing it almost immediately. Like cutting methane emissions, restoring blue carbon sinks can be a powerful tool to put off the worst impacts of climate change while the more far-reaching measures that are needed can be put into place. It also has the benefit of maintaining the many ecosystem services provided by these habitats.

Reduced fossil-fuel use would reduce reactive nitrogen emissions from burning the fuels, as would rolling out existing technologies that reduce nitrogen emissions from fossil-fuel burning. But fossil-fuel burning accounts for only about 16% of reactive nitrogen emissions and reducing it won't fix the nitrogen cascade. Controlling the main sources of anthropogenic reactive nitrogen, fertilizers and nitrogen-fixing crops, without compromising the food supply of a growing population is a challenge, but scientists have already identified promising new technologies. Research is still needed on better ways to give plants only the nitrogen they need to reduce waste to the environment, on better ways to manage livestock wastes, and on recycling reactive nitrogen instead of making it anew and dumping it in the environment. Reducing government subsidies that encourage wasteful fertilizer use would help. Again it is essential to maintain and restore habitats like wetlands, estuaries, and bays that lock up both reactive nitrogen and carbon, and remove reactive nitrogen by denitrification. The restoration of streamside vegetation and wetlands, for example, is a key strategy to reduce the size of the Gulf of Mexico "dead zone" to a target of 5,000 km^2 (1,930 mi^2; see Figure 17).

Global change can only be addressed through international actions and agreements. Greenhouse gases and reactive nitrogen flow across borders, fishing fleets roam far and wide across the oceans, and economic incentives and pressures operate on global scales. Developing countries often lack the technology, finance, and other resources to implement urgently needed measures, and can only do so with assistance from developed countries. Unfortunately, governments have generally been slow to take action on most aspects of global change. There are signs that this is changing, and in recent years more and more countries have taken steps internally to reduce carbon emissions and protect habitats, and made international commitments to this as well. The next decade or two will reveal whether this is too little, too late or if the global community finally took meaningful action just in time to avert catastrophe.

FOR MORE INFORMATION

Climate Change and Its Effects

Ashton, G. V., S. A. Morley, D. K. A. Barnes, M. S. Clark, and L. S. Peck, 2017. Warming by 1 °C drives species and assemblage level responses in Antarctica's marine shallows. *Current Biology*, vol. 27, September 11, pp. 2698–2705.

Altieri, A. H. and K. B. Gedan, 2015. Climate change and dead zones. *Global Change Biology*, vol. 21, pp. 1395–1406.

Burge, C. A., C. M. Eakin, C. S. Friedman, et al., 2014. Climate change influences on marine infectious diseases: Implications for management and society. *Annual Review of Marine Science*, vol. 6, pp. 249–277.

Cohen, J., L. Agel, M. Barlow, C. I. Garfinkel, and I. White, 2021. Linking Arctic vulnerability and change with extreme winter weather in the United States. *Science*, vol. 373, pp. 1116–1121.

Dahlke, F. T., S. Wohlrab, M. Butzin, and H.-O. Pörtner, 2020. Thermal bottlenecks in the life cycle define climate vulnerability of fish. *Science*, vol. 369, pp. 65–70.

Hastings, R. A., L. A. Rutterford, J. J. Freer, et al., 2020. Climate change drives poleward increases and equatorward declines in marine species. *Current Biology*, vol. 30, pp. 1572–1577.

Howard, J. et al., 2013. Oceans and marine resources in a changing climate. *Oceanography and Marine Biology: An Annual Review*, vol. 51, pp. 71–192.

International Energy Agency, 2017. CO_2 emissions from fuel combustion. Overview 2017.

IPCC, 2021: Summary for Policymakers. In: *Climate Change 2021: The Physical Science Basis. Contribution of Working Group I to the Sixth Assessment Report of the Intergovernmental Panel on Climate Change.* Cambridge University Press.

IPCC, 2022. Summary for Policymakers. In: *Climate Change 2022. Impacts, Adaptation and Vulnerability. Contribution of Working Group II to the Sixth Assessment Report of the Intergovernmental Panel on Climate Change.* Cambridge University Press.

Jonkers, L., H. Hillebrand, and M. Kucera, 2019. Global change drives modern plankton communities away from the pre-industrial state. *Nature*, vol. 570, pp. 372–375.

O'Leary, J. K., F. Micheli, L. Airoldi, et al., 2017. The resilience of marine ecosystems to climatic disturbances. *BioScience*, vol. 67, pp. 208–220.

Ripple, W. J., C. Wolf, T. M. Newsome, et al., 2020. World scientists' warning of a climate emergency. *BioScience*, vol. 70, pp. 8–12.

Slater, T., I. R. Lawrence, I. N., Otasaka, et al., 2021. Review article: Earth's ice imbalance. *The Cryosphere*, vol. 15, pp. 233–246.

Tyne, R. L., P. H. Barry, M. Lawson, et al., 2021. Rapid microbial methanogenesis during CO_2 storage in hydrocarbon reservoirs. *Nature*, vol. 600, pp. 670–674.

Watts, N., M. Amann, S. Ayeb-Karlsson, et al., 2017. The *Lancet* Countdown on health and climate change: From 25 years of inaction to a global transformation for public health. *The Lancet*, vol. 391, no. 10120, pp. 581–630.

Welsby, D., J. Price, S. Pye, and P. Ekins, 2021. Unextractable fossil fuels in a 1.5 °C world. *Nature*, vol. 597, pp. 230–234.

Ocean Acidification

Andersson A. J. and D. Gledhill, 2013. Ocean acidification and coral reefs: Effects on breakdown, dissolution, and net ecosystem calcification. *Annual Review of Marine Science*, vol. 5, pp. 321–348.

Di Giglio, S., E. Lein, M. Y. Hu, et al., 2020. Skeletal integrity of a marine keystone predator (*Asterias rubens*) threatened by ocean acidification. Journal of *Experimental Marine Biology and Ecology*, vol. 526, p. 151335.

Hoffman, G. E., J. P. Barry, P. J. Edmunds, R. D. Gates, D. A. Hutchins, T. Kllinger, and M. A. Sewell, 2010. The effect of ocean acidification on calcifying organisms in marine ecosystems: An organism to ecosystem perspective. *Annual Review of Ecology, Evolution, and Systematics*, vol. 41, pp. 127–147.

McNicholl, C., M. S. Koch, P. W. Swarzenski, et al., 2020. Ocean acidification effects on calcification and dissolution in tropical reef macroalgae. *Coral Reefs*, vol. 39, pp. 1635–1647.

Schwaner, C., M. Barbosa, P. Connors, et al., 2020. Experimental acidification increase susceptibility of *Mercanaria mercenaria* to infection by *Vibrio* species. *Marine Environmental Research*, vol. 154, p. 104872.

Waldbusser, G. G. and J. E. Salisbury, 2014. Ocean acidification in the coastal zone from an organism's perspective: Multiple system parameters, frequency domains, and habitats. *Annual Review of Marine Science*, vol. 6, pp. 221–247.

The Nitrogen Cascade

Diaz, R. J. and R. Rosenberg, 2008. Spreading dead zones and consequences for marine ecosystems. *Science*, vol. 321, pp. 926–929.

Howarth, R. W., 2008. Coastal nitrogen pollution: A review of sources and trends globally and regionally. *Harmful Algae*, vol. 8, pp. 14–20.

Jikells, T. D. et al., 2017. A reevaluation of the magnitude and impacts of anthropogenic atmospheric nitrogen inputs on the ocean. *Global Biogeochemical Cycles*, vol. 31, no. 2, pp. 289–305.

Seitzinger, K. and R. Lee, 2008. Land-based sources of nutrients to large marine ecosystems. Pp. 81–97 in: Sherman, K. and G. Hempel (eds.), *The UNEP Large Marine Ecosystems Report. A perspective on changing conditions in LMEs of the world's regional seas.* UNEP Regional Seas Reports and Studies No. 182, United Nations Environment Programme, Nairobi, Kenya.

UNESCO-SCOPE, 2007. Human alteration of the nitrogen cycle. Threats, benefits and opportunities. UNESCO-SCOPE Policy Briefs, April 2007, No. 4.

Habitat Loss

Burke, L., Y. Kura, K. Kassem, C. Ravenga, M. Spalding, and D. McAllister, 2000. *Pilot assessment of global ecosystems: Coastal Ecosystems.* World Resources Institute, 100 pp.

Javeline, D., J. J. Hellmann, R. Castro Cornejo, and G. Shufeldt, 2013. Expert opinion on climate change and threats to biodiversity. *BioScience*, vol. 63, no. 8, August, pp. 666–673.

Molnar, J. L., R. L. Gamboa, C. Revenga, and M. D. Spalding, 2008. Assessing the global threat of invasive species to marine biodiversity. *Frontiers in Ecology and the Environment*, vol. 6, pp. 485–492.

Polunin, N. V. (Ed.), 2008. *Aquatic ecosystems: trends and global prospects.* Cambridge University Press, 512 pp.

UNEP, 2006. *Marine and Coastal Ecosystems and Human Well-being: A Synthesis Report Based on the Findings of the Millennium Ecosystem Assessment.* United Nations Environment Programme, 64 pp.

The Fisheries Crisis

Arnason, R., K. Kelleher, and R. Willmann, 2009. *The Sunken Billions: The economic justification for fisheries reform.* The World Bank, Washington D.C., 100 pp.

Cheung, W. L. W., C. Close, V. W. Y. Lam, J. Sarmiento, K. Kearney, R. Watson, and D. Pauly, 2009. Projections of global marine biodiversity impacts under climate change scenarios. *Fish and Fisheries,* vol. 10, pp. 235–251.

Christiansen, J. S., C. W. Mecklenburg, and O. V. Karamushko, 2014. Arctic marine fishes and their fisheries in light of global change. *Global Change Biology,* vol. 20, pp. 352–359.

Daskalov, G. M., A. N. Grishin, S. Rodionov, and V. Mihneva, 2007. Trophic cascades triggered by overfishing reveal possible mechanisms of ecosystem shift regimes. *Proceedings of the National Academy of Sciences,* vol. 104, pp. 10518–10523.

Jennings, S., A. D. Smith, E. A. Fulton, and D. C. Smith, 2014. The ecosystem approach to fisheries: Management at the dynamic interface between biodiversity conservation and sustainable use. *Annals of the New York Academy of Sciences,* vol. 13221, pp. 48–60.

Worm, B., E. B. Barbier, N. Beaumont, et al., 2006. Impacts of biodiversity loss on ocean ecosystem services. *Science,* vol. 314, pp. 787–790.

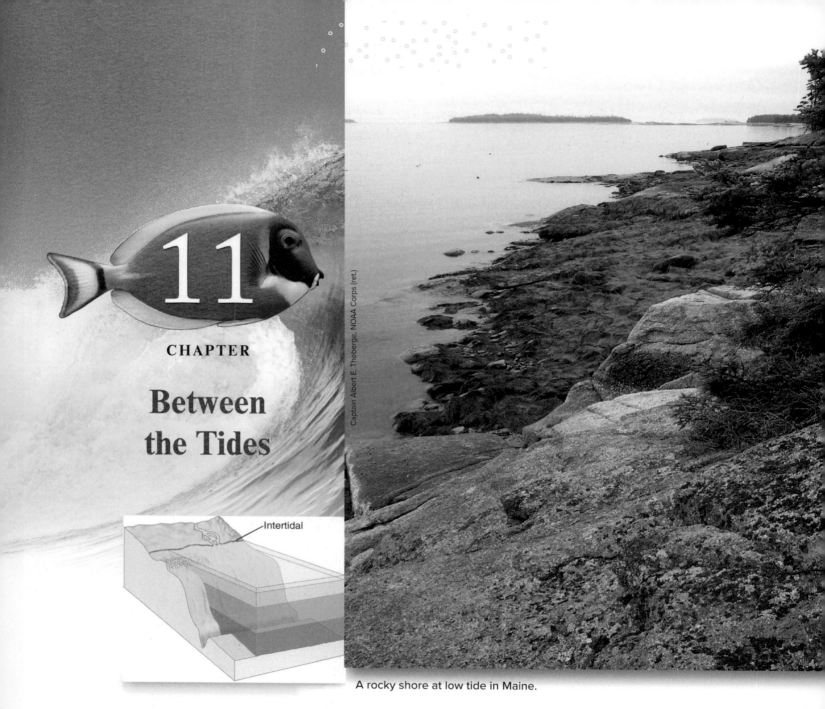

11 CHAPTER

Between the Tides

Captain Albert E. Theberge, NOAA Corps (ret.)

Intertidal

A rocky shore at low tide in Maine.

Of all the vast ocean, the **intertidal zone,** sometimes called the **littoral zone,** is the best known to marine biologists and the public alike. The intertidal zone is the narrow fringe along the shoreline that lies between the highest high and the lowest low tides. It is the only part of the marine world that we can experience firsthand without leaving our own natural element. We don't need a boat, and, at least at low tide, we can see it without a face mask and move through it without swim fins. More importantly from the scientist's point of view, we can work in the intertidal without cumbersome and expensive equipment, can return to the exact same place time after time, and it occupies a relatively small area. These aspects make the intertidal easier to study than many other marine environments. In some places crashing waves or rough terrain make it harder to work, and the time available is

often restricted by the tides, but in general intertidal communities are among the most-studied and best-understood of all marine communities. Although the intertidal zone constitutes only a tiny fraction of the marine environment, lessons learned there have added immensely to our understanding of ecology in general.

The intertidal is unique among marine environments in that it is regularly exposed to the air. Organisms in the intertidal must cope with this exposure, even if it means giving up characteristics that would be advantageous below the tides. Being out of the water and exposed to air is called **emersion**—the opposite of **immersion,** or being submerged.

The nature of intertidal **communities** depends critically on the type of bottom. The bottom—that is, the material on or in which an organism lives—is called the **substrate.** Hard, rocky bottoms are a

very different habitat than soft bottoms made of mud or sand. In this chapter we consider intertidal communities on both kinds of substrate, beginning with the rocky intertidal. The major coastal communities of North America are shown in Appendix D.

The intertidal zone is the shoreline between the high and low tide marks. It is the only part of the marine world that faces regular exposure to air, or emersion. Intertidal communities differ greatly depending on whether they have rocky or soft bottoms.

11.1 ROCKY SHORE INTERTIDAL COMMUNITIES

Rocky shores generally occur on steep coasts without large amounts of sediment. Such areas have often been recently uplifted or are still rising as a result of geological processes. These uplifted coasts have not had time to erode or accumulate sediment. The west coast of the Americas, for example, is mostly rocky because its **active margin** has been uplifted by geological processes. Eastern Canada and New England were covered by huge sheets of ice during the last ice age (see "The Geological History of Planet Earth," in 2.2). The ice sheets scraped sediment from the continental shelf, exposing the bare rock underneath. Under the tremendous weight of the ice, the coast actually sank partially down into the **mantle.** When the ice melted, the coast slowly rose, or rebounded, leaving a coastline of exposed rock. Sea level began to rise, however, and eventually sea level rise overtook the rebound of the coast. The sea flooded the rocky coast, forming a deeply sculptured shoreline north of Cape Cod. This is the only part of the Atlantic coast of North America that has much rocky shore. The southern Atlantic and Gulf coasts of North America are slowly sinking, or **subsiding,** weighed down by huge amounts of sediment that are accumulating on the **passive continental margin.** Rocky areas are uncommon on these coasts.

Not all rocky shores are formed by uplift. Waves and currents can carry sediments away, leaving bare rock behind. Similarly, outcrops of hard, erosion-resistant rock may be left behind after softer surrounding rocks erode away. Much of the coast of the island of Hawai'i is rocky because it is geologically very young. Formed by successive flows of lava into the sea, the coast hasn't had time to accumulate sediment. In fact, the coast is still being formed by periodic eruptions of the Kīlauea volcano (Fig. 11.1).

Rocky shores usually occur on recently uplifted or geologically young coasts or on coasts where erosion is removing sediments and soft rock. In North America, rocky shores are common on the west coast and on the east coast north of Cape Cod.

Chris Johns/Getty Images

FIGURE 11.1 Lava flows create new rocky shorelines on the island of Hawai'i.

It is difficult to burrow through rock, though rock-boring clams (*Zirfaea, Penitella*) can do it in soft rock like sandstone. Most rocky intertidal organisms live on the rock surface. Animals that live on the surface of the substrate—be it rock, sand, mud, or even other organisms—are called **epifauna.** Some epifauna move around on the rocks, but many are **sessile** and stay attached to the rock.

Living on the rock surface, organisms in the rocky intertidal are fully exposed to the elements. This subjects them to considerable physical stress.

Exposure at Low Tide

Low tide presents problems for rocky intertidal organisms. Left high and dry, they are exposed to the air, a harsher environment than water. The higher the organisms live in the intertidal, the more time they have to spend out of the water. The upper part of the intertidal zone is only immersed at the peak of high tide and then only briefly. The very upper edge may only be submerged during

Community All the different populations of organisms that live in a defined area.
• 4.2, Living Machinery; Table 4.1

Active Continental Margin One that is colliding with another plate and therefore has a lot of geological activity.
Passive Continental Margin One that is on the "trailing edge" of a continent and has little geological activity.
• 2.3, The Geological Provinces of the Ocean; Figure 2.23

Mantle One of the three main internal layers of the earth. The mantle lies between the crust, the outermost layer, and the core, the innermost layer.
• 2.1, The Water Planet; Figure 2.3

exceptionally high **spring tides.** The highest part of the "intertidal," in fact, is almost never immersed. It is kept wet by wave splash, and then only at high tide.

Organisms living low in the intertidal, on the other hand, are submerged most of the time and have to cope with emersion only for short periods or, at the lowermost edge, only at the most extreme low tides.

Emersion time, or time spent out of the water, gets longer the higher in the intertidal you go.

Water Loss Marine organisms tend to dry out, or **desiccate,** when exposed to air. To survive, intertidal organisms must be able to prevent desiccation, tolerate it, or both. Most cope with the problem of drying out in one of two basic ways: They either run and hide or they "clam up."

The run-and-hide strategy is simple. When the tide goes out, the organism goes somewhere wet until the tide comes back in. Shore crabs, hermit crabs, snails, and other rocky shore denizens are often seen huddled in moist, shady cavities or crevices in the rocks (Fig. 11.2). **Tide pools,** depressions in the rocks that hold seawater after the tide goes out, are also favorite places to hide (Fig. 11.3). Some areas are kept moist by spray from waves or by water that slowly leaks out of tide pools. The hiding place may even be provided by other organisms: Dense clumps of mussels, algae, and other organisms provide a moist, shady habitat where smaller inhabitants of the intertidal can hide.

Seaweeds and sessile animals can't run, but many can hide. Instead of moving to moist areas when the tide goes out, they only live where it stays wet (Fig. 11.4). This may be because the larvae or spores settle only in moist, shady places or because those that settle elsewhere dry out and die.

Organisms that use the "clam-up" strategy have some sort of protective covering, like a shell, to hold in water. Some, like barnacles and mussels, are completely enclosed and can seal in moisture simply by closing their shell. Others, like limpets, have an opening that cannot be completely shut. These organisms typically clamp themselves tightly to the rock to seal the opening. Some use mucus to make a better seal. They may also carve out shallow depressions, or "home scars," in the rock that make the seal more effective. They do this by scraping the rock with their shell or their **radula.** Every strategy has disadvantages, however: Clamming up makes it harder for animals to obtain oxygen and food.

Some organisms use a combination of strategies. The periwinkles (*Littorina*) shown in Figure 11.2, for example, clamp themselves to the rocks to seal in moisture. They can also seal off the opening of their shell by closing the **operculum,** a stiff plate that fits the opening like a door. Periwinkles

FIGURE 11.2 These periwinkles (*Littorina cincta*) get through low tide by clustering in a moist, shady crevice. They also seal against the rock to retain moisture.

FIGURE 11.3 When the tide goes out, a little bit of the ocean stays in this small tide pool in New Zealand. Organisms like these chitons (*Sypharochiton pelliserpentis*) and snails (*Diloma atrovirens*) move to such pools to stay moist. Even in tide pools, however, life can be tough. The water often undergoes drastic changes in salinity, oxygen content, and temperature.

Michael E. Huber

Michael E. Huber

FIGURE 11.4 These seaweeds can't move to moist depressions at low tide, so they live there permanently. They don't grow on the surrounding rock because it dries out.

FIGURE 11.5 The shell ridges on this tropical snail (*Nerita plicata*) help it stay cool by radiating heat. The snail's white color probably helps by reflecting sunlight.

Michael E. Huber

are still not immune to desiccation, so at low tide they congregate in moist, shady places, especially on hot days. Desiccation is a particular problem in hot, tropical climates, where intertidal organisms are often confined to tide pools or cool spots.

Finally, some intertidal organisms use neither the run-and-hide nor the "clam-up" approach. Instead, they simply tolerate drying out. Some intertidal **chitons** can survive the loss of 75% of the water in their tissues. Some intertidal seaweeds, such as rockweeds (*Fucus;* see Fig. 6.5), can withstand a water loss of as much as 90%, becoming almost completely dry and practically crunchy. They quickly recover when the tide comes in and wets their tissues.

> Some intertidal organisms avoid drying out by moving to or living in wet spots. Others can close a shell to retain water. Still others are able to dry out and then recover when the tide returns.

Temperature and Salinity Emersion creates problems other than desiccation for intertidal organisms. Sea temperatures are relatively constant and mild because of the high **heat capacity** of water, but air temperatures can be much more extreme. At low tide, intertidal organisms are at the mercy of the sun's heat or, in cold climes, the freezing cold of winter. Because tide pools are shallow, they too experience extreme temperatures, though usually not as extreme as air temperatures.

Most intertidal organisms can tolerate a wide temperature range. Tide-pool fishes, for example, are much more tolerant of extreme temperatures than related fishes living below the tides. Certain species of periwinkle from high in the intertidal show remarkable heat tolerance. One can survive temperatures as high as 49 °C (120 °F) in the laboratory.

Organisms deal with temperature extremes in ways besides simply being tough. Those that move to moist hiding places to avoid drying out, for example, also avoid high temperatures because such places are usually cool as well as damp. Some snails, especially in the tropics, have pronounced ridges on their shells. Like the fins on a car radiator, these ridges help the snail lose heat (Fig. 11.5).

The color of a snail's shell can also help it tolerate high temperatures. Snails that are regularly subjected to extreme high temperatures tend to be light in color. The light color helps reflect sunlight. On Atlantic shores, for example, the dog whelk or dog winkle (*Nucella lapillus*) has two color forms: white-shelled and brown-shelled. On shores with heavy wave action, brown whelks predominate. On sheltered shores the white form is most common. The difference appears to be related to temperature. Brown whelks absorb more heat than white ones and die in temperatures that don't harm the white snails. On the exposed coasts where brown snails live, there are dense mussel beds, which stay moist and relatively cool. Wave spray also helps cool the snails. Sheltered coasts have few mussels and little wave spray so they are hotter, and white whelks have an advantage.

Turban snails (*Lunella coreensis*) on intertidal shores in Japan take things even further. They grow dense mats of a green alga (*Pseudocladophora conchopheria*) on their shells. The algal mats retain moisture and keep the snails cool.

Spring Tides Tides with a large range that occurs around times of the full or new moon.
Tidal Range The difference in height between a high tide and the next low tide.
• 3.3, Waves and Tides

Radula A rasping ribbon of small teeth that is present in most molluscs.
• 7.5, Molluscs: The Successful Soft Body; Figure 7.23 inset

Chitons Molluscs whose shells consist of eight overlapping plates on their upper, or dorsal, surface.
• 7.5, Molluscs: The Successful Soft Body

Heat Capacity The amount of heat energy required to raise the temperature of a substance; also, its ability to hold heat. Water has one of the highest heat capacities of any natural substance.
• 3.1, The Waters of the Ocean

Intertidal organisms also have to deal with extremes of salinity. When it rains, they have to endure freshwater, which is fatal to most marine organisms. Many simply keep the freshwater out by closing their shells—another benefit of the "clam-up" strategy. Even so, rainstorms during low tide sometimes cause the mass mortality of intertidal organisms. Tide-pool residents, too, face extreme variation in salinity. Rain dilutes the pools and lowers their salinity, while on hot days the salinity can increase markedly because of evaporation. To cope, most tide-pool organisms tolerate a wide range of salinity as well as temperature. They may also burrow or reduce their activity to ride out extreme conditions and wait for high tide.

> The intertidal has more extremes of temperature and salinity than other marine environments because it is regularly exposed to the air. Intertidal organisms have evolved various mechanisms to avoid or endure these extremes.

Restriction of Feeding Because little sediment accumulates in the rocky intertidal, **deposit feeders** are uncommon. Most of the sessile animals are **filter feeders** that have to be immersed in the water to filter it, and therefore can't feed at low tide. Even animals that are not filter feeders have trouble feeding at low tide. Many mobile animals in the rocky intertidal are grazers that scrape algae, bacteria, and other food from the rocks. Others feed on pieces of seaweed and other large **detritus** that drift in with the tide. Some are predators and move over the rocks in search of prey. When mobile animals seek shelter or clamp to the rocks to avoid water loss at low tide they can't move around to find food.

Being unable to feed when the tide is out is not much of a problem for animals low in the intertidal. They are immersed most of the day and have plenty of time to feed. Higher in the intertidal, however, animals may not be underwater long enough to get adequate feeding time. This can cause them to grow more slowly or even prevent them from living in the high intertidal at all.

> Many intertidal animals are unable to feed when exposed at low tide. This may prevent them from living higher on the shore than they do.

The Power of the Sea

Even when the tide is in, life in the rocky intertidal is not easy. Waves expend tremendous energy as they crash on the shore. Rocky intertidal organisms are exposed to the full power of the sea (Fig. 11.6).

The Distribution of Wave Energy Along the Shore The impact of waves varies along the shoreline. Some areas are sheltered from the surf, others are fully exposed. Enclosed bays, for example, are usually protected from wave action, which is why they are used for harbors. It is not always easy to predict which areas will be sheltered and which exposed, however.

Recall from Chapter 3 (see "Waves," in 3.3) that when a wave enters shallow water it "feels" the bottom and slows down. Thus, the same wave travels faster in deep than in shallow water.

Waves almost never approach the shore straight on, but instead come in at an angle (Fig. 11.7). One "end" of the wave reaches

FIGURE 11.6 Ocean waves expend tremendous energy when they break on the shore.

FIGURE 11.7 Nearly all waves approach the coast at an angle. As a result, they refract, or bend toward the coast. By the time the waves break they are almost parallel to shore.

shallow water before the other. The end in shallow water slows down, but the end in deep water continues to travel at its original speed. As a result, the wave bends, just as a two-wheeled cart will turn to one side if one wheel sticks. This bending, called **refraction,** causes the waves to become nearly parallel to the shore (Fig. 11.8). They never quite get perfectly parallel, however.

Refraction produces complex wave patterns when the coast is not a straight line. In particular, wave action tends to focus at headlands (Fig. 11.9). Bays, even if they are not physically sheltered from incoming waves, generally get less wave energy.

> Incoming waves refract, or bend, to become more parallel to the shore. This increases wave impact at headlands and decreases it in bays.

FIGURE 11.8 Wave refraction. A series of waves approaches the coast at an angle; the numbered lines represent the wave crests. The left end of wave 1 is in shallower water than the right end, so the left end slows down. The right end catches up, and the wave will bend a bit to the left. The waves closer to shore continue to experience this effect, each becoming more parallel to shore. Wave refraction greatly influences the way wave energy affects intertidal environments.

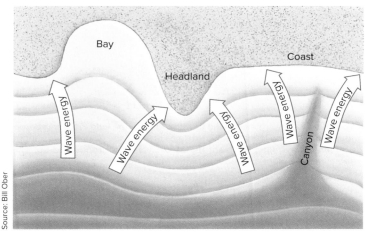

FIGURE 11.9 Both the coastline and bottom affect wave refraction. For example, an incoming wave first hits shallow water straight out from a headland. This part of the wave slows, lagging behind the sections on either side. As a result the wave wraps around the headland, which gets most of the wave energy. The opposite occurs in bays or over submarine canyons: The central part of the wave is in the deepest water, and the wave turns off to the sides. This deflects wave energy away from the bay or the shore behind the canyon. Variation in wave energy along the shore due to refraction and other factors greatly influences the natural of intertidal communities.

Offshore bottom features can influence the effect of waves on the coast. Submarine canyons, for example, may cause wave refraction. Also, waves often break on reefs or sand bars and expend their energy before they reach the shore.

The result of all this is that there is tremendous variation in the amount of wave energy along the shore. Exposure to waves strongly affects intertidal organisms (Fig. 11.10). The complex patterns of water circulation in the surf zone affect larval settlement, food availability, and many other factors, and are responsible for much of the variation in rocky intertidal communities.

Coping with Wave Shock The force of striking waves, or **wave shock,** strongly affects intertidal organisms. Some intertidal organisms simply can't withstand wave shock and are only found in sheltered locations. Such species are often delicate or unable to keep a firm grip on the rocks. Because sediment tends to accumulate in the sheltered spots where they live, these organisms often cope with sedimentation better than those that live on exposed shores.

Organisms exposed to the waves need some way to deal with wave shock. Sessile organisms attach firmly to the rocks to keep from being washed away. Seaweeds use their **holdfasts** or simply encrust on the rocks. Barnacles secure themselves with a glue so strong that several companies have tried to duplicate it. Mussels attach with their **byssal threads,** strong fibers made of protein that the mussel produces with a special gland in its foot. These threads form the mussel's "beard." Though we usually think of them as stationary, mussels can slowly move around by putting out new threads and detaching old ones.

Mobile animals, too, often cling strongly to the rocks. Limpets and chitons, for example, use their muscular foot like a powerful suction cup. Gobies (*Gobius*) and clingfishes (*Gobiesox*), which are common tide-pool fishes, also have suction cups, formed by modified pelvic fins. The fishes don't stick as strongly as limpets, but unlike limpets they can swim home if dislodged. Intertidal fishes also tend to lack **swim bladders,** so they sink and stay on the bottom.

Rather than resist the waves, many intertidal animals find shelter when wave action gets too strong. This is especially true of highly mobile animals like shore crabs (*Pachygrapsus, Grapsus*). In fact, there is a trade-off between being able to move fast and having a strong grip on the rocks. Holding on tightly slows an animal down. Many intertidal snails are easier to knock off the rocks when they are moving than when they stop and clamp down. Not surprisingly, they usually stop and hold on when wave action is heavy. This limits their feeding, which prevents some species from living in highly exposed areas.

Intertidal organisms have other adaptations to withstand wave shock. Animals in exposed locations tend to have thicker shells than those in sheltered ones. A compact shape can also help reduce the impact of the waves (Fig. 11.11). Many intertidal animals, including barnacles, mussels, limpets, and chitons, have low profiles close to the rocks. Colonies of the sand-castle worm *Phragmatopoma*

Deposit Feeders Animals that eat organic matter that settles to the bottom.

Filter Feeders Animals that actively filter food particles from the water. They are a common type of *suspension feeder*.

• 7.1, Sponges; Figure 7.4

Detritus Particles of dead organic matter.

• 10.3, The Flow of Energy and Materials

Holdfast A structure used by many seaweeds to anchor themselves to the bottom.

• 6.1, Multicellular Algae: The Seaweeds; Figure 6.1

Swim Bladder A gas-filled sac that provides many bony fishes with buoyancy.

• 8.2, Types of Fishes; Figure 8.12*b*

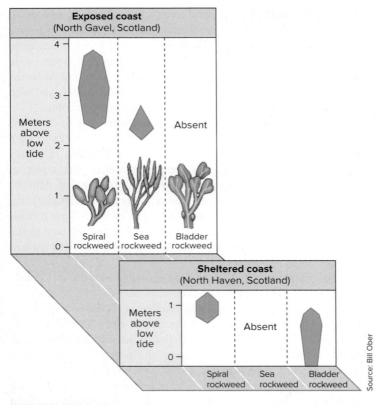

FIGURE 11.10 Even closely related species may be affected differently by wave exposure. On the Scottish coast the bladder rockweed (*Fucus vesiculosus*) occurs only in sheltered locations, the sea rockweed (*F. inflatus*) only at exposed sites. The spiral rockweed (*F. spiralis;* see Fig. 6.5) occurs in both environments but lives higher up on the exposed coast. This is probably because wave splash reaches higher at exposed locations. Such differences may be caused by the effects of waves on competitors or predators rather than the direct effects of wave shock. Diagrams like this are known as "kite diagrams." A wider blue "kite" indicates that more individuals of that species are at that elevation above low tide.

FIGURE 11.11 The giant green sea anemone (*Anthopleura xanthogrammica;* see Fig. 11.25) lives low in the intertidal zone on the Pacific coast of North America. (*a*) In sheltered locations the anemone grows relatively tall. (*b*) Anemones from areas with heavy wave action are much shorter. This reduces the body area that is exposed and allows more water to slide over the top of the anemone. In other words, drag is reduced.

FIGURE 11.12 Organisms like this brown alga, the kelp *Eisenia arborea,* withstand waves by being flexible. (*a*) In calm water the plant stands upright. (*b*) When a wave hits, the plant bends over and the fronds fold up. This streamlines the plant and reduces water resistance.

californica provide another example of the importance of shape. These colonies are not especially strong and are easily crushed, but they can withstand considerable wave shock because of their domed shape. Some organisms, especially seaweeds, are flexible and can "go with the flow" (Fig. 11.12). There may also be safety in numbers (Fig. 11.13).

> Organisms on exposed coasts deal with wave shock in different ways, including strong attachments, thickened shells, low profiles, and flexibility.

Even the firmest grip on the rocks is of little help if the wave smashes a boulder or drifting log onto the rocks, crushing whatever is there. Waves can also turn rocks over, even large boulders. When this happens the organisms on top of the rock may be smashed or buried, and sunlight for any algae is blocked. The underside of the rock supports different organisms than the top, and these fare no better. Once nestled snugly under the rock, they are suddenly exposed to sun and waves, not to mention hungry predators. The organisms on both the top and bottom of overturned rocks usually die. People can have the same effect. If you happen to go looking

under rocks at the shore, don't forget to turn them back over the way you found them.

Because wave action varies from place to place, and organisms differ in how waves affect them, sheltered and exposed areas have very distinct communities. Marine communities in quiet bays are much different from those at exposed headlands. The effect of wave action can also be seen on a smaller scale. The organisms in a sheltered crevice usually differ from those on exposed rocks nearby, for example, and variation in surf zone circulation produces considerable variation from place to place, even on exposed shores.

The Battle for Space

Despite the intertidal zone's physical extremes, there is usually plenty of food. The high light levels and nutrient-rich coastal waters supply the basic requirements for **photosynthesis,** so algae grow vigorously. High tide brings in abundant plankton as well as drifting seaweed fragments and other detritus (Fig. 11.14), which is actually the most important food source in many rocky intertidal communities. Limpets, snails, and other small, slow-moving animals that graze algae from the rocks are often limited by food

availability because they are unable to range over a wide enough area. For most other intertidal animals, particularly sessile ones, food is not usually a **limiting resource,** though feeding time can be restricted near the upper end of a species' range.

Unoccupied space, on the other hand, is often in short supply. Sessile organisms need a permanent place to attach. Often there isn't enough room to go around, and the availability of space commonly limits rocky intertidal populations. Nearly all the space in the intertidal is usually occupied (Fig. 11.15), except on some tropical shores where the intense sun and high temperatures prevent anything from growing on the rocks. When habitable space does open up, colonizers usually quickly take it over. Space is so scarce that organisms often attach to other organisms instead of the rocks.

(a) (b) (c)

Source: Bill Ober

FIGURE 11.13 Intertidal animals may get some protection from wave shock by growing in dense groups. (*a*) Mussels (*Mytilus*) growing as isolated individuals, for example, get the full impact of the waves. Small individuals, which are closer to the rock, may be able to hang on but larger mussels, with more exposed surface area, can be torn away. (*b*) When the mussels grow in dense clusters, the waves do not get a direct shot at any of them but slide over the tops. Eddies created as the water flows over the mussels may also hold plankton near the mussels, increasing their food supply, and the dense clumps retain moisture at low tide. (*c*) If the clumps get *too* dense, however, many of the mussels attach to other mussels instead of the rock. Waves can cause more strain than the mussels on the bottom can bear and rip away entire clumps. This opens up space for other organisms, including other mussels.

Rocky intertidal populations are often limited by space, not food or nutrients.

Not surprisingly, competition for space is a dominant ecological factor in the rocky intertidal. There are many ways to compete for space. One is to be the first to get to open spots. For intertidal organisms, this means having an effective way

Photosynthesis

$CO_2 + H_2O + \text{sun energy} \rightarrow \text{organic matter} + O_2$
$\qquad\qquad\qquad\qquad\qquad\qquad\qquad$ (glucose)

• 4.1, The Ingredients of Life

Limiting Resource A resource that is so scarce that it restricts the growth of a population.

• 10.1, The Organization of Communities

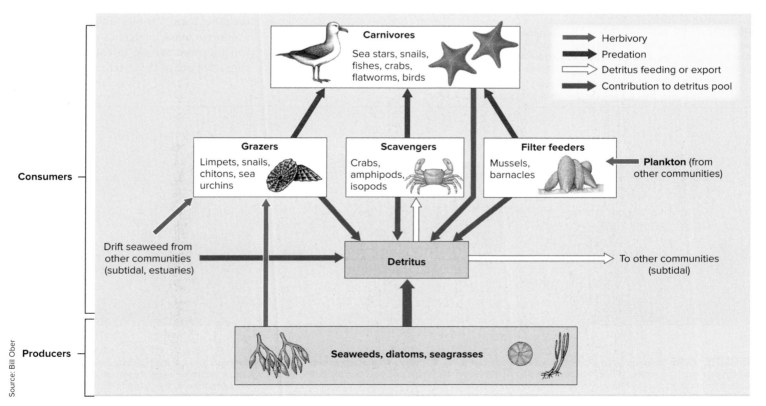

FIGURE 11.14 A generalized food web on a rocky shore.

Source: Bill Ober

of **dispersal.** Organisms that depend on being the first to occupy new patches of open space must be good at getting themselves or their offspring from place to place. Most rocky intertidal species disperse via larvae or spores, which settle on the rocks to colonize open space. Having taken over the space, the organism must either be good at holding on to it or be able to reproduce rapidly to disperse its young to the next opening. Both strategies are used in the intertidal.

Rather than colonizing open patches, some intertidal organisms take over space that is already occupied. Barnacles, for instance, undercut their neighbors, loosening them from the rock. Owl limpets (*Lottia gigantea*) maintain a territory by bulldozing out intruders. Less forceful methods also work. Many intertidal organisms simply grow over their competitors, making them vulnerable to waves (Fig. 11.16), smothering them, or in the case of seaweeds, blocking precious sunlight. Some species grow in colonies, gradually increasing the amount of space they hold as the colony grows.

Two species of mussel provide an example of how competition and physical factors can interact to determine the distribution of organisms. On the west coast of North America the blue mussel (*Mytilus galloprovincialis;* also called the Mediterranean or bay mussel) is found mainly in sheltered locations, whereas the California mussel (*M. californianus*) is found on the wave-exposed open coast. As you might expect, the California mussel has a thicker shell and attaches more strongly to the rocks than the blue mussel. On the other hand, the blue mussel does just fine on open coasts as long as the California mussel is absent. The blue mussel is apparently rare on open coasts not because it can't take the waves but because it is out-competed by the California mussel. The California mussel, with its thicker shell, crushes the blue mussel when the two grow together. On the other hand, the blue mussel, unlike the California mussel, tolerates a lot of silt and can therefore survive in calm bays where silt settles out of the water.

FIGURE 11.15 Most organisms in the intertidal zone live attached to the rocks, and most of the available space is occupied. This little patch of rock supports two species of mussels and two of barnacles, plus limpets and sea anemones. What little open space there is doesn't last for long: A small bare patch (arrow) has already been colonized by newly settled barnacles.

FIGURE 11.16 The sea palm (*Postelsia palmaeformis;* see Fig. 6.7) takes advantage of wave action to compete for space. (*a*) Adults literally drip spores, which develop into young sporelings near the parent. (*b*) When the space below is occupied, the sporelings grow on these competitors, which are eventually pulled from the rocks. (*c*) This clears space for a new generation of young sea palms. Sea palms are typically seen from early spring to early winter; though they can withstand considerable wave shock they are usually wiped out by winter storms and must recruit to available space each year.

Vertical Zonation of Rocky Shores

Rocky intertidal communities vary markedly from place to place, but there is one feature that is remarkably common. The rocky intertidal community is usually divided into distinct bands, or **zones,** at characteristic heights in the intertidal (Figs. 11.17 and 11.18). Thus, a given species is usually found only within a particular vertical range, and not throughout the intertidal. Biologists call this pattern of banding **vertical zonation.**

When the shore consists of an evenly sloping rock face, the zones are often sharply defined belts that can be easily distinguished by the colors of the organisms (Fig. 11.17). Many shores are much more uneven, with scattered boulders, channels, and gullies. Zonation may not be as obvious in such areas, but it usually exists nonetheless.

Marine biologists have studied the causes of vertical zonation in great detail. Though there is still much to be learned, we know that zonation results from the complex interaction of physical and biological factors. A general rule is that the upper limit at which a species occurs is usually determined mainly by physical factors, whereas the lower limit is usually determined by biological factors, especially predation and competition.

Michael E. Huber

FIGURE 11.17 Intertidal organisms often form distinct bands, or zones, at different heights on the shore (see Fig. 5.14). The white band at the top of the intertidal is dominated by a lichen (*Pertusaria*) and is rarely if ever submerged. It gets it moisture from wave splash. Just below that is a thin black zone dominated by another lichen (*Verrucaria*). The brown below that is dominated by barnacles (*Austrominius*) and patches of a red alga (*Apophlaea*). The dark zone at the water's edge is dominated by mussels (*Mytilus, Perna*) and several species of seaweed.

> Most rocky shores have a distinct pattern of vertical zonation. The upper limit of a zone is often set by physical factors, the lower limit by biological ones.

This rule is a useful starting point in understanding the causes of vertical zonation. As with all generalizations, however, there are exceptions. For example, zonation can be produced if the larvae of a species settle only at a particular height on the shore. A species might be perfectly able to live higher on the shore than it does, but is outcompeted by species even better adapted to those conditions. One cannot just *assume* that the upper limit of a certain species is set by physical factors. Instead, this hypothesis must be *tested* by experiment (see Box 11.1, "Transplantation, Removal, and Caging Experiments"). Furthermore, different factors often interact to determine the limits, and sometimes the line between physical and biological factors is fuzzy. As noted previously, for example, some filter feeders do not live high in the intertidal because they are not submerged long enough to feed. Is this upper limit due to a physical factor—emersion by the tide—or a biological one—feeding?

Many rocky shores around the world show a pattern of vertical zonation that is quite similar in its general nature but highly variable in its particulars. Biologists studying a certain area sometimes name the zones after the dominant organism, as in the "limpet zone" or the "mussel zone." These zones actually contain a variety of organisms. The mussel zone, for example, is also home to worms, crabs, snails, seaweeds, and many other species. Also, the specific organisms found in the intertidal vary from place to place. On the east coast of North America, for example, the mussel zone is often replaced by a rockweed zone.

Instead of naming the zones after organisms, we will simply divide the intertidal into the *upper, middle,* and *lower zones.* While not especially creative, at least these names apply everywhere!

Bear in mind that the following sections are general descriptions of "typical" intertidal communities and don't apply exactly to any particular place. Furthermore, the boundaries between zones are not absolute and some species occur in more than one zone. The next time you go to the shore, think about how these descriptions apply. Perhaps more importantly, think about how the place you visit is different. What might cause the differences?

The Upper Intertidal Seldom submerged, the inhabitants of the upper intertidal zone must be well adapted to withstand exposure to air. This zone actually lies mostly above the high tide mark, and the organisms are wetted mainly by wave splash and spray. It is often called the "splash zone." On exposed coasts with more wave splash the upper intertidal extends farther above the high tide line than on sheltered coasts.

In many places, **lichens** (*Verrucaria*) form black, tar-like blotches on rocks in the upper intertidal. The fungus part of the lichen soaks up water, storing it for long dry periods. Dark green mats of cyanobacteria (*Calothrix*) are abundant. They are protected from drying out by a jelly-like coating and have the advantage of being able to **fix nitrogen** from the air. Small tufts of a filamentous green alga (*Ulothrix*) that is also resistant to drying out may spring up here and there. Other green (*Prasiola, Enteromorpha*), brown

Lichens Close, *mutualistic* associations between fungi and microscopic algae; mutualism is a type of *symbiosis*.
- 5.5, Fungi; and 10.1, The Organization of Communities

Nitrogen Fixation Conversion of nitrogen gas (N$_2$) into nitrogen compounds that can be used by primary producers as nutrients.
- 5.2, Prokaryotes; Table 5.1

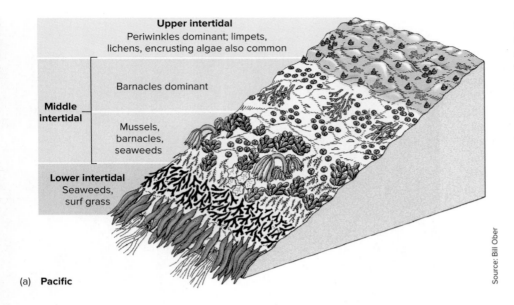

(a) **Pacific**

Upper intertidal
Periwinkles dominant; limpets,
lichens, encrusting algae also common

Barnacles dominant

Middle intertidal

Mussels,
barnacles,
seaweeds

Lower intertidal
Seaweeds,
surf grass

Source: Bill Ober

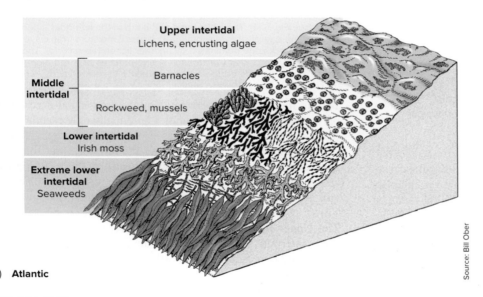

(b) **Atlantic**

Upper intertidal
Lichens, encrusting algae

Middle intertidal

Barnacles

Rockweed, mussels

Lower intertidal
Irish moss

Extreme lower
intertidal
Seaweeds

Source: Bill Ober

FIGURE 11.18 Generalized patterns of zonation on temperate rocky shores on the (*a*) Pacific and (*b*) Atlantic coasts of North America. At any particular place on the coast the exact pattern will probably be different. Only organisms that characteristically dominate the various zones are shown. Hundreds of other species live in the intertidal.

algae off the rocks with their claws, but also eat animals and detritus. Sea lice or sea roaches (*Ligia;* see Fig. 7.35) breathe air and live above the intertidal, but move down into the upper intertidal at low tide.

Most of the upper intertidal zone lies above the high tide line and is kept wet by wave splash. The dominant primary producers are lichens and cyanobacteria. Periwinkles are the most common animals.

Few marine predators can reach the upper intertidal. Shore crabs occasionally eat periwinkles and limpets. From time to time predatory snails, such as unicorn shells (*Acanthina*), also venture into the splash zone. On the other hand, land predators often visit the upper intertidal. Birds such as oyster-catchers (*Haematopus*) eat large numbers of limpets and snails. Raccoons, rats, and other land animals are also known to enjoy these tasty molluscs, as do people in most of the world.

The Middle Intertidal Unlike the upper intertidal, which is affected only by wave splash and the highest spring tides, the middle intertidal is regularly submerged and then uncovered by the tides. A **diurnal tide** exposes the organisms once a day, a **semidiurnal tide** twice (see Fig. 3.34). If the tide is **mixed,** the lower of the two successive high tides may not submerge the high part of the zone, and the higher of the two lows may not expose the bottom part. Thus, even in places with a semidiurnal tide, parts of the middle intertidal zone may be submerged or exposed only once a day. With so much variation in emersion time, different heights within the middle intertidal often support different organisms. In other words, the middle intertidal is often made up of several separate vertical zones.

(*Pelvetia*), and red (*Porphyra, Bangia*) algae are occasionally found in the upper intertidal, usually in moist spots.

Large numbers of periwinkles (*Littorina*) graze on the algae, scraping it from the rocks with their radulas. Periwinkles are so abundant that the upper intertidal is often called the "*Littorina* zone." Not all of the many species of periwinkles live high in the intertidal, but those that do are well adapted to it. They can breathe air like land snails, live out of water for months, and tolerate extreme temperatures. They do have limits, however, and may have to seek shelter on hot days (see Fig. 11.2).

Limpets (*Acmaea, Lottia*) also live in the high intertidal. Like periwinkles, limpets are hardy grazers. Shore crabs occasionally venture into the upper intertidal, scurrying over the rocks. They mostly scrape

The upper boundary of the middle intertidal is almost always marked by a band of barnacles. In many places at least two species of barnacles, such as little gray (*Chthamalus*) and rock barnacles (*Balanus, Semibalanus*), form distinct bands, with little gray barnacles living higher up.

Experiments (see Box 11.1, "Transplantation, Removal, and Caging Experiments") show that this zonation results from a combination of the barnacles' larval settlement pattern, desiccation tolerance, competition, and predation (Fig. 11.19). The larvae of both species settle over a wider range than adults occupy. The upper limit of both species appears to result from emersion, because larvae that settle too high in the intertidal die. Little gray barnacles tolerate drying better than rock barnacles and can therefore live higher up. At lower levels,

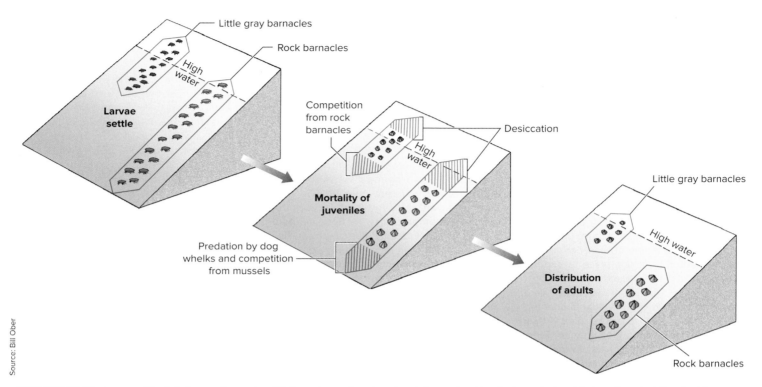

Source: Bill Ober

FIGURE 11.19 Larvae of both little gray barnacles (*Chthamalus stellatus*) and rock barnacles (*Semibalanus balanoides*) settle out of the plankton over a wider range of the intertidal zone than is occupied by adults. At the upper edge, young barnacles dry out and die. Little gray barnacles are more resistant so they can live higher on the shore. Little gray barnacles that settle where the rock barnacles can survive, however, are outcompeted. The lower edge of the rock barnacle zone occurs where predatory snails, called dog whelks (*Nucella lapillus*), can easily reach them. In some places, competition from mussels also helps determine the lower limit.

where the rock barnacles can survive, they outcompete the little gray barnacles. Adult little gray barnacles, then, live perched in a narrow band above their competitors where they can survive emersion.

The lower limit of rock barnacles, like that of little gray barnacles, is determined by biological factors, in this case both predation and competition. Dog whelks are major predators of barnacles (Fig. 11.20). These snails use their radula to drill holes in barnacles' shells. They also secrete chemicals that soften the shells. If protected from the snails by wire cages, rock barnacles flourish below their normal limit. Unprotected barnacles, however, suffer heavy losses to snail predation. The only thing that saves the rock barnacles is that the whelks do most of their feeding during high tide. When emersed they lose a lot of water if they move around hunting barnacles, so to avoid desiccation at low tide they cease feeding or move lower in the intertidal.

In the zone where rock barnacles are common, the snails don't have enough time at high tide to eat the barnacles. Sea stars, which also eat barnacles, have the same problem as the snails. Rock barnacles also face competition from mussels. In some places the lower limit of barnacles is set not by whelk predation but by competition with mussels. Like the little gray barnacles, the rock barnacles persist in a narrow zone between the level where they desiccate and die and the level where their enemies can reach them.

Acorn barnacles usually occupy the top of the middle intertidal zone. Their upper limit is determined by how high they can live without drying out. Their lower limit is set by competition with other barnacles or mussels or by snail or sea star predators.

Many other organisms live in the middle intertidal among or below the barnacles. Which organisms are present, how many there are, and where they occur all depend on the unique combination of physical and biological factors at that site. The pattern of the tides, steepness of the shore, exposure to waves, and local weather all have an influence. Predation, competition, and larval settlement patterns are almost always involved. Considering all the possible ways in which these factors might interact gives you some idea of how complicated the story can be.

Depending on all these factors, mussels (*Mytilus*), gooseneck barnacles (*Pollicipes*), and brown seaweeds, particularly rockweeds (*Fucus, Pelvetia*), often dominate the middle intertidal below the barnacles. Many rockweeds have air bladders called **pneumatocysts** that float their fronds closer to the light. They sometimes form a thick canopy that shelters many smaller organisms. If the rockweeds are experimentally removed, the algae and animals under the canopy typically bleach in the sun and die back, but small filamentous

Primary Producers Organisms that manufacture organic matter from carbon dioxide (CO_2), usually by photosynthesis.
• 4.1, The Ingredients of Life

Semidiurnal Tide A tidal pattern with two high and two low tides each day.
Diurnal Tide A tidal pattern with one high and one low tide each day.
Mixed Tide A tidal pattern in which two successive high tides are of different heights.
• 3.3, Waves and Tides; Figure 3.34

Box 11.1 Transplantation, Removal, and Caging Experiments

In the intertidal zone, a rule of thumb is that physical factors, especially desiccation, limit how high in the intertidal a species can live. Biological factors such as competition and predation set the lower limit. Where does this rule of thumb come from? How can you tell why a certain species is found where it is?

Like many scientific questions, this one is best answered by experiment—altering natural conditions to see what happens. Three general types of experiments have been particularly effective. In one of these, organisms are **transplanted** from one place to another to see if they can survive under the new conditions. In one experiment barnacles were grown on panels at various heights on intertidal pier pilings. The barnacles died if they were moved higher than they normally lived. Tests showed they had lost a lot of water, and the cause of death was drying out at low tide. Thus, the barnacles cannot survive the conditions above their normal range. Their upper limit is set by a physical factor—desiccation.

Transplantation can also tell us when physical factors are not important. When barnacles are transplanted lower in the intertidal than they normally live, they do just fine if protected from enemies. The same is true of many other intertidal species, including certain mussels, snails, and seaweeds. In fact, some actually grow faster when moved below their normal range. Their lower limit, therefore, is not set by the physical environment.

If organisms can live lower in the intertidal, why don't they? Experiments show competitors or predators often set a species' lower boundary. In **removal experiments,** one species is removed from an area, which is then compared to an untouched **control** area. A classic experiment examined competition between rock barnacles (*Semibalanus balanoides*) and little gray barnacles (*Chthamalus stellatus*), which normally live higher on the shore (see Fig. 11.19). Rocks with newly settled juveniles of both species were collected and placed at different heights. The rock barnacles were removed from some of the rocks, while other rocks were not disturbed.

High in the intertidal, little gray barnacles survived better than rock barnacles because they tolerate drying better. Lower in the intertidal, little gray barnacles do fine as long as the rock barnacles are removed, but when the two species grow together the bigger, faster-growing rock barnacles crush, undercut, or smother the little gray barnacles. The lower limit of little gray barnacles is determined by a biological factor: competition.

Removal experiments also show the importance of grazing and predation. When limpets are removed from test areas, for example, a profusion of seaweeds usually results. When limpets are present the algae cannot establish because limpets scrape young algae off the rocks. If the seaweeds get a foothold, however, they are often able to persist because adult seaweeds can stand up to the grazing limpets. Another removal experiment, involving a sea star, is summarized in Figure 11.21.

It may be time-consuming, difficult, or downright impossible to remove all the organisms of interest from an area, or they may quickly move back after removal. Instead, **caging experiments** can be used to keep them out. On the Channel Islands off the coast of Southern California, the intertidal is covered by a carpet of seaweeds. When marine biologists discovered that large numbers of spiny lobsters (*Panulirus interruptus*) move into the intertidal during nighttime high tides, they wondered what effect the lobsters were having. They installed cages to keep the lobsters out. To make sure that the seaweed wasn't affected by the shade of the cages, they also installed control cages that had roofs but no ends, allowing lobsters to enter unimpeded. Seaweeds continued to flourish in these control areas and in adjacent open areas, but within the fully enclosed cages the seaweeds were soon replaced by mussels. This demonstrated that seaweeds dominate because the lobsters eat the mussels, which are superior competitors.

Caging experiments don't have to use actual cages, just some sort of barrier. Strips of artificial turf, for example, will keep out sea stars, limpets, and snails, which can't crawl over the turf. Cages can also be used to hold animals inside an area, rather than keep them out, to determine their effects.

The ochre sea star (*Pisaster ochraceus*) has been shown to be a keystone predator in the rocky intertidal on the Pacific coast of North America, in particular preventing the competitively superior California blue mussel (*Mytilus californianus*) from dominating space in the lower intertidal. But in recent years disease has caused mass sea star mortality (see Box 11.2, "Sea Star Wasting Disease"), with possible flow-on effects on the entire intertidal ecosystem. Researchers combined removal and caging experiments, removing viable sea stars from the study area and installing cages that prevented predatory crabs (*Cancer,*

Carlos Robles

These cages were used in California to test the effects of spiny lobsters (*Panulirus interruptus*) in the intertidal zone. The lower cages have closed ends to keep lobsters out. The upper cages have open ends to allow lobsters free access and are controls for the effects of the cages themselves.

Carlos Robles

The mussels in this dark patch have taken over the space inside a closed cage, which was removed for the photo. The surrounding rock is dominated by red algae, as are areas inside open-ended cages, not visible in this photo. The conclusion of the experiment is that mussels would dominate the community if not eaten by lobsters.

Romaleon) from getting to the mussels. In the lower intertidal, mussels protected by cages flourished, but those outside suffered heavy crab predation. The cages made no difference higher in the intertidal, probably because the crabs could not move that high up to feed. The experiment showed that at least in some situations predators besides *Pisaster* can prevent mussels from taking over.

Caging experiments have also been used to study the effects of physical rather than biological factors. Efforts to restore degraded seagrass beds in the Netherlands have met with limited success because many transplanted seagrass seedlings do not survive. To help understand why, researchers enclosed plots in cages that reduced wave and current energy in the plots. Seedlings in these areas survived much better, indicating that protection from the physical effects of waves and currents can improve seagrass transplantation success.

Stephen P. Parker/Science Source

FIGURE 11.20 A dog whelk (*Nucella lapillus*) preying on rock barnacles (*Semibalanus balanoides*) on a rocky shore in Maine. In moist conditions like these the whelk is able to feed at low tide, but it will cease activity if the rock dries out.

and branching alga often form a thick algal turf. The turf makes it more difficult for new rockweeds to settle, and recovery of the canopy and its associated community may take as long as a decade.

Mussels are especially common on stormy, exposed shores. They cannot live as high on the shore as barnacles, because they dry out and also because at high levels they don't spend enough time underwater to filter feed. At heights where they *can* live, however, mussels are dominant competitors, smothering or crowding out other organisms.

Sea stars (*Pisaster, Asterias*) are voracious mussel predators. Sea stars do not force open a mussel's shell to eat it. Instead, they insert their stomach into the shell and begin digesting the mussel from the inside. Sea stars need only a tiny crack to insert their stomach—only 0.2 mm (0.008 in) for the ochre sea star (*Pisaster ochraceus;* see Fig. 11.25). The shell opens after the mussel is weakened.

Sea stars don't tolerate desiccation very well and need to be underwater to search for food, though they may finish a meal after the tide goes out. In the lower part of the middle intertidal this is no problem, and sea stars take a heavy toll on mussels. Higher in the intertidal they don't have enough time while immersed to complete their feeding and digestion. Thus, mussels are only found above the level of heavy sea star predation. As with other intertidal species, the lower limit of mussels is set by a biological factor: predation by sea stars.

Mussels are the dominant competitors for space on many rocky shores. Their upper limit is set by desiccation and filter feeding time, their lower limit by sea stars and other predators.

In some places spiny lobsters (*Panulirus*) instead of sea stars are the main mussel predators. Lobsters can almost completely eliminate mussels from the intertidal zone.

Sea stars and other mussel predators can have a strong effect even above the level where they completely wipe out the mussels. They venture into the mussel bed at high tide and eat some of the mussels before retreating with the tide. This opens up space for other organisms—such as acorn barnacles, gooseneck barnacles, and seaweeds—that would otherwise be crowded out. The sea stars also eat dog whelks, doing the barnacles another favor. If the barnacles live long enough, they get too big for the dog whelks to eat. By reducing the number of dog whelks, the sea stars give the barnacles more of a chance to grow big before a whelk eats them.

The sea stars are absent from areas with extremely strong wave action. In such areas, or if the predators are experimentally removed (Fig. 11.21), mussels take over. They outcompete and crowd out other sessile organisms. Thus, many species can live in the middle intertidal only if sea stars keep mussel numbers under control.

Note that many intertidal species are more abundant than the sea stars, but the sea stars profoundly affect the entire community. This demonstrates a common feature of biological communities: Just because a species is relatively uncommon does not mean it is unimportant. Predators whose effects on their communities are proportionately much greater than their abundance are known as **keystone predators.**

The ochre sea star is an important keystone predator, but other predators also influence rocky intertidal community structure. Six-armed sea stars (*Leptasterias*) are another common predator in the middle intertidal of North America's Pacific coast. In 2011, six-armed sea stars along a 100 km (60 mi) stretch of coast were killed by toxins from a harmful algal bloom (see Box 15.1, "Red Tides and Harmful Algal Blooms"). Populations of an important algal grazer, the black turban snail (*Tegula funebralis*) rapidly increased with the decreased number of predatory six-armed sea stars. Populations of the snail hardly changed after a similar crash of ochre sea star populations in 2014 (see Box 11.2, "Sea Star Wasting Disease"). Thus, six-armed sea stars have more effect on black turban snail populations than ochre sea stars, which in turn affects seaweed populations. This series of events demonstrates how much biologists can learn from "natural experiments."

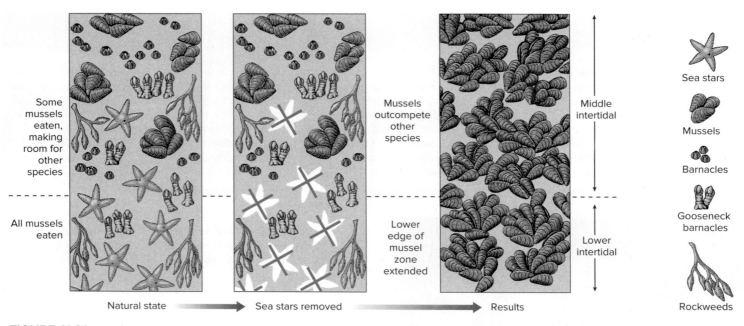

FIGURE 11.21 Removing predatory sea stars—or keeping them out with cages—shows how they affect the middle intertidal community. Below a certain level the sea stars can easily reach the mussels, their favorite food, and eat them all. Above this level the sea stars cannot eat all the mussels, but they eat enough to make space available for other species. When there are no sea stars around, the mussels are able to live lower, and they monopolize the available space by overgrowing and crowding out other species. Sea stars thus maintain the diversity of the middle intertidal community.

Predators don't even necessarily need to eat their prey to affect community structure. Six-armed sea stars eat more black turban snails than ochre sea stars, but the snails can smell both and evacuate tide pools when a sea star enters (especially when the snails aren't hungry). The absence of the snails gives seaweeds in the tide pool a respite from grazing, allowing them to grow in greater profusion.

Natural disturbances can have effects similar to predators. When mussel beds get too dense, clumps of mussels can be torn away by waves (see Fig. 11.13), exposing bare rock. Drifting logs that batter the rocks and, in cold places, scouring ice and severe freezes, have the same effect of opening up new space. This prevents mussels from monopolizing the available space, allowing other organisms to persist.

When a patch of space is cleared, new organisms often move into the patch and get replaced by others in a regular sequence (Fig. 11.22). The term **ecological succession** refers to such regular patterns of regrowth. In the rocky intertidal the first stage is usually a thin film of bacteria and microscopic algae, such as diatoms, that covers the rock. This film may condition the rock surface, since the settling larvae of some species prefer surfaces with the film over bare rock. Seaweeds often move in next, followed by barnacles and finally mussels, the dominant competitor. The final stage in an ecological succession is called the **climax community.**

The typical steps of ecological succession in the middle intertidal of many rocky shores are, first, a bacterial and algal film, then seaweeds, barnacles, and finally the climax mussel community.

What actually happens usually deviates, to varying degrees, from the idealized pattern shown in Figure 11.22. Grazers like limpets and chitons may remove newly settled larvae and spores. If such grazers move into a patch early, the succession may never get past the bacterial and algal film stage and in some places grazers limit even the film.

On the other hand, stages in the succession may be skipped. Seaweeds may never colonize a patch, for example, if barnacles get there first (see Fig. 11.15). Timing is critical: If the patch opens up when barnacle larvae are abundant and seaweed spores are rare, barnacles have the upper hand. Thus, there is an element of chance in the development of the community. Stages may also be skipped if the bare patch is small. A small patch cleared in the middle of a mussel bed may be taken over by other mussels that move in from the sides before the succession gets started. Furthermore, the physical environment can have more subtle influences on the community than smashing it with waves or logs. For example, the sea star *Pisaster ochraceus* eats less when it's cold, so its influence as a keystone predator can vary with the seasons. Other seasonal factors may come into play. On the Pacific Northwest coast of North America, low tides tend to occur during the day in spring and summer, but at night in autumn and winter. Rockweeds higher in the intertidal have difficulty growing in spring because of desiccation during the daytime tides, but in fall actually grow faster than rockweeds lower in the intertidal because they don't desiccate during the nocturnal low tides and are less exposed to predators and waves.

Without predation and other disturbances, the best competitors take over and many species disappear from the area. Disturbance can prevent this. Mussels, for instance, are often unable to completely cover middle intertidal rocks because sea stars eat them or waves tear them away. This gives other species a chance. Disturbance can thus increase the number of species that live in an area, that is, the **diversity,** by interfering with **competitive exclusion.** The rocky intertidal in some places can be thought of as a mosaic of patches that were cleared at different times and have developed differently. Each patch supports a different set of organisms, so the number of species in the area as a whole increases. On the other hand, if predation and other disturbances happen too often, the community keeps getting knocked back to the starting point. It

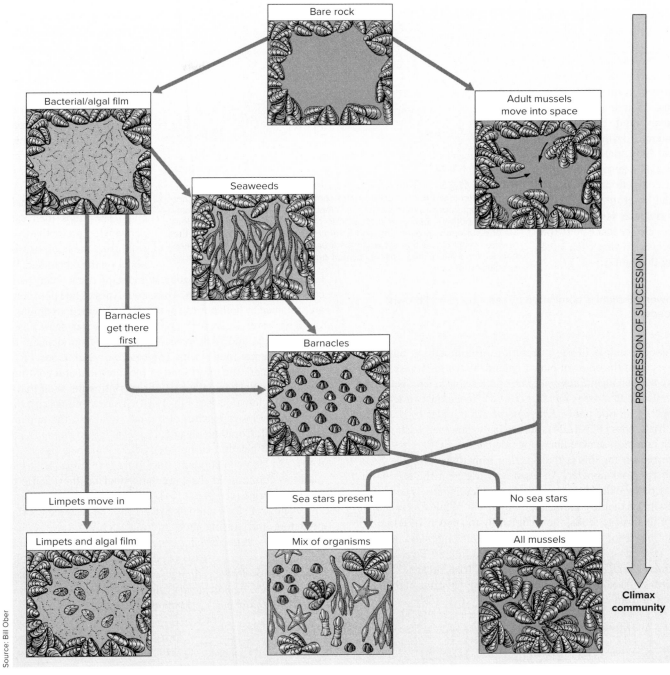

FIGURE 11.22 Ecological succession following the clearing of a patch in a mussel bed. The pathway taken and the end result depend on the size of the patch, when it opens up, and just plain luck—which organisms get there first.

never gets a chance to develop, and not many species are able to live there. The highest diversity occurs when there is enough disturbance to prevent the dominant competitors from taking over, but not so much that the community is unable to develop (Fig. 11.23).

In the absence of disturbance a few dominant competitors, especially mussels, take over the space in the middle intertidal zone. Moderate predation and other disturbance prevents this and allows other species to live there. Too much disturbance, however, removes most species.

The Lower Intertidal The lower intertidal is immersed most of the time. This makes it easy for predators like sea stars and dog whelks to feed, so mussels and barnacles are rare. Recent mass mortality of sea stars (see Box 11.2, "Sea Star Wasting Disease") has created the prospect that mussels would come to dominate the lower intertidal on the Pacific coast of North America. At least

Competitive Exclusion The elimination of one species by another as a result of competition.

• 10.1, The Organization of Communities

in some places other predators including crabs (*Carcinus, Romaleon*) can help keep the mussels in check.

The lower intertidal is dominated by seaweeds, which form a thick carpet on the rocks. These seaweeds, including species of red, green, and brown algae, can't tolerate drying out but in the lower intertidal they grow in profusion. Not surprisingly, grazing and competition are important in the lower intertidal. Light, as well as space, is an important resource. Seaweeds often compete by overgrowing each other, blocking the light.

FIGURE 11.23 Other things being equal, the number of species depends on how often disturbances occur. In this context, predation on the dominant competitors counts as a disturbance. When disturbance is rare, the dominant competitors take over and exclude other species. Intermediate levels of disturbance prevent this and give other species a chance. Thus, the number of species is highest when disturbance is moderate. If disturbance happens too often, most species cannot get a foothold and the number of species drops.

> The lower intertidal is dominated by red, green, and brown seaweeds.

A good example of the interaction of competition and grazing comes from the coast of New England. Two common seaweeds there are a green alga, *Enteromorpha,* and a red alga (not actually a moss) called Irish moss (*Chondrus crispus*). When the two seaweeds grow together in tide pools, *Enteromorpha* dominates by overgrowing the Irish moss (Fig. 11.24). Surprisingly, however, Irish moss is the most common seaweed in many tide pools.

The reason for this is that grazing sometimes prevents *Enteromorpha* from taking over. An abundant grazer in the area is the common periwinkle (*Littorina littorea*), which is closely related to the periwinkles that live in the upper intertidal. While *Enteromorpha* is one of its favorite foods, the snail hardly touches Irish moss. If a tide pool has a lot of snails, they eat the *Enteromorpha* and make way for Irish moss. If snails are transplanted into an *Enteromorpha* pool, *Enteromorpha* quickly disappears and Irish moss takes over. On the other hand, *Enteromorpha* soon moves in after periwinkles are removed from an Irish moss pool.

The story doesn't end there. If the periwinkles like *Enteromorpha* so much you'd think that they would move into *Enteromorpha* pools, but they don't. For one thing, large periwinkles do not move around a lot and prefer to stay in one tide pool. Young periwinkles are eaten by green crabs (*Carcinus maenas*), which also live in tide pools. The crabs, in turn, are eaten by gulls (*Larus*). *Enteromorpha* provides cover for the crabs, protecting them from gulls. The crabs then eat young periwinkles, preventing *them* from colonizing the pool. In Irish moss pools, on the other hand, the crabs lack cover and are eaten by gulls. Without the crabs, young periwinkles can survive in the tide pools. Thus, both types of tide pool community are sustained by both positive and negative interactions among species.

The lower intertidal supports many other seaweeds besides *Enteromorpha* and Irish moss. These range from delicate reds and greens to large, tough kelps (*Egregia, Laminaria;* see Fig. 13.21). The kelps mark the lower limit of the intertidal and continue down into the **subtidal zone,** the part of the continental shelf that is never exposed by low tide (see Fig. 10.12). There is no precise boundary between the lower reaches of the intertidal and the upper edge of the subtidal. **Coralline algae** (*Corallina, Lithothamnion*), red algae that deposit calcium carbonate ($CaCO_3$) in their tissues (see Fig. 6.10), can also be abundant. Surf grass (*Phyllospadix*), a flowering plant, is common in the lower intertidal on the Pacific coast of North America (see Fig. 6.13e).

A host of small animals live among the seaweeds, hiding from predators and staying moist during very low tides. Sea urchins (*Strongylocentrotus, Echinometra;* see Fig. 13.19) are common grazers on the seaweeds. Also present in the lower intertidal are sea anemones (*Metridium, Anthopleura;* Fig. 11.25), polychaete worms (*Spirorbis, Phragmatopoma*), snails (*Tegula, Nucella*), sea slugs (*Aplysia, Dendronotus*), and many others.

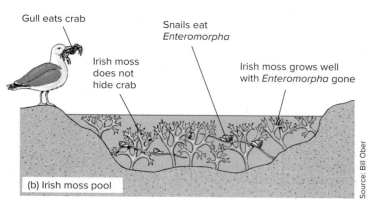

FIGURE 11.24 Biological interactions determine what type of seaweed predominates in New England tide pools. Unless something interferes, both types of pool are self-sustaining.

EYE ON SCIENCE

Box 11.2 Sea Star Wasting Disease

They started dying in 2013. Up and down the Pacific Coast of North America, marine biologists began seeing ochre sea stars (*Pisaster ochraceus*) practically melting. Their arms literally pulled away from their bodies and crawled away, and what was left of the sea stars wasted away into blobs of white goo. By 2014, this phenomenon, dubbed "Sea Star Wasting Syndrome" (SSWS) spread along the entire coast, from Alaska to Baja California, Mexico. Sea star populations suffered up to 90% mortality at many locations and were wiped out entirely at others. Similar outbreaks had been observed in previous decades but restricted to small areas, mainly in Southern California and the Gulf of California.

Mass mortality of this magnitude, not surprisingly, was a major concern to marine biologists, especially because the ochre sea star is a keystone predator important in the structure of rocky intertidal communities (see "The Middle Intertidal," above). An early suggestion was that SSWS was caused by radiation transported across the Pacific from the Fukushima disaster (see Box 3.3, "Waves That Kill"), but this was quickly ruled out. Restricted outbreaks of SSWS had been observed long before the Fukushima disaster, and have also been seen on the Atlantic Coast of North America, isolated from any effects of Fukushima. The most recent evidence is that the syndrome is caused by microorganisms.

It was clear that single research teams could not adequately understand an event of this geographic scale. Fortunately, marine scientists along the Pacific coast of North America had formed the Partnership for Interdisciplinary Studies of Coastal Oceans (PISCO) in 1999. PISCO had already had formed common monitoring methods and long-term monitoring records at many sites along the coast, and this network was ideal for studying the ecological effects of SSWS. The ability to quickly begin assessing the extent and effects of SSWS demonstrates the value of long-term, integrated research partnerships. PISCO continues to work with other partners to study SSWS and its effects on intertidal, as well as subtidal, communities.

Pathogenic microorganisms are the most likely cause of SSWS, which eventually spread to affect at least 22 species of sea stars. Given the ochre sea star's keystone role in controlling populations of mussels, the dominant competitor for space, it was expected that mussel populations would rapidly increase in the absence of the

Mark Mortin/Shutterstock

A sea star affecting by wasting disease rots away.

sea stars. Mussels have indeed increased at many locations, but not at others. Indications are that other factors including water circulation, larval settlement, and other predators (see Box 11.1, "Transplantation, Removal, and Caging Experiments") may play a greater role than previously thought.

There was some recovery from the massive outbreak of SSWS in 2013–2014, but intermittent, more localized outbreaks continue. Research on the causes and consequences also continues.

For more information, explore the links provided on the Marine Biology *Online Learning Center.*

Bill Coster/Panthe/Mary Evans Picture Library/Superstock

FIGURE 11.25 The bright green color of these giant green sea anemones (*Anthopleura xanthogrammica*) comes from zooxanthellae, symbiotic algae that live within the anemones' tissues and provide them nutrition, although the anemones also catch small prey with their tentacles. The anemones are surrounded by the sea star *Pisaster*, a keystone predator in the rocky intertidal.

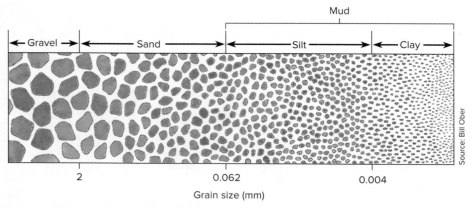

FIGURE 11.26 Sediments are classified by the size of the particles. Sand is relatively coarse; clay is very fine. Together, silt and clay are called mud.

Most rocky intertidal fishes live in the lower intertidal or in tide pools. Gobies, clingfishes, sculpins (*Oligocottus*), prickle-backs (*Cebidichthys*), and gunnels (*Xererpes*) are among the most common. These are all small fishes adapted to the environmental extremes of the intertidal. Most are carnivorous.

11.2 SOFT-BOTTOM INTERTIDAL COMMUNITIES

Any bottom that is composed of sediment, as opposed to rock, is considered a **soft bottom.** The dividing line isn't always clear. Boulder fields are usually thought of as rocky, but how small the rocks have to be before the bottom is considered soft is not precisely defined. In this text we refer to a bottom as soft if organisms are able to burrow in it easily.

Soft bottoms occur where sediments accumulate. In North America, soft bottoms dominate on the east coast south of Cape Cod and virtually all of the Gulf coast (see Appendix D). The rocky west coast is often interrupted by sandy beaches and mudflats, especially in and near river mouths. Whether and what kind of sediment accumulates in an area depends on how much water motion there is and on the source of the sediment. In turn, the type of sediment strongly influences the community.

The Shifting Sediments

While rocky intertidal organisms have a firm substrate to latch onto, soft bottoms tend to be unstable and shift in response to waves, tides, and currents. Thus, soft-bottom organisms do not have a solid place for attachment. Not many seaweeds have adapted to this environment. Seagrasses are the most common large primary producers on soft bottoms and often form dense intertidal beds. In this chapter, we deal only with intertidal soft-bottom communities that lack seagrasses. Seagrass communities are discussed in Chapter 13 (see "Seagrass Meadows," in 13.2).

Soft-bottom animals also lack solid attachment sites. Some are epifauna and live on the sediment surface, but most burrow in the sediment for protection and to keep from being washed away.

Animals that burrow in the substrate are called **infauna** because they live *in* the sediment.

The kind of sediment on the bottom, especially the size of the grains, is one of the most important physical factors affecting soft-bottom communities. Most people use the terms "sand," "silt," "clay," and "mud" without much thought. To a geologist these terms refer to sediments with specific particle sizes (Fig. 11.26).

Careful analysis is needed to determine grain size precisely, but a "quick and dirty" test will literally give you a feel for the different sediment types. Rub a pinch of sediment or soil between your fingers. Any grittiness is caused by sand. Silt and clay, which together are called mud, feel smooth. Also, the finest sand particles are the smallest you can see. To tell silt and clay apart, you can rub a little on your teeth. Silt feels gritty, but clay is still smooth. If you try to test this for yourself, be aware that it is pretty hard to get a sample of pure clay from a mud flat!

> The terms "sand," "silt," and "clay" refer to sediments of particular grain sizes. Sand is the coarsest, followed by silt and then clay. "Mud" refers to silt and clay together.

Most sediments are made up of a mixture of different particle sizes. They are described according to the most common grain size. Sand, for instance, has mostly sand-sized grains but may also have small amounts of mud or a few large rocks.

Sediment composition is directly related to the degree of water motion. Imagine, or better yet actually perform, the following experiment. Take a handful of sediment or soil that contains a wide range of particle sizes, from large pebbles down to clay. Put it in a glass container with some water and shake it up. As soon as you stop shaking, the pebbles will sink to the bottom. As the water gradually stops moving, first the coarse sand and then finer particles will begin to sink. Very fine material will remain suspended for a long time, making the water look muddy. You might have to let the container sit for weeks before the finest clay settles out completely. If the container is stirred even gently, the fine material will never settle out.

This demonstrates a general rule: Fine sediments remain suspended with even a small amount of water motion, whereas coarse sediments settle out unless there is considerable flow. Bottom sediments thus reflect prevailing conditions. Calm, sheltered areas have muddy bottoms because fine sediment can settle out. Organic particles sink at about the same rate as clay particles, so the two tend to settle out together. Some organic material also binds to clay particles. Clay sediments are therefore usually organic-rich. Places with stronger waves and currents have coarser bottom sediments. If the water motion is strong enough, it may carry away *all* the loose material, leaving bare rock or large boulders.

> Fine sediments are found in calm areas such as bays and lagoons. Coarser sediments are found in areas affected by waves and currents.

In our sediment experiment, all the particles would eventually settle out if the container were kept still. A constant flow of water through the container, however, would carry away the fine material and only certain particles, the coarse ones, would remain. The coarse particles would be sorted out from the fine ones.

Living in the Sediment

Living in sediment has advantages in the intertidal. Soft bottoms stay wet after the tide is out, so the problem of desiccation is not as critical as in the rocky intertidal. This depends on the grain size, however. Coarse sands drain, and therefore dry out, quite rapidly (Fig. 11.27). Partially because of this, coarse sand beaches have relatively little animal life. Sand beaches are also constantly shifting with the waves and tides, and this instability is another challenge for organisms living there.

Oxygen Availability The amount of organic matter in bottom sediments is particularly important to deposit feeders. Because there are relatively few primary producers, detritus is the main source of food for intertidal soft-bottom communities. Deposit feeders extract this organic matter from the sediments. The amount of detritus depends on grain size (see Fig. 13.12). Coarse sands contain very little organic matter. That is why we tend to think of sand as clean. Silt and clay, on the other hand, are usually rich in detritus, which is why they can be smelly.

The grain size also affects the amount of available oxygen in the sediments. Oxygen in sediments is used up by the **respiration** of animals and, more importantly, decay bacteria. Below the sediment surface there is no light and therefore no photosynthesis, so the infauna depend on the circulation of water through the sediments to replenish the oxygen supply. Grain size and the degree of sorting strongly affect how porous a sediment is (Fig. 11.27). Every backyard gardener knows that water flows more easily through sand than clay. Water circulation through fine sediments is greatly restricted.

Muddy bottoms, then, have a double problem. First, they have more organic material to decay and use up oxygen. Second, the flow of water that brings in new oxygen is reduced. Except for the upper few centimeters of mud the **interstitial water,** or water between the grains, is deficient in oxygen. If you go very far down at all, in fact, the oxygen is completely used up. Sediments with absolutely no oxygen are said to be **anoxic.**

Well-sorted (coarse)	Well-sorted (fine)	Poorly sorted
(a) Water drains quickly	(b) Water drains slowly	(c) Water blocked

Source: Bill Ober

FIGURE 11.27 "Sorting" refers to the uniformity of grain size in the sediment. In well-sorted sediments (*a* and *b*) the grains are all about the same size. There is a lot of space between the grains, so water can flow through. The grain size, as well as sorting, affects how well water circulates; larger grains have larger spaces and are thus more porous. Poorly sorted sediments (*c*) have many different-sized grains. Small grains fill in the spaces between the larger ones, making water flow difficult.

Anoxic conditions are no problem at all for bacteria that are capable of **anaerobic respiration,** in which they break down organic matter without oxygen. They produce a noxious gas called **hydrogen sulfide (H_2S)** as a by-product (see Table 5.1). If you have ever had to unclog the drain of your kitchen sink, you have probably run into hydrogen sulfide. It turns things black and smells like rotten eggs. In the sediments, just as in your drain, hydrogen sulfide is produced when bacteria continue to decompose organic material after all the oxygen has been used up. A distinct black layer appears where anoxic conditions begin in the sediments (Fig. 11.28).

The decay of organic matter in the sediments uses up oxygen. Because of this, the interstitial water beneath the sediment surface is often depleted of oxygen, especially in fine sediments.

Infauna must adapt to oxygen shortage, especially in muddy bottoms. Many animals pump oxygen-rich water from the sediment surface with siphons or through their burrows (see Fig. 12.11). Such animals are never actually exposed to low oxygen levels. Their burrows, and the effects of **bioturbators**—infauna that burrow through, turn over, or otherwise disturb the sediment—help oxygenate the sediment.

Nevertheless, muddy sediments are often oxygen-deficient. Animals living in

Michael E. Huber

FIGURE 11.28 The black layer in the sediments shows where the oxygen has been completely depleted and hydrogen sulfide (H_2S) is produced by anaerobic bacteria.

Respiration
Organic matter + $O_2 \rightarrow CO_2 + H_2O$ + energy (glucose)
• 4.1, The Ingredients of Life

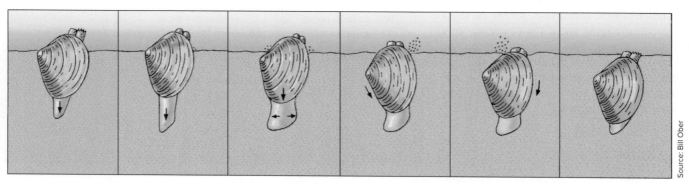

Source: Bill Ober

FIGURE 11.29 Burrowing in clams and cockles. The foot does all the work. The clam first pushes its foot down through the sediment. Then the clam expands the end of the foot, which anchors the clam as it pulls its body down.

them have adapted to low-oxygen environments. They often have special **hemoglobins** and other adaptations to extract as much as possible of what little oxygen there is in the interstitial water. Some are sluggish, which reduces their oxygen consumption. They may even have a limited capability to carry out anaerobic respiration. A few animals have symbiotic bacteria that help them live in low-oxygen sediments. Even so, hydrogen sulfide is toxic to most animals, and anoxic sediments have relatively little animal life.

Getting Around Soft-bottom animals use a variety of methods to burrow through the sediments. Clams (*Macoma, Donax*) and cockles (*Cardium*) take advantage of being able to change the shape of their muscular foot. First, they make the foot thin and reach forward with it (Fig. 11.29). Then, the end of the foot thickens and acts as an anchor while they pull the rest of the body along. Many soft-bodied animals do something similar, using their body the way clams use the foot (Fig. 11.30). Some worms force their pharynx into cracks in the sediment to expand the crack before pulling their bodies along behind. Heart urchins (*Lovenia, Echinocardium;* see Fig. 13.7) burrow or plough through the sediment with their spines and tube feet. The many crustaceans that live on soft bottoms—such as amphipods (*Talitrus, Corophium*); sand, or mole, crabs (*Emerita*); and ghost (*Callianassa*) and mud (*Upogebia*) shrimps—use their jointed appendages to dig.

Quite a few deposit feeders solve two problems at once by eating their way through the sediment. Sea cucumbers, certain worms, and other animals use the same inchworm style of locomotion as do the clams and worms described previously, with one important exception. Rather than push through the sediments, they push the sediments *through them.* They digest the organic matter and leave the rest of the sediment behind (Fig. 11.31).

Some soft-bottom animals are so small that instead of burrowing through the sediments they live in the interstitial spaces between the grains. These animals are collectively called the **meiofauna.** There are many different types of animals in the meiofauna, but most have independently evolved a worm-like shape (see Box 13.2, "Life in Mud and Sand").

Feeding As already noted, detritus is the main source of food in the soft-bottom intertidal (Fig. 11.32). **Diatoms** sometimes form highly productive mats on the sediment surface, but most of the time they don't account for much primary production. In any case, most animals don't distinguish between the diatoms and detritus. **Plankton** brought in by the tides also make a small contribution to the food supply.

Many methods of deposit feeding have evolved. One of the most common has already been described: Animals such as sea cucumbers and various worms take in sediment as they burrow, digest the detritus and small organisms, and leave the rest of the sediment in their wake. This technique is more common on mud bottoms than sand, probably because mud contains more organic matter. Sand is also abrasive and hard on the digestive system.

Sand dollars (*Mellita, Dendraster;* see Figs. 7.48b and 13.8) are more selective. They use their tube feet to pick up organic particles. Sand dollars burrow near the sediment surface, where detritus

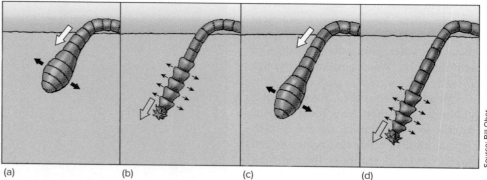

Source: Bill Ober

FIGURE 11.30 Burrowing in the lugworm (*Arenicola*). (*a*) The worm expands the end of its body (black arrows). The expanded end acts as an anchor and the rest of the body is pulled along behind (white arrow). (*b*) The worm then flares its segments (black arrows), which prevents it from sliding backward when the contraction of the circular muscles in the anterior body extends the proboscis forward (blue arrow). As the process is repeated (*c* and *d*), the worm moves forward through the sediment.

is still accumulating and is therefore more abundant. The bent-nosed clam (*Macoma;* see Fig. 12.11) also concentrates on the upper layer of sediment. It uses a long siphon to suck up food particles from the surface. Other animals catch particles as they settle out and are thus on the line between suspension feeding and deposit feeding. Some polychaete worms (*Terebella*) have long, sticky tentacles that they spread out on the bottom to gather food (see Fig. 13.11). Other polychaetes use a mucus net instead of tentacles.

Suspension feeders, which don't wait for the detritus to settle, also inhabit intertidal soft bottoms. An olive shell (*Olivella*) from Central America makes a mucus net, but instead of spreading the net on the bottom the snail holds the net up in the water to filter food. Sand, or mole, crabs hold a pair of large, bushy antennae up into the water to trap food. By quickly burying and uncovering themselves, they combine feeding and locomotion. When the tide is coming in and they want to move up the beach, they uncover just before a wave hits, ride the wave up, and raise their antennae. Then they burrow to keep from

FIGURE 11.31 After digesting out the organic matter, this tropical sea cucumber (*Holothuria edulis*) has deposited a pile of undigested sand pellets.

being washed back down. As the tide recedes, they do the opposite, burrowing before the wave arrives, then popping out to ride the backwash down the beach.

Soft bottoms also have their share of predators. Moon snails (*Polinices*) burrow through the upper sediments looking for clams. When a snail finds a clam, it drills a hole in the clam's shell and eats it. Several polychaetes and other worms are also important predators. Birds can be major predators during low tide (see Fig. 12.12). At high tide, fishes can come in. Fishes often don't eat an entire animal. Instead, they just nip off clam siphons or other bits that stick out.

Zonation Because the organisms live in the sediments and can't be seen, zonation on intertidal soft bottoms is not as obvious as in the rocky intertidal. Zonation does exist, however, especially on sandy beaches (Fig. 11.33). Water drains rapidly from the sand, and because the beach slopes, the upper part is drier than the lower part.

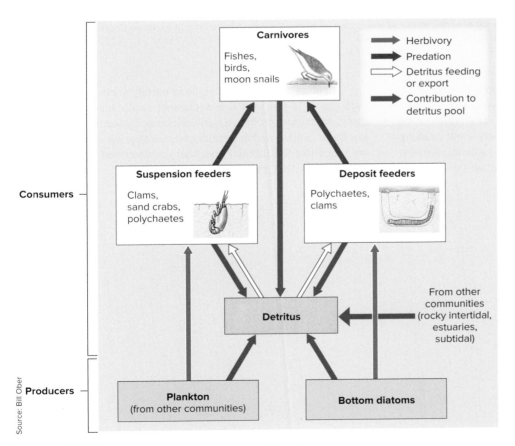

FIGURE 11.32 A generalized food web on a sandy beach.

Hemoglobin Red protein in the blood of vertebrates and some invertebrates that transports oxygen.
• 8.3, Biology of Fishes

Diatoms Single-celled algae with a shell, or test, made of silica.
• 5.3, Unicellular Algae; Figure 5.6

Plankton Primary producers (*phytoplankton*) and consumers (*zooplankton*) that drift with the currents.
• 10.2, The Major Marine Lifestyles and Environments; Figure 10.11

FIGURE 11.33 Generalized zonation pattern on sandy beaches of the Atlantic coast of North America. Sheltered and exposed beaches have different communities, and the animals shown here don't usually all occur on the same beach.

The upper beach is inhabited by beach hoppers, or sand fleas, which are really amphipods, and by isopods. In warmer areas, these small crustaceans are replaced by ghost (*Ocypode*) and fiddler crabs (*Uca;* see Box 12.1, "Fiddler on the Mud") that scurry about catching smaller animals, scavenging bits of dead meat, and gathering detritus. Polychaetes, clams, and other animals appear lower on the beach.

Zonation is even less obvious in muddy areas. The bottom in such places is flat, and fine sediments retain water. The habitat therefore does not change very markedly between the high- and low-water marks, and intertidal communities on muddy bottoms are much like the subtidal ones that are described in Chapters 12 and 13 rather than here in Chapter 11.

Interactive Exploration

McGraw-Hill Connect® is a great place to check your understanding of chapter material. Visit **www.mcgrawhillconnect.com** for access to interactive chapter summaries, chapter quizzing, and more! Further enhance your knowledge with video clips and weblinks to chapter-related material.

Critical Thinking

1. There are marked differences in the type of organisms found at four different locations at the same tidal height along a rocky shore. What might account for this? Offer at least three possible explanations.

2. Most marine biologists hypothesize that space, not food, limits populations in the rocky intertidal. What kind of experiments could be performed to test this hypothesis?

For Further Reading

Some of the recommended reading may be available online. Look for live links on the *Marine Biology* Online Learning Center.

General Interest

Denny, M. and S. D. Gaines, 2007. *Encyclopedia of tidepools and rocky shores.* Stanford University Press.

Howgego, J.,2022. The grown-up guide to rock pooling. *New Scientist*, vol. 255, no.3, 16 July, pp. 48–50. Exploring tide pools can provide a close connection to the natural world.

Pfister, C. A., R. T. Paine, and J. T. Wootton, 2016. The iconic keystone predator has a pathogen. *Frontiers in Ecology and the Environment*, vol. 14, no. 5, June, pp. 285–286. How intertidal communities will change as a result of the mass mortality of the ochre sea star and other predatory sea stars remain to be seen.

Pinchin, K., 2022. Protecting Alaska's Harvest. *Scientific American*, vol. 326, no. 1, January, pp. 56–69. Intertidal food resources are important to indigenous Alaskan communities, but are threatened by pollution.

Robles, C., 1996. Turf battles in the tidal zone. *Natural History*, vol. 105, no. 7, July, pp. 24–27. During their nighttime forays into the intertidal zone, spiny lobsters gobble up mussels and make way for a luxurious carpet of seaweeds.

Smith, C. S., M. E. Rudd, R. K. Gittman, et al., 2020. Coming to terms with living shorelines: A scoping review of novel restoration strategies for shoreline protection. *Frontiers in Marine Science* [https://doi. org/10.3389/fmars.2020.00434].

White, M., 2011. Brimming pools. *National Geographic*, vol. 219, no. 6, June, pp. 100–115. A detailed look at the Pacific Coast's rocky intertidal zone.

Wolcott, T. G. and D. L. Wolcott, 1990. Wet behind the gills. *Natural History*, vol. 99, no. 10, October, pp. 46–55. Land and shore crabs carry salt water with them in order to breathe.

In Depth

Demes, K. W., C. D. G. Harley, L. M. Anderson, E. Carrington, and C. Nilsson, 2013. Shifts in morphological and mechanical traits compensate for performance costs of reproduction in a wave-swept seaweed. *Journal of Ecology*, vol. 101, pp. 963–970.

Demes, K. W., J. N. Pruitt, C. D. G. Harley, and E. Carrington, 2013. Survival of the weakest: Increased frond mechanical strength in a wave-swept kelp inhibits self-pruning and increases whole-plant mortality. *Functional Ecology*, vol. 27, pp. 439–445.

Fales, R. J. and J. R. Smith, 2022. Long-term change in a high-intertidal rock-week (*Pelvetiopsis californica*) and community consequences. *Marine Biology*, vol. 169, [https://doi.org/10.1007/s00227-022-04022-1]

Hull, W. W. and P. E. Bourdeau, 2017. Can crabs kill like a keystone predator? A field test of the effects of crab predation on mussel mortality on a northeast Pacific rocky shore. *PLoS One*, vol. 12, no. 8, p. e0183064.

Martínez, B., R. M. Viejo, F. Carreño, and S. C. Aranda, 2012. Habitat distribution models for intertidal seaweeds: Responses to climatic and non-climatic drivers. *Journal of Biogeography*, vol. 39, pp. 1877–1890.

McQuaid, C. D., F. Porri, K. R. Nicastro, and G. I. Zardi, 2015. Simple, scale-dependent patterns emerge from very complex effects—an example from the intertidal mussels *Mytilus galloprovincialis* and *Perna perna*. *Oceanography and Marine Biology: An Annual Review*, vol. 53, pp. 127–156.

Menge, B. A., T. C. Gouhier, T. Freidenburg, and J. Lubchenco, 2011. Linking long-term, large-scale climatic and environmental variability to patterns of marine invertebrate recruitment: Toward explaining "unexplained" variation. *Journal of Experimental Marine Biology and Ecology*, vol. 400, pp. 236–249.

Morgan, S. G., A. L. Shanks, J. H. MacMahan, A. J. Reniers, and F. Feddersen, 2018. Planktonic subsidies to surf-zone and intertidal communities. *Annual Review of Marine Science*, vol. 10, pp. 345–369.

Murray, N. J., S. R. Phinn, M. DeWitt, et al., 2019. The global distribution and trajectory of tidal flats. *Nature*, vol. 565, no. 7738, pp. 222–225 plus supplements.

Ramos, E., A. Puente, and J. A. Juanes, 2016. An ecological classification of rocky shores at a regional scale: A predictive tool for management of conservation values. *Marine Ecology*, vol. 37, pp. 311–328.

Wahl, M., V. Jormalainen, B. K. Eriksson, J. A. Coyer, M. Molis, H. Schubert, M. Dethier, R. Karez, I. Kruse, M. Lenz, G. Pearson, S. Rohde, S. A. Wikström, and J. L. Olsen, 2011. Stress ecology in *Fucus*: Abiotic, biotic and genetic interactions. *Advances in Marine Biology*, vol. 59, pp. 37–105.

12

Estuaries: Where Rivers Meet the Sea

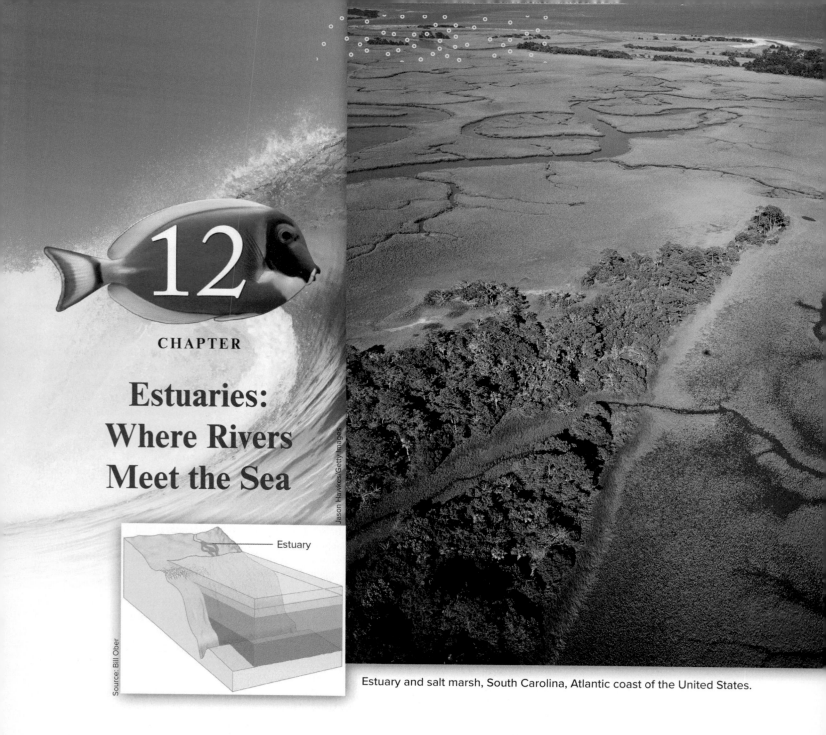

Estuary

Source: Bill Ober

Estuary and salt marsh, South Carolina, Atlantic coast of the United States.

A unique environment develops where fresh water from rivers enters the sea. **Estuaries** are semi-enclosed areas of the coast where fresh water and seawater meet and mix. They therefore represent a close interaction between land and sea. Estuaries are typically inhabited by fewer species, and therefore lower **species diversity,** or **biodiversity,** than rocky shores. They are nevertheless among the most productive environments on Earth and as a result the breeding ground of many human-food species.

Estuaries also rank among the environments most affected by humans (see "Human Impact on Estuarine Communities," below). Most natural harbors are estuaries, and many of the world's great cities—New York, London, and Tokyo, among others—developed along them.

12.1 ORIGINS AND TYPES OF ESTUARIES

Estuaries are scattered along the shores of all the oceans and vary widely in origin, type, and size. They may be called lagoons, sloughs, or even bays, but all share the mixing of fresh water with the sea in a partially enclosed section of the coast. Some oceanographers go as far as classifying enclosed seas with restricted circulation, like the Baltic and Black seas, as estuaries.

Estuaries are partially enclosed coastal regions where fresh water from rivers meets and mixes with seawater.

FIGURE 12.1 Two types of estuaries are found along the eastern coast of the United States. Chesapeake Bay and the mouth of the Delaware River are drowned river valley estuaries; the Cape Hatteras islands form a bar-built estuary.

Delaware River

Chesapeake Bay

Cape Hatteras

Jacques Descloitres, MODIS Rapid Response Team, NASA/GSFC

Many estuaries were formed when sea level rose because of the melting of ice at the end of the last ice age during the **Pleistocene,** about 18,000 years ago. The sea invaded low-lands and river mouths in the process. These estuaries are called **drowned river valleys** or **coastal plain estuaries.** They are the most common type of estuary. Examples are Chesapeake Bay and the mouth of the Delaware River on the east coast of the United States (Fig. 12.1), the mouth of the St. Lawrence River in eastern Canada, and the mouth of the River Thames in England. Also considered estuaries are the extensive **bayous** that are affected by tides along the low-lying mouth of the Mississippi River and adjacent coastal areas on the northern Gulf of Mexico.

A second type of estuary is the **bar-built estuary.** Here, the accumulation of sediments along the coast builds up **sand bars** and **barrier islands** that act as a wall between the ocean and fresh water from rivers. Bar-built estuaries are found, for instance, along the Texas coast of the Gulf of Mexico, the section of the North Carolina coast protected by the Outer Banks and Hatteras barrier islands (Fig. 12.1), and along the North Sea coast of the Netherlands and Germany. Barrier islands (see Fig. 2.24) protect coastlines by absorbing the stress of storms and currents, and their sand dunes are often used as nesting sites by seabirds.

Other estuaries, like San Francisco Bay in California, were created not because sea level rose but because the land sank, or **subsided,** as the result of movements of the crust. These are known as **tectonic estuaries.**

Another type of estuary was created when retreating glaciers cut deep, often spectacular, valleys along the coast. The valleys were partially submerged when sea level rose, and rivers now flow into them. These estuaries, or **fjords,** are common in southeastern Alaska, British Columbia, Norway, Greenland, southern Chile, and the South Island of New Zealand (Fig. 12.2). Large glaciers, currently melting faster as a result of **global climate change** (see Special Report: Climate Change), are still found in many fjords, particularly in Alaska, Greenland, and southern Chile.

FIGURE 12.2 Milford Sound (*Piopiotahi* in Māori), on the southwestern coast of New Zealand's South Island, is a fjord. It is a finger-like inlet surrounded by sheer walls that rise 1,200 m (3,900 ft) above sea level and plunge to depths of 500 m (1,640 ft). Its entrance is only 55 m (180 ft) deep. As in other fjords, the shallow entrance restricts the exchange of water between the fjord and the open sea, resulting in stagnant, oxygen-depleted, deep water.

Peter Castro

Estuaries can be classified into four basic groups based on their origins: drowned river valleys, bar-built, tectonic, and glacier-carved estuaries, or fjords.

Broad, well-developed estuaries are particularly common in regions with flat coastal plains and wide continental shelves, a feature typical of **passive margins.** This is the case along the Atlantic coast of North America. The opposite is true for the steep coasts and

Pleistocene Geological period that began around 2.5 million years ago and during which sea levels fluctuated during several ice ages.
Plate Tectonics The process in which large sections of Earth's crust move about.
• 2.2, The Origins and Structure of the Ocean Basins

Passive Continental Margin Margin that is on the "trailing edge" of a continent and therefore has little geological activity.
Active Continental Margin Margin that is colliding with another plate and therefore has a lot of geological activity.
• 2.3, The Geological Provinces of the Ocean; Figure 2.23

narrow continental shelves of the Pacific coast of North America and other **active margins.** Here, narrow river mouths carved along the steep coast have typically restricted the formation of estuaries.

12.2 PHYSICAL CHARACTERISTICS OF ESTUARIES

Influenced by the tides and the mixing of fresh water and seawater, estuaries have a unique combination of physical and chemical characteristics. These factors govern the lives of the organisms that live there.

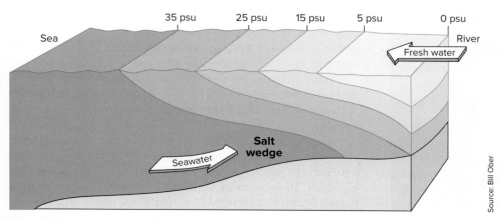

FIGURE 12.3 Profile of an idealized estuary. The lines across the estuary connect points of similar salinity and are known as *isohalines.*

(a)

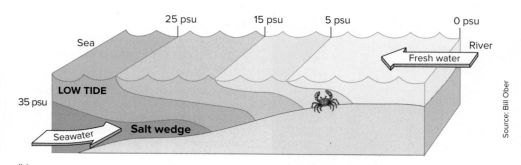

(b)

FIGURE 12.4 The salt wedge in a typical estuary moves in and out with the tide. (*a*) At high tide the crab is covered by water with a salinity of 35 psu. (*b*) At low tide it is covered by water with a low salinity, between 5 psu and 15 psu.

Salinity

The salinity of estuaries fluctuates dramatically both from place to place and from time to time. When seawater, averaging a salinity of about 35‰ (parts per million), or 35 psu (practical salinity units), mixes with fresh water (nearly 0 psu) from rivers or melting glaciers the mixture has a salinity somewhere in between. The more fresh water that is mixed in, the lower the salinity. Salinity therefore decreases as one moves upstream (Fig. 12.3).

Salinity also varies with depth in the estuary. The salty seawater is more dense and stays on the bottom (see "Salinity, Temperature, and Density," in 3.1). It flows in along the bottom in what is frequently known as a **salt wedge.** Meanwhile, the fresher, less dense water from the river flows out on the surface.

The salt wedge moves back and forth with the daily rhythm of the tides (Fig. 12.4). It moves up the estuary on the rising tide, then recedes as the tide falls. This means that organisms that stay in one place are faced with dramatic fluctuations in salinity. They are submerged under the salt wedge at high tide and under low-salinity water at low tide. If the area has a **diurnal tide,** the organisms are subjected to two shifts in salinity every day: one as the tide moves upstream and a second as it retreats. In an estuary with **semidiurnal tides,** salinity changes four times a day.

Estuaries are subject to wide fluctuations in salinity.

The behavior of water masses in estuaries is not always this simple. The shape of the estuary and its bottom, the wind, evaporation of water from the surface, and changes in the tide (because of storms and other factors) all influence the distribution of salinity. Also of importance are seasonal variations in freshwater runoff from rivers as a result of rainfall patterns or snowmelt. Currents are especially important. Because most estuaries, including fjords, are long and narrow, the tide doesn't just rise; it rushes in, often creating strong **tidal currents.** In a few places the tide actually comes in as a nearly vertical wall of water known as a **tidal bore.** Tidal bores in the Qiantang River, China, can generate waves as high as 6 m (20 ft)! Similar tidal bores, up to 4 m (14 ft high) are also observed near the mouth of the Amazon River in Brazil. Such strong water movements greatly affect the pattern of salinity in an estuary.

Another factor that affects circulation in estuaries is the **Coriolis effect.** North of the Equator, the fresh water that flows from rivers toward the sea is deflected toward the

Source: Bill Ober

right. South of the Equator, the flow is to the left. This means that in estuaries located in the Northern Hemisphere marine organisms can penetrate farther upstream on the left side when one faces seaward, whereas they extend up the right side in the Southern Hemisphere.

In regions of little freshwater runoff and high evaporation, the salinity of the water increases. An example is Laguna Madre, a shallow bar-built estuary with limited access to the open ocean that parallels the Texas coast for 185 km (115 mi). The average salinity is more than 50 psu in some areas, and it can reach 100 psu or more during dry spells. These high-salinity estuaries are called **negative estuaries.**

Substrate

Rivers carry large amounts of sediment and other materials, including pollutants, into most estuaries. Sand and other coarse material settle out in the upper reaches of the estuary, where the river current slows. The fine, muddy particles, however, are carried further down the estuary. There, many of the particles settle out when the current slows even more, though the finest particles can be carried far out to sea. The **substrate,** or type of bottom, of most estuaries is therefore sand or soft mud.

Mud, which is actually a combination of silt and clay (see Fig. 11.26), is rich in organic material. As in other organic-rich sediments, respiration by decay bacteria uses up oxygen in the **interstitial water,** the water between sediment particles. Water cannot easily flow through the fine sediments to replenish the oxygen supply. As a result, the sediments in estuaries are often devoid of oxygen, or are **anoxic,** below the first few centimeters (see Fig. 11.28). They have the black color and rotten-egg smell typical of anoxic sediments, in which **hydrogen sulfide (H_2S),** which is toxic to most organisms, accumulates. Anoxic sediments are not completely devoid of life. **Anaerobic bacteria,** which do not need oxygen to carry out respiration, thrive under these conditions.

> Fine, muddy sediments brought into estuaries by rivers settle out in the relatively quiet waters. Bacterial respiration in these organic-rich sediments depletes the oxygen in them.

In estuaries that have unimpeded tidal flow, which includes most shallow ones, there is plenty of oxygen dissolved in the water. Some deep-water estuaries like fjords (see Fig. 12.2), however, have a shallow "sill" at the entrance that restricts water circulation. Low-salinity water flows out unimpeded on the surface. The sill, however, prevents seawater from flowing in along the bottom. The stagnant deep water can become depleted in oxygen because of bacterial respiration associated with the decomposition of organic matter that sinks and accumulates on the bottom.

Other Physical Factors

Water temperature in estuaries, except fjords, varies markedly because of their shallow depths and large surface area. Organisms that are exposed at low tide have to face even more drastic daily and seasonal temperature fluctuations.

Large amounts of suspended sediments are typical of estuaries, greatly reducing the water clarity. Very little light thus penetrates through the water column. The particulate material in the water can also clog the feeding surfaces of some filter feeders and even kill organisms, like some sponges, that are sensitive to sediment.

12.3 ESTUARIES AS ECOSYSTEMS

To the uninitiated, an estuary may at first look bare. This impression is far from the truth. Estuaries are tremendously productive and are home to large numbers of organisms, many of which are of commercial importance. Estuaries also provide vital breeding and feeding grounds for many birds, fishes, shrimps, and other animals. Estuarine ecosystems consist of several distinct communities, each with its own characteristic assemblage of organisms.

Living in an Estuary

Life in an estuary revolves largely around the need to adapt to extremes in salinity, temperature, and other physical factors. Though other marine environments can be more extreme—they can be colder or more saline, for instance—none changes so rapidly or in so many ways as an estuary. Accumulation of sediment or the opening up of barrier islands as a result of storms can bring even faster changes. Living in an estuary is not easy, so relatively few species have successfully adapted to estuarine conditions. These species, however, typically occur in large numbers.

Coping with Salinity Fluctuations Maintaining the proper salt and water balance of cells and body fluids is one of the greatest challenges facing estuarine organisms. Most estuarine organisms are marine species that have developed the ability to tolerate low salinities as a consequence of fresh water from rivers or melting glaciers (Fig. 12.5). How far they can move up the estuary depends on just how tolerant they are. Most estuarine organisms are **euryhaline** species, that is, they tolerate a wide range of salinities. The relatively few **stenohaline** species, those that tolerate only a narrow range of salinities, are limited to the upper or lower ends of the estuary and rarely penetrate into the middle estuary. Stenohaline species can be either marine or freshwater in origin. Some species are adapted to live in **brackish water,** or water of intermediate salinity. Some of these species are stenohaline; others are euryhaline.

Because of their marine background, most estuarine organisms face the problem of the water in estuaries being diluted with fresh water. Those having an internal salt concentration higher than that of the surrounding water tend to take on water through **osmosis** (see Fig. 4.13*a*). Some animals adapt by simple changes in behavior. They hide in their mud burrows, close their shells, or swim away as the salinity drops. These strategies are not widespread in estuaries, however, and most organisms rely on other mechanisms.

Semidiurnal Tide A tidal pattern with two high and two low tides each day.
Diurnal Tide A tidal pattern with one high and one low tide each day.
Mixed Semidiurnal Tide A tidal pattern in which two successive high tides are of different heights.
• 3.3, Waves and Tides; Figure 3.34

Coriolis Effect As a result of Earth's rotation, anything that moves large distances on Earth's surface tends to deflect to the right in the Northern Hemisphere and to the left in the Southern Hemisphere.
• 3.2, Ocean Circulation

Osmosis The movement of water from high to low concentrations across a membrane.
• 4.3, Challenges of Life in the Sea

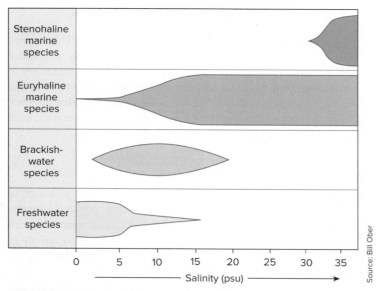

FIGURE 12.5 Types of species living in an idealized estuary in relation to salinity. The width of the bars represents the relative number of species, or biodiversity.

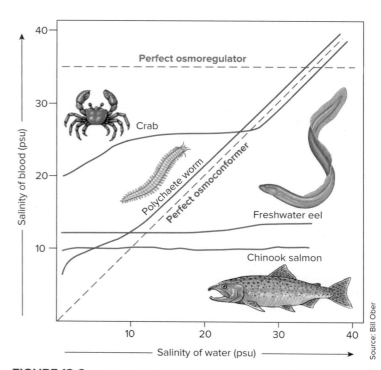

FIGURE 12.6 The salinity of the body fluids of estuarine animals responds in various ways to the salinity of the surrounding water. In a perfect osmoconformer, the salinity of the blood exactly matches that of the water. In a perfect osmoregulator, blood salinity stays the same no matter what the water salinity is. We have drawn the line for an imaginary perfect osmoregulator at 35 psu. The salmon and freshwater eels are nearly perfect osmoregulators even though their bloods are more dilute. The important point is not the actual salinity of the blood but the fact that it remains relatively constant. Notice that some organisms, like the crab in the diagram, can only osmoregulate within a certain range of salinity; they are osmoconformers outside this range.

Soft-bodied estuarine animals, like many molluscs and polychaete worms, often maintain osmotic balance simply by allowing their body fluids to change with the salinity of the water. They are called **osmoconformers** (Fig. 12.6). Many fishes, crabs, molluscs, and polychaetes are instead **osmoregulators.** They keep the salt concentration of their body fluids more or less constant regardless of the water salinity. They can nevertheless adapt to different salinities by regulating the concentration of solutes in their body fluids. For example, when the salinity of the water becomes lower than that of the blood, osmoregulators get rid of excess water and, via **active transport,** absorb some solutes from the surrounding water to compensate for those lost in the elimination of water. The gills, kidneys, and other structures accomplish this.

Bony fishes that inhabit estuaries also need to osmoregulate, since their blood is less salty than seawater (see Fig. 4.14 and "Regulation of the Internal Environment," in 8.3). Salmon and freshwater eels migrate back and forth between rivers and the sea and still maintain a stable internal environment, thanks to the active transport of solutes by their kidneys and gills.

> Organisms in estuaries have adapted to salinity fluctuations in various ways. Osmoconformers let the salinity of their body fluids vary with that of the water. Osmoregulators keep the salt concentration of their body fluids more or less constant.

Few animals can be neatly classified as perfect osmoconformers or perfect osmoregulators. Many invertebrates, for instance, osmoregulate

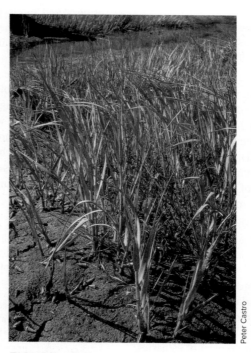

FIGURE 12.7 Cordgrass (*Spartina*) is an important component of salt marshes on both the Atlantic and Pacific coasts of North America and other temperate shores worldwide.

at low salinities and osmoconform at higher salinities. Even efficient osmoregulators like salmon and freshwater eels do not keep *exactly* the same concentration of salts and other solutes in their blood as salinity changes.

Estuarine plants must also handle salinity variations. Grasses and other salt-marsh plants are land plants that have developed high salt tolerance. Some of these plants actively absorb salts and concentrate harmless solutes like sugars to match the outside concentrations and prevent water from leaving their tissues. Notice that this is opposite to the situation in marine organisms that live in estuaries, which have to adapt to reduced, not increased, salinities.

Several types of adaptations have evolved in some estuarine plants. Cordgrasses (*Spartina;* Fig. 12.7), other salt-marsh plants, and some mangroves actually excrete excess salts by way of **salt glands** in their leaves. Other estuarine plants, like pickleweed (*Salicornia*), accumulate large amounts of water to dilute the salts they take up (Fig. 12.8). Such fleshy plants are known as **succulents.**

Adapting to the Mud As discussed in Chapter 11 (see "Living in the Sediment," in 11.2), living in mud has its problems. There is nothing to hold on to, so most animals either burrow or live in permanent tubes beneath the sediment surface. Clams do well because they can extend their siphons through the mud to get water for food and oxygen. Because it is difficult to move through mud, the animal inhabitants tend to be stationary or slow-moving. Living in mud, however, has a benefit: Salinity fluctuations are less drastic than in the water column.

The depletion of oxygen caused by the decay of organic matter in the mud presents another challenge. This is no problem to burrowers that pump oxygen-rich water into their burrows. Burrowers without this luxury have special adaptations to low-oxygen environments. Some have blood that contains **hemoglobin,** which has a particularly high affinity for oxygen. It can hold and carry oxygen even when only minute quantities are available. Some clams and a few other mud-dwellers can even survive for days without oxygen.

Types of Estuarine Communities

Several distinct communities are associated with estuaries. One consists of the **plankton,** fishes, and other open-water organisms that come in and leave with the tide. Other communities are permanent parts of the estuarine ecosystem.

Estuarine communities show low biodiversity. The relatively low number of estuarine species, however, are typically represented by many individuals. The low biodiversity is therefore compensated by a high **biomass,** the amount of living material measured as weight. A surprising number of estuarine species, particularly those inhabiting temperate estuaries, are widely distributed around the world. Humans have introduced many of these species, often with undesirable consequences (see Box 18.2, "Biological Invasions, the Uninvited Guests").

Open Water The type and abundance of plankton inhabiting estuaries vary tremendously with the currents, salinity, and temperature. The murky water restricts the penetration of light and can limit **primary production** by phytoplankton, even when the density of plankton is typically very high because of the high amount of nutrients. Most of the phytoplankton and zooplankton in small estuaries are marine species flushed in and out by the tides. Larger estuaries can also have their own, strictly estuarine, species of plankton.

One reason many of the world's great cities developed around estuaries is the rich supply of fish and shellfish in or near estuaries. Many species of commercially important fishes and shrimps use estuaries as nurseries for their young, taking advantage of the abundant food and relative safety from predators. About 90% of the marine commercial catch in the northern Gulf of Mexico, for example, is of fishes like the menhaden (*Brevoortia*; Fig. 12.9) and shrimps that depend on estuaries at some point in their lives.

A relatively rich variety of fishes live in most estuaries. Many are the juveniles of marine species that breed at sea but use estuaries as nurseries. Examples are the menhaden, anchovies (*Anchoa*), striped bass (*Merone*), red drum (*Scianeops*), and many species of flatfishes. Some fishes move through estuaries during their migrations. Such

FIGURE 12.8 Pickleweed (*Salicornia*) is a common succulent plant in salt marshes around the world. Farmed pickleweed is being studied as a source of biofuel.

fishes are either **anadromous**—those, like salmon, smelts, and shad, that migrate from the sea to spawn in fresh water or **catadromous**—those, like freshwater eels, that migrate from fresh water to spawn at sea. Relatively few fishes spend their entire lives in estuaries. Killifishes (*Fundulus*) are one example.

Mudflats The bottoms of estuaries that become exposed at low tide often form **mudflats** (see Fig. 12.14). Mudflats are especially extensive in estuaries where there is a large **tidal range** and a gently sloping bottom. It all looks pretty much the same, but the mudflat can vary widely in particle size. Sand often accumulates to create sand flats near river mouths and in the tidal creeks that form as the tide changes. The calmer central part of the mudflat contains more fine, silty material. Mudflats can also be found in fjords (see Fig. 12.2),

Active Transport The transfer of substances across membranes by a cell against a *concentration gradient.*
• 4.3, Challenges of Life in the Sea

Plankton Primary producers (*phytoplankton*) and consumers (*zooplankton*) that drift with the currents.
• 10.2, Major Marine Lifestyles and Environments; Figure 10.11

Primary Production The conversion of carbon from an inorganic form, carbon dioxide, into organic matter by autotrophs—that is, the production of food.
• 4.1, The Ingredients of Life

Hemoglobin A blood protein that transports oxygen in many animals; in vertebrates it is contained in *erythrocytes,* or red blood cells.
• 8.3, Biology of Fishes

Tidal Range Difference in water level between successive high and low tides.
• 3.3, Waves and Tides

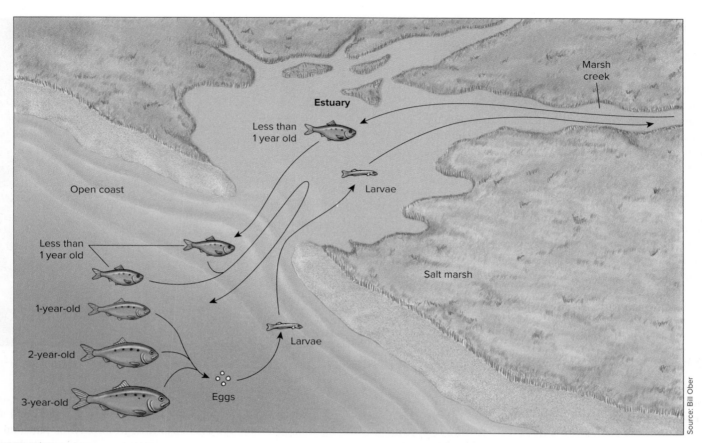

Source: Bill Ober

FIGURE 12.9 The Atlantic menhaden (*Brevoortia tyrannus*) is one of the most important commercial fishes in the United States. Adult fish (one to three years old) spawn offshore and the larvae drift with the tides and currents into estuaries, moving into shallow areas in the salt marshes to grow.

FIGURE 12.10
The California horn snail (*Cerithidea californica*), a deposit feeder, is abundant on mudflats. The green alga is *Enteromorpha,* which tolerates wide fluctuations in salinity and temperature as well as pollution. It can be found on rocky shores as well as along the shores of estuaries. It thrives during the long, sunny days of summer, when it can turn mudflats into bright-green "meadows."

Peter Castro

mudflat communities could be classified as intertidal communities. In estuaries, however, mudflat organisms must also withstand the regular, often drastic, variations in salinity that define estuaries.

Although not always evident, **primary producers** do flourish on mudflats. A few seaweeds, like the green algae *Enteromorpha* (Fig. 12.10) and *Ulva,* the sea lettuce, and the red alga *Gracilaria* grow on bits of shell. These and other primary producers can be particularly common during the warmer months. Large numbers of benthic diatoms grow on the mud and often undergo extensive blooms, forming golden-brown patches. These patches become coated with oxygen bubbles as intense photosynthesis takes place in the sunlight in tide pools left by the receding tide.

Bacteria and archaea are extremely abundant on mudflats. They decompose the huge amounts of organic matter brought in by rivers and tides. When the oxygen is used up by decay, some bacteria produce hydrogen sulfide. This in turn is used by **sulfur bacteria, chemosynthetic bacteria** that derive energy by breaking down sulfur compounds like hydrogen sulfide (see Table 5.1). Diatoms and bacteria, including photosynthetic bacteria, actually account for most of the primary production on mudflats.

The dominant animals on mudflats burrow in the sediment and are known as **infauna** (Fig. 12.11). Burrowers, like the fat innkeeper (*Urechis caupo*), polychaete worms, and ghost shrimps, actively excavate burrows in the sediment. Though there are not many types of burrowing animals, they often occur in immense numbers. At low tide their presence is often revealed only by small sediment mounds topped by a hole or piles of feces and other refuse. They feed on the abundant

where they occur mostly at the head of the fjord because the sides of fjords are steep and the bottom rapidly slopes to deep water.

Mudflat communities in estuaries are similar to those on muddy shores (see 11.2, Soft-Bottom Intertidal Communities). Low tides expose organisms to desiccation, wide variations in temperature, and predation, just as in any other intertidal community. For these reasons

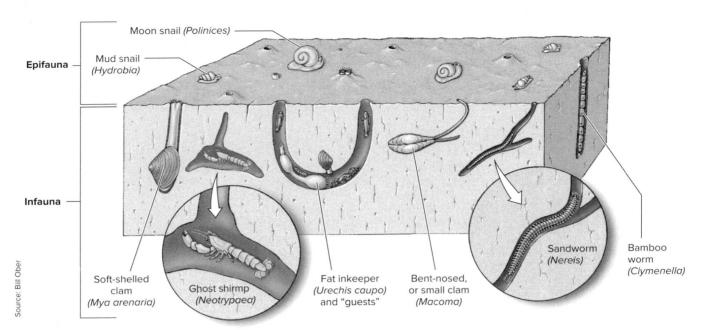

Source: Bill Ober

FIGURE 12.11 Some representative inhabitants of mudflats in temperate estuaries. Many mudflat organisms also can be found on muddy bottoms outside estuaries (see Fig. 13.6). The mud and moon snails are examples of *epifauna;* the clams, ghost shrimp, fat innkeeper, and the worms are examples of *infauna.* The snails and the bent-nosed clam are *deposit feeders,* whereas the soft-shelled clam and the ghost shrimp are *filter feeders.*

detritus in the sediment and water. Most of the food for these animals is brought in by the rivers and tides and is not actually produced on the mudflat. Very few mudflat animals can be classified as **epifauna,** those that either live *on* the sediment surface or are attached to a surface as **sessile** forms (Fig. 12.11). Crabs and some other animals can temporarily bury by covering themselves with sediment.

Mudflat inhabitants that feed on detritus are **deposit** and **suspension feeders,** including **filter feeders.** Deposit feeders are more common than suspension feeders on mudflats and other muddy bottoms (see Fig. 13.12). Suspension feeders are at a disadvantage because their filtering mechanisms tend to get clogged by the high amounts of sediment that rains on soft bottoms. Furthermore, deposit feeders actually exclude many suspension feeders by disturbing the sediments, which clogs the suspension feeders' feeding structures and buries their newly settled larvae.

Suspension feeders, on the other hand, dominate where the sediment is more sandy. The wider interstitial spaces between the larger sand particles hold less detritus for deposit feeders to eat, and the abrasive sand is hard on their digestive systems.

Many deposit feeders and some other members of the infauna are known as **bioturbators** because they move and mix sediment when burying or digging. Bioturbation helps in the oxygenation of sediment, a most important role in the case of the typically anoxic sediments of estuaries.

Estuarine communities are characterized by low biodiversity but high biomass. The dominant primary producers on mudflats are diatoms and bacteria. Most of the animals are burrowing deposit and suspension feeders that feed on detritus.

Protozoans, nematodes, and many other minute animals that compose the **meiofauna** (see Box 13.2, "Life in Mud and Sand") also thrive on detritus. The meiofauna are also known as **interstitial**

animals. The larger burrowing animals, or infauna, include many polychaetes (see Figs. 11.30 and 12.11). Most are deposit feeders. Other polychaetes are suspension feeders that filter water or extrude tentacles to collect the detritus that falls from the water column. Yet another detritus-feeding strategy among some polychaetes is to switch back and forth between suspension and deposit feeding, depending on the amount of suspended material in the water.

Bivalves often abound on mudflats. Many are filter feeders that are also found on muddy and sandy shores outside estuaries (see Fig. 11.29). Examples from temperate waters are the quahog, or hard clam (*Mercenaria mercenaria*), the soft-shelled clam (*Mya arenaria;* Fig. 12.11), and razor clams (*Ensis*). Some of these are of considerable commercial importance. Bent-nosed, or small, clams (*Macoma;* Fig. 12.11) are deposit feeders that use their long incurrent siphons to vacuum the surface.

The ghost (*Neotrypaea,* Fig. 12.11) and mud (*Upogebia*) shrimps make elaborate burrows that, as bioturbators, help oxygenate the sediment. These shrimps feed on detritus that they filter from the water and sift from the mud. Fiddler crabs (*Uca*) also live in burrows but are active on the mudflats at low tide (see Box 12.1, "Fiddler on the Mud"). They process the mud and extract the detritus, which they eat.

Chemosynthetic Bacteria *Autotrophic bacteria* that use energy contained in inorganic compounds rather than sunlight to make organic matter.
• 5.2, Prokaryotes; Table 5.1

Detritus Particles of dead organic matter.
• 10.3, The Flow of Energy and Materials

Deposit Feeders Animals that feed on organic matter that settles in the sediment.
Suspension Feeders Animals, including *filter feeders,* that feed on particles suspended in the water column.
• 7.1, Sponges; Figure 7.4

Box 12.1 Fiddler on the Mud

What lives in mud, literally feeds on mud, and finds mates by calling and waving across the mud? But, of course, fiddler crabs, creatures remarkable in many ways but best known as the ultimate experts in mud.

The many species of fiddler crabs (*Uca* and other genera) are inhabitants of mud and sand flats in estuaries and other sheltered coasts. They are found mostly in the tropics and subtropics, but some species are found as far north from the Equator as New Hampshire, United States, and as far south as Chile. Fiddlers are deposit feeders. They feed at low tide, using their pincers to scoop mud up into feeding appendages close to the mouth. The detritus in the mud is extracted with the help of brush-like mouthparts. Water is pumped from the gill chambers into the mouth to make the lighter detritus float and thus help separate it from the mud. The detritus is swallowed, and the clean mud is spat out on the substrate in neat little balls.

Fiddlers are active at low tide and retreat into their burrows at high tide. Each burrow has an entrance (revealed by the neat little balls of mud around it) that the occupant can plug when the tide comes in. At the next low tide, crabs emerge from home to feed and do whatever healthy, active fiddlers like to do. The tidal cycle means everything to them. Tides are so crucial that if crabs are taken away and isolated in an environment of constant light and temperature, they will continue to be active at the times that correspond to low tide and sit quietly when they were expected to be at home! Not only activity patterns but also color changes that normally take place in their natural environment (darker color during the day, lighter at night) continue to be observed in isolation. These patterns are examples of **biological clocks,** repeated rhythms that are synchronized with time. In the case of fiddlers, activity patterns and color changes are synchronized with tides, which depend on lunar cycles, and with day–night changes, which depend on the sun.

Fiddlers have an exciting sex life. Males feature one tremendously enlarged claw, either right or left. It is brightly colored or highlighted with markings in many species. Females have a much smaller pair of claws that are used in feeding, as is the males' small pincer. Males use their big claw to advertise their sex—to tell females they mean business and to threaten any other males that may be in their way. They wave the claw at low tide on territories established around their burrows. In one species, males build a mud shelter around the burrow to heighten the effect. Claw-waving gets so heated sometimes that a whole mudflat seems to move up and down with hundreds of displaying males. Males entice any interested females into their burrows, and a female can visit a few pads before deciding on a particular one. Males often fight for prospective mates but are also known to establish partnerships with neighbor males to defend their territories against intruders. Fighting with a stronger neighbor can cause a fiddler to end up with a lost claw, a more costly alternative than peaceful cooperation. A lost claw means disaster, meaning not only a deprived sex life but also not being as cool as the neighbors: the enlarged claw is used in temperature regulation, and crabs with an enlarged claw cool faster than those without it! It takes many molts to regenerate one that is big enough to get the crab back in action, and crabs whose claws are too small or that don't have the right moves can get pretty lonely!

In those areas coinhabited by several species of fiddlers, waving is used to prevent a male from attracting females of the wrong species. Some species wave up and down, others sideways. The angle and frequency of waving also vary, and bowing, fancy steps, and other body movements often form part of the ritual. Some beat the claw on the ground, and males of many species even produce sound by vibrating a joint of the large claw. It pays to advertise!

Signaling in a male fiddler crab (*Uca*).

Source: Bill Ober

On the Pacific coast of North America the fat innkeeper (Fig. 12.11), a soft-body echiuran worm, secretes a funnel-shaped net of mucus. It pumps water through this net to filter out food. It gets its common name because it shares its U-shaped burrow with a polychaete (*Hesperonoe adventor*), a crab (*Scleroplax granulata*), one or more fish (*Clevelandia ios*), and other guests.

Some animals live on the surface of the mud or move in and out with the tide. These include deposit feeders like mud snails (*Cerithidea, Hydrobia;* Figs. 12.10 and 12.11), amphipods, and shrimps. Carnivores include polychaete worms (*Nereis;* Fig. 12.11), moon snails (*Polinices;* Fig. 12.11) and other predatory snails (*Busycon*), and swimming crabs (*Callinectes*).

By far the most important predators in the mudflat community are fishes and birds. Fishes invade mudflats at high tide, whereas birds congregate at low tide to feed. Estuaries are important stopover and wintering areas for many species of migratory birds. The open spaces offer them safety from natural enemies, and food is plentiful. The most significant predators on mudflats are wading shorebirds (Figs. 12.12 and 12.13). These include the willet (*Tringa*), godwits (*Limosa*), dowitchers (*Limnodromus*), and many species of plovers (*Charadrius, Pluvialis*) and sandpipers such as curlews (*Nomenius*) and phalaropes (*Phalaropus*). They feed on polychaetes, ghost shrimps and other small crustaceans, clams, and mud snails. Oystercatchers (*Haematopus*) specialize on clams and other bivalves. Most of these birds exploit different types of prey. The varying lengths of their bills represent a specialization in prey because different types of prey live at different depths in the mud (see Fig. 12.12).

In addition, shorebirds use different strategies to locate their food. Birds like sandpipers rely mostly on their bills, probing in the mud as they walk around (Fig. 12.13*a*). Others, like plovers, use their eyesight to detect slight movements on the surface of the mud (Fig. 12.13*b*). Biologists think that these differences in feeding habits are an example of **resource partitioning.**

FIGURE 12.12 Differences in the bill length of wading shorebirds from the west coast of North America allow them to feed on particular mudflat animals.

FIGURE 12.13 Feeding behavior also varies among shorebirds. (*a*) Sandpipers use their bills to search for food and follow a roughly straight path. (*b*) Plovers rely mostly on their vision, turning their heads sideways as they move.

Herons and egrets comprise yet another group of wading birds. They specialize in catching fishes, shrimps, and other small swimming prey. Birds that feed by swimming or diving in the estuary, like ducks, terns, and gulls, are often seen resting on mudflats.

Salt Marshes Estuaries in temperate and subarctic regions worldwide are usually bordered by extensive grassy areas that extend inland from the mudflats. These intertidal areas are partially flooded at high tide and are known as **salt,** or **tidal, marshes** (Fig. 12.14). Sometimes they are grouped with freshwater marshes and collectively called **wetlands. Coastal wetlands** now cover as much as 200,000 km² (77,200 mi²) worldwide. Though mostly associated with estuaries, salt marshes can also develop along sheltered open coasts. They develop as long as disturbance from wave action is minimal to allow the accumulation of muddy sediments. Salt marshes may also develop along the inner margins of fjords as long as there

is an accumulation of muddy sediments free from the ice of glaciers. Tidal creeks, freshwater streams, and shallow pools frequently cut through the marsh (see photo at the beginning of the chapter). Salt marshes are typically replaced by mangrove forests along sheltered coasts in the tropics (see "Mangrove Forests," below).

In North America, salt marshes are particularly extensive along the Atlantic and Gulf of Mexico coasts (see map in Appendix D). The broad estuaries and shallow, protected bays of these gently sloping coastlines provide optimal conditions for the development of salt marshes. The Pacific coast of North America, on the other hand, is generally steeper, exposed to wave action, so that most of the estuaries have formed along narrow river valleys.

Resource Partitioning The sharing of a resource by two or more species to avoid competition.

• 10.1, The Organization of Communities

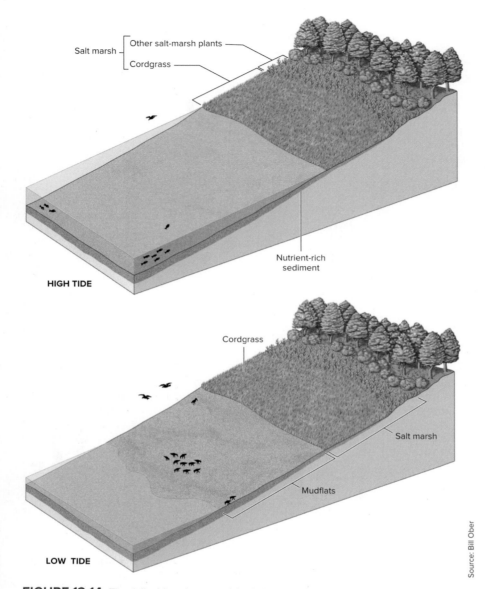

FIGURE 12.14 The daily tides play a crucial role in salt marshes. They help circulate detritus and nutrients and expose mudflat organisms to predation by shorebirds and other animals.

Source: Bill Ober

This has resulted in less extensive development of salt marshes. In the Northern Hemisphere salt marshes tend to be more extensive on the left side than on the right side of estuaries, since the turbulence caused by the flow of fresh water from rivers is stronger on the right side as a result of the Coriolis effect.

Salt marshes are subject to the same extremes in salinity, temperature, and tides that affect mudflats. Salt marshes also develop on a muddy bottom, but the mud is held together by the roots of marsh plants and thus is more stable.

Salt-marsh communities are dominated by a few hardy grasses and other salt-tolerant land plants. These plants thrive in the marsh, though the environment is too harsh for most other land plants. There is a pronounced zonation of plants in salt marshes (Fig. 12.15). The location of a given zone is related to the height relative to the tide, but it varies according to geographical location, type of substrate, and other factors. For instance, soil salinity can become particularly high at intermediate heights as a result of higher evaporation in marshes closer to hot, dry regions. This can result in areas bare of vegetation.

Cordgrasses (the smooth cordgrass, *Spartina alterniflora,* on the Atlantic coast; the California cordgrass, *S. foliosa,* on the Pacific coast; see Fig. 12.7) are typically the most common plants along the seaward limit of the salt marsh, where it meets the mudflats (Figs. 12.14 and 12.15). These grasses invariably occupy the fringe above the mean low tide level. Plants do better here because the soil is well drained and therefore richer in oxygen and less salty. The tops of their tall leaves remain exposed to the air even when the bottom is covered at high tide. The plants have extensive horizontal stems, or **rhizomes,** that stretch out underground. (see Fig. 6.14).

Cordgrass can gradually invade mudflats because the plants slow down the tidal flow and thus increase the amount of sediment trapped among the roots. The landward extension of the salt marsh is eventually limited by the height of the highest tide. In addition to providing a significant portion of the high primary production of estuarine communities because such a high density of plant biomass (see "Feeding Interactions Among Estuarine Organisms," below), salt-marsh plants like cordgrass help stabilize soils by decreasing the effects of wave action. Smooth cordgrass from the Atlantic has been introduced in other parts of the world for the protection of shorelines, sometimes with negative effects (see Box 12.2, "Restoration of Salt Marshes").

Cordgrass gives way to other plants in the higher parts of the marsh. On the Atlantic coast, a second species of cordgrass (the salt-meadow, or salt-marsh hay, *Spartina patens*) dominates (Fig. 12.15), but rushes (*Juncus*), pickleweed, and several other plants often form distinct zones. The higher levels of salt marshes on the Pacific coast are usually dominated by pickleweed (see Fig. 12.8). The landward limit of salt marshes is a transition zone with adjacent terrestrial, or land, communities. It is characterized by a large variety of plants resistant to salt spray, like salt grasses (*Distichlis*) and several species of pickleweed. It appears that in most salt marshes zonation is determined not only by the effects of flooding by tides but also by the combined effect of other factors. They include competition for space among salt-marsh plants, increased soil salinity in warm areas due to evaporation, and even the effect of burrowing animals.

The muddy salt-marsh substrate is home to decay bacteria, diatoms, and thick mats of filamentous green algae and cyanobacteria. Bacteria play a crucial role by decomposing the large amounts of dead plant material produced in the salt marsh. These bacteria and the partially broken-down organic matter are a major source of the detritus that feeds many of the inhabitants of the estuary. Some bacteria are **nitrogen fixers** that enrich the sediment.

Salt marshes are dominated by grasses and other marsh plants. Bacteria in the mud decompose dead plant material and contribute a large portion of the detritus in the estuary.

Box 12.2 Restoration of Salt Marshes

The degradation and destruction of salt marshes by human disturbance is a major worldwide problem (see "Human Impact on Estuarine Communities," above). The enhancement or restoration of disturbed salt marshes to their natural condition is nevertheless being carried out as part of efforts to protect and preserve coastal wetlands.

Some biologists encourage the natural regeneration of disturbed salt marshes, but others prefer to accelerate recovery by replanting dominant species, particularly cordgrass (*Spartina*). The University of Southern Mississippi, for example, operates a nursery that grows salt-marsh plants, which are then transplanted to restore salt marshes. The success of replanting, however, depends on factors like wave action and tides, water chemistry (salinity, dissolved nutrients), and the substrate (slope, sediment size, oxygen content). Recovery, which can last years, depends, among other factors, on the type and degree of disturbance, environmental factors, and the relative maturity of marshes, with the more mature ones taking longer to recover. Systematic monitoring is essential as marsh plants spread and tides bring in the larvae of invertebrates, and as other plants, fishes, seabirds, and other organisms become established. Restoration does not always follow a trouble-free recovery to a community where species diversity matches that of a targeted natural state, usually nearby marshes that serve as points of reference. Invasive plants, feral animals, unusual weather, and other unpredictable disruptions often slow down restoration.

The technology behind salt-marsh restoration is also being applied to restoring flooded areas previously cut off from the ocean, mitigation projects where salt marshes are created to offset marshes destroyed or affected by dredging or construction, and salt marshes affected by the 2010 *Deepwater Horizon* oil spill in the Gulf of Mexico. Lands once reclaimed from the sea for agricultural purposes in England and the North Sea are being re-exposed to tidal fluctuations and restored as salt marshes, a defense against erosion by rising sea levels because marshes dissipate wave action.

Industrial salt ponds are also being transformed into salt marshes and other tidal wetlands in San Francisco Bay, California, a project that is creating new habitats for seabirds and other wildlife as well as providing flood management. The South Bay Salt Pond Restoration Project aims to eventually restore 6,040 ha (15,100 acres). Full tidal restoration of nearly 1,520 ha (3,750 acres) had been completed by 2020, in addition to almost 1,620 ha (4,000 acres) in the planning stage. Already the number of birds has doubled, and leopard sharks and other predators have returned. Another objective of restoring salt marshes is to prevent tidal erosion and flooding.

Restoration is also undertaken in salt marshes impacted by invasive species of cord grass, as in the case of smooth cordgrasses (*Spartina alterniflora*), a native to the Atlantic coast of North America that has become a pest on the Pacific coast. Seeds were probably accidentally introduced when oysters were transplanted to the Pacific, but some could have come in ships' ballast water. The plant was also intentionally introduced on the Pacific and other coasts for erosion control. Problems have resulted, as with many other invasive species (see Box 18.2, "Biological Invasions: The Uninvited Guests"). Smooth cordgrass has spread over mudflats, tidal creeks, oyster grounds, and eelgrass meadows, its roots accumulating additional sediment, turning natural habitats into swampy land within a decade or so. Smooth cordgrass hybridizes with the native Pacific cordgrass (*Spartina foliosa*), and the hybrids are taller, spread into deeper water, and release more pollen and seeds than the native cordgrass. Spreading is accelerated because smooth cordgrass, unlike the native species, can self-pollinate. These hybrids are by now the dominant cordgrass in many Pacific salt marshes. Efforts to control invasive cordgrass are being undertaken in places like San Francisco Bay and Willapa Bay on the west coast of the United States.

For more information, explore the links provided on the Marine Biology *Online Learning Center.*

Some animals burrowing in mudflats also inhabit salt marshes. In addition, nematodes, small crustaceans, larvae of land insects, and other small invertebrates live among the algal mats and decaying marsh plants. Crabs are conspicuous inhabitants of salt marshes. Fiddler crabs build burrows along the mudflat edges, where they increase the oxygenation of the substrate, another example of bioturbation. Other marsh crabs (*Sesarma, Hemigrapsus*) are scavengers that eat dead organic matter. Some of these species live in burrows.

Marsh plants provide shelter and food to many marine and land animals. Coffee bean snails (*Melampus*) and marsh periwinkles (*Littorina, Littoraria*) are air-breathing snails that feed on detritus, minute algae, and fungi that grow on marsh plants. They move up the plants as the high tide moves in. Though they are air-breathers, they lay their eggs in the water and the larvae that hatch develop in the plankton. The ribbed, or horse, mussel (*Geukensia demissa*) is a suspension feeder that lives half buried in the mud among the cordgrass (Fig. 12.16). Killifishes and juvenile silversides (*Menidia*) are examples of fishes that inhabit tidal creeks and pools in the marsh at low tide. They move into the salt-marsh grass at high tide to escape predators like crabs and larger fishes, which enter the creeks with the rising tide. Crustaceans and small fishes retreat to pools or tidal creeks at low tide. Rails and American coots are among the birds that feed and nest here. Many other land birds and mammals, from ospreys to raccoons, are common visitors.

Mangrove Forests Mangrove forests are not limited to estuaries or close to the seashore, but in some ways they are the tropical equivalents of the temperate salt marshes. **Mangroves** are flowering land plants adapted to live in the intertidal (see 6.2, Flowering Plants, for a discussion of the most important species of mangroves and their morphological adaptations). These trees and shrubs often form dense forests, sometimes called **mangals**, to distinguish them from the actual plants themselves, or mangroves (see Figs. 6.16 and 6.17). Mangroves are typical of tropical and subtropical regions, where they replace the temperate salt marshes (see Fig. 6.15 and map in Appendix D).

Nitrogen Fixation Conversion of nitrogen gas (N_2) into nitrogen compounds that can be used by primary producers as nutrients.
• 5.2, Prokaryotes; Table 5.1

Peter Castro

FIGURE 12.16 The Atlantic ribbed, or horse, mussel (*Geukensia demissa*) lives half buried in the mud. It has the unusual ability to slightly open its valves, or gape, at low tide and take in oxygen from the air.

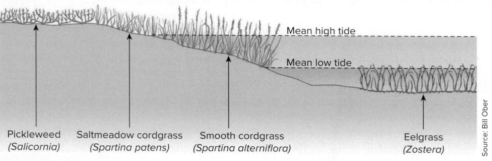

Source: Bill Ober

Mean high tide

Mean low tide

Pickleweed
(*Salicornia*)

Saltmeadow cordgrass
(*Spartina patens*)

Smooth cordgrass
(*Spartina alterniflora*)

Eelgrass
(*Zostera*)

FIGURE 12.15 A salt marsh near Atlantic Beach, North Carolina. As in other Atlantic marshes, the smooth cordgrass (*Spartina alterniflora*) occupies the edge of the marsh that is flooded the most by seawater. It is replaced higher up in the marsh by saltmeadow grass, or salt-marsh hay (*Spartina patens*), a shorter and finer grass that is less salt tolerant and can form extensive meadows. It grows where the marsh is flooded only at high tide. Many of these marshes have been filled in and destroyed.

The two communities nevertheless coexist in some areas, as on the northern coast of the Gulf of Mexico, southeastern Australia, and northern New Zealand. It has been estimated that most (around 75%) of all sheltered tropical shores were at one time fringed with mangroves, a figure that suggests their tremendous importance.

Mangroves are killed by frost so their worldwide northern and southern limits are determined by low temperatures. A change in the distribution of mangroves as a result of global climate change has already been noted. Florida mangroves have been growing farther north along the Atlantic coast and those in southern Australia have been expanding into salt marshes. Similar extensions of the geographical range of mangroves have also been recorded in Perú and on the Pacific coast of Mexico. Mangrove forests are been directly affected by humans in many other ways (see "Human Impact on Estuarine Communities," below).

Mangrove forests are formed by mangroves, tropical and subtropical trees and shrubs adapted to the marine intertidal environment, mostly on estuaries.

Mangroves grow on sheltered, unexposed coasts where muddy sediments accumulate (Fig. 12.17). Though mangroves usually grow in tropical and subtropical estuaries, they are not restricted to them. As in salt-marsh plants, the various species of mangroves have different tolerances to immersion by high tide. Partly as a result of these differences in tolerance, they show a distinctive zonation in the intertidal, from a marine to a progressively terrestrial environment.

As land plants growing at the sea edge, mangroves live under very stressful conditions. They are nevertheless adapted to the marine environment in several ways. Mangroves must get rid of salts from the water that is taken in by the roots. Most salts are actually not taken in by the roots of the red mangrove (*Rhizophora mangle*), a process that requires energy. Salt glands on the leaves of the black (*Avicennia germinans*) and white (*Laguncularia racemosa*) mangroves in the Western Hemisphere and several other mangrove species excrete salts, with salt crystals usually visible on the leaves as the drops containing the salts dry up (Fig. 12.18). Living in anoxic mud is also stressful, and the mangrove roots of all mangrove species have different types of root extensions, like the prop roots of the red mangrove (see Fig. 6.16), for obtaining oxygen from the atmosphere. Other species of mangroves, like the black mangrove and the **Indo-West Pacific** species of *Sonneratia*, develop **pneumatophores,** conspicuous, unbranched extensions of the roots. Pneumatophores grow upward from the anoxic mud to help aerate the plant tissues (Fig. 12.19). Also helping in aeration are lenticels, pores in the bark and roots. Root **lenticels** are connected to **aerenchyma**, soft tissue with air spaces, that, as in cordgrasses in saltmarshes, transports air to the submerged parts of trees.

Many marine and land animals live in mangrove forests. Crabs are particularly common. Some of these crabs, like species of *Sesarma* and *Cardisoma,* feed on the abundant leaf litter that accumulates below the mangrove trees. Some species of crabs also feed on leaves, flowers (Fig. 12.18), and seedlings still attached to mangrove trees. Mangrove crabs spend most of their lives on land, but when eggs are ready to hatch, females must release the planktonic larvae into the water.

Many types of organisms attach to, or take shelter among, the submerged mangrove roots (Fig. 12.20). Particularly common are seaweeds, sponges, oysters, barnacles, and tunicates. The number

and diversity of the attached organisms are especially rich in mangrove roots subject to a wide tidal range. Large sponges are particularly important because they are used as shelter by a good number of small fishes.

The muddy bottom around mangroves is inhabited, like in mudflats, by a variety of deposit and suspension feeders. These include polychaetes, mud shrimps, and clams. Several species of fiddler crabs (see Box 12.1, "Fiddler on the Mud") excavate burrows in the mud. As in temperate mudflats and salt marshes, burrowing crabs help oxygenate the sediment. Mudskippers (*Periophthalmus;* Fig. 12.21) are unique fishes found in Indo-West Pacific mangrove forests and mudflats. They have burrows in the mud but spend most of their time out of the water, skipping over the mud and crawling up mangrove roots to catch insects and crabs. When out of the water, mudskippers can take oxygen from the air through blood-rich surfaces in the mouth and on the skin as long as the surfaces remain moist.

The channels that cross mangrove forests are rich nurseries for many species of commercially important shrimps, spiny lobsters, crabs, and fishes (Fig. 12.22). They are also nurseries for coral reef fishes. Several species of oysters and other bivalve molluscs that live on or even within the roots of mangroves (like shipworms, *Teredo*) are used as food in some places around the world. Oyster farms are sometimes located near mangroves (see Fig. 17.15), a case where humans take advantage of the nutrient-rich waters of mangrove forests.

Many species of land animals use mangrove forests for shelter and food. Insects feed on leaves, flowers, and the attached seedlings,

FIGURE 12.17 Aerial view of a mangrove forest on the southern coast of Puerto Rico. The outer seaward edge of the forest is dominated by the red mangrove (*Rhizophora mangle*), shown here as a slightly higher belt along the shore. As in Florida and most of the Western Hemisphere, the inner margin behind the red mangrove is bordered by a broad belt of black mangrove (*Avicennia germinans*). Farther away from the black mangrove is the white mangrove (*Laguncularia racemosa*).

while bees and bats feed on the pollen and nectar of some mangrove flowers. Birds make their homes in the branches and feed on fishes, crabs, and other prey. Snakes, frogs, lizards, bats, and other land animals also live in the mangrove trees.

FIGURE 12.18 Leaves of the Indo-West Pacific black mangrove (*Aegiceras corniculatum*) from Australia, showing the salt crystals that form as the salty secretions of the salt glands dry up under the sun. Notice the large flower buds.

FIGURE 12.19 Pneumatophores, the vertical extensions of shallow roots, obtain additional oxygen in mangroves like *Sonneratia alba.* Here in Palau, western Pacific, this species is found along the seaward fringe of mangrove forests.

FIGURE 12.20 Seaweeds, sponges, oysters, sea anemones, barnacles, sea squirts, and many other types of organisms live attached to the roots of the red mangrove (*Rhizophora mangle*).

FIGURE 12.21 A mudskipper (*Periophthalmus*) from the mudflats of a mangrove forest in Singapore. Its protruding eyes are adapted to see in air. Each eye can be retracted into a moist pocket to keep it from drying out.

Large amounts of leaves and other dead plant material accumulate in the mangrove forest. Considerable amounts are eaten by crabs, and some is exported to other ecosystems. Much of the detritus, however, is broken down by bacteria and fungi. This makes the mud among the mangrove roots black and oxygen-deficient, much like that in salt marshes. Because of the oxygen-poor sediments, and

FIGURE 12.22 Small fishes, many of which are juveniles of coral reef fishes and commercially important species, seek shelter from predators and find food among the roots of mangrove. Shown here is the red mangrove (*Rhizophora mangle*) in a Florida mangrove forest.

toxic substances released by the leaves, life on muddy bottoms in mangrove forests is less abundant than on similar bottoms elsewhere.

Mangrove forests are of a tremendous ecological significance, but directly or indirectly are also of great economic importance to humans. The subject is discussed in "Economic Importance," in 6.2.

Other Estuarine Communities The bottom of estuaries beyond the intertidal mudflats and salt marshes is typically muddy and inhabited by organisms similar to those characteristic of muddy subtidal communities (see 13.2, Soft-Bottom Subtidal Communities). Brackish-water species are gradually replaced by euryhaline marine species and ultimately by stenohaline marine species (see Fig. 12.5). Fjord bottoms are typically anoxic and support communities that are characterized by low biodiversity but high biomass. The abrasive effect of drift ice from glaciers is also an important factor in some fjords. Deep-water coral "reefs" high in biodiversity have nevertheless been discovered in some fjords (see Box 14.3, "Deep-Water Coral Communities").

The muddy bottoms below low tide levels are sometimes covered by beds, or meadows, of grass-like flowering plants known as **seagrasses.** They include eelgrass (*Zostera;* see Fig. 6.13*b*), which is restricted to temperate waters, and turtle grass (*Thalassia;* see Fig. 6.13*d*), a warm-water species often found near mangrove forests. The roots of seagrasses help stabilize the sediment, and their leaves provide shelter to many organisms as well as being an additional source of detritus. Seagrass meadows are not restricted to estuaries and are discussed in more detail in Chapter 13 (see "Seagrass Meadows," in 13.2).

Oysters (*Ostrea, Crassostrea*; Fig. 7.26*a*) can form extensive beds on the muddy bottoms of estuaries in temperate waters in North America, Europe, and Australia. These **oyster reefs,** sometimes known by the more general name of **shellfish reefs,** gradually develop as successive generations of oysters grow on the shells of their predecessors (Fig. 12.23). They provide a complex, three-dimensional surface for many organisms. The oyster-reef community includes seaweeds, sponges, tubeworms, barnacles, and other organisms that attach to the hard shells. Other animals take shelter among or even inside the shells. A similar estuarine community develops in association with mussel (*Mytilus*) beds, though the mussels require a hard substrate for attachment.

Oyster reefs, once an important feature of many estuaries along the Atlantic coast of North America and elsewhere, have sharply declined as a result of pollution, overharvesting, disease, and disturbance by boats. This decline has had a major impact on the biodiversity of these estuarine communities. In addition to providing a habitat to many species, oysters increase the clarity and light transmission of water for seagrasses and other plants by filtering the water; an adult oyster filters as much as 270 l (60 gallons) of water daily. Oyster reefs also help protect shores from erosion by waves.

CP Cheah/Moment/Getty Images

Blanca Laviers/National Geographic/Getty Images

Feeding Interactions Among Estuarine Organisms

Though estuaries are low in biodiversity when compared to coral reefs and rocky shores, they reap the benefits of living in a very productive ecosystem. The generalized food webs shown in Figure 12.24 summarize the feeding relationships among different organisms in estuarine ecosystems.

Why do estuaries have such a high primary production? There are several reasons. Nutrients brought in by the tide and rivers, together with those generated by nitrogen-fixing organisms and the decomposition of detritus, are used by plants, algae, and bacteria, the primary producers. Primary production is especially high in the communities that surround estuaries. The high biomass of cordgrass and other salt-marsh plants (or mangroves in the tropics) are particularly adapted to live on the mud and thus take advantage of the high concentration of nutrients in the sediments. The diatoms and bacteria in the mud and the phytoplankton in the water also contribute significantly to primary production.

Detritus also tends to sink to the bottom. Bottom water, which has a higher salinity and density than shallower water, thus acts as a nutrient trap in deep estuaries. Some species of phytoplankton are known to migrate to deep water at night, where they take in nutrients and move up to shallow, sunlit water the next day to carry out photosynthesis.

Primary production by estuary plants and other organisms varies geographically and seasonally, as does their relative contribution to the ecosystem as a whole. Estimates of primary production range from 130 to nearly 6,000 g dry weight/m^2/year for cordgrasses in salt marshes on the Atlantic coast of the United States. Refer to Table 10.1 for a summary of the typical rates of primary production for salt marshes, mangroves, and seagrass meadows.

The organic material manufactured by primary producers is made available to consumers mainly in the form of detritus. A distinctive feature of estuarine ecosystems is that most of the animals feed on dead organic matter. Except for insects, a few types of birds like geese, and some land animals on the fringes, relatively few herbivores actually graze on salt-marsh plants. Many detritus feeders obtain more energy from the bacteria and other decomposers in the detritus than from the dead organic matter itself. They excrete any detritus that remains undigested, however, returning it to the detritus pool. The surplus detritus is exported to the open ocean and neighboring ecosystems in a process known as **outwelling.** The exported detritus serves as a valuable source of food and nutrients to other ecosystems. The amount of exported detritus varies among estuaries, and some are actually net importers. Nonetheless, outwelling is an important role of estuaries, an additional reason that they should be preserved and protected.

Both salt marshes and mangrove forests are coastal ecosystems where natural **carbon sinks**, or **blue carbon**, result from the long-term accumulation of large amounts of organic matter that sink and are buried in sediments (see Box 10.3, "Carbon Sinks and Blue Carbon"). Carbon dioxide (CO_2), removed from the atmosphere and transferred into organic matter by photosynthesis, is thus ultimately stored in these carbon sinks. Because of the high primary production of salt marshes and mangrove forests, the amount of carbon in these sinks

FIGURE 12.23 An oyster reef formed by the eastern oyster (*Crassostrea virginica*) on the Atlantic coast of North America, exposed at low tide.

Scott Taylor, Duke Marine Laboratory

has been found to be very high, in many cases much higher than in land forests. The absorption of carbon as CO_2 from the atmosphere by the primary producers of these wetlands is greater than the amount they release. Such release of CO_2, an important **greenhouse gas**, accelerates global climate change as well as **ocean acidification** (see "Special Report: Climate Change").

Estuaries include plant-dominated communities with very high primary production. Much of the food manufactured by these plants is made available to consumers by way of detritus. Important carbon sinks are found in coastal wetlands.

12.4 HUMAN IMPACT ON ESTUARINE COMMUNITIES

The value of coastal wetlands as sources of food and as nurseries of many food species, in the protection against land erosion and flood surges caused by storms and hurricanes, and their role as carbon sinks (see Box 10.3, "Carbon Sinks and Blue Carbon") and in the maintenance of biodiversity and water quality, is enormous (see "Economic Importance," in 6.2). Estuaries also serve as critical stopovers for migratory seabirds around the world. Furthermore, mangrove forests and seagrass meadows that often develop in tropical estuaries help reduce terrestrial runoff that protects coral reefs from sedimentation. Yet, the environmental consequences of human intrusion in coastal wetlands, particularly in salt marshes and mangrove forests, have been disastrous. Countless have been obliterated (see Fig. 18.2), and many surviving ones are in danger of disappearing. As an example, three-quarters of the Southern California salt marshes have already been lost, and the surviving ones could be gone within 100 years. What's more, oyster reefs are now considered one of the world's most imperiled marine habitats.

All around the globe estuaries are being dredged to make marinas, artificial harbors, and seaports. Others are filled to create everything from industrial parks and urban development to garbage

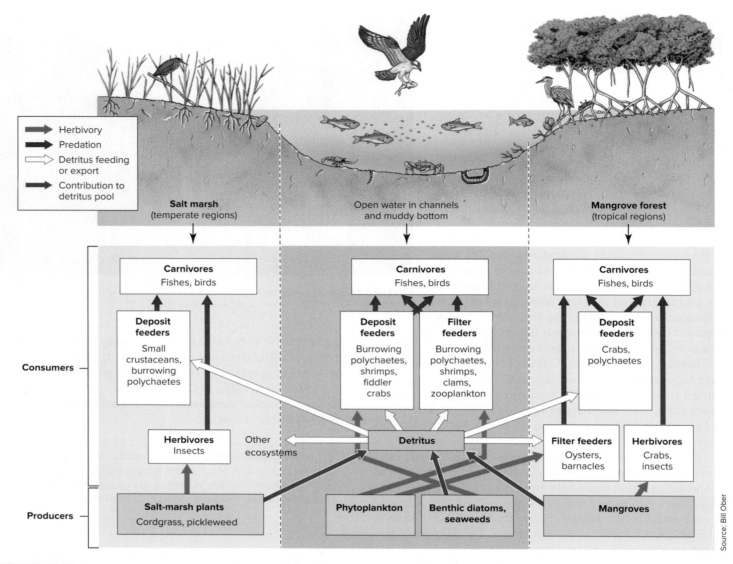

FIGURE 12.24 Generalized food webs in estuarine ecosystems. Salt marshes (left) occur in temperate regions, mangroves (right) in the tropics.

Source: Bill Ober

dumps. The dredging of navigation channels increases the exposure of estuaries to wave action, which often results in the destruction of salt marshes. Another problem in some estuaries is the reduction or disappearance of the usual freshwater input when rivers are dammed or diverted. Sediment input from rivers is decreased so that erosion of sediments by tides is not replenished. The opposite can also be a problem. Deforestation and agriculture brings about an increase in sediment, which in estuaries like Chesapeake Bay, decreases water quality and increases pollution. Oil spills can be particularly harmful to salt marshes, as evidenced by the 2010 *Deepwater Horizon* spill in the Gulf of Mexico. Wetlands along the Louisiana coast of the Gulf of Mexico, among the most extensive in the world, have also been gradually eroded away as the result of the cutting of canals to install pipelines and haul oil-drilling equipment. One reason why the city of New Orleans was badly impacted by Hurricane Katrina in 2005 was that coastal salt marshes between the Gulf of Mexico and the city had been greatly reduced. Another threat, particularly along the Pacific coast of North America, is the effect of cordgrass **invasive species**

(see, Box 12.2, "Restoration of Salt Marshes"). About one-third of all estuaries in the United States have disappeared altogether; close to 70% of those in California have been lost, and all are at risk of vanishing. Similar or even higher losses have been documented in many countries. Erosion and flooding as a result of sea level rise brought about by global climate change (see Special Report: Climate Change) is another potential threat to salt marshes.

The same factors that threaten salt marshes are menacing mangrove forests in the tropics. Mangrove forests once fringed around 75% of all sheltered tropical coastlines, but 35 to 50% of these forests have been destroyed. The figure is higher for the very diverse mangrove forests of Southeast Asia. It has been estimated that mangrove forests are disappearing at an annual rate of at least 1 to 2% worldwide, possibly higher than coral reefs and tropical rain forests. The United Nations' Environment Program estimated that about 20% of mangrove forests were lost worldwide between 1980 and 2005.

Mangrove forests have been cleared at this alarming rate to provide space for agriculture, urban and industrial development, roads,

and garbage dumps. Countless mangrove forests have been destroyed and replaced by tourist resorts, which, like in East Africa, has resulted in a decrease of fish populations in nearby coral reefs, hurting tourism in the end. Shrimp aquaculture, a booming operation and an important source of revenue and employment in the developing nations of Southeast Asia, South America, and other tropical and subtropical regions (see "Aquaculture," in 17.1), has nevertheless been particularly destructive. Forests have been destroyed to build the ponds to raise the shrimp; many others have been built to raise fish (Fig. 12.25). Water from the ponds, which contains large amounts of waste, excess nutrients, and uneaten food, is often flushed out to sea, causing serious pollution. Excess nutrients are responsible for **eutrophication.**

The growing use of mangrove wood as fuel and timber in some areas is another cause for concern. Mangrove forests have also been impacted by increased boat traffic, oil spills (see "Effects of Oil on Marine Life," in 18.2), and pollution by plastics and solid waste (Fig. 12.26). Together with salt marshes, it has been predicted that mangrove forests will be among the first marine ecosystems to be adversely affected by sea level rise due to global climate change. Increased temperatures, however,

FIGURE 12.25 Shrimp and fish aquaculture has been responsible for the destruction of many mangrove forests, particularly in Southeast Asia and South America. Waste that is released into coastal waters from fish-farming ponds like this, is an important source of pollution.

are promoting the extension of mangroves further north or south from the Equator (see above). Such increases in temperature have nevertheless caused severe droughts that decrease freshwater input in estuaries, which result in increased salinities that kill mangroves.

Mangrove forests remove carbon dioxide (CO_2) from the atmosphere and trap an unusually high proportion of their primary production as organic carbon in the leaves and detritus that are deposited in the sediments. When the mangroves are destroyed, much of this trapped CO_2 is released back to the atmosphere when the organic matter decays. Mangrove deforestation accounts for an estimated 10% of all CO_2 emissions caused by deforestation, even though mangrove forests occupy only 0.7% of the area of tropical forests.

Conservation efforts through protective legislation, restoration projects involving the mass replanting of mangrove seedlings, proper management, and the creation of marine protected areas and reserves have nevertheless resulted in a reduction in the rate of loss of mangrove forests in some areas. Of particular importance is the development of sustainable exploitations of fishery resources in developing countries, where economic development is often in conflict with the conservation of natural resources. Many conservation programs thus emphasize the education of local communities on the economic and ecological values of mangrove forests and on providing economic alternatives to practices that lead to mangrove destruction.

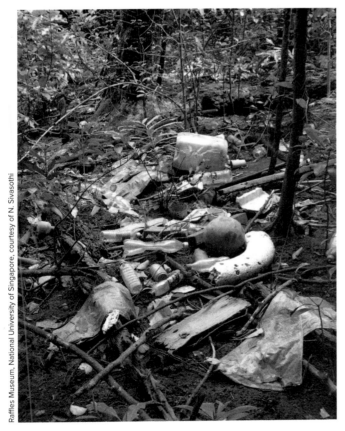

FIGURE 12.26 Solid waste, especially plastics and other durable materials, often accumulate in mangrove forests. Some of the waste is brought in by high tide, but forests are sometimes used as convenient garbage dumps.

Eutrophication Increased growth of algae as a consequence of excess nutrients.

• 18.2, Pollution

Interactive Exploration

McGraw-Hill Connect® is a great place to check your understanding of chapter material. Visit **www.mcgrawhillconnect.com** for access to interactive chapter summaries, chapter quizzing, and more! Further enhance your knowledge with video clips and weblinks to chapter-related material.

Critical Thinking

1. A proposal is made to deepen the entrance and main channel of an estuary. What do you think will happen to the salt marshes that surround the channel? What do you predict will happen to the primary production of the estuary as a whole?

2. Mangroves of a species of *Rhizophora* living along the northern coast of a bay are subject to a much wider tidal range than those on the southern shores of the same bay. What differences could be expected in the diversity and density of the organisms living on the roots (see Fig. 12.20) of the northern mangroves in contrast to those living on the southern shores? Explain the reason for the differences, if any.

3. Some of the organic material manufactured in estuarine communities is exported to other ecosystems. What type of ecosystems receive this material? How is this material transported?

4. Shorebirds most certainly impact the populations of invertebrates living as infauna in mud flats. Many of these shorebirds are seasonal migrants. What kinds of impact could you predict?

For Further Reading

Some of the recommended reading may be available online. Look for live links on the *Marine Biology* Online Learning Center.

General Interest

Byerly, P., B. G. Merkle, and M. Hepner, 2019. Renewed hope for coastal marshes in Louisiana. *American Scientist*, vol. 107, no. 2, March–April, pp. 198–202. Several efforts are being made to save Louisiana salt marshes, the most extensive in the United States.

Carey, J., 2013. Architects of the swamp. *Scientific American,* vol. 309, no. 6, December, pp. 74–79. Wetland restoration, not an easy task, can be successful if one or two goals are achieved rather than trying to fully restore the entire ecosystem.

Gies, E., 2018. Fortress of mud. *Nature,* vol. 562, pp. 178–180. Salt-marsh restoration in San Francisco Bay offers hope to overcome rising seas.

Jacobsen, R., 2019. Beyond seawalls. *Scientific American,* vol. 32, no. 4, April, pp. 32–37. Restored salt marshes rather than seawalls promise the best protection to shorelines threatened by storms and sea-level rise.

Popkin, G., 2015. Breaking the waves. *Science,* vol. 350, 13 November, pp. 756–759. Salt-marsh plants can be used as a defense against rising sea levels.

In Depth

Bayraktarov, E., S. Brisbane, V. Hagger, C. S. Smith, K. A. Wilson, C. E. Lovelock, C. Gillies, A. D. L. Steven, and M. I. Saunders, 2018. Priorities and motivations of marine coastal restoration research. *Frontiers in Marine Science* [https://doi.org/10.3389/fmars.2020.00484].

Cadier, C., E. Bayraktarov, R. Piccolo, and M. F. Adame, 2020. Indicators of coastal wetlands restoration success: A systematic review. *Frontiers in Marine Science* [https://doi.org/10.3389/fmars.2020.600220].

Cai, W.-J., R. A. Feely, J. M. Testa, M. Li, W. Evans, S. R. Alin, Y.-Y. Xu, G. Pelletier, A. Ahmed, D. J. Greeley, J. A. Newton, and N. Bednaršek, 2021. Natural and anthropogenic drivers of acidification in large estuaries. *Annual Review of Marine Science,* vol. 13, pp. 23–55.

Carrasquilla-Henao, M. and F. Juanes, 2017. Mangroves enhance local fisheries catches: A global meta-analysis. *Fish and Fisheries,* vol. 18, pp. 79–93.

Duarte, C. M, 2017. Hidden forests, the role of vegetated coastal habitats in the ocean carbon budget. *Biogeosciences,* vol. 14, pp. 301–310.

Ermgassen, P., S. E. Zu, T. Grove, and I. Nagelkerken, 2020. Global affiliation of juvenile fishes and invertebrates with mangrove habitats. *Bulletin of Marine Science,* vol. 96, pp. 403–414.

Friess, D. A., E. S. Yando, J. B. Alemu, L.-W. Wong, S. Soto, and N. Bhatia, 2020. Ecosystem services and disservices of mangrove forests and saltmarshes. *Oceanography and Marine Biology: An Annual Review,* vol. 58, pp. 7–142.

Gaskins, L. C., A. B. Paxton, and B. R. Silliman, 2020. Megafauna in salt marshes. *Frontiers in Marine Science* [https://doi.org/10.3389/fmars.2020.561476].

Himes-Cornell, A., S. O. Grose, and L. Pendleton, 2018. Mangrove ecosystem service values and methodological approaches to valuation: Where do we stand? *Frontiers in Marine Science* [https://doi.org/10.3389/fmars.2018.00376].

Lacerda, L. D., R. Borges, and A. C. Ferreira, 2019. Neotropical mangroves: Conservation and sustainable use in a scenario of global climate change. *Aquatic Conservation: Marine and Freshwater Ecosystems,* vol. 29, pp. 1347–1364.

Smith, C. S., M. E. Rudd, R. K. Gittman, E. C. Melvin, V. S. Patterson, J. J. Renzi, E. H. Wellman, and B. R. Silliman, 2020. Coming to terms with living shorelines: A scoping review of novel restoration strategies for shoreline protection. *Frontiers in Marine Science* [https://doi.org/10.3389/fmars.2020.00434].

Wiberg, P. L., S. Fagherazzi, and M. L. Kirwan, 2020. Improving predictions of salt marsh evolution through better integration of data and models. *Annual Review of Marine Science,* vol. 12, pp. 389–413.

A shallow rocky subtidal community, including kelp, other seaweeds, and many types of invertebrates.

Subtidal zone

Continental shelf

Simon Shin kwangsig/Shutterstock

13

CHAPTER

Life on the Continental Shelf

The submerged edge of the continents, the **continental shelf,** was once considered the beginning of the unknown ocean. But when the shelf came under scrutiny during the 1800s, the unknown began to give up its secrets. We have learned more because the use of scuba and underwater habitats has allowed firsthand study and observation (Fig. 13.1). Tropical coral reefs, seagrass meadows, and kelp forests, among the most productive ecosystems in the ocean, are found on the shelf. The shelf also includes the world's most important fishing grounds, which yield about 90% of the total marine global catch. Oil and minerals have been found on the shelf, and nations have extended their international borders to protect their new-found, or yet-to-be-found, resources. The continental shelf, being close to shore, is also profoundly affected by pollution and other activities of humans on land.

This chapter looks at life on the continental shelf. Life in the water column above the shelf is discussed in Chapter 15, and the shelf's fisheries in Chapter 17. Coral reefs, most of which are found on the shelf, are covered separately in Chapter 14.

13.1 PHYSICAL CHARACTERISTICS OF THE SUBTIDAL ENVIRONMENT

The part of the continental shelf that is never exposed at low tide constitutes the **subtidal zone** of the marine environment. The subtidal zone, sometimes called the **sublittoral zone,** extends from the low tide level on shore to the **shelf break,** the outer edge of the

Bill Ober

FIGURE 13.1 Scuba diving has dramatically expanded the possibilities for the study of the subtidal environment. These two marine biologists are using a grid to determine the density (number per area) and spacing, or distribution, of bottom organisms (see Fig. 13.4).

continental shelf (see Fig. 10.12). The depth of the shelf break varies, but it averages around 150 m (490 ft). The width of the shelf is also highly variable. It is much wider on the trailing edge of plates (**passive margins**) than on the leading edge of plates (**active margins**), where the plates are colliding with other plates (see "Active and Passive Margins" in 2.3, The Geological Provinces of the Ocean). The shelf is therefore much wider on the Atlantic margins of North and South America than on the Pacific side of the same continents (see Fig. 2.23). The width can also vary in a particular stretch of the coast, as in the case of the coast of California (see Fig. 2.22). It ranges from less than 1 km (0.6 mi) to more than 750 km (470 mi), with an average of approximately 80 km (48 mi).

The **benthos** of the continental shelf live in the subtidal zone, which is discussed in this chapter. Chapter 15 covers the **plankton** and **nekton** of the water column over the continental shelf, which constitutes the **neritic zone.**

> The subtidal zone consists of the sea floor from the low tide level to the shelf break, the outer edge of the continental shelf.

The physical factors that affect subtidal organisms are linked to two of the shelf's fundamental characteristics: its relatively shallow water and its proximity to land. Because the bottom is shallow, temperature varies more from place to place in the subtidal zone than on the deeper bottom beyond the shelf. This is significant because temperature is one of the most important factors influencing the distribution of marine organisms, and the kinds of organisms found in the subtidal change dramatically from the Equator to the poles. There are also *more,* not just different, species in the tropics than in temperate or polar waters. The sea floor beneath the Arctic and Antarctic ice, however, is far from being a desert (see Box 13.1, "Under the Polar Ice").

The bottom in shallow water is also much more affected by waves and currents than in deep water. The rise and fall of tides can produce particularly strong **tidal currents** on the shelf, especially in bays and narrow straits. Wind waves can affect the bottom even at depths of 200 m (650 ft). Water motion, or **turbulence,** stirs up the water column and prevents **stratification.** As a result, the temperature and salinity of the water at the bottom of the subtidal are not much different from those at the surface. More importantly, nutrients do not concentrate in the bottom layer and become unavailable to primary producers at the surface, as they do in deep water (see "Nutrients," in 15.3). Nutrients are also brought in by rivers, sometimes as by-products of the highly productive salt marshes or mangrove forests that may fringe the shore. As a result, the water over the continental shelf is far more productive and plankton-rich than the open ocean, so much more food is available.

Rivers also bring in large amounts of fresh water. Freshwater runoff dilutes the seawater, reducing its salinity. The huge freshwater plumes of large rivers like the Mississippi and the Amazon extend many miles offshore. Freshwater fishes causes stratification of the water column. Away from the influence of rivers, however, the salinity of coastal water is about the same as that beyond the shelf.

The combination of proximity to land and shallow water greatly influences **sedimentation,** the settling of sediment particles from the water. Most of the sediment on the shelf is **lithogenous,** and rivers bring in huge quantities of sediment from the continents. Water motion sorts out the particles by size and density, especially on the shallower parts of the shelf. Large-grained material like gravel and sand settles out even in areas with strong waves and currents. On the other hand, turbulence keeps fine particles like silt and clay in suspension. Fine particles are deposited only in quiet areas or in deeper water when turbulence does not reach the bottom.

The abundant phytoplankton plus the sediment that is brought in by rivers and stirred up by waves and currents make shelf water murkier or with a greenish tint than that of the deep-blue of open-ocean water. Light does not penetrate as deeply, which reduces the depth at which primary producers—phytoplankton and attached seaweeds and seagrasses—can carry out photosynthesis and grow.

Other factors affecting subtidal communities, particularly those close to land, are disturbance by ice in polar and subpolar regions or close to glaciers, trawling by commercial fishing (see "Trawling," in 18.1), and pollution by fertilizers, sewage, oil, and other chemicals (see 8.2, Pollution).

> The type of bottom, depth, turbulence, temperature, salinity, and light are among the most important physical factors that influence life on the continental shelf. Disturbance by pollution, fish trawlers, and ice are also significant in many regions.

13.2 SOFT-BOTTOM SUBTIDAL COMMUNITIES

The type of bottom, or **substrate,** is most important in determining which particular organisms inhabit the floor of the continental shelf. It also dictates how they are sampled by marine biologists (Fig. 13.2). In fact, subtidal communities are often classified according to the type of substrate. The most common of these are communities associated with soft bottoms.

Sandy and muddy **substrates** dominate the world's continental shelves. Large areas covered by soft sediments stretch from the shore to the edge of the shelf. Even along rocky shores, rocks eventually give way to sand or mud in deeper water. The organisms that inhabit these often flat and seemingly homogeneous bottoms (Fig. 13.3) are not necessarily distributed by chance. It has long been recognized that these organisms form distinct communities whose distribution is greatly influenced by factors like the particle size and stability of the sediment, light, and temperature.

The shelf's soft-bottom communities share many traits with the communities of sandy beaches and mudflats covered in Chapters 11 and 12. **Infauna,** animals that burrow or dig in the sediment, predominate in all these communities. There are also, however, some **epifauna,** animals that live on top of the sediment (see Fig. 13.6). Some members of the epifauna can temporarily bury by covering themselves with sediment. Because the soft bottom offers nothing to hold on to, **sessile,** or attached, forms are rare.

> Most of the continental shelf is covered by mud or sand. The subtidal communities in these areas are dominated by infauna.

The number of species living on subtidal soft bottoms is usually higher than the number of species on soft bottoms in the intertidal zone. This is largely because of the relatively more stable physical conditions below the low tide mark. Desiccation is not a problem.

Furthermore, there are none of the drastic temperature changes caused by exposure at low tide or the salinity variations of estuarine mudflats.

The close relationship between particle size and the distribution of organisms is particularly evident in the infauna, which for the most part are very selective as to where they live. Different species can also partition their environment and thus reduce competition by living at different depths in the substrate. Because only the upper layer of sediment contains enough oxygen, however, the depth at which the infauna can live is limited. Oxygen is quickly used up by decomposition in mud that is rich in organic matter. In contrast, sand usually contains less organic matter. It is also more porous, so water can circulate through the sediment and replenish the oxygen (see Fig. 11.27). The infauna can thus burrow deeper in sand than in mud. Even in mud, however, the presence of burrows aids circulation, helping organisms obtain oxygen.

Soft substrates often contain patches of different types of sediment. As a result, the distribution of organisms along the bottom is typically **patchy**—that is, the organisms occur in distinct

Benthos Organisms that live on the bottom.
Plankton Those that drift with the currents.
Nekton Those able to swim against the currents.

• 10.2, Major Marine Lifestyles and Environments; Figure 10.11

Stratification Separation of the water column into layers, with the densest, coldest water at the bottom, which prevents the mixing of the nutrient-rich deep water with the less dense, warmer upper layer.

• 3.2, Ocean Circulation; Figure 3.22

Lithogenous Sediment Sediment that comes from the physical or chemical breakdown of rocks on land.
Biogenous Sediment Sediment composed of the skeletons and shells of marine organisms.

• 2.2, The Origin and Structure of the Ocean Basins

Source: Bill Ober

FIGURE 13.2 Though scuba diving is an excellent method for sampling and studying subtidal environments, its use is limited to relatively shallow depths. Soft bottoms at greater depths can be studied by using various sampling gears. *Bottom grabs* (*a*), like the Van Veen grab, are lowered from the surface. The jaws close, grabbing a sample of bottom sediment, as the grab is retrieved. Different types of *bottom trawls* (*b*) are used to collect the larger inhabitants of soft bottoms. They are similar to the bottom trawls used by fishers (see Fig. 17.6*d*). *Dredges* (c) with heavy metal frames are used to scrape organisms off rocky bottoms.

Box 13.1 Under the Polar Ice

The polar regions are among the very few unspoiled wildernesses remaining on Earth. Though less familiar than the animals we see on the surface or ice in the Arctic and Antarctic polar regions, life on the polar continental shelves is as unspoiled and fascinating as life on the surface.

Even if both Arctic and Antarctic regions are dominated by ice and low temperatures, their marine environments are surprisingly very different. The Arctic Ocean is the smallest and shallowest of the four major ocean basins (see Table 2.1). It is almost completely surrounded by continents and islands and thus has limited links with the Atlantic and Pacific oceans (see map in Fig. 2.2b). In contrast, the Antarctic, the second polar region, consists of a continent, Antarctica, circled by the Southern Ocean, which is an extension of all major oceans (see map in Fig. 2.2a). The North Pole lies underwater, whereas the South Pole is in the middle of a continent. In contrast to the permanent ice shelves around Antarctica, the Arctic winter ice melts to varying degrees during summer. The continental shelf is broad and relatively shallow in the Arctic and narrower and deeper around Antarctica (see map in Appendix C). The Arctic Ocean receives runoff from rivers, whereas there is none in the Southern Ocean in Antarctica. Primary production in the Southern Sea is higher than that in the Arctic, where it can nevertheless be high in some areas during the summer. Another difference is that disturbance of soft sediments from the feeding of large mammals like the gray whale and the walrus, which are found only in the Arctic, is absent in the Antarctic shelf.

Ice is a major physical factor for shelf organisms in both polar regions. A layer of

Bottom under the ice, McMurdo Sound, Antarctica. Benthic invertebrates include sea urchins (*Sterechinus neumayeri*), Antarctic scallops (*Adamussium colbecki*), and a brittle star (*Ophionotus victoriae*). An underwater camera of the Remotely Operable Micro-environment Observatory (ROMEO) is connected to onshore equipment and linked by radio to the Internet, allowing the year-round study of the benthos.

Andia/Photoshot

ice several meters thick freezes and eventually crushes any organisms living on the bottom. Winds and currents push the ice, scouring the bottom and crushing even more organisms. Ice can also form around the organisms to depths of 30 m (100 ft) or more. The ice, less dense than the water, often floats to the surface, carrying with it these trapped, often frozen, organisms. Ice can also carry large amounts of sediment with it, forming large depressions and holes. Year-round low temperatures also mean that life processes, including growth, proceed at a slow pace. Polar marine life is unique, the result of adaptations to a particularly harsh environment.

Periods of high primary production in the Arctic result in large amounts of detritus from dead plankton in the water and diatoms that grow on the ice. The detritus feeds a large variety of deposit and suspension feeders like polychaetes, soft corals, and large numbers of clams, which support the walrus. Isopods

and amphipods, small crustaceans that are an important food source for the gray whale, are common scavengers; echinoderms like brittle stars, sea urchins, and sea cucumbers also abound. More mobile animals like predatory crabs and fishes can also be abundant. Patches of kelp (*Laminaria*) manage to develop on rocks along Arctic coasts (see Fig. 13.22), providing habitats to other algae and many invertebrates.

The invertebrate fauna of Antarctica is rich, colorful, and highly diverse. Biodiversity of the shelf fauna is much higher than in the Arctic, and many of these species are found nowhere else. They evolved in Antarctica over a long period of isolation from the continental shelves of other continents. The strong current system that rings Antarctica also serves as a barrier. Though kelps are present on several of the sub-Antarctic islands (see Fig. 13.22), they are surprisingly absent in mainland Antarctica. Here they are replaced by a few brown seaweeds that are not considered kelps, though they can be large in size. Benthic animals are rare at the shelf's shallower depths because of the scouring effect of winter ice. Below this depth, however, benthic invertebrates are plentiful. Life on the hard bottoms deep under the ice shelves is plentiful, as shown by videos made through holes bored through the thick ice.

The nutrient-rich waters around Antarctica result in very high primary production when sunlight becomes available during the long summer days. Rich blooms of phytoplankton and from ice diatoms provide food for the many suspension feeders. Sponges in particular are so common that they cover most of the bottom in many places.

Sponges are represented by many species and several growth forms.

clumps or patches rather than in a random or regular pattern (Fig. 13.4). Some species have a patchy distribution because their planktonic larvae select a particular environment on which to settle and undergo **metamorphosis.** Some larvae are known to postpone metamorphosis and "taste" the bottom until they find

a certain type of substrate. Metamorphosis can be triggered by highly specific chemical, physical, and biological factors (Fig. 13.5). The larvae of some species can sense adults and prefer to settle near them. This can cause the species to be distributed in clumps even if there is a uniform bottom. The arrival of new

Volcano-like sponges can grow to 2 m (close to 7 ft) or more in height. These large sponges are probably hundreds of years old. Others are fan-shaped or resemble bushes or branching corals. Sponges provide refuge and perches for many fishes and other mobile animals, much as kelps or corals do elsewhere. Sponges are so common that the bottom below 30 m (100 ft) or so is nothing but a thick mat of siliceous, or glass, sponge spicules—truly a glass bottom.

Glass spicules can play an amazing role in some Antarctic sponges that harbor symbiotic algae. The green algae can provide some nutrients to the sponges but must obtain light in order to carry out photosynthesis. How these symbiotic algae survive deep inside sponges that live in water covered by a thick sheet of ice seems to be explained by the glass spicules efficiently transmitting to the algae what little light reaches the sponges, a real network of fiber-optic cables!

Other invertebrates can occur in large numbers: sea anemones, soft corals, sea stars, clams, nudibranchs, and sea urchins. Many of these, like sponges, are suspension feeders, but others feed on the sponges. Potential predators like crabs, lobsters, sharks, and other large fishes are absent in Antarctica as a result of the low temperatures. To protect themselves against the relatively few predators, mostly sea stars, many sponges produce toxic substances. These chemical defenses are especially common in those sponges with bright colors. Not all of these subtidal invertebrates are unique to Antarctica. Some are found elsewhere, but in progressively deeper water as one gets closer to the Equator.

Antarctic fishes are remarkable in their own right because they can remain active at temperatures that are close to the freezing point of seawater. Many have a chemical

An emerald notothen (*Trematomus bernacchii*), an icefish with a chemical "antifreeze" in its blood, on an Antarctic sponge.

WaterFrame/Alamy Stock Photo

"antifreeze" in their blood. The cold water holds so much dissolved oxygen that some, like some icefishes, have colorless blood that lacks hemoglobin.

Although sparsely populated by humans, life in polar regions is threatened by the far-reaching impact of humans that directly or indirectly affect life on the continental shelves. The most alarming threat is **global climate change** (see Special Report: Climate Change), which is responsible for the rapid transformation of polar regions as the sea ice shrinks. In fact, both the Arctic and Antarctica are frequently used as indicators of global warming. Potential pollution is a complicating factor in the Arctic because the melting ice facilitates oil and gas drilling. It is estimated that the Arctic holds 13% of the world's remaining oil and 30% of its gas. The reduced sea ice has put at risk the polar bear, the walrus, seals, and some cetaceans. There is evidence of shifts in the distribution of some fishes as water temperatures slowly increase, with cold-adapted species declining and warm-adapted ones moving north. The opening of the Northwest Passage will allow some species to migrate across the Arctic, as in the cases of gray whales that found their way into the Mediterranean

and southern Africa (see Fig. 9.33). The erosion of natural barriers increases the chances that different but close species of some marine mammals now geographically isolated by ice could meet and mate. There is a known case of a polar-grizzly bear hybrid in nature, and narwhal-beluga and right-bowhead whale hybrids are suspected. Hybrid mammals tend to be unfertile and not as healthy as normal individuals, which could be disastrous in these endangered or threatened species. Other threats are global distillation (see "PCBs and Other Persistent Organic Pollutants," in 18.2) and an ozone hole (see Special Report: The No-Zone).

The loss of coastal ice is also impacting the Inuit and other aboriginal peoples of the Arctic. The consequences of the loss of available wildlife and of the crumbling shores as the frozen soil thaws are transforming these unique cultures.

Life below and above the Antarctic ice is also threatened. An ozone hole over the continent and, most importantly, the increasing temperatures and the melting ice as a result of global climate change could have drastic consequences to life in Antarctica. Average water temperatures west of the Antarctic Peninsula have already increased by 1 °C (1.8 °F) since the 1950s. King crabs (*Neolithodes*) from further north, previously unrecorded in Antarctica because of the low temperatures, have been found in large numbers at the edge of the continental shelf. The effects of these predators on Antarctic shelf life remain unknown.

Also unknown are the potential effects of increased light on the bottom as the ice melts, with algae displacing invertebrate communities, and of stratification as fresh water from the melting ice accumulates on the ocean surface.

individuals to a population, either by settling larvae or by migrating juveniles or adults, is known as **recruitment**. The presence and abundance of a particular species on the bottom is nevertheless not always dependent on the supply of larvae. Interactions with other species after larval settlement, factors like predation,

Metamorphosis The transformation of one stage of a life cycle into another, as when a larva changes into a juvenile.

• 7.1, Sponges

Primary Producers Organisms that can create organic matter from carbon dioxide (CO_2), usually by photosynthesis.

• 4.1, The Ingredients of Life

FIGURE 13.3 Conspicuous life on shallow sandy bottoms includes occasional clumps of seaweeds that manage to grow on small rocks or shells as well as large predators like flatfishes.

Charlie Arneson

(a) Random (b) Regular (c) Patchy

Source: Bill Ober

FIGURE 13.4 The spacing, or distribution, of organisms can be classified into three basic types: *(a)* *random,* in which animals are scattered with no particular pattern, *(b)* *regular,* where they are spaced at even intervals, and *(c)* *patchy,* or *clumped,* where they cluster together. These patterns of distribution can be obtained by using a grid as shown in Figure 13.1. Many marine species show a patchy distribution. Besides the larvae of some bottom invertebrates that randomly settle on the bottom, random and regular distribution is expected to be rare on marine bottoms. Can you think of a reason organisms like clams might show random or regular distributions? Figure 13.5 provides hints!

competition, and bioturbation, most probably enter into the equation (see "Larval Ecology," in 10.1).

Unvegetated Soft-Bottom Communities

The great majority of the shelf's soft-bottom communities lack large amounts of seaweeds or seagrasses (Fig. 13.3). They can therefore be classified as **unvegetated** communities. Sea lettuce (*Ulva*) and other seaweeds may grow as long as there is enough light, but only on hard surfaces like rocks and shell fragments. The main primary producers are diatoms and a few other microscopic algae and bacteria that grow on sand or mud particles. The scarcity of seaweeds and plants means that, as on sandy beaches, primary production by benthic **primary producers** is usually very low. Nearly all primary production is by phytoplankton that are not part of the bottom communities.

The benthic animals that are part of subtidal soft-bottom communities vary widely across the world, but four groups of large-size invertebrates dominate for the most part: polychaetes, molluscs, crustaceans, and echinoderms. Though there are exceptions, temperate soft bottoms, which constitute roughly 45% of the planet's continental shelves, are inhabited by communities that are typically dominated by molluscs and polychaetes. Tropical soft-bottoms, about 30% of all continental shelves, are dominated by communities dominated for the most part by crustaceans and molluscs. Tropical subtidal communities, in contrast to temperate ones, can be particularly influenced by sharp seasonal variations in salinity and sedimentation due to heavy seasonal rainfall typical of the tropics. Polar (Arctic and Antarctic) subtidal communities, which are found in the remaining 25% of the continental shelf, are unique and very different from each other (see Box 13.1, "Under the Polar Ice").

Because there is little primary production by benthic organisms, **detritus** is a very important food source for many inhabitants. Detritus is brought in by currents from estuaries, rocky shores, and other more productive coastal communities. It is also present as feces, dead individuals, and other debris from the plankton and nekton in the water column. Detritus is also generated by the bottom inhabitants themselves.

The detritus is used by bacteria and by the many types of minute animals that live between the sediment particles, the **interstitial** animals, or **meiofauna** (see Box 13.2, "Life in Mud and Sand").

Larger benthic invertebrates also feed on detritus. They are mostly burrowing **deposit feeders** (Fig. 13.6). Polychaetes are the most diverse group of deposit feeders in the soft sediments of the shelf. Trumpet (*Pectinaria;* Fig. 13.6) and bamboo worms (*Clymenella;* see Fig. 12.11) are deposit-feeding polychaetes that inhabit tubes they build from sediment particles. Lugworms (*Arenicola*) and others live in burrows. These polychaetes and other worms eat detritus and other organic matter by collecting it with their tentacles or by ingesting sediment and extracting food from it.

Some sea urchins are uniquely adapted to living as deposit feeders on soft bottoms. Heart urchins (*Spatangus*) have abandoned the round shape of most urchins, becoming more streamlined with shorter spines that lie flat (Figs. 13.6 and 13.7). Sand dollars (*Dendraster*) are almost completely flat and have very short spines (Figs. 13.8 and 7.48*b*). They typically feed on detritus and use mucus to carry particles to the mouth. Other deposit feeders among the infauna include echiurans (Fig. 13.9), peanut worms, sea cucumbers, and ghost shrimps (*Neotrypaea;* see Fig. 12.11).

The infauna also include **suspension feeders** that eat drifting detritus and plankton from the water column. Many of these suspension feeders are **filter feeders,** which actively filter the water to obtain suspended particles by pumping water or sweeping filtering structures through the water (see Fig. 7.4). In contrast, **passive suspension feeders** only use mucus or cilia to move suspended particles into the mouth. Soft-bottom suspension feeders include many types of clams (Fig. 13.6): razor clams, the quahog (*Mercenaria*

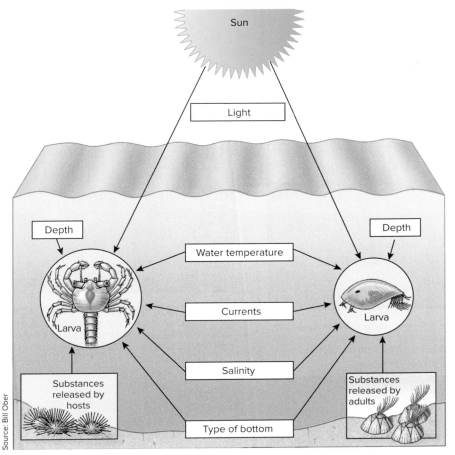

FIGURE 13.5 Many factors are known to influence the settlement and metamorphosis of planktonic larvae. The larva illustrated on the left, a megalopa (see Fig. 7.41), belongs to a crab (*Echinoecus pentagonus*) that as an adult lives on tropical sea urchins. The larva on the right is the cypris larva of a barnacle. Many barnacle larvae settle near adults of their species. Both larvae are tiny when compared to the adults and are enlarged to show their characteristic shapes.

mercenaria), cockles, the soft-shelled clam (*Mya arenaria*), and others. Most clams are filter feeders, but some—like the bent-nosed, or small, clams and the file yoldia—are deposit feeders. They collect detritus and microscopic organisms with their siphons or specialized appendages (Fig. 13.10). Also among the filter feeders are some amphipods (Fig. 13.6), polychaetes like parchment worms (Fig. 13.6), and bryozoans (Fig. 13.11).

The distribution of burrowing deposit and suspension feeders is influenced by several factors. Already mentioned in the previous section is the type of substrate. Deposit feeders tend to predominate in muddy sediments because more detritus settles in areas of low turbulence and is ultimately retained in the smaller interstitial spaces between mud particles (Fig. 13.12). Suspension feeders, on the other hand, are more common on sandy bottoms. Suspension feeders like sea pens (*Stylatula;* Fig. 13.13) and sea pansies (*Renilla*) can often be found in dense stands.

The types of organisms present also affect the establishment of others. Deposit feeders, for instance, are known to exclude suspension feeders (see "Mudflats," in 12.3). Some deposit feeders, other members

Detritus Particles of dead organic matter.
• 10.3, The Flow of Energy and Materials

Deposit Feeders Animals that feed on organic matter that settles in the sediment.
Suspension Feeders Animals, including *filter feeders,* that feed on particles suspended in the water column.
• 7.1, Sponges; Figure 7.4

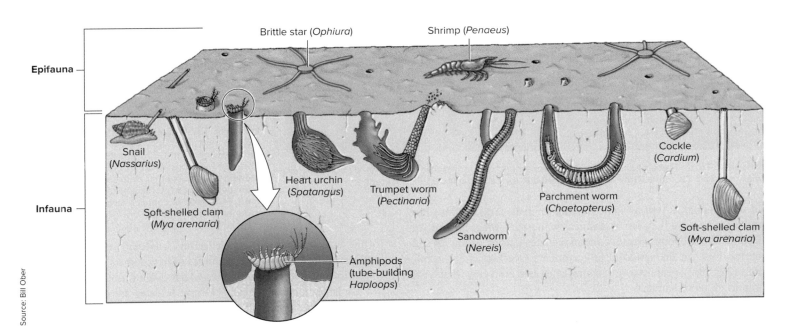

FIGURE 13.6 Representatives of the infauna and epifauna of subtidal soft bottoms in different parts of the world. Also see Figure 12.11 for a sample of mudflat inhabitants.

FIGURE 13.7 Like all heart urchins, *Spatangus purpureus* is specialized for living in sediments. Heart urchins burrow below the surface (see Fig. 13.6) and use modified tube feet for feeding. This photo was taken in the Mediterranean Sea at night, when the urchin emerged from the sediment.

FIGURE 13.9 *Thalassema steinbecki* is a deposit-feeding echiuran that inhabits soft bottoms along the Pacific coast of North and South America from Baja California to the Galápagos Islands.

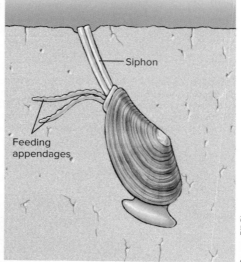

FIGURE 13.8 These sand dollars (*Dendraster excentricus*) form dense beds on sandy bottoms from Alaska to Baja California. They lie partially buried in the sand, angled into the current.

FIGURE 13.10 The file yoldia (*Yoldia limatula*) inhabits mud and muddy sand from shallow water to depths of 30 m (100 ft) in the North Atlantic. The siphon brings water in but is not used for feeding as in most other clams. Instead, this clam uses two grooved, tentacle-like appendages to feed. Each groove contains cilia that bring small organisms to the mouth.

of the infauna, as well as some burying animals, are known as **bioturbators** because they move sediment while burrowing, burying, or feeding. Bioturbation uncovers and oxygenates deeper sediments and buries those on the surface. Sea cucumbers (see Fig. 11.31), echiurans (Fig. 13.9), peanut worms, some fishes, and even gray whales are important bioturbators.

Many tube builders are deposit feeders, but they help stabilize the substrate, making it more suitable for suspension feeders. Their tubes can also interfere with the activities of burrowing deposit feeders. The tubes slow down the flow of water over the sediment, which decreases the rate of particle suspension. The modification of the environment by deposit feeders, especially of bioturbators, and the effects of tubes are examples of how some species can indirectly influence the recruitment and survival of others.

A large number of epifaunal invertebrates are deposit feeders. These include most amphipods and other small crustaceans as well as many species of brittle stars (see Fig. 13.6). Most of these brittle stars use their tube feet to collect detritus from the bottom. Other brittle stars are suspension feeders that raise their arms up into the water to catch suspended particles with their tube feet. Still others are

FIGURE 13.11 Colonies of bryozoans, or moss animals (see Fig. 7.44), consist of tiny individuals that filter-feed using a lophophore provided with ciliated tentacles.

FIGURE 13.13 Sea pens are suspension-feeding cnidarians. Each individual is a colony that includes numerous minute polyps and a fleshy stalk that is anchored in soft substrates. This is *Stylatula elongata* from the Pacific coast of North America.

Water turbulence	Less turbulence ⟶ More turbulence	
Size of sediment particles	Mud	Sand
Oxygen and detritus concentration	Less oxygen, more detritus	More oxygen, less detritus
Type of animals	Deposit feeders	Suspension feeders

Source: Bill Ober

FIGURE 13.12 The distribution of suspension and deposit feeders in soft bottoms is largely influenced by the size of the sediment particles. This relationship, however, is not clear-cut. Animals already established in the sediment, for instance, influence colonization by others.

FIGURE 13.14 Sea stars like *Astropecten* prey on clams and other burrowing invertebrates.

and moon snails (*Polinices;* see Fig. 12.11) feed on clams by drilling a hole in the shell and rasping away the flesh. Sea stars (*Astropecten;* Fig. 13.14) prey on clams, brittle stars, polychaetes, and other animals. Predatory amphipods influence subtidal communities by preying on the settling larvae of other species. Crabs are common predators and scavengers on soft bottoms. Examples are the blue crab (*Callinectes sapidus*) and other swimming crabs like the lady crab (*Ovalipes ocellatus*), and many other crabs that partially bury themselves in the sand or mud. Other predatory crabs, hermit crabs, lobsters, and octopuses take shelter on rocky bottoms but move to soft bottoms to feed.

Many fishes are common predators. Most bottom-dwelling, or **demersal,** fishes in these soft-bottom communities are carnivores. Rays and skates scoop up clams, crabs, and other infauna and epifauna. Flatfishes like flounders, halibuts, soles, and turbots lie camouflaged or covered on the bottom and forage for a wide variety of prey. **Pelagic** fishes and squids also feed on the inhabitants of the shelf's soft bottoms. Some only nip off the siphons of molluscs instead of eating the entire animal. A very large predator indeed is the gray whale (*Eschrichtius robustus*), which filters the sediment for amphipods and other small animals (see Fig. 9.19*h*). Large predators like gray whales, walruses,

scavengers and feed on dead animals. Shrimps, including commercially valuable species (*Penaeus*), are another type of epifaunal scavenger.

Most soft-bottom subtidal communities lack large seaweeds and plants. They are mostly inhabited by deposit and suspension feeders.

Some members of the soft-bottom epifauna are predators. They can burrow through the sediment to get their prey or catch it on the surface. As in other communities, predators are important in regulating the number and type of bottom inhabitants. They remove individuals and cause disturbances in the sediment that allow recolonization by different types of organisms. Snails like whelks (*Nassarius;* see Fig. 13.6)

Pelagic Pertaining to the water column away from the bottom or other structure.
• 10.2, Major Marine Lifestyles and Environments; Figure 10.11

Biomass The total weight of living organisms.
• 10.3, The Flow of Energy and Materials

Box 13.2 Life in Mud and Sand

The space between sediment particles, largely invisible to us, is an important part of the marine environment. This microscopic world, which extends from sandy beaches and estuaries to deep water, is inhabited by highly specialized **interstitial** organisms, often called the **meiofauna.**

The meiofauna are adapted to their unique environment in several ways. They are typically slender and worm-like, a shape that evolved for efficient movement between sediment particles and increase surface area for better uptake, not only of oxygen (which tends to be deficient in sediments) but also perhaps of **dissolved organic matter (DOM).** Some meiofauna glide freely among the sediment particles, whereas others attach to them. Though detritus is probably an important food source, many meiofauna are predators and scavengers of other meiofauna. There also are grazers that eat the diatoms and other tiny algae that live in the upper few millimeters of the sediment. The meiofauna, in turn, are part of the diet of many deposit feeders.

The underground world of the meiofauna is packed with bizarre creatures. There are protozoans, tiny attached hydroids that capture their food with snake-like tentacles, and vacuum-cleaning worms. Some members are just miniature versions of flatworms, polychaetes, copepods, and other more familiar animals that

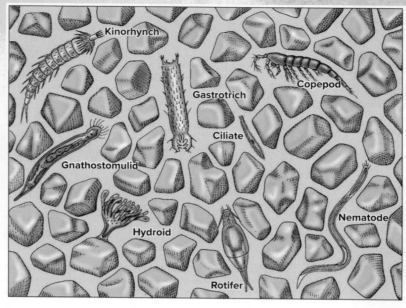

Examples of the meiofauna living among sand grains.

Source: Bill Ober

live elsewhere. **Nematodes** (see "Nematodes," in 7.4), which are found practically everywhere, are one of the most common members of the meiofauna. Other groups, however, are restricted to the meiofauna. Such is the case of **gnathostomulids** (phylum **Gnathostomulida**; see Box 7.2, "How to Discover a New Phylum") and **kinorhynchs** (phylum **Kinorhyncha**). Only about 270 species of kinorhynchs are known, all restricted to marine mud and sand. Their bodies are divided into segments armed with spines. The head, which is also surrounded by spines, can be retracted into the body.

Gastrotrichs (phylum **Gastrotricha**) use suction to eat detritus and smaller members of the meiofauna. They have short, hair-like cilia on the head and the ventral surface of the body. Many of the about 840 species

known are marine, including estuaries. Gastrotrichs look like protozoans, but have many cells and true tissues and organs.

Rotifers (phylum **Rotifera**) are a group of slightly more than 2,030 known species, of which only about 100 are marine. Of these, several species are part of the meiofauna. They are known as "wheel animals" because of a crown of cilia on their heads. This structure is used in locomotion and feeding.

The **archiannelids** are segmented worms (phylum **Annelida**) that are common members of the meiofauna. They are simple in structure and minute in size. Unlike polychaetes, the group of segmented worms in which they are often included, archiannelids typically lack distinct segments, parapodia, or bristles.

Oligochaetes are segmented worms that are widely distributed on land and in fresh water. They include the earthworms but are less common at sea, with some members part of the meiofauna, especially in polluted bays.

Collecting and extracting live meiofauna is not particularly complicated. The easiest procedure is to take moist mud or sand and let it stagnate in a container for an hour or so. The meiofauna will move to the top layer of sediment as they run out of oxygen. Samples are taken close to the surface with an eyedropper and observed under a dissecting or, even better, a compound microscope. The show is about to begin.

and rays have important effects on soft-bottom communities. They not only remove their prey but also are bioturbators that dig pits in the bottom while feeding, killing large numbers of infauna that aren't eaten and changing the characteristics of the sediment.

Seagrass Meadows

Soft bottoms along the coast are occasionally carpeted by **seagrasses.** These flowering plants, grass-like in appearance but unrelated to true grasses, have evolved to become established in the marine environment (see 6.2, Flowering Plants, for a discussion of the most important species of seagrasses, their morphological adaptations, and reproduction). Seagrass meadows, or beds, develop best in sheltered, shallow water. They are also found in estuaries and in association with mangrove

forests (see "Other Estuarine Communities," in 12.3). Seagrass communities are estimated to cover about 1.65 million km² (637,000 mi²) of coastal waters, the second most extensive coastal community after *Laminaria* kelp beds (see below). Seagrasses can grow as gigantic **clones,** as in *Posidonia australis,* which has grown to cover 180 km² (70 mi²) in Western Australia and estimated to be 4,500 years old!

Seagrasses can grow into thick, luxuriant meadows (Fig. 13.15), which often consist of more than one species of seagrass and many species of seaweeds. Their roots and a network of underground stems (see Fig. 6.13) keep them anchored in the face of turbulence. The roots and stems also help stabilize the soft bottom, and the leaves help slow down wave action and currents. This decrease in turbulence causes more and finer sediment to be deposited, which in turn affects

colonization by other organisms. Turtle grass (*Thalassia testudinum;* see Figs. 6.14*d* and 13.18) is particularly important in Florida and Caribbean coral reefs, where it helps stabilize the landward, shallow sides of the reefs. Reduced turbulence also improves water clarity because less sediment remains suspended in the water column.

Seagrass meadows contain a very high plant **biomass**, as high as 1 kg dry weight/m² for turtle grass. With such a high density of photosynthesizing plants, seagrass meadows have a higher primary production than anywhere else on soft bottoms. In fact, they rank among the most productive communities in the entire ocean. Values as high as 8 gC/m²/day (where gC is grams of carbon fixed) have been recorded for seagrasses alone. Part of the reason for such high primary production is the fact that seagrasses, unlike seaweeds, have true roots (see Fig. 6.12) and are therefore able to absorb nutrients from the sediment. Phytoplankton and seaweeds, by contrast, must depend on nutrients dissolved in the water column. Some typical rates of primary production in seagrass meadows and other marine environments are summarized in Table 10.1.

Another point highlighting the importance of seagrasses is that they remove more CO_2 from seawater by photosynthesis than the CO_2 they produce by respiration, thus helping reduce the problem of **acidification** (see Special Report, Ocean Acidification: The Other Problem).

FLPA/Bob Gibbons/Getty Images

FIGURE 13.15 Eelgrass (*Zostera marina*) at low tide on the Pacific coast of North America.

Many small algae grow on the surface of seagrass leaves. These algae, known as **epiphytes,** further increase primary production in seagrass communities, although they can shield seagrasses from some of the light needed for photosynthesis. Microscopic diatoms are particularly abundant. Some epiphytic cyanobacteria also carry out **nitrogen fixation** and release nutrients in the form of nitrogen compounds.

The number of grazers, or herbivores, in seagrass meadows varies with geographical location. Herbivores, not many of which eat seagrass leaves, directly consume much less than half of seagrass primary production. Herbivores that do eat seagrasses include sea turtles, manatees, sea urchins, and some parrotfishes. Seagrasses are also important in the diet of some birds like ducks and geese in the Arctic and other regions.

Animals take advantage of the high primary production of seagrasses in several ways, even when they do not actually eat the seagrasses themselves (Fig. 13.16). Many feed on the large amounts of

Nitrogen Fixation Conversion of nitrogen gas (N_2) into nitrogen compounds that can be used by primary producers as nutrients.
• 5.2, Prokaryotes; Table 5.1

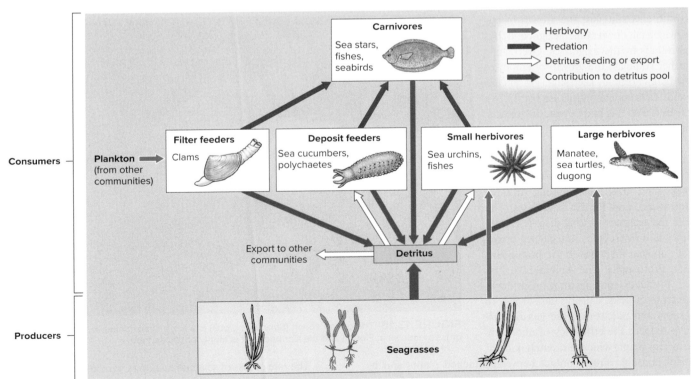

Source: Bill Ober

FIGURE 13.16 Generalized food web in a seagrass community. As in estuaries (see Fig. 12.24), detritus generated from dead plants is an important source of food for many animals.

decaying leaves. Deposit-feeding polychaetes, clams, and sea cucumbers live in or on the detritus-rich sediment. Detritus is also exported to other communities, like the unvegetated soft bottoms of deeper water. Some detritus, however, is buried in the sediment.

The dense seagrasses also offer shelter to many animals that do not feed on detritus. More animals live in or on the sediments in seagrass meadows than in the surrounding unvegetated sediments. A variety of small sessile or crawling animals live on the leaves: hydroids, snails, tiny tube-dwelling polychaetes, amphipods, shrimps, and the like (Fig. 13.17). Larger animals, like the queen conch (*Strombus gigas;* Fig. 13.18), live among the plants. Filter feeders that live in the sediment include clams and the pen shell (*Pinna carnea*). Several species of fishes and the West Indian sea star (*Oreaster reticulatus*) are examples of carnivores. Seagrass meadows also serve as nurseries for commercially valuable species like the Atlantic bay scallop (*Argopecten irradians*) and shrimps.

> Highly productive seagrass communities are restricted to soft bottoms in shallow, sheltered water. The plants are not heavily grazed but produce a lot of detritus that is used by deposit feeders and exported to other communities.

Human Impact on Seagrasses

The total area covered by seagrass meadows around the world has decreased by about a third since the late 1800s—and the loss is speeding up. They have been decreasing at a rate of more than 7% since 1990. Seagrasses have been adversely affected by sediment deposition from dredging, damage by boat propellers, and pollution, most especially excess nutrients from agriculture and urban runoff (see Special Report, Overwhelming the Nitrogen Cycle). Excess nutrients stimulate the growth of epiphytes, which cut down available light and thus photosynthesis by the seagrasses. Overfishing can further stimulate the growth of epiphytes because fishes normally keep small grazers like crabs and snails under control (see Fig. 13.28).

Disease also has had devastating effects. An epidemic of seagrass wasting disease killed about 95% of meadows on the Atlantic coasts of North America and Europe in the 1930s. More recent but less dramatic outbreaks have taken place among Atlantic, Mediterranean, and Pacific seagrasses. The cause of the seagrass wasting disease is *Labyrinthula,* a microscopic, ameba-like organism with unclear affinities to the protozoans (see 5.4, Protozoans: The Animal-Like Protists). It produces enzymes that break down the contents of cells, causing dark-brown to black spots and patches on the leaves. *Labyrinthula* reduces the efficiency of photosynthesis by the plant, which ultimately kills it. It spreads through direct contact between attached plants and by drifting leaves. Wasting disease, as well as other outbreaks of diseases among marine organisms, seems to be somehow related, directly or indirectly, to the impact of humans on the marine environment.

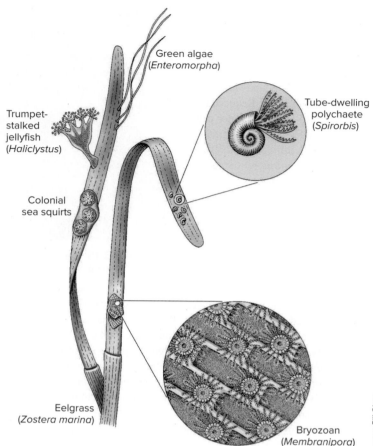

Source: Bill Ober

FIGURE 13.17 Eelgrass (*Zostera marina*) leaves are often inhabited by sessile, or attached, organisms.

Charlie Arneson

FIGURE 13.18 The queen conch (*Strombus gigas*) is a large snail commonly associated with turtle grass meadows in Florida and the Caribbean. It is highly prized as food.

The rate of loss of seagrass meadows parallels that of other highly productive but endangered marine ecosystems: mangrove forests and salt marshes (see 12.4, Human Impact on Estuarine Communities) and coral reefs (see 14.4, Human Impact on Coral Reefs). The loss of

seagrass meadows is more widespread, however, because they extend into both tropical and temperate regions in contrast to the tropical coral reefs and mangroves and the temperate salt marshes.

As a result of the high primary production of seagrass meadows, a large amount of organic carbon is stored not only in the plants themselves but buried as a **carbon sink**, or **blue carbon** (see Box 10.3, "Carbon Sinks and Blue Carbon"), very much as in salt marshes and mangrove forests (see "Feeding Interactions among Estuarine Organisms" in 12.3). The loss of seagrasses is therefore of considerable significance because much of this organic carbon, some trapped over thousands of years, will be decomposed and released back to the atmosphere as CO_2, the most important of the greenhouse gases responsible for global climate change (see Special Report: Climate Change).

Efforts to restore seagrass meadows are taking place in several parts of the world, especially in estuaries. These measures involve transplanting individual plants taken from healthy meadows, applying seeds, or planting seedlings reared in the laboratory. Spreading seeds has been very successful in coastal lagoons in Virginia, USA, where 3,600 ha (8,896 acres) of previously lost seagrass beds have so far been restored. Such restoration has resulted in an increase in the production and diversity of animals (including previously depleted bay scallops, *Argopecten irradians*, which support an important fishery) and a decrease in water turbidity.

13.3 HARD-BOTTOM SUBTIDAL COMMUNITIES

Hard bottoms make up a relatively small portion of the continental shelf. They usually represent the submerged extensions of rocky shores as well as many subtidal rocky reefs of varying size. **Calcareous algae,** the calcareous tubes of polychaete worms and the aggregations of oyster shells (see Fig. 12.23) can form three-dimensionally complex hard bottoms are often called reefs, but they should not be confused with the tropical or deep-water coral reefs.

Rocky Bottoms

Unlike those in the intertidal, the communities that develop on subtidal rocky bottoms are never subject to desiccation. This means that a wider variety of organisms can live there than in the intertidal.

Rocky-bottom communities in shallow water are rich and productive as long as enough light penetrates through the water column. Oil and gas rigs, although human-made, provide a hard bottom that can support a wide variety of organisms. Seaweeds are the most conspicuous inhabitants, especially on flat or gently sloping bottoms. They occur in an awesome array of colors, growth forms, textures, and sizes. Most are brown and red seaweeds, and can be filamentous (*Chordaria, Ceramium*), branched (*Agardhiella, Desmarestia*), thin and leafy (*Porphyra, Gigartina*), or **encrusting** (*Lithothamnion*). The dense growth of mostly filamentous seaweeds is often called the **algal turf**. Many of these seaweeds can also be found in the lower intertidal.

As in the intertidal, one of the main problems for subtidal seaweeds and sessile animals is to find a place to attach so there is intense competition for living space on the rocks. Practically all seaweeds have a **holdfast** (see Fig. 13.21) to anchor them to the substrate. Every bit of space is occupied, even if it seems clean to our naked eye. Different species of seaweed have different competitive abilities. They also vary in their tolerance to wave action, grazing by

sea urchins and other herbivores, temperature, light, and the stability of the substrate.

The effect of light is obviously important for seaweeds. As depth increases, the amount of light available for photosynthesis decreases, making it harder for seaweeds to live there. Not all colors of light penetrate to equal depths. In clear ocean water, blue light penetrates the deepest, red the least (see Fig. 3.11). Some species are better adapted to deep water than others. Several can live at depths of over 200 m (650 ft) in clear water. Deep-water seaweeds have increased levels of chlorophyll and other pigments that capture light energy. These adaptations can be found in all groups of seaweeds and are not restricted to the red algae, once thought to be the best adapted to deep water. Depth zonation is not determined by light alone. It is affected by grazing, competition for space, and other factors.

Seaweeds also vary in their life history strategies. Some are **perennial** and the holdfast survives more than a year, whereas others are found only at certain times of the year. Though some grow fast and are short-lived, others grow slowly and are sturdy and long-lived. Fast growers are typically the first to colonize surfaces recently disturbed by grazers, turbulence, or other phenomena. Some seaweeds use both strategies by alternating a fast-growing, short-lived stage with a slow-growing, perennial one. Many have different growth forms at different times of their lives (see Fig. 6.11). These growth forms belong to the same species but look and function differently.

Seaweeds must compete for space not only with each other but also with many sessile animals. Invertebrates tend to dominate on steeply sloping bottoms and vertical walls, where light limits seaweed growth (see photo at the beginning of this chapter). Hard substrates provide a good place for organisms to attach but are much harder to burrow through than sand or mud. As a result, hard-bottom communities tend to have a rich epifauna and a poor infauna, the reverse of soft-bottom communities. Sponges, hydroids (see Fig. 7.8), sea anemones, soft corals, bryozoans (see Fig. 7.44), tube-dwelling polychaetes, barnacles, and sea squirts (see Fig. 7.53) are among the most common groups. Many form colonies that outcompete other species by simply growing over them. A few, like the rock-boring clam (*Pholas*), live embedded in rocks.

Grazers on subtidal rocky bottoms are usually small, slow-moving invertebrates. Perhaps most important are sea urchins (*Arbacia, Diadema, Strongylocentrotus;* Fig. 13.19). Chitons, sea hares, limpets, abalones (*Haliotis*), and other gastropod mollusks, as well as several groups of fishes, are also important grazers (Fig. 13.20).

Some seaweeds have evolved defenses against grazing. These include chemicals like sulfuric acid and phenols, which make them unpalatable and the ability to rapidly regrow tissue lost to grazers. Some seaweeds even have life history stages that bore into mollusc shells. Upright seaweeds tend to be tough and leathery. Calcareous algae, which include coralline (*Lithothamnion, Clathromorphum*) and calcareous green (*Halimeda;* see Fig. 14.10) algae, deposit calcium carbonate in their cell walls, making them particularly resistant to grazing.

Carnivores, including nudibranchs and other gastropods as well as sea stars, feed on attached invertebrates. Sea urchins feed not only on seaweeds but also on some of the flimsier attached invertebrates.

Encrusting Seaweeds Those that grow as a thin layer over rocks, like some of the coralline algae.

• 6.1, Multicellular Algae: The Seaweeds

FIGURE 13.19 Sea urchins, like *Strongylocentrotus purpuratus* from the Pacific coast of North America, are important in influencing the composition of hard-bottom subtidal communities. They graze on seaweeds and on some of the encrusting animals and thus uncover new surfaces where other sessile organisms can settle.

Charlie Arneson

Other carnivores, like crabs, lobsters, and many types of fishes, prey on grazers and smaller carnivores.

Grazers and predators strongly influence the composition of hard-bottom communities. As in the rocky intertidal (see Fig. 11.21), they remove residents from the rocks, opening up space for other organisms. Settling larvae and seaweed spores colonize the patches cleared by grazers and carnivores. Because these planktonic stages are often seasonal, patches formed at different times can be colonized by different species. This increases the total number of species, or **species diversity,** or **biodiversity,** in a given area. Carnivores can also act as a check on the grazers, helping maintain a relatively stable situation. This balance can be easily upset, however. For example, explosive increases in sea urchin populations have been reported in several subtidal communities (see below), as have mass mortalities. Like all biological communities, subtidal communities are constantly changing.

The species composition of rocky-bottom subtidal communities is influenced by factors like light, competition for space, grazing, and predation.

Kelp Communities

Among the most fascinating of marine communities, **kelp communities** are also one of the most productive. Kelps are a group of large, fast-growing brown seaweeds that live in relatively cold water and are restricted to temperate and subpolar regions (see "Brown Algae," in 6.1). They are true giants compared with other subtidal seaweeds or seagrasses, creating luxuriant forests (see Fig. 6.8) that are home to a vast assortment of organisms.

There are several species of kelp. In the North Atlantic, Arctic, and on the Asiatic coast of the North Pacific, species of *Laminaria* (Fig. 13.21) predominate. Their simple or cleft blades can be 3 m (10 ft) long. The giant kelp (*Macrocystis*), the planet's largest benthic organism, dominates kelp communities on the Pacific coasts of North and South America and other parts of the Southern Hemisphere (Fig. 13.22). Each kelp individual is attached to the rocky bottom by a large holdfast (see Fig. 6.1). Several long **stipes,** intertwined to form a trunk-like foundation, grow from a single holdfast. The **fronds,** leaf-like blades, grow

FIGURE 13.20 Generalized food web in a hard-bottom subtidal community. Most of the detritus generated is in the form of drift seaweeds.

Source: Bill Ober

FIGURE 13.21 Examples of North Atlantic kelps. The hollow-stemmed kelp reaches lengths of 12 m (40 ft) in deeper water.

Source: Bill Ober

from the stipes. A single stipe can reach 20 to 30 m (65 to 100 ft) or more. In some Southern Hemisphere communities, *Ecklonia* rather than *Macrocystis* is the main species. Kelp communities on the Pacific coast of North America are particularly diverse. A number of species, including the bull kelp (*Nereocystis*), the elk kelp (*Pelagophycus;* Fig. 13.23), *Alaria,* and *Pterygophora,* can be important or even replace *Macrocystis.* The bull kelp consists of many blades, each up to 5 m (16 ft) long, that hang below the surface suspended by a gas-filled

pneumatocyst located at the end of a long stipe. *Alaria* (Fig. 13.21), which like many other species of kelp is edible, is also important in the North Atlantic.

Large, dense patches of kelp are known as **kelp beds.** They are called **kelp forests** when the fronds float on the surface in a thick mat (Fig. 13.24). This floating **canopy** is characteristic of Pacific kelp forests dominated by the giant and bull kelps. *Ecklonia* and some species of *Laminaria* and *Alaria* also form a canopy. *Laminaria* beds are thought to be the most extensive coastal community in the world, covering an estimated 2 million km² (772,200 mi²), about 36% of coastal waters. Kelp forests can be extensive enough to be visible from space!

Physical factors have a major influence on kelp communities. Temperature is of particular importance because kelps are restricted to cold water. This is partially because kelps don't do well in warm water and partially because warm waters tend to lack the rich supply of nutrients that kelps need (see "Patterns of Production," in 15.3). This dependence on cold water is reflected in the geographic distribution of kelps (Fig. 13.22). The surface waters of the oceans flow in great clockwise gyres in the Northern Hemisphere and counterclockwise gyres in the Southern Hemisphere (see Fig. 3.21). The currents that flow toward the poles on the western sides of the oceans carry warm water from equatorial regions. Because of this, kelps are restricted to high latitudes on the eastern sides of the continents, but extend well down western shores, where cold, nutrient-rich currents flow down from high latitudes. *Ecklonia* occurs in low latitudes not far from the Equator along the Arabian Sea coast of the Arabian Peninsula (Fig. 13.22). It is found there only during the summer, when the **monsoons** that blow from Africa northeastward across the Arabian Sea cause strong **upwelling** that lowers water temperature

Source: Bill Ober

FIGURE 13.22 The geographic distribution of kelps is greatly affected by surface temperatures, which are influenced by the surface circulation of the ocean. Currents along the western coasts of the continents transport cold water from polar regions; on the eastern coasts of continents, warm water is transported from the Equator. As a result, kelps extend farther toward the Equator along the western coasts of the continents than on the eastern coasts. The opposite is true for reef-building corals, which require warm water (see Fig. 14.11). Also see map in Appendix D.

Charlie Arneson

FIGURE 13.23 The elk kelp (*Pelagophycus porra*) grows on the outer, deeper edges of some giant kelp forests (see Fig. 13.26). It has two impressive, antler-like branches from which large blades hang at the mercy of the currents.

Dale Glantz

FIGURE 13.24 Giant kelp (*Macrocystis pyrifera*) forest at Cedros Island, Baja California, Mexico.

deep as light allows. This can be quite deep, up to 40 m (130 ft) in some species. Their fronds float at the surface, basking in sunlight, while their stipes connect them to the bottom far below.

Kelp communities are restricted to hard substrates in cold, nutrient-rich water.

Kelps are actually quite fragile largely *because* of their size. The fronds cause a lot of drag, but the long, thin stipes can break even if they are adapted to stretch in storm surge. Holdfasts are more often torn from the bottom as the result of storm waves and damage by grazers. Drifting kelps cause more damage by entangling other fronds. Kelps don't do well where there is heavy wave action, and storms can be disastrous. Though they must extend their blades to the surface, many species prefer to attach to the bottom in relatively deep water, where wave action is reduced. Thus, the very adaptations that allow these species of kelp to live in deep water, large size, and floating fronds, also tend to restrict them there.

Kelps can grow fast, and, not surprisingly, kelp communities are very productive. Primary production reaches 1,000 gC/m²/year in *Ecklonia* in Australia and South Africa, close to 2,000 gC/m²/year in *Laminaria* in the North Atlantic, and as high as 5,400 gC/m²/year in giant kelp (also see Table 10.1).

Because of their fast growth and high productivity, kelps remove large amounts of CO_2 from seawater and the atmosphere and hence, like seagrasses, help reduce acidification (see Special Report, Ocean Acidification: The Other Problem). Some envision expanding kelp farming not only for food, fertilizers, and fuel, but to help reduce CO_2, which is responsible for global climate change and acidification.

Kelp forests, as in seagrass meadows, salt marshes, and mangrove forests, act as an important **carbon sink** (see Box 10.3, "Carbon Sinks and Blue Carbon"). Instead of extra carbon being buried in sediment, drift kept and detritus sink to deep water. Some biologists have suggested that kelp beds represent the most important carbon-sink system in the ocean.

The large kelps we see are only one stage in their life history. All kelps go through two stages: a large, spore-producing **sporophyte** and a microscopic **gametophyte,** which produces male and female gametes (Fig. 13.25). The sporophyte is the organism we see.

In some kelps, the sporophyte is an annual. In contrast, the giant kelp and others are perennial and can live for several years. These

(see Fig. 15.31). The disappearance of the monsoons when the winds reverse direction during the winter causes an increase in water temperature, which kills the kelp.

All but a few species of kelp are limited to hard surfaces, which can include substrates like worm tubes and the holdfasts of other seaweeds. Given a suitable place to attach, kelps will grow in water as

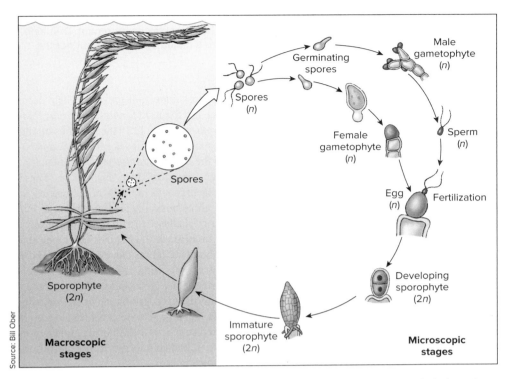

FIGURE 13.25 The life history of the giant kelp (*Macrocystis*) and other kelps includes a large, spore-producing sporophyte. Spores settle on the bottom and develop into minute male or female gametophytes. Each gametophyte releases male or female gametes, which, after fertilization, develop into the sporophyte, thus completing the cycle (also see Fig. 6.11c).

long-lived kelps often lose fronds to grazers, storms, and waves. They are able to grow them back because, unlike many seaweeds, growth takes place at the holdfast as well as at the end of the stipes.

Kelp forests along the Pacific coast of North America are arranged in distinct depth zones, each made up of species that grow at a characteristic height above the bottom (Fig. 13.26). This structure results from the interaction of several physical and biological factors. The floating canopy of the giant kelp, for instance, develops only where the water is deep enough to reduce wave action but shallow enough for light to reach the bottom, permitting growth from the holdfasts.

Monsoons Winds in the northern Indian Ocean that blow from the southwest in summer but from the northeast in the winter.

• 15.3, Epipelagic Food Webs; Figure 15.31

Upwelling The upward flow of cold, nutrient-rich deep water to the surface.

• 15.3, Epipelagic Food Webs

Ecological Niche The combination of what a species eats, where it lives, how it behaves, and all the other aspects of its lifestyle.

• 10.1, The Organization of Communities

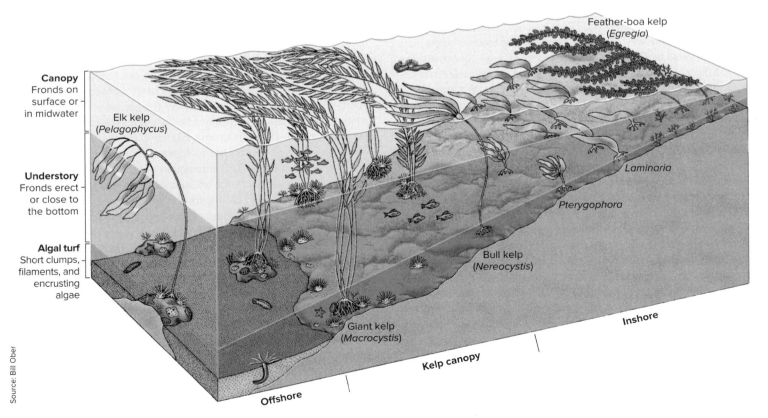

FIGURE 13.26 Distribution of the major types of kelps and other seaweeds in a generalized giant kelp (*Macrocystis*) forest on the Pacific coast of North America. The complex distribution of kelps and other seaweeds results from the effects of factors like light, type of substrate, wave action, depth, number and type of grazers, and even time of year because some of the seaweeds are annuals.

Other kelps can contribute to the surface canopy. These include the bull kelp, found closer inshore, and the feather-boa kelp (*Egregia*), which lives in shallower water subject to wave action. The elk kelp forms a midwater canopy in deeper water along the outer edge of the giant kelp canopy.

The dense canopy of giant kelp forests cuts down the amount of light underneath. Diving under the canopy is like walking into a dense forest on land. The kelps that live there also have to adapt to the reduced light level, but life under the canopy is rich and varied. Smaller kelps exploit the **understory,** the area below the canopy. They include *Laminaria, Pterygophora,* and other kelps that have either erect fronds that stand above the bottom or fronds that lie right on it.

Branching and encrusting coralline algae and other red algae are common. Some seaweeds are more abundant in shallow water, where increased wave action reduces the size of the canopy.

North Atlantic kelp forests are dominated by species of *Laminaria* that typically do not form a canopy. They are similar to Pacific kelp forests by including many species of seaweeds that are distributed in depth zones.

The complex, three-dimensional structure of kelp forests is exploited by many different animals, which explains the high species diversity of kelp communities. Polychaetes, small crustaceans, brittle stars, and other small invertebrates live on the kelp holdfasts. Tube-dwelling polychaetes and other sessile organisms are common on the blades and stipes. Like the animals that live associated with the holdfast, they are mostly suspension feeders. One conspicuous inhabitant of the blades is a bryozoan (*Membranipora*) that forms thin, lace-like colonies. Its calcareous encrustations weigh the blades down and cover photosynthetic tissues, but their effect appears to be minimal. The rocky bottoms around kelps are inhabited by sponges, sea squirts, lobsters, crabs, hermit crabs, sea stars, abalones (Fig. 7.24*b*), and octopuses, among others.

Fishes are also very common. They use the food resources and habitats provided by the kelp community in many ways, thus occupying many different **ecological niches.** Fishes often use the available resources by feeding and taking shelter in different areas within the forest. Some species feed close to the bottom. In kelp forests along the Pacific coast of North America, bottom feeders include many species of rockfishes (*Sebastes*), the kelp bass (*Paralabrax clathratus*), and the Garibaldi (*Hypsypops rubicundus*), a bright-orange damselfish that establishes territories on rocky bottoms. The California sheephead (*Semicossyphus pulcher*) uses its dog-like teeth to crush sea urchins, crabs, and other bottom invertebrates. Topsmelt (*Atherinops*) are plankton feeders that take advantage of large swarms of opossum shrimps, or mysids, and other planktonic animals found around kelps. Fishes can define additional ecological niches by being active at different times of the day or night.

Small algae are grazed by snails, crabs, sea urchins, and fishes, but surprisingly few grazers eat the large kelps. One giant grazer of kelp, the Steller's sea cow, is now extinct (see Fig. 18.14). Isopods (*Phycolimnoria*) are small crustaceans that burrow into the holdfast, weakening it. A few fishes graze on kelps, but they do not appear to cause much mortality. Rather than grazing on the attached kelp, animals use most of the huge production of kelps in the form of drift kelp, pieces that break loose and sink to the bottom or are washed ashore. Many species of filter feeders (sponges, polychaetes, bivalves, and sea squirts) feed on the small particles of detritus generated from drift kelp (see Fig. 13.20). As with seagrasses, salt-marsh plants, and mangroves, however, much of the drift kelp is exported to other communities.

Kelp forests form a multistoried, complex environment. Drift kelp and understory seaweeds are a major food source but not the live kelp themselves.

Sea urchins are by far the most important grazers in kelp communities. Of special importance are the red (*Strongylocentrotus franciscanus*) and purple (*S. purpuratus*; see Fig. 13.19) sea urchins on the Pacific coast of North America and the green sea urchin (*S. droebachiensis;* see Fig. 7.47*a*) in both the North Atlantic and North Pacific. Urchin populations sometimes "explode" (see Fig. 10.3). These explosions have had devastating impacts on kelp communities in different parts of the world. Urchins normally feed on drift kelp but during population explosions, or "plagues," the urchins eat live kelps and other seaweeds. When the urchins eat the holdfasts or stipes, the kelps break loose, float away, and die. Urchins can even climb up the kelp, weighing down the fronds and allowing other urchins to reach them. The urchins can completely clear large areas, which are then known as "urchin barrens." Encrusting coralline algae are virtually the only seaweeds left on these barrens. A widespread explosion of the purple sea urchin has affected kelp beds in California and Oregon during recent years. About 90% of bull-kelp forests in northern California were lost to sea urchins during 2014–2019.

The reasons for such outbreaks of urchins remain unclear. A possible cause in the North Pacific is the decline in sea otters (*Enhydra lutris;* see Fig. 9.12), an urchin predator that has disappeared from most of its former range. A study of kelp forests (mostly *Alaria* and *Laminaria*) in the Aleutian Islands, Alaska revealed that kelp forests were healthier where sea otters were common. In contrast, there were many urchins and few kelps on islands where sea otters were absent (Fig. 13.27). There is evidence that otter populations have declined because of predation by orcas, or killer whales, which normally prefer seals and sea lions. Seals and sea lions have become increasingly scarce since the late 1980s, perhaps because overfishing has reduced their food supply. Orcas also appear to have changed their feeding habits when an important food source, the carcasses of harpooned whales tied to whaling ships, dwindled when most commercial whaling was banned. Overfishing thus can have affected kelp forests by way of a chain of events that includes seals and sea lions, orcas, sea otters, and urchins. This interaction is an example of a **trophic cascade,** when changes in the abundance of an organism, usually a predator, extend throughout the food chain.

Observations in the Aleutians, however, do not help explain the situation in Southern California, where sea otters were wiped out almost 200 years ago, but the destruction of giant kelp forests by urchins was not observed until the 1950s. Heavy fishing on other urchin predators, including lobsters, crabs, and fishes, probably plays a role in the increase in urchin populations in Southern California and other places. The harvesting of Pacific abalones for food could have been a cause of urchin plagues. These large molluscs compete with urchins for shelter in rock crevices. Removal of the abalones, now rare, can provide more space for urchins.

Another possibility is that a decrease in the amount of drift algae in Southern California might have caused the urchins to switch to feeding on live kelps. Pollution from sewage and stormwater runoff and temperature increases are factors that could have caused a drop in the availability of drift kelp. Some of these factors can also stimulate the growth and survival of urchins. Some organic

FIGURE 13.27 The effect of predation of sea otters (*Enhydra lutris*) by orcas, or killer whales (*Orcinus orca*) on the populations of sea urchins (*Strongylo-centrotus*) and kelps (*Alaria, Laminaria*) in kelp forests in the Aleutian Islands, Alaska is an example of a trophic cascade, so called because the effects of a predator extend throughout the food chain. The years without bars in the graphs indicate years without data and not zero values.

compounds released in sewage, for example, are used as nutrients by juvenile urchins.

Fluctuations in the number of urchins could be also caused by the higher survival of their planktonic larvae, perhaps the result of more favorable temperatures or more abundant food. It is likely that a combination of factors causes urchin plagues, which probably are natural fluctuations in population size.

In addition to grazing by sea urchins, another factor affecting the health of kelp forests is climate. A strong **El Niño** in 1997–1998 produced severe storms and unusually warm currents, which caused high kelp mortality in California and other regions along the eastern Pacific (see "The El Niño-Southern Oscillation," in 15.3). A **La Niña** that followed, however, brought cold, nutrient-rich currents to the same region, helping in the recovery of kelp forests. Recovery nevertheless proved to be slow in kelp forests as well as in

subtidal seaweed communities, but recovery has been aided in part by the relative success of forests developing on artificial rocky reefs (see "Restoration of Habitats," in 18.4). Increased water temperatures during recent summers associated with global climate change, and increased populations of urchins helped by a decrease in the numbers of a predatory sea star, *Pycnopodia helianthoides* (see Fig. 7.46*a*), because of a disease, have slowed down recovery.

Devastation of kelp forests has been particularly severe along northern California, where more than 95% of the forests have vanished since 2014. Long-term studies in southern California, however, have shown that recent mass mortalities of urchins due to a bacterial infection have triggered a reversal of fortunes. Urchin barrens returned to being kelp-dominated rocky reefs after as little as six months. Such results thus support the proposal that the removal, or culling, of urchins does help in the recovery of kelp forests.

EYE ON SCIENCE

Box 13.3 *Toxoplasma:* From Cats to Sea Otters

A growing number of marine mammals, notably the threatened sea otter, have been found sharing diseases with land animals. One of these diseases is caused by *Toxoplasma gondii,* a single-cell parasite that causes brain infections in humans and other land animals.

Toxoplasma infects the tissues of many land mammals and birds, but it typically doesn't cause any symptoms. It is estimated that about 20% of the United States population is infected with *Toxoplasma* without causing any ill-effects. If anything, it will go as far as being responsible for flu-like symptoms. Some humans, however, are of particular concern. *Toxoplasma* can be lethal in the immunocompromised, or immune-deficient, individuals, where the immune system, which is in charge of defending the body against infections, is not performing properly. Immunocompromised individuals include HIV and AIDS patients, people who have inherited an immunodeficiency condition, and those given immunosuppressant drugs to prevent the rejection of transplants or treat inflammation and certain diseases. *Toxoplasma* invades the brain of immunocompromised individuals and causes toxoplasmosis, which is often lethal. The human fetus is also susceptible. Humans who are pregnant or infected with the parasite but having no symptoms can pass the parasite to the fetus and cause congenital toxoplasmosis, which can lead to blindness or the death of the fetus.

Mammals get infected with *Toxoplasma* by eating animals infected with the non-sexual stage of the parasite or by food or water contaminated by a resistant stage, the oocyst, which is found only in the feces of the domestic cat and other members of the cat family. *Toxoplasma* reproduces sexually only in the intestines of cats and the oocyst is the resulting stage. Oocysts, which are fairly resistant, are never produced by other infected mammals or birds. *Toxoplasma* infections are readily diagnosed by a blood test that detects very specific antibodies that target specific proteins in the parasite.

The California sea otter has been particularly affected by *Toxoplasma.* The parasite is responsible for approximately 17% of sea otter deaths. It has been found mostly in the sea otter brains, where it causes inflammation, or encephalitis. The analysis of antibodies in sea otter blood between 1998 and 2004 in California showed positive infection with *Toxoplasma* in 52% of 305 recently dead animals and 38% of 257 live individuals. The parasite has been pointed out as the main reason of the slow recovery of the California sea otter. *Toxoplasma* has also been found in an increasing number of marine mammals around the world, including seals, sea lions, Hawaiian monk seals, dolphins, the walrus, manatees, and the beluga, Bryde's, and humpback whales. Congenital toxoplasmosis has been discovered in a one-day-old harbor seal and in the fetus of a bottlenose dolphin.

How can a cat parasite infect sea otters and other marine mammals remains a mystery. The search for an answer is the subject of current research. The most obvious source of infection is coastal water runoff contaminated with oocysts from cat feces and cat litter. Areas of high marine mammal infection are near urban centers with coastal runoff, and oocysts in the water could be filtered by bivalve molluscs or filter-feeding fishes that are then eaten by sea otters and other marine mammals. There is experimental evidence for this: *Toxoplasma* DNA was found in the gills of anchovies exposed to oocysts under laboratory conditions.

Cats, domestic as well as those living in the wild, are the main source of infection. Domestic cats that are allowed outside the house are easily infected by eating rodents or birds, which carry the non-sexual stage of the parasite but never produce oocysts as in cats. Oocysts are highly resistant and can survive sewage treatment. They can even also survive in landfills for as long as 18 months. The best recommendation to cat owners is to bag and dispose of cat feces in approved landfills where runoff is strictly controlled.

For more information, explore the links provided on the Marine Biology *Online Learning Center.*

Kelp communities can be severely disrupted by strong wave action, grazing by sea urchins, warm currents, and pollution.

To appease fishers, who were angry at the possibility of sea otters feeding on shellfish, it was agreed that sea otters were to be kept from naturally migrating from central to Southern California. The "otter-free" zone was abandoned in 2012 and sea otters were allowed to roam free in Southern California. An estimated 16,000 sea otters lived from Oregon to Baja California, Mexico in the nineteenth century. A 2019 survey showed that 2,962 sea otters inhabited California, lower than the 3,272 peak recorded in 2016. A total of 114 sea otters were counted in 2020 in San Nicolas Island off Southern California, where 140 individuals were relocated there from central California between 1987 and 1990. The 89 sea otters transplanted from Alaska to Vancouver Island, British Columbia, Canada between 1969 and 1972 now number about 7,000. Sea otters are being infected by bacteria that thrive in water polluted by nutrients and by parasites like *Toxoplasma* (see Box 13.3, "*Toxoplasma:* From Cats to Sea Otters"). Mortality due to "exploratory" bites by great white sharks has been on the increase in California.

Sea otters also appear to have helped in the recovery of seagrass meadows in Elkhorn Slough, a large estuary in Monterey Bay, central California. Fertilizer runoff carrying nutrients from the many farms nearby has stimulated the growth of algae that live as epiphytes on the seagrass leaves, shading the leaves from sunlight. Seagrass meadows nearly disappeared from the estuary. Marine biologists have provided evidence that the return of sea otters to Elkhorn Slough in the mid-1980s signaled the recovery of the seagrass meadows. Crabs are a major part of the sea otter's diet in the estuary. Increased predation by sea otters has decreased the number of crabs, which feed on gastropod molluscs and other small invertebrates like isopods that graze on the epiphytes. A smaller number of crabs triggers an increase in the abundance of grazers, which then eat more of the seagrass epiphytes, resulting in an increase in the amount of sunlight reaching the leaves (Fig. 13.28). Such interaction is another example of a trophic cascade involving sea otters.

Another example of a trophic cascade has been described in the Gulf of Maine on the Atlantic coast of the United States. Overfishing

FIGURE 13.28 The effect of predation of crabs (*Cancer productus* and *Romaleon antennarium*) by the California sea otter (*Enhydra lutris*) on eelgrass (*Zostera marina*) in Elkhorn Slough, California is another example of a trophic cascade involving sea otters (also see Fig. 13.27). Crabs feed on grazers like an isopod (*Idotea resecata*) and a gastropod (the sea slug *Phyllaplysia taylori*), both of which feed on epiphytes (like the red alga *Smithora naiadum*) that grow on the eelgrass, shading leaves from sunlight. An increase in the number of sea otters has therefore helped in the recovery of seagrass meadows because a decrease in the number of crabs has resulted in a larger number of epiphyte grazers.

of the Atlantic cod (*Gadus morhua*) and other bottom-feeding fishes reduced pressure on young American, or Maine, lobsters (*Homarus americanus*), crabs, and sea urchins. The number of sea urchins steadily increased and they grazed on kelp, which is used by lobsters as shelter. Heavy harvesting of sea urchins for export to Japan led to a reduction in their numbers in the early 1990s. This development and continued overfishing of bottom fishes initially resulted in a sharp increase in the number of lobsters. Catches have nevertheless decreased in recent years as a result of increased water temperatures. Warmer water has also caused a decrease in the harvests of soft-shelled clams as an invasive predator, the green crab (*Carcinus maenas*), which does better in warm water.

Evidence from other parts of the world, however, seems to indicate that catastrophic disturbances of kelp communities are usually followed by a recovery, all in recurring cycles. Urchins and kelps are apparently kept in a delicate "balance" that can be tipped one way or the other by factors like climate change, the effects of nutrient pollution on the survival of urchin larvae, and the removal of urchin predators.

El Niño A warming of the surface water in the Eastern Pacific, part of large-scale changes in atmospheric and ocean current patterns, or *ENSO*.
La Niña A cooling trend of the surface water in the Eastern Pacific.
• 15.3, Epipelagic Food Webs

Interactive
Exploration

McGraw-Hill Connect® is a great place to check your understanding of chapter material. Visit **www.mcgrawhillconnect.com** for access to interactive chapter summaries, chapter quizzing, and more! Further enhance your knowledge with video clips and weblinks to chapter-related material.

Critical Thinking

1. The settling and metamorphosis of planktonic larvae can be triggered by the type of bottom (see Fig. 13.5). What kind of bottom features might be involved?

2. Eelgrass communities were severely affected by wasting disease in the 1930s, which caused many eelgrass meadows to disappear. What changes would you expect to take place if an eelgrass community vanished from a given area? Consider changes to the substrate, the benthos, and other types of marine animals. Are there any possible changes among animals living on land? What type of community do you think would replace the eelgrass communities after they disappeared?

3. The life history of kelps consists of a large sporophyte and a tiny gametophyte. Sea lettuce and some other seaweeds, however, have a gametophyte that is as big as their sporophyte (see Fig. 6.11*a*). Do you see any advantages for kelps having such an inconspicuous, puny gametophyte?

4. The outer, deeper margin of giant-kelp forests is typically even, whereas the inner, shallower margin is uneven and patchy (see Fig. 13.24). Can you present a possible explanation for such observation?

For Further Reading

Some of the recommended readings may be available online. Look for live links on the *Marine Biology* Online Learning Center.

General Interest

Ballesta, L., 2017. The beauty below the ice. *National Geographic,* vol. 232, no. 1, July, pp. 50–73. The Antarctic subtidal is home to an amazing variety of unique organisms.

Hall, S., 2020. Life in the dark Arctic. *Science News,* vol. 197, no. 7, pp. 14–19. Scientists spend a year, including the dark winter, studying Arctic food webs.

Harmon Courage, K., 2020. Prairies of the sea. *Smithsonian,* vol. 51, no. 8, pp. 52–65. Seagrass meadows are in sharp decline around the world despite their importance in the economy of the seas.

Isaacson, A., 2016. Into thin ice. *National Geographic,* vol. 229, no. 1, January, pp. 98–117. Exploitation of the Arctic Ocean intensifies with the reduction of the ice cap as a consequence of global warming.

McGrath, S., 2014. The urchin keepers. *Audubon,* vol. 116, no. 1, January–February, pp. 38–45. Sea otters have been successfully relocated from the Aleutian Islands, Alaska to Washington State.

In Depth

Deininger, A. and H. Frigstad, 2019. Reevaluating the role of organic matter sources for coastal eutrophication, oligotrophication, and ecosystem health. *Frontiers in Marine Science* [https://doi.org/10.3389/fmars.2019.00210].

Duarte, C. M. and D. Krause-Jensen, 2017. Export from seagrass meadows contributes to marine carbon sequestration. *Frontiers in Marine Science* [https://doi.org/10.3389/fmars.2017.00013].

Duarte, B., I. Martins, R. Rosa, A. R. Matos, M. Y. Roleda, T. B. H. Reusch, A. H. Engelen, E. A. Serrão, G. A. Pearson, J. C. Marques, I. Caçador, C. M. Duarte, and A. Jueterbock, 2018. Climate change impacts on seagrass meadows and macroalgal forests: An integrative perspective on acclimation and adaptation potential. *Frontiers in Marine Science* [https://doi.org/10.3389/fmars.2018.00190].

Filbee-Dexter, K. and T. Wernberg, 2018. Rise of turfs: A new battlefront for globally declining kelp forests. *BioScience,* vol. 68, pp. 64–76.

Folkard, A. M., 2019. Biophysical interactions in fragmented marine canopies: Fundamental processes, consequences, and upscaling. *Frontiers in Marine Science* [https://doi.org/10.3389/fmars.2019.00279].

Hancock, A. M., C. K. King, J. S. Stark, A. McMinn, and A. T. Davidson, 2020. Effects of ocean acidification on Antarctic marine organisms: A meta-analysis. *Ecology and Evolution,* vol. 10, pp. 4495–4514.

Morris, R. H., E. M. A. Strain, S. E. Reeves, A. Vergés, E. M. Marzinelli, C. Layton, V. Shelamoff, T. D. J. Graham, M. Chevalier, and S. E. Swearer, 2020. Key principles for managing recovery of kelp forests through restoration. *BioScience,* vol. 70, pp. 688–698.

Peck, L. S., 2018. Antarctic marine biodiversity: Adaptations, environments and responses to change. *Oceanography and Marine Biology: An Annual Review,* vol. 56, pp. 105–236.

Pondella, D. J., S. E. Piacenza, J. T. Claisse, C. M. Williams, J. P. Williams, A. J. Zellmer and J. E. Caselle, 2019. Assessing drivers of rocky reef fish biomass density from the Southern California Bight. *Marine Ecology Progress Series*, vol. 628, pp. 125–140.

Valdez, S. R., Y. S. Zhang, T. van der Heide, M. A. Vanderklift, F. Tarquinio, R. J. Orth, and B. R. Silliman, 2017. Positive ecological interactions and the success of seagrass restoration. *Frontiers in Marine Science* [https://doi.org/10.3389/fmars.2020.00091].

Wernberg, T., M. A. Coleman, R. C. Babcock, S. Y. Bell, J. J. Bolton, S. D. Connell, C. L. Hurd, C. R. Johnson, E. M. Marzinelli, N. T. Shears, P. D. Steinberg, M. S. Thomsen, M. A. Vanderklift, A. Vergés, and J. T. Wright, 2019. Biology and ecology of the globally significant kelp *Ecklonia radiata*. *Oceanography and Marine Biology: An Annual Review,* vol. 57, pp. 265–324.

Williams, J. P., J. T. Claisse, D. J. Pondella II, C. M. Williams, M. J. Robart, Z. Scholtz, E. M. Jaco, T. Ford, H. Burdick, and D. Witting, 2021. Sea urchin mass mortality rapidly restores kelp forest communities. *Marine Ecology Progress Series,* vol. 664, pp. 117–131.

Zarco-Perello, S., N. E. Bosch, S. Bennett, M. A. Vanderklift, and T. Wernberg, 2021. Persistence of tropical herbivores in temperate reefs constrains kelp resilience to cryptic habitats. *Journal of Ecology,* vol. 109, pp. 2081–2094.

Coral reef in the Red Sea. A Caribbean coral reef in Panamá.

CHAPTER

14

Coral Reefs

Damsea/Shutterstock

Coral reef

There is something special about tropical coral reefs. The warm, clear water, spectacular colors, and multitude of life captivate almost everyone. Coral reefs rival that other great tropical ecosystem, the rain forest, in their beauty, richness, and complexity. Tropical rain forests and coral reefs are also similar in that the basic physical structure of both communities is produced by organisms. Like the giant trees of a rain forest, reef-building corals create a three-dimensional framework that supports a vast assortment of organisms. Coral reefs are massive—in fact, they are not only biological communities but also geological structures, the largest geological features ever built by organisms.

Oysters, polychaete worms, and red algae also form reefs, and some cold-water corals slowly build mounds on the sea floor (see Box 14.2, "Deep-Water Coral Communities"). None of these features are as widespread, as large, or as structurally complex as tropical coral reefs.

14.1 THE ORGANISMS THAT BUILD REEFS

Coral reefs are made of huge amounts of **calcium carbonate** (**CaCO₃**), or limestone, deposited by organisms. Of the thousands of species in coral reef communities, only a fraction produce the limestone reef. The most important of these reef-building organisms, not surprisingly, are corals.

317

Table 14.1 Major Groups of Corals and Related Cnidarians on Coral Reefs

Common Name	Importance as Reef Builders	Notes
ANTHOZOANS (Lack medusa stage and live only as polyps; same group as sea anemones)		
Scleractinian corals	The main reef builders	Produce a calcareous skeleton; nearly all have zooxanthellae.
Soft corals	Not reef builders	Common on coral reefs (Fig. 14.27); most have zooxanthellae but do not produce a rigid calcareous skeleton.
Organ-pipe corals (*Tubipora*)	Minor	Named for pipe-like structure of skeleton; have zooxanthellae and produce a calcareous skeleton.
Blue coral (*Heliopora*)	Significant in some places	Named for distinct blue color of skeleton; has zooxanthellae and produces a calcareous skeleton.
Gorgonians	Not reef builders	Sea fans (Fig. 7.12) and sea whips; hard skeleton is made mostly of protein and not calcareous; some have zooxanthellae.
Precious corals	Not reef builders	Gorgonians with a pink, red, or gold calcareous skeleton used for jewelry; occur mainly in deep water rather than on coral reefs and do not contribute to reef growth; lack zooxanthellae.
Black corals	Not reef builders	Used to make jewelry and sometimes called "precious corals" but are a different group from gorgonian precious corals; hard skeleton is made of protein and is not calcareous; commonly occur in deep and cold surface waters as well as on coral reefs.
HYDROZOANS (Have both medusa and polyp stages but are seen on reef only as polyps; same group as some jellyfishes)		
Fire corals (*Millepora*)	Significant in some places	Named because touching them produces a burning sensation from their powerful nematocysts; have zooxanthellae and produce a calcareous skeleton.
Lace corals (*Stylaster*)	Insignificant	Named for their delicate, branched colonies; lack zooxanthellae but produce a calcareous skeleton; commonly occur in deep and cold surface waters as well as on coral reefs.

Reef Corals

"Coral" is a general term for several different groups of **cnidarians,** only some of which help build reefs (Table 14.1). In reef-building, or **hermatypic,** corals the **polyps** produce calcium carbonate skeletons. The skeletons built by billions of these tiny polyps form a massive reef. The most important reef builders are a group known as **scleractinian corals,** sometimes called the stony or "true" corals.

Nearly all reef-building corals contain symbiotic **zooxanthellae** (Fig. 14.1) that help the corals make their calcium carbonate skeletons. Corals can produce their skeletons without zooxanthellae but only very slowly, not nearly fast enough to build a reef. It is the zooxanthellae as much as the corals themselves that help construct the reef framework, and without zooxanthellae there would be no reefs. There are, however, a few exceptions. A scleractinian coral (*Tubastrea*) that lacks zooxanthellae is an important reef builder in some places, for example. **Ahermatypic** corals, like precious corals and black corals, do not help build reefs and often lack zooxanthellae.

The primary architects of coral reefs are reef-building corals that produce calcium carbonate skeletons with the help of symbiotic zooxanthellae.

The Coral Polyp You have to look close to see the little polyps that build coral reefs. Coral polyps are not only small but also deceptively simple in appearance. They look much like little sea anemones, consisting of an upright cylinder of tissue with a ring of

tentacles on top (Figs. 14.2 and 14.3*b*). Like anemones and other cnidarians, they use their nematocyst-armed tentacles to capture food, especially zooplankton. The tentacles surround the mouth, the only opening to the sac-like gut.

Most reef-building corals are colonies of many polyps, all connected by a thin sheet of tissue. The colony starts when a planktonic coral larva, called a **planula,** settles on a hard surface. Coral larvae generally do not settle on soft bottoms. The larva transforms, or **metamorphoses,** into a single "founder" polyp that, if it survives, divides over and over to form the colony. The digestive systems of the polyps usually remain connected via the surface tissue layer,

FIGURE 14.1 The microscopic, golden-brown zooxanthellae that pack these polyp tentacles help corals build reefs. They also occur in giant clams, some sea anemones (see Fig. 11.25), and other invertebrates. Cells in the white, bulbous tips of the tentacles are packed with nematocysts.

and they share a common nervous system (Fig. 14.4). A few reef-building corals consist of only a single large polyp (Fig. 14.3*a*).

Coral polyps lie in a cup-like skeleton of calcium carbonate that they make themselves. The polyps continually lay down new layers of calcium carbonate, building up the skeleton so that it grows upward and outward (Fig. 14.5). The skeleton forms nearly all the bulk of the colony (Fig. 14.6) and can take many different shapes (Fig. 14.7). The actual living tissue is only a thin layer on the surface. It is the calcareous coral skeletons that form the framework of the reef.

Coral Nutrition Zooxanthellae nourish the host coral as well as help it deposit its skeleton. They perform **photosynthesis** and pass some of the organic matter they make on to the coral (Fig. 14.8). Thus, the zooxanthellae feed the coral from the inside. Many corals can survive and grow without eating, as long as the zooxanthellae have enough light.

Although corals get much of their nutrition from their zooxanthellae, most eat when they get the chance, preying voraciously on zooplankton. The billions of coral polyps on a reef, along with all the other hungry reef organisms, are very efficient at removing zooplankton brought in by currents. The reef has been called a "wall of mouths."

Coral polyps catch plankton and **detritus** with their tentacles, or in sheets of mucus that they secrete on the colony surface. Mucus feeding allows the corals to catch much smaller particles than they can with their tentacles. Tiny, hair-like cilia gather the mucus into threads and

Cnidarians Animals in the phylum Cnidaria; they have radial symmetry, tissue-level organization, and tentacles with *nematocysts,* specialized stinging structures.
Life stages of cnidarians:
Polyp The sessile, sac-like stage, with the mouth and tentacles on top.
Medusa The swimming, bell-like stage, with the mouth and tentacles underneath.
• 7.2, Cnidarians: Radial Symmetry

Plankton Primary producers (*phytoplankton*) and consumers (*zooplankton*) that drift with the currents.
• 10.2, Major Marine Lifestyles and Environments; Figure 10.11

Zooxanthellae Dinoflagellates (single-celled, photosynthetic algae) that live within animal tissues.
• 5.3, Unicellular Algae

Symbiosis The living together in close association of two different species, often divided into *parasitism,* where one species benefits at the expense of the other; *commensalism,* where one species benefits without affecting the other; and *mutualism,* where both species benefit.
• 10.1, The Organization of Communities

Photosynthesis
$$CO_2 + H_2O + \text{sun energy} \rightarrow \text{organic matter} + O_2 \text{ (glucose)}$$
• 4.1, The Ingredients of Life

Detritus Particles of dead organic matter.
• 10.3, The Flow of Energy and Materials

Source: Bill Ober

FIGURE 14.2 Cutaway view of one of the polyps in a coral colony and of the calcium carbonate skeleton underneath. The polyps are interconnected by a very thin layer of tissue.

Michael E. Huber

(a)

Bill Ober

(b)

Charlie Arneson

(c)

FIGURE 14.3 Coral polyps. (*a*) A few corals consist of a single polyp, which as in this mushroom coral (*Fungia*) can be free-living, or not attached to the bottom. Most corals are colonies of many individual polyps. (*b*) In some of these, like the large-cupped boulder coral (*Montastrea cavernosa*) from the Caribbean, each polyp has its own individual cup, called a corallite. (*c*) In coral colonies like this brain coral (*Diploria*) from the Caribbean, meandering lines of polyps lie in a common corallite.

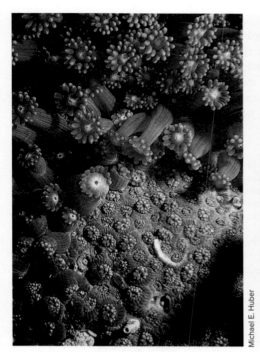

FIGURE 14.4 The polyps in a coral colony are interconnected. If you touch an extended polyp, it will contract, and so will its neighbors, followed by their neighbors, and so on, so that a wave of contraction passes over the colony. In this colony of the coral *Goniopora lobata* the wave of contraction is moving up from the bottom.

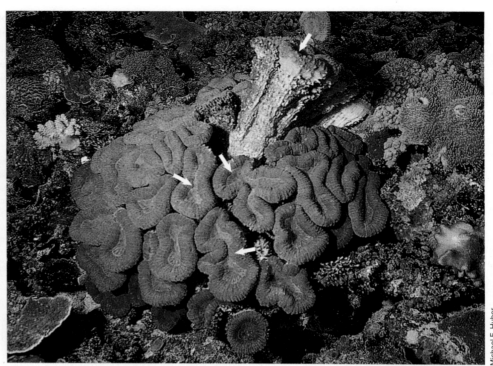

FIGURE 14.5 This coral (*Lobophyllia hemprichii*) shows particularly well how corals build up their skeleton. Each of the irregular rings (arrows) is a single polyp that has built up a column of calcium carbonate skeleton.

FIGURE 14.6 The calcium carbonate skeleton makes up most of a coral colony. A live colony (*Pocillopora verrucosa*) is on the right. On the left is a colony with the living tissue removed. The main difference is the color; the live part is only a thin layer of tissue on the surface. The "corals" sold in shell and aquarium shops are actually only the skeletons of live corals that were taken from the reef and bleached. Some reefs have been devastated by collectors who supply these shops to feed their families.

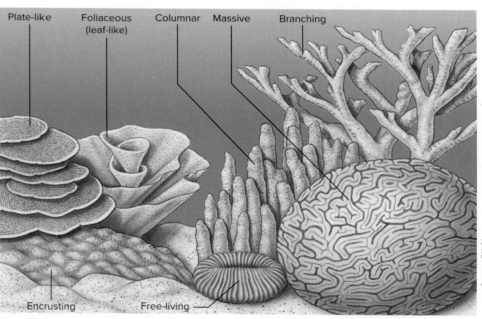

Plate-like Foliaceous (leaf-like) Columnar Massive Branching

Encrusting Free-living

FIGURE 14.7 Corals come in a multitude of shapes, or growth forms.

pass them along to the mouth. Some corals hardly use their tentacles and rely on the mucus method. A few have even lost tentacles altogether.

Corals have still other ways of feeding themselves. Attached to the wall of the gut are a number of long, coiled tubes called **mesenterial filaments** (Fig. 14.2). The mesenterial filaments secrete digestive enzymes. The polyp can extrude the filaments through the mouth or body wall to digest and absorb food particles outside the body. Corals also use the mesenterial filaments to digest organic matter from the sediments. In addition, corals can absorb **dissolved organic matter (DOM**; see "Trophic Structure," in 10.3).

Coral polyp

Source: Bill Ober

FIGURE 14.8 Zooxanthellae in a coral's tissue perform photosynthesis and transfer some of the organic matter they manufacture to the coral host. Carbon dioxide and nutrients are continually recycled between the coral and its zooxanthellae.

> Corals nourish themselves in a remarkable number of ways. Zooxanthellae are the most important source of nutrition. Corals can also capture zooplankton and detritus with tentacles or mucus nets, digest organic material outside the body with mesenterial filaments, or absorb dissolved organic matter (DOM) from the water.

Other Reef Builders

Although they are the chief architects, corals don't build a reef alone. Algae in particular are essential to reef growth. In fact, some marine biologists prefer to call coral reefs "algal reefs" or "biotic reefs." One reason for this is that zooxanthellae, which are algae, are essential to most reef-building corals. There are other algae, however, that also have key roles in building the reef. Encrusting **coralline algae** (*Porolithon, Lithothamnion*) grow in rock-hard sheets on the reef. They deposit considerable amounts of calcium carbonate, sometimes more than corals, and thus contribute to reef growth. Coralline algae are more important on Indian and Pacific Ocean reefs than Atlantic ones.

Encrusting coralline algae not only help build the reef, they also keep it from washing away. The stony pavement they make is tough enough to withstand waves that would smash even the most rugged corals. The algae form a distinct ridge on the outer edge of many reefs, especially in the Pacific. This **algal ridge** absorbs the force of the waves and prevents erosion from destroying the reef.

Encrusting algae do another job that is vital to reef growth. Coral skeletons and fragments create an open network, full of spaces, that traps coarse carbonate sediments (Fig. 14.9). Sediment, especially fine sediment, damages corals when it settles directly on them, but the buildup of coarse sediment in the reef framework is an essential part of reef growth. The structure of a reef is formed as much by the accumulation of calcareous sediment as by coral growth. Encrusting algae grow over the sediment as it builds up, cementing it in place. Encrusting coralline algae are the glue that holds the reef together. Some invertebrates, notably sponges and **bryozoans,** also help bind sediments.

> Encrusting coralline algae help build the reef by depositing calcium carbonate, by resisting wave erosion, and by cementing sediments.

Nearly all the sediment that accumulates to help form the reef comes from corals and the shells or skeletons of other organisms. In other words, nearly all the sediment is **biogenous. Coral rubble,** fragments of broken coral, is one important source. Another important sediment-forming organism is a calcareous green alga (*Halimeda*; Fig. 14.10). *Halimeda* deposits calcium carbonate in its tissues to provide support and discourage grazers—a mouthful of limestone is pretty unappetizing. The remnants of *Halimeda* accumulate on reefs in huge amounts, to be bound together by encrusting organisms.

Many other organisms make calcium carbonate sediments and contribute to reef growth. The tests of **forams,** as well as snails, clams, and other molluscs, are very important. Sea urchins, bryozoans, crustaceans, sponges, bacteria, and a host of other organisms add or help bind carbonate sediments. Reef growth is truly a team effort.

> The accumulation of calcium carbonate sediments is important in reef growth. A calcareous green alga, *Halimeda,* and coral rubble account for most of the sediment, but many other organisms contribute.

A great deal of the sediment on reefs comes from the activities of organisms that don't deposit calcium carbonate but instead break down the solid reef structure. Many animals scrape or bite their food off the reef with some sort of hard structure. Parrotfishes, for example, are named for their fused teeth that form a parrot-like beak. Sea urchins scrape algae off the reef with their **Aristotle's Lantern.** In the process, these and many other

Coralline Algae Red algae that deposit calcium carbonate ($CaCO_3$) in their tissues.

• 6.1, Multicellular Algae: The Seaweeds

Bryozoans Small, colonial, encrusting animals that make delicate, often lace-like, skeletons.

• 7.7, Lophophorates; Figure 7.44

Foraminiferans (Forams) Protozoans, often microscopic, with a calcium carbonate test.

• 5.3, Unicellular Algae; Figure 5.11

Aristotle's Lantern A complicated set of calcium carbonate ($CaCO_3$) teeth and associated muscles that is found in sea urchins.

• 7.8, Echinoderms: Five-Way Symmetry; Figure 7.49

Source: Bill Ober

FIGURE 14.9 Reef growth involves several processes. (*a*) The framework is made when reef-building corals settle and grow on some hard surface, usually a preexisting reef. (*b*) The spaces in this framework are partially filled in by coarse carbonate sediments. (*c*) When the sediments are glued together by encrusting organisms, new reef "rock" is formed and the reef has grown. On a real reef the corals continually grow upward while the sediments consolidate, so all three steps go on at the same time. Reefs are not actually completely solid as depicted here but are porous, with many holes and crevices that serve as home to a multitude of organisms.

grazers remove bits of calcium carbonate from the reef to form sediment. The erosion caused by such organisms, or **bioerosion,** tends to wear the reef away, although some of the sediment they create does get reincorporated into the reef structure. Many other organisms—including sponges, clams, polychaete and other worms, and algae—cause bioerosion by burrowing into or through the reef limestone, either scraping it away to form sediment or dissolving it. A reef grows only if corals, coralline algae, and

Michael E. Huber

FIGURE 14.10 This calcareous green alga (*Halimeda*) is one of the main sediment-forming organisms on most reefs. Up to 99% of the plant's weight is calcium carbonate.

sediment-forming and -binding organisms build it up faster than bioeroders wear it away.

Bioeroders have another important role in reef communities. Their burrowing creates spaces in the reef framework, nooks, and crannies where other organisms can hide. More species live inside the reef framework, in fact, than on its surface.

Conditions for Reef Growth

Other organisms are important, but coral reefs do not develop without reef-building corals. Corals have very particular requirements that determine where reefs develop. Reefs are rare on soft bottoms, for example, because coral larvae need to settle on a hard surface.

Light and Temperature Corals can grow only in shallow water, where light for their zooxanthellae can penetrate. Calcareous algae need sunlight, too. Different corals and algae have different depth limits—some can live deeper than others—but reefs rarely develop in water deeper than about 50 m (165 ft). Because of this, coral reefs are found only on the continental shelves, around islands, or on top of seamounts. Many types of coral live in deep water and do not need light, but these corals do not contain zooxanthellae or build massive reef structures (see Box 14.2, "Deep-Water Coral Communities"). Corals tend to prefer clear water, since water clouded with sediment or plankton reduces light penetration.

Reef-building corals are limited to warm water and can grow and reproduce only if the average water temperature is above about 20 °C (68 °F). Most reefs grow in considerably warmer areas. Figure 14.11 illustrates the relationship between coral reefs and water temperature.

Water that is *too* warm is also bad for corals. The upper temperature limit varies, but is usually around 30 to 35 °C (86 to 95 °F). The first outward sign of heat stress, or stress of other kinds, is **bleaching,** in which the coral expels its zooxanthellae (see Fig. 14.35). It is called bleaching because the golden-brown or greenish zooxanthellae give corals most of their color; without zooxanthellae the

Box 14.1 Coral Reproduction

Corals are amazingly adaptable animals. They come in all shapes and sizes and have many ways to feed themselves. It should come as no surprise, then, that they also have more than one way to reproduce.

One form of reproduction in corals is essentially the same as growth. As individual polyps reproduce vegetatively by dividing into new polyps, the colony as a whole grows. The process is taken a step further when a piece of a coral colony breaks off and grows into a new "daughter" colony. Reproduction by fragmentation seems to be important for some species, which may even be adapted to break easily to produce fragments. The growth of fragments into new colonies can be an important part of the recovery of reefs from storm damage and other disturbances, and transplanting fragments is one way that scientists and conservation groups help restore damaged reefs (see "Restoration of Habitats," in 18.4). Some corals, especially free-living ones, reproduce asexually by budding (see Fig. 4.19a).

Corals also reproduce sexually. They produce eggs and sperm, which fuse and develop into planulae, the characteristic larvae of cnidarians. Some species have separate sexes, but about 75% are hermaphrodites and make both eggs and sperm. The fertilization method varies.

In some corals, whether or not they are hermaphrodites, the egg is fertilized and initially develops inside the polyp. Most corals, however, are broadcast spawners and release eggs and sperm into the water.

The most spectacular form of sexual reproduction in corals is mass spawning, in which many different coral species on a reef all spawn at the same time. Mass spawning was first reported from the Great Barrier Reef, where it takes place a few nights a year between October and early December, just after a full moon. At a given place the time of the mass spawning event can usually be predicted down to the night. Since its discovery on the Great Barrier Reef, mass spawning has been found on many other reefs around the world.

Spawning corals release their eggs and sperm through their only body opening, the mouth. Some species package the gametes in little bundles, which can contain both eggs and sperm or only one or the other. The bundles float to the surface and break up, allowing the eggs and sperm to mix. Some corals that fertilize their eggs internally release larvae, rather than separate eggs and sperm, during mass spawning events.

Nobody knows why corals spawn all at once. Maybe egg predators get so full that most eggs go uneaten. It might have something to do with the tides. There may be an explanation that no one has thought of. Another interesting thing is that mass spawning happens on some reefs but not on others. Is there something different about these reefs? Finding answers to these questions will occupy coral biologists for some time to come.

The release of sperm and egg bundles by the coral *Acropora* during the mass coral spawning on the Great Barrier Reef.

coral's tissue is almost transparent and the coral looks white. Corals also slough off large amounts of slimy mucus when stressed. If the bleaching isn't too severe, corals sometimes recover, regaining their symbionts either from the regrowth of the few that remain or by acquiring new ones from the water. If the high temperatures last too long or the temperature gets too high, however, the coral dies.

Temperature limits vary among coral species and from place to place. Corals from warm locations, tolerate higher temperatures than corals from cooler waters (Fig. 14.12). Corals can also adapt to fluctuating conditions. For instance, reefs grow in parts of the Persian Gulf where the water temperature ranges from 16 to 40 °C (60 to 104 °F).

One way that corals adapt to temperature may be to have different species or strains of zooxanthellae that vary in temperature tolerance. Corals may even bleach as a way to expel zooxanthellae that can't take the heat and acquire different strains that are better adapted to warm conditions. On the Great Barrier Reef, for example, corals sometimes harbor more high-temperature zooxanthellae after recovering from temperature-induced bleaching.

In any case, the upper thermal tolerances of corals are usually not far above the normal temperature range where they live. Corals suffer in temperatures above the normal range. This sometimes happens during extreme low tides, when shallow pools on the reef may be cut off from circulation. Heated by the sun, the water can warm up to fatal temperatures. By discharging heated water, power stations and other industrial plants can also kill corals. Global warming has caused increasing widespread, frequent, and severe mass coral bleaching (see 14.4).

Corals need light and warm temperatures, so tropical coral reefs grow only in shallow, warm water. Temperatures that are too high, however, cause coral bleaching and mortality.

Salinity, Sediments, and Pollution Most corals are sensitive to reduced salinity and don't do well near river mouths, for example, where there is a lot of freshwater input. This is not only because of the lowered salinity but also because rivers bring in a lot of silt,

| ● Coral reefs | ▨ Reef-building corals | ---- Average 20 isotherm | ← Warm current | ← Cold current |

FIGURE 14.11 The distribution of reef coral communities, including those that do not form structural reefs. Note that the distribution of reef corals, like that of kelps, is related to temperature. Reef corals require warm water, however, while kelps need cold water. Compare the distribution of reefs with that of kelps shown in Fig. 13.22. Note that because of warm surface currents corals extend further north and south on the east sides of continents than on the west sides.

which is generally unfavorable to corals. It clouds the water, cutting down light for the zooxanthellae. Sediment on the colony surface can smother the coral or cause disease, though corals can clean themselves to some extent by sloughing off mucus that carries the sediment away. Sediment also covers up hard substrate that coral larvae need to settle on, and even when they do find a place to settle the new coral polyps are especially susceptible to sediment because they are so small, and therefore easily smothered.

Some corals do thrive in silty environments and even feed on organic-rich sediment particles. Sediment-tolerant corals can build diverse, productive reefs in silty environments. Reefs in clear, low-sediment waters, however, are dominated by species that are sensitive to sediment unless there is enough wave or current action to wash the sediment away (Fig. 14.13). Many reefs around the world have been damaged by human activities like mining, logging, and agriculture that greatly increase the flow of sediment onto the reef.

Corals are also sensitive to pollution of many kinds. Even low concentrations of pesticides and toxic wastes can harm them. Again, larvae are especially sensitive. Large amounts of nutrients can also be harmful (see "Pollution, Overfishing, Disease, and Habitat Destruction," in 14.4).

> Corals are very sensitive to freshwater, fine sediment, and pollution, including pollution by high nutrient levels.

14.2 KINDS OF CORAL REEFS

Coral reefs are usually divided into three main categories: **fringing reefs, barrier reefs,** and **atolls.** Some reefs don't fit neatly into any particular category or fall between two categories. Still, the division of reefs into the three major types works well for the most part.

> The three main types of reefs are fringing reefs, barrier reefs, and atolls.

Fringing Reefs

Fringing reefs are the simplest and most common reefs. They develop along the shore throughout the tropics, wherever there is a hard bottom where coral larvae can settle. Rocky shorelines provide the best conditions for fringing reefs. Fringing reefs also grow on soft bottoms if there is even a small hard patch where corals can get a foothold. Once they get started, the corals create their own hard bottom and the reef slowly expands.

As their name implies, fringing reefs grow in a narrow band or fringe along the shore. Occurring close to land, they are especially exposed to sediment, freshwater runoff, and human disturbance. Under the right conditions, however, fringing reefs can be impressive. In fact, the longest reef system in the world (though not the one with the largest coral area) is not the famous Great Barrier Reef

The bottom is primarily sand, mud, or coral rubble. There are some living corals, but neither as many colonies nor as many species as on the reef slope. Seaweeds, seagrasses, and soft corals can also occupy the reef flat, sometimes in dense beds.

The reef slope can be quite steep, even vertical. It is the part of the reef with the densest cover (Fig. 14.16) and the most species of coral, because the slope is not exposed at low tide and is away from shore and the effects of sediment and freshwater. Also, the waves that bathe the slope provide good circulation, bring in nutrients and zooplankton, and wash away fine sediments. The **reef crest** is the shallow upper edge of the reef slope. The crest sometimes has even more luxuriant coral growth than the rest of the reef slope. If there is intense wave action, however, the crest can consist of an algal ridge, with the richest coral growth just below. Because there is less light in deep water, the deepest part of the reef slope usually has less live coral and fewer coral species.

Fringing reefs grow close to shore and consist of an inner reef flat and an outer reef slope.

Large amounts of sediment and coral rubble tumble down the reef slope and settle at the base. As this material builds up, reef organisms may begin to grow on it, depending on the water depth and other factors. Thus, the reef can grow outward as well as upward. Beyond the base of the slope, the bottom is usually fairly flat and composed of sand or mud. On many Caribbean reefs, turtle grass (*Thalassia testudinum*) dominates the bottom beyond the slope.

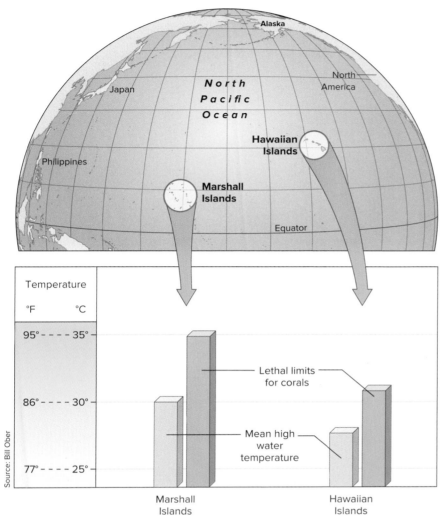

FIGURE 14.12 The upper temperature limit of corals is related to the temperature at their home sites. For example, the water in the Marshall Islands is warmer on average than that in Hawai'i. During the hottest months of the year the average high temperature is several degrees higher in the Marshalls. Corals from the Marshalls can tolerate correspondingly higher temperatures. Why do you think the highest temperature that the corals can tolerate would be higher than the average high temperature at their location?

in Australia but a fringing reef that runs some 4,000 km (2,500 mi) along the coast of the Red Sea. Part of the reason this reef is so well developed is that the climate is dry and there are no rivers that bring in sediment and freshwater.

The typical structure of a fringing reef is shown in Figure 14.14. Depending on the place, the shore can be steep and rocky or have mangroves or a beach. The reef itself consists of an inner **reef flat** and an outer **reef slope.** The reef flat is usually the widest part of the reef. It is shallow, sometimes exposed at low tide (Fig. 14.15), and slopes very gently toward the sea. Being closest to land, it is the part of the reef most strongly affected by sediments and freshwater runoff.

FIGURE 14.13 Corals often flourish where there is plenty of wave action. The water motion keeps sediment from settling on the corals and brings in food, oxygen, and nutrients.

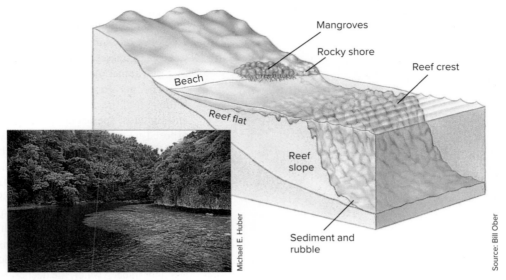

FIGURE 14.14 Typical structure of a fringing reef. Fringing reefs, like this one in the Bismarck Archipelago in the southwest Pacific (photo), can grow right up to the shore.

FIGURE 14.15 The upward growth of most reefs is limited by the tides. When extreme low tides occur, shallow areas like this reef flat on the Great Barrier Reef are exposed. If the corals are exposed for only a short time, they can survive, but they will die if exposed for too long. It is this occasional exposure at extreme low tides that keeps reef flats flat because all the corals above a certain depth are killed.

FIGURE 14.16 The elkhorn coral (*Acropora palmata*) is a dominant coral on the reef slopes of fringing reefs in the Caribbean and Florida. Its broad branches rise parallel to the surface to collect light. This colony suffers from a disease known as white-band disease (see 14.4).

Barrier Reefs

The distinction between barrier reefs and fringing reefs is sometimes unclear because the two types grade into one another. Like fringing reefs, barrier reefs lie along the coast, but barrier reefs occur considerably farther from shore, occasionally 100 km (60 mi) or more. Barrier reefs are separated from the shore—which may also have a fringing reef—by a relatively deep **lagoon** (Fig. 14.17). Largely protected from waves and currents, the lagoon usually has a soft sediment bottom. Seagrass beds often grow in shallow parts of the

lagoon. Scattered coral formations variously known as **patch reefs, coral knolls,** or **pinnacles,** depending on their size and shape, can grow up nearly to the surface.

The barrier reef consists of a **back-reef slope,** a reef flat, and a **fore-reef slope,** which corresponds to the reef slope of a fringing reef and has a reef crest. The back-reef slope can be gentle or as steep as the fore-reef slope. It is protected from waves by the rest of the reef, but waves wash large amounts of sediment from the reef down the slope. As a result, coral growth is often not as vigorous on the back-reef slope as on the fore-reef slope. This isn't always true, though,

and some back-reef slopes, especially gentle ones, have luxuriant coral growth (Fig. 14.18).

The reef flat, like that on fringing reefs, is a shallow, nearly flat platform. Sand and coral rubble patches are interspersed with sea-grass or seaweed beds, soft corals, and patches of dense coral cover.

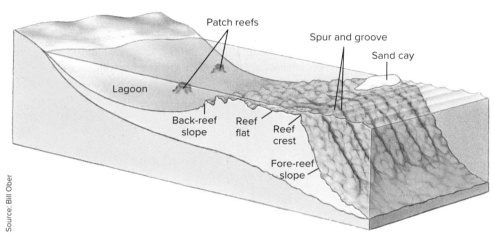

Source: Bill Ober

FIGURE 14.17 Typical structure of a barrier reef.

Michael E. Huber

FIGURE 14.18 A rich back-reef slope on a Pacific barrier reef.

Waves and currents can pile up sand to form small sand islands called **sand cays** or, in the United States, **keys.**

The richest coral growth is usually at the outer reef crest. There can be a well-developed algal ridge if there is strong wave action, with coral growth most luxuriant just below the crest. Exposed fore-reef areas often have a series of finger-like projections alternating with sand channels (Figs. 14.17 and 14.19). There is still debate about what causes these formations, known as **spur-and-groove** formations or **buttresses.** The wind, waves, or both are definitely involved, because spur-and-groove formations develop primarily on reef slopes that are exposed to consistent strong winds. These formations are found on atolls and some fringing reefs as well as barrier reefs.

Fore-reef slopes on barrier reefs vary from relatively gentle to vertical. The steepness depends on the geological setting, the action of wind and waves, the amount of sediment flowing down the slope, the depth and nature of the bottom at the reef base, and other factors. As with other types of reefs, the abundance and diversity of corals on the fore-reef slope generally decrease with depth. Corals' growth form also changes down the slope. At the crest, under the pounding of the waves, corals below the algal ridge are mostly stout and compact. Below the crest there is great variety in form. Whether they form branches, columns, or whorls, corals in this zone often grow vertically upward. This could be an adaptation for competition. Corals that grow upward like skyscrapers rather than outward need less space to attach. They are also less likely to be shaded, and if they spread out at the top can shade out competing corals and algae. Deeper on the reef slope, corals tend to grow in flat sheets to collect light (see Fig. 10.1*b*).

The largest and most famous barrier reef is the Great Barrier Reef. It runs more than 2,000 km (1,200 mi) along the northeastern coast of Australia, varying in width between about 15 and 350 km (10 and 200 mi) and covering an area of over 225,000 km² (80,000 mi²). Though not the longest reef in the world, it covers such a large area and is so complex and well developed that it is generally regarded as the largest reef structure. Actually, the Great Barrier Reef is not a single reef but a complex system of some 3,000 reefs and associated lagoons, channels, islands, and sand cays (Fig. 14.20).

The largest barrier reef in the Caribbean, the Mesoamerican Barrier Reef, lies off the coast of Belize, Central America. Other major barrier reefs include the Florida Reef Tract

David Burdick/NOAA

FIGURE 14.19 Spur-and-groove formation on Guam, one of the Mariana Islands in the western Pacific Ocean.

Image Professionals GmbH/Alamy Stock Photo

FIGURE 14.20 The Great Barrier Reef is a complicated system of thousands of small reefs, sand cays, and lagoons. Shown here are two reefs, the one in the foreground with a sand cay and spur-and-groove formations (see Fig. 14.19) on its outer margin.

and barrier reefs associated with the islands of New Caledonia, New Guinea, and Fiji in the Pacific. There are many other smaller barrier reefs, especially in the Pacific. Like the Great Barrier Reef, these are usually not single reefs but complex systems of smaller reefs.

Atolls

An atoll is a ring of reef, and often islands or sand cays, surrounding a central lagoon (Figs. 14.21 and 14.22). The vast majority of atolls occur in the **Indo-West Pacific region,** that is, the tropical Indian and western Pacific oceans. Atolls are rare in the Caribbean and the rest of the tropical Atlantic Ocean, although some ring-like reefs that grow on shallow banks and superficially resemble atolls do occur there. Unlike fringing and barrier reefs, atolls can be found far from land, rising up from depths of thousands of meters. With practically no land around, there is no river-borne silt and little or no freshwater runoff. Bathed in clean blue ocean water, atolls display spectacular coral growth and breathtaking water clarity. They are a diver's dream.

Atoll Structure Atolls range in size from small rings less than a mile across to systems more than 50 km (30 mi) in diameter. The world's largest growing atoll, with an area of some 12,600 km^2 (4,900 mi^2), is the Great Chagos Bank in the Indian Ocean. Mostly submerged, it has only a few tiny islands and is now uninhabited, though in the past it supported a small plantation and was used by sailors. The largest inhabited atolls are Suvadiva, in the Maldive Islands of the Indian Ocean, and Kwajalein, one of the Marshall Islands in the central Pacific. These atolls cover areas of more than 1,200 km^2 (700 mi^2). Atolls can have dozens of islands and be home to thousands of people.

An atoll's reef flat is much like the reef flat on a fringing or barrier reef: flat and shallow, with low coral abundance and diversity. The fore-reef and back-reef slopes can now be thought of as outer and inner slopes, respectively, since they extend all the way around the ring-shaped atoll.

Atoll reef crests are strongly influenced by wind and waves. Because most atolls lie in the **trade winds** belt, winds come from a consistent direction. Consequently, the wind affects various parts of the atoll in different ways. Encrusting coralline algae, which can endure the constant pounding of waves, build a distinct algal ridge on the reef crest of the **windward** side of the atoll, the side that faces the prevailing wind. On the few Caribbean atolls, coralline algae can be replaced by especially wave-resistant corals. The algal ridge is less prominent or absent on the **leeward,** or sheltered, side of the atoll. Spur-and-groove formations, too, are better developed on the windward side.

The fore-reef, or outer, slope is vertical or nearly so, usually with ledges and overhangs. The rocky wall of the reef extends down to great depths, far beyond the limit of living corals themselves. The water can be hundreds, even thousands, of meters deep just a stone's throw from the reef.

The lagoon, on the other hand, is relatively shallow, usually no more than about 60 m (195 ft) deep. The bottom of a lagoon is uneven, however, and some pinnacles rise almost to the surface, where they can form "mini-atolls," small rings of coral within the lagoon.

Atolls are rings of reef, with steep outer slopes, that enclose a shallow lagoon.

How Atolls Form When European explorers first saw atolls, scientists were at a loss to explain them. They knew corals can only grow in shallow water, yet atolls grow right from the depths of the open ocean. Therefore, the atoll could not have grown up from the ocean floor. If the reefs grew on some kind of shallow structure that was already there, like a seamount, why is there no sign of it? The islands on atolls are simple sand cays that have been built by the accumulation of reef sediments and would not exist without the reef. They are *products* of the reef and could not provide the original foundation for reef growth. Finally, why do atolls always form rings?

The puzzle of atoll formation was solved by Charles Darwin in the mid-nineteenth century. Darwin is most famous, of course, for proposing the theory of evolution by natural selection, but his theory of atoll formation was another of his many important contributions to science.

Darwin reasoned that atolls are formed by reef growth on a **subsiding** island. The atoll gets its start when a deep-sea volcano erupts to build an island or seamount. Corals soon colonize the shores of the new island, and a fringing reef develops (Fig. 14.23*a*). As with most fringing reefs, coral growth is most vigorous at the outer edge of the reef. The inner reef is strongly affected by sediment and runoff from the island. As the island subsides, the outer reef continues to grow faster than corals inside the lagoon,

> **The trade winds,** the steadiest winds on Earth, blow from latitudes of about 30° toward the Equator.
>
> • 3.2, Ocean Circulation; Figure 3.18

FIGURE 14.21 A small atoll in the Republic of Belau (Palau), western Pacific.

Douglas Faulkner/Science Source

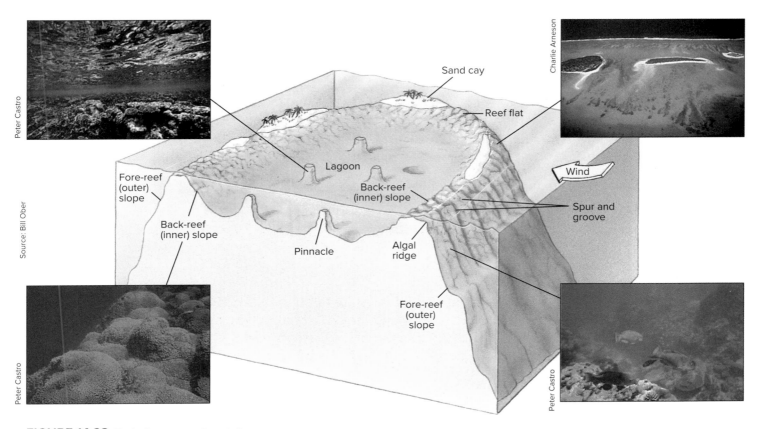

Peter Castro

Source: Bill Ober

Peter Castro

Charlie Arneson

Peter Castro

Sand cay

Reef flat

Lagoon

Fore-reef (outer) slope

Back-reef (inner) slope

Back-reef (inner) slope

Pinnacle

Algal ridge

Wind

Spur and groove

Fore-reef (outer) slope

FIGURE 14.22 Typical structure of an atoll.

Box 14.2 Deep-Water Coral Communities

Tropical coral reefs bask in sunlit shallow water, but over 700 species of corals live in the cold and darkness of deep water. Deep-water corals occur in all the oceans to depths of over 6,000 m (20,000 ft). They do not harbor zooxanthellae, which in the absence of sunlight would be of no use. They feed by capturing zooplankton with their tentacles, and generally grow in strong currents that bring in food.

Over 20 deep-water coral species build or contribute to large seabed mounds known as bioherms. The mounds are usually on the continental slope or seamounts and other underwater features at depths of up to 1,500 m (5,000 ft). In some places, Norwegian fjords, for example, they occur in water as shallow as 40 m (130 ft). These structures are sometimes called "coral reefs," but the term "reefs" was originally a nautical term for areas of hard bottom shallow enough for ships to run aground, and the geological definition of coral reefs refers to solid calcium carbonate structures built by corals. Although deep-water coral mounds contain large amounts of calcareous coral fragments, they are mostly mud. The mounds also appear to be a product of circulation patterns that favor the passive accumulation of sediment and coral fragments, rather than structures actively built by the corals. Scientists have also speculated that the mounds might form around cold seeps and rely in part on chemosynthesis.

The largest known deep-water coral mounds, dominated by the branching coral *Lophelia pertusa,* are in the northeastern Atlantic off the coast of Britain and Scandinavia. *Lophelia* is a scleractinian coral, like most tropical reef-building corals, but lacks zooxanthellae. Individual mounds grow more than 300 m (1,000 ft) above the surrounding muddy bottom, with a base more than 5 km (3 mi) in diameter. Mound complexes can extend for as far as 45 km (30 mi).

Lophelia mounds support rich and diverse communities. The coral branches and broken fragments provide shelter and a hard surface where other sessile species can attach. Relatively few fishes, about 25 species, are known to associate with *Lophelia* mounds, but biologists have found more than 1,300 invertebrate species. There could well be more. The *Lophelia* mounds in the northeastern Atlantic have been known since the nineteenth century but have only really been studied in the last two decades when advances in deep-sea exploration technology revealed their true extent and diversity. Mounds made by *Lophelia* and other deep-water corals occur in many other

A *Lophelia* mound devastated by trawling.

MAREANO/Institute of Marine Research

parts of the ocean, and new mounds are regularly discovered as deep-sea exploration continues. The communities can be ancient: A deep-sea coral in Hawai'i has been found to be more than 4,000 years old.

Like seamount communities (see Box 16.2, "Biodiversity in the Deep Sea"), deep-water coral communities on the continental slope are increasingly threatened by trawl fishing. As shallow-water fisheries are depleted, trawlers are forced into ever-deeper water. The trawls shatter the fragile corals and dig great gouges in the seabed. Some countries have prohibited trawling in areas of known coral mounds, and international measures for additional protection have been agreed.

Alberto Lindner/NOAA

This coral community at a depth of 150 m (490 ft) in the Aleutian Islands, Alaska, includes soft corals, lace corals, sponges, and other animals.

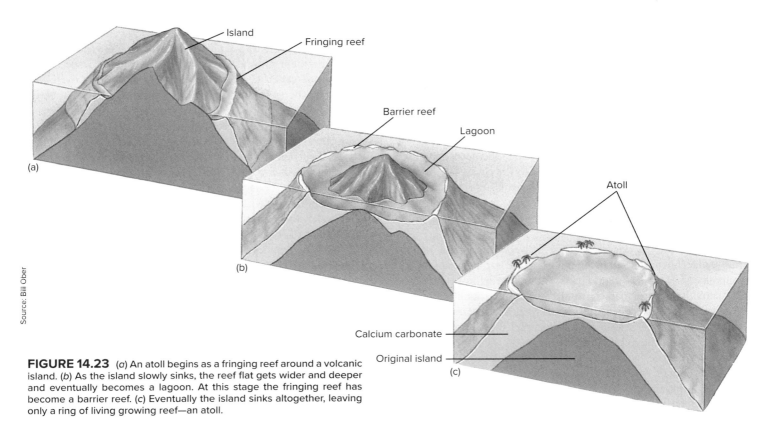

Source: Bill Ober

FIGURE 14.23 (*a*) An atoll begins as a fringing reef around a volcanic island. (*b*) As the island slowly sinks, the reef flat gets wider and deeper and eventually becomes a lagoon. At this stage the fringing reef has become a barrier reef. (*c*) Eventually the island sinks altogether, leaving only a ring of living growing reef—an atoll.

so the lagoon gets progressively deeper, though scattered coral pinnacles continue to grow to near the surface.

Surprisingly, Darwin's explanation of atoll formation was pretty much ignored for a century while scientists proposed various other hypotheses, none of which held up under testing. That is the strength of the scientific method. Eventually, scientists got conclusive evidence that Darwin was right. Unlike other hypotheses for atoll formation, Darwin's hypothesis predicted that below the thick calcium carbonate cap formed by the reef there should be volcanic rock—the original island. In the 1950s the United States Geological Survey drilled several deep holes on Enewetak atoll in the Marshall Islands. These cores revealed exactly what Darwin predicted: volcanic rock far beneath the calcium carbonate of the reef. The thickness of the carbonate cap is impressive: The living reef has built up more than 1,400 m (4,600 ft) of calcium carbonate over the volcanic island underlying Enewetak!

There were, of course, a few details to be added to the picture, in particular the effects of changes in sea level. When sea level is low, atolls can be stranded above the surface. The reef dies and is eroded by wind and rain. If sea level rises rapidly, the atoll can be drowned, unable to grow in deep water. There are a number of such atolls, drowned and with only a few small living reefs, in the Indo-West Pacific.

14.3 THE ECOLOGY OF CORAL REEFS

Coral reefs are impressive to geologists, but to biologists they are simply awesome. They are easily the richest and most complex of all marine ecosystems. Thousands of species may live on a single reef.

How do all these species live? How do they affect each other? What is their role in the reef ecosystem?

These questions are hard to answer because reefs are so complex. Just identifying the vast number of different organisms is hard enough; the task of figuring out what they all *do* is mind-boggling. Furthermore, until the last half century or so most marine biologists lived and worked in the temperate regions of the Northern Hemisphere, far from the nearest reef. As a result, relatively few biologists studied reefs. There has been tremendous progress, but there is still much to learn. The rest of this chapter summarizes the ecology of coral reefs and a few of the many important questions that remain.

The Trophic Structure of Coral Reefs

The tropical waters where coral reefs are found are usually nutrient-poor and therefore have very little phytoplankton and **primary production**. In these barren waters, coral reefs are oases of abundant life. How can such rich communities grow when the surrounding sea is so unproductive?

Subsidence The slow sinking into the *mantle* of a part of the earth's crust that contains a landmass.

• 11.1, Rocky Shore Intertidal Communities

Primary Production The conversion of carbon from an inorganic form, carbon dioxide, into organic matter by autotrophs, that is, the production of food.

• 4.1, The Ingredients of Life

A big part of the answer lies in the mutualistic relationship between corals and their zooxanthellae. We have already learned what the zooxanthellae do for the coral: They provide food and help make the calcium carbonate skeleton. In return, the zooxanthellae get a protected place to live and a steady supply of carbon dioxide and nutrients like **nitrogen** and **phosphorus.** Most of the coral's nitrogen and phosphorus waste products are not excreted into the water. Instead, they are taken up and used as nutrients by the zooxanthellae. Using sunlight, the zooxanthellae incorporate the nutrients into organic compounds, which are passed back to the coral. When the coral breaks down the organic matter, the nutrients are released and the whole process begins again (see Fig. 14.8). The nutrients are recycled, so that far fewer new nutrient input is needed than would otherwise be the case.

Nutrient recycling occurs not just between corals and their zooxanthellae, but among all the members of the coral reef community. Sponges, sea squirts, giant clams, and other reef invertebrates have symbiotic algae or bacteria and recycle nutrients like corals do. Recycling also takes place outside the bodies of reef organisms. When fishes graze on seaweeds, for example, they excrete nitrogen, phosphorus, and other nutrients as waste. These nutrients are quickly taken up by other algae. Many corals provide shelter to schools of small fish. The fish leave the coral at night to feed and return during the day. The waste products of the fish can be an important source of nutrients and help the coral grow faster. In this way nutrients are cycled from the fish's prey to the fish to the coral. Nutrients pass through the community again and again in this cycle of feeding and excretion.

Coral reef communities use nutrients very efficiently as a result of recycling. The recycling isn't perfect, however, and some nutrients are lost, carried away by the currents. Thus, the reef still needs a supply of new nutrients. Recycling alone is not enough to account for the high productivity of reefs.

The reef provides some of its own nutrients. Coral reefs have among the highest rates of **nitrogen fixation** of any natural ecosystem. The main nitrogen fixers are cyanobacteria, especially a free-living one called *Calothrix* and another group that lives symbiotically in sponges. Corals, too, may have symbionts that fix nitrogen, providing nutrients for the zooxanthellae. Because of this nitrogen fixation, nitrogen probably does not limit most coral reef communities, though not all reef biologists agree.

Ocean currents bring in additional nitrogen and, more importantly, phosphorus and other nutrients that are not produced on the reef. Corals, bacteria, algae, and other organisms absorb nutrients directly from the water. Even though the water is nutrient-poor, if enough water washes over the reef the nutrients add up. In business terms, this is a low-margin, high-volume proposition. More importantly, the water carries zooplankton, a rich nutrient source. When zooplankton are captured by the "wall of mouths," the nutrients in the zooplankton are passed on to the reef community. In fact, many biologists think that corals eat zooplankton to get nutrients for their zooxanthellae as much as to feed themselves. Animals like seabirds, dolphins, and large fishes that spend part of their time around reefs but venture out into the open ocean to feed also transfer nutrients from oceanic waters to the reef community.

> Coral reefs are very productive even though the surrounding ocean water lacks nutrients because nutrients are recycled extensively, nitrogen is fixed on the reef, and the zooplankton and nutrients brought in by currents and predators are used efficiently.

The production and efficient use of nutrients by coral reef communities result in high primary productivity. This is reflected in the richness of the community. Scientists aren't sure, however, just how much primary production there is on coral reefs, or which particular organisms are the most important producers. There is no doubt that zooxanthellae are very important, but because they live inside corals, it is hard to measure exactly how much organic matter they produce. For a time it was thought that very few animals eat coral, since there is so little live tissue on a coral colony. It was therefore believed that, even though zooxanthellae produce a lot of organic matter, most of it is consumed by the coral and not much passed on to the rest of the community. As biologists looked closer, however, they found more and more animals that eat corals or their products (Fig. 14.24). Primary production by coral zooxanthellae therefore can be important not only to corals but also to the community at large. Exactly how much production corals and their zooxanthellae contribute is still unknown.

Seaweeds are also important primary producers on the reef (Fig. 14.25),

FIGURE 14.24 A number of animals eat coral directly, and many others feed on the mucus that corals produce or on coral eggs and larvae. The primary production of coral zooxanthellae is thus passed on to coral feeders, and then to the animals that eat them.

Source: Bill Ober

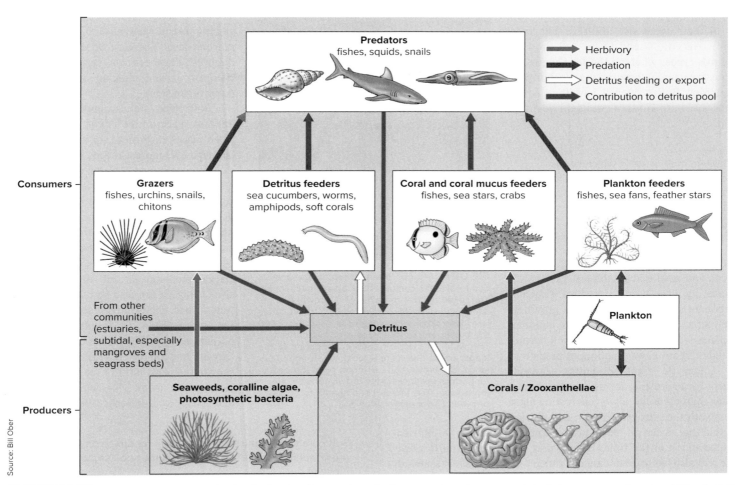

Source: Bill Ober

FIGURE 14.25 A generalized coral reef food web. Coral reefs are extremely diverse, and most components include many organisms in addition to those listed here.

especially small, fleshy, or filamentous types that are called **turf algae** because they often grow in a short, thick turf. A great many fishes, sea urchins, snails, and other animals graze on these seaweeds. Turf algae may perform more photosynthesis on the reef than zooxanthellae, but biologists are not sure.

> Zooxanthellae and turf algae are probably the most important primary producers on coral reefs.

Cyanobacteria and coralline algae are also primary producers on coral reefs. They probably account for less primary production than do zooxanthellae and turf algae.

Coral Reef Communities

With so many species on coral reefs, the interactions among them are exceedingly complex. What is known about these interactions is fascinating; what remains to be learned will be even more so.

Competition Space is at a premium on coral reefs, as it is in the rocky intertidal (see "The Battle for Space," in 11.1). Corals, seaweeds, and many others need to attach to a hard surface. Cor-

als, seaweeds, many soft corals and sponges, and some other reef inhabitants need not just space but space in the sunlight. The reef is crowded, and most of the space is taken. As a result the sessile organisms, those that stay in one place, must compete for space.

> Sessile coral reef organisms must compete for space. Corals, seaweeds, and many other reef organisms must compete for space in the sunlight.

Corals compete for space in different ways. The fast-growing ones tend to grow upward and then branch out, cutting their neighbors off from the light. Other corals take a more direct approach and actually attack their neighbors (Fig. 14.26). Some use their mesenterial filaments for this. When they contact another coral, they extrude the filaments and digest away the tissue of the other coral. Still other corals develop special long tentacles called **sweeper tentacles** that are loaded with nematocysts

Nitrogen Fixation The conversion of nitrogen gas (N_2) into nitrogen compounds that can be used by primary producers as nutrients.
• 5.2, Eukaryotes; Table 5.1

and sting neighboring colonies. Corals differ in their aggressive abilities. The most aggressive corals tend to be slow-growing, massive types, whereas the less aggressive forms are usually fast-growing, upright, and branching. Both strategies have their advantages, and both kinds of corals thrive on the reef.

> The two main ways in which corals compete for space are by overgrowing their neighbors and by directly attacking them.

Corals compete for space and light not only with each other but also with seaweeds and sessile invertebrates. Like corals, encrusting algae have to produce a calcium carbonate skeleton and therefore grow relatively slowly. They tend to be most abundant in places where corals don't do well because of sedimentation, wave action, or predation.

Under the right conditions seaweeds, except for encrusting forms, can grow much faster than either corals or encrusting algae. Even with the nitrogen fixation and nutrient cycling that occur on reefs, most are probably somewhat nutrient-limited much of the time. Hence, they usually grow fairly slowly. The reef also has an abundance of hungry grazers that eat seaweeds.

FIGURE 14.26 When different species of coral come in contact, they attack each other. The pink band separating the brown (*Porites lutea*) and blue (*Mycedium elephantotus*) corals is a dead zone where the blue coral has killed the brown one in the process of overgrowing it. The width of the pink band corresponds to the length of the blue coral's tentacles. To the upper left of the brown coral is a soft coral (*Sarcophyton*), which is attacking the brown coral by releasing poison. The brown coral seems to be stuck between a rock and a soft place!

Michael E. Huber

The combination of nutrient limitation and grazing keeps seaweeds in check. If the nutrient levels increase or the grazers are removed, seaweeds can rapidly take over, overgrowing and choking out corals and other organisms.

Soft corals are also important competitors for space on reefs (Fig. 14.27), and in some places they make up almost half the biomass. Like most seaweeds, soft corals lack a calcium carbonate skeleton and are able to grow faster than hard corals. Some soft corals contain sharp little calcium carbonate needles, or **sclerites,** that discourage predation. Many of them also contain chemicals that are toxic or distasteful to predators. Because of these defense mechanisms, only a few specialized predators eat soft corals. The defensive chemicals can also be released into the water, where they kill hard corals that come too close (Fig. 14.26). Another competitive advantage enjoyed by some soft corals is that they are not completely sessile. Though they stay in one place most of the time, they can slowly move about. This helps them invade and occupy available space on the reef.

> Soft corals are important competitors for space on reefs. They grow rapidly, are resistant to predators, and can occasionally move about.

With all these competitive weapons at their disposal, why don't soft corals take over? Not much is known about how soft corals compete with reef-building corals and other reef organisms or what determines the winner. Many soft corals appear to have shorter lives than reef-building corals, although some live for decades. They are also more easily torn away by storm waves. They have symbiotic zooxanthellae like reef-building corals but are much less efficient photosynthesizers. They also seem to depend on favorable physical conditions. It is not known how these factors interact to determine when and where soft corals successfully compete for space on the reef.

Like soft corals, sponges often have needle-like structures, spicules, and nasty chemicals that protect them from predators. They can be important users of space on reefs, much more so in the Caribbean than in the Pacific and Indian oceans. Part of the reason for this seems to be that there are fewer species of coral in the Caribbean than in the Indo-West Pacific, a result of geological history. During the most recent series of ice ages, the sea surface was cooler. Corals survived in the heart of the Indo-West Pacific region, around Indonesia and New Guinea, but many species became extinct in other parts of the ocean. When the ice age ended,

FIGURE 14.27 Soft corals can form dense patches on coral reefs, as on this reef in Papua New Guinea.

Michael E. Huber

corals spread out again across the Pacific. The Isthmus of Panamá emerged in the meantime, however, and blocked the dispersal of corals back into the Caribbean. It is thought that the Caribbean contains only coral species that survived the ice ages or have evolved since. Sponges are even more abundant in the Caribbean now than in the past, however, because Caribbean corals have been hard-hit by pollution, disease, and bleaching (see 14.4), making way for the sponges.

Coral reef fishes are another group in which competition is important. Along with corals, fishes are probably the most conspicuous and abundant animals on the reef (Fig. 14.28). Many of these fishes share similar diets; for example, many species eat coral, many graze on algae, and many are carnivores. Different species of fishes of the same feeding type at least potentially compete with each other.

Along with competition, the abundances of individual species can also be determined mainly by how many of their larvae settle out from the plankton. With favorable currents and other conditions, many larvae of a given species will settle out and the species becomes abundant. If larval supply is low, for example, if currents carry larvae away from the reef, the species becomes rare. This is called a **pre-settlement** hypothesis because it holds that the nature of reef fish communities is determined by the availability of different species' larvae before they settle.

An alternative, **post-settlement,** hypothesis is that most species have plenty of settling larvae. The abundant species are those that compete successfully for space, food, and other resources after the larvae settle, that is, as juveniles and adults. This hypothesis holds that so many different fish species can live on the reef because each does something a little different from other species, thereby avoiding competition and the risk of **competitive exclusion.** In other words, each species has its own particular **ecological niche.** According to this view, the structure of the fish community on a reef is determined by the range of resources available on that reef, and the fish communities of reefs vary because different reefs offer different resources.

The relative importance of the supply of settling larvae and post-settlement competition in structuring reef fish communities hasn't been established. It probably varies from species to species and reef to reef. Physical factors and natural disturbances are probably also important, as are predation and other biological interactions. The presence of cleaner wrasses, for example, promotes the larval settlement of damselfishes (see Box 10.2, Cleaning Associations).

The abundances of reef fish species are determined by how many larvae are available to settle out from the plankton and by competition among juveniles and adults after the larvae settle out. Other factors are probably also important.

Predation on Corals As in other communities, predation and grazing are important in structuring coral reef communities. A variety of animals eat corals, but instead of killing the coral and eating

Competitive Exclusion The elimination of one species by another as a result of competition.
Ecological Niche The combination of what a species eats, where it lives, how it behaves, and all the other aspects of its lifestyle.
• 10.1, The Organization of Communities

FIGURE 14.28 Diving on a coral reef is like taking a swim in a tropical fish aquarium—brightly colored fishes seem to be everywhere. The competitive relationships among the various species of fishes are poorly understood.

FIGURE 14.29 The chevron butterflyfish (*Chaetodon trifascialis*) is one of many reef animals that feed on corals without killing the entire coral colony. Its mouth is adapted for nipping off individual coral polyps (also see Fig. 8.27).

it entirely, most coral predators eat individual polyps or bite off pieces here and there (Fig. 14.29). The coral colony as a whole survives and can grow back the portion that was eaten. In this respect, coral predation is similar to grazing by herbivores. Fishing grazing on corals appears to release symbiotic zooxanthellae from the corals, so it might play a role in corals' acquisition of new symbionts.

Coral predation affects both the number and type of corals that live on a reef, as well as how fast the reef as a whole grows. In Kāne'ohe Bay, for example, a butterflyfish (*Chaetodon unimaculatus*) slows the growth of a particular coral (*Montipora verrucosa*) it likes to eat. When the coral is protected from the fish by a cage, it grows much faster. If it were not for the fish, this fast-growing coral would probably dominate other corals in the bay. Coral-eating snails (*Coralliophila, Drupella*) have similar effects on some reefs.

The Crown-of-Thorns Sea Star Another example of the effect of coral predators is the **crown-of-thorns sea star** (COTS; *Acanthaster planci;* Fig. 14.30). COTS feed by pushing their stomach out through the mouth, covering all or part of the coral colony with the stomach, and digesting away the live coral tissue. COTS have distinct preferences for certain types of coral and avoid others—some corals must taste bad. Other corals harbor symbiotic crabs (see the photo at the beginning of Chapter 7), shrimps, and fishes that discourage the sea stars by pinching and biting their **tube feet.**

FIGURE 14.30 The crown-of-thorns sea star (*Acanthaster planci*) is an important and controversial coral predator.

COTS have had a major impact on some reefs. Beginning in the late 1950s, people began to notice large numbers, sometimes thousands, of the sea star on reefs scattered across the Pacific (Fig. 14.31). The sea stars in these large aggregations move en masse across the reef, consuming almost every coral in their path. Healthy reefs recover in 10 to 15 years, though it may take longer for certain slow-growing coral species to grow back.

The first response to the problem was panic. Coral reefs are valuable resources: They support fisheries, tourism, and recreation and protect coastlines from tsunamis, storms, and erosion. With COTS apparently threatening reefs, people decided to take action and control the sea star. The first attempt backfired. With limited knowledge of the animal's biology, some people cut the sea stars into pieces and dumped them back in the sea. Because sea stars can regenerate, the pieces grew into new sea stars! More sophisticated methods, like poisoning the sea stars, have been used, but are time consuming and expensive, and sometimes did more harm than good. COTS outbreaks eventually go away by themselves, though they can inflict a lot of damage on the reef before they do. Unfortunately, COTS outbreaks are becoming more frequent and more severe, probably because of human activities (see 14.4).

When COTS outbreaks were first observed it seemed obvious that humans must be to blame. After all, the plagues had never occurred before. Or had they? People had only begun using scuba a short time before the sea star plagues were noticed. Even if the plagues had been occurring for a long time, there were no scientists around to see them. Geologists found fossil evidence of crown-of-thorns outbreaks dating back thousands of years, and there are old stories and other historical evidence for past outbreaks. Occasional COTS outbreaks are probably a natural part of the reef ecosystem, and periodic outbreaks part of the sea star's biology.

Even if outbreaks did occur in the past, though, they have become more frequent. The removal of COTS predators by humans may favor outbreaks, but this effect is probably minor. The problem, at least on the Great Barrier Reef, is that floods carry massive amounts of nutrients onto the reef. The nutrients favor the survival of larval and juvenile COTS, leading to an outbreak a few years later. Land clearing, river modification, fertilizer runoff, and other activities have increased both the frequency of flooding and the associated nutrient input.

COTS outbreaks may be a natural part of the ecosystem, but it has become clear that the Great Barrier Reef is in serious decline. Coral bleaching, cyclone damage (while cyclones are natural, global warming is increasing their frequency and severity), and other stresses have taken a heavy toll. COTS outbreaks are one more major source of damage to the reef probably made worse by human activities, and have accounted for considerable coral mortality. They are also a stress we

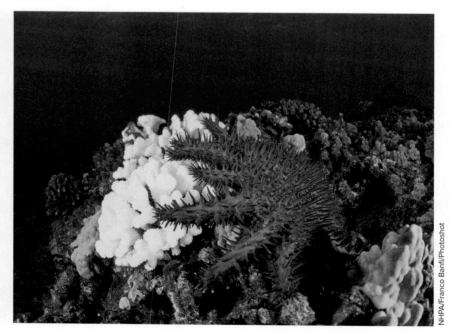

FIGURE 14.31 An outbreak of crown-of-thorns sea stars (*Acanthaster planci*) in the Hawaiian Islands. The white colony of *Pocillopora* shows the bare calcium carbonate skeleton left behind after the sea star has digested away the coral's tissue.

can do something about right now, so the managers of the Great Barrier Reef have not only taken steps to address nutrient runoff to the reef, but actively control COTS outbreaks by killing the sea stars when they get out of control (see "Promoting Reef Resilience", in 14.4).

These issues are by no means restricted to the Great Barrier Reef, and those responsible for protecting coral reefs around the world are faced with similar problems.

> Population explosions of the crown-of-thorns sea star periodically damage many Pacific reefs. These explosions have probably occurred naturally but are increasing, and are an additional threat to reefs already in decline.

Bill Ober

FIGURE 14.32 The long-spined black sea urchin (*Diadema antillarum*) is one of the most important grazers on Caribbean reefs. Closely related species are found on reefs in other parts of the world.

increase in seaweed cover occurred after a decline in urchin populations in the Red Sea.

Fishing can reduce fish grazing on reefs—even if the grazers themselves aren't fished—through a **trophic cascade.** Sharks, the top fish predators on many reefs, have been severely depleted by fishing because they reproduce slowly and are highly targeted, mostly for their valuable fins. Without shark predation, large predatory fishes like groupers become more abundant, and in turn eat smaller grazing fishes. It is not yet clear how widespread this phenomenon is, because the predatory fishes are usually targeted as well as sharks. It is probably most common in remote areas where there isn't a lot of local fishing pressure but fishing vessels targeting sharks come in from far away.

Grazing Herbivore grazing on algae is at least as important in coral reef ecosystems as is predation on corals. Many fishes, especially surgeonfishes (*Acanthurus*), parrotfishes (*Scarus, Sparisoma*), and damselfishes (*Pomacentrus, Dascyllus*), graze intensively on reefs. Among the invertebrates, sea urchins (*Diadema, Echinometra*) are especially important. Many **microherbivores,** small invertebrates like snails, **chitons,** crustaceans, and polychaete worms, also eat algae.

Many seaweeds grow rapidly and can potentially outcompete and overgrow corals. Under natural conditions they are common on the reef but are kept in check by grazers and nutrient limitation. Caging experiments (see Box 11.1, "Transplantation, Removal, and Caging Experiments") demonstrate the importance of grazers. For example, seaweeds are abundant on sand flats next to many Caribbean reefs but relatively scarce on the reef itself. Unprotected seaweeds transplanted from the sand flat to the reef are quickly eaten by grazing fishes. If the seaweeds are protected by cages, however, they grow faster than on the sand flat! The seaweeds are perfectly capable of living on the reef, but are rare there because they get eaten. Caging experiments on the Great Barrier Reef show similar results.

If grazers are removed, seaweeds can flourish and take over space from corals and other organisms. In many parts of the Caribbean, fishing has reduced populations of grazing reef fishes. When this happened another important grazer, a sea urchin (*Diadema antillarum;* Fig. 14.32), became more common. The urchin apparently benefited from the reduced competition. For years, the urchin seems to have picked up the slack for the fishes, and seaweed populations remained more or less stable. In 1983, however, a disease wiped out populations of the urchin over much of the Caribbean. Seaweeds, released from grazing pressure, became much more abundant on many reefs, at the expense of corals. In Jamaica they took over many reefs almost completely, and the formerly rich coral reefs are now more seaweed bed than coral reef. A similar

> Grazers help prevent fast-growing seaweeds from overgrowing other sessile organisms on the reef.

In addition to controlling how *much* algae there is, grazers affect which particular *types* of seaweed live on the reef and where. Coralline algae, for example, are abundant because the calcium carbonate in their tissues discourages grazers. Other seaweeds produce noxious chemicals that are poisonous or taste bad; these seaweeds also tend to be abundant. Seaweeds that lack such defenses are most heavily grazed and thus tend to be rare. Even so, they generally grow rapidly and are an important food source.

Damselfishes provide some interesting examples of the effects of grazing on reefs. Many damselfishes graze on seaweeds inside territories that they vigorously defend, chasing away other fishes. Many such damselfishes actually "farm" their territories. They weed out unpalatable algae, pulling them up and carrying them outside the territory. What is left in the territory is a dense mat of tasty seaweeds, usually fine, filamentous types. Protected by the damselfish, these algae grow very rapidly and outcompete corals and coralline

Tube Feet Water-filled tubes possessed only by echinoderms, many of which end in a sucker and can be extended and contracted to grip things and to move around.
- 7.8, Echinoderms: Five-Way Symmetry; Figure 7.45

Chitons Molluscs whose shells consist of eight overlapping plates on their upper, or dorsal, surface.
- 7.5, Molluscs: The Successful Soft Body

Trophic Cascade A process in which an effect on one species flows through an ecosystem because of indirect interactions via the food web.
- 10.1, The Organization of Communities

Box 14.3 "Must Have Been Something I Ate"

Ahhhh! You're relaxing on a warm tropical night after a delicious fish dinner. The palm trees sway, a warm tropical breeze blows—and suddenly your bowels begin to churn. Before long your lips burn and tingle, and your hands and feet feel like pins and needles. You go into the kitchen for a drink, but the cool water feels warm. The cool floor and the cold compress you put on your forehead are also warm to the touch: The sensations of hot and cold are reversed. As you stagger to the bathroom, your arms and legs are heavy and weak. Now feeling really sick, you mumble, "Must have been something I ate."

You're right. What you have is a case of **ciguatera**—tropical fish poisoning. You're not alone. Tens, perhaps hundreds, of thousands of people get ciguatera every year. And relax, you probably won't die, though you might be a little sick (if you're unlucky, *very* sick) for months or even years. Don't count on a cure, though there are various folk remedies that might help a little.

So what *is* ciguatera, anyway? The disease has been known for hundreds of years. The name comes from the Spanish word for a Caribbean snail: You can also get ciguatera from eating molluscs, and perhaps sea urchins, though fish dinners are the most common cause. Ciguatera is caused by a group of toxic dinoflagellates (*Gambierdiscus*, and possibly others) that live on the surface of seaweeds. Herbivorous fishes like surgeonfishes and parrotfishes ingest the dinoflagellates, and their toxins, along with the seaweeds. Predatory fishes like jacks, barracudas, and groupers pick up the toxin when they eat the herbivores. An intense, localized bloom of the dinoflagellates can mean that herbivorous fishes feeding in that spot become toxic, while fishes a short distance away are unaffected. If the dinoflagellates are widespread at relatively low levels, herbivorous fishes may remain safe, while predators that range over larger distances steadily accumulate toxins and become poisonous. Thus, it is hard to predict which fish are safe to eat, although certain

species are known to have a higher risk than others. Which species are risky varies from place to place, so local knowledge is essential. It is sometimes claimed that larger fish are more risky, but the data don't support this.

It is possible to tell if fish are affected—all you need is a laboratory. The toxins can be identified through chemical analysis or by exposing test organisms like mice or mosquito larvae to extracts. A simpler test is to feed a bit to a cat: Cats are highly sensitive to ciguatera. If any mongooses are handy, they're good tasters, too. This isn't very kind to the animals, who usually die if the fish carries ciguatera. Test sticks that change color when rubbed into the flesh of toxic fish were developed but were unreliable and are no longer sold.

To complicate matters, there are at least 20 toxins involved, not just one, and it is hard to develop a test to reliably pick them all up in any combination. For now, at least, the best strategy is to avoid eating fish species that are known to be risky. Otherwise, it's go hungry or take your chances.

algae. Outside the territory, parrotfishes and surgeonfishes gobble up the algae, clearing space for other organisms. Thus, the community inside the territory is very different from that outside. One interesting point is that cyanobacteria, which are nitrogen fixers, are more common inside damselfish territories than outside. Damselfishes may indirectly have a role in the nutrient balance of the reef.

Symbiosis Among the vast number of species that live on coral reefs, many have evolved special symbiotic relationships. There are far too many instances of symbiosis on reefs to describe here. In fact, coral reefs probably have more different symbiotic relationships than any habitat on Earth. The few examples discussed here will give you some idea of how fascinating these relationships are.

> Symbiotic relationships are very important in coral reef communities. Coral reefs probably have more examples of symbiosis than any other biological community.

We have already seen how mutualism between corals and their zooxanthellae is the essential feature of reef formation. Many other organisms also have photosynthetic symbionts. Sea anemones, snails, and giant clams (*Tridacna*) all harbor zooxanthellae. The

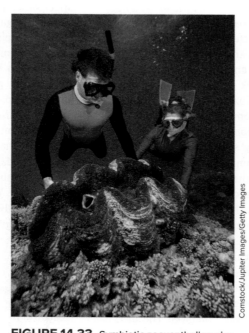

FIGURE 14.33 Symbiotic zooxanthellae give the upper surface of the giant clam (*Tridacna gigas*) its blue and green colors, and provide food that allows the clam to get so big. The clam also filter-feeds. The hole visible on the clam's fleshy upper surface is one of the siphons through which it pumps water to feed and obtain oxygen. Giant clams do not occur in the Caribbean. Stories of people getting trapped in them and drowning are myths.

"deal" between the two partners is the same as in corals: The zooxanthellae get nutrients and a safe place to live, and the host gets food. Giant clams grow so large (Fig. 14.33) because their zooxanthellae provide a constant food supply.

There are primary producers other than zooxanthellae that live inside reef animals. As mentioned previously, some sponges have cyanobacteria that fix nitrogen in addition to performing photosynthesis. Some sea squirts house a photosynthetic bacterium called *Prochloron*. *Prochloron* is especially interesting because it could be similar to the symbiotic organisms that eventually became the chloroplasts of plants (see Box 4.1, "From Snack to Servant: How Complex Cells Arose").

Another important example of mutualism on the reef is the relationship between corals and the crabs, shrimps, and fishes that help protect them from COTS and other predators. Most corals host a number of **facultative** and **obligate symbionts,** especially crustaceans. Some of the obligate

symbionts are parasites and harm the coral, some are commensals and apparently have no effect, and some are mutualists that benefit the coral. It is often hard to tell which is which, because for most symbionts the nature of the relationship between coral and symbiont is not well understood. The crabs that protect their coral from predators, for instance, were once thought to be parasites.

Anemonefishes (*Amphiprion;* Fig. 14.34) have an interesting relationship with several kinds of sea anemones. The anemones inhabited by anemonefishes have a powerful sting and are capable of killing the fish. The fish have a protective mucus, however, that keeps the anemone from stinging. It is not known whether mucus is produced by the fish themselves, by the anemone, or both. When anemonefish are newly introduced to an anemone, they typically rub against the anemone's tentacles. They could be coating themselves with the anemone's mucus. Anemones have no eyes and no brain, but lots of tentacles. If they simply stung everything they touched they would sting themselves. The anemone recognizes itself by the "taste" of its own mucus, and the anemonefishes could be taking advantage of this. On the other hand, the fishes' own mucus could protect them from the anemone, and the fish sometimes safely enter an anemone without rubbing on the tentacles first.

Anemonefishes are protected by the anemone's stinging tentacles and brood their eggs under the anemone. The anemone also benefits. Anemonefishes drive away other fishes that eat anemones, and could benefit their hosts nutritionally. Anemones with anemonefish survive longer, grow faster, and reproduce by asexual division more often than anemones without anenomefish.

FIGURE 14.34 Orange-fin anemonefish (*Amphiprion chrysopterus*) and their sea anemone host.

Bill Ober

1997–1998. Reefs in some places, including the Caribbean and the Great Barrier Reef, recovered when the water cooled. Reefs in the Indian Ocean, Southeast Asia, and the far western Pacific, however, suffered major long-term damage.

Mass global bleaching almost certainly occurred long before it was first observed in 1997–1998, given that El Niño events have been happening for millennia at least. Bleaching continued to be seen on various reefs around the world after 1997–1998, but for a while was not as widespread and generally localized. Individual reefs often had years or decades to recover between bleaching events.

But climate change (see Special Report, Climate Change) is bringing more intense and frequent El Niño events and marine heat waves. Not surprisingly, mass coral bleaching is also becoming more frequent, intense, and widespread. A second global-scale bleaching event occurred in 2010. The most severe global bleaching so far lasted from early 2014 to 2017, with record-breaking water temperatures in 2014 even without an El Niño. An estimated 75% of the world's reefs suffered serious bleaching. Reefs in Kāne'ohe Bay, Hawai'i, bleached in 2014 and 2015, as did those in Florida. Reefs in the Mariana Islands bleached three years in a row, and those in Guam four years straight. In 2016 the Great Barrier Reef had its worst bleaching ever to that point, with 80% coral loss on the worst-affected reefs. Intense bleaching came on the Great Barrier Reef in 2017, 2020, and 2022. Major bleaching events are occurring without an El Niño, and in fact even during La Niña, the reverse of El Niño, which normally brings relatively cool conditions. With

14.4 HUMAN IMPACT ON CORAL REEFS

Earth's tropical coral reefs are in serious trouble. Coral reefs are not only beautiful, diverse, and productive, they provide a wide range of concrete benefits, including food, other products, employment, coastal protection, recreation, and cultural meaning, to people throughout the tropics. But, more than a quarter of the world's reefs have been lost entirely, or are in immediate danger. Most of the rest are in decline: Live coral cover, the most widely used indicator of coral reef health, has declined by at least half in the last 50 years. Human activities threaten reefs at all levels from global to very local.

Global Warming and Ocean Acidification

The most serious threat to reefs is global warming, and the mass coral bleaching caused by marine heat waves (Fig. 14.35). **El Niño** (see "The El Niño-Southern Oscillation" in 15.3) brings unusually warm water to many parts of the ocean, and the first time global-scale coral bleaching was observed during an unusually strong El Niño in

FIGURE 14.35 Mass coral bleaching on Australia's Great Barrier Reef.

Brett Monroe Garner/Getty Images

Facultative Symbiont A symbiont that is not completely dependent on its partner and can live outside the symbiosis.
Obligate Symbiont One that depends on its partner and does not occur outside the symbiosis.
• 10.1, The Organization of Communities

bleaching events occurring so often, reefs have little time to recover, and the effects become cumulative. Coral communities on many reefs around the world are changing dramatically. Reefs often have less coral, and fewer coral species.

The other global effect of human CO_2 emissions, ocean acidification (see Special Report, Ocean Acidification: The Other CO_2 Problem) makes it harder for corals to deposit their calcium carbonate skeletons, so they grow slower, and for new coral colonies to establish. It also increases how fast exposed calcium carbonate surfaces on reefs dissolve. Slow coral growth and faster calcium carbonate dissolution means that reefs are becoming less effective carbon sinks, that is, they are likely to remove less CO_2 from the atmosphere. There are also indications that coral reefs may not be able to grow upward fast enough to keep up with sea level rise caused by global warming.

Pollution, Overfishing, Disease, and Habitat Destruction

Even before mass coral bleaching became a global problem, most coral reefs, especially in populated areas, were being negatively affected by human activities. **Eutrophication** (see "Eutrophication," in 18.2) is a problem on many reefs around the world. Humans release tremendous quantities of nutrients in sewage, in fertilizers that are washed from farmland to the sea, and in emissions to the atmosphere from agricultural waste and burning fossil fuels. Most coral reefs grow in water that is naturally nutrient-poor. This isn't a problem for the corals because of the nutrient recycling between the corals and their symbiotic zooxanthellae. But without human influence, seaweeds are generally nutrient limited, and their growth is also slowed by grazers. This allows corals to compete successfully for space and light. When large amounts of nutrients are added, seaweeds can grow much faster, and shade and choke out the slower-growing corals.

Coastal development for tourism and urban development has increased in many tropical areas near reefs. Such development typically leads not only to greater release of nutrients from sewage and fertilizer for agriculture, golf courses, and other uses, but to more intensive fishing. Nutrient discharges can be controlled by sewage treatment and a variety of other measures, but these often lag behind development. More and more nutrients are ending up in waters that support coral reefs, and there are many cases of reefs damaged by eutrophication.

This is a particular problem when, as is often the case, fishing reduces populations of herbivorous fishes. Such changes are common as fishing pressure on reefs escalates because of the population increase and demand for fish that accompany coastal development. High demand for coral-reef fish in distant markets increases fishing pressure. Thus, seaweed growth is often artificially enhanced by eutrophication at the same time that the grazers that keep the seaweeds under control are removed.

Increased sediment inputs to reef habitats, both chronic inputs from land-use changes and acute events caused by road construction, mining, dredging, and other activities, have also damaged many coral reefs (see "Salinity, Sediments, and Pollution" in 14.1). Acute sedimentation events may be becoming less common as

communities and environmental managers become more aware, but still occur. Chronic increases in sediment runoff due to land-use changes for agriculture, forestry, mining, and urban development are more difficult to address and often require broad-scale societal change that involves multiple economic sectors.

In recent decades there have been more and more observations of previously unknown coral diseases. This first started in the Florida Keys and Caribbean, but coral disease outbreaks have since been reported on a number of reefs around the world. Many infections start as a line of dead or discolored tissue that advances over the colony (see Fig. 14.16), leaving exposed white skeleton in its wake. The diseases are often named after the color of the band (white-band, black-band, yellow-band, brown-band disease), though the disease doesn't always form bands and sometimes there are just growing patches of dead tissue on the coral. Bacteria, fungi, protozoans, and other pathogens cause the diseases. It is highly unlikely that these pathogens, and therefore the diseases they cause, are new, but coral diseases were never reported until the 1970s, and not observed to cause significant coral mortality until the 1990s. Almost certainly, the recent increase in coral disease around the world reflect increased stress on reefs due to bleaching, acidification, eutrophication, sediment, and other human impacts.

Many reefs around the world have been impacted by direct physical habitat damage. Sometimes the individual causes are relatively minor. Reef walkers, snorkelers, scuba divers, boat anchors, and fishing lines can all break corals. The damage from a single event is usually small, but the damage can accumulate to become major damage on heavily used reefs. More severe damage has occurred on many reefs because of fishing with explosives or poisons, dredging and blasting for navigation channels, coral mining to provide building materials (see Fig. 18.3), coral collection for the aquarium and tourist trades, and ship groundings and trawler damage. Environmental managers in most countries have become more aware of the value of coral reefs and the damage caused by such practices, and they are becoming less common. They do still occur at localized scales, however.

Promoting Reef Resilience

The world's coral reefs are in such bad shape that many biologists fear that coral reefs as we know them now will no longer be around in a generation or maybe two. It is clear that the most important thing we can do to save coral reefs is to reduce CO_2 emissions. This, however, requires major international action beyond the reach of any individual country, especially the developing countries where many reefs occur, and may take time that reefs just don't have. A growing number of scientists are looking for ways to buy time by promoting the resilience of reefs to global change and other stresses.

A critical first step is to reduce the many other stresses on reefs from nutrients, sediments, overfishing, and so on. Reducing these stresses gives reefs a better chance to withstand and recover from bleaching and acidification damage—that is, it enhances reef resilience. This doesn't require global action and can be accomplished at levels from national down to local communities. And in most cases we already pretty much know what needs to be done. More and more countries are implementing improved sewage treatment, better agricultural and other land-use practices, reserves that

Box 14.4 The Kāne'ohe Bay Story

One of the best-known examples of the harmful effects of nutrient enrichment occurred in Kāne'ohe Bay, a partially enclosed bay on the northeast shore of the island of O'ahu, which once had some of the most luxuriant reefs in Hawai'i. Until the 1930s the area around the bay was sparsely populated. In the military buildup of O'ahu before World War II, the population increased. The increase continued after the war with residential development around the bay.

Sewage from the expanding population was discharged directly into the bay. By 1978, about 20,000 m³ (over 5 million gallons) of sewage were entering the bay every day. The sewage was treated, but not to a level where the nutrients were removed. Long before then, by the mid-1960s in fact, marine biologists began to see changes in the middle part of the bay. Loaded with nutrients, the sewage was a great seaweed fertilizer. One seaweed in particular, a green alga called bubble weed (*Dictyosphaeria cavernosa*), found the conditions particularly to its liking and exploded, literally covering the bottom in many parts of the bay. Bubble weed overgrew and smothered corals. Phytoplankton also bloomed, clouding the water. Kāne'ohe Bay's reefs began to die. Such accelerated algal growth due to nutrient input is called **eutrophication** (see "Eutrophication," in 18.2).

For a time it seemed the story had a happy ending. As the once-beautiful reefs smothered, scientists and the general public cried out. It took a while, but in 1978 public pressure finally forced the diversion of the treated sewage offshore, greatly reducing nutrient input to the bay. The response was dramatic. Bubble weed died back in much of the bay, and the corals began to recover faster than expected. By the early 1980s, bubble weed were fairly scarce and corals were growing back. The reefs weren't what they once were but seemed to be on track to recover.

Then the ghost of pollution past reared its ugly head. In November 1982, Hurricane Iwa struck Kāne'ohe Bay. Layers of coral skeleton that formed during the years of pollution were fragile and crumbly. When the hurricane hit, this weak layer collapsed and many reefs were severely damaged.

Fortunately, the corals were already beginning to recover, and some of the broken pieces were able to grow back. If the hurricane had hit during the years of pollution, the reefs of Kāne'ohe Bay—and their benefits to fishing, tourism, and recreation—might have disappeared forever.

The rapid recovery of Kāne'ohe Bay's reefs during the early 1980s did not continue. By 1990 recovery leveled off, and bubble weed came back. Nutrients are still a problem. A lot of nutrients from the old sewage outfalls were stored in the sediments and are still being released. New nutrients enter from lawn and golf course fertilizers, boats, and the septic tanks of private homes. Fishing reduced populations of fishes that graze on bubble weed. Furthermore, the grazing fishes that remain prefer to eat other species of seaweed introduced from outside Hawai'i and have shifted away from eating bubble weed. Bubble weed started to dominate again, but then in 2006 declined steeply. No one is sure why or if bubble weed will make another comeback. But bubble algae are no longer the only problem. While some species of algae introduced to Kāne'ohe Bay are favorite foods of grazing fishes, others are not. These species are also able to grow without a lot of nutrients and proliferated, smothering the bay's reefs. To fight back, biologists and conservationists used an underwater vacuum cleaner to suck up the dense mats of invasive algae, and grew a native urchin (*Tripneustes gratilla*) that eats the invasive algae in nurseries, then releasing them.

This combination of manual and biological controls has had some success in keeping the invasive algae in check.

Jennifer E. Smith, Ph.D.

The red alga *Eucheuma denticulatum* is one of several species of red algae introduced to Kāne'ohe Bay for experimental mariculture that have gotten out of control. The algae are overgrowing and smothering corals in many parts of the bay.

protect reef fishes from fishing pressure, and restrictions or bans on practices that physically destroy reefs. There is no doubt that these steps have beneficial results. A major role for scientists in this regard is to determine which steps—Improved sewage treatment or reforestation? A new no-fishing zone or reduced bag limits?—provide the most "bang for the buck" in protecting reefs. Social scientists have critical roles. For example, people in many developing countries depend completely on reefs for food and income, so reducing pressure on the reefs means providing alternative livelihoods - ones that people want and not ones that outside parties think they should have.

FIGURE 14.36 A coral nursery in the Philippines.

Steve De Neef/VW Pics/Universal Images Group/Getty Images

Reducing existing stress on reefs is a necessary and urgent first step, but an increasing number of reef biologists consider that reefs need even more help, and that active measures to promote reef resilience are needed. Current research on promoting reef resilience originates in large part from careful observations of the effects of coral bleaching and other reef stresses. For example, surveys show that the deeper parts of many reefs are less affected by bleaching because the most dangerously warm seawater tends to stay near the surface. These deep, or mesophotic, communities generally support fewer species than undisturbed shallow-water ones, but may provide refugia for corals and reef fishes that can re-seed damaged reefs after bleaching. This points to a special need to protect such reefs.

Careful surveys and monitoring have also identified a very few reefs that may be especially important to reef resilience on much larger scales. Satellite data, current modelling, and genetic analysis show that a few reefs in the Red Sea happen to be positioned to provide eggs and larvae that seed many other reefs. Similarly, there are perhaps 100 of some 3,000 reefs on the Great Barrier Reef whose location not only favors widespread dispersal of their eggs and larvae to other reefs but also helps protect them from damage by cyclones, COTS, and other disturbances. Such "mother reefs" are being identified in other reef systems. Targeting these reefs for special protection provides benefits for reef resilience far out of proportion to the size of the reefs.

Researchers have also discovered small reefs on the Great Barrier Reef, and in the Red Sea, Caribbean, and elsewhere, that for unknown reasons are unexpectedly vibrant and healthy despite bleaching and other stresses that have degraded surrounding reefs. Again, it is important to protect such reefs to re-seed surrounding areas, but, probably more importantly, researchers are racing to learn what makes these particular reefs and corals so resilient. They are already learning to selectively breed heat-tolerant strains of not only corals but also their symbiotic zooxanthellae. The symbionts can possibly be introduced to a variety of coral species to promote bleaching resistance. Tolerant coral strains can potentially be raised in large numbers in coral nurseries (Fig. 14.36). Though not yet technically feasible, one can envision that someday the refinement of heat-resistant zooxanthellae and identification of specific coral genes for resilience, coupled with the ability to grow coral larvae in large amounts, might make it possible to produce "super-corals" to seed degraded reefs.

One thing is for sure: without our help—and soon—the world's priceless coral reefs are headed for disaster.

Interactive Exploration

McGraw-Hill Connect® is a great place to check your understanding of chapter material. Visit **www.mcgrawhillconnect.com** for access to interactive chapter summaries, chapter quizzing, and more! Further enhance your knowledge with videoclips and web links to chapter-related material.

Critical Thinking

1. What factors might account for the fact that the vast majority of atolls occur in the Indian and Pacific oceans and that atolls are rare in the Atlantic?
2. There are only a few reefs off the northeast coast of Brazil (see map in Fig. 14.11), even though it lies in the tropics. How would you explain this? But a new reef has recently been discovered near the mouth of the Amazon. What would you expect this reef to be like?

For Further Reading

Some of the recommended reading may be available online. Look for live links on the *Marine Biology* Online Learning Center.

General Interest

Albright, R., 2018. Can we save the corals? *Scientific American,* vol. 318, no. 1, January, pp. 37–49. Many efforts are in progress to protect, restore, and enhance the resilience of corals.

Dance, A., 2019. Hope for coral reefs. *Nature*, vol. 575, no. 7784, 28 November, pp. 580–581. The discovery of bleaching-resistant reefs gives hope that biologists can unravel secrets of reef resilience.

Eddy, T. D., V. W. Y. Lam, G. Reygondeau, et al., 2021. Global decline in capacity of coral reef to provide ecosystem services. *One Earth*, vol. 4, pp. 1278–1285. Climate change, pollution, overfishing, and other human impacts have greatly reduced the capacity of the world's coral reefs to provide benefits to humans.

Karkareky, R. and A.-H. Theo, 2016. Homeward bound: Fish larvae use dispersal corridors when settling on corals reefs. *Frontiers in Ecology and the Environment*, vol. 14, no. 10, December, pp. 569–570. Reef fish larvae don't just disperse at random, but follow distinct corridors to locate and settle on reefs.

Lirman, D. and S. Schopmeyer, 2017. Ecological solutions to reef degradation: Optimizing coral reef restoration in the Caribbean and Western Atlantic. *PeerJ*, 4:e2597; DOI 10.7717/peerj.2597. Scientific, conservation, and citizen's organizations plant tens of thousands of seed corals on damaged reefs in the Caribbean and Western Atlantic, with increasing success.

McDermott, A., 2016. Rebuilding reefs. *Science News*, vol. 190, no. 9, 29 October, pp. 18–22. Multiple faces of reef restoration efforts.

Pitz, K., 2016. Trouble in the tropics. *Oceanus*, vol. 51, no. 2, winter, pp. 60–63. Research tries to unveil some of the mysteries about ciguatera—tropical fish poisoning.

Sheehy, S., 2022. The mainland and the Mesoamerican Barrier Reef: An uneasy symbiosis. *Natural History*, vol. 130, no. 1, December/January, pp. 16–23. The world's second-largest barrier reef is intimately linked to mangroves, seagrass beds, and other ecosystems—and like all barrier reefs to what happens on the adjacent coastline.

Schiffman, R., 2016. Supercharged coral vs climate change. *New Scientist,* vol. 230, no. 3068, 9 April, pp. 26–28. An interview with the marine biologist who is trying to breed highly resilient corals.

Slezak, M., 2016. The starfish terminator. *New Scientist,* vol. 229, no. 3056, 16 January, pp. 35–37. A new underwater robot has a seek-and-destroy mission against the crown-of-thorns starfish.

In Depth

Albright, R., Y. Takeshita, D. A. Koweek, *et al.,* 2018. Carbon dioxide addition to coral reef waters, suppresses net community calcification. *Nature,* vol. 555, no. 7697, pp. 516–519.

Altman-Kurosaki, N. T., C. M. Smith, and E. C. Franklin, 2021. O'ahu's marine protected areas have limited success in protecting coral reef herbivores. *Coral Reefs*, vol. 40, pp. 305–322.

Blackall, L. L., B. Wilson, and M. J. H. Oppen, 2015. Coral—the world's most diverse symbiotic ecosystem. *Molecular Ecology*, vol. 24, pp. 5330–5347.

Camp, E. F., V. Schoepf, P. J. Mumby, *et al.,* 2018. The future of coral reefs subject to rapid climate change: Lessons from natural extreme environments. *Frontiers in Marine Science,* https://doi.org/10.3389/fmars.2018.00004.

Goldberg, W. M., 2018. Coral food, feeding, nutrition and section: A review. pp. 377–421. In: *Marine organisms as model systems in biology and medicine*, M. Kloc and J. Z. Kubiak, eds. Springer.

Green, A. L., A. P. Maypa, G. R. Almany, K. L. Rhodes, R. Weeks, R. A. Abesamis, M. G. Gleason, P. J. Mumby, and A. T. White, 2015. Larval dispersal and movement patterns of coral reef fishes, and implications for marine reserve network design. *Biological Reviews,* vol. 90, pp. 1215–1247.

Hall, M. R., K. M. Kocot, K. W. Baughman, *et al.,* 2017. The crown-of-thorns starfish genome as a guide for biocontrol of this coral reef pest. *Nature,* vol. 544, no. 7649, pp. 231–234.

Harborne, A. R., A. Rogers, Y.-M. Bozec, and P. J. Mumby, 2017. Multiple stressors and the functioning of coral reefs. *Annual Review of Marine Science,* vol. 9, pp. 445–468.

Hock K., N. H. Wolff, J. C. Ortiz, S. A. Condie, K. R. N. Anthony, P. G. Blackwell, and P. J Mumby, 2017. Connectivity and systemic resilience of the Great Barrier Reef. *PLoS Biology,* vol. 15, no. 11, e2003355, doi.org/10.1371/journal.pbio.2003355.

Hughes, T. P., J. T. Kerry, M. Álvarez-Noriega, *et al.,* 2018. Global warming transforms reef assemblages. *Nature,* vol. 556, pp. 492–496.

Muehllehner, N., C. Langdon, A. Venti, and D. Kadko, 2016. Dynamics of carbonate chemistry, production, and calcification of the Florida Reef Tract (2009–2010): Evidence for seasonal dissolution. *Global Biogeochemical Cycles,* vol. 30, pp. 661–668.

Perry, C. T., L. Alvarez-Filip, N. A. J. Graham, *et al.,* 2018. Loss of coral reef growth capacity to track future increases in sea level. *Nature,* vol. 558, pp. 396–400.

Sweet, M. J. and B. E. Brown, 2016. Coral responses to anthropogenic stress in the twenty-first century: An ecophysiological perspective. *Oceanography and Marine Biology: An Annual Review,* vol. 54, pp. 271–314.

Thurber, R. V., L. D. Mydlarz, M. Brandt, *et al.,* 2020. Deciphering coral disease dynamics: Integrating host, microbiome, and the changing environment. *Frontiers in Ecology and Evolution*, vol. 8:575927.

Wolfe, K., T. M. Kenyon, and P. J. Mumby, 2021. The biology and ecology of coral rubble and implications for the future of corals reefs. *Coral Reefs*, vol. 40, pp. 1769–1806.

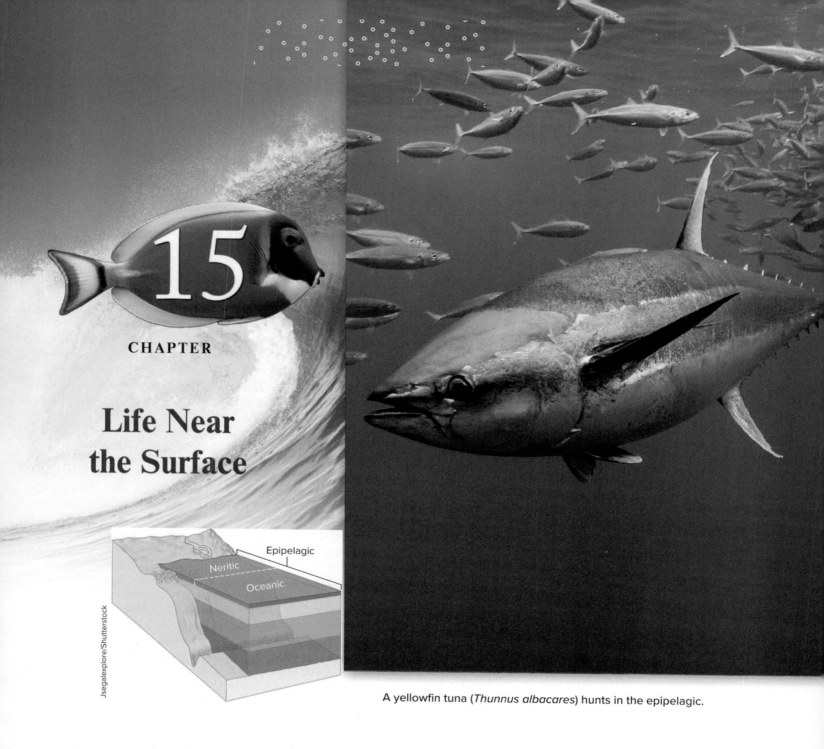

Jsegalexplore/Shutterstock

A yellowfin tuna (*Thunnus albacares*) hunts in the epipelagic.

15

CHAPTER

Life Near the Surface

"The ocean," for most of us, conjures up images of beaches and cliffs, breaking surf, or quiet bays. Such familiar nearshore waters, however, make up only a small fraction of the world ocean. The rest is the vast open sea, the **pelagic realm.** Though distant and unfamiliar, the open ocean affects us all. It regulates our climate and atmosphere and provides food and other resources. The pelagic realm holds practically all the liquid water on Earth, the water planet.

The pelagic environment is the water column itself, away from the bottom or the shore. Pelagic organisms live suspended in their liquid medium. With few exceptions, the pelagic lacks the solid physical structure provided either by the bottom and other geological features or by large organisms like corals and kelps. There is

no place for attachment, no bottom for burrowing, nothing to hide behind. Imagine spending your life floating in the air, never touching the ground. This is what life is like for pelagic organisms.

Chapter 15 deals with the surface layers of the pelagic environment: the **epipelagic,** or upper pelagic, realm. The epipelagic is often defined as the zone from the surface down to 200 m (650 ft) depth. Being the shallowest part of the pelagic realm, the epipelagic is the warmest, and, of course, the best lit. The epipelagic is therefore much the same as the **photic zone,** the zone from the surface to the depth where there is no longer enough light to support photosynthesis. The depth of the photic zone varies, depending on water clarity and the amount of sunlight. The difference between the epipelagic and photic zones is not stressed in this chapter.

The epipelagic is divided into two main components. Epipelagic waters over the continental shelf are referred to as **neritic** (see Fig. 10.12). The neritic environment is only a small part of the epipelagic, but it is important to humans because it is near shore and supports most of the world's marine fisheries production (see "Food from the Sea," in 17.1). Surface waters beyond the continental shelf are known as the **oceanic** part of the epipelagic.

The epipelagic realm is the layer of the ocean from the surface to a depth of 200 m. It is divided into neritic waters, which lie over the continental shelf, and oceanic waters beyond the shelf. The epipelagic contains the photic zone, the surface layer where there is enough light for photosynthesis.

(a)

FIGURE 15.1 (*a*) A typical phytoplankton net is small and has fine netting that prevents many microscopic plankton from passing through. (*b*) A bongo net, so called because of the two rings that hold the mouth of the net open, is used to sample zooplankton. Zooplankton nets are usually larger and have coarser mesh than phytoplankton nets. The coarse mesh lets phytoplankton pass through but retains the larger zooplankton.

15.1 THE ORGANISMS OF THE EPIPELAGIC

Like nearly all ecosystems, the pelagic realm is fueled by solar energy captured in photosynthesis. Epipelagic ecosystems differ from many shallow-water ones in that nearly all the **primary production** takes place within the epipelagic system itself. Coastal ecosystems often receive large amounts of food from elsewhere. The intertidal zone, for example, gets plankton and drifting seaweeds from offshore, and rivers carry organic material into estuaries. The pelagic realm, far from the shore and bottom, gets little external input of organic matter.

The epipelagic does supply food to other communities. Large amounts of organic matter sink out of the epipelagic to feed organisms in deeper water or, in the neritic zone, on the bottom (see Chapter 16). Ocean currents carry epipelagic **plankton** into shallow water, where it is consumed by a profusion of **suspension feeders.** Epipelagic fishes and zooplankton provide food not only to other marine communities but also to land-dwelling birds and mammals, including humans.

The epipelagic lacks **deposit feeders** because it does not include the bottom where organic material can be deposited. Suspension feeders, on the other hand, abound. After all, the food is suspended in the water column. There are also many large predators, like fishes, squids, and marine mammals.

The Plankton: A New Understanding

For more than a century the main way that scientists studied plankton was to catch them by towing nets through the water (Fig. 15.1), or sometimes by pumping water through a filter. This reliance on plankton nets profoundly affected our understanding of the epipelagic. Imagine if our only way to study flying organisms was with nets. If our nets were too small or too slow, we might never know there were birds. Nets with too coarse a mesh would leave us completely ignorant of mosquitoes. Imagine organisms with the consistency of clouds that slipped through any net! Similar misunderstandings resulted from oceanographers' dependence on plankton nets to study the epipelagic.

New techniques including better microscopes, underwater photography, satellites, chemical procedures, and, yes, even improved nets and filters have revolutionized our understanding of the epipelagic. **Genomics** has been a particularly revolutionary tool. Genomics is the study of entire genomes, or at least DNA sequences containing multiple genes, so that the interactions among genes, and distinctive sequences that identify the type of organism the DNA came from, can be analyzed. Sometimes genomes are obtained from living organisms, but often the DNA is simply extracted from seawater—all organisms are constantly shedding their DNA into the environment. **Metagenomics** is the study of multiple species' genomes and how they interact (see Box 5.2, "Tiny Cells, Big Surprises"). Genes that are involved in nutrient and carbon cycling, and information about when the activity of the genes is switched on and off, tell us about both the timing of such key processes and interactions among the species involved. These are just examples of the vast wealth of information genomics is providing.

These new discoveries have raised even more questions, and it has become clear that we don't understand the plankton nearly as well as we once thought. Vast numbers and a mind-boggling diversity of plankton that are too small to be caught in standard plankton nets have been and are still being discovered. These are often subdivided on the basis of the size (Fig. 15.2). The **femtoplankton** is composed almost entirely of **viruses** and is also called the **virioplankton.** Most of the **picoplankton** consists of **archaea** and **bacteria.** The larger **net plankton,** so called because they *can* be caught in nets, are also subdivided on the basis of size into the **micro-, meso-, macro-,** and **megaplankton,** but these categories are not stressed in this book. Categorizing the plankton by size should not be confused with the division between

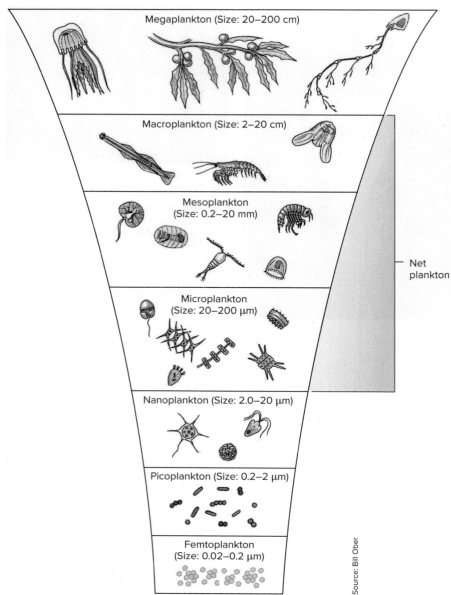

Source: Bill Ober

FIGURE 15.2 Plankton are often separated into categories based on their size (also see Appendix A). Note that the size of the organisms in each category increases logarithmically, that is, the size range of each category is 10 times that of the next smaller category.

phytoplankton—plankton that perform photosynthesis—and **zooplankton.** The phytoplankton, for example, include species of all size classes from the picoplankton to the megaplankton.

The Phytoplankton

Large producers like seaweeds and seagrasses are mostly absent from the epipelagic because they have no place to attach. Floating seaweeds are important in a few places, like the Sargasso Sea (see Fig. 8.23), but in most of the epipelagic the only primary producers are single-celled or simple chains of cells. These tiny organisms make up the phytoplankton, which occur virtually everywhere in the epipelagic, often in huge numbers. Phytoplankton perform more

than 95% of the photosynthesis in the epipelagic. This amounts to nearly half the world's primary production and produces nearly half the oxygen in our atmosphere.

Because net phytoplankton are relatively easy to catch, their importance has long been known. The most important net phytoplankton are **diatoms** (Fig. 15.3) and **dinoflagellates.** Before the discovery of the nanoplankton and picoplankton, it was thought that diatoms dominated the phytoplankton and accounted for most photosynthesis in the epipelagic. Although we now know this isn't the case, diatoms are still extremely important. They are especially common in temperate and polar regions and other nutrient-rich waters. They are abundant both near the coast and in the open ocean.

Dinoflagellates are also important in both neritic and oceanic waters but tend to prefer warm waters. In the tropics they often replace diatoms as the most abundant members of the net phytoplankton. In some places diatoms and dinoflagellates replace each other seasonally, with diatoms preferring cooler temperatures. Dinoflagellates may be adapted better to low-nutrient conditions than diatoms. Given nutrients, on the other hand, dinoflagellates may **bloom,** or grow explosively into huge numbers, sometimes causing **red tides** (see Box 15.1, "Red Tides and Harmful Algal Blooms").

Most cyanobacteria are too small, but one important group, *Trichodesmium,* does get caught in nets because its cells form larger masses known as trichomes. *Trichodesmium* can be very abundant, sometimes forming red tides. They are particularly abundant in nutrient-poor waters, perhaps because they can fix nitrogen (see "Nutrients," below).

Because they are so small and hard to catch, or even to see under a microscope, photosynthetic picoplankton and nanoplankton are not as well known as net phytoplankton, and their immense importance has only been appreciated in recent decades. Photosynthetic picoplankton and nanoplankton are far more abundant in terms of cell numbers than net phytoplankton and contribute most of the epipelagic's photosynthesis, 90% or more in many places.

Cyanobacteria are the most abundant picoplankton and account for at least half the ocean's total primary production. One group, the single-celled *Prochlorococcus,* with a typical density of 100,000 cells in a milliliter of seawater, is the most abundant of all marine phytoplankton. *Prochlorococcus* is especially dominant in nutrient-poor tropical and subtropical waters. The closely related *Synechococcus* is also very abundant in all but polar waters.

Although cyanobacteria dominate the photosynthetic picoplankton, various protists are also important. These **eukaryotes** typically make up less than 5% of the total picoplankton cells in the water but have been known to account for over 30%. An ample supply of nutrients appears to favor an increased abundance of protists relative to cyanobacteria. Many of the photosynthetic protists in the picoplankton have not been isolated and are only known through genomics. Their ecological role in the phytoplankton is poorly understood.

(a) (b)

FIGURE 15.3 Diatoms have sculptured shells, or frustules, made of silica. (a) *Thalassiosira allenii* (top and side views) consists of a single cell. (b) *Fragilaria* is a diatom that forms chains of cells. Each division in the long, green filaments is an individual cell (also see Fig. 5.6).

Table 15.1 shows the major groups of marine phytoplankton. Various other groups may form blooms, but relatively rarely, and are of secondary importance in the overall ecology of the seas.

Although protists have an uncertain role in the picoplankton, they dominate the nanoplankton, and many are photosynthetic. **Coccolithophorids** (see Fig. 5.10) are one of the more abundant groups, and probably the best known. They do best in the open ocean but also occur in coastal waters.

Another group of minute phytoplankton known as **cryptophytes** are plentiful in neritic waters. They appear to be very important in epipelagic food webs but not much is known about them. **Silicoflagellates** (see Fig. 5.9) occasionally bloom and become important primary producers. Several other groups of protistan nanoplankton are important primary producers in the epipelagic. Most diatoms and dinoflagellates belong to the net plankton, but a few unusually small species are part of the nanoplankton.

Phytoplankton are the main primary producers in the epipelagic. The most abundant phytoplankton are cyanobacteria and various groups of protistan pico- and nanoplankton, including coccolithophorids, cryptophytes, and silicoflagellates. Among the larger net phytoplankton, diatoms and dinoflagellates are dominant.

Primary Production The conversion of carbon dioxide (CO_2) into organic matter by autotrophs, that is, the production of food.
• 4.1, The Ingredients of Life

Plankton Primary producers (*phytoplankton*) and consumers (*zooplankton*) that drift with the currents.
• 10.2, Major Marine Lifestyles and Environments; Figure 10.11

Deposit Feeders Animals that eat organic matter that settles to the bottom.

Suspension Feeders Animals, including *filter feeders,* that eat particles suspended in the water column.
• 7.1, Sponges; Figure 7.4

Genome The complete genetic information of an organism.
• 4.1, The Ingredients of Life

Viruses Particles composed of nucleic acids and proteins that are not usually considered to be alive.
• 5.1, Viruses

Archaea Single-celled, *prokaryotic* organisms once thought to be bacteria but now known to be as different from bacteria as from humans.
• 5.2, Prokaryotes

Dinoflagellates Single-celled organisms that use two flagella to swim.
• 5.3, Unicellular Algae

Table 15.1 The Major Groups of Marine Phytoplankton

Size Category	Group	Neritic or Oceanic	Latitude/Temperature	Notes
Net plankton	Diatoms	Both	Everywhere, but most common in temperate and polar waters	Important primary producers
	Dinoflagellates	Both	Everywhere, but most common in warm waters	Common red tide organisms
	Colonial cyanobacteria (*Trichodesmium*)	Oceanic	Mainly tropical	Can fix atmospheric nitrogen; causes red tides in the Red Sea and elsewhere
Nanoplankton	Coccolithophorids	Oceanic	Everywhere, but most common in tropical waters	Important primary producers in nutrient-poor waters
	Cryptophytes	Both	Everywhere, but most common in temperate and polar waters	Very important primary producers; poorly known
	Silicoflagellates	Neritic	Temperate and polar waters	Sometimes form blooms
Picoplankton	Unicellular cyanobacteria (*Prochlorococcus, Synechococcus*)	Both	Everywhere, but most important in warm waters	Dominant primary producers, especially in nutrient-poor waters
	Various protists	Not known	Not known	Presence of many groups recently discovered

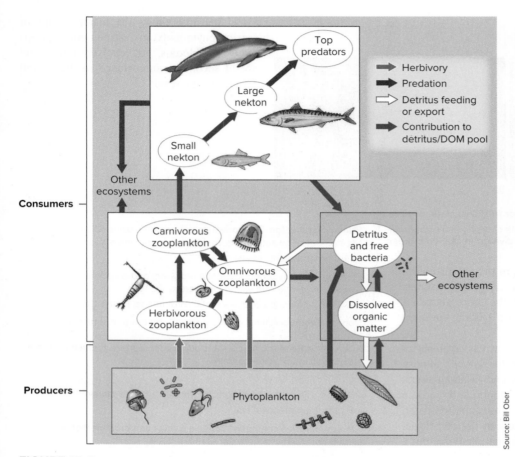

Consumers

Producers

Herbivory
Predation
Detritus feeding or export
Contribution to detritus/DOM pool

Source: Bill Ober

FIGURE 15.4 A simplified epipelagic food web.

Dr. Howard Spero

FIGURE 15.5 A planktonic foramaniferan (*Orbulina universa*) captures a copepod on its long, sticky pseudopodia. The copepod will be drawn to the surface of the foram's shell, where it will be digested. The shell is 0.5 mm (0.02 in) in diameter.

The most important of these protozoans are various **flagellates,** protozoans that move around by means of flagella. **Ciliates, foraminiferans** (Fig. 15.5), and **radiolarians** (see 5.4) are also important protozoan grazers, on net plankton as well as pico- and nanoplankton. Many grazing protozoans are capable of photosynthesis, so they also act as members of the phytoplankton.

The Zooplankton

Phytoplankton form the base of the food web. The solar energy that they capture and store in organic matter is passed on to the other creatures of the epipelagic, from minute zooplankton to gigantic whales. The first step in this flow of energy occurs when **herbivores** eat the phytoplankton. Herbivores are the vital link between the primary producers in the phytoplankton and the rest of the community. Large epipelagic animals cannot feed directly on the tiny phytoplankton. They rely instead on herbivorous zooplankton, which can. Thus, a fundamental part of the epipelagic food web is the flow of energy from phytoplankton to herbivorous zooplankton.

Very few zooplankton are strict herbivores and most that eat phytoplankton also eat other zooplankton when they can. Most zooplankton species, however, are primarily carnivorous and hardly eat phytoplankton at all. These carnivores may feed directly on herbivorous zooplankton and thus reap the production of phytoplankton with only one intermediate step, or **trophic level,** in the food web. They may also eat other carnivores, adding links to the food web (Fig. 15.4).

Protozoan Zooplankton The tiny picoplankton and nanoplankton are too small for most multicellular animals to catch and eat. **Protozoans,** however, can catch them. When it was discovered that pico- and nanoplankton are the most abundant phytoplankton, the importance of protozoans was also recognized. Without protozoans, much of the primary production in the epipelagic would go unused.

Copepods Small crustaceans, especially **copepods** (Fig. 15.6), dominate the net zooplankton practically everywhere in the ocean, typically numbering 70% or more of the community. Copepods are probably the most numerous group of animals on Earth.

Nearly all epipelagic copepods eat at least some phytoplankton. It was once thought that they use the bristles on their mouthparts and antennae (Fig. 15.7*a*) to sieve phytoplankton cells out of the water, eating whatever particles happen to be the right size to snag in the bristles. In fact, this is not the case. For small organisms like copepods, water is much more viscous, or syrupy, than it seems to us. The bristly appendages of copepods act more like paddles than sieves, and are used to create water currents that draw individual phytoplankton cells close enough for the copepod to grab. At least some copepods can see and smell individual phytoplankton cells, and actively select cells to eat rather than passively consuming whatever happens to get caught on their bristles.

Though most copepods eat at least some phytoplankton, many also eat other zooplankton, including other copepods, when they can. A few copepods are exclusively carnivorous. These generally have claw-like appendages to seize their prey (Fig. 15.7*b*).

Other Crustaceans Crustaceans other than copepods are also important in the zooplankton. Though not as abundant globally as copepods, shrimp-like **krill** often aggregate into huge, dense swarms. In polar seas krill sometimes dominate the zooplankton,

and they are a major part of epipelagic food webs in the Antarctic (see Figs. 10.13, 10.14, and 10.15). They are efficient filter feeders, capturing phytoplankton, especially diatoms, with their bristly appendages. Krill also eat small zooplankton and **detritus,** including **fecal pellets,** the solid waste excreted by other zooplankton.

Copepods are so small that most large animals can't catch them. Krill, by contrast, are relatively big, up to 6 cm (2.5 in) in Antarctic krill (*Euphausia superba;* see Fig. 17.12). Fishes, seabirds, and even great whales eat them (see Fig. 10.14).

FIGURE 15.6 This widely distributed copepod, *Gaussia princeps*, reaches body lengths over 10 mm (3/8 in), larger than most copepods.

Although copepods and krill are by far the most abundant, there are many other crustaceans, both herbivorous and carnivorous, in the zooplankton. At certain times and places, these other crustacean groups can be very abundant. Amphipods and most other planktonic crustaceans are small, like copepods. A few larger crustaceans, however, also occur in the net zooplankton. These include a number of decapods—crabs, shrimps, and their relatives (see "Crustaceans," in 7.6). Although relatively few of these large crustaceans inhabit the epipelagic realm as adults, many do so during their larval stages (see "Meroplankton," below). The decapods are almost exclusively carnivorous.

Copepods, krill, and other crustaceans dominate the net zooplankton. Copepods are the main herbivores in the epipelagic and are by far the most abundant group of zooplankton.

Non-Crustacean Zooplankton The zooplankton include many animal groups other than crustaceans. **Salps** (Fig. 15.8) are transparent, planktonic relatives of the sea squirts, or tunicates, that live on the bottom (see "Tunicates," in 7.10). Salps catch phytoplankton by filtering water through a sieve-like sac or a fine mucus net.

Larvaceans (Fig. 15.9) are also relatives of sea squirts, though they hardly look it—except for their larvae. Sea squirt larvae, known as tadpole larvae, are very similar to larvaceans (see Fig. 7.52*b*). Larvaceans live inside a "house" they make of mucus. By beating its tail, the larvacean pumps water through passages in the house. Food particles are caught in a mucus net secreted inside the house. At least some larvaceans also secrete a net that can extend as far as 2 m (6.5 ft) outside the house. The use of sticky mucus nets allows larvaceans to capture extremely small food particles. Larvaceans and some salps are among the few animals that can catch pico- and nanoplankton. They are therefore important in linking primary production by pico- and nanoplankton to the rest of the epipelagic community.

The openings through which water enters the house filter out particles too large for the larvacean to eat. These filters eventually get clogged. Some species can reverse the water flow to clear the

Nitrogen Fixation The conversion of nitrogen gas (N_2) into nitrogen compounds that can be used by primary producers as nutrients.
• 5.2, Eukaryotes; Table 5.1

Eukaryotes Organisms with cells that contain a nucleus and other organelles that are enclosed by membranes.
• 4.2, Living Machinery; Figure 4.8

Protozoans Single-celled organisms that are animal-like in that they ingest food and usually can move around.
• 5.4, Protozoans: The Animal-Like Protists

Copepods Tiny crustaceans that are often planktonic.
• 7.6, Arthropods: The Armored Achievers

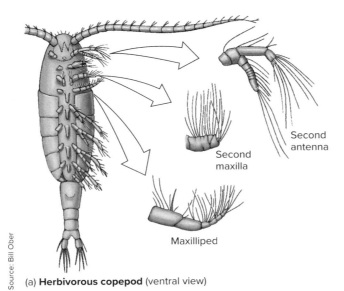

(a) **Herbivorous copepod** (ventral view)

Source: Bill Ober

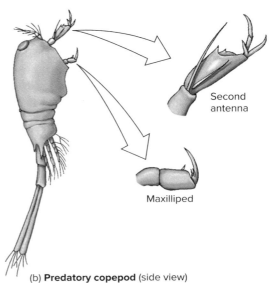

(b) **Predatory copepod** (side view)

FIGURE 15.7 (*a*) The mouthparts and appendages of copepods that feed mainly on phytoplankton, like *Calanus,* have many long bristles. (*b*) Copepods that prey on other zooplankton, like *Corycaeus,* have appendages with fewer and shorter bristles. Their appendages are better adapted for grasping. All appendages are paired, but (*a*) shows only those on one side.

Carver Mostard/Alamy Stock Photo

FIGURE 15.8 A pelagic salp (*Tethys vagina*). These gelatinous animals feed by filtering phytoplankton. Like larvaceans (Fig. 15.9), some can capture bacteria and other very tiny plankton. They sometimes provide a home to other animals.

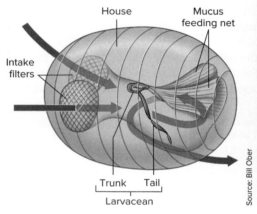

Source: Bill Ober

FIGURE 15.9 A larvacean spends most of its time inside a mucus "house." By beating its tail, the larvacean draws water into the house (blue arrows) through two intake filters. Food particles are caught on the mucus feeding net, and the filtered water flows outward.

Russ Hopcroft, University of Alaska Fairbanks, NOAA, Census of Marine Life.

FIGURE 15.10 In pteropods, like this *Clio pyramidata,* the foot is typically expanded into "wings" that the animal swims with. Pteropods have a shell like most other molluscs, but it is thin and light to help in flotation.

filters. If the filters get too clogged or a predator threatens, the larvacean simply abandons the house and swims away. It can produce a new house within minutes and resume feeding. When disturbed, some species build and discard houses every 10 minutes! Even under normal circumstances, most species change houses every four hours or so. Discarded houses are an important source of detritus and transport large amounts of carbon to the deep sea as they sink.

A group of molluscs called **pteropods** also includes phytoplankton grazers. Pteropods are small snails in which the foot has been modified to form a pair of "wings" that they flap to stay afloat (Fig. 15.10). Some feed by capturing phytoplankton, including picoplankton and nanoplankton, in mucus nets or threads; others are carnivorous.

Larvaceans, salps, and some pteropods feed with mucus nets or threads. They are among the few zooplankton that can eat pico- and nanoplankton. Discarded larvacean houses are an important source of detritus in the epipelagic.

Arrow worms, or **chaetognaths,** feed mostly on copepods. This may not be because they actually prefer copepods but because copepods are so abundant. Arrow worms consume an assortment of other prey when it is available. They can be very abundant and have a major role in epipelagic food webs.

Not all carnivorous zooplankton are small. Jellyfishes, or sea jellies, and **siphonophores,** for example, can be quite large. They drift in the plankton as they don't swim strongly enough to oppose currents. They can, however, swim up and down in the water column or to approach prey over short distances, and in terms of energy use they are the most efficient swimmers for their size in the ocean. Sea jellies are carnivorous, and many eat small fishes as well as zooplankton. The somewhat similar **comb jellies** (see Fig. 15.20*b*) are also carnivorous. The ocean sunfish (*Mola mola:* Fig. 15.11), which grows to 2,300 kg (5,000 lb), swims weakly and is sometimes considered a member of the zooplankton.

Meroplankton The zooplankton discussed so far, except for most sea jellies, spend their whole lives in the plankton and are called **holoplankton.** In addition to these permanent members of the zooplankton, there are a vast number of organisms that have planktonic larvae. These animals—whether from estuaries, the rocky intertidal, kelp beds, coral reefs, or even the deep sea—release their eggs or young into the water column, and the larvae spend the early part of their lives in the plankton. Such temporary members of the plankton are called **meroplankton.** Coastal waters are particularly rich in meroplankton, but meroplankton are found throughout the ocean.

FIGURE 15.11 Ocean sunfish (*Mola mola*) have almost no tail and swim only very weakly. These fish are in shallow water but the species is usually found away from the bottom in deeper water.

Many invertebrates have a characteristic larva (Fig. 15.12). Some have a whole series of different larval stages (see Fig. 7.41). Nearly all marine fishes also have planktonic larvae.

The meroplankton are the larval stages of invertebrates and fishes that spend only part of their lives in the zooplankton.

Small larvae tend to feed mostly on phytoplankton; larger ones eat zooplankton. If there is a series of stages, as in crustaceans, the larvae may feed on phytoplankton initially and later switch to zooplankton. Fish larvae, too, often change from herbivores to carnivores as they grow (see Fig. 15.25).

The Nekton

Plankton are by far the most abundant organisms in the sea, and they form the base of the epipelagic food chain. Most of us, however, are more familiar with the **nekton,** the large, strong swimmers. Fishes, marine mammals, and squids are the most abundant nekton. Turtles, sea snakes, and penguins are also nekton.

Nearly all nekton are carnivorous. **Planktivorous** nekton, those that eat zooplankton, include small fishes like herrings, sardines, and anchovies. They also include the world's largest fishes, the whale shark (*Rhincodon typus*) and basking shark (*Cetorhinus maximus*). The largest nekton of all, baleen whales, also eat plankton, mostly krill. Seals, penguins, squids, and an assortment of fishes, including salmon, tunas, and flying fishes, also eat krill.

Some fishes, like lanternfishes, stay in deeper water during the day and swim up into the epipelagic at night (see "Adaptations of Midwater Animals," in 16.1). They also consume large amounts of zooplankton. These fishes are important foods for some large epipelagic nekton, like tunas and dolphins, that dive into deeper water to feed.

Krill Planktonic, shrimp-like crustaceans.
- 7.6, Arthropods: The Armored Achievers

Detritus Particles of dead organic matter.
- 10.3, The Flow of Energy and Materials

Arrow Worms or **Chaetognaths** Small, worm-like predators with fins along the body and spines on the head.

- 7.4, Bilaterally Symmetrical Worms

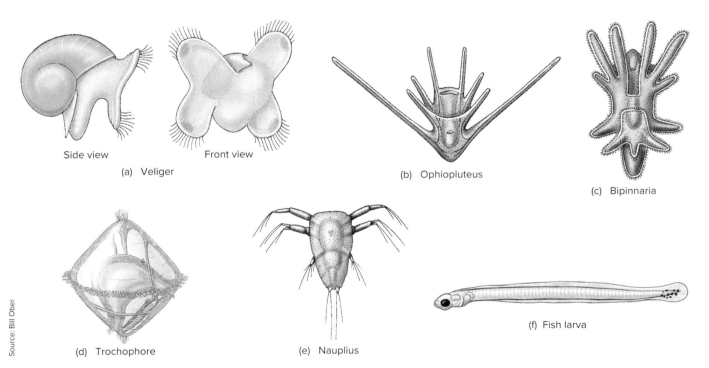

(a) Veliger — Side view / Front view

(b) Ophiopluteus

(c) Bipinnaria

(d) Trochophore

(e) Nauplius

(f) Fish larva

Source: Bill Ober

FIGURE 15.12 There is tremendous variety of larvae in the meroplankton. Some examples are (*a*) the veliger of molluscs, (*b*) the ophiopluteus of brittle stars, (*c*) the bipinnaria of sea stars, (*d*) the trochophore of polychaete worms and some molluscs, (*e*) the nauplius of many crustaceans, and (*f*) fish larvae.

Box 15.1 Red Tides and Harmful Algal Blooms

From time to time, especially near the coast, the sea becomes bright red literally overnight. This phenomenon, called a red tide, has been known for thousands of years. The Old Testament (Exodus 7:20–21) contains what may be the earliest reference to a red tide when it describes the waters of the Nile turning to blood. The Red Sea is named for the red tides that often occur there.

The term "red tide" is here to stay, but red tides have nothing to do with the tide. They are massive blooms of phytoplankton. At their peak there can be hundreds of thousands of cells in a single drop! Furthermore, red tides aren't always red. The sea may instead turn orange, brown, or bright green. The term "brown tide" is sometimes used for blooms of phytoplankton called chrysophytes, but the basic phenomenon is the same.

Red tides are different from ordinary phytoplankton blooms like the spring bloom that occurs in cold waters (see "Seasonal Patterns," below). The spring bloom includes many different species and is predictable, occurring in response to increased light or nutrients. Red tides, by contrast, are usually blooms of a single species and are unpredictable because we don't fully understand what causes them.

Out of more than 10,000 species of marine phytoplankton, only about 200 cause harmful red tides. About half are dinoflagellates, but many other organisms, including diatoms, cyanobacteria, and chrysophytes, can cause red tides.

Red tides that cause problems, or **harmful algal blooms (HABs),** are receiving increasing attention from both scientists and society at large. Of course, what is harmful depends on your point of view. If you are on a beach vacation, a foul brown foam caused by a bloom may be nothing more than an annoying reason to cut the vacation short. To the motel owner depending on your business it is a disaster.

Some blooms are more than just a nuisance. They are deadly. About a third of red tide organisms produce toxins, including some of the most powerful toxins known. Normally there are too few of the organisms around to worry about, but when they bloom they can cause serious problems. Mussels, clams, crabs, and other shellfish often tolerate the toxins by storing them away in the digestive gland, kidney, liver, or other tissues. People who eat the shellfish, however, can suffer nausea, diarrhea, vomiting, numbness and tingling, loss of balance and memory, slurred speech, shooting pains, paralysis, and even death. Toxic algae cause an estimated 100,000 to 200,000 cases of serious poisoning a year, including ciguatera (see Box 14.3, "Must Have Been Something I Ate"). These lead to 10,000 to 20,000 deaths and a similar number of cases of paralysis and other consequences. You don't have to eat shellfish to suffer. Swimming or boating in affected water, even breathing sea spray, can cause sore throats, eye irritation, and skin complaints. Some of the toxins may be carcinogenic.

The effects of HABs aren't confined to humans. Blooms of the toxic dinoflagellate *Karenia brevis,* an increasing problem in the Gulf of Mexico in recent years, can kill clam,

Kevin Schafer/The Image Bank/Peter Arnold/Getty Images

Bloom of a dinoflagellate called *Noctiluca* caused this red tide in Mexico. The organism is bioluminescent, and blooms like this produce spectacular blue-green light at night.

oyster, and scallop larvae, potentially disrupting fisheries for those species. HABs can turn the surface into a sea of dead fish. A dinoflagellate called *Pfiesteria* is a particular problem along parts of the U.S. east and Gulf coasts (see "Dinoflagellates," in 5.3), but many other HAB organisms cause fish kills. Fish-eating whales and seabirds have also been killed. Though they eat aquatic vegetation, Florida manatees have been killed by red tides just by being exposed in the water, and perhaps by breathing toxic spray at the surface.

Most species of nekton, however, eat other nekton rather than plankton. Fishes, squids, and large crustaceans are the main foods. Epipelagic predators are usually not fussy and will eat many different prey, provided they are the right size. In general, the larger the predator, the larger the prey, though there are exceptions like baleen whales and whale sharks. Thus, small fishes like herrings have small prey: zooplankton. Bigger fishes eat these small fishes and in turn are eaten by even bigger predators. At the top of the food chain are the largest predators of all, the top predators, which eat the largest prey. The sperm whale (*Physeter catodon;* see Fig. 1.18), the largest of all nekton except baleen whales, eats giant squid more than 10 m (33 ft) long. There are other top predators that eat massive prey. Among predators, killer whales (*Orcinus orca*) are second in size only to the sperm whale. They not only eat porpoises and seals, but by hunting in groups can also attack and kill baleen whales. Large sharks like the great white (*Carcharodon carcharias*) and mako (*Isurus*) sharks eat seals, billfishes like marlins and sailfishes, and even other sharks.

Nearly all the epipelagic nekton are predators. A few eat plankton, but most species eat other, usually smaller, nekton.

15.2 LIVING IN THE EPIPELAGIC

Every environment places special demands on the organisms that live there, and the epipelagic is no exception. The adaptations of epipelagic organisms largely center around two main needs: the need to stay in the epipelagic and the need to eat and avoid being eaten.

Staying Afloat

To live in the epipelagic, organisms must *stay* in the epipelagic. Epipelagic organisms face a fundamental problem: Cells and tissues are denser than water. Shells and skeletons are even more dense. Thus, organisms sink unless they have some adaptation to

The harmful effects of algal blooms are not always caused by toxins. Blooms of some diatoms kill fish because the diatoms' sharp spines damage the fishes' gills. Even when algal blooms don't harm fish directly, they can cause fish kills when the masses of phytoplankton die, decompose, and use up all the oxygen.

Red tides cost billions of dollars in losses to fisheries and tourism. Fish farms can be wiped out and valuable shellfish beds are often closed because of red tides, or during seasons when red tides are likely. Perfectly safe seafood can be rendered nearly worthless if the public perceives it as dangerous.

HABs have been around since long before biblical times. There is fossil evidence of red tides from more than 100 million years ago. Scientists have been concerned, however, that HABs may be becoming more frequent, widespread, intense, and persistent than in the past. Some of the apparent increase could just reflect better monitoring and reporting.

One reason HABs might be increasing is eutrophication, increased algal growth due to nutrient pollution. Nutrient pollution has been associated with increasing HABs in the Seto Inland Sea of Japan, Black Sea, and East China Sea, among other areas. The link between nutrients and HABs is not always straightforward. HAB organisms vary in the types of nutrients they use, so nutrient pollution in some forms may not stimulate algal growth. The types of nutrients added is also important. Humans add a lot of nitrogen (N; see Special Report, Overwhelming the Nitrogen Cycle), and not so much phosphorus (P) and silicon (Si). Dams actually reduce the natural supply of phosphorus and silicon. Most marine systems are nitrogen-limited, and when nitrogen is added the phytoplankton grow until they run out of something else. In particular, diatoms can run out of the silicon needed to make their shells, shifting the balance in favor of dinoflagellates. While some diatoms produce toxins, dinoflagellates are much more likely to do so. Not only that, some dinoflagellates produce more toxin when their supply of phosphorus runs low, which is likely to happen if we pump in nitrogen and not phosphorus. Other factors, including currents, temperature, and the abundance of zooplankton grazers and disease-causing viruses, also play a role. In a few places, scientists are beginning to develop models to predict HABs, but in most places we still don't understand what triggers HABs well enough to predict them. It is clear, however, that in many places controlling nutrient pollution is a key to reducing HABs.

HABs are also spreading to new places. Ships can transport hundreds of millions of HAB organisms in their ballast water. Natural events can also spread HABs. For example, shellfish poisoning was unknown in the Gulf of Maine until 1972, when a tropical storm carried in a seed population of toxic dinoflagellates. There have since been outbreaks almost annually. There is some evidence that climate change might contribute to HABs, because of changes in water circulation and other disruption to ecological processes. Recent major HABs in California, Chile, and Australia, for example, have been linked to unusual climate-related conditions.

Overall, it is not clear whether HABs are an increasing problem at a global scale. Certainly, some local areas have experienced unprecedented HABs in recent years. But data show that the various diseases caused by HABs are increasing in some places and decreasing in others, at least in the last few decades. Monitoring and reporting of HABs varies widely, so the data may not reflect what is actually happening. There is significant investment in improved technologies, including satellite imagery, sensors that detect harmful algae in the water, and toxicological analysis of seawater, shellfish, and algae, to detect HABs and shellfish poisoning.

prevent it. This is not a problem for organisms on the bottom, but organisms that live near the surface must somehow avoid sinking to stay in their habitat.

Phytoplankton have to stay in relatively shallow water to get enough light for photosynthesis. Once a phytoplankton cell sinks or is carried by water movement out of the photic zone it is doomed, unless it can somehow get back into the sunlit layer. Animals, too, whether zooplankton or nekton, must be able to stay near the surface, not because they need sunlight but because their food is found in the shallow waters.

Organisms that can't swim have two basic ways to keep themselves from sinking out of the epipelagic. One is to increase their water resistance so they sink slower. The other is to be more buoyant so they don't sink in the first place. Buoyancy also benefits organisms that swim because it allows them to stay at a given depth with less work. This applies not only to the nekton, which by definition are strong swimmers, but also to zooplankton and even some phytoplankton, like dinoflagellates. They swim up and down in the water column even though they can't swim strongly enough to move against the currents.

Organisms must avoid sinking to stay in the epipelagic. They do so by increasing water resistance and increasing buoyancy.

Increased Resistance How fast an organism of a given weight sinks depends on how much water resistance, or **drag,** it encounters. The drag depends on how much water a moving organism pushes in front of it and the amount of friction between the water and the organism's surface. For small organisms like most plankton, drag depends mostly on surface area: the more surface area, the higher the water resistance and the slower the organism sinks.

Siphonophores Drifting colonial cnidarians in which different members of the colony are specialized for different tasks.
• 7.2, Cnidarians: Radial Symmetry

Comb Jellies or **Ctenophores** Radially symmetrical animals that resemble jellyfishes, or sea jellies, but have eight rows of cilia and no *nematocysts.*
• 7.3, Comb Jellies: Radial Symmetry Revisited

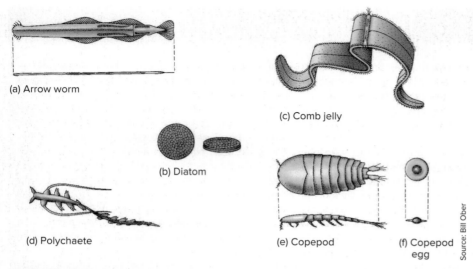

(a) Arrow worm

(c) Comb jelly

(b) Diatom

(d) Polychaete

(e) Copepod

(f) Copepod egg

Source: Bill Ober

FIGURE 15.13 Planktonic organisms with flat shapes include (*a*) some arrow worms (*Sagitta*), (*b*) many diatoms, (*c*) *Cestum,* a highly modified comb jelly, (*d*) *Tomopteris,* a planktonic polychaete worm, (*e*) certain copepods, such as *Sapphirina,* and (*f*) some copepod eggs.

This is one reason plankton are usually small: Small organisms have more surface area per unit volume than large organisms (see "Surface-to-Volume Ratio," in 4.3) and thus a slower sinking rate. It also helps that, to tiny plankton, water is much more viscous, or syrupy, than it is to larger organisms (see "Copepods," above), helping to slow the rate of sinking.

An organism's shape can also increase its surface area to make it sink slower. The parachute-like shape of many sea jellies helps slow sinking. Many plankton have extremely flat shapes (Fig. 15.13). You can see how this helps slow sinking with a simple experiment. Take two sheets of paper and crumple one into a ball. Drop both pieces from the same height. The flat sheet will take much longer to hit the ground because it offers more air resistance. Exactly the same principle applies in water. A flat shape has another advantage for phytoplankton. Note how the flat sheet of paper zigzags from side to side as it falls. Flat phytoplankton cells do the same thing. The back-and-forth motion keeps seawater flowing over the cell's surface, renewing the layer of water with which the cell exchanges gases, nutrients, and waste products.

Long projections or spines are another common adaptation to increase surface area in planktonic organisms (Fig. 15.14). Spines have the added advantage of making the organism harder to eat. Many phytoplankton form chains. Chains sink slower than the individual cells would if the chain were broken up.

Epipelagic nekton, by contrast, rarely have pronounced spines or other features that increase water resistance. Since swimming burns a lot of energy, nekton usually have adaptations to *reduce* drag and make it easier to swim.

Increased Buoyancy One common adaptation epipelagic organisms have to be more buoyant is to store **lipids,** such as oils or fats. Lipids are less dense than water and float. Many plankton—notably diatoms, copepods, and fish eggs and larvae—contain oil droplets. Many adult epipelagic fishes also gain buoyancy by storing lipid. This is especially true of sharks, tunas and their relatives, and other fishes in which the swim bladder is poorly

developed or missing altogether. Epipelagic sharks, for example, have enlarged livers with a very high oil content. Whales, seals, and other marine mammals have a thick layer of fatty, buoyant blubber under the skin (see Fig. 4.2).

Oils and fats also serve other functions. They are the most efficient way to store energy. In marine mammals the blubber provides insulation from the cold as well as buoyancy. Insulation is especially important to warm-blooded animals, which must burn energy to maintain their body temperatures (see "Temperature," in 4.3).

Pockets of gas are another adaptation for buoyancy. Cyanobacteria have tiny gas bubbles, or vacuoles, inside their cells. They are able to change the number and buoyancy of the vacuoles. This allows them to increase buoyancy to move up in the water column or decrease it to sink. Some other plankton, especially large ones, have special gas-filled floats. Such floats are especially common in organisms that live right at the sea surface, as described in the next section. Most epipelagic bony fishes have **swim bladders** for buoyancy.

A gas-filled bladder or float provides much more buoyancy than lipid, but it has a major disadvantage. Gas expands and contracts as the animal moves up and down in the water column and the pressure changes. When the volume of gas changes, so does the amount

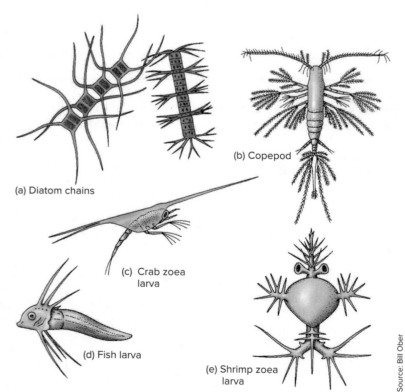

(a) Diatom chains

(b) Copepod

(c) Crab zoea larva

(d) Fish larva

(e) Shrimp zoea larva

Source: Bill Ober

FIGURE 15.14 Some planktonic organisms have long spines or projections. They can also form chains. Examples are (*a*) diatoms, (*b*) copepods like *Augaptilus,* (*c*) zoea larvae of porcellanid crabs, (*d*) fish larvae (*Lophius*), and (*e*) zoea larvae of *Sergestes,* a shrimp.

of buoyancy. To control its buoyancy, a fish must be able to regulate the amount of gas in its swim bladder. Most fishes can do this, but the mechanism varies. Some fishes pump gas in and out of the bladder through a special duct, and can adjust fairly rapidly to pressure changes. Other fishes regulate the amount of gas in their swim bladders much more slowly and can't cope well with depth changes. Many fishers have pulled up fish with bulging eyes or the stomach protruding from the mouth (see Fig. 3.15). This happens when the gas in the swim bladder expands as the fish is brought to the surface. In normal life the fish would never come to the surface or would surface much more slowly than it did on the end of the line.

The swim bladder is often poorly developed or absent in active fishes that frequently change depth, such as tunas. It never evolved in sharks. Such fishes must compensate for the loss of buoyancy. In addition to their large oily livers, sharks have large, stiff fins and asymmetrical tails that provide lift when the shark swims (see Fig. 8.4). Members of the tuna family also rely on stiff, almost wing-like fins and must swim constantly to provide lift.

Yet another way to gain buoyancy is to control the composition of the body fluids. Organisms can reduce their density by excluding heavy ions, like sulfate (SO_4^{-2}) and magnesium (Mg^{+2}), and replacing them with lighter ones, especially ammonium (NH_4^{+1}) and chloride (Cl^{-1}). Some dinoflagellates do this, and there is evidence that other phytoplankton do too. So do various zooplankton, including salps, comb jellies, and some squids.

> Mechanisms to increase buoyancy in epipelagic organisms include lipid storage, gas-filled floats, and the substitution of light ions for heavy ones in internal fluids.

The Floaters The plankton include an unusual and highly specialized group of organisms that live at the very surface of the ocean. Organisms that live right at the sea surface but remain underwater are known as **neuston,** and those whose bodies project through the sea surface into the air are called **pleuston.**

All plankton need to keep from sinking, but the neuston and pleuston have to go one step further and actually float. The most common method of doing this is to have some sort of gas-filled structure to provide buoyancy. There are many variations on this seemingly simple theme.

The upper surface of the by-the-wind sailor (*Velella*), a colonial, jellyfish-like cnidarian, is specialized as a float (Fig. 15.15). The float protrudes into the air and acts like a sail, pushing the colony along in the wind. The Portuguese man-of-war (*Physalia*), a siphonophore, is famous for its powerful sting (see Box 7.1, "The Case of the Killer Cnidarians"). Like the by-the-wind sailor, part of the colony acts as a sail (Fig. 15.16). Several other

cnidarians live at the sea surface. Some can even control the buoyancy of their floats and sink below the surface for shelter during storms.

Despite their powerful stinging cells, these relatives of sea jellies have enemies. The violet snail (*Janthina*) makes a raft of mucus filled with bubbles from which it hangs upside down. These inch-long snails drift about, eating Portuguese men-of-war and other delicacies when they find them. Another mollusc, a sea slug (nudibranch) called *Glaucus,* stays afloat by swallowing a bubble

> **Swim Bladder** A gas-filled sac that lies inside the body cavity of most bony fishes.
> • 8.2, Type of Fishes; Figure 8.12*b*

Peter Parks/Image Quest Marine

FIGURE 15.15 The by-the-wind sailor (*Velella*).

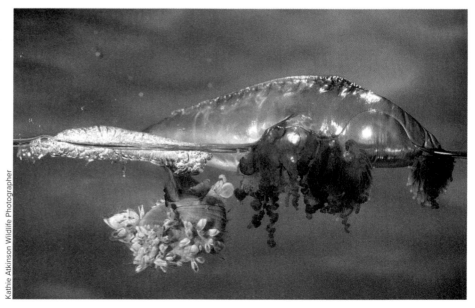

Kathie Atkinson Wildlife Photographer

FIGURE 15.16 A violet snail (*Janthina janthina;* left), covered with gooseneck barnacles, eats a Portuguese man-of-war (*Physalia physalis;* right).

FIGURE 15.18 The marine water strider (*Halobates sericeus*) relies on greatly elongated legs and the water's surface tension to skate on the surface.

Lanna Cheng, Scripps Institution of Oceanography

FIGURE 15.17 The pelagic sea slug (*Glaucus*) feeding on *Porpita,* a relative of jellyfishes, or sea jellies. The sea slug not only gets a meal but also uses *Porpita's* stinging cells for defense.

Kathie Atkinson Wildlife Photographer

of air. It feeds on the by-the-wind sailor and its relative, the small, disk-shaped *Porpita* (Fig. 15.17). *Porpita's* stinging cells, still capable of firing, end up in the flaps that protrude from the sea slug's back and will sting animals that disturb it. Thus, *Porpita* provides not only food but also protection for the sea slug.

Not all surface inhabitants have special adaptations to float. Another sea slug (*Fiona pinnata*), for example, looks much like sea slugs that live on the bottom, but it is only found on objects—both other organisms and debris—floating at the surface. It feeds on barnacles that attach to these objects (Fig. 15.16), and possibly also on floaters like *Physalia* and *Vellela.* While it has no specific adaptation to float, *Fiona* has a short larval time span and a fast growth rate once the larvae settle, which may be adaptations to rapidly colonize floating material. There are plenty of "rafts" of material at the sea surface and *Fiona* is globally distributed.

Another globally distributed surface inhabitant doesn't float at all. The water strider (*Halobates*), the only insect that lives in the open ocean, skims over the water surface (Fig. 15.18). It is closely related to the water striders common in lakes and ponds. The water strider isn't marine in the strict sense because it cannot swim and drowns if it falls through the surface. Still, it manages to live all over the oceans.

Predators and Their Prey

Epipelagic animals need to find food and at the same time avoid being eaten in an environment where there are few places to hide.

Sense Organs Predators and their prey play a continual game of hide-and-seek. The predator tries to find its prey and attack before the

victim can escape, while the prey wants as much warning of approaching enemies as possible. Most animals in the epipelagic have highly developed sense organs to help them detect their prey and enemies.

The epipelagic has plenty of light to see by, at least during the day, so it is no surprise that vision is important to many epipelagic animals. Many zooplankton have well-developed eyes. Most can't see actual images, but they can detect motion, shapes, and shadows. Copepods and other zooplankton probably use vision to locate their prey and avoid predators.

Squids, fishes, and marine mammals all have good eyesight. Vision is especially important to nekton in the epipelagic because there are no solid structures that can be used for concealment. In other environments, animals can hide in the sediments, under rocks, or behind seaweeds. There are no such hiding places in the epipelagic. The large, well-developed eyes of most epipelagic fishes (Fig. 15.19) and other nekton are used not only to find prey and watch for predators but also to find mates and stay together in schools (see "Behavior," in 8.3).

Fishes have another remote sensing system: the **lateral line.** Like all fishes, those in the epipelagic are extremely sensitive to vibrations in the water. Fishes use their lateral lines to stay in touch with schoolmates and to detect predators. Even blind fishes can school and react to the lunge of an enemy. Most predatory fishes—including

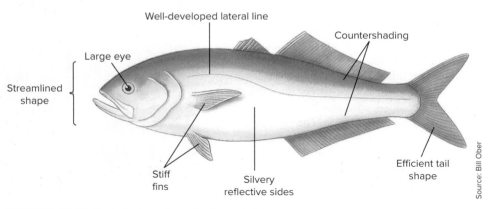

Well-developed lateral line

Countershading

Large eye

Streamlined shape

Stiff fins

Silvery reflective sides

Efficient tail shape

Source: Bill Ober

FIGURE 15.19 Typical adaptations of epipelagic fishes.

FIGURE 15.20 Many species of zooplankton are transparent or nearly so. Examples include (*a*) hyperiid amphipods, which have two giant eyes that cover most of the head, (*b*) comb jellies, and (*c*) squids. These photos have been taken to make the organisms more visible than they actually are.

sharks, tunas, and billfishes—also have well-developed hearing and are strongly attracted to splashes on the surface and irregular vibrations in the water, the kinds of vibrations made by an injured fish. Dolphins and many other cetaceans have another remote sensing system, **echolocation.** This sophisticated built-in sonar allows them to locate their prey at a distance (see "Biology of Marine Mammals," in 9.3).

Epipelagic animals have well-developed sense organs, especially vision, the lateral lines and hearing of fishes, and echolocation in cetaceans.

Coloration and Camouflage Just because there are no hiding places doesn't mean that epipelagic organisms cannot conceal themselves. Indeed, **protective coloration,** or camouflage, is nearly universal among epipelagic animals. This isn't surprising in a world where the hunters rely so heavily on vision to find their victims, and the prey use vision to get away.

One way to be inconspicuous in the vast, watery world of the epipelagic is to be transparent. This adaptation is seen in a variety of zooplankton, some of which are almost perfectly clear (Fig. 15.20). Gelatinous zooplankton like some sea jellies, salps, larvaceans, and comb jellies are probably the best at being invisible. Many other groups of zooplankton are at least partially transparent, with perhaps only the eyes, a few spots of pigment, or the internal organs visible. Some nearly transparent zooplankton have a faint, bluish tinge, possibly helping them blend in with the surroundings. The nearly transparent, bluish coloration of many neuston and pleuston (Figs. 15.15–15.17) serves the same purpose; in their case, the color also helps them blend in with the sky when viewed from below.

Another common form of protective coloration, particularly in nekton, is **countershading,** where the back (dorsal surface) is dark, usually green, blue, or black, and the belly (ventral surface) is white or silver. Countershading is particularly well suited to the epipelagic. To a predator looking down, the ocean depths are a dark blue. Viewed from above, the dark back of a countershaded fish blends in against the dark background. Looking up, on the other hand, the predator sees the bright light filtering down from above and the silvery-white sea surface. Against this bright background a dark object stands out like a sore thumb, but the silvery-white undersides of epipelagic nekton reflect light and match the bright surface. Laterally compressed bodies, also common, reduce the size of the silhouette, whether viewed from above or below (Fig. 15.21).

Countershading, in which the dorsal surface is dark and the ventral surface is white or silver, is a widespread adaptation among epipelagic nekton. Countershaded organisms blend in against the background whether they are viewed from above or below.

Most epipelagic fishes have silvery sides that reflect light. This helps them blend in when viewed from the side as well as from above or below. It is also common for them to have vertical bars or irregular patterns that help break up their outline in the dappled underwater light.

Lateral Line A system of canals on the head and sides of fishes that helps them detect vibrations in the water.
• 8.3, Biology of Fishes; Figure 8.19

FIGURE 15.21 Like many epipelagic fishes, the sailfish (*Istiophorus platypterus*) has a laterally compressed body; that is, it is high and narrow when viewed in cross section.

Box 15.2 Swimming Machines

Tunas, mackerels, and billfishes swim continuously. Feeding, courtship, reproduction, and even "sleep" are done in constant motion. Consequently, practically every aspect of the body form and function of these swimming machines is adapted to enhance swimming.

The swimming feats of tunas and billfishes are amazing. They routinely cover vast distances in their annual migrations (see Fig. 8.22). One Pacific bluefin tuna (*Thunnus orientalis*) tagged southeast of Japan was recaptured off the Pacific coast of Baja California, Mexico, 10,800 km (6,700 mi) away. Most other tunas and billfishes also make long-distance migrations.

These long journeys are made in an impressively short time. Tagged Atlantic, or northern, bluefin tuna (*T. thynnus*), have crossed the Atlantic in 119 days, averaging a straight-line distance of over 65 km (40 mi) per day. The fish actually cover a much greater distance as they dash around to feed. Some tunas could cross the Atlantic in less than two months at their *slowest* cruising speed if they took a direct route.

Tunas and billfishes are primarily endurance swimmers, adapted for sustained cruising, but they are also accomplished sprinters and can make blistering high-speed bursts. The fastest fish of all is the Indo-West Pacific sailfish (*Istiophorus platypterus;* see Fig. 1.15), which can exceed 110 km/h (70 mph) for short periods. No other fish can match this, but most tunas and billfishes are fast swimmers. Several large species can reach 75 km/h (50 mph); some smaller ones are just as fast for their size. Most are so fast that they can easily outdistance their prey. Their phenomenal speed has probably evolved not so much to catch prey—they can do that at slower speeds—as to compete with schoolmates. The first one to the prey, after all, gets the meal.

Many adaptations of these fishes reduce water resistance. Several of these hydrodynamic adaptations resemble aerodynamic features of high-speed jets. Human engineers are new to the game— tunas and their relatives evolved their "high-tech" designs long ago.

Tunas, mackerels, and billfishes have made streamlining an art form. The sleek body shapes of tunas are nearly ideal from an engineering perspective. Most species lack scales over most of the body, making it smooth and slippery. The eyes lie flush instead of protruding and are covered with a slick, transparent lid that reduces drag. The fins are stiff, smooth, and narrow, also cutting drag. When not in use, the fins tuck into grooves so they lie flush with the body and not break up its smooth contours. Jets retract their landing gear in flight for the same reason.

These fishes have even more complex adaptations to improve their hydrodynamics. The long bill of marlins, sailfishes, and swordfish (*Xiphias gladius*) helps them slip through the water. Many supersonic aircraft have a similar needle at the nose. Most tunas and billfishes have a series of keels and finlets near the tail. Although most of their scales have been lost, tunas and mackerels retain a patch of coarse scales near the head called the corselet. The keels, finlets, and corselet help direct the flow of water over the body surface in such a way as to reduce resistance. Again, supersonic jets have similar features.

Vertebrates, including fishes, have a lymphatic system that helps regulate body fluids, carries away wastes, and supports the immune system. Tunas have adapted their lymphatic system for another purpose: dealing with the high stresses that arise when maneuvering with their stiff fins at high speed. Their lymphatic system also acts as a hydraulic system akin to the hydraulics used in heavy machinery. It magnifies the force of the muscles that control the fins and makes them more efficient.

Always swimming, tunas can force water over their gills by simply opening their mouth. They have lost most of the muscles that other fishes use to pump water past their gills. In fact, tunas must swim to

Natural light waves vibrate in planes from horizontal to vertical and everything in between. Filtering out light except in one polarized plane can greatly improve vision; that is why polarized sunglasses reduce glare. Many epipelagic fishes have polarization-sensitive vision that helps them find prey even if they have reflective surfaces. But the prey have adapted: some epipelagic fishes modify their reflective sides to match the surrounding polarized light and make their camouflage more effective.

Flying fishes (*Cypselurus*) have evolved a distinctive defense that is not exactly camouflage but does make them hard to see, at least temporarily. When threatened, flying fishes launch out of the water and glide through the air on their greatly enlarged pectoral fins (Fig. 15.22). To a predator, the flying fish seems to have disappeared, because it is difficult to see beyond the reflective sea surface. This strategy is only partly effective, however, and flying fishes are a favorite food of many epipelagic predators.

Swimming: The Need for Speed Protective coloration or not, the keen senses of epipelagic predators enable them to find their prey.

FIGURE 15.22 Flying fishes (*Cypselurus*) can't actually fly, but they glide long distances using their large pectoral fins. To launch themselves they flap the back of their body; the lower lobe of their tail fin is elongated to provide lift and steering until they are completely in the air.

When this happens the prey's only hope is to flee, because there are no hiding places. Whether the prey gets away or the predator gets a meal often depends on which swims faster. The emphasis is on sheer speed, as opposed to maneuverability, or being able to burrow in the bottom or hide in crevices in the rocks. It is no coincidence that the epipelagic is home to the ocean's most powerful swimmers (see "Swimming Machines," below).

As noted above, whereas plankton are typically adapted to increase drag to slow their sinking, epipelagic nekton typically reduce drag to swim fast. Nearly all epipelagic nekton have streamlined bodies for efficient swimming (see Fig. 9.15). They rarely have bulging eyes, long spines, or other projections that increase resistance. Instead, they are sleek and compact. They often have smooth body surfaces to help them slide through the water. Epipelagic fishes usually have small scales, or none at all, and dolphins and whales have lost nearly all their hair. Fishes produce oils and mucus that lubricate the skin to slip through the water even more easily.

breathe. They must also keep swimming to avoid sinking, since most have largely or completely lost the swim bladder.

A potential problem is that opening the mouth to breathe detracts from the streamlining of these fishes and tends to slow them down. Some tunas have specialized grooves in their tongue. The grooves help channel water through the mouth and out the gill slits to reduce water resistance.

Tunas and billfishes have adaptations to increase forward thrust as well as to reduce drag. Again, they are the envy of engineers. Their high, narrow tails with swept-back tips are almost perfectly adapted for propulsion with the least possible effort. Perhaps most important of all to these and other fast swimmers is their ability to sense and make use of eddies in the water. They can slide past eddies that would slow them down and then gain thrust by "pushing off" the eddies. The race car driver who "slipstreams" and then "slingshots" past a leading car uses much the same principles, but not nearly as well. Scientists and engineers are hoping to learn from these fishes to design more efficient propulsion systems for ships.

These swimming machines are also very efficient in maintaining a warm body temperature. A bluefin tuna in water of 7 °C (45 °F) can maintain a core temperature of over 25 °C (77 °F). This helps not only the muscles, but probably also the brain and eyes work better. Billfishes have gone one step further. They have evolved special "heaters" of modified muscle tissue that warm the eyes and brain, maintaining peak performance of these critical organs.

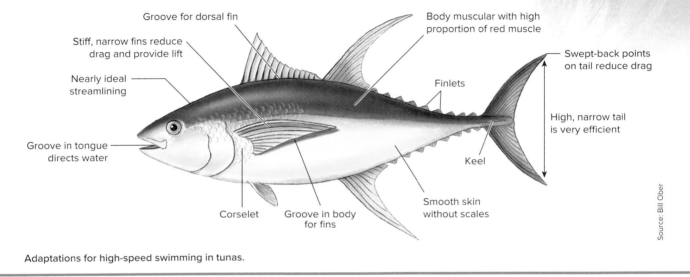

Groove for dorsal fin

Stiff, narrow fins reduce drag and provide lift

Nearly ideal streamlining

Groove in tongue directs water

Corselet

Groove in body for fins

Body muscular with high proportion of red muscle

Swept-back points on tail reduce drag

Finlets

High, narrow tail is very efficient

Keel

Smooth skin without scales

Source: Bill Ober

Adaptations for high-speed swimming in tunas.

Epipelagic nekton are also firm and muscular, another adaptation for swimming. The force produced by the muscles is delivered almost entirely by the tail. Epipelagic fishes rarely swim with their pectoral fins, which are used only for steering and lift. Most epipelagic fishes have a high, narrow tail, which in engineering terms is the most efficient shape for high-speed swimming. Tunas and sharks have independently evolved specialized long tendons, not found in other fishes, that efficiently transfer the muscles' power back to the tail.

Bony fishes in other habitats typically have fins with movable spines connected by a thin membrane, making them dexterous and flexible. By contrast, the fins of epipelagic bony fishes tend to be stiff, giving them the strength to provide lift at high speed, and maneuverability with just small movements of the fins. These stiff fins aren't much good for hovering, swimming backward, poking into holes and crevices, or other activities that require tight maneuvers at slow speed. Epipelagic fishes don't do such things.

Epipelagic nekton not only have a lot of muscle, but their muscles are strong and efficient. Fishes have two kinds of muscle, red and white—the equivalent of the white and dark meat on a turkey. Red muscle gets its color from a high concentration of **myoglobin** and can store a lot of oxygen. It is best suited for long, sustained effort. White muscle, on the other hand, provides short bursts of power. Epipelagic fishes use their red muscle for sustained cruising, and typically have more red muscle than coastal fishes, which don't do as much sustained swimming. Epipelagic fishes still have white muscle that kicks in when they need an extra burst of speed.

Typical epipelagic nekton have sharp eyesight, countershading, streamlined bodies, well-developed and efficient muscles, and high, relatively narrow tails.

Muscles work more efficiently at warm temperatures. Epipelagic sharks, tunas, and billfishes have evolved a system to conserve the heat their muscles generate to keep their internal temperature warmer than the surrounding water. These fishes can almost be considered "warm-blooded." In most fishes, heat generated in the muscles is carried by the blood to the skin and then lost to the water. "Warm-blooded" fishes have a special arrangement of the blood

Myoglobin A red muscle protein in vertebrates that stores oxygen.
• 8.3, Biology of Fishes

Source: Bill Ober

FIGURE 15.23 In "warm-blooded" epipelagic fishes, small veins and arteries are arranged in such a way that heat generated by muscular activity at the body core is carried back to the core in returning blood. The veins and arteries are packed into a complex network known as the rete mirabile, or "wonderful net."

vessels known as the **rete mirabile,** or "wonderful net." In this arrangement (Fig. 15.23), body heat carried outward in the blood is transferred to inward-flowing blood and taken back into the body core. This greatly reduces heat loss. The fish's core temperature remains higher than the surrounding water, while the skin is nearly at water temperature.

Vertical Migration The surface layers of the ocean contain by far the most food in the pelagic realm. They can be a dangerous place, though, with voracious predators zooming around and nowhere to hide. Some zooplankton spend only part of their time near the surface and retreat to safer territory when not feeding. These animals undertake **vertical migration.** During the day they live at considerable depth, usually at least 200 m (650 ft; Fig. 15.24). At these depths there isn't much light, so the zooplankton are relatively safe from predators that use vision. At night, the zooplankton swim up to the surface layers to feed on phytoplankton and other zooplankton. Experiments in deep tanks have shown that zooplankton vertically migrate only if predatory fish are in the tank; they stop migrating when the predators are removed.

Vertically migrating zooplankton stay below the photic zone during the day. At night they migrate to the surface to feed.

These daily movements require a lot of energy. For an organism that is 2 mm long, a 200-m (220-yd) migration is the rough equivalent of a 200-km (120-mi) swim for a human! That is a long way to go to avoid predators when many other zooplankton

survive predation without migrating. Various explanations for vertical migrations in addition to escaping predation have been proposed. Zooplankton may be able to slow their metabolism and conserve energy by spending part of their time in the deep water, which is cold and reduces their body temperature. This is somewhat like sleep or hibernation. It has also been suggested that zooplankton migrate to avoid toxins produced by some phytoplankton. The phytoplankton produce more toxins during the day, when they are actively photosynthesizing.

Many species of nekton, mainly fishes and some large shrimps, also make vertical migrations. These animals generally migrate to much greater depths than zooplankton (see "Adaptations of Midwater Animals," in 16.1).

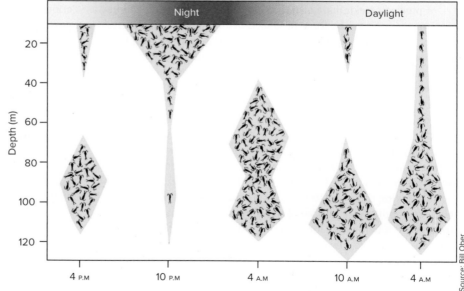

Source: Bill Ober

FIGURE 15.24 The depth distribution at different times of day of a vertically migrating copepod.

15.3 EPIPELAGIC FOOD WEBS

Epipelagic food webs are of great interest, especially because epipelagic fisheries provide food and employment to millions (see "Food from the Sea," in 17.1). Species that are caught commercially can be understood and managed only if we understand the rest of the food web on which they depend.

Trophic Levels and Energy Flow

The trophic structure of the epipelagic is extremely complex. The feeding habits of most epipelagic species are known poorly, if at all. It's hard to describe the trophic structure of a community if you don't even know what many of the animals eat!

Another difficulty in understanding epipelagic food webs is that most of the animals eat a variety of prey, often from different trophic levels. Zooplankton such as copepods often eat both phytoplankton and zooplankton; thus, they function as both herbivores and carnivores. Nekton, too, consume prey at different levels on the

food web. A tuna, for example, can act as a secondary consumer when it eats krill, as a third-level consumer when it eats a sardine that ate zooplankton, and as a fourth-level consumer when it eats a mackerel that ate a flying fish that ate zooplankton. This makes it difficult to assign many animals to a particular trophic level.

Yet another complication is that most epipelagic animals consume different prey at different times in their lives. Most eat different food as larvae than they eat as adults, and even the larvae often switch from phytoplankton to zooplankton. Even after they leave the larval stage, many fishes eat different prey as they grow larger (Fig. 15.25).

The basic flow of energy in the epipelagic can be depicted as phytoplankton → zooplankton → small nekton → large nekton → top predators. The top predators, of course, are also nekton. This scheme is greatly simplified, and each level contains a mini-web. Within the zooplankton, for example, there are herbivores and several levels of carnivores, forming a food web among themselves. There is also an important side branch called the microbial loop, which is described in the next section.

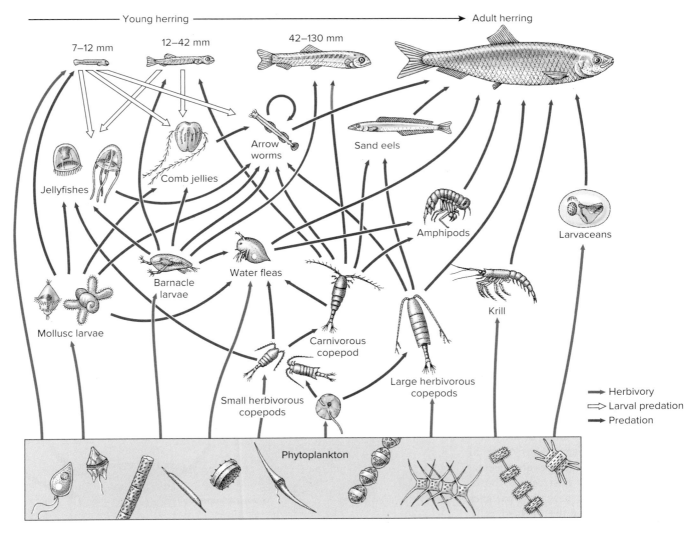

FIGURE 15.25 The North Sea herring (*Clupea harengus*) eats different foods at different stages of its life. Its larval stages are eaten by predators that do not feed on adult herring (open arrows). Many, if not most, epipelagic animals have similarly complex feeding relationships. Illustrations of food webs are usually greatly simplified and gloss over such complexities. For example, how would this partial food web fit into the scheme shown in Figure 15.4?

Source: Bill Ober

Epipelagic food chains usually have many steps and are generally longer than in other ecosystems. The number of steps varies: Tropical food webs tend to have more levels than those in colder waters. Even in cold waters there can be five or six steps between the primary producers in the phytoplankton and a top predator. There are exceptions, of course. The diatoms-to-krill-to-whales chain (see Fig. 10.13), for example, is among the shortest of food chains.

The epipelagic is an exception to the rule of thumb that only about 10% of the energy contained in one trophic level is passed on to the next (see "Trophic Structure," in 10.3). Epipelagic herbivores convert more than 20%, on average, of the energy derived from phytoplankton into growth. Epipelagic carnivores, too, are more than 10% efficient, though not as efficient as the herbivores.

Even with their high efficiency, the length of epipelagic food webs means that most of the energy fixed by phytoplankton is lost before it reaches the top carnivores. After all, even an efficiency of 20% means that 80% of the energy is lost in just one step. Large animals that feed directly on plankton have an advantage in that they have more food available than do predators that eat other high-level carnivores. By feeding directly at low trophic levels, they eliminate many intermediate steps. It is no accident that the largest epipelagic nekton, baleen whales and whale sharks, and the most abundant epipelagic fishes, like anchovies and herrings, eat plankton.

We may not think of DOM as food in the ordinary sense, but it contains a lot of energy. Calorie counters who like sugar in their coffee are familiar with this fact. Very few animals, however, are able to use DOM as an energy source. Though some phytoplankton can use it, it was once thought that the huge pool of energy in DOM went largely unused.

The Microbial Loop

The DOM in the ocean isn't just sitting there, but is the basis of a major energy pathway called the **microbial loop** (Fig. 15.26). The DOM is not lost to the food web, but is used by **heterotrophic** bacteria and archaea. The most abundant plankton in the epipelagic are a group of heterotrophic bacteria collectively known as **SAR11.** SAR11 bacteria were first discovered by genomics: Marine biologists found their DNA without ever observing the cells. Eventually some cells were collected and biologists learned how to culture them—these have been named *Pelagibacter*, but there are many other strains of SAR11, sometimes referred to as *Pelagibacterales*, that haven't yet been collected or cultured. Many other microbes in addition to SAR11 process DOM through the microbial loop.

The microbial loop heterotrophs are so small that most animals can't eat them, but tiny protozoans in the nanoplankton can.

Epipelagic food chains tend to be long and complex. The transfer of energy between trophic levels is more efficient than in many other ecosystems, but because there are often many levels, not much of the energy fixed in primary production reaches the top of the food chain.

Most of the primary production in the epipelagic was once thought to flow through the simplified food chain of phytoplankton → zooplankton → nekton. "Phytoplankton" and "zooplankton" referred to the relatively large net plankton. The discovery of vast numbers of picoplankton and nanoplankton in the ocean greatly changed our understanding of epipelagic food webs.

The ocean contains huge amounts of **dissolved organic matter (DOM),** organic material that exists not as particles but in dissolved form. Some of the DOM simply leaks out of cells. Zooplankton spill a lot of DOM when they eat and excrete it as waste. Viruses (see 5.1), however, account for most of the DOM released into the epipelagic. They occur in vast numbers, and most microbes are infected. **Lytic viruses** cause their host cells to burst, releasing not only many new virus particles but also the contents of the infected cells. Phytoplankton of all sizes also release large amounts of DOM—as much as half the organic matter they produce. Every other component of the ecosystem also releases DOM, but in much smaller amounts.

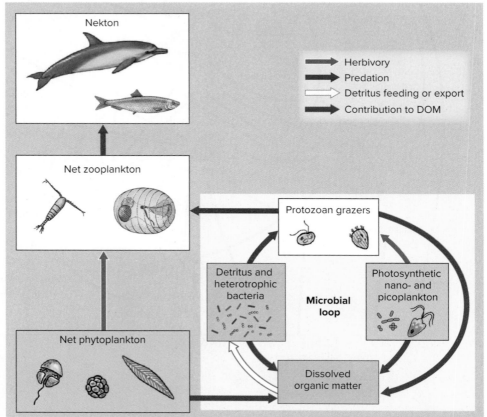

FIGURE 15.26 A modern view of epipelagic food webs (compare with the food web in Fig. 15.4). The left side shows the flow of energy from the net phytoplankton to the nekton. This part of epipelagic food webs has been known for decades. The right side of the diagram shows the more recently discovered microbial loop. Much of the flow from organisms into dissolved organic matter (blue arrows) is caused by viruses.

Source: Bill Ober

The energy from DOM is finally passed up the rest of the food chain when net zooplankton eat the protozoans.

> The "microbial loop," in simplified form, refers to the flow of energy through the series phytoplankton → DOM → bacteria/archaea → protozoans → zooplankton. Without the microbial loop, the energy in DOM would largely go unused. As much as half the primary production in the epipelagic is channeled through the microbial loop.

The microbial loop channels not only DOM but also the energy in living pico- and nanoplankton up the food chain. Photosynthetic cyanobacteria like *Prochlorococcus* and *Synechococcus* are consumed directly by protozoan grazers that are able to eat such small cells. Biologists have discovered that the cyanobacteria live in close association, perhaps even symbiosis, with heterotrophic bacteria, so that the photosynthetic production is transferred to the heterotrophic bacteria before moving up the food chain through the microbial loop.

Detritus—particulate rather than dissolved organic matter—is also important in the epipelagic, as in other marine food webs. Two important sources of detritus have already been mentioned: fecal pellets and abandoned larvacean houses. Larvacean houses and other accumulations of mucus can be very abundant and support rich populations of bacteria. They are often called **marine snow** because underwater they look like snowflakes.

Many zooplankton and fishes eat marine snow. Much of the detritus, however, sinks out of the epipelagic zone to deeper water before epipelagic organisms can get to it. As previously noted, the epipelagic does not get much detritus from other systems.

Patterns of Production

Epipelagic food webs are complex, but they all share one simple feature: Primary production by phytoplankton, be they pico-, nano-, or net plankton, is the base. All other organisms, from the smallest zooplankton to the largest predators, depend on this primary production. Some parts of the epipelagic rank among the most productive ecosystems on Earth (see Table 10.1). There are also large areas that are among the least productive, the "deserts" of the ocean. The abundance of animals, from zooplankton to whales, generally follows the pattern of primary production (Fig. 15.27). It is therefore essential to understand the factors that control primary production by phytoplankton.

Phytoplankton need two main things to perform photosynthesis. They need sunlight, the ultimate source of energy for the ecosystem, and they need a supply of essential nutrients. Without sunlight and nutrients, phytoplankton cannot grow and produce the food that fuels the food web.

Light Limitation The epipelagic is the sunlit layer of the ocean, but there is not always enough light for photosynthesis. In other words, primary production can be **light-limited.** There is no light at night, of course, so phytoplankton must get enough light during the day to grow. At high latitudes, phytoplankton become light-limited during winter, when the days are short and the sunlight weak. In winter, phytoplankton at these latitudes store less energy in photosynthesis than they burn up in respiration. In tropical and subtropical waters, on the other hand, there is enough light to support photosynthesis throughout the year, at least at the surface.

The total primary production in the water column depends not only on the intensity of light at the surface but also on how deep the light penetrates. If only a thin layer at the surface is sufficiently well lit for photosynthesis, there will not be as much production as if the photic zone is deep. Photic zone depth varies with the season, being deepest in summer. It also depends on the weather. On cloudy days, light does not penetrate as deep as on bright, sunny days. Especially important is the amount of sediment and other material in the water. Light penetrates deeper in clear than in cloudy water, so the photic zone is deeper. The phytoplankton themselves affect photic zone depth. Because they absorb light for photosynthesis, the phytoplankton reduce the light available to phytoplankton below. This phenomenon, known as **self-shading,** is especially important in highly productive waters, which are rather murky because they contain so much plankton. Conversely, the barren waters of the **central gyres,** in the middle of the ocean basins (see Fig. 3.20), are incredibly clear.

Nutrients Nutrients, especially nitrogen, iron, and phosphorus, play a major part in controlling primary production. Even with plenty of light, producers cannot perform photosynthesis if there are not enough nutrients, that is, if primary production becomes **nutrient-limited.** Over much of the ocean the nutrient in shortest supply, that is, the **limiting nutrient,** is nitrogen. **Nitrate (NO_3^{-1})** is the most important source of nitrogen. Some nitrogen enters the ocean from rivers or the atmosphere (see Fig. 10.21). A few phytoplankton supply nitrogen to the epipelagic by **fixing** free nitrogen (N_2), which is otherwise not usable by organisms. The colonial cyanobacterium *Trichodesmium* is thought to be the most important of these, especially in tropical waters, where it can provide most of the fixed nitrogen supply, but the importance of some recently discovered single-celled cyanobacteria that can fix nitrogen is not known. Some diatoms have symbiotic nitrogen-fixing cyanobacteria, which can also be significant in certain areas.

Oceanographers are increasingly concerned that human activities are adding huge amounts of nitrogen to the ocean, with currently unknown but potentially devastating consequences. It is possible that the extra nitrogen will enhance fisheries or have other beneficial impacts, but it could also lead to widespread increases in harmful algal blooms and oxygen-deficient "dead zones" or disrupt food webs (see Special Report, Overwhelming the Nitrogen Cycle).

Large areas of the open ocean, including the Southern Ocean (see Fig. 2.2) and the equatorial south Pacific, are limited by iron instead of nitrogen. This has been demonstrated in dramatic experiments where phytoplankton grow explosively after iron is added, becoming so abundant they turn the water pea-soup green. There are highly controversial proposals to attempt to reduce global warming by fertilizing these parts of the ocean with iron, hoping that the resulting huge phytoplankton blooms will remove carbon dioxide (CO_2) from the atmosphere. Experiments to date, however, indicate that this "geoengineering" would not be effective because only a small fraction of the organic matter produced sinks out of surface waters. Most of it is rapidly used and exchanged back to the atmosphere. The ecological consequences can only be guessed

Heterotrophs Organisms that cannot make their own food and must use the organic matter produced by autotrophs.
• 4.1, The Ingredients of Life

FIGURE 15.27 (*a*) The distribution of average daily primary productivity in the oceans. Note the relationship of productivity to current and upwelling systems. Because primary production is the base of the food web, this pattern is reflected at higher levels, for example, in the average distribution of zooplankton (*b*) and of sperm whales, as indicated by whale catches from 1760 to 1926. Some areas with low primary production, like the Hawaiian Islands, show high catches because of whale migration and the proximity to land bases.

at, and the risks to the planet are immense. Still, given the urgency of dealing with climate change, research continues on whether and where deliberate fertilization of the epipelagic might pull significant amounts of CO_2 out of the atmosphere.

Phosphate (PO_4^{-3}) and various other nutrients can also limit phytoplankton growth at certain times and places. The supply of silicon sometimes limits diatom growth, for example, and a shortage of "micronutrients," including vitamin B_{12}, cobalt, and nickel, that phytoplankton need in minuscule amounts may sometimes affect productivity. Biologists are also learning that sometimes things are

more complicated than having a single limiting nutrient. *Trichodesmium* needs phosphorus to fix nitrogen, for example, and when phosphorus shortage prevents its nitrogen fixation, other phytoplankton may become nitrogen-limited.

Significant amounts of nutrients are transported to the epipelagic in the atmosphere. Atmospheric nutrient transport is especially important in the open oceans far from land. Human activities are increasing this atmospheric nutrient transport through our emissions and by changes in land use that increase the amount of dust blown into the atmosphere.

Nutrient recycling is critical to the ocean's primary productivity. The cycle begins when dissolved nutrients are incorporated into living organic matter by phytoplankton. Later, when the living material dies, the nutrients are **regenerated,** or released, as bacteria decompose the material.

The dependence on recycled nutrients profoundly affects production in the epipelagic. Much of the organic material produced by phytoplankton eventually ends up as detritus: fecal pellets, dead bodies, marine snow, and other organic particles. These organic particles sink, and many sink out of the epipelagic into deeper waters before they decay. The nutrients they contain are released below the photic zone (Fig. 15.28). The net result of this process is to continually strip nutrients out of the epipelagic zone into the dark, cold waters below. The epipelagic is often depleted in nutrients, and phytoplankton growth is often nutrient-limited. Deep water, on the other hand, is nutrient-rich, but there is not enough light for photosynthesis, so the nutrients can't be used in primary production. The general nutrient profiles shown in Figure 15.29 are characteristic of most of the pelagic realm.

Because many organic particles sink out of the epipelagic before the nutrients they contain are regenerated, surface waters are nutrient-poor and phytoplankton growth is often nutrient-limited. Deep waters are nutrient-rich because of the rain of organic particles from the surface.

The phytoplankton that support epipelagic food webs, then, have a problem: At the surface there is sunlight but nutrients are often limiting, whereas in deep water there are plenty of nutrients but not enough light. Neritic phytoplankton have it somewhat easier than oceanic forms. Neritic areas are relatively shallow, so the bottom traps sinking organic particles and a lot of the regenerated nutrients are returned to the water column by mixing. Storms can mix the water column all the way to the bottom in shallower parts of the neritic zone. This is one reason the continental shelves are highly productive. Another reason is that rivers bring in fresh nutrients from land. Even so, neritic waters can have very low surface concentrations of nitrate, phosphate, and other nutrients, especially in summer when warm surface waters reduce mixing.

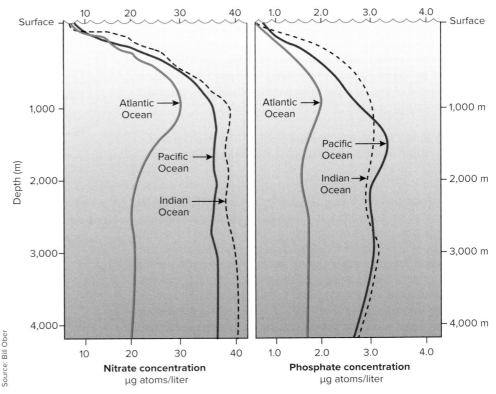

FIGURE 15.28 The amount of nutrients at different depths is controlled by photosynthesis, respiration, and the sinking of organic particles. In primary production, dissolved nutrients are removed from the water and incorporated into organic matter. Respiration, in this case mainly by bacterial decay, breaks down the organic matter and regenerates the nutrients. The uptake of nutrients can occur only at the surface, where there is light. Because organic particles sink, however, much of the regeneration occurs below the photic zone. This process strips nutrients from the surface layer and carries them into deeper water.

FIGURE 15.29 Typical profiles of nitrate and phosphate in the open ocean. Note that surface waters generally have very low levels of these nutrients.

Neritic waters are usually highly productive because the shallow bottom holds organic particles and the nutrients they contain near the photic zone and because rivers bring in additional nutrients.

For primary production to occur in oceanic areas, the nutrients contained in the deep water must somehow get to the surface. The most effective way for this to happen is for the nutrient-rich deep water itself to move to the surface. This sounds simple enough, but it occurs only at certain times and places. The ocean is usually **stratified;** that is, warm surface layers float on the denser water below (see "Thermohaline Circulation and the Great Ocean Conveyor," in 3.2). A **thermocline,** a zone of transition, lies between the warmer, less dense layer at the surface and the cooler, denser layer below. Just as energy is needed to push a cork below the surface or lift a weight up from the bottom, it takes energy to push surface water down across the thermocline into the denser water below, mixing it with the deep water, or to bring dense, nutrient-rich deep water to the surface. Much of the time this simply doesn't happen, and surface production is often nutrient-limited.

Seasonal Patterns One way that deep-water nutrients get to the surface is for the water column to mix. On the continental shelf, strong wind and waves can mix the water column all the way to the bottom. Often, however, wind and waves do not mix the water deeply enough to bring nutrients to the surface, especially in the open ocean.

If the surface water gets denser, however, it loses its tendency to float. This happens at high latitudes when winter cold and winds cool the surface water. If the surface water gets denser than the water below, **overturn** occurs (see Fig. 3.23). The thermocline breaks down, the surface water sinks, and nutrient-rich deep water is mixed up to the surface. Overturn depends on very cold conditions and is not usually widespread except in polar waters. Even in the absence of overturn, however, surface cooling can promote mixing. Since the cooler surface water becomes more dense, less energy is needed to mix it with deeper water. The mixing of deep nutrients to the surface is assisted by winter storms, which bring strong winds and large waves. Because of overturn and mixing during the winter, polar and temperate waters are highly productive (Fig. 15.27).

Oceanic waters at high latitudes are highly productive because winter overturn and mixing bring nutrient-rich deep water to the surface.

The productivity figures in Figure 15.27 and Table 10.1 refer to production over the entire year. This obscures the fact that primary production often varies during the year. In warm temperate and tropical waters such seasonal variation is relatively small. The water column remains stable throughout the year, restricting the transport of deep nutrients up into the photic zone. For this reason, most tropical waters have low but fairly constant levels of production throughout the year (Fig. 15.30a), although there are occasional bursts of production as small-scale mixing events push localized plumes of nutrient-rich water up into the photic zone.

In temperate waters the effects of the seasons are profound. Overturn and mixing during the winter bring large amounts of nutrients to the surface. The phytoplankton are light-limited in winter, however, and unable to use the nutrients in photosynthesis.

Primary production during winter months, therefore, is low at temperate latitudes (Fig. 15.30b).

When spring comes, the days get longer and the sunshine more intense. Light is no longer limiting, and the surface water contains plenty of nutrients because of overturn and mixing during the preceding winter. The availability of both light and nutrients provides ideal conditions for phytoplankton and produces a period of rapid growth called the **spring bloom** (Fig. 15.30b). In many temperate areas the spring bloom represents most of the primary production for the entire year.

As the spring bloom develops, two things occur, neither beneficial for phytoplankton growth. First, the increase in sunlight warms the surface water, making it less dense. This increases the stability of the water column, eliminating overturn and greatly reducing the mixing of nutrient-rich deep water to the surface. Second, the phytoplankton rapidly use up nutrients as they photosynthesize and grow. Thus, nutrients are removed from the water at the same time that the supply is blocked. The available nutrients in the water drop, and the phytoplankton become nutrient-limited. Nitrate is usually the nutrient that runs out first.

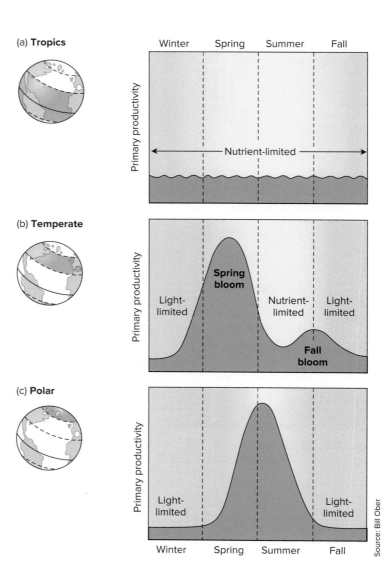

FIGURE 15.30 Generalized seasonal cycles of primary productivity (mg C/m²/d) in (_a_) tropical, (_b_) temperate, and (_c_) polar waters.

Source: Bill Ober

During most of the summer, primary production is nutrient-limited. Productivity depends on nutrient recycling and the new input of nutrients. If the water column never becomes very stable, some mixing and therefore some production takes place. If the surface water warms considerably and the water column becomes stratified, nutrient input by mixing is low and primary production falls. Temperate waters generally have low productivity during the summer months because of stratification.

Production in autumn depends largely on which comes first: the short days and weak sunlight that bring light limitation, or surface cooling and storms, which increase mixing of nutrients. If the days are cool and sunny, for example, a strong wind can mix up nutrients while the phytoplankton still have enough light to grow. If so, there will be a burst of production known as the **fall bloom** (Fig. 15.30b). If warm, mild conditions persist late into the fall the phytoplankton become light-limited before overturn and mixing begin. Even though production at temperate latitudes is light-limited during the winter and nutrient-limited during the summer, enough production takes place during blooms to give these waters a high total production over the year (Fig. 15.27).

> In temperate waters, primary production shows a seasonal cycle. During winter, production is light-limited but overturn and wind mixing bring nutrients to the surface. In spring, increased sunlight allows the phytoplankton to use the nutrients and a spring bloom occurs. During summer production is nutrient-limited because the phytoplankton use up the nutrients and stratification prevents mixing. A fall bloom occurs if stratification breaks down while there is enough light for photosynthesis.

Cold polar waters may not become stratified at all and may continue to produce at very high levels throughout the short summer when the sun shines most of the day (Fig. 15.30c). Primary production falls as the days shorten and is greatly reduced by light limitation during the long winter months. Polar waters can be extremely productive, as is true in some parts of the Southern Ocean. Production in much of the Southern Ocean, however, is limited by a shortage of iron.

The Arctic Ocean lies at such a high latitude and is so extensively covered by ice that in the past it was generally light-limited and unproductive in spite of overturn and mixing. Climate change, however, is strongly affecting the Arctic, which is warming twice as fast as the rest of the planet. The extent of summer sea ice is rapidly shrinking (see Special Report, Climate Change) and primary productivity in parts of the Arctic Ocean has already increased. The ecological consequences of these changes are not known.

Upwelling and Productivity Overturn and mixing caused by the cooling of surface waters are not the only processes that transport nutrients up into the photic zone. At certain times and places, large amounts of nutrient-rich water move up to the surface from below. This phenomenon, known as **upwelling,** is caused by **Ekman transport.**

Along some coasts, mainly on the eastern sides of the ocean basins, the prevailing winds blow parallel to the coast in a direction that causes Ekman transport to carry the surface layer offshore. At the edge of the continental shelf deeper water moves up to the surface to replace it (Fig. 15.31), typically from a depth of 50 to 300 m (165 to 1,000 ft). When this intense **coastal upwelling** comes from deep enough to tap into cold, nutrient-rich waters below the surface, it carries huge amounts of nutrients into the photic zone. Major coastal upwelling areas (Fig. 15.32) are among the most productive waters of the epipelagic (Fig. 15.27) and therefore among the richest fishing grounds (see Fig. 17.4).

On some coasts, like the Pacific coast of South America, upwelling is fairly steady and takes place over a large geographic area. On other coasts, like that of California, upwelling tends to occur as localized, short-lived events (Fig. 15.33). If the wind is strong for a few days, strong upwelling occurs, only to fade away when the wind dies and spring up somewhere else. Even on the Pacific coast of South America, upwelling is usually most intense in small, localized patches.

Coastal upwelling tends to be seasonal, occurring mainly during the time of year when winds are strong and blow in the right direction along the coast. Such seasonality is most pronounced on the coast of Somalia, in eastern Africa (Fig. 15.32). This area is

Ekman Transport The net movement of the upper layer of the water column, or *Ekman layer,* at 90° to the wind direction, to the right in the Northern Hemisphere and the left in the Southern Hemisphere. This occurs as a result of the *Coriolis effect.*

• 3.2, Ocean Circulation

Source: Bill Ober

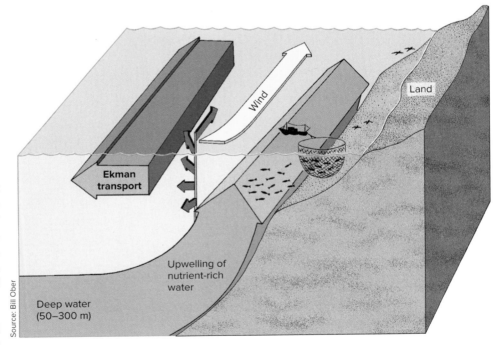

Source: Bill Ober

FIGURE 15.31 When prevailing winds blow in the right direction along the coast, Ekman transport carries surface water offshore. Deeper water rises into the photic zone to replace the surface water, carrying nutrients with it. This phenomenon is called coastal upwelling. Is the example in this figure from the Northern or Southern Hemisphere?

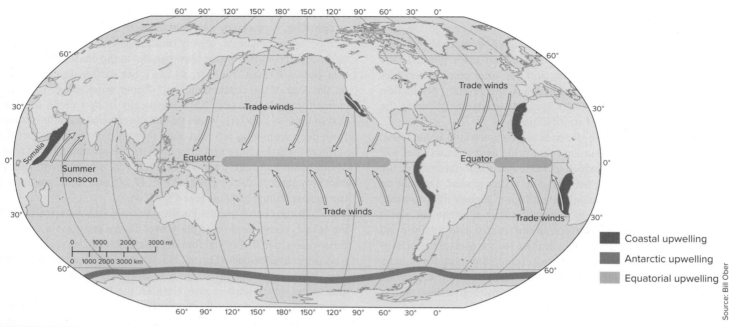

FIGURE 15.32 The major upwelling areas of the world in relation to the prevailing winds. These areas are among the most productive parts of the ocean (see Fig. 15.27). Less intense or more sporadic upwelling occurs in many other areas.

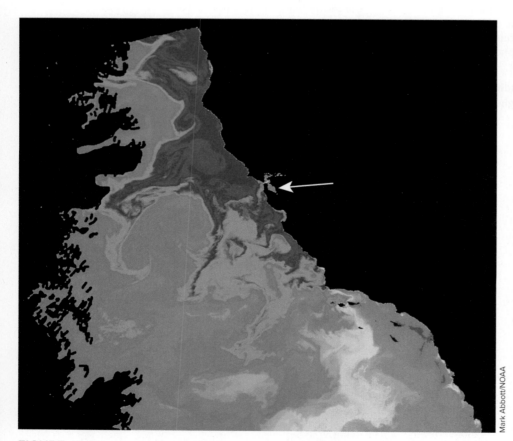

FIGURE 15.33 This satellite image shows summer upwelling along the California and southern Oregon coast. The red area in the lower right is warm surface water off Southern California. The purple water to the north is very cold deep water that has upwelled along the coast. Water farther offshore (green) is warmer. The small red patch near the center of the image (arrow) is San Francisco Bay. The black area to the left was obscured by clouds from the satellite's view and the black area on the right is land.

dominated by **monsoons,** strong winds that blow northward in summer and southward in winter. The summer monsoon causes very intense coastal upwelling, which dies when the winds change to the winter monsoon. When the upwelling stops, production falls dramatically.

Coastal winds are not the only source of upwelling. The Coriolis effect also produces **equatorial upwelling,** especially in the Pacific. Note that the direction of the Coriolis effect changes from right to left at the equator. Thus, the north equatorial currents transport surface water to the right (north), whereas the south equatorial currents transport water to the left (south; Fig. 15.34). As a result, in equatorial regions the sea surface is being pulled apart, or diverging, and deep water moves up to fill the void, typically from a depth of a few hundred meters. Equatorial upwelling is not as intense as coastal upwelling, but it still raises primary production significantly and occurs over much larger areas.

Upwelling also occurs in a ring around Antarctica as a result of complex wind and current patterns between the continent and the Antarctic Circumpolar Current (see Fig. 3.20). While coastal and equatorial upwelling typically come from depths of a few hundred meters at most, Antarctic upwelling brings water from as deep as 4,000 m (12,000 ft) to the surface. This upwelling, along with

EYE ON SCIENCE

Box 15.3 Biological Nutrient Pumps

Primary production in the epipelagic critically depends on nutrient transport into the photic zone. Oceanographers have traditionally looked at this in terms of physical processes, like upwelling, overturn, and mixing by wind and waves, that move vast amounts of cold, nutrient-rich deep water into the sunlit surface layer. Decades ago a leading oceanographer commented that animals might also pump nutrients up to the surface. He was joking, because at the time it was inconceivable that marine organisms could have any perceptible effect, but marine biologists now know it isn't a joke.

When marine animals swim, their waggling fins, pulsating bodies, or paddling appendages create turbulence. Nobody thought much about this in terms of ocean mixing until researchers calculated that the total turbulent energy that organisms could impart to mixing the ocean is comparable to wind and waves. Then, measurements showed that vertically migrating krill in a Canadian fjord increased mixing by a factor of 100. Such biological mixing might be a major contributor to primary production in the ocean after all! One krill can't do much, but there are billions of them. Larger animals like fishes and whales are not as numerous but are a lot more powerful. Unlike wind and wave mixing, this "biomixing" can occur throughout the water column, not just at the surface. Furthermore,

marine animals often congregate near the boundaries of ocean layers, where mixing is most effective in pumping nutrients up from one layer to another.

Like all scientific hypotheses, this one was tested. A study in Europe failed to detect significant biomixing by vertically migrating zooplankton. Theorists calculated that much of the turbulent energy that swimming animals generate is dissipated as heat instead of driving mixing. But in addition to generating turbulence, animals carry water along with them as they push through the water. This gives the water momentum, so it keeps moving for a while after the animal stops. Thus, in addition to stirring the water with turbulence, the animal creates a "mini-current." Experiments with swimming jellyfish confirm this. Unlike turbulence generation, this mechanism doesn't lose energy through heat dissipation, and new calculations show that the total mixing by the ocean's animals could indeed be more than that imparted by winds and waves.

Animals also pump nutrients into the epipelagic by moving not just nutrient-rich water, but nutrients themselves. Iron is critically limiting in Southern Ocean waters around Antarctica. Antarctic krill (*Euphausia superba*) have a high iron content. But the iron in their tissues isn't available to support primary production by phytoplankton, and the sinking of their iron-rich fecal pellets tends to strip iron from the epipelagic. Antarctic krill, however, have been

recently discovered to feed at depths of up to 2,000 m (6,500 ft) on iron-rich detritus and copepods, carrying the iron with them when they ascend to the surface layer. Many other epipelagic animals regularly feed at depth and return to the surface, a major biological pump of nutrients back into the epipelagic.

Antarctic baleen whales eat huge amounts of krill both at the surface and at depth. When they defecate they release iron in concentrations 10 million times that of the surrounding water. Similarly, whales and seals release more nitrogen into the Gulf of Maine than all of the inflowing rivers. Thus, large animals may have a major role in maintaining primary production—and with it fisheries, oxygen production, and other benefits—by recycling nutrients from depth back up into the epipelagic. Primary production in many parts of the epipelagic has declined over the last century or so. The drastic reduction of baleen whale and top predator populations by humans could be one reason. In fact, where decades of effort by conservationists have not achieved a complete ban on commercial whaling (see "Whales, Dolphins, and Porpoises," in 9.3), there is increasing support for a ban in recognition of the importance of whales in pumping nutrients into the epipelagic and supporting primary production.

For more information, explore the links provided in the Marine Biology Online Learning Center.

the relative lack of stratification (see "Seasonal Patterns," above), contributes greatly to the high productivity of the Southern Ocean. Antarctic production is being reduced by ocean acidification, however (see Special Report, Ocean Acidification: The Other CO_2 Problem). The Southern Ocean is particularly vulnerable to acidification because CO_2 is more soluble in the cold waters.

Upwelling brings nutrients to the surface and results in high primary production. Coastal upwelling is very intense. It occurs when winds cause the Ekman transport of surface water offshore. Equatorial upwelling is caused by the divergence of equatorial surface currents. Antarctic upwelling occurs in a ring around Antarctica and brings very deep water to the surface.

Geographic Patterns Water depth and temperature, prevailing winds, and surface currents all affect the ocean's productivity, as we have seen in the previous sections. The geographic distribution of

productivity (Fig. 15.27) reflects these factors. Coastal waters are highly productive because the shallow bottom prevents nutrients from sinking out of the photic zone and because wind and waves mix the water column. Coastal areas that experience upwelling are especially productive. Equatorial waters, too, are productive because of upwelling, but not as productive as coastal upwelling zones. Polar and cold temperate regions have high productivity because overturn and upwelling bring nutrients up into the sunlit layer.

None of the processes that bring nutrients to the surface operate in the vast central gyres. These lie in relatively warm latitudes, so the surface waters never cool enough for overturn or mixing. Far from both the coast and the equatorial currents, the central gyres never experience upwelling, either. The gyre regions are permanently limited by nutrients; with the exception of the light-limited Arctic Ocean, they have the lowest productivity in the epipelagic. In fact, the central gyres are among the least productive ecosystems on Earth (see Table 10.1).

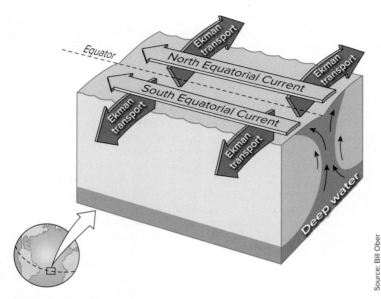

Source: Bill Ober

FIGURE 15.34 The Coriolis effect influences the equatorial currents differently on opposite sides of the equator. Surface water therefore moves away from the equator. To replace it, deep water moves up into the sunlit zone. This is called equatorial upwelling (see Fig. 15.27).

Climate change is expected to reduce the ocean's primary productivity. The warming surface waters will make the water column more stable, reducing the mixing of nutrients up to the surface. Ocean acidification will also reduce productivity. There are already signs that plankton productivity is declining, with flow-on effects on fish populations and even up to marine mammals.

The El Niño–Southern Oscillation

The interplay of winds, currents, and upwelling affects not only the ocean's primary production but also fisheries, climate, and ultimately human welfare. This is brought home most strongly when normal patterns suddenly change, as in the phenomenon known as the **El Niño–Southern Oscillation (ENSO).** ENSO, often simply called El Niño, has received widespread attention not only from marine scientists but also, because of its impact on humans, from economists, politicians, and the general public.

The term "El Niño" originally referred to a change in the surface currents along the coasts of Perú and Chile. For much of the year the winds along this coast blow from south to north, producing strong upwelling. The upwelling brings nutrients to the surface, making these waters one of the world's richest fishing grounds. Every year, usually in December, upwelling decreases, and the water gets warmer. Locals have been familiar with this event for centuries because it signals the end of the peak fishing season. Because this change in currents comes around Christmas, they called it *El Niño,* or "The Child." Every few years, however, the change is much more pronounced than usual. The surface water gets much warmer, and upwelling ceases completely. Primary production drops to almost nothing, and the fishes that normally teem in these waters disappear. Fisheries along the Perú-Chile coast are devastated, and seabirds die in huge numbers (see Box 17.1, "Of Fish and Seabirds, Fishers and Chickens").

The "Southern Oscillation" part of ENSO has also been known for a long time. Like El Niño, the Southern Oscillation was first noted because of its impact on humans. People in India depend on summer monsoon winds to bring rain for their crops. Sometimes the monsoons fail, producing famine and hardship. Beginning in 1904, a British administrator, Gilbert Walker, tried to predict when the monsoons would fail by analyzing weather records from around the world. He never achieved his goal, but did discover a major atmospheric phenomenon that he named the Southern Oscillation.

The Southern Oscillation refers to a long-distance linkage in atmospheric (or barometric) pressure. When the pressure is high over the Pacific Ocean, it tends to be low over the Indian Ocean, and vice versa (Fig. 15.35). Over a period of months or years, the air pressure swings back and forth like a giant seesaw that extends halfway around the world. The changes in atmospheric pressure bring dramatic changes in wind and rainfall, including the failure of the summer monsoon.

In the late 1950s it became apparent that El Niño and the Southern Oscillation were two sides of the same coin: Instead of being isolated phenomena in a particular region, they are part of a complex interaction of ocean and atmosphere that links the entire planet. El Niño corresponds closely to dramatic changes in the Southern Oscillation. Scientists use the term "ENSO" to signify that El Niño and the Southern Oscillation are two aspects of the same global phenomenon.

When the strongest El Niño in at least a century occurred during 1982 and 1983, it became clear that El Niño has profound global effects on weather, wildlife, and society. The 1982–83 El Niño brought extreme weather to much of the planet—storms and floods in some places, in others drought, forest fires, and heat waves. These extreme conditions focused scientific and public attention on understanding and dealing with El Niño.

In the ensuing years scientists carefully analyzed information from the 1982–83 El Niño, as well as milder El Niño events in 1986–87 and 1991–95. Based on what they learned, they developed a Pacific-wide system of oceanographic and atmospheric monitoring equipment in the hope of getting early warning of new ENSO events. The system was soon put to the test. In late 1996 there were early signs, and by early 1997 the prediction was official: Another El Niño was on its way.

The prediction turned out to be accurate, with a vengeance. The 1997–98 El Niño was one of the strongest known El Niños of all time, even stronger than in 1982–83. Its severity caught even the scientists who predicted it by surprise, and the devastating effects were felt over much of the globe (Fig. 15.36). Another very strong El Niño occurred in 2015–16, and milder events have occurred in various years before and since.

El Niño begins to develop when the atmospheric "seesaw" of the Southern Oscillation brings lower than usual atmospheric pressure in the southeastern Pacific and high pressure to the eastern Indian Ocean (Fig. 15.35). This weakens the trade winds, and therefore coastal upwelling along South America also weakens or, in strong events, stops entirely. Not only does the interrupted upwelling bring a failure in fisheries, the absence of cold water coming up from depth means that seawater near the coast is warmer than usual. Furthermore, in El Niño years the trade winds no longer push a mass of very warm surface water, the Pacific Warm Pool (see Fig. 3.10), to the far western Pacific. When the trade winds

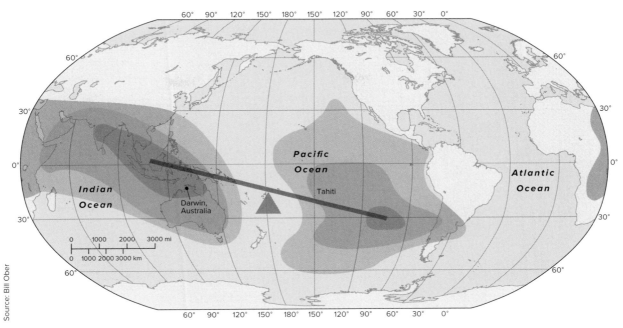

FIGURE 15.35 In the Southern Oscillation, atmospheric pressure "seesaws" between two gigantic systems half a world apart. When the pressure is unusually high in the western Pacific, it tends to be unusually low over the Indian Ocean, and vice versa. The shaded areas represent the linked zones of atmospheric pressure. The darker the blue, the more closely the atmospheric pressure is linked to pressure on the other side of the oscillation.

slack off the Warm Pool "sloshes" eastward, warming the surface near the coast of South America even more. The high surface temperatures result in increased evaporation and more moisture in the atmosphere. Thus, El Niño brings high rainfall to the coasts of South America and Southern California. In the extreme 1997–98 event the rainfall was torrential, causing widespread floods and mudslides, and hurricanes lashed the Pacific coast. Because of the weaker trade winds and associated changes in the jet stream, however, storms developing in the Caribbean and western Atlantic don't spin as fast as they otherwise would. This inhibits hurricane formation, and the Caribbean and southern United States enjoyed a mild hurricane season in 1997–98. The reduced storm activity, however, brought drought and wildfires to eastern South America, including the Amazon basin, and the input of energy to the atmosphere from the warm surface waters along the coast resulted in swarms of killer tornados in central Florida, where tornados are uncommon.

On the other side of the Pacific and into the Indian Ocean, the pattern was more or less reversed. The eastward movement of the Pacific Warm Pool means cooler sea temperatures, a dryer atmosphere, and lower rainfall for Indonesia, New Guinea, and Australia, which suffered drought and wildfires in the 1997–98 El Niño. Perversely, although the bigger picture was for relatively cool and dry conditions, decreased rainfall and winds meant that water temperatures on Australia's Great Barrier reef spiked, resulting in widespread coral bleaching (see "Climate Change and Ocean Acidification," in 14.4). The 1997–98 El Niño also had more far-reaching effects, including torrential rain and floods in East Africa and drought in southern Africa.

Worldwide, several thousand people at least were killed in floods and storms during the 1997–98 El Niño, and there were many secondary effects. Crop and livestock losses were enormous, bringing hardship to farmers, especially in poorer countries, and

in some places famine. The financial losses from agricultural failure amounted to hundreds of millions of dollars, and markets were affected widely as prices rose because of reduced supply. The fisheries crash in Perú and Chile had similar effects: Much of the catch is processed into animal feed and farmers as far away as Ireland faced higher feed prices. Fires, often lit by farmers using the opportunity to clear land, raged out of control in drought-stricken Indonesia and the Amazon basin. Thousands of square miles of rain forest were destroyed. The fires in Indonesia were so bad that much of Southeast Asia endured months of haze and air pollution, and an accompanying increase in respiratory ailments. The thick smoke even caused several plane crashes.

Disease outbreaks from water contamination sometimes followed storms and floods. Warmer temperatures led to increases in mosquito-borne diseases like malaria, encephalitis, and dengue fever. In North America, outbreaks of bubonic plague and an often fatal respiratory disease known as hantavirus are associated with severe El Niños. This is because the growth in vegetation after the high rainfall provides more food for rats and mice, which spread the diseases. There were even more unusual problems. After its floods were over, for example, Kenya suffered a plague of a kind of beetle that, when crushed, releases a poison that causes burning, itching, and blindness.

The effects of El Niño are not necessarily all bad, or at least not bad for everyone. Cyclone activity during the 1997–98 event was down in Hong Kong and the Philippines, as were hurricanes in the Caribbean. Farmers lucky enough to escape El Niño's wrath enjoyed higher prices for their crops. In Chile and the southwestern United States, heavy rains filled dams and replenished water supplies. Heavy snowfall delighted skiers and resort owners. Deserts bloomed when the rains brought spectacular displays of wildflowers. Indeed, El Niño's periodic soakings could be a vital

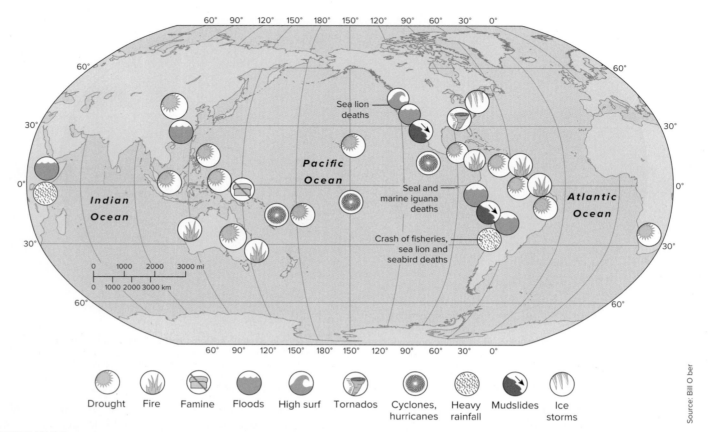

Drought Fire Famine Floods High surf Tornados Cyclones, hurricanes Heavy rainfall Mudslides Ice storms

Source: Bill O ber

FIGURE 15.36 Some of the worldwide events linked to strong El Niños. This is just a sampling; most parts of the world are affected.

part of desert ecology. El Niño brought a relatively mild winter to much of the northern United States and Europe, saving millions of dollars on heating bills. While the normal fisheries in Perú and Chile crashed, warm-water fishes like dolphin and tunas appeared in record numbers. Salmon fishers in Oregon even caught striped marlin, normally confined to the subtropics.

The effects of ENSO are harmful not so much in and of themselves as because they are extreme changes in the normal pattern. Heavy rain where it is rare can cause floods, while the lack of heavy rain in places that depend on it causes drought and famine. Indeed, scientists now realize that El Niño is not really an abnormal occurrence, but simply one extreme of a regular weather cycle. **La Niña,** the other extreme, brings weather conditions that are roughly the opposite of El Niño's. Places that experience drought during El Niño, for example, can expect wet weather during La Niña years. After a mild hurricane season during the 1997–98 El Niño, Central America and the Caribbean suffered devastating hurricanes in the La Niña that followed.

Damage estimates from the record-breaking El Niño of 1997–98 range upward of $20 billion, but it could have been much worse. Because scientists could predict El Niño the world

had advance warning and time to prepare. Many countries intensified their disaster preparedness efforts and built up food reserves. Industry and agriculture adjusted their planning. Cattle ranchers in Australia, for example, reduced their herds, cutting the losses from drought. In southern Africa farmers planted more drought-resistant crops. Countries around the world continue to monitor El Niño development and plan accordingly. Though another very strong event occurred in 2015–16, damage was considerably reduced because there was time to prepare. There were still major impacts from fires, floods, and other extreme weather, however. Every El Niño is different, and in a given place the exact effects are hard to predict. Climate change is expected to increase the intensity and frequency of strong ENSO events.

Since the discovery of ENSO, a number of other global-scale climate cycles have been identified. The North Pacific Decadal Oscillation, for example, is superimposed on ENSO, but operates on a longer cycle of around 10 years, as its name suggests. The North Atlantic Oscillation profoundly influence weather patterns bordering the Atlantic Ocean. These and other cycles all influence each other in complex ways that are not understood and are likely to change significantly in an era of global climate change.

Interactive Exploration

McGraw-Hill Connect® is a great place to check your understanding of chapter material. Visit **www.mcgrawhillconnect.com** for access to interactive chapter summaries, chapter quizzing, and more! Further enhance your knowledge with videoclips and weblinks to chapter-related material.

Critical Thinking

1. Plankton are unable to swim effectively and drift about at the mercy of the currents. You might think that the currents would scatter planktonic organisms throughout the oceans, but many species are restricted to particular regions. What mechanisms might allow a species to maintain its characteristic distribution?

2. Spiny species of diatoms are found in both warm subtropical waters and colder areas. Because warm water is less dense than cold water, would you predict any differences between the spines of warm-water and cold-water individuals? Why?

For Further Reading

Some of the recommended reading may be available online. Look for live links on the *Marine Biology* Online Learning Center.

General Interest

Almada, A. A., 2016. Journey into the ocean's macrobiomes. *Oceanus,* vol. 51, no. 2, winter, pp. 68–71. Revelations about the interactions between bacteria and zooplankton.

Brower, K., 2014. Quicksilver. *National Geographic,* vol. 225, no. 3, March, pp. 66–87. The Atlantic bluefin tuna, which is being over-fished, is a truly magnificent swimming machine.

Chisolm, S. W., 2017. Quick Guide: *Prochlorococcus. Current Biology,* vol. 27, no. 11, 5 June, pp. R431–R510. All your questions answered about one of the ocean's most important phytoplankton groups.

Courage, K. H., 2022. Stealth migrations. *Scientific American,* vol. 327, no. 2, August, pp. 48–53. Mass vertical migrations by tiny plankton profoundly affect the whole planet.

Fischetti, M., 2022. Dynamic seas. How the ocean organizes itself. *Scientific American,* vol. 327, no. 2, August, pp. 65–67. The traditional layered representation of the ocean is broadly true, but the real ocean is much more complicated.

Fishman, J., 2016. Swimmers under pressure. *Scientific American,* vol. 314, no. 5, May, pp. 58–59. Pound for pound, jellyfish are the most efficient swimmers in the ocean.

Hallaegraf, G. M., K. Aligizaki, Z. Azmil, et al., 2021. Global HAB Status Report. A Scientific Summary for Policy Makers. IOC Information Document 1399, UNESCO, Paris. A review of global data on harmful algal blooms.

Ham, Y.-G., 2018. El Niño events set to intensify. *Nature,* vol. 564, no. 7735, pp. 192–193. Models predict that climate change will cause strong El Niños.

Hamilton, G., 2016. The secret lives of jellyfish. *Nature,* vol. 531, no. 7595, 24 March, pp. 432–435. Once thought of as dead ends in the food web, and a downright nuisance, jellyfish are eaten by seabirds, tunas, and other marine animals, and may have an important role in nutrient cycling.

Nicol, S., 2018. Oceans of krill. *Natural History,* vol. 126, no. 4, April, pp. 28–33. The vast populations of krill in the Southern Ocean are at a crossroads.

Ohnemus, D., 2016. Uncovering the ocean's biological pump. *Oceanus,* vol. 51, no. 2, winter, pp. 52–55. A former "science kid" studies the biological pump that moves carbon from the epipelagic to the deep sea.

Sardet, C., 2015. *Plankton. Wonders of the drifting world.* A detailed exploration of ocean plankton and their role in the oceans, with stunning photos.

Stelling, T., 2016. March of the jellies. *New Scientist,* vol. 231, no. 3082, 16 July, pp. 26–29. Despite concerns that jellyfish (sea jellies) are taking over the oceans, they may have important ecological roles.

Tara Oceans studies plankton at a planetary scale. *Science,* vol. 348, no. 6237, 22 May 2015, pp. 873–875. A special section describes a major oceanographic expedition to study plankton, with abstracts of resulting research articles.

In Depth

Anderson, D. M., E. Fensin, C. J. Gobler, et al., 2021. Marine harmful algal blooms (HABs) in the United States: History, current status, and future trends. *Harmful Algae,* vol. 102, p. 101975.

Behrenfeld, M. J. and E. S. Boss, 2014. Resurrecting the ecological underpinnings of ocean plankton blooms. *Annual Review of Marine Science,* vol. 6, pp. 167–194.

Brady, P. C., A. A. Gilerson, G. W. Kattawar, *et al.,* 2015. Open-ocean fish reveal an omnidirectional solution to camouflage in polarized environments. *Science,* vol. 350, pp. 965–969.

Chust, G., M. Vogt, F. Benedetti, et al., 2017. Mare incognitum: A glimpse into future plankton diversity and ecology research. *Frontiers in Marine Science,* doi.org/10.3389/fmars.2017.00068.

Dam, H. G., 2013. Evolutionary adaptation of marine zooplankton to global change. *Annual Review of Marine Science,* vol. 5, pp. 349–370.

Giovannoni, S. J., 2017. SAR11 bacteria: The most abundant plankton in the oceans. *Annual Review of Marine Science,* vol. 9, pp. 231–255.

Jickells, T. and C. M. Moore, 2015. The importance of atmospheric deposition for ocean productivity. *Annual Review of Ecology, Evolution, and Systematics,* vol. 46, pp. 481–501.

Johnson, Z. I. and A. C. Martiny, 2015. Techniques for quantifying phytoplankton biodiversity. *Annual Review of Marine Science,* vol. 7, pp. 299–324.

Johnsen, S., 2014. Hide and seek in the open sea: Pelagic camouflage and visual countermeasures. *Annual Review of Marine Science,* vol. 6, pp. 369–392.

Kunze, E., 2019. Biologically generated mixing in the ocean. *Annual Review of Marine Science,* vol.11, pp. 215–226.

Murphy, G. E., T. N. Romanuk, and B. Worm, 2020. Cascading effects of climate change on plankton community structure. *Ecology and Evolution,* vol. 10, pp. 2170–2181.

Steinberg, D. K. and M. R. Landry, 2017. Zooplankton and the ocean carbon cycle. *Annual Review of Marine Science,* vol. 9, pp. 413–444.

Tiltade, P. R. and E. I. Olalekan, 2015. The importance of marine genomics to life. *Journal of Ocean Research,* vol. 3, no. 1, pp. 1–13.

Westwood, K. J., P. G. Thomson, R. L. van den Enden, L. E. Maher, S. W. Wright, and A. T. Davidson, 2018. Ocean acidification impacts primary and bacterial production in Antarctic coastal waters during austral summer. *Journal of Experimental Marine Biology and Ecology,* vol. 498, pp. 46–60.

Williams, P. J. and H. W. Ducklow, 2019. The microbial loop concept: A history, 1930–1974. *Journal of Marine Research,* vol. 77, supplement 1, pp. 23–81. The history of a concept that revolutionized our understanding of epipelagic food webs.

Yebra, L., T. Kobari, A. R. Sastri, F. Gusmão, and S. Hernández-León, 2017. Advances in biochemical indices of zooplankton production. *Advances in Marine Biology,* vol. 76, pp. 157–240.

16

CHAPTER

The Ocean Depths

Source: Bill Ober

Bathyal — Mesopelagic ⎤
Abyssal — Bathypelagic ⎬ Deep sea
Hadal — Abyssopelagic ⎦

NOAA Office of Ocean Exploration and Research

The deep-sea gorgonian coral *Iridigorgia*, with unidentified crustaceans living on the branches.

"Inner space" it's been called. Dark, cold, and inhabited by bizarre, fearsome-looking creatures, it *is* reminiscent of the outer space of science-fiction movies. As in outer space, humans can venture into this mysterious realm only in elaborate, specially designed craft. Even then there is an element of risk. But "inner space" is here on Earth: the ocean waters below the sunlit surface layer.

The ocean depths include a number of distinct habitats. Immediately below the epipelagic lies the **mesopelagic,** or "middle pelagic," **zone** (Fig. 16.1). The epipelagic is roughly equivalent to the **photic zone,** the surface layer down to 150 to 200 m (500 to 650 ft) where there is enough light to support primary production by photosynthesis. In the mesopelagic there is still some dim light, but not enough for photosynthesis. It has been called the "twilight zone."

Below the mesopelagic there is no sunlight at all. This inky darkness is the world of the **deep sea.** The term "deep sea" is sometimes used to include the mesopelagic zone, but in this text we use it only for the perpetually dark waters below the mesopelagic.

The waters below the epipelagic can be divided into the mesopelagic zone, where there is some light but not enough for primary production, and the deep sea, where there is no sunlight at all.

The deep sea is by far the least-known part of the ocean. In some ways we know more about other planets than about our own deep sea. Breakthroughs in technology and major research programs

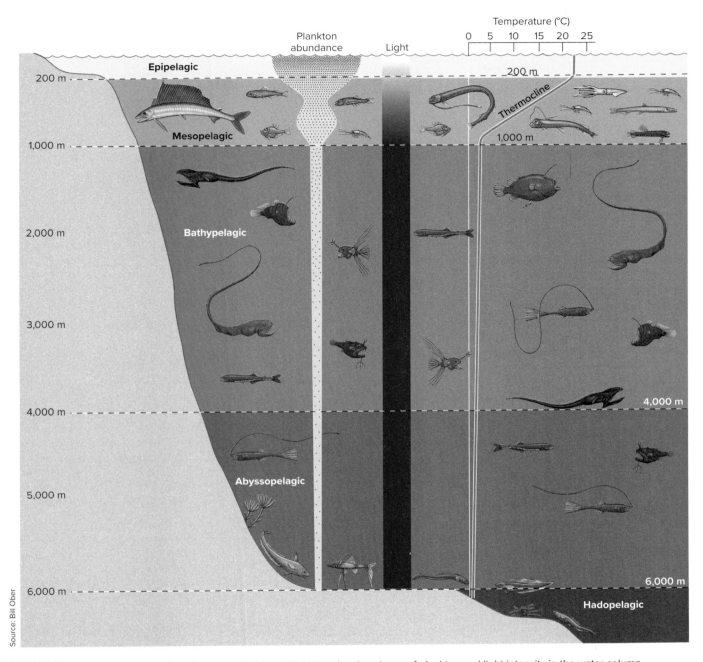

FIGURE 16.1 Life in the mesopelagic and deep sea is closely linked to the abundance of plankton and light intensity in the water column.

like the Census of Marine Life (see "The Census of Marine Life", in 1.1) have greatly improved our knowledge of the deep sea, but one of the main things we've learned is how much we still don't know.

Several different habitats are discussed in this chapter; each supports a distinct community of organisms. These communities share one important feature: the lack of **primary production** by **photosynthesis.** Without primary production to support the food web, most organisms below the photic zone depend on organic material produced in the surface layers. Some of this surface

production sinks into the dark waters below. Without a steady supply of food from above, there could be little life below the sunlit layer of the sea. Exceptions to this are discussed in the section "Hot Springs, Cold Seeps, and Dead Bodies" (see below).

Primary Production The conversion of carbon dioxide into organic matter by *autotrophs,* that is, the production of food.
Photosynthesis
$CO_2 + H_2O + \text{sun energy} \rightarrow \text{organic matter} + O_2$
$\phantom{CO_2 + H_2O + \text{sun energy} \rightarrow \text{organic matter}}$ (glucose)

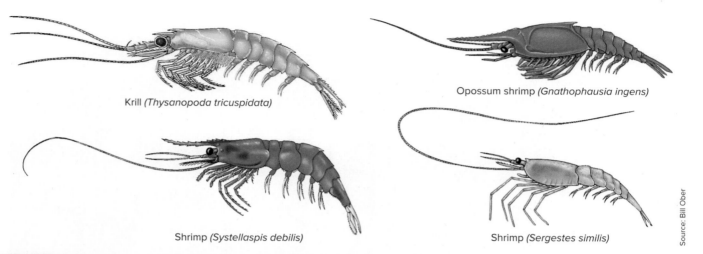

Krill *(Thysanopoda tricuspidata)*

Opossum shrimp *(Gnathophausia ingens)*

Shrimp *(Systellaspis debilis)*

Shrimp *(Sergestes similis)*

Source: Bill Ober

FIGURE 16.2 Some crustaceans that inhabit the mesopelagic zone include krill, opossum (lophogastrid) shrimps, and true (decapod) shrimps like *Systellaspis debilis* and *Sergestes similis*.

Because of the dependence on surface production for food, life is much less abundant below the photic zone than in the sunlit surface layer. Most food particles get eaten before they sink into deeper water. With food in short supply, pelagic organisms become more and more scarce at greater depths. There are typically 5 to 10 times fewer organisms at 500 m (1,600 ft), for example, than there are at the surface, and perhaps 10 times fewer again at 4,000 m (13,000 ft).

Deep-water organisms depend on the surface not only for food, but also for oxygen (O_2). If the ocean were stagnant, the oxygen below the surface would be quickly used up by **respiration** and animal life would be impossible. Fortunately, however, **thermohaline circulation** and the **great ocean conveyor** constantly replenish the supply of oxygen to the deep sea. Oxygen still becomes depleted in some places (see "The Oxygen Minimum Zone," below), but by and large the ocean depths have enough oxygen for respiration.

16.1 THE TWILIGHT WORLD

The mesopelagic is a world of twilight. In the upper part of the mesopelagic the dim light during the day is enough to see by, but not enough to support phytoplankton growth. The sea gets darker with depth and, typically at a depth of about 1,000 m (3,300 ft), there is no light at all. The absence of light marks the bottom of the mesopelagic zone, which thus stretches from the bottom of the epipelagic, around 200 m (660 ft) deep, to about 1,000 m deep.

The mesopelagic zone extends from about 200 m to about 1,000 m deep.

The temperature at a given depth in the mesopelagic generally varies much less than in the epipelagic. The mesopelagic, however, is the zone where the **main thermocline** occurs (Fig. 16.1), so organisms that move up and down in the water column encounter large changes in temperature. Mesopelagic organisms that stay at about the same depth experience more constant temperatures.

The Animals of the Mesopelagic

Though phytoplankton and other photosynthetic organisms cannot grow in the dim light, the mesopelagic supports a rich and varied community of animals, which are often called **midwater** animals.

Zooplankton The major groups of animals in the mesopelagic zooplankton are much the same as those in the epipelagic (see "The Zooplankton," in 15.1), though the particular species are different. **Krill** and **copepods** are dominant, as they are in surface waters. Several kinds of shrimps (Fig. 16.2) are relatively more common in the mesopelagic than in the epipelagic. Krill and most mesopelagic shrimps have a common adaptation of midwater animals: **photophores**, or **light organs**, which are specialized structures that produce "living light," or **bioluminescence** (see "Bioluminescence," below).

A group of crustaceans known as **ostracods** can be very abundant in the mesopelagic. Ostracods have a characteristic shell, or **carapace**, that makes them look like tiny clams with legs (Fig. 16.3). They are crustaceans, however, and unrelated to clams. Like copepods, most ostracods are small, usually only a few millimeters (1/8 in) long. One (*Gigantocypris*), however, can reach 1 cm (1/2 in). *Gigantocypris* is thought to have the most sensitive vision of all midwater animals. Amphipods and other crustaceans are also part of the midwater plankton.

Arrow worms, or **chaetognaths,** are important midwater predators. At times they are among the most abundant midwater zooplankton, especially in the upper parts of the mesopelagic.

Respiration
Organic matter + O_2 → CO_2 + H_2O + energy
 (glucose)

• 4.1, The Ingredients of Life

Thermohaline Circulation Ocean circulation that is driven by differences in water density, due to variations in water temperature and salinity, rather than by the wind or tides.
Great Ocean Conveyor A global circulation pattern in which water cycles throughout the ocean basins.

• 3.2, Ocean Circulation; Fig. 3.25

Box 16.1 The Chambered Nautilus

Nearly all cephalopods—the squids, octopuses, and cuttlefishes—have at most only vestiges of the hard shell that characterizes most other molluscs. Only the chambered nautiluses (*Nautilus, Allonautilus, Eutephoceras*), the last living relatives of a group of animals that once ruled the seas, retain the large, heavy shell of their ancestors.

Most early animals in the sea lived on the bottom, crawling and scratching for survival. Around 500 million years ago a group of molluscs evolved a new trick: the ability to partially fill their shells with gas. Buoyed by the gas, these ancient ancestors of modern nautiluses, called nautiloids, could float up off the bottom, away from predators. They soon evolved the ability to move by squirting out water—probably the first form of jet propulsion.

These innovations were immensely successful. For 200 million years nautiloids and their descendants, especially a group with coiled shells called the ammonites, dominated the ocean. They had the water column more or less to themselves and could drop onto prey from above.

Then fishes, which had been around for some time, evolved a swim bladder. They could maintain neutral buoyancy and compete with the nautiloids. More importantly, they could now swim faster and more efficiently than the nautiloids, with their cumbersome shells. Out-competed by fishes, most nautiloids went extinct. One group of cephalopods, the squids, became more fish-like. They abandoned the shell and became streamlined, active swimmers. Of all the heavy-shelled cephalopods, only the nautiluses remain.

Nautilus lives in a coiled shell partitioned into a series of chambers. The chambers are walled off one by one as the animal grows. The animal lives only in the last chamber. The others are filled with gas and provide buoyancy, without which the heavy shell would sink the animal to the bottom. When a chamber is first partitioned it is filled with seawater. Rather than pumping gas in, *Nautilus* removes ions from the water in the chamber. This makes the water more dilute than the animal's blood, so the water flows into the blood by osmosis and gas diffuses into the chamber to replace it. After that, the chamber is more or less sealed and doesn't need repeated filling and emptying like a fish's swim bladder. This allows *Nautilus* to move rapidly up and down in the water column.

Nautilus is found near coral reefs but is not really a coral reef animal because it generally lives deeper than corals, typically from 100 to 400 m (330 to 1,300 ft). Occasionally it ventures into shallow water. The upper limit of its normal depth range is set by temperature; water temperatures above 25 °C (77 °F) are lethal, and those below 20 °C (68 °F) are preferred. If the water is cool enough, *Nautilus* can live at the surface, and specimens can be maintained in aquaria. The lower depth limit is set by pressure. The shell chambers are sealed, so gas cannot be pumped in to counteract the pressure at great depth. Instead, the animal relies on the strength of its shell, like a submarine relies on its hull. When the pressure gets too great, at about 750 m (2,500 ft), the shell is crushed. Water begins to leak into the chambers at shallower depths of about 350 m (1,150 ft).

Nautilus appears to be primarily a scavenger, locating animal remains and molted lobster shells by smell. Its neutral buoyancy reduces its energy expenditure as it moves up and down the water column looking for scent trails. When it senses food, the animal swims to it by jet propulsion, squirting water out of a muscular funnel. It can also prey on live crustaceans. When not feeding, it spends most of its time "asleep" in the cool, deep water, conserving energy. A single meal can last a *Nautilus* at least two months!

Interestingly, *Nautilus* tolerates conditions of almost zero oxygen. It can use oxygen stored in the chambers of its shell, a trick it evolved long before humans invented the scuba tank. The benefits of this ability are not known, since the waters where *Nautilus* lives normally have plenty of oxygen.

Another puzzle is that the vast majority of *Nautilus* caught in traps are males. Maybe females are hard to catch or in short supply.

A chambered nautilus (*Nautilus belauensis*).

Longitudinal section of a shell of *Nautilus pompilius* showing the gas chambers.

Eighteen species of *Nautilus* and its relatives are currently recognized. Only eight species were recognized just a few years ago. These were considered "living fossils," the last remnants of an ancient group. But studies indicate there are more species than thought and that they undergo regular episodes of dispersal and evolution into new species. Instead of being a few forlorn vestiges hanging on in the face of extinction, the group is actually going through a burst of evolutionary radiation. The chambered nautilus still holds plenty of secrets.

Main Thermocline The layer between about 200 and 1,000 m (650 and 3,300 ft) where the temperature drops rapidly as depth increases. This is a transition zone between the warm surface layers and the cold deep water.
• 3.2, Ocean Circulation; Figure 3.22

Krill Planktonic, shrimp-like crustaceans.
• 7.6, Arthropods: The Armored Achievers

Copepods Tiny crustaceans that are often planktonic.
• 15.1, The Organisms of the Epipelagic

Arrow Worms or **Chaetognaths** Small, worm-like predators with fins along the body and spines on the head.
• 7.4, Bilaterally Symmetrical Worms

Jellyfishes, siphonophores, comb jellies, larvaceans, and pteropods are also common. Most of the other major groups that are part of the epipelagic zooplankton are also represented in the mesopelagic.

Cephalopods, especially **squids** (Fig. 16.4), are also prominent members of the midwater community. Some squids swim weakly and are planktonic, while strong-swimming squids are part of the nekton. Mesopelagic squids usually have photophores, typically arranged in a species-specific pattern. The vampire squid (*Vampyroteuthis;* Fig. 16.5) also has photophores. It looks something like an octopus, but is neither a squid nor an octopus. In most cephalopods, females produce one batch of eggs and then die, but female vampire squid can produce eggs over at least 20 and possibly as many as 100 reproductive cycles.

There are also a few species of true octopuses in the mesopelagic. Bioluminescence is not as common in mesopelagic octopuses as in squids, but some species do have photophores. One (*Stauroteuthis*) has light-emitting suckers. Like the vampire squid, mesopelagic octopuses have evolved membranes that connect their tentacles like the web on a duck's feet. This may help them float like a parachute in the water or envelop prey.

Midwater Fishes Nearly all mesopelagic fishes are small, typically 2 to 10 cm (1 to 4 in) long, although a few species are larger. Bristlemouths and lanternfishes (Fig. 16.6) are the most abundant fishes in the mesopelagic, and can account for 90% or more of the fishes collected by midwater trawls (Fig. 16.7). Bristlemouths are the most common of all. One species (*Cyclothone signata*) is the most abundant fish on Earth, surprising and impressive when you consider the huge schools of fishes like sardines and herrings in the epipelagic. Bristlemouths are named for their many sharp teeth. They have rows of photophores on their underside, or ventral surface.

Lanternfishes get their name from the photophores adorning their heads and bodies. Like squids, each species typically has a distinctive photophore pattern. Lanternfishes have blunt heads, relatively large mouths, and large eyes, probably an adaptation to help them see in the dim light. They are very general in their food habits, eating just about anything they can get down.

FIGURE 16.3 A mesopelagic ostracod (*Gigantocypris*). This one is about 1 cm (0.5 in) long. Most ostracods are much smaller.

The most common mesopelagic, or midwater, organisms are krill, copepods, shrimps, and small fishes like bristlemouths and lanternfishes.

Bristlemouths and lanternfishes are the most numerous, but many other fishes live in the mesopelagic. Marine hatchetfishes look somewhat like the unrelated fresh water hatchetfishes sold in pet shops, except for their large eyes and mouths and ventral photophores. Viperfishes, dragonfishes, barracudinas, sabertooth fishes, lancetfishes, snake mackerels, and cutlassfishes are all long, eel-like fishes with large mouths and eyes. Many have photophores, usually in rows on the ventral surface. Most are less than 30 cm (1 ft) long, but there are exceptions. A lancetfish (*Alepisaurus ferox;* Fig. 16.6) grows to about 2 m (6.5 ft), and the black scabbard fish (*Aphanopus carbo;* Fig. 16.8) to over 1 m (3.3 ft) long.

Adaptations of Midwater Animals

By the standards of the surface world, many of the animals that live below the photic zone seem bizarre. Though they look strange to us, they are well adapted to their unique environment. Species from the same depth often have very similar characteristics even though they are unrelated. On the other hand, closely related species from different depths can differ markedly in appearance and other characteristics.

Feeding and Food Webs Most of the food produced in the epipelagic is used there; only about 20% of surface primary production sinks to the mesopelagic. This means that the mesopelagic is chronically short of food, which is why there are fewer organisms in the mesopelagic than in the epipelagic. The abundance of midwater organisms in a particular geographic area reflects the productivity of the waters above. There is more mesopelagic life under highly

Abraliopsis

Chiroteuthis

Thelidioteuthis

Pterygioteuthis

FIGURE 16.4 Most mesopelagic squids have photophores (shown in black), usually arranged in a different pattern in each species.

FIGURE 16.5 The vampire squid (*Vampyroteuthis infernalis*) differs from true squids in that 2 of its 10 tentacles are modified into long, retractable sensory tentacles and the other 8 tentacles aren't used for feeding. The vampire squid only grows to about 30 cm (12 in).

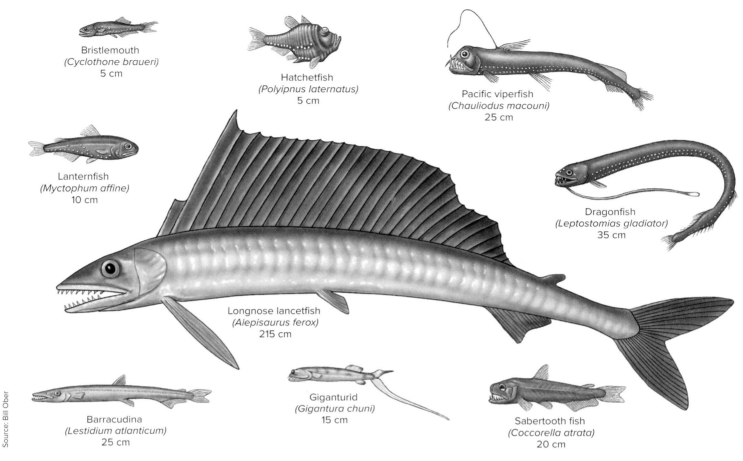

Bristlemouth
(*Cyclothone braueri*)
5 cm

Hatchetfish
(*Polyipnus laternatus*)
5 cm

Pacific viperfish
(*Chauliodus macouni*)
25 cm

Lanternfish
(*Myctophum affine*)
10 cm

Dragonfish
(*Leptostomias gladiator*)
35 cm

Longnose lancetfish
(*Alepisaurus ferox*)
215 cm

Barracudina
(*Lestidium atlanticum*)
25 cm

Giganturid
(*Gigantura chuni*)
15 cm

Sabertooth fish
(*Coccorella atrata*)
20 cm

Source: Bill Ober

FIGURE 16.6 Some typical mesopelagic fishes and their approximate maximum length.

Cephalopods Squids, octopuses, and related molluscs that use sucker-bearing arms to capture prey and, with a few exceptions, lack a shell.
• 7.5, Molluscs: The Successful Soft Body

Michael E. Huber

(a)

Michael E. Huber

(b)

FIGURE 16.7 Nets called rectangular midwater trawls are commonly used to collect mesopelagic organisms. The net can be opened and closed by remote control when it is at the desired depth. This prevents surface organisms from being caught while the net is being lowered and retrieved. In both (*a*) and (*b*) the mouth of the net is open.

Michael E. Huber

FIGURE 16.8 A black scabbard fish (*Aphanopus carbo*) for sale by a Madeiran fisherman. Known locally as *espada,* it is a relatively rare example of a midwater fish that is caught for food. Mesopelagic fishes are increasingly being exploited, however, because shallower fish stocks are depleted (see "Food from the Sea," in 17.1).

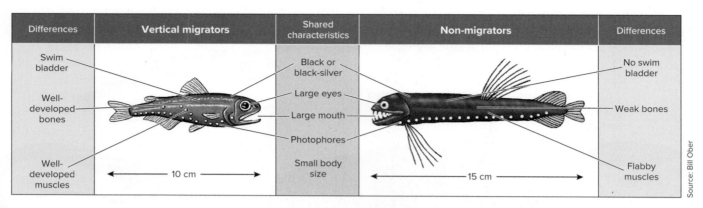

FIGURE 16.9 Some adaptations of typical mesopelagic fishes, including some differences between vertical migrators like lanternfishes (left) and non-migrators like dragonfishes (right). Compare these with the adaptations of epipelagic and deep-sea fishes shown in Figures 15.18 and 16.19.

productive surface waters than under areas with low primary production.

Many of the characteristics of midwater animals are directly related to food shortage. The small size of midwater fishes, for example, is probably an adaptation to the limited food supply. Animals need a lot of food to grow large, so there is an evolutionary advantage to limited growth and small size.

Midwater fishes usually have large mouths, and many have hinged, extendible jaws equipped with fearsome teeth (Figs. 16.9 and 16.10). The long, sharp teeth help keep prey from escaping. With food scarce, midwater fishes can't afford to be picky. They usually have very broad diets and eat just about anything they can fit into their mouths. The large, protrusible jaws allow them to eat a wide range of prey. They don't have to pass up potential meals because they are too large to eat. Some mesopelagic fishes can eat prey larger than they are!

FIGURE 16.10 (*a*) The viperfish (*Chauliodus*) has hinged jaws that can accommodate large prey. (*b*) The rattrap fish (*Malacosteus*) has a similar jaw arrangement.

Common adaptations of midwater fishes include small size, large mouths, hinged and extendible jaws, needle-like teeth, and unspecialized diets. These adaptations result from the limited food supply in the mesopelagic.

Midwater animals can be divided into two major groups: those that stay in the mesopelagic and those that migrate to the surface at night. The non-migrators include a few species of small zooplankton, mainly copepods and krill, that filter out **detritus** and the small amount of phytoplankton that sinks out of the photic zone. The fecal pellets of epipelagic copepods and other surface grazers form an important part of the detritus eaten by mesopelagic filter feeders. Fecal pellets sink much faster than individual phytoplankton cells, so they stand a better chance of making it to the mesopelagic before being eaten.

Most non-migrating midwater animals, however, are not zooplankton but fishes, shrimps, and squids. They are sit-and-wait predators that lurk in the dim light, gulping down anything that comes

within range. With food hard to come by, these animals are adapted to conserve energy. Instead of energy-consuming muscle, non-migrating midwater fishes have flabby, watery flesh. To fill their **swim bladder,** fishes must produce a gas pressure inside the bladder that matches the external water pressure. Because pressure is greater at depth than at the surface, filling the swim bladder requires more energy in the mesopelagic. To save energy most non-migrating midwater fishes have lost the swim bladder. To compensate, they have evolved soft, weak bones and lost defensive structures like spines and scales. These adaptations reduce weight and make them more neutrally buoyant, so they can float at a constant depth without wasting energy swimming. Since they don't swim much, they have little need for the streamlining characteristic of epipelagic fishes.

Vertical Migration and the Deep Scattering Layer Instead of staying put and waiting for food to fall from above, many mesopelagic organisms make **vertical migrations.** They swim up at night to feed in the rich surface layers and descend during the day to depths of several hundred meters or more. In the dim light they are probably relatively safe from predators. Some vertical migrators spend the day in a lethargic stupor, conserving energy until their next foray to the surface. Vertical migration is also seen in

many zooplankton that live in the deeper parts of the epipelagic (see "Predators and Their Prey," in 15.2).

Vertically migrating fishes differ in several important ways from those that stay in the mesopelagic (Fig. 16.9). Well-developed muscles and bones are needed to make the daily swim up and down the water column. These structures are heavy, so mesopelagic fishes that vertically migrate have retained the swim bladder for buoyancy. As they move up and down, they experience dramatic changes in pressure. Some vertically migrating fishes can rapidly adjust the volume of gas in the swim bladder to prevent it from collapsing or exploding when they change depth. Many, however, have a swim bladder filled with fat instead of gas. Fat, unlike gas, does not expand and contract with pressure changes, making it much easier for the fishes to regulate their buoyancy. Vertically migrating fishes can also tolerate the temperature changes they experience as they move up and down across the thermocline.

Midwater animals that vertically migrate have well-developed bones and muscles, wide temperature tolerances, and, in fishes, swim bladders. Non-migratory midwater fishes have soft bones, flabby muscles, and lack swim bladders.

Vertical migration by mesopelagic animals was discovered during World War II, when sonar came into use. Sonar showed a series of sound-reflecting layers, or "false bottoms." The real bottom gives a sharp, clear echo, but these layers, collectively dubbed the **deep scattering layer (DSL),** give a soft, diffuse echo that makes a shadowy trace on sonar plots. During the day the DSL lies at depths of 300 to 500 m (1,000 to 1,600 ft), but at sunset it rises to the surface. The depth of the DSL is clearly related to light intensity: The DSL stays deeper when there is a full moon than on moonless nights and even moves up and down when clouds pass over the moon.

The DSL is composed of fishes—especially lanternfishes—krill, shrimps, copepods, jellyfishes, squids, and other midwater animals. Most of these organisms, though they are part of the DSL, do not contribute to its sound-reflecting properties. Because organisms are made mostly of water, sound passes through them much as it does through seawater, without bouncing off. Air pockets, however, reflect sound quite strongly. The echo of the DSL comes mostly from sound waves bouncing off the gas-filled swim bladders of some vertically migrating fishes.

The deep scattering layer (DSL) is a sound-reflecting layer made up of vertically migrating midwater animals. Lanternfishes, krill, shrimps, copepods, jellyfishes, and squids are the dominant organisms of the DSL.

When lanternfishes, krill, and other animals return to the mesopelagic after feeding near the surface, they carry the products of surface production down with them. Thus, vertical migration greatly increases the food supply in the mesopelagic. Many non-migratory midwater predators feed heavily on vertically migrating species. The migrators are more muscular than non-migrators and provide a nutritious meal.

Sense Organs To help them see in the dim light, midwater fishes characteristically have eyes that are large and highly sensitive. Large, light-sensitive eyes also occur in squids, shrimps, and other groups. Some midwater fishes have developed **tubular eyes** (Fig. 16.11), a complex visual system that is almost like having two pairs of eyes. Tubular eyes give very acute vision in the direction that the eyes are pointed, either upward or forward, but are not good for lateral vision. Some fish species with tubular eyes can rotate the eyes to look in different directions. In addition, in many fishes with tubular eyes the **retina,** the light-sensitive part of the eye, extends partway up one side of the eye (Fig. 16.12a). This allows the fish to see to the side and below as well as upward (Fig. 16.13). In normal fish eyes the retina lies only at the back of the eye.

Adaptations very similar to tubular eyes are found in at least one octopus (*Amphitretus;* Fig. 16.12a) and in the bilobed eyes of some krill (*Stylocheiron;* Figs. 16.12c and 16.14). One squid, *Histioteuthis,* has taken a different path to the same apparent end. One of the squid's eyes is much larger than the other. The squid floats in the water column with the large eye pointed upward and the small eye downward.

Many midwater animals have evolved large, light-sensitive eyes that provide good vision in dim light. Other adaptations include tubular eyes in fishes and bilobed eyes in krill.

Coloration and Body Shape Like their epipelagic counterparts, mesopelagic predators rely heavily on vision. Because midwater

Detritus Particles of dead organic matter.
• 10.3, The Flow of Energy and Materials

Swim Bladder A gas-filled sac in the body cavity of most bony fishes that helps them control their buoyancy.
• 8.2, Types of Fishes; Figure 8.12

FIGURE 16.11 Many midwater fishes, like this barreleye (*Dolichopteryx longipes*), have tubular eyes that give them very acute upward vision. The large white lens at the top of the eye is very effective at gathering the dim light in the mesopelagic. The small black dot below the white lens is a mirror structure that provides downward vision.

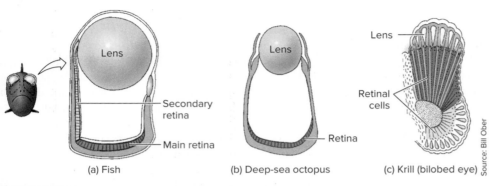

(a) Fish (b) Deep-sea octopus (c) Krill (bilobed eye)

Source: Bill Ober

FIGURE 16.12 (*a*) The tubular eye of a midwater fish (*Scopelarchus*). The retina is the light-sensitive part of the eye. The part of the retina at the bottom of the eye, colored red, provides good upward vision. The yellow part extending up the side of the eye provides lateral vision (Fig. 16.13), which is less acute. Eyes with a similar structure have evolved in (*b*) octopuses (*Amphitretus pelagicus*) and (*c*) krill (*Stylocheiron suhmii*).

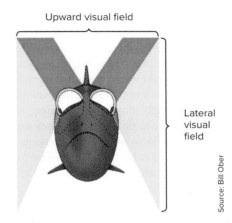

Source: Bill Ober

FIGURE 16.13 The field of vision of a midwater fish (*Scopelarchus*). The fish has two main visual fields corresponding to the two parts of the retina shown in Figure 16.12*a*.

prey cannot afford the energetic costs of fast swimming or heavy defensive spines and scales, camouflage is perhaps even more important than in the epipelagic. The basic strategies, however, are very similar: **countershading,** transparency, and reduction of the silhouette. There are many variations on these basic strategies, especially in relation to depth and light levels.

Transparency is particularly common in the shallower and better-lit parts of the mesopelagic. Copepods, jellyfishes, shrimps, bristlemouths, and other animals that live in the upper mesopelagic tend to be transparent, some almost completely so. Deeper in the mesopelagic, fishes tend to be more silvery, or black or red in the deepest, darkest part. Zooplankton from the deeper mesopelagic are often red, orange, or purple. These colors might be conspicuous at the surface, but colors change underwater (see "Seawater," in 3.1, The Waters of the Ocean). Our eyes see a fish as red at the surface because its skin absorbs most of the colors in sunlight but reflects red. Red light doesn't penetrate to mesopelagic depths, however, and the red pigment absorbs the blue light that does, so the organism appears dark against the dark background of the surrounding water.

Mesopelagic fishes often have black backs and silvery sides, reminiscent of the countershading of epipelagic animals (see "Predators and Their Prey," in 15.2, Living in the Epipelagic). In the mesopelagic, however, there isn't enough light to reflect off the white or silver belly typical of epipelagic countershading to mask the animal's outline. Even a white object produces a silhouette in twilight. A silhouette makes the animal conspicuous and vulnerable to all those sharp eyes peering up from below. To reduce their silhouettes, some mesopelagic fishes, like hatchetfishes, have laterally compressed bodies. This reduces the size of the body outline whether the animal is viewed from above or below.

Some mesopelagic squids and octopuses can switch between camouflage strategies. Many cephalopods have a chameleon-like ability to change color, and some midwater species can change from being practically transparent to a mottled reddish-orange depending on light level and the presence of predators.

Bioluminescence Most midwater animals have evolved an even more effective way to mask their silhouettes. Their bioluminescent

photophores, found mostly on their undersides, produce light that breaks up the silhouette and helps the animal blend in with the background light filtering down from the surface (Fig. 16.15). This adaptation, which functions in a similar manner to countershading, is called **counterillumination.**

The light produced by midwater animals is closely matched to the background light. Like the natural light at these depths, nearly all midwater bioluminescence is blue-green. Many mesopelagic animals can control the brightness of the light they produce to match the brightness of the background. This has been shown experimentally by placing special blinders on shrimps and other animals. The blinders allow experimenters to control how much light the animal sees (Fig. 16.16). When the animal is exposed to bright light, it produces bright bioluminescence; when the light is dim, so is the bioluminescence. When opaque blinders are put on the shrimp so that it sees no light, it turns off its photophores completely. This control of the bioluminescence is essential. It is easy to see an animal if it produces light at night or if the light is brighter than the background. On the other hand, the animal creates a silhouette during the day if the light isn't bright enough.

Cheryl Clarke-Hopcroft, Institute of Marine Science, Fairbanks, AK

FIGURE 16.14 This midwater krill (*Stylocheiron elongatum*) has bilobed eyes.

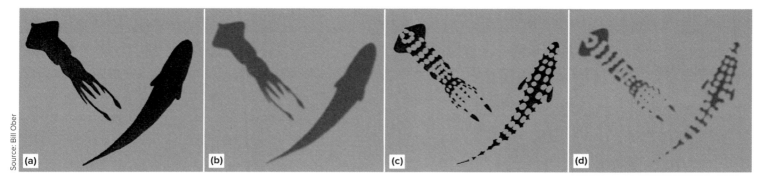

Source: Bill Ober

(a) **(b)** **(c)** **(d)**

FIGURE 16.15 The value of having photophores on the lower, or ventral, surface of midwater animals is shown in this simple demonstration. (*a* and *b*) Silhouettes of two midwater organisms as they would appear without photophores. (*c* and *d*) The same animals with the photophores in white to match the background. The photophores break up the silhouette, making the animal much less visible. This effect is more pronounced when the animals are a little out of focus (*b* and *d*), as they are when viewed through the water.

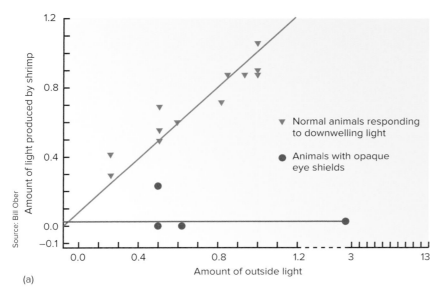

Source: Bill Ober

(a)

Cookie-cutter sharks (*Isistius*) use a twist on counterillumination to attract prey rather than avoid predators. Cookie-cutter sharks cut out round chunks of flesh from much larger fishes, whales and dolphins, and seals, and also eat whole squids. The sharks swim only weakly, however, making it hard to attack their faster-moving prey. The sharks have diffuse photophores on their undersides, as in normal counterillumination. Just behind their mouth, however, is a black band without photophores that creates a false silhouette. The silhouette attracts predators from below, which the shark attacks as they approach.

Midwater organisms have evolved ways to defeat counterillumination. The bioluminescence of most mesopelagic organisms nearly matches the color of natural light from above, but is just a bit greener. The visual pigments of some midwater fishes allow them to distinguish subtle color differences in the blue-green range, and others have yellow filters that serve the same purpose. Some midwater squids can also tell the difference between bioluminescence and natural light, but they do it by having the equivalent of polarized sunglasses rather than color discrimination—natural light in the mesopelagic and bioluminescence are polarized differently. The use of counterillumination to avoid predators, and even attract prey, and the evolution of measures to defeat counterillumination, is a classic example of the "arms races" that evolve between predators and prey (see "Ways that Species Interact," in 10.1).

Most midwater animals are bioluminescent, and midwater organisms have evolved many different ways to produce light. Photophores, as we have seen, are common. In some species the light is produced by the animal's own specialized tissue. In other species, symbiotic

Michael Latz, Scripps Institution of Oceanography

(b)

FIGURE 16.16 (*a*) This experiment showed that a midwater shrimp (*Sergestes similis;* Fig. 16.2) produces bioluminescence to match the background light intensity. Shrimp having both eyes covered with blinders did not produce any light (lower line), no matter how much outside light there was. Those with clear blinders produced more light as the outside level was increased (upper line). (*b*) The experimental setup, in this case using a control shrimp with clear blinders.

Countershading A pattern of coloration common in open-water nekton in which the back is black or dark blue and the underside white or silver.

• 15.2, Living in the Epipelagic

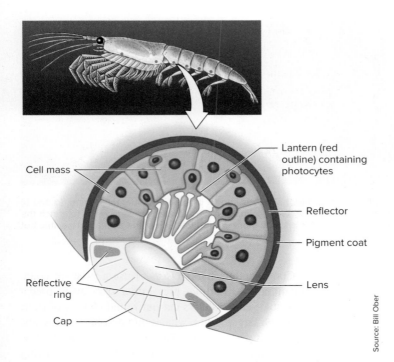

Cell mass

Lantern (red outline) containing photocytes

Reflector

Pigment coat

Reflective ring

Lens

Cap

Source: Bill Ober

FIGURE 16.17 Cross section of a krill photophore.

bit of bioluminescent tissue, on the end. The fishes dangle the glowing lure in front of their mouths. Anglerfishes use the same tactic, though they are more common in the bathypelagic zone than the mesopelagic (see "The Lack of Food," below). The mesopelagic squid *Chiroteuthis* (see Fig. 16.4) has light organs on the end of long modified tentacles that hang down as lures. Even the bioluminescent suckers of the octopus *Stauroteuthis* are thought to attract prey. Some midwater fishes and squids seem to use bioluminescence to stun or confuse their prey. Some have light organs around their eyes that may help them see their prey. In a few species, such photophores produce red light instead of the usual blue-green. The red light is invisible to most other midwater organisms, but these fishes can see it and probably use it to spy undetected on potential prey.

Mesopelagic animals also use bioluminescence for purposes unrelated to predation. The distinctive pattern of photophores on many species, which often differ between males and females, could help them identify potential mates. Some mesopelagic fishes, squids, and octopuses probably use bioluminescence to communicate.

> Most midwater animals are bioluminescent. Bioluminescence is used in counterillumination to mask the silhouette, to escape from predators, to attract or see prey, and in communication and courtship.

bacteria live inside the light organ and produce the light. In either case, the photophore can be quite complex (Fig. 16.17).

Bioluminescence is not always produced by specialized photophores. Many jellyfishes and other gelatinous animals produce light with cells that are scattered over the body surface. Some copepods, ostracods, shrimps, and other animals secrete bioluminescent fluids that they squirt out through special glands, either in addition to or instead of having photophores. Some squids and octopuses produce bioluminescent ink, and the vampire squid can release luminescent fluid from the ends of its tentacles.

Mesopelagic animals use bioluminescence to defend against predators in other ways than counterillumination. Many flash or emit a sudden spurt of bioluminescent fluid when attacked, startling the predator while the prey darts away. Bioluminescent fluid emitted by some squids, octopuses, and shrimps acts as a "smoke screen," hiding the escape route, or as a decoy, with the predator attacking the glowing cloud of fluid instead of the prey. The midwater squid *Octopoteuthis* goes one better. It attaches its tentacles to attacking predators and then detaches, or autotomizes, the tentacles. The tentacles, glowing and wriggling like a worm, probably distract the predator. Bioluminescence can also attract a predator's predators, making it riskier to attack the bioluminescent prey. This applies even if the prey is eaten, since the prey, or its body parts, may continue to glow inside the predator. As a counter-strategy, many mesopelagic predators that are otherwise transparent have an opaque lining around their gut to black out their glowing meals.

Bioluminescence has offensive as well as defensive functions. The cookie-cutter shark is not the only mesopelagic animal that uses bioluminescence to attract prey. Mesopelagic fishes like viperfishes and dragonfishes (see Figs. 16.6 and 16.10) have a modified, elongated fin spine or a barbel under the chin, with a lure, a fleshy

Many squids apparently use distinctive photophore patterns to identify their own species and the opposite sex, but finding the opposite sex isn't necessarily paramount. Males of the bioluminescent squid *Octopoteuthis* fertilize females by attaching a packet of sperm, or **spermatophore,** to the female. The spermatophore then injects the sperm into the female's body, where the sperm remain ready to fertilize the female's eggs when she produces them. But male *Octopoteuthis* don't discriminate between other males and females, instead attaching spermatophores to any member of their own species they encounter. Making sperm doesn't require much energy, and it must be more efficient for the males to attach their spermatophores indiscriminately than to bother telling males from females.

The Oxygen Minimum Zone In many places, midwater organisms have to deal with a lack of oxygen. Oxygen enters the ocean in two ways: by gas exchange with the atmosphere (see "Seawater," in 3.1) and as a by-product of photosynthesis. Both processes occur only at the surface, and once a water mass descends to mesopelagic depths, there is no way for it to gain oxygen. **Respiration** by decay bacteria, however, continues to use up oxygen (Fig. 16.18). As a result, the water becomes depleted in oxygen, often in fairly well-defined layers around 500 m (1,600 ft) deep known as **oxygen minimum zones (OMZs).** The amount of oxygen in OMZs can drop to practically nothing. Below the OMZ there is very little food and therefore very little respiration and decomposition, so oxygen is not used up so quickly. Thus, the water below the OMZ retains most of the oxygen it had when it left the surface.

Animals live in OMZs despite the low oxygen levels. Fishes, krill, and shrimps that live there usually have large, well-developed gills to help extract what little oxygen there is. They also tend to be

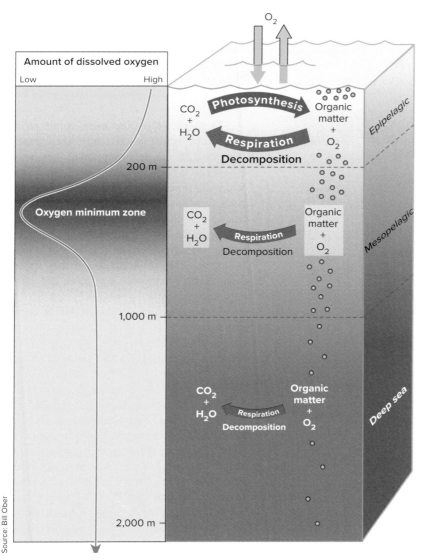

Source: Bill Ober

FIGURE 16.18 Surface waters are rich in oxygen, because oxygen both enters from the atmosphere and is released by photosynthesis. In the mesopelagic zone neither the atmosphere nor photosynthesis can contribute oxygen to the water, but there is extensive bacterial decomposition of organic matter sinking from shallow water. This uses up oxygen and results in an oxygen minimum zone. Below the oxygen minimum zone, most of the organic matter has already decayed on its way down, and oxygen remains dissolved in the water. Additional oxygen is brought in by the deep thermohaline circulation (see Figs. 3.24 and 3.25).

16.2 THE WORLD OF PERPETUAL DARKNESS

Below the mesopelagic lies the little-known world of the deep sea, where sunlight never penetrates. This alien environment is vast, indeed. It is the largest habitat on Earth and contains about 75% of our planet's liquid water. The deep sea can be divided into several pelagic depth zones. The **bathypelagic zone** includes depths between 1,000 and 4,000 m (3,300 and 13,000 ft), and the **abyssopelagic zone** lies from 4,000 to 6,000 m (13,000 to 20,000 ft). The **hadopelagic,** or **hadal pelagic, zone** consists of the waters of the ocean **trenches,** from below 6,000 m to just above the sea floor, as deep as 11,000 m (36,000 ft). Each of the depth zones supports a distinct community of animals, but they also have much in common. Here we stress the similarities, rather than the differences, among the depth zones of the deep sea.

The conditions of life in the deep pelagic environment change relatively little. Not only is it always dark, it is always cold: The temperature remains nearly constant, typically at 1 to 2 °C (35 °F). Salinity and other chemical properties of the water are also remarkably uniform.

The deep sea also includes the ocean bottom beyond the continental shelf. Bottom-living organisms are covered separately (see "The Deep-Ocean Floor," below).

The deep sea includes the bathypelagic, from 1,000 to 4,000 m; the abyssopelagic, 4,000 to 6,000 m; and the hadopelagic, 6,000 m to the bottom of trenches. The physical environment in these zones is quite constant. The deep sea also includes the deep-sea floor.

In the darkness of the deep sea there is no need for countershading. Many animals, especially zooplankton, are a drab gray or off-white. Deep-sea fishes are generally black or a reddish brown, which in the deep sea has the same effect as being black. A few deep-sea fishes are bright red, as are many deep-sea shrimps.

As in mesopelagic animals, bioluminescence is very common in animals that live in the upper part of the deep sea. Deep-sea animals don't use bioluminescence for counterillumination, since there is no sunlight to create a silhouette. They have fewer photophores than midwater species, and the photophores are usually on the head and sides of the body rather than on the ventral surface. In the deep sea the primary uses of bioluminescence are prey attraction, defense against predators,

Hemoglobin A blood protein that transports oxygen in many animals; in vertebrates it is contained in erythrocytes (red blood cells).
• 8.3, Biology of Fishes

Trenches Deep depressions in the sea floor that are formed when two plates collide and one sinks below the other.
• 2.2, The Origin and Structure of Ocean Basins; Figures 2.12 and 2.13

relatively inactive, which lowers their oxygen consumption. Many have biochemical adaptations like **hemoglobin** that functions well at low oxygen concentrations.

Vampire squid are a good example of adaptation to the OMZ. Their hemoglobin has a high affinity for oxygen to extract it from oxygen-depleted water, they have the lowest metabolic rate known in any cephalopod, and they are neutrally buoyant so they can hover in the water column without expending energy swimming. Vampire squid can capture live prey, but in the OMZ prey are scarce and vampire squid mostly eat detritus. Marine snow, the remains of gelatinous zooplankton and crustaceans, discarded larvacean houses, and fecal pellets, has been found in their gut contents.

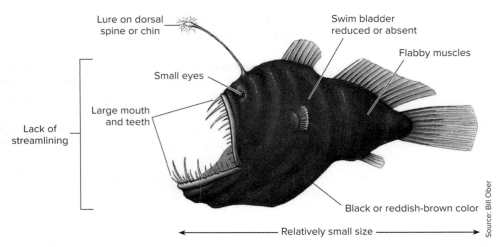

FIGURE 16.19 Some typical characteristics of deep-sea pelagic fishes. Compare these with the adaptations shown in Figures 15.18 and 16.9.

FIGURE 16.20 Comparison of typical adaptations in mesopelagic and deep-sea pelagic fishes. Shown are closely related bristlemouths from the mesopelagic (*G. denudatum*) and the deep sea (*G. bathyphilum*). The deep-sea fish has smaller eyes, less muscle, and fewer light organs. It also has less-developed nervous and circulatory systems, as indicated by the smaller brain and gill filaments.

all the hungry mouths in the waters above to reach the deep sea. Deep-sea animals do not make vertical migrations to the rich surface waters—the surface is too far away and the pressure change too great. With food critically scarce, deep-sea animals are few and far between.

Deep-sea fishes, the most common of which are bristlemouths and anglerfishes (Fig. 16.22), are relatively small, generally 50 cm (20 in) or less, but on average they are larger than mesopelagic fishes. This is somewhat surprising, given there is even less food available in the deep sea than in the mesopelagic. Deep-sea fishes apparently put their energy into growth, reproducing slowly and late in life, while mesopelagic fishes spend less energy on growth and more on early reproduction.

The energy-saving adaptations to food shortage seen in midwater organisms are accentuated in the deep sea. Deep-sea fishes are even more sluggish and sedentary than midwater fishes. They have flabby, watery muscles, weak skeletons, no scales, and poorly developed respiratory, circulatory, and nervous systems. Nearly all lack functional swim bladders. These fishes hang in the water column, expending as little energy as possible, until a meal comes along. Most deep-sea fishes have huge mouths and often fearsome teeth (Fig. 16.21), and can consume prey much larger than themselves. This trend reaches its peak in the swallowers (*Saccopharynx*) and gulpers (*Eurypharynx;* Fig. 16.22), which look like swimming mouths. To go along with their large mouths, many species have stomachs that can expand to accommodate the prey once it has been engulfed.

communication, and courtship. Bioluminescence becomes less common in the deeper parts of the deep sea, for reasons that are not understood.

The large eyes of midwater animals are not needed in the deep sea, where not even dim sunlight penetrates. The deep sea is not *completely* dark, however, because of bioluminescence. Many deep-sea animals have functional eyes, especially in the upper parts of the deep sea, but the eyes are generally small (Figs. 16.19 and 16.20). Animals from the deepest regions tend to have even smaller eyes or be blind altogether. Deep-sea fishes that are blind are not bioluminescent, one indication that the main function of vision in the deep sea is to see bioluminescence.

The Lack of Food

Deep-sea organisms face a continual shortage of food. Very little, only about 5%, of the food produced in the photic zone makes it past

Deep-sea pelagic fishes are typically small and black, with small eyes, large mouths, expandable stomachs, flabby muscles, weak bones, and poorly developed swim bladders. Bristlemouths and anglerfishes are the most common.

Like their mesopelagic counterparts, bathypelagic anglerfishes have the first spine on their dorsal fin modified into a "pole" that dangles a bioluminescent bait to attract prey. In some species the bait even resembles a shrimp or a worm. In most species only the females have a pole and bait. Many other deep-sea fishes also attract prey with bioluminescent lures.

Sex in the Deep Sea

Food is not the only thing that is scarce in the deep sea. In such a vast, sparsely populated world, finding a mate can be difficult—even harder than finding food. Deep-sea animals will eat just about

FIGURE 16.21 The fearsome jaws and teeth of a deep-sea dragonfish, the scaleless black dragonfish (*Melanostomias biseriatus*). The long barbel below the chin has a lure with bioluminescent tissue.

anything they can get, but to reproduce they generally need to find a member of their own species and the opposite sex.

Many deep-sea fishes have solved the problem by becoming **hermaphrodites.** After all, it would accomplish nothing if two members of the same species finally got together but were both the same sex. If every individual can produce both eggs and sperm, the ability to breed is guaranteed. There could also be deep-sea species whose males, like the mesopelagic squid *Octopoteuthis,* mate indiscriminately with both sexes of their species, getting it right when the other individual happens to be female.

Deep-sea animals probably actively attract mates. Bioluminescence is one way to signal other members of the same species. The lure of female anglerfishes differs among species, so it could have a role in attracting mates as well as prey. Chemical attraction is also important. Male anglerfishes have a very powerful sense of smell, which they use to locate females. The females apparently release a special chemical that the male can detect and follow. Such chemicals are called **pheromones.**

Some anglerfishes (*Cryptopsaras, Ceratias*) have evolved an extreme solution to the problem of finding mates. When a male locates a female, who is much larger, he bites into her side, where he remains attached for the rest of his life (Fig. 16.22). In some species the male's modified jaws fuse with the female's tissue. Their circulatory systems join, and the female ends up nourishing the male. In some species the female absorbs the entire male except his testes. This arrangement, often called **male parasitism,** ensures the male is always available to fertilize the female's eggs.

Neither hermaphroditism nor male parasitism are common in deep-sea invertebrates. The mechanisms that bring males and females together are unknown. There is evidence that some groups aggregate to breed, perhaps attracted by bioluminescent signals.

Finding mates, a problem for deep-sea animals, is eased by the use of bioluminescent and chemical signals and by the development of hermaphroditism and male parasitism.

Living Under Pressure

Under the weight of the overlying water column, the pressure in the deep sea is tremendous. This is one reason so little is known about the deep sea. The submersibles and equipment needed to study the deep sea must withstand the pressure without being crushed and are very expensive. Only a very few submersibles can venture into the deepest trenches, where the pressure can exceed

Deep-sea anglerfish
(*Gigantactis macronema*)
35 cm

Deep-sea devilfish
(*Caulophryne pelagica*)
15 cm

Deep-sea bristlemouth
(*Gonostoma bathyphilum*)
20 cm

Attached male

Female deep-sea anglerfish
with attached male
(*Cryptopsaras couesii*)
45 cm

Swallower
(*Saccopharynx ampullaceus*)
160 cm

Gulper
(*Eurypharynx pelecanoides*)
100 cm

FIGURE 16.22 Some deep-sea fishes and their approximate maximum length.

Hermaphrodites Individuals with both male and female gonads.

• 7.5, Molluscs: The Successful Soft Body

1,000 atmospheres (14,700 psi). It is just as difficult to bring animals up from the deep sea as it is to go down to them. Unable to endure the enormous change in pressure, they usually die when brought to the surface. A few deep-sea organisms have been brought up from the deep sea in special pressurized chambers. Much has been learned from such work, but it is frustratingly difficult.

Pressure has important effects on deep-sea organisms. The lack of a functional swim bladder in most deep-sea fishes, for example, is probably due to the high energetic cost of filling the bladder with gas under extreme pressure. Along with food availability, pressure is a major factor causing zonation in deep-sea pelagic organisms, that is, dividing the deep sea into bathypelagic, abyssopelagic, and hadopelagic zones.

In shallow-water organisms the **enzymes** that control metabolism are strongly affected by pressure, and would cease to function at the pressures of the deep sea. Deep-sea organisms, however, have much more pressure-resistant enzymes. Some also have high concentrations of a chemical that helps stabilize the enzymes. Such molecular adaptations enable deep-sea organisms to survive under pressures that would kill any surface-dweller.

Nonetheless, pressure probably limits the depth range of most organisms, and the number of species declines going deeper and deeper. The deepest known fish was recorded at a depth of 8,370 m (27,460 ft). Invertebrates and protozoa have been found at the deepest depths.

> Hydrostatic pressure is great in the deep sea and partially controls the depth distribution of deep-sea organisms. Deep-sea organisms have molecular adaptations that allow their enzymes to function at high pressure.

16.3 THE DEEP-OCEAN FLOOR

The floor of the deep sea shares many characteristics with the pelagic waters immediately above: the absence of sunlight, constant low temperature, and great hydrostatic pressure. Nevertheless, the biological communities of the deep-sea floor are very different from pelagic communities because of one key factor: the bottom.

Marine biologists have learned a bit more about the **benthos,** or bottom-inhabiting organisms, of the deep sea than about deep-water pelagic communities, because it is easier to study a fixed bottom than an environment that is suspended in space and constantly moving. Much, however, is still unkown about the deep-sea floor. Of the 270 million km^2 (105 million mi^2) of deep-sea floor, only a small fraction has been quantitatively sampled. What we do know has been learned using a variety of techniques. Devices called epibenthic sleds are dragged along the bottom, scooping up organisms, and corers bring a piece of the bottom to the surface. Deep-sea cameras photograph fast-swimming animals like fishes

FIGURE 16.23 The ROV (remotely operated vehicle) *Hercules. Hercules* is used to take samples, install equipment, and take photographs and videos to depths of 4,000 m (13,000 ft).

Courtesy Mountains in the Sea Research Team, the IFE Crew, and NOAA/OAR/OER

that are hard to catch in nets. Miniature transmitters can be hidden in bait and used to track the movements of a fish that swallows it. Deep submersibles like *Alvin* (see Fig. 1.10) have also been very useful, even more so than in the water column, as have remotely operated vehicles, or ROVs (Fig. 16.23), which are used to collect samples, take photos, and perform experiments. In 1995 one such craft succeeded for the first time in reaching the deepest part of the ocean. The Japanese-built *Kaiko* descended 10,991 m (36,061 ft) to the floor of the Challenger Deep in the Mariana Trench. This broke the long-standing record of the manned submersible *Trieste,* which in 1960 descended to 10,919 m (35,810 ft), also in the Mariana Trench. The one-person submersible *Deepsea Challenger* also made it to the bottom of the Challenger Deep, to a depth of 10,908 m (35,756 ft) in 2012. Completely autonomous submersibles, which are pre-programmed to operate independently of direct human control, are also making contributions.

Feeding in the Deep-Sea Benthos

Food shortage is critical on the floor of the deep sea. Very little of the surface production makes it all the way to the bottom. Benthic organisms, however, have a major advantage over the deep-sea pelagic ones above. In the water column, food particles that are not immediately located and eaten sink away and are lost. Once food reaches the bottom, by contrast, it stays put until it is found. Thus, although pelagic animals can get first crack at food sinking out of the photic zone, benthic animals have more time to find and eat it. Food particles that reach the bottom tend to be those that sink fairly rapidly, minimizing the chance that they will be eaten on the way down. Fecal pellets, for example, are an important source of organic matter for the deep-sea benthos.

Still, the rain of organic matter to the sea floor is actually more like a drizzle. Very little food is available to the benthic community. Much of the material that does reach the sea floor, like the chitinous remains of crustacean zooplankton, is not immediately digestible. On the sea floor, however, bacteria decompose the **chitin** and become food for other organisms. Still, deep-sea benthic community structure is largely determined by how much food energy is available.

Most of the deep-sea floor is covered in fine, muddy sediment. The **meiofauna,** tiny animals that live among the sediment particles (see Box 13.2, "Life in Mud and Sand"), are the most abundant organisms on the deep-sea floor, typically outnumbering larger organisms by a factor of 10. The meiofauna graze on bacteria and absorb dissolved organic matter (DOM) from the water between the sediment grains. The energy in the bacteria and DOM is thus made available to larger animals, or **macrofauna,** that graze on the meiofauna.

Suspension feeders are rare among the larger organisms in the deep-sea benthos. Instead, **deposit feeders** dominate. Many of these are **infauna,** burrowing in the sediments. Others, the **epifauna,** rest on the sediment surface.

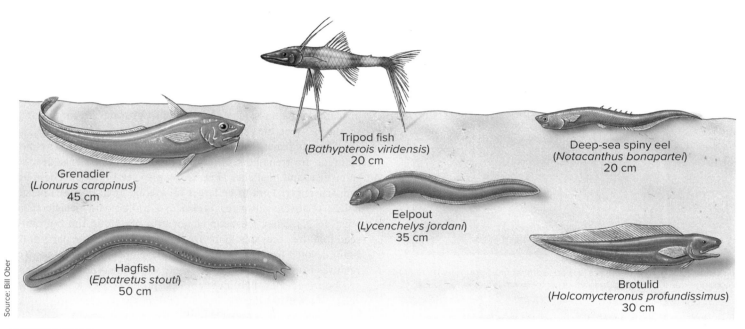

Source: Bill Ober

FIGURE 16.24 Some typical deep-sea bottom fishes and their approximate maximum length.

Polychaete worms are usually the most abundant macrofauna on the deep-sea floor, followed by crustaceans and bivalve molluscs, but there is considerable variation from place to place. Sea cucumbers are sometimes dominant, for example. Sea cucumbers from the deep sea often have strange, highly modified body forms. Some have leg-like appendages and walk across the bottom in search of organic-rich sediment. "Herds" of some species have been observed from submersibles. Other species can swim above the sea floor by undulating their bodies or squirting jets of water. Some parts of the deep sea are dominated by brittle stars, and sea stars can also be abundant. The makeup of deep benthic communities changes more with depth than over distance at the same depth.

The deep-sea benthos is dominated by deposit feeders. The dominant animal groups are the meiofauna, polychaete worms, crustaceans, bivalve molluscs, sea cucumbers, brittle stars, and sea stars.

There are predators in the deep-sea benthos, but they seem to be fairly rare. The main predators on deposit-feeding animals are probably sea stars, brittle stars, and crabs. Members of the nekton, like fishes and squids, are also important predators. Sea spiders, or pycnogonids, prey on other invertebrates by sucking out their soft parts.

Tripod fishes are another interesting group of deep-sea benthic predators. Nearly blind, these fishes sit on the bottom on their elongated fins (Fig. 16.24), facing into the current and snapping up passing plankton.

The slow rain of food to the bottom is interrupted by an occasional "storm." Large pieces of food that sink rapidly, like the dead bodies of large fishes or whales, are an important source of food to the benthos. Mobile deep-sea animals rapidly congregate around such "baitfalls" (Fig. 16.25). Among the most common of these are crustaceans, especially amphipods, which arrive soon after the bait

touches down. Many deep-sea benthic amphipods are generalists that feed on detritus and perhaps prey on live organisms if nothing else is available. Some, however, seem to specialize as scavengers.

Enzymes Proteins that speed up and control chemical reactions in organisms.
Chitin Highly resistant carbohydrate found in the skeleton of crustaceans and other structures.
• 4.1, The Ingredients of Life

Suspension Feeders Animals, including *filter feeders,* that eat particles suspended in the water column.
Deposit Feeders Animals that eat organic matter that settles to the bottom.
• 7.1, Sponges; Figure 7.4

Deep Sea Fish Ecology Lab, Astrid Leitner and Jeff Drazen, Department of Oceanography, SOEST University of Hawaii Manoa, DeepCCZ expedition. Used with permission.

FIGURE 16.25 A variety of fishes quickly locate large pieces of food on the deep-sea floor. These cutthroat eels (*Ilyophis arx*), have come to fish placed as bait on a seamount more than 3,000 m (9,800) deep. This was the largest aggregation of deep-sea fishes ever observed.

FIGURE 16.26 The deep-sea isopod (*Bathynomus giganteus*) is related to common garden pillbugs, but can grow to 36 cm (14 in) long.

Robert S. Carney, Louisiana State University

They apparently have a well-developed sense of smell to help them find new baitfalls. When caught in traps, these amphipods often have nothing in their guts except the bait, which indicates that they hadn't fed for some time. This, and the fact that they have an expandable gut, could mean that the amphipods are adapted for large but infrequent meals.

While most deep-sea benthic animals are small, the deep-sea members of some groups are giants compared to their shallow-water relatives (Fig. 16.26). Most amphipods, isopods, and sea spiders are less than 1 cm (0.4 in) in size, but deep-sea isopods can reach 36 cm (14 in), and amphipods 34 cm (13 in), in length, and deep-sea sea spiders can reach 80 cm (30 in) across. This phenomenon, known as **deep-sea gigantism,** is thought to be an adaptation for fast, efficient locomotion so that the animals can cover a larger area in search of baitfalls. The giant size also provides for more energy storage between meals.

Various fishes also find freshly placed bait quickly. The most common are grenadiers, or rattails, brotulas and cusk eels, deep-sea spiny eels, and hagfishes (Fig. 16.24, also see Fig. 8.2). These bottom scavengers tend to be larger on average than deep-sea pelagic fishes, relatively muscular, and active, unlike bathypelagic fishes (Fig. 16.27). They are adapted for cruising along the bottom in search of the occasional bonanza. In several groups the parts of the brain devoted to olfaction are highly developed compared to close relatives from the mesopelagic, where visual areas dominate. Deep-sea bottom fishes, like invertebrates, probably rely a lot on their sense of smell. At depths above 2,000 m, sharks can also show up at deep-sea bait falls, quickly putting an end to the feed.

The Nature of Life in the Deep-Sea Benthos

There is a growing realization that life in the deep sea proceeds at a very different pace than at the surface. Most deep-sea animals seem to grow very slowly, probably because of the lack of food. On the other hand, they live for a long time. Some deep-sea clams

	Epipelagic	Mesopelagic (vertical migrators)	Mesopelagic (non-migrators)	Deep Pelagic	Deep-sea Bottom
Appearance					
Size	Wide range from tiny to huge	Small	Small	Relatively small, larger than mesopelagic	Relatively large
Shape	Streamlined	Relatively elongated and/or laterally compressed	Relatively elongated and/or laterally compressed	No streamlining, often globular in shape	Very elongated
Musculature	Strong muscles, fast swimming	Moderately strong muscles	Weak, flabby muscles	Weak, flabby muscles	Strong muscles
Eyes	Large	Very large, sensitive	Very large, sensitive; sometimes tubular	Small, sometimes absent	Small
Coloration	Typical counter-shading: dark back and white or silver belly	Black or black with silver sides and belly; counter-illumination	Black or black with silver sides and belly; counter-illumination	Black or reddish brown, occasionally bright red, often lack coloration at greatest depths; no counter-illumination	Dark brown or black
Bioluminescence	Relatively uncommon	Common	Common	Common	Only in a few groups

Source: Bill Ober

FIGURE 16.27 Comparison of the typical characteristics of fishes from different depth zones in the pelagic realm.

Box 16.2 Biodiversity in the Deep Sea

With its immense pressure, near-freezing waters, absence of sunlight, and chronic food shortage, the deep sea seems like one of Earth's least hospitable environments. Indeed, in the nineteenth century the pioneering oceanographer William Forbes (see "The *Challenger* Expedition," in 1.1, The Science of Marine Biology), observing that fewer and fewer organisms were caught in nets as depth increased, hypothesized that no life at all existed below about 600 m (2,000 ft). This "azoic hypothesis" was quickly proved wrong when other scientists caught animals from greater depths. Nevertheless, animal abundance does decrease with depth—animals are scarce in the deep sea.

It was once thought that in addition to low abundance there were relatively few animal species in the deep sea. Just the opposite is true: The deep sea could be the most biologically diverse environment on Earth. Biologists are unable to collect and identify every species present in most environments, so they never know the exact number of species there. They can estimate species numbers, however, from "species accumulation curves." This involves analyzing how often they find new species as they collect more and more individual organisms. The first organism collected will always be a species new to the study. The second organism could be from the same species, leaving the total number of species collected at one, or it might be a new

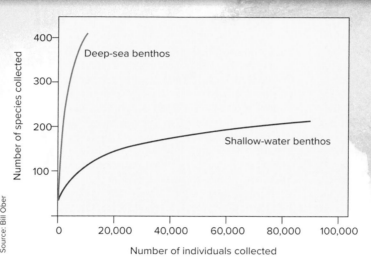

Source: Bill Ober

Species accumulation curves from the deep-sea and shallow-water benthos off the coast of New England.

species, bringing the species total to two. If the number of species in the habitat—one measure of its biodiversity—is small, then as more and more individuals are collected the number of new species increases relatively slowly and soon starts to level off near the total number of species that live in the environment. In highly diverse habitats, ones with many species, the number of species increases rapidly as more individuals are collected and takes longer to level off.

When this was done on the deep-sea floor, the species curve went through the roof, leading researchers to estimate that as many as 1 million species live on the deep-sea floor. Other estimates of the number of species in the ocean—not just the deep sea—are much lower. It is clear that nobody really

knows how many marine species there are, but in any case that the deep-sea floor is among the planet's most diverse habitats.

Seamounts, which like the rest of the deep sea have hardly been studied, also have very high diversity. Samples from only 24 seamounts in the southwest Pacific near Australia produced more than 850 species, and the species accumulation curve was still rising, indicating that many more species would have been found had more samples been taken. About a third of these species were new to science. Seamounts seem to be deep-sea islands, each holding a collection of organisms found nowhere else. The ocean's 30,000 seamounts must hold vast numbers of seamount waiting to be discovered, but many may go extinct before that happens. Seamounts are home to the orange roughy (*Hoplostethus atlanticus*) and several other commercially valuable fishes. These fishes live for more than a hundred years, but take decades to reach reproductive age and reproduce very slowly. This makes them highly vulnerable to overfishing (see "Food from the Sea," in 17.1). The orange roughy population on some Indian Ocean seamounts, for example, was completely fished out less than three years after their exploitation began. Even worse, the bottom trawls used to catch these fish rip animals from the bottom, reducing the abundance of benthic organisms by 80% or more.

are estimated live up to 100 years, some deep-sea fishes to more than 200 years, and cold-seep tubeworms (see "Hot Springs, Cold Seeps, and Dead Bodies," below) to 300 years or more. The low temperature, high pressure, and chronic food shortage slow down the processes of life in the deep sea.

It may also be that deep-sea animals need to live a long time to store up enough energy to reproduce. The larvae of deep-sea forms do not spend time in the food-rich photic zone. The chances of making it all the way to the surface and then back to the deep-sea floor are simply too small. Instead, deep-sea animals tend to produce large eggs, with enough yolk to see the larva through its early stages without eating. It takes a lot more energy to produce a large egg than a small one, so deep-sea animals produce only a few eggs. In at least some animals, reproduction could be tied to feeding.

In some species of amphipods, individuals caught in baited traps are all sexually immature. Biologists speculate that they do not reproduce until they manage to find a good meal.

Microbes in the Deep Sea

Bacteria, archaea, and viruses play many important roles in deep-sea benthic ecosystems that we are only beginning to understand. In 1968 a famous unplanned "experiment" gave an early indication of how much there is to learn. As the crew of *Alvin* was preparing for a dive the submersible was swamped by a wave, its supporting cable snapped, and *Alvin*, hatch open, dropped 1,540 m (5,000 ft) to the bottom. The crew escaped but left their lunch on board. It's the most famous lunch in marine biology.

Box 16.3 *Alvin* Reborn

The research submersible *Alvin* (see Fig. 1.10) has played a central role in some of the greatest discoveries in deep-sea biology, but she wasn't getting any younger. Launched in 1964, and with more than 4,600 dives under her belt, *Alvin* had been a starring tool for deep-sea science for nearly five decades. Over the years *Alvin* often had facelifts and upgrades, and not much of the original sub remained. Even so, moving into the twenty-first century *Alvin* seemed to have reached the end of her working life, and her depth limit of 4,500 m (14,800 ft) meant that much of the deep ocean was out of reach. In 2004, a plan was developed to retire *Alvin* and build her replacement.

Escalating costs and tight research funding meant that the plan to replace *Alvin* had to be scrapped. Instead, from late 2010 to 2014, *Alvin* was transformed by her largest upgrade ever. The upgrade replaced the heart of *Alvin,* the titanium sphere that houses the crew. The new sphere is capable of depths to 6,500 m (21,300 ft). Instead of the original three windows, the new sphere has five larger windows to increase visibility. The interior was redesigned to be more comfortable—or, perhaps more accurately, less uncomfortable—during the long descents into the abyss. Other improvements in Phase 1 included lighting, communication, and control systems, and high-definition video cameras. *Alvin*'s support vessel, *Atlantis,* was also upgraded with improved facilities to launch and store the sub. Also improved was *Alvin*'s launch system and storage in its support vessel, the research vessel *Atlantis.*

Some of *Alvin*'s components still don't allow her to reach the 6,500 m maximum depth the titanium sphere can withstand, and additional upgrades have been planned. Even these won't allow *Alvin* to reach the very deepest trenches. But some ROVs—"landers," or equipment packages that are simply dropped to the bottom and retrieved—and glider-like manned submersibles can reach the deepest parts of the ocean to reveal the secrets of the least-explored places on Earth.

For more information, explore the links provided on the Marine Biology *Online Learning Center.*

When *Alvin* was recovered 10 months later, scientists discovered that the long-lost lunch was in amazingly good condition. Though soggy, the sandwiches looked almost fresh; the bologna was still pink inside. The rest of the lunch—apples and a thermos of soup—also looked good enough to eat. Once brought to the surface the food soon spoiled, even though it was refrigerated.

Why was the food preserved in the deep sea? The deep sea is cold, but so is a refrigerator. Are bacteria absent from the deep sea? Does the pressure inhibit bacterial decay? Is there some other explanation? These questions sparked a flurry of research.

It is now known that bacteria live in huge numbers in the deep sea, as in every other environment on Earth. Pressure and cold slows bacterial growth, however, and most shallow-water bacteria cannot grow at the pressure and temperature of the deep sea. Therefore, the bacteria that were already in the lunch probably died when *Alvin* sank.

Even if the surface bacteria died, there are still plenty of bacteria already living in the deep sea. Deep-sea bacteria don't just tolerate the prevailing cold and high pressure, many of them grow best or even *only* under these conditions. Even though these cold-loving (**psychrophilic**) and pressure-loving (**barophilic**) bacteria grow best under deep-sea conditions, they still grow slower than shallow-water bacteria and can take up to 1,000 times longer to decompose organic matter. Some deep-sea bacteria may be adapted to use organic matter in low concentrations, and are overloaded by rich fare like a bologna sandwich. Furthermore, the lunchbox could have prevented many bacteria, like those that live on or in amphipods and other deep-sea animals, from getting to the food.

Vast numbers of microbes live in deep-sea sediments. Until the last few years it was thought that bacteria dominate, but archaea are as or more abundant. Viruses are key drivers of the microbial ecosystem in deep-sea sediments. Researchers estimate that viruses kill some 80% of the bacteria and archaea in the sediment, causing their cells to burst and release large amounts of dissolved organic carbon (DOC). Other microbes take up the DOC as an energy source, so the viruses promote rapid carbon recycling, as well as recycling of nutrients like nitrogen and phosphorus. Thus, microbes and viruses play key roles in deep-sea carbon and nutrient cycles.

Deep-sea sediments also contain large numbers of **chemosynthetic prokaryotes,** which are probably an important food source for deposit feeders. They could be involved in the formation of polymetallic nodules and other mineral deposits (see "Ocean Mining," in 17.2, Non-Living Resources from the Sea Floor). Chemosynthetic bacteria are even gradually digesting the wreck of the *Titanic!*

16.4 HOT SPRINGS, COLD SEEPS, AND DEAD BODIES

The year 1977 marked one of the most exciting discoveries in the history of biology, and it wasn't even made by biologists! A group of marine geologists and chemists was using *Alvin* to look for **hydrothermal vents** on a section of mid-ocean ridge near the Galápagos Islands in the eastern Pacific. When the scientists found the vents, they also found something completely unexpected: a rich, flourishing community unlike anything ever imagined (Fig. 16.28). In the days that followed, more vents were found, each teeming with animals. There were gigantic worms up to 1 m (3.3 ft) long, 30-cm (12-in) clams, dense clusters of mussels, shrimps, crabs, fishes, and a variety of other unexpected life. The vents were like oases of life on the barren deep-sea floor.

Expeditions were soon mounted to hydrothermal areas around the world. With every dive, it seems, come new discoveries. Over 400 new animal species—and counting—have been found in hydrothermal-vent communities, which vary considerably from place to place. Tubeworms, clams, crabs, and shrimps typically dominate the eastern Pacific vent communities that were first discovered. Unusual snails and barnacles are most common at vents in the western Pacific, while vents on the Mid-Atlantic Ridge are typically dominated by a shrimp (*Rimicaris*).

With no sunlight to support photosynthesis, the primary producers in hydrothermal-vent communities are chemosynthetic archaea and bacteria. Around the mid-ocean ridge, seawater trickles down through cracks and fissures in the earth's crust and is heated to very high temperatures. Rich in sulfide minerals, it emerges at hydrothermal vents to form "black smokers," "chimneys," and other mineral deposits. The hot water also contains large amounts of **hydrogen sulfide** (H_2S), which is toxic to most organisms but is an energy-rich molecule. Chemosynthetic prokaryotes that use the energy in hydrogen sulfide and sulfide minerals to make inorganic matter are the base of the food chain. Some of these microbes are extremophiles that can live at temperatures over 120 °C (250 °F), the highest temperature at which life is known to occur (see "Archaea," in 5.2). New studies are expected to shatter this record.

> Deep-sea hydrothermal vents harbor rich communities. The primary production that supports these communities comes from microbial chemosynthesis, not photosynthesis.

Water near the vents contains so many microbes that they cloud the water. Some vent animals feed by filtering them from the water, but this isn't the principal mode of feeding. One of the dominant tubeworms in eastern Pacific vent communities (*Riftia*), does not filter feed. In fact, it doesn't even have a mouth or digestive tract! Instead, these worms have a highly specialized organ called a trophosome ("feeding body"; Fig. 16.29), packed with symbiotic bacteria. The bacteria perform chemosynthesis inside the worm's body and pass much of the organic matter they produce on to the worm. The worm, in turn, supplies the bacteria with raw materials. The bright-red plume acts like a gill, exchanging not only carbon dioxide and oxygen, but also hydrogen sulfide. The tubeworm's blood has special hemoglobin that chemically binds the hydrogen sulfide, protecting the worm from its toxic effects, and transports it to the bacteria in the feeding body. Most other vent animals chemically process hydrogen sulfide to avoid being poisoned.

Many other vent animals, including mussels (*Bathymodiolus*) and large clams (*Calyptogena*), contain symbiotic bacteria, though they can filter-feed as well. Non-symbiotic microbes are also an important food source. For example, the shrimp (*Rimicaris*) that dominates vent communities on the Mid-Atlantic Ridge scrapes off and eats bits of microbe-covered mineral from the chimneys that form at vents (see Fig. 2.26). The microbes are digested and the mineral eliminated.

Rimicaris do not have recognizable eyes, but they do have two light-sensitive patches on their upper surface. The patches can detect much fainter light than humans can see. Before the discovery that these shrimp could "see," no one suspected there was any light at all at deep-sea vents. A special low-light camera similar to those used to study distant stars revealed a faint glow, invisible to the human eye, around the vents. The source of the glow is uncertain, although some of it can be explained by the heat of the emerging water. Biologists speculate that the shrimp use this dim light both to locate active vents and to avoid getting cooked by coming too close to the scalding water.

Boiling-hot black smokers are not the only hydrothermal habitat in the deep sea. "White smokers" occur a little further away from the active rift and are cooler, so that black sulfide minerals precipitate out before the water emerges from the sea floor. White minerals remaining in the water form the "smoke." "Snowblower vents" form where chemosynthetic bacteria living in rocks beneath the sea floor produce filaments of sulfur that coalesce into snowflake-like particles when they emerge from the vent into cold water. Cooler vents at greater distance from the mid-ocean ridge or associated with transform fault and trenches (see "The Mid-Ocean Ridge and Hydrothermal Vents," in 2.3) support snails, sponges, deep-sea corals, and other organisms, but not in the abundance seen at mid-ocean ridge vents. Thick mats of chemosynthetic archaea and bacteria also grow in some of these areas, using carbonate minerals rather than sulfide minerals as an energy source. "Blue smokers" have also been discovered.

Communities based on chemosynthesis have even been found on deep-sea "graves." As previously discussed, occasional baitfalls like dead whales are an important source of food for deep-sea scavengers. When the scavengers are through, the decomposing remains produce hydrogen sulfide and methane, supporting communities similar in many ways to those at vents and seeps.

Other chemosynthetic communities are found at **cold seeps,** places mostly along continental margins or in sediment-rich basins like the Gulf of Mexico, where hydrogen sulfide and **methane** (CH_4) produced by the decay of organic matter seep out from the sea floor. Primary production by chemosynthetic prokaryotes that can use one or the other of these energy-rich molecules supports communities that are similar in many ways to those at hydrothermal vents, though the individual species are mostly different. Hydrothermal vents and whale carcasses are relatively short-lived, lasting perhaps a few decades. Though cold seeps can be wiped out by major disturbances, they can also persist for centuries or more, fed by the steady decay of organic matter deep in the sediments. Some cold-seep tubeworms live for 300 years or more.

Unlike most deep-sea organisms, those at hot springs, cold seeps, and dead bodies enjoy an energy-rich environment and grow fast and large. On the other hand, their specialized habitats are tiny oases separated by vast distances. These oases are also unreliable. Hot springs can be wiped out by volcanic eruptions, undersea landslides, and other disturbances. As long as the flow of energy-rich

Chemosynthetic Prokaryotes Autotrophic *bacteria* and *archaea* that use energy contained in inorganic chemicals rather than sunlight to make organic matter.
- 5.2, Prokaryotes; Table 5.1

Hydrothermal Vents Undersea hot springs associated with mid-ocean ridges.
- 2.3, The Geologic Provinces of the Ocean

FIGURE 16.28 Rich, colorful animal communities live at many hydrothermal vents. This community at a depth of over 2,500 m (8,200 ft) on the East Pacific Rise includes giant tube worms (*Riftia*), zoarcid fish, or eelpouts, and crabs (*Bythograea*). Image courtesy of Richard A. Lutz.

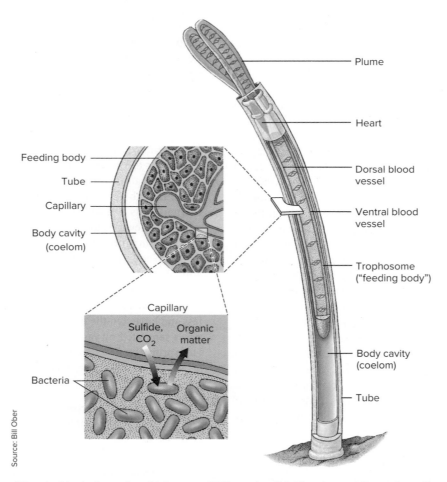

FIGURE 16.29 The anatomy of the giant hydrothermal-vent tubeworm (*Riftia pachyptila*). The plume at the end acts like a gill, except that it exchanges hydrogen sulfide (H_2S) as well as carbon dioxide (CO_2) and oxygen (O_2). The carbon dioxide and sulfide are carried in the blood to the feeding body, where symbiotic bacteria use them to make organic matter by chemosynthesis.

molecules continues the communities recover fairly quickly as new larvae recolonize the vent (see Box 3.2, "Larval Transport Near Hydrothermal Vents") but sometimes the flow is blocked or dries up. In 2002 scientists returned to the Rose Garden, a hydrothermal vent near the Galápagos Islands first discovered in 1979 and revisited multiple times, to find no trace of the rich vent community—only fresh lava flows. To avoid extinction, species in chemosynthetic communities have to disperse to new oases. Only 200 m (660 ft) from the Rose Garden site scientists discovered a new vent, dubbed "Rosebud," already colonized by juvenile tubeworms, clams, and mussels. The communities recolonizing new vents or areas wiped out by an eruption, however, can be different from those that came

before, with species that were common becoming rare and *vice versa,* and vents can be colonized by species from hundreds of kilometers away.

The carcasses of large organisms quickly rot away, so the species they support must also "island hop." The remains of whales, seals, sharks, and other large organisms are particularly tiny habitats in the expanse of the deep sea, but compared to hot springs and cold seeps there are a lot of them. Or at least there were. By hunting the giants of the sea to the brink of extinction, we may have already removed these stepping stones and doomed an entire ecosystem that we have only just discovered.

McGraw-Hill Connect® is a great place to check your understanding of chapter material. Visit **www.mcgrawhillconnect.com** for access to interactive chapter summaries, chapter quizzing, and more! Further enhance your knowledge with video clips and web links to chapter-related material.

Critical Thinking

1. The deep-sea floor has been considered as a potential site for the disposal of toxic and radioactive wastes. What questions about the biology, geology, and chemistry of the deep-sea environment do you think should be answered before such plans are approved?
2. How do you think non-migratory midwater fishes, with their flabby muscles, are able to prey on vertical migrators, which have well-developed muscles?
3. Fats are highly energy-rich molecules that require a great deal of energy to produce, but in the mesopelagic, where food is scarce, many fishes have swim bladders filled with fat. How might this be explained?

For Further Reading

Some of the recommended reading may be available online. Look for live links on the *Marine Biology* Online Learning Center.

General Interest

Conquering the Deep. *New Scientist,* vol. 231, no. 3084, 30 July 2016, pp. 32–39. A series of articles about how new technology is helping people study the deep sea.

Copley, J., 2020. Into the deep. *New Scientist,* vol. 248, no. 3307, 7 November 2020. A new wave of deep sea exploration is driven by the desire to mine the sea floor.

Heffernan, O. 2020. Help for the high seas. *Nature,* vol. 580, no. 7801, 2 April, pp. 20–23. The international community is trying to regulate the destruction of deep-sea communities.

Kaplan, M., 2011. Once more unto the deep. *New Scientist,* vol. 211, no. 2828, 3 September, pp. 38–41. Private companies are developing high-tech subs to visit the very deepest parts of the ocean.

Kunzig, R., 2007. Sweeping the ocean floor. *Discover,* June, pp. 30–37. The Census of Marine Life looks at the deep sea.

Lutz, R. A., 2003. Dawn in the deep. *National Geographic,* vol. 203, no. 2, February, pp. 92–103. A scientific film project lights up the world of hydrothermal vent communities.

McClain, C., 2010. An empire lacking food. *American Scientist,* vol. 98, no. 6, November/December, pp. 470–477. Food shortage is a primary driver of the many adaptations of deep-sea animals. http://www.americanscientist .org/issues/pub/2010/6/an-empire-lacking-food/1.

Maxmen, A., 2018. Hidden lives of deep-sea animals. *Nature,* vol. 561, 20 September, pp. 216–217. Video technology reveals deep-sea life.

Nevala, A. E., 2010. Building the next-generation *Alvin. Oceanus,* vol. 48, no. 2, December, pp. 12–15. The venerable research submarine *Alvin* is being reborn.

Nicholls, H., 2004. Sink or swim. *Nature,* vol. 432, no. 7013, 4 November, pp. 12–14. Biodiversity on seamounts and in other open-ocean habitats is in trouble.

Qui, J., 2010. Death and rebirth in the deep. *Nature,* vol. 465, no. 7296, 20 May, pp. 284–286. Hydrothermal vents are precarious places to live and routinely get wiped out by natural disasters—but the organisms that live there carry on.

Schrope, M., 2014. Robots explore the world's deepest ocean trenches. *Scientific American,* vol. 310, no. 4, April, pp. 60–69. The exploration of trenches is facilitated by robotics.

Stone, G. S., 2012. Mountains in the sea. *National Geographic,* vol. 222, no. 3, September, pp. 66–79. An expedition explores seamounts and life in and around them.

Switek, B., 2013. Deep-sea secrets. *Discover,* September, pp. 58–59. Bacteria and worms specialize in digesting the bones of deep-sea whale burials.

The deep, 2005. *New Scientist,* vol. 188, no. 2525, 12 November, pp. 36–51. A 15-page special with spectacular photos and articles about new deep-sea discoveries.

The once & future *Alvin,* 2015. *Oceanus,* vol. 51, no. 1, Summer 2015. A special issue of nine articles commemorating the 50th anniversary of *Alvin.*

Tucker, A., 2013. Light fantastic. *Smithsonian,* vol. 43, March, pp. 50–59. A scientist explores bioluminescence in the deep sea.

Ward, P., 2008. Chambers of secrets. *New Scientist,* vol. 198, no. 2650, 5 April, pp. 40–43. New findings show that *Nautilus* is far from a "living fossil."

In Depth

Burford, B. P. and B. H. Robison, 2020. Bioluminescent backlighting illuminates the visual signals of a squid in the deep sea. *Proceedings of the National Academy of Sciences,* vol. 117, no. 15, pp. 8524–8531.

Drazen, J. C. and T. T. Sutton, 2017. Dining in the deep: The feeding ecology of deep-sea fishes. *Annual Review of Marine Science,* vol. 9, pp. 337–366.

Fernandez-Arcaya, U., E. Ramirez-Llodra, J. Aguzzi, *et al.,* 2017. Ecological role of submarine canyons and need for canyon conservation: A review. *Frontiers in Marine Science,* vol. 4, January, article 5.

Gallo, N. D. and L.A. Levin, 2016. Fish ecology and evolution in the world's oxygen minimum zones and implications of ocean deoxygenation. *Advances in Marine Biology,* vol. 74, pp. 117–198.

Hoving, H.-J., J. A. Perez, K. S. R. Bolstad, *et al.,* 2014. The study of deep-sea cephalopods. *Advances in Marine Biology,* vol. 67, pp. 235–359.

Jamieson, A.J., 2021. A global assessment of fishes at lower abyssal and upper hadal depths (5000 to 8000 m). *Deep Sea Research Part I: Oceanographic Research Papers* [https://doi.org/10.1016/j.dsr.2021.103642].

Levin, L. A. and N. Le Bris, 2015. The deep ocean under climate change. *Science,* vol. 350, no. 6262, 13 November, pp. 766–768.

McClain, C. R. and M. A. Rex, 2015. Toward a conceptual understanding of β-diversity in the deep-sea benthos. *Annual Review of Ecology, Evolution, and Systematics,* vol. 46, pp. 623–642.

Priede, I. G. and R. Froese, 2013. Colonization of the deep sea by fishes. *Journal of Fish Biology,* vol. 83, pp. 1528–1550.

Puig, P., A. Palanques, and J. Martín, 2014. Contemporary sediment-transport processes in submarine canyons. *Annual Review of Marine Science,* vol. 6, pp. 53–77.

Smith, C. R., A. G. Glover, T. Treude, N. D. Higgs, and D. J. Amon, 2015. Whale-fall ecosystems: Recent insights into ecology, paleoecology, and evolution. *Annual Review of Marine Science,* vol. 7, pp. 571–596.

Wooley, S. N. C., D. P. Tittensor, P. K. Dunstan, G. Guillera-Arroita, J. J. Lahoz-Monfort, B. A. Wintle, B. Worm, and T. D. O'Hara, 2016. Deep-sea diversity patterns are shaped by energy availability. *Nature,* vol. 533, no. 7603, 19 May, pp. 393–396.

17

CHAPTER

Resources from the Sea

People have used the many resources that the oceans offer ever since the first humans ventured to the shore. Evidence of the use of marine life as food goes back to our African ancestors more than 150,000 years ago. More recent prehistoric evidence includes fishhooks, seashell artifacts, and mounds of empty mollusc shells. Our exploitation of marine resources is now much more sophisticated, but, unfortunately, it has also become more destructive. Fishers cross the oceans assisted by satellites, marine chemists extract wonder drugs from marine organisms, genetic engineers develop faster-growing fish, and ocean engineers investigate better ways of harvesting energy from waves and tides.

Chapter 17 examines the resources of the sea and their use, and misuse, by humans. In discussing them we will draw on our knowledge of the sea floor and the chemical and physical features of the ocean (discussed in Part One of the book) and of the types and distribution of marine life (discussed in Parts Two and Three).

17.1 THE LIVING RESOURCES OF THE SEA

The oceans are the planet's largest factory of organic matter. Humans take advantage of this productivity and harvest many different kinds of marine organisms, mostly for food.

Food from the Sea

The oceans provide food as well as employment for millions of people. The vast majority of the harvest consists of fishes, which are known in fisheries terminology as **finfish.** Finfish constitute 85% of the total world marine catch (Fig. 17.1). Molluscs and crustaceans, which together are called **shellfish,** are less important than finfish in the size of their catches but their economic value is highly significant.

Most of the world's food is grown on land, and food from the sea represents only about 1% of all the food eaten. Still, seafood is one of the world's most important foods. It is rich in protein, which is essential for normal growth. Dependence on seafood for protein is much higher in most coastal nations, especially nations dealing with poverty. The world's population is rapidly growing (Fig. 17.2), and it is increasing much faster in the places where it hurts the most: the poor, already crowded developing world.

> The marine organisms that are most widely used as food are fishes, molluscs, and crustaceans. Seafood is important to the world's population because it is a good source of protein.

Marine fisheries provide much-needed food and employment, but the world's most important fisheries are already overexploited, and some are exhausted. After increasing almost fivefold since the 1950s, worldwide catches have been decreasing (Table 17.1). It is becoming increasingly more difficult for fish catches and world fish catch nor the world grain output to catch up with global population growth. The amount of grain and fish per person has already started to decrease. The increase in fish production needed to meet the demand is being met not by marine catches but by farming of mostly freshwater fishes. The world's oceans have actually been running out of fish because of **overfishing.**

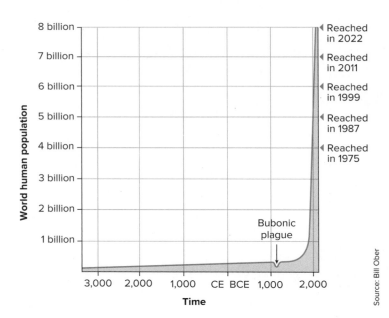

Source: Bill Ober

FIGURE 17.2 The curve illustrating the growth of the world human population over the centuries looks like a giant "J": Very slow, almost non-existent population growth followed by a sudden explosion of very fast growth. This J-shaped curve indicates that the more people there are, the faster the population grows, as was the case with the dinoflagellates shown in Figure 10.2. Growth was slow for millennia because of food shortages and disease. The domestication of plants and animals helped provide more food, but periodic famines and plagues, like the bubonic plague in Europe during the 1300s, kept the population in check. Better sanitation, advances in medicine, and more efficient agriculture eventually helped sharply reduce the death rate, and within a few centuries the population began to increase rapidly. A decrease in the birth rate of many countries, however, has slowed down global population growth. The population of the United States nevertheless continues to grow, reaching 333 million in 2021. The global population is expected to reach 8.5 billion by 2030, 9.7 billion by 2050, and could peak at 10.4 billion during the 2080s. The U.S. population is projected to reach 478 million by 2100, whereas that of Africa will rise from 1 billion in 2010 to 3.6 billion in 2100. The full effects of the COVID-19 pandemic on worldwide population growth are yet to be assessed.

Michael Melford/Getty Images

Fishing is one of the oldest human endeavors. Small-scale fisheries that involve simple gear and methods are still practiced around the world, especially in developing countries. These fisheries employ most of the world's fishing people, and provide animal protein to people whose diets are often protein-deficient.

The increased demand for seafood in affluent countries and the expansion of the world's population have steadily increased the pressure on the food resources of the

FIGURE 17.1 Although threatened by overfishing, marine fisheries provide food to millions. The importance of fish as a source of protein has increased the value of marine catches. Catches are consumed in many ways and the by-products processed into food for farmed fish, chickens, and pets, as well as, fertilizer and other products.

Table 17.1 World Commercial Catches of Selected Marine Fishes, Molluscs, and Crustaceans in Millions of Metric Tons

Catch	1975	1985	1995	2000	2005	2015	2018
Herrings, sardines, and other clupeoid fishes.	13.43	21.10	22.01	24.90	22.27	16.73	19.82
Miscellaneous pelagic fishes	Not listed	Not listed	13.93	10.64	11.30	11.14	11.06
Cods, haddocks, hakes, pollocks	11.85	12.46	10.74	8.68	8.07	8.93	9.32
Tunas, bonitos, billfishes	2.06	3.18	4.89	5.82	6.51	7.39	7.91
Salmon, smelts	0.55	1.17	1.15	0.80	1.03	1.10	1.13
Flounders and other flatfishes	1.16	1.35	0.92	1.01	0.90	0.97	0.97
Sharks, rays	0.59	0.62	0.76	0.87	0.78	0.80	0.68
Total marine fishes	**51.93**	**64.40**	**72.00**	**71.84**	**69.60**	**65.93**	**70.29**
Freshwater fishes	**5.96**	**8.74**	**5.80**	**6.80**	**8.17**	**10.13**	**10.71**
Squids, octopuses	1.18	1.79	2.94	3.66	0.73	4.71	3.64
Scallops	0.29	0.60	0.54	0.66	0.73	0.57	0.50
Clams, cockles	0.94	1.51	0.96	0.80	0.65	0.61	0.76
Oysters	0.85	1.09	0.19	0.25	0.16	0.15	0.15
Mussels	0.53	0.97	0.24	0.26	0.13	0.12	0.08
Total marine molluscs	**4.03**	**6.18**	**6.38**	**7.25**	**6.49**	**7.10**	**5.96**
Shrimps	1.33	2.12	2.44	3.08	3.20	3.44	3.46
Crabs	0.75	0.89	0.95	1.09	1.23	1.63	1.65
Lobsters	0.10	0.20	0.22	0.23	0.23	0.31	0.30
Krill	0.04	0.19	0.12	0.11	0.13	0.25	0.32
Total marine crustaceans	**2.35**	**3.42**	**4.77**	**5.91**	**5.20**	**6.06**	**6.00**
World total marine catch	**61.22**	**75.68**	**85.04**	**86.80**	**83.06**	**81.16**	**84.41**

Note: Catches tabulated in groups defined by the Food and Agriculture Organization (FAO) of the United Nations; only selected groups are listed and, when added, will not equal totals.

sea. The application of technology has greatly increased the efficiency with which many nations harvest these resources (Fig. 17.3). Nations like China, Japan, Russia, and the United States have developed high-tech fishing fleets that can remain on the fishing grounds away from the home port for long periods. Factory, or mother, ships process and store the fish taken by smaller fishing boats. The catch is processed, marketed, and sold in a multitude of ways: fresh, frozen, canned, dried and salted, smoked, as fish sticks, and as fish meal. Modern fishing ventures provide jobs not only to fishers but also to technicians, marine biologists, marketing specialists, economists, and other experts. Women and the elderly often undertake processing and marketing in developing countries, which contributes to social equity. Commercial fisheries provide a considerable portion of the export earnings of countries like Canada and Iceland and help sustain these nations' economies.

Annual global consumption of fish, both wild-caught and farmed marine and freshwater, reached 20.2 kg (45 lb) per capita in 2020, which provide about 17% of the animal protein intake and 7% of all protein, plant and animal. Worldwide fish consumption, especially in developing countries, is higher than the consumption of poultry, beef, or pork, providing almost 20% of the protein intake of more than 3.1 billion people. Seafood (marine fish and shellfish) consumption has been steadily increasing as consumers broaden their tastes and look for healthy, low-fat sources of protein. Annual per capita

consumption of seafood in China (about 38 kg [84 lb]) and Japan (43.5 kg [95.9 lb]) is the highest in the world. Annual consumption was 8.6 kg (19.0 lb) in the United States in 2020. The developed world is for the most part buying more fish rather than catching it. Japan, home to 2% of the world's population but consuming about 10% of the world's catch, buys more than twice what it catches.

Major Fishing Areas An estimated 95% of the world's major fisheries are located on coastal waters and over half of the catches are taken from less than 7% of the ocean surface (Fig. 17.4). These coastal fisheries exploit the rich waters of the **continental shelf.** Because shelf waters are shallow compared with the open ocean, it is relatively easy to harvest bottom-dwelling, or **demersal,** species. Coastal fisheries also include **pelagic** catches: fishes, squids, and other animals that live in the water column. **Primary production** is

Continental Shelf The shallow, gently sloping edge of the continents, extending from the shore to the *shelf break,* the point where the slope gets steeper.
• 2.3, The Geological Provinces of the Ocean; Figure 2.20

Primary Production The conversion by autotrophs of carbon dioxide into organic carbon, that is, the production of food.
• 4.1, The Ingredients of Life

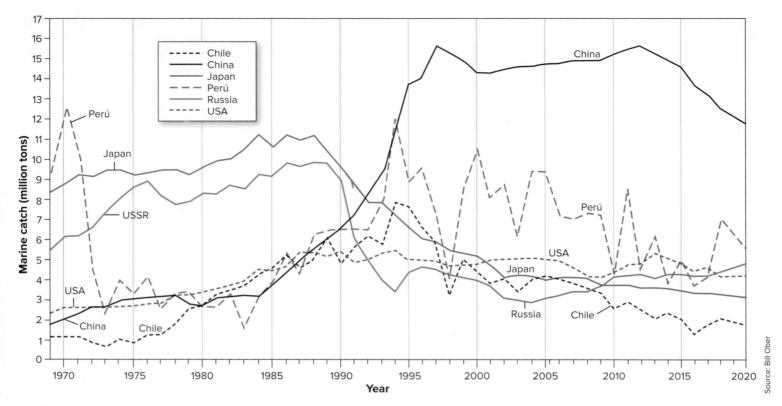

FIGURE 17.3 Marine catches by six of the major fishing nations. Indonesia, India, Vietnam, and Norway complete the top 10 fishing nations. Marine fishes constitute the bulk of the catches, but shellfish are also included, not seaweeds and marine plants. Russian catches included those from the former Soviet Union until 1990. The figures for Perú and Chile show the dramatic changes of their anchovy fisheries (see Box 17.1, "Of Fish and Seabirds, Fishers and Chickens").

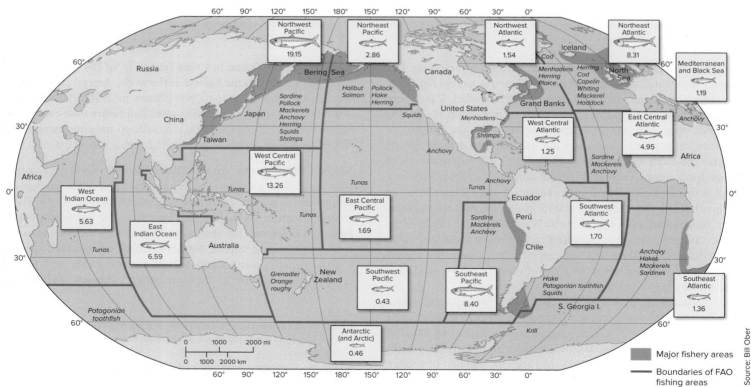

FIGURE 17.4 The major marine fishing areas of the world, based on boundaries established by the Food and Agriculture Organization (FAO) of the United Nations. Statistics refer to the 2020 marine fish and shellfish catches (in million metric tons) reported for each region. Ten of the 16 showed lower catches in 2020 than in 2019.

higher over the shelf than farther offshore, supporting much more abundant life (see Table 10.1 and Fig. 15.26). Significant coastal fisheries are found where the continental shelf is particularly wide, as in the case of the Grand Banks of Newfoundland off eastern Canada, the North Sea, and the Bering Sea.

> Most of the world's fisheries are coastal. Coastal fisheries take both bottom, or demersal, and open-water, or pelagic, catches. Other valuable fisheries are found in the open ocean far from the coast.

Notice from the map in Figure 17.4 that the largest catches are taken from the western Pacific because they are closer to nations where large populations consume large amounts of fish. Most fishing grounds in the Atlantic, Pacific, and Mediterranean are in decline or exhausted. A few other areas like the Indian Ocean and Antarctica are less exploited and still have some underexploited resources. These regions are more remote and therefore more expensive to exploit.

The open ocean, about 92% of the total area of the ocean, supports fewer fisheries than the continental shelf, but they are nevertheless very valuable. Some of the richest fishing grounds are located in **upwelling** areas just beyond the continental shelf, including those of Perú and northwestern and southwestern Africa (Fig. 17.4). Other fisheries, like those for tunas and other migratory species, extend far into the open ocean.

Major Food Species There are thousands of species of fishes, crustaceans, and molluscs, but relatively few support major fisheries. A summary of the major commercial catches is given in Table 17.1.

The largest catches are those for **clupeoid fishes,** small, **plankton-feeding** fishes that form huge schools. They include herrings (often sold as "sardines"), anchovies, sardines (sometimes called "pilchards"), menhadens, and shads (Table 17.2). Clupeoid fishes are usually concentrated over the continental shelf, but some species can also be found offshore near upwelling areas. They are caught with large **purse seines** that surround and trap the schools (Fig. 17.5b).

Herrings, anchovies, and sardines are eaten fresh, canned, or pickled. **Fish flour,** an odorless powder used as protein and dietary food supplements for human consumption, is also made from these and other fishes. About 90% of the clupeoid catch, however—particularly that of menhadens and herrings—is ground into **fish meal** to feed farmed fish, poultry, and livestock. The fish are also pressed to obtain **fish oil,** used in the manufacture of products like margarine, cosmetics, and paints as well as food for farmed fish and in omega-3 fatty acid supplements. Some of the catch is used as fertilizers and pet food. **Industrial fisheries** like these, where the catch is used for purposes other than direct human consumption, accounted for 12% of fishery products in 2018.

> Clupeoid fishes, herrings and related fishes, provide the largest catches of fish. Most are used not directly as food but in fish meal and other products.

Cods and related fishes—the pollock, haddock, hakes, and whiting (Table 17.2)—make up another important component of the worldwide catch. These fishes are all demersal, cold-water species. They are mostly caught with **trawls** that are dragged along the bottom (Fig. 17.5d). The Alaska, or walleye, pollock is the largest fishery in United States waters and in 2020 second in the world (3.5 million metric tons) after the Peruvian anchovy (see below). Overfishing threatened the fishery, but it is now considered to be well managed and **sustainable** (see below).

The Atlantic cod (*Gadus morhua*) supported a most important fishery for centuries. European fishers were already fishing for it on the Grand Banks of Newfoundland a century before the arrival of the first colonists (and probably before Columbus). It was a vital source of inexpensive protein in many parts of the world. In an age before refrigeration, cod was salted and dried before being sent to Europe (when no meat could be eaten on Fridays) and the Caribbean. The dried fish was soaked in water before cooking. Now, however, salted cod is expensive and most cods and related fishes are sold fresh or frozen.

Atlantic cod catches in Canadian and other Western Atlantic waters peaked to close to 2 million metric tons in the 1960s before collapsing in the early 1990s. The cod fishery on the Grand Banks lasted until 1992 when a moratorium was declared in an attempt to save the fishery from extinction. The Georges Bank fishery off New England was similarly closed in 1994, that off Newfoundland and Labrador, Canada in 2003. Cod was listed as an endangered species in Newfoundland, unthinkable a few decades ago. North Sea catches were also affected, dropping from 277,000 metric tons in 1971 to 59,000 metric tons in 2000. As a result, vast areas of the North Sea were closed to cod fishing in 2001. Closures caused high unemployment among fishers and related workers on both sides of the Atlantic, also threatening to destroy traditional fishing cultures.

The closing of cod fisheries across the North Atlantic is working, and cod is making a comeback. Recovery has been slow because fishes such as herring and mackerel, which are normally eaten by adult cod, became more common, and they feed on juvenile cod. Fortunately, cod began maturing at younger ages, perhaps as a response to depletion.

A total of 1.1 million metric tons of cod were taken in 2020 mostly on the northeastern Atlantic, but the 1992 Grand Banks moratorium is still in effect. The recovery of the fishery is still shaky.

Jacks (*Caranx*), mullets (*Mugil*), rockfishes (*Sebastes*) (including the ocean perches, also known as redfishes), and mackerels (Table 17.2) are also important in terms of worldwide tonnage. Canned mackerel from Asia, South America, and elsewhere has become an important source of cheap protein in some parts of

Upwelling The upward flow of nutrient-rich deep water to the surface, resulting in greatly increased primary production.
• 15.3, Epipelagic Food Webs

Plankton-feeding fishes use gill rakers, slender projections of the gills, to strain plankton from the water.
• 8.3, Biology of Fishes

Table 17.2 Examples of Commercially Important Fishes Around the World

Species	Distribution and Habits	Species	Distribution and Habits
Herrings (*Clupea*)	North Atlantic and Pacific; schooling, plankton feeders; 38 cm (15 in)	Hakes and whiting (*Merluccius*)	Temperate worldwide; demersal, feed on bottom invertebrates and fishes; 1 m (3 ft)
Sardines, or pilchards (*Sardinops, Sardinella, Sardina*)	Mostly temperate worldwide; schooling, plankton feeders; 30 cm (12 in)	Flatfishes: flounders, halibuts, soles, and others (*Platichthys, Hippoglossus*)	Mostly temperate worldwide; demersal, feed on bottom invertebrates and fishes; 2 m (6.5 ft) in some halibuts
Anchovies (*Engraulis*)	Worldwide; schooling, plankton feeders; 20 cm (8 in)		
Menhadens (*Brevoortia*)	Temperate and subtropical Atlantic; schooling, plankton feeders; 38 cm (15 in)	Tunas (*Thunnus, Katsuwonus*)	Tropical and temperate; schooling, carnivores; 4.3 m (14 ft) in the northern bluefin tuna
Cods (*Gadus*)	North Atlantic and Pacific; demersal, feed on bottom invertebrates and fishes; 1.5 m (5 ft) in the Atlantic cod (no longer this large)	Mackerels (*Scomber, Scomberomorus*)	Tropical and temperate worldwide; schooling, carnivores; 2.4 m (8 ft)
Alaska, or walleye, pollock (*Theragra chalcogramma*)	Temperate North and Central Pacific; demersal, feeds mostly on bottom invertebrates and fishes; 90 cm (35 in)	Salmon (*Oncorhynchus, Salmo*)	North Pacific and Atlantic; open ocean and rivers, carnivores; 1 m (3 ft)
Haddock (*Melanogrammus aeglefinus*)	North Atlantic; demersal, feeds mostly on bottom invertebrates; 90 cm (35 in)		

Source: Bill Ober

Note: Fishes are not drawn to scale. The measurements given are of the approximate maximum length.

the world. Flounders, halibuts, and other flatfishes are important catches in the United States, Canada, and other countries. Salmon, though now caught in much smaller numbers than formerly, is a very valuable catch, especially in the North Pacific. Salmon are caught both along the coast and in the open ocean. The fishery is threatened, however, by overfishing and environmental degradation, especially the destruction of salmon breeding sites (see "Migrations," in 8.3). Practically all salmon consumed now is farmed (see below).

The most important open-ocean fisheries are those for several species of tunas (Table 17.2). The migration routes of tunas crisscross the oceans, mostly in tropical waters (see Fig. 8.22). Skipjack, yellowfin, albacore, bigeye, and bluefin tunas command high prices in world markets (see Box 17.2, "Aquaculture of Bluefin Tunas"). They are caught by modern fleets that use sophisticated techniques to spot the schools in mid-ocean. Tunas are caught with large seines, surface **longlines,** or **gill nets** (Fig. 17.5). The fishing boats are equipped with freezers so that the tuna can be brought to port long after they are caught. Besides these high-tech fleets, some local, small-scale fisheries continue to exploit bonito, skipjack, and other tunas. Most tunas are eaten in affluent countries, either canned or raw (Fig. 17.7).

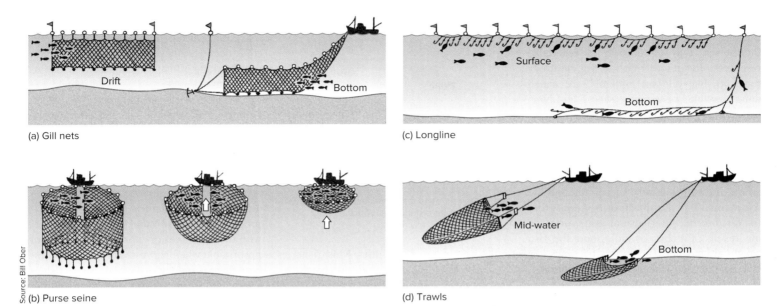

Source: Bill Ober

(a) Gill nets

(b) Purse seine

(c) Longline

(d) Trawls

FIGURE 17.5 Examples of fishing methods. *Gill nets* (*a*) can be highly effective, and their mesh size and length are often regulated for taking particular catches (see Fig. 17.10) or for reducing by-catch. *Purse seines* (*b*) are especially important for capturing schooling fishes like clupeoid fishes and tunas. The use of *longlines* (*c*) and *trawls* (*d*) is controversial due to the large, unintentional by-catch (see below).

Molluscs are the second most valuable group of marine food species after fishes. Several types of cephalopods provide the largest catches of molluscs (Table 17.1). Squids (Fig. 17.6), cuttlefishes, and octopuses are especially popular. Other important food molluscs are clams (*Macoma, Mercenaria, Mya,* and many others), oysters (*Ostrea*), mussels (*Mytilus*), scallops (*Pecten*), abalones (*Haliotis*), and a few other gastropods like conch (*Strombus*; Fig. 13.18) in some regions.

Crustaceans are prized as food the world over. Major fisheries exploit many species of shrimps (or "prawns") and lobsters, all of which bring a high price. Crabs like the blue (*Callinectes sapidus*), king (*Paralithodes camtschaticus*), and Dungeness (*Cancer magister*) are also harvested.

Other groups of marine organisms are also eaten, though they do not contribute much to global fisheries production. Seaweeds, particularly kelp, are consumed in many cultures, especially in Asia (see Box 6.1, "Seaweeds for Gourmets"). Most seaweeds are farmed for **carrageenan**, which is used as an emulsifier. Sea urchins are esteemed for their gonads, or roe, which command a high price, particularly in Japan. There is a fishery for the red sea urchin (*Strongylocentrotus franciscanus*) in California. Most of the roe is exported to Japan or sold to Japanese restaurants where, known as *uni*, it is eaten raw. Some species of sea cucumbers, known as *trepang* or *bêche-de-mer*, are dried, boiled, smoked, or eaten raw in China and other Asian countries. Examples of other invertebrates used as food are jellyfishes in Asia, gooseneck barnacles in Spain, and polychaete worms in the South Pacific.

Sea turtles are still hunted and their eggs gathered, even where they are protected. Seals and whales are also eaten in some places, and there are traditional fisheries for marine mammals in the Arctic (see Fig. 4.2), North Atlantic, West Indies, and South Pacific. These traditional fisheries are a source of considerable controversy because most of the species involved are endangered.

Optimal Yields and Overfishing Like all living things, species we harvest for food reproduce to replace the individuals that are lost

Journey is bliss/Shutterstock

FIGURE 17.6 Squids are often dried in Japan, Korea, and other Asian countries. Dry squid is popular as a dry snack or eaten cooked in many ways. Fishers use lighted boats to catch the squid at night.

to disease and predators, including humans. Because these living resources can replace themselves, they are known as **renewable resources.** Resources that are not naturally replaced, like oil and minerals, are called **non-renewable resources** (see Non-Living Resources from the Sea Floor, below). Experience has shown, however, that, though the food resources of the ocean are renewable, they are not inexhaustible.

If, for example, a new, untapped population of sardines is very successful, and the fishers make handsome profits, soon other fishers join in. After several years, **overfishing** results: Catches dwindle, and the fish caught are smaller. The fishery becomes unprofitable, and many, if not most, of the fishers go out of business.

What happened? The reproductive rate of sardines—or salmon, or scallops—depends, at least in part, on the size of the population, or **stock,** as it is known to fisheries biologists. Like dinoflagellates growing in a jar (see Fig. 10.2), fish stocks grow fastest when there are neither too few nor too many individuals in the population. If the population size is very small, the number of young being born is also small because there are not many potential parents. If the population is too large, competition, overcrowding, and diseases slow down the growth rate. The number of new young, that is, the population growth rate, is highest at some intermediate population density (Fig. 17.8).

To harvest the stock in the optimal way, one must consider this feature of population growth. Obviously, it would be foolish to harvest the entire stock at once, because no individuals would be left to reproduce, and the fishery would be destroyed forever. If the fishery is to last indefinitely, or to be **sustainable,** the number of fish caught can be no more than the number of new fish added through reproduction; if more are caught, the population will decline. The **sustainable yield** of a population is the amount that can be caught and just maintain a constant population size. In other words, the catch is just large enough to prevent the population from growing but not so large as to reduce it.

Because the growth rate depends on the population size, so does the sustainable yield. When the stock is large, it is held in check by natural mortality, and even a small harvest causes a reduction in the population. Very small populations also have a low growth rate, and fishing is more dangerous because it can threaten the stock and drive the species to the brink of extinction.

The highest catch that can be repeated year after year without threatening the stock is called the **maximum sustainable yield.** It occurs at medium population size, when the natural growth rate is highest. From the point of view of profit and food production, this can be thought of as the optimal catch.

The size of the catch, and therefore of the stock, is directly related to **fishing effort:** how many boats and fishers there are, how long they stay at sea, and so forth. When little effort is put into the fishery, the catch is obviously small. Only a small fraction of the stock is removed by fishing, and the population grows until limited by natural factors. The population remains secure, but the fishery yields less food and less profit than it could safely sustain. With

FIGURE 17.7 Raw fish, shrimp, seaweed, scallops, and sea urchin roe are used in *sushi* and *sashimi,* Japanese delicacies that have become popular around the world.

more intense effort, the catch exceeds the maximum sustainable yield. Before long the stock declines and catches fall no matter how much fishing effort is expended: Overfishing has occurred.

A plot of the sustainable yield versus fishing effort gives us a **catch-effort curve,** which is very similar to a plot of the population growth rate versus the size of the stock (Fig. 17.9). The maximum sustainable yield occurs at moderate levels of effort, which result in intermediate stock sizes.

Another problem is that the biological properties of most stocks do not mix well with the principles of economics or with politics. Most fisheries are profitable when harvested at the level of the optimum catch. As long as there is money to be made, more fishers and more boats will be attracted to the fishery, and the catch will exceed the optimal level. In an open fishery, one that is completely unregulated, market forces inevitably lead to overfishing. A fishery can still be profitable to some fishers, even if catches are below the maximum sustainable yield. The total profit from the fishery, however, decreases.

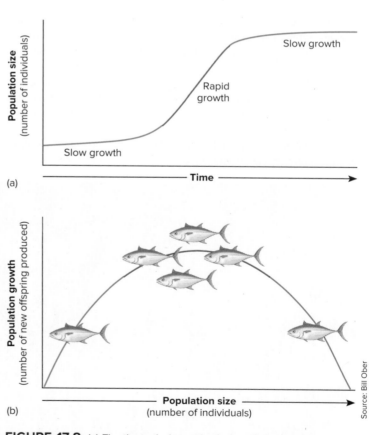

FIGURE 17.8 (*a*) The theoretical growth of a population begins with just a few individuals. At first, with only a few adults to produce offspring, the population increases very slowly (blue line). As the population size gradually increases, so does the number of offspring, and the rate of growth begins to increase (red line). Eventually, the population reaches the point where limiting factors like food shortage and crowding prevent further growth (blue line). (*b*) The rate of growth is directly related to population size and is maximal, thus at intermediate abundances. Also see Figure 10.4.

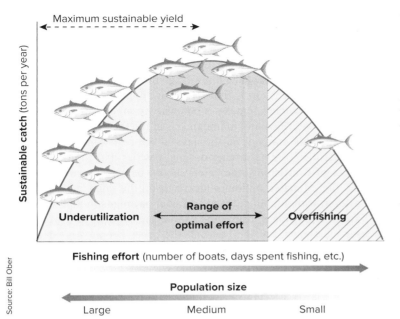

FIGURE 17.9 A generalized, theoretical curve showing that as fishing effort increases, so does the catch, but only up to a point, which is the biologically optimal catch at the maximum sustainable yield. After this point the overexploited fishery will yield smaller and smaller catches as the effort increases. The curve is called a catch-effort curve.

Overfishing results when catches are higher than the maximum sustainable yield, or optimal catch. Supply-and-demand forces almost always result in overfishing if a profitable fishery is left unregulated.

The Food and Agriculture Organization (FAO) of the United Nations estimated in 2011 that out of the 600 stocks of marine fishes it monitors, 52% were **fully exploited** and were close or had reached the maximum sustainable yield, 17% were **overexploited** (or **overfished**), and 7% were already **depleted,** both being below the maximum sustainable yield. Only 3% were **underexploited.** FAO estimated that only 65.8% of fisheries were sustainable, a drop from 90% in 1974. Progress has been made and 82.5% of the 2019 landings were from sustainable stocks, a 3.8% improvement over 2018. Still, 34% of the stocks were classified as overfished in 2017. Most of the top-10 commercial species, which account for almost a third of global catches, are fully depleted (see Special Report, Stripping the Sea Bare, Fig. 19). Good examples are the stocks of cod, herring, halibut, salmon, Alaskan king crab, and other species in the North Sea and the North Atlantic and North Pacific. As with the great whales (see "Conservation of Cetaceans," in 9.3), fishing effort in these fisheries has long surpassed the optimal catch (see Special Report, Stripping the Sea Bare, Fig. 20). Overfishing is by far the biggest threat for fish species listed as endangered or vulnerable to extinction (see Table 18.1). The traditional major fishing areas of the world are not the only ones becoming exhausted. Small-scale local, or **artisanal**, fisheries in the tropics, where most people live and where food is needed the most, are being rapidly decimated. Artisanal fisheries contribute a third to half of all global catches that are directly consumed by humans. Their decline constitutes a major cultural loss as well.

Most of the world's fisheries are already fully exploited, and at least a quarter or more are overexploited or even exhausted.

The danger of overfishing can be particularly serious in herrings, anchovies, and other clupeoid fishes. These species often undergo dramatic population cycles and can therefore be especially vulnerable to fishing pressure. This is the situation in the Peruvian anchovy, or *anchoveta* (*Engraulis ringens;* see Box 17.1, "Of Fish and Seabirds, Fishers and Chickens").

Overfishing is threatening many other species, particularly large fishes like tunas, swordfish, and sharks. Around 90% of the biggest fishes in the world oceans are already gone, taken by commercial fishing fleets. Only around 10% of the original stocks remain. The remaining fishes are also smaller than before the intensive fishing started, an average of half the size 20 years ago in the case of tunas. Small females produce less eggs than large females, and, at least in some species, larvae from small females are smaller and grow slower than larvae from larger females.

The disappearance of the most valuable fishes, which happen to be higher in the trophic pyramid, has forced fishing lower on the pyramid, or fishing down the food web (see Special Report, Stripping the Sea Bare, Fig. 21). Such a shift can cause unknown changes in the whole ecosystem, like an increase in the number of non-utilized plankton or in undesirable predators like jellyfishes, or sea jellies, and comb jellies.

Bigeye tuna (*Thunnus obesus*), for example, were about two times as heavy and eight times more abundant in the 1950s than at present. The northern, or Atlantic, bluefin tuna (*Thunnus thynnus*) is among the largest of bony fishes and the most valuable. Bluefin stocks are overfished, but recovering thanks to the enforcement of regional fishing quotas (see Box 17.2, "Aquaculture of Bluefin Tunas"). Sharks, also large in size and slow to grow and reproduce, have critically declined in many parts of the world (see Box 8.1, "Shark!"). Recent estimates show that 37% of the species of sharks and rays are threatened with extinction.

The swordfish (*Xiphias gladius*), another prized food fish, has also been victim of overfishing. North Pacific populations fell approximately 70% between 1960 and the late 1990s, and most of the fish were caught before they were old enough to reproduce. A campaign to reduce consumption of swordfish was very successful, and ultimately swordfish fisheries closed in large areas of United States waters in the Atlantic and Gulf of Mexico. Longline fishing for tunas was also closed in some areas because many swordfish are caught and killed on longlines. Swordfish stocks have now recovered and no longer overfished, at least in the North Atlantic and Pacific, an example of the effect of consumer pressure and successful management.

Habitat destruction is another threat to fishery resources. Estuaries, mangrove forests, seagrass beds, and other threatened environments are critical breeding grounds and nurseries for fishes, lobsters, shrimps, scallops, and other valuable species. Three-quarters of the commercial catch of the United States consists of species that inhabit estuaries during part of their life (see 12.4, Human Impact on Estuarine Communities). Bottom trawls are very destructive to seafloor life, another form of habitat damage (see "Trawling," in 18.1). Seamounts, inhabited by many unique species, are particularly vulnerable (see Box 16.2, "Biodiversity in the Deep Sea").

By-catch, the species that are caught unintentionally while fishing for other species, is another problem (see Fig. 18.14). It is estimated that around 25% of the worldwide catch, roughly 23 million metric tons, is by-catch. A good portion of the by-catch, however, goes unreported. The swordfish caught and killed on longlines set for tunas are one example of by-catch; longlines also catch sharks, marlin, turtles, seabirds, dolphins, and other marine life. Trawling also produces a lot of by-catch. This is particularly true of shrimp fisheries, where as much as 95% of the total catch is by-catch because of the small size of the net's mesh. Some of the by-catch is kept but much of it is discarded. Even if it is released alive, most of the discarded by-catch dies. A large part of the by-catch in trawl fisheries is juveniles of valuable species sought in other fisheries, or worse, of protected species like cod in the North Atlantic. **Ghost fishing,** trapping by abandoned fishing gear like gillnets, longlines, and various kinds of traps, also kills uncounted numbers of marine life each year.

Another threat to fisheries is pollution from sewage, oil spills, and toxic chemicals. The high level of mercury in large fishes like tunas and swordfish is of particular concern (see "Heavy Metals," in 18.2). **Global warming** (see Special Report: Climate Change) is also a problem. Some species of fish are spreading away from the tropics by moving to cooler or deeper waters. Such changes could disrupt breeding cycles and cause shifts in food requirements and in the effect of predators. A 2019 study found that rising water temperatures worldwide for 80 years have reduced the catch of 124 fish and shellfish species by an average of 4.1%.

Managing the Resources A fishery is regarded as collapsed if catches fall below 10% of historic highs. Nearly one-third of all the species that are fished have already collapsed, and around 60% are predicted to collapse by 2025. Some scientists have concluded that *all* of the world's fishing stocks will collapse by mid-century if no drastic measures are taken to curb overfishing, by-catch, destruction of habitats, and pollution. Good management, however, has yielded some signs of improvement in some regions. Fisheries should be harvested in a way that does not deplete them beyond recovery. Fisheries must then be managed to ensure their long-term value. The wise management of fisheries stocks is not an easy task. For one thing, the maximum sustainable yield can be very difficult to estimate as fisheries biologists need detailed information about the size of fisheries stocks, how fast individuals grow and reproduce, how long they live, and what they eat (which often changes at different stages of the life cycle; see Fig. 15.24). Such information is rarely easy to obtain and is often unavailable. Biologists may have to rely on rough assumptions, making their estimates of the optimal catch less reliable.

Furthermore, real fisheries are much more complex than we have indicated. The smooth catch-effort curve shown in Figure 17.9 represents a simplified model and does not take many natural features into account. For example, the harvested species could be **competing** with other species, and fishing pressure might alter the competitive balance. Schools can get smaller as a result of fishing. This might not only make the fish harder to catch but also affect their behavior and reproduction. Simple models do not consider the size of the fish caught, but it makes a difference whether large, older individuals or small, younger ones are caught, for example,

because large individuals typically produce more eggs than small ones. The time of year when fishing is done and whether the catch is taken before or after the breeding season can be important. These complexities can have dramatic consequences and could cause a fishery to fail unexpectedly if not taken into account.

A major problem is that the actual population size of most commercial catches remains unknown. We may assume that fishing at an "intermediate" abundance is at the theoretical "optimal" level and this may not be the case in the real world. Given the uncertainties of determining optimal catches and the disastrous effects of overfishing, the catch should be set somewhat lower than the estimated optimum just to be on the safe side. A fisher, however, with a family to feed and boat payments to make, might have different ideas. The same can be said of dockyard workers, gear merchants, bankers, and all the other people who depend directly or indirectly on the fishery. If the catch is harvested by more than one nation, international relations also come into play. Thus, fisheries management is a complex, often controversial, matter that is affected by economic and political factors as well as biological ones.

There are a number of ways to manage the fishery once a catch level is agreed on. The total could may be limited by closing the season as soon as the target catch is reached or by restricting the length of the season, the number of boats or fishers, or the areas open to fishing. The size and power of boats can be limited or certain methods of fishing can be banned altogether. By regulating the mesh size of nets, fishers could be prohibited from taking individuals of certain sizes (Fig. 17.10). Leaving the largest individuals to reproduce can help in the recovery of overfished stocks. If sexes can be told apart, fishers could be prohibited from taking females.

The total collapse of once thriving fisheries has sometimes forced the use of drastic measures. Governments could reduce their fishing subsidies, they could pay fishers to give up fishing, or a fishery could be closed altogether. Complete closures, however, are in effect less than 1% of the world's fishing grounds. Besides preventing overfishing, management measures can be undertaken to help restore stocks that have become depleted. These measures could involve the improvement and protection of essential habitats or the transplantation of artificially raised young.

The management of fisheries to prevent overfishing includes the establishment of quotas, restrictions on the type of fishing gear, establishing marine protected areas, and other measures.

Fishing rights over a nation's territorial waters are a complicating factor in the management of resources. A country's territorial waters traditionally extended 3 nautical miles (5.5 km) offshore. Some nations, however, began to exclude fishing fleets from other nations by extending their territorial waters. Fishing disputes even led to wars. A general compromise was finally reached in 1982 with the **United Nations Convention on the Law of the Sea (UNCLOS;** see 18.5, Prospects for the Future), so far ratified by 168 nations, but not by the United States. It allows nations to establish an **exclusive economic zone (EEZ)** 200 nautical miles (370 km) offshore. Nations can completely control their fisheries, oil, and mineral resources within this zone. Nations are required to use their resources in a

Box 17.1 Of Fish and Seabirds, Fishers and Chickens

The ocean has been good to Perú. As the cold Perú Current flows northward, coastal upwelling (see Fig. 15.30) pumps nutrients from the depths. The resulting increase in primary production supports a rich harvest of plankton that in turn feeds immense schools of the Peruvian anchovy, or *anchoveta* (*Engraulis ringens*). This high productivity is a critical part of a complex cycle that has had tremendous consequences for the economy of Perú.

Clouds of cormorants, boobies, and other seabirds have gorged themselves on the anchovy schools for centuries. The birds roost and nest on small islands along the coast. With hardly any rain to wash them away, the birds' droppings slowly build up in the dry climate. The droppings have accumulated into layers as thick as 45 m (150 ft). This thick crust, called **guano,** is rich in nitrogen and phosphorus and is an excellent fertilizer.

The fertilizer starts out miles away, when organic matter sinks to the depths of the Pacific. When the organic material decomposes, nitrate and phosphate, the main nutrients for phytoplankton, are released into the water. The nutrients remain in the dark depths, unavailable to phytoplankton, until upwelling eventually brings them into shallow water along Perú's coast. Here they are taken up by phytoplankton, which form the base of the food web. The plankton are eaten by the anchovies that feed the guano-producing seabirds. Nutrients thus travel from the depths of the Pacific to the coastal islands of Perú with the help of upwelling, plankton, anchovies, and seabird droppings!

And then people came along. Guano, a valuable agricultural fertilizer, was mined and exported. The guano industry brought considerable wealth to Perú, and by the end of the nineteenth century millions of tons had been mined. Though it is still harvested from around 20 guano islands as valuable sustainable organic fertilizer (94,900 metric tons by 2022) what took thousands of years to deposit was mostly used up in a matter of decades.

The anchovies were next. A commercial anchovy fishery was established in the

Fishers unloading a net full of Peruvian anchovies.

Islas Ballestas, guano islands off Pisco, Perú.

1950s and grew to unprecedented dimensions. It became the world's largest single fishery and made Perú number three in terms of total marine catches (after China and Indonesia) in 2020 (Fig. 17.3). Catches continued to increase, except in years when El Niño, the warm currents that occasionally arrive at the end of the year, interfered with upwelling (see "The El Niño–Southern Oscillation," in 15.3).

Most of the catch is exported as fish meal for fish farming (aquaculture) and chicken feed. Fish meal from Perú became the world's largest source of protein meal.

By the late 1960s, the annual catch surpassed the estimated optimal, or maximum sustainable, yield of around 10 million metric tons a year. After the 12.3-million-metric-ton catch of 1970, the fishery collapsed. The 1972 El Niño added to these woes. The guano-producing seabirds suffered a dramatic decline. Around 4 million now live on the Peruvian coast, down from 20 million in the 1950s.

The early 1970s collapse had widespread effects. The price of other protein meals, particularly soybean meal, increased. In Brazil alone, several million acres of rain forest were cleared to grow soybeans.

Another dramatic collapse of a fishery is that of the Pacific sardine (*Sardinops caerulea*), which supported a booming fishery in California immortalized by John Steinbeck in *Cannery Row* (see Box 1.3, "John Steinbeck and Ed Ricketts"). The fishery crashed in the 1940s. The reasons for its collapse and that of the Peruvian anchovy are not entirely clear. Overfishing was not the only cause. Clupeoid fishes like anchovies and sardines naturally undergo population cycles. It may well have been that the combination of heavy fishing pressure and a dip in the natural cycle pushed these fishes over the brink. El Niño also enters into the picture. Harvest records since the beginning of the twentieth century show that, when the Peruvian anchovy was thriving, the Pacific sardine occurred in low numbers, and vice versa. Populations of these two Eastern Pacific species thus appear to have cycles that are opposite to each other for reasons that are not clear. It has been speculated that warm water in the Pacific due to a strong El Niño translates into high sardine and poor anchovy harvests; cool water has the opposite effect.

Since its collapse, annual catches of the Peruvian anchovy have varied from a low of 93,654 metric tons in 1983 to 9.8 million metric tons in 1994 (Fig. 17.3), becoming again the world's largest marine fish catch. The El Niño caused a 78% drop in the catch, to 1.7 million metric tons, in 1998. It soon recovered, however, and by 2000 the catch was 11.3 million metric tons. The annual catch fluctuated around 7.0 million metric tons from 2006 to 2009, decreasing to 3.1 million metric tons in 2014, but rebounding to 7.0 million metric tons in 2018 (but decreasing to 4.9 million metric tons in 2020), still the largest fishery in the world. The Peruvian government has now established annual fishing quotas but the exact maximum sustainable yield remains unknown.

sustainable way. They can keep foreign fishers out if they wish or sell fishing licenses to foreign fleets. EEZs cannot always be policed, of course, and foreign fishers can sneak in and fish without permission or with illegal gear.

More than 90% of the ocean's present fisheries, lie within the EEZ of one nation or another, but the high seas are still considered common property. A number of potential new fisheries lie outside territorial boundaries and thus are open to all nations.

 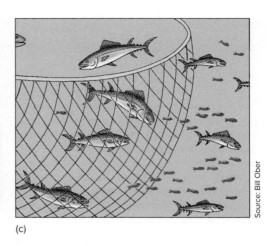

(a) (b) (c)

Source: Bill Ober

FIGURE 17.10 Both the size and species of fishes caught by nets can be controlled by the net's mesh size. A fine net might catch both sardines and tunas (*a*). With a larger mesh size the sardines escape and only tunas are caught (*b*). With an even larger mesh size only large tuna are taken (c).

Furthermore, fishing regulations are being increasingly ignored as catches diminish.

> The establishment of an exclusive economic zone (EEZ) allows nations to protect fishing and other resources 200 nautical miles around their shores.

In the United States, which has signed but not yet ratified UNCLOS, the **Sustainable Fisheries Act** of 1996 required federal fisheries managers to develop management plans to prevent over-fishing, restore depleted stocks, and reduce by-catch, the first time protection has been extended to non-commercial species. Vessels of foreign nations that have signed fishing agreements with the United States are allowed to fish in United States waters only after receiving a fishing permit. The 2003 **Pew Oceans Commission** went further by calling for policies to protect marine ecosystems. Such policies are beginning to yield results. By the end of 2021, of the 460 commercial and recreationally important marine stocks being monitored in United States waters, 80% (201) of 252 previously overfished stocks are no longer being overfished.

Efforts toward the better management of fisheries have already brought about positive results elsewhere. Several important fisher-ies around the world are now being successfully managed, as in the case of the Atlantic cod fishery (see above). Fish from these sus-tainable fisheries or farms are often "eco-labeled" so that consum-ers differentiate them from seafood from overexploited or poorly managed sources. The role of consumer awareness is most import-ant. We should choose fish from fisheries that are sustainable and as a result, have less of an impact on the environment. DNA tests will be widely used to identify fish caught from unsustainable or illegal fisheries.

The establishment of **marine protected areas,** or **MPAs,** in many parts of the world (see map in Appendix D) is another way of restoring and protecting fisheries. Fishing in MPAs can be either banned or strictly managed. A banning of all commercial fishing

for at least 16 years in most of the Arctic Ocean was agreed upon in 2018. It has been demonstrated that **biodiversity** (number of species) and **biomass** (abundance of particular species) in MPAs are higher than in non-protected areas. Non-protected areas open to fishing benefit by offspring and adults settling in from protected areas (see 18.4, Conserving and Enhancing the Marine Environment).

Illegal Fishing. Illegal, unreported, and **unregulated fishing (IUU fishing)** account for an estimated 20–50% of the worldwide catches. IUU fishing could be as high as 20 million metric tons a year, but we will obviously never know the size of the catch. Many illegal fishing boats do not enforce international maritime law and enter into other countries' exclusive economic zones (EEZs). Ille-gal fishing has become a common practice off the coasts of Africa, Southeast Asia, South America, and the Pacific Islands (including the Galápagos), threatening the livelihood of local (and legal) fish-ers and depriving millions of much-needed proteins. Squid, a pop-ular human food across East Asia, is particularly sought. Squid is also a crucial food of many marine species, particularly tuna. Some boats licensed to catch tuna are also known to illegally take shark fins, swordfish, Antarctic toothfish, and other valuable catches. Others use drift nets to illegally catch tuna. Illegal bottom-trawling particularly damaging to the marine environment (see "Trawling," in 18.1), and illegal longline fishing kills seabirds and other by catch (see 18.3, Threatened and Endangered Species).

Tracing illegal fishing boats on the high seas, as well as their catches, is a challenging task. Satellite-based surveillance systems and other electronic monitoring are used to trace illegal fleets. Some of these technologies are based on the radar detection of GPS-based automatic signals (AIS) from radio beacons that large ships are required to keep turned on to avoid collisions. Illegal boats, however, often turn off their beacons, but satellites pro-vided with a new technology can detect these boats by detect-ing faint signals from the radars and radio communication of the boats. Also used are satellites that sensor the night lights used in squid fishing. Helping in the task is a 2016 international agreement so far ratified by 55 nations that forbids the landing

Dale Glantz

FIGURE 17.11 *Pleuroncodes planipes,* also called the lobster krill or tuna crab, is a pelagic crab that has been suggested as a potential source of human food. Large swarms of the crab, each having a maximum length of 13 cm (5 in), are often washed ashore on the Pacific coast of California and Mexico, turning beaches bright red. A possible problem with this plan is that *Pleuroncodes* is an important food for tunas.

of vessels suspected of illegal fishing. DNA samples are also used to identify suspected illegal catches that make their way into markets.

New Fisheries Fisheries biologists have long been interested in tapping new or underexploited fisheries. One possibility is to increase the use of by-catch. The main problem with much of the by-catch is that many consumers simply will not buy it. What is considered a delicacy in one place is junk in another. Hake (*Merluccius;* Table 17.2), for instance, is prized in Europe but not in the United States. Croakers and sea robins are common throwaway fishes in the United States that are eaten elsewhere. California market squid (*Doryteuthis opalescens*; Fig. 7.28*b*) is caught in large numbers in California, but most of the catch is exported, primarily to China. Some of it is repacked, and sent back for consumption in California. Squids are a delicious source of lean protein, but some consumers were suspicious of the sucker-armed molluscs, though marketing squid by its Italian name of *calamari* has increased its appeal. A name change also helped overcome consumer resistance to eating dolphinfish (*Coryphaena hippurus*), a fish and not a dolphin. The more seductive Hawaiian name of *mahimahi* helped enhance its marketability.

One use of the by-catch is to process it into products that have more market appeal. In the *surimi* process, for example, low-value fish is washed to remove fat, minced, and mixed with flavorings and preservatives. Appropriately shaped, it is sold as imitation crab, lobster, shrimp, or scallop. Alaskan pollock has been the main component, but less desirable fish species are also be used. Processed fish products like fish sticks could also open the market to less popular catches. Unwanted catches could also be converted into fish flour and used to protein-enrich all sorts of processed foods.

The highly productive waters around Antarctica are often mentioned as potential sources of commercial catches. Antarctic catches include various fishes, squids, and krill (Fig. 17.12). Even in the harsh conditions of Antarctic waters, however, overfishing is taking its toll. The Patagonian and Antarctic toothfishes (*Dissostichus*), marketed as "Chilean sea bass" in the United States, has been seriously depleted, mostly by illegal fishing.

There are other potential sources of seafood. Some of these are underutilized. Others are unconventional species like squid and other cephalopods, flying fishes, and pelagic crabs (*Pleuroncodes*; Fig. 17.11). Lanternfishes (*Myctophum;* see Fig. 16.6) represent another potential fishery. They are found in deep water but migrate to the surface at night in the **deep scattering layer** forming dense schools. These and other species of the mesopelagic zone remain underexploited or completely unexploited mainly because of lack of consumer acceptance or the absence of efficient fishing methods. Some could eventually support successful fisheries, though probably for fish meal rather than for human consumption. The development of a new fishery must nevertheless be undertaken only after a careful investigation of the biology of the species in question, particularly on their interactions with other species in the community.

Measures to increase the supply of food from the sea include an increase in the exploitation of by-catch, underutilized species, and the development of new fisheries.

Aquaculture Instead of overfishing the dwindling natural food resources of the oceans, why not raise marine organisms as we do farm animals? This is not a new idea. The Chinese have been doing it with freshwater fishes for thousands of years, the Romans farmed oysters, and the early Hawaiians built walled fish ponds along the coast to raise mullet and milkfish (*Chanos chanos*). The

Deep Scattering Layer Animals, mostly fishes and shrimps, that migrate vertically between the mesopelagic and epipelagic zones.
• 16.1, The Twilight World

application of farming techniques to the growth and harvesting of aquatic organisms is known as **aquaculture. Mariculture,** the agriculture of the sea, is specifically applied to the farming of marine and brackish-water, or estuarine, organisms. The worldwide culture of marine and brackish-water fishes reached 8.3 million metric tons in 2020 with an estimated value of $36.2 billion. Figures for mollusks, mostly oysters, reached 17.5 million tons worth $29.8 billion, and crustaceans, mostly shrimps, 6.8 million tons worth $81.5 billion. Figures for all groups of marine and brackish-water species combined are almost three times the volume and almost nine times their value in 2000 (11.9 million metric tons with a value of $16.7 billion), show the rapid growth of marine aquaculture (see Fig. 17.13). The 2020 figures double if the culture of seaweeds (35.0 million metric tons with a value of $16.5 billion) is included. The culture of freshwater animals (mostly fishes) in 2020 was 54.4 million metric tons, with a value of $265 billion. Aquaculture has also grown more than three times faster than livestock production on land, making aquaculture the world's fastest-growing food-production sector. In fact, farming salmon is about seven times more efficient than raising beef. Demand for seafood is expected to grow more than 3% annually (against 2% in meat) as the result of the growth in population and incomes as well as in the status of fish

FIGURE 17.12 Krill (*Euphausia superba*) form dense schools in Antarctic waters and was considered potential human food. Predictions of annual catches in millions of tons did not materialize (see Table 17.1). Overfishing could also affect the many Antarctic species that depend on krill as a food source (see Figs. 10.14 and 10.15). It is one of the world's largest underexploited catches, although it is now harvested to feed farmed salmon and is used as a source of omega-3 fatty acids.

Gerald Corsi/Getty Images

as a healthy food. It is clear that this increased demand must be met by aquaculture because of the stagnant growth in global fish catches. Dwindling catches mean an even higher consumer price for wild-caught fish. Nearly half of all the fish and shellfish consumed around the world today is farmed, although consumption is

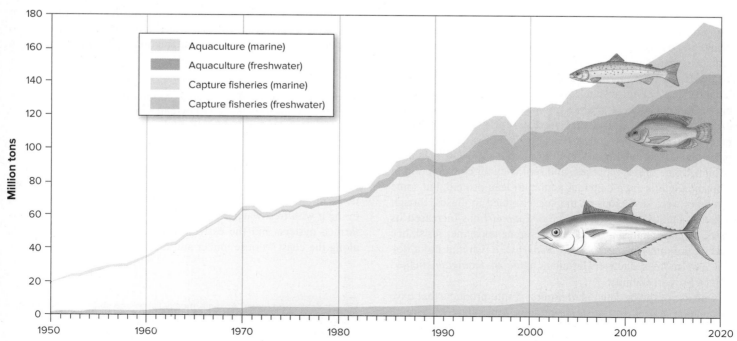

FIGURE 17.13 Global aquaculture production is increasing, whereas catches, especially of marine species, have remained steady. Notice the reduction in catches as a result of the effect of the COVID-19 pandemic on fishing effort worldwide.

Source: Adapted by Bill Ober from Science, vol. 370, no. 6519, 20 Nov. 2020.

EYE ON SCIENCE

Box 17.2 Aquaculture of Bluefin Tunas

The International Seafood Sustainability Foundation reported in 2017 that 48% of the 23 stocks of the seven major commercial species of tunas are being overfished or are already overfished. Only a few, like skipjack tuna (*Katsuwonus pelamis*), remain underexploited. Of particular importance are the three species of bluefin tunas, all of which are overfished: the Atlantic, or northern (*Thunnus thynnus*) tuna, the Pacific (*Thunnus orientalis*), and the southern (*Thunnus maccoyii;* see Fig. 1.17), which is found across the Southern Hemisphere. As a result of overfishing, the southern bluefin is listed as endangered by the International Union for Conservation of Nature and Natural Resources (IUCN) (see Table 18.1). The Pacific is listed as vulnerable, just below endangered, with an estimated 2.6% of the pre-exploitation numbers remaining. The most valuable species of tunas are nevertheless recovering, the result of the enforcement of fishing quotas.

The value of bluefin tunas, which *sashimi* and *sushi* connoisseurs value for their dark-red meat, increases as the fish, particularly large ones, become scarcer. Bluefins constitute a luxury food, with individual fish sold in Tokyo for as much as $3 million (about $11,000 per kg or $5,000 per lb) in 2019!

The Atlantic fisheries of about 30 species of tunas and related fishes are managed, in part through fishing quotas, by the International Commission for the Conservation of Atlantic Tunas (ICCAT). The Mediterranean populations of the Atlantic bluefin have been halved in size since the 1970s, but efforts to ban fishing or to stop international trade have failed and in 2014 ICCAT allowed a 20% increase in the fishing quotas for the Mediterranean and eastern Atlantic bluefin. There is also the problem of illegal fishing. Although ICCAT has implemented an electronic system for recording bluefin catches since 2011, there is evidence that catches have been far higher than those declared by boat skippers. Bluefin is also part of the by-catch of longliners targeting other catches. Differences of opinion between economists, politicians, biologists, and conservationists, as in the case of whales, have slowed down progress toward an agreement.

High prices, high demand, particularly in Japan, which consumes 80% of all bluefin tunas, and dwindling stocks have encouraged the farming of bluefins. Atlantic bluefin is farmed throughout the Mediterranean, Pacific bluefin in Japan and on the Pacific coast of Mexico, and southern bluefin in Australia (see Table 17.3). Schools are caught in giant purse seines, slowly grown and fattened in floating pens (a practice known as "tuna ranching"), harvested, and flown refrigerated or frozen to fish markets. Tuna ranching unfortunately does not help in replenishing the dwindling natural populations because bluefins normally do not reproduce in floating pens. Tuna ranching only helps by slightly decreasing the number of fish that are taken from the wild.

Attempts are consequently being made to raise bluefins from eggs to sexually mature adults that have never been in the wild. This domestication process could provide highly priced fish for human consumption and ultimately help save bluefins from eventual extinction. Major breakthroughs in the breeding of bluefins in captivity have been made by researchers in Japan, Australia, Spain, and Italy. In 2002 a team at Kindai University, Japan raised for the first time the complete life cycle from eggs to reproducing adult bluefins. Other efforts, including land-based projects replacing floating pens, are underway in other countries, including the United States. One technique involves implanting into adults a device that slowly releases a synthetic version of a hormone, gonadotropin-releasing hormone, or GnRH, that triggers spawning of sperm and eggs. This hormone appears to not be naturally produced in captive bluefins. Fertilization results in minute larvae that slowly develop into spawning adults in at least four years. Japanese scientists have so far been able to breed domesticated bluefin to a third generation. A Spanish team first reported in 2010 spontaneous spawning without the use of hormonal induction in the Atlantic bluefin, a major breakthrough in the domestication of bluefins.

After more than 50 years of effort, the Aquaculture Technology and Production Center at Kindai University is commercially raising Pacific bluefins from eggs. They reported shipping 21,460 metric tons in 2021. Two-year-old fish, each weighing as much as 20 kg (44 lb), are being sold in Japan and other countries. The hope is to ultimately produce bluefins in a sustainable, environmentally friendly way in enough quantities to relieve pressure on the dwindling wild stocks.

For more information, explore the links provided on the Marine Biology *Online Learning Center.*

mostly of freshwater fishes. Aquaculture has made China the largest producer and exporter of seafood in the world. Though aquaculture is used primarily to grow food species, it is also used to grow commodities like cultured pearls (see "Bivalves," in 7.5) and fishes for the aquarium, or ornamental, trade.

Aquaculture of marine species is a growing activity due to the dwindling marine catches and an increase in the demand for seafood.

Traditional aquaculture is still practiced in several parts of the world, particularly in Asia. Milkfish is farmed in ponds filled with brackish water (Fig. 17.14). The immature fish, or fry, are captured from the wild, transferred to the ponds, and fed with agricultural by-products. In this way, wastes are converted to fish flesh that is cheaper to produce than pork or beef. These fish farms provide not only high-protein food but jobs as well. FAO estimated in 2018 that 20.5 million people (of which 19% were women) were employed by aquaculture operations worldwide. This figure is still lower than capture fisheries, which employed 39.0 million people, of which 12% were women.

With various modifications, similar operations are used to farm other fishes, molluscs, shrimps, and seaweeds in many parts of the world. The fry or spat (immature bivalve molluscs) are transplanted to favorable sites in bays or even along mangrove forests (Fig. 17.15) and estuaries (including fjords). Shrimp aquaculture has shown tremendous growth, and the farming of marine species is a significant source of foreign exchange earnings for several developing countries. Farmed shrimp now account for a substantial portion of the shrimp consumed around the world. Salmon and other fishes are raised in large floating pens or cages (Fig. 17.16). Oysters, mussels, and other molluscs are grown on racks, in baskets, hanging from rafts. Aquaculture of these filter-feeding molluscs can be particularly successful because it is a self-supporting system that does not involve adding food, fertilizers, or antibiotics. These kinds of fish, shellfish, and seaweed farming are examples of **extensive aquaculture**, farming that relies only on natural conditions and food sources. A reward of extensive aquaculture of shellfish and seaweeds is that it can provide food and habitats to native marine species, thus helping local biodiversity. Mussel farms, for example, have been found to have as many as three times more invertebrates and fishes than nearby areas.

Sometimes, however, the farming of high-value food species is a different story. In what can best be described as the domestication of marine organisms, growth is maximized by almost totally controlling the organisms and their environment (see Box 17.2, "Aquaculture of Bluefin Tunas"). Aquaculture is then said to be **intensive** because food, often in the form of pellets, is provided, and water quality in artificial ponds or tanks is controlled in order to maximize production.

Aquaculture, be extensive or intensive, poses many problems, and relatively few marine food species can be farmed (Table 17.3). Most species need specialized sites and equipment to be farmed successfully. Water pumped into tanks or other holding facilities must be free of pollutants and carefully checked for temperature, salinity, and other factors. Food can be a problem because the various stages of a species usually have different food requirements. This is a particular problem when trying to culture planktonic larval stages because they require specially cultured food. Still, it takes less food to grow a pound of fish than it takes to grow a pound of chicken, pork, or beef. With a few exceptions, fishes are "cold-blooded" and don't need energy, and hence extra food, to keep a relatively constant body temperature as birds and mammals do. Predators and disease-causing organisms must be periodically removed or killed. Parasites and disease can be devastating under the crowded conditions typical of culture operations. Viral infections are a serious problem in salmon and shrimp

FIGURE 17.14 Milkfish (*Chanos chanos*) is harvested from floating cages and brackish-water ponds in Southeast Asia. Some will be eaten, others allowed to mature and spawn to replenish the cages and ponds. The fish are shown in the insert.

The Vanzi Library

FIGURE 17.15 An oyster farm (*Crassostrea*) in a mangrove forest in Thailand photographed at low time.

Tapui/Shutterstock

farming. Crowded conditions also tend to cause cannibalism among fishes and crustaceans.

Commercial aquaculture is nevertheless a challenge that many fisheries scientists are willing to accept. It is now possible, for example, to freeze shrimp sperm, ensuring year-round reproduction. We have learned to induce the settlement of the planktonic larvae of abalone, a valuable mollusc. Scientists have created oysters with three sets of chromosomes, instead of the normal two, which makes them sterile. Normal oysters develop a strong taste when their eggs mature, but sterile ones, which do not produce eggs, are always

Table 17.3 Examples of Marine and Brackish-Water Species Used in Commercial Aquaculture

Farmed Species	Examples of Regions Where Farmed
FISHES	
Atlantic salmon (*Salmo salar*)	Australia, Canada, Chile, Europe, U.S.
Cobia (*Rachycentron canadum*)	Central America, Southeast Asia, U.S., West Indies
Cod (*Gadus*)	Europe, U.S.
Flatfishes (*Solea* and others)	Europe, U.S.
Horse mackerel (*Trachurus*)	Japan
Milkfish (*Chanos chanos*)	Southeast Asia
Mullets (*Mugil*)	Mediterranean, Southeast Asia
Pacific and southern bluefin tunas (*Thunnus*)	Australia, Japan, Mediterranean, Mexico
Pacific salmon (*Oncorhynchus*)	Canada, Chile, Japan, U.S.
Puffer (*Fugu*)	Japan
Red seabream (*Pagrus major*)	Japan
Yellowtail (*Seriola*)	Japan
MOLLUSCS	
Abalone (*Haliotis*)	Australia, Japan, South Africa, U.S.
Clams, cockles (*Anadara, Ruditapes*, and others)	China, Korea, Japan, Southeast Asia
Mussels (*Mytilus, Perna*)	Europe, New Zealand, U.S.
Oysters (*Crassostrea, Ostrea*)	Australia, China, Europe, Japan, Korea, Taiwan, U.S.
Scallops (*Pecten, Patinopecten*)	Europe, Japan, U.S.
CRUSTACEANS	
Shrimps (*Penaeus* and others)	Bangladesh, China, Ecuador, India, Japan, Mexico, Southeast Asia, U.S.
SEAWEEDS	
Red (*Gracilaria, Kappaphycus, Porphyra*) and brown (kelp: *Laminaria, Undaria*) algae	Japan, Chile, China, Indonesia, Japan, Korea, South Pacific, Southeast Asia, U.S.

The farming of lobsters from eggs to marketable individuals is a major challenge, mostly because of difficulties in raising the planktonic larvae. Juveniles of several species are nevertheless being commercially ranched in holding cages. Several ambitious projects, however, have been successful in experimentally raising the eggs of a few species of lobsters to a marketable product, a technology that one day hopes to be applied commercially.

Expensive equipment and specialized personnel further restrict the number of farmed species. Species that are farmed are usually those that command high prices, and some of those that can be farmed are not farmed because it is not profitable. Instead of mass-producing cheap protein for a hungry world, aquaculture tends to provide variety in the diet of the affluent.

Another drawback of aquaculture is pollution. Fish farming in which thousands of fish are concentrated in ponds along the coast or in extensive floating pens releases huge amounts of feces, urine, and uneaten food, which ultimately degrade water quality. The decomposition of these wastes depletes oxygen in the water and releases nutrients that can trigger harmful algal blooms. Farmed fishes also concentrate toxic chemicals. Furthermore, the production of fish meal, often used as food in fish farming, is an energy-consuming process that releases greenhouse gases. Aquaculture now uses almost 70% of the fish meal and 90% of the fish oil produced worldwide. There is pressure to develop plant-based food to at least partially replace fish meal.

Some fish farms also use chemicals like antibiotics, pesticides, and synthetic pigments, which could be harmful to surrounding marine life. Another risk is the introduction of parasites and diseases to local marine species in the wild. Even more devastating can be the destruction of the natural environment. Clearing for shrimp and fish farms (see Fig. 12.25), for example, has caused the destruction of mangrove forests, salt marshes, and other coastal communities (see 12.4, Human Impact on Estuarine Communities). This destruction has reduced the stocks of local species that use mangrove forests and salt marshes as nurseries. Though shrimp is a profitable product, less food is actually produced than in the destroyed environments. Introduced farmed species that escape are potentially harmful to native species and the communities they live in, and catching fish from the wild to feed farmed fish, a common practice, can also deplete wild fisheries. Escaped Atlantic salmon breed with wild populations and dilute the **genome** of the wild populations, perhaps making the offspring more vulnerable to diseases and other natural stresses.

tasty. Different strains of oysters are being bred in efforts to develop faster-growing and larger hybrid oysters, very much as in plants.

Rather than raising them all the way to harvest, salmon and other species are grown for only a short time, then released as fry or juveniles to enrich natural populations in a process known as **seeding.** In some places salmon are held in captivity their entire lives, from hatching to harvest. In other places the salmon are released as juveniles to feed and grow at sea. Several years later they return as full-grown adults to the stream where they were released. Not only can they be caught by commercial and sport fishers, but they swim right back to the hatchery, where the ones not used for breeding can be caught and harvested. This practice is known as **salmon ranching**. Salmon raised from young stages in offshore enclosures, which is known as **salmon farming** (Fig. 17.16), is responsible for making salmon the most important fish raised at sea. Although more expensive, salmon is now being raised in inland freshwater farms in several parts of the world. One advantage is that these farms are not responsible for coastal pollution.

piola666/Getty Images

FIGURE 17.16 Most salmon consumed worldwide is farmed Atlantic salmon (*Salmo salar*), which has made Norway the most important salmon-producing nation in the world. Fish-meal-fed salmon is raised in cages anchored offshore, and the harvested fish flown to consumers around the world. There have been serious environmental problems related to salmon ranching in second-ranked Chile (where Atlantic salmon was introduced, with more than 1 million tons produced in 2020) and elsewhere. Decomposition of feces and uneaten food depletes bottom oxygen in once-pristine waters. Salmon farming in Norway is sustainable and rigorously monitored.

There are also major concerns about the effects that harmful **polychlorinated biphenyls,** or **PCBs,** antibiotics, and other chemicals could have on human consumers. These contaminants accumulate on farmed fishes, particularly salmon.

Some fisheries scientists and economists are nevertheless optimistic. They predict that aquaculture will provide relatively cheap food. They pin these hopes on the development of technological improvements such as new ways to farm species

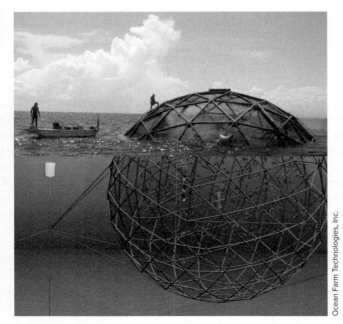

Ocean Farm Technologies, Inc.

FIGURE 17.17 Mobile, wire-mesh pens of different shapes and sizes are being used in the offshore, or open-ocean, aquaculture of shrimps and of many types of fishes. Food is piped in from barges or boats.

(Fig. 17.17). Other options are pumping nutrient-rich water from the deep sea to provide better culture conditions or from sewage discharges and use it to grow the planktonic algae that are fed to the larvae of fish and other species. The application of **genetic engineering** and other forms of **biotechnology** to aquaculture allows scientists to identify genes carrying desired traits or alter genes of a species to produce **genetically modified (GMO)** varieties that grow faster or larger, are disease resistant, better tasting, or more nutritional. A GMO Atlantic salmon that grows faster and larger than conventionally farmed salmon has been approved for human consumption in the United States. This GMO salmon carries a chinook salmon gene that, together with a gene from a third unrelated fish, regulates growth hormone. There is experimental evidence that the GMO salmon is at a disadvantage when it tries to reproduce, easing concerns that escaped fish could breed with wild populations. The development of sterile individuals can also result in fish that use energy, not for reproduction but for growth.

Even if the number of marine species that can be farmed is limited, together with concerns about pollution and destruction of habitats, new technologies such as genetically modified (GMO) varieties offer improved prospects for the future of marine aquaculture.

Marine Life as Items of Commerce and Recreation

The living resources of the sea are used in many ways other than food. Chemical compounds that are obtained from marine organisms, or **marine natural products**, are used in medicine (see Box 17.3, "Take Two Sponges and Call Me in the Morning"). Timber and charcoal are obtained from mangroves. Jewelry is made from pearls, shells, and black and precious corals; leather from sharks and other fishes. Many of these resources, however, are being overexploited. Mangrove forests are being rapidly cleared, and black and precious coral have disappeared in many areas.

For millions, the living resources of the sea provide relaxation. Divers, surfers, and marine recreational fishers support a multibillion-dollar business worldwide, buying gear and traveling long distances to pursue their hobbies. Whale-watching cruises and diving tours offer opportunities for nature lovers, also supporting the tourist industry that provides jobs and help many local and national economies. Marine resources, however, need to be protected and managed in a sustainable way with a minimum of disturbance, something that unfortunately is not always the case.

Business and recreation are also combined in the thriving aquarium trade. Though the aquarium hobby is dominated by freshwater fishes, marine aquaria enjoy much popularity, with at least 2 million keeping them worldwide. The export of colorful marine tropical fishes is a significant component of trade in

Box 17.3 Take Two Sponges and Call Me in the Morning

Obtaining drugs from the sea is not an easy task. It involves a sharp eye, intuition, good luck, and lots of frustration. It means diving in awesome coral reefs as well as working countless hours in the chemistry lab.

Colorful attached invertebrates that live in coral reefs—sponges, soft corals, sea squirts—are good candidates for biomedical research. Though seemingly defenseless, these very visible, soft, attached animals are rarely eaten by hungry fishes or crabs. This fact suggests that they have some type of defensive mechanism. Many of these colorful invertebrates are known to produce unique natural products that make them taste bad or allow them to get rid of hostile neighbors, and these chemical substances could have properties that can be beneficial to humans as well.

Resistance in humans to known antibiotics has prompted the search for new ones, particularly among deep-water microbes. Bacteria living in sea squirts and other invertebrates are sources of new drugs useful in drug-resistant fungal infections.

Marine organisms of potential value as drugs are collected, frozen, and sent to the lab for analysis. Crude extracts undergo trials to test their ability to kill or inhibit the growth of bacteria (that is, to act as antibiotics), fungi, and viruses as well as their effect on cancer cells and for their potential use as anti-inflammatory agents. Laboratory animals and cultures of cells or tissues are used in these

This sponge from coral reefs in Fiji (*Acanthella cavernosa*) contains a potent chemical that kills worms, including some human parasites. The chemical is being tested for its potential use as a drug. The sponges are cultured on ceramic plates tied to plastic netting.

Reprinted by permission of D. Mendola. ©CalBioMarine Technologies, Leucadia, California.

trials. Any promising extracts are further separated and chemically identified. Chemicals with particularly promising properties are then used by pharmaceutical companies to develop new drugs. This process entails another long series of tests that ultimately includes rigorous clinical testing on humans.

Sponges and gorgonians are a rich source of natural products; some act as antibiotics, whereas others have anti-inflammatory or painkilling properties. A bryozoan (*Bugula neritina*) is the source of bryostatin, a promising drug in the fight against cancer. So is didemnin B from a Caribbean sea squirt (*Trididemnum*). Squalamine, which circulates in the blood of sharks, has antibiotic and antifungal properties. It is being tested for its

ability to starve tumors by cutting off blood supply. Shark cartilage, however, has shown not to be effective against cancer, as some had claimed. Horseshoe crab blood is used to test for contaminant bacteria in vaccines, injections, and space probes. Deep-sea bacteria and archaea, dinoflagellates, and seaweeds are cultured to study their anti-tumor capabilities.

The toxins, or poisonous substances, found in many marine organisms are also of potential value in medicine. Tetrodotoxin, the powerful toxin from certain pufferfishes and porcupine fishes (see Box 5.3, "Symbiotic Bacteria—the Essential Guests"), for example, is used in Japan as a local anesthetic and as a painkiller in terminal cancer patients. Some conotoxins, a group of toxins from cone shells (*Conus,* see Fig. 10.7), are used to treat chronic pain. Other conotoxins are undergoing clinical tests as painkillers and to treat epilepsy and depression.

Marine organisms are also used as remedies in traditional medicine, mostly in Asia, a practice that has resulted in devastating effects on many species (see 18.3, "Threatened and Endangered Species").

Although the use of marine natural products in medicine can sound promising, only relatively few of them have made their way into pharmacies and hospitals. Nevertheless, one never knows what's waiting to be discovered in the tissues of a sponge, sea cucumber, or sea anemone on a distant coral reef.

countries like the Philippines and Indonesia. The worldwide trade of aquarium marine life is estimated to be worth more than $330 annually, with the United States as the largest importer. The unrestricted collection of marine life for the trade can nevertheless be very destructive to the natural environment. Aquarium fishes are often collected by using poisons or explosives that kill hundreds or thousands of fish for every one that makes it to the pet shop. The management of aquarium-species harvests, however, has helped reduce the impact of collecting in some places by harvesting reef fishes in a sustainable way.

17.2 NON-LIVING RESOURCES FROM THE SEA FLOOR

Oil and Gas

Oil and natural gas were among the first of the sea's non-renewable resources to be used commercially. In the late 1800s it was discovered

that some California oil fields extended well offshore beneath the seabed. The oil was extracted using oil rigs mounted on wooden piers that extended out from shore. Underwater oil and gas deposits have resulted from millions of years of decomposition under high pressure of buried sediments rich in diatoms and other organic matter.

The offshore oil industry has undergone tremendous expansion since the 1970s because the high price of oil and gas makes offshore drilling immensely profitable. Oil and gas production on the continental shelf now occurs in the Persian Gulf, the Gulf of Mexico, the North Sea, in the South Atlantic off Brazil, and in other areas on all continents except Antarctica. A large percentage of the continental shelves around the world is considered a potential source of oil and gas, and drilling has now extended into deeper water beyond the shelf. The melting of the Arctic ice cap due to climate change

Genome The complete genetic information of an organism.
• 4.1, The Ingredients of Life

has made the Arctic seabed particularly attractive. The enormous economic potential of these reserves was one of the factors that prompted the establishment of EEZs to protect national interests.

The continental shelves are a major source of oil and natural gas.

Exploiting offshore oil and gas can be a difficult and costly operation, especially when the deposits lie many miles offshore as they do in the North Sea. Powerful currents, huge waves, and miserable weather compound the problems.

Overcoming these difficulties has been a major accomplishment of ocean engineering. Exploratory drilling is done from drill ships or partly submerged or elevated platforms that can be towed from place to place and anchored in position on the sea floor. Once oil or gas is found, huge steel or concrete platforms are erected and secured to the bottom to extract it (Fig. 17.18). Remotely controlled submarines are being used to build facilities on the bottom, which include pipelines to transport the oil or gas to terminals on land.

Another potential source of energy from the sea floor is **methane (CH4),** a major constituent of natural gas. Vast stores of methane, both as bubbles and in the form of frozen compounds, **methane hydrate** (or **clathrates**), have been found in frozen Arctic soil or deep under the ocean floor worldwide. Methane hydrates consist of methane molecules locked within ice. Methane is a product of microbial decomposition of organic matter but the gas can be locked into the ice due to low temperature and/or high pressure. If warmed, methane hydrates revert back to water and methane, which can be used as fuel. It has been suggested that the energy contained in all methane hydrate deposits could be higher than that contained in all other known fossil fuels. Japan was the first nation to successfully extract natural gas from methane hydrates taken 25 km (15.5 mi) offshore in 2013. Some methane hydrate deposits have been found at shallower depths, which could require scooping rather than drilling. It will be some time, however, before the technology needed to exploit this resource is developed. One drawback is that methane is a **greenhouse gas** that may escape into the atmosphere and accelerate **global climate change** (see Special Report: Climate Change).

The potential threat of oil pollution, however, is a factor of great concern (see "Effects of Oil on Marine Life," in 18.2). Pollution from drilling operations can affect coastal ecosystems, fisheries, and recreation. As a consequence, oil and gas drilling have been banned or strictly regulated in many coastal regions.

Ocean Mining

The seabed is a potential source of many minerals, and perhaps the planet's richest source. Though most marine deposits are not presently exploited, ocean mining will become more viable as we develop new technologies and as high-grade ores on land become exhausted.

Sand and gravel for the construction industry are mined along beaches and offshore in many parts of the world, exceeding quantities extracted on land. Some tin and even diamonds and gold are mined from offshore deposits brought to the seabed by rivers.

One potential source of minerals is the offshore deposits of phosphates, which are used as fertilizers. Another potential source are **polymetallic nodules,** lumps of minerals that are scattered on the deep-ocean basins beyond the shelf. Polymetallic nodules contain manganese, nickel, copper, and cobalt, all of which are important to industry. Large amounts of "rare-earth" minerals, needed for hybrid-car batteries and other types of electronic technologies, have been found as deep as 6,000 m (nearly 20,000 ft) in the Pacific along a tract running from south of Hawai'i to off the coast of Mexico.

Perhaps the most promising source of minerals are the seafloor **massive sulfide deposits** that are found along the mid-ocean ridges and **hydrothermal vents.** The minerals are extracted from deep in Earth's crust as hot water percolates through volcanic fissures and vents. They are deposited when the hot water emerges and hits the cold ocean water. These deposits are rich in copper, lead, and zinc.

Polymetallic nodules and other mineral-rich deep-sea deposits are potential sources of valuable minerals.

There are huge technical problems associated with mining the deep-sea floor. It is expensive, mainly because of the tremendous depths. The detrimental effects of mining on the surrounding environment, similar to the destruction of habitats caused by trawling (see "Trawling," in 18.1), have also been raised. The ownership of mineral resources that lie outside the EEZ is another issue. The United Nations' International Seabed Authority oversees mining in international waters, granting licenses to contractors to explore

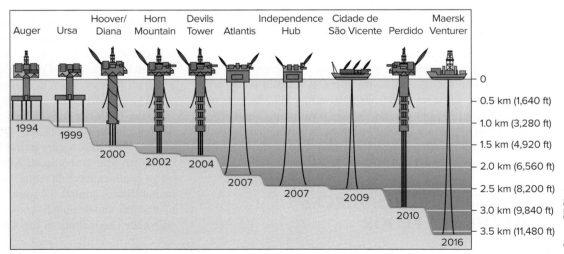

FIGURE 17.18 Offshore oil-drilling rigs and ship platforms have been built to get oil from deeper water farther offshore than ever before.

Source: Bill Ober

resources at particular places. As metal prices rise, however, deep-sea mining could become more attractive. Several private companies continue to investigate the prospects of deep-water mining (Fig. 17.19), but there have been increasing demands for a moratorium or an outright ban on commercial deep-sea mining.

17.3 NON-LIVING RESOURCES FROM SEAWATER

Energy

The ocean is a vast reservoir of renewable energy that can be put to human use. Harnessing this energy is the objective of several concepts that could help ease our dependency on fossil fuels and reduce carbon dioxide (CO_2) emissions.

Mill wheels have been used since ancient times to harness **tidal energy,** the energy contained in the normal ebb and flow of the tides. Modern schemes call for the construction of large barriers across narrow bays and river estuaries in areas where the **tidal range** is high, at least 3 m (10 ft). Water moving in with the high tide is caught behind the barrier, and locks are opened to release the water at low tide. The flowing water drives turbines that generate electricity from mechanical energy, just as in the hydroelectric plants in river dams. One such plant has been operational in northwestern France since 1966, and another has started generating electricity in the Orkney Islands north of Scotland (Fig. 17.20).

The use of tidal energy is pollution-free and relatively efficient, but the resulting changes in the tidal patterns can be risky. The rich marshes in estuaries can be damaged or destroyed, and pollutants from other sources tend to accumulate upstream because normal tidal flushing is restricted. River flows can also be altered, increasing the risk of floods. The artificial lagoon created upstream, however, can be used in recreation, as in the case of the French plant.

Wave energy from wind-generated waves and strong ocean currents is another potential source of energy, particularly in areas subject to powerful waves. As with tidal energy, water flow can be converted into electricity by turbine generators. Wave energy is being used to power navigation buoys. Several projects, mostly experimental, are being developed in Europe, Australia, and the United States (Fig. 17.21).

Another way to harvest energy from the ocean is to take advantage of the temperature difference between surface and deep water, a process called **ocean thermal energy conversion (OTEC).** Several pilot plants already in operation or planned throughout the Pacific and Indian oceans and the Caribbean. OTEC plants circulate ammonia, propane, or another liquid that boils at low temperature through pipes bathed in warm surface water (Fig. 17.22). The liquid evaporates and the gas is forced through turbine generators to produce electricity. The pipes then flow through cold water pumped up from the deep, condensing the gas back into a liquid, and the cycle repeats. Temperature differences of at least 20 °C (36 °F) between the surface and below are needed, a condition met in the tropics. Electricity generated by OTEC could be sent ashore by power lines, or used at sea for various industrial operations, including the desalination of seawater into fresh water (see below). The

FIGURE 17.19 ROVs (remotely operated vehicles) were used to explore the ocean floor off Papua New Guinea for minerals containing gold, silver, zinc, and, in an underwater photo, copper. The proposal collapsed in 2019, partially because of potential environmental problems.

cold, nutrient-rich water pumped from the deep could be used for aquaculture or to grow algae for animal feed, fertilizers, or biofuels (see Box 6.2, "Marine Algae as Biofuels").

An indirect way of using the ocean as a source of energy are the offshore solar-panel plants that are already operational or planned, offshore wind farms already common in the North Sea and China, and floating nuclear power plants in the planning stage.

Hydrothermal Vents Undersea hot springs associated with the mid-ocean ridges encircling Earth, where new material is added to Earth's crust.
• 2.3, The Geological Provinces of the Ocean

Ions Charged atoms or groups of atoms that are formed when salts are dissolved in water.
• 3.1, The Waters of the Ocean

Tidal Range The difference in height between successive high and low tides.
• 3.3, Waves and Tides

 Source: Bill Ober

FIGURE 17.20 A tidal-power scheme became operational in 2021 in the Orkney Islands north of Scotland. As the strong tidal currents flow, blades rotate and turbines in the device generate up to 2 megawatts of electricity, enough to power 2,000 homes. The device, 72 m (236 ft) long, is anchored at a depth of 35 m (115 ft). A subsea cable connects to the local electricity grid.

Several challenges have affected the development of new technologies to harness energy from the ocean. Problems include not only corrosion and the effects of exposure to the elements, but **biofouling,** the unwanted growth of seaweeds, encrusting animals, and microorganisms.

Potential sources of electricity from the sea include tides, waves, currents, and the temperature difference between surface and deep water.

Fresh Water

Desalination plants that convert seawater into fresh water were first built in desert and semi-desert coastal regions that lack a sufficient supply of fresh water, for human consumption or to grow crops. Widespread water shortages, however, have now made desalination a more feasible source of fresh water, so that the number of people using water from desalination plants has more than doubled in the past decade. Nearly 17,000 desalination plants have been built around the world. The largest so far, like one in Saudi Arabia that produces more than 1 million m³ (260 million gallons) of fresh water daily, are in the Middle East. Several small nations elsewhere now produce more desalinated water than that they obtain from natural sources.

Several desalination systems are used. The process of reverse osmosis, for example, uses a membrane that allows water to pass through but blocks the passage of ions, thus desalinating the water. Reverse osmosis plants are becoming common in small-scale projects like resorts as well as in large desalination plants. Desalination, however, requires a great deal of energy and is therefore expensive. It also produces a highly saline residue that can cause environmental problems (see "Thermal Pollution," in 18.2). New methods that use a renewable energy sources like solar panels, or wind or wave power, should make desalination more practical and economical. Still, saving fresh water is cheaper than desalination or recycling it.

Minerals

Every naturally occurring element on Earth is present in seawater, but mostly in extremely small quantities (see Table 3.1), the result of chemical dissolution from rocks on land or from hydrothermal vents (see "Seawater," in 3.1). The chief product obtained from seawater is **table salt,** or sodium chloride (NaCl), which is composed of the two most abundant ions in seawater, sodium and chloride. Salt, a

Simon Waldman/Alamy Stock Photo

(a) (b) (c)

FIGURE 17.21 Several experimental devices have been designed to tap energy from waves. The sea snake (a) consists of several long, floating segments that rise and fall in relation to each other as the result of wave action. Internal hydraulic rams drive generators that produce electricity. Small turbines secured on the bottom (b) or paddles with buoyant flaps (c) have also been envisioned as ways of generating electricity.

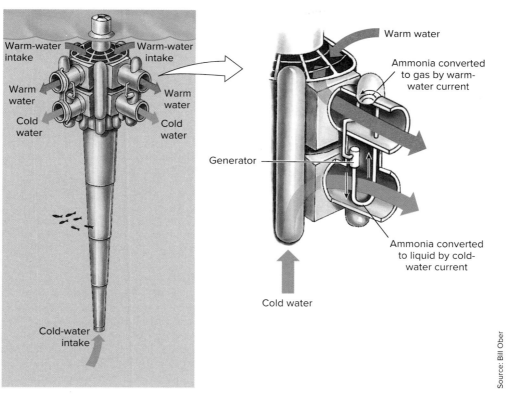

Source: Bill Ober

FIGURE 17.22 This ocean thermal energy conversion (OTEC) plant is an experimental model consisting of a platform containing generators and a long tube for obtaining cold water.

precious commodity to ancient civilizations, has been produced for centuries by evaporating seawater. Most of the other constituents of seawater are difficult to extract because they are present in such small amounts. Magnesium and bromine are also obtained from seawater but valuable trace metals like uranium could one day be commercially extracted.

Seawater is a potentially rich source of renewable energy, fresh water, and minerals.

Interactive Exploration

McGraw-Hill Connect® is a great place to check your understanding of chapter material. Visit **www.mcgrawhillconnect.com** for access to interactive chapter summaries, chapter quizzing, and more! Further enhance your knowledge with video clips and web links to chapter-related material.

Critical Thinking

1. For the last three years the annual catches of a commercially important fish have been above the maximum sustainable yield. One option is to decrease the fishing effort by decreasing the number of fishers. This, however, would cause unemployment in a region where unemployment is already high. What other options might ensure a lower fishing effort? How could they be carried out?

2. Aquaculture of many food species is expensive, and often only high-priced species are raised, being of little help to the poor nations where food is needed the most. What measures and new developments might help increase the value of aquaculture to these poor nations?

3. It has been suggested that cheap electricity generated from tides, waves, or currents could be used to pump nutrient-rich water from the deep. The water could then be used to grow algae to feed the larvae of farmed fishes and invertebrates. How else could this energy be used to decrease the costs of aquaculture?

4. A species of shrimp is being considered for farming in coastal areas. List the major questions and issues that must be investigated before deciding to go ahead and farm the species.

For Further Reading

Some of the recommended reading may be available online. Look for live links on the *Marine Biology* Online Learning Center.

General Interest

Bourne, J. K., 2014. How to farm a better fish. *National Geographic,* vol. 225, no. 6, June, pp. 92–113. Recent developments in aquaculture have resulted in the production of more farmed fish than beef.

Bourzac, K., 2018. The briny deep. *New Scientist,* vol. 239, no. 3194, 8 September, pp. 32–35. Seawater desalination is becoming a more viable solution to the problem of severe freshwater shortage in many regions.

Brower, K., 2014. Quicksilver. *National Geographic,* vol. 225, no. 3, March, pp. 66–87. The Atlantic bluefin tuna is threatened by relentless overfishing.

Drahl, C., 2019. Shell game. *Science News,* vol. 195, no. 11, pp. 18–21. Biodegradable seafood-shell waste can be converted into plastic substitutes.

Fagan, B., 2017. *Fishing: How the sea fed civilization.* Yale University Press, New Haven, CT. Commercial marine fisheries have had a major impact on societies around the world.

Harris, M., 2016. Saltwater solution. *Scientific American,* vol. 315, no. 1, July, pp. 68–71. Plants genetically modified to survive salt could be farmed for food.

Kish, S. W., 2020. The bounty of the sea. *Oceanus,* vol. 55, no. 2, Fall, pp. 22–27. The oceans provide not only food and pharmaceuticals, but are a source of mental and physical health to humans.

Korten, T., 2020. Chasing the pirates. *Smithsonian,* vol. 51, no. 5, September, pp. 38–51, 82. Efforts are being made to stop or at least decrease pirate fishing that illegally targets fragile species worldwide.

Kwok, R., 2016. Runaway fish. *Science News,* vol. 190, no. 6, September 17, pp. 22–26. Fishes escaping from marine farms can have a serious effect on native wildlife.

Lawton, G., 2021. Plenty more fish in the sea? *New Scientist,* vol. 249, no. 3321, 14 February, pp. 36–40. The author examines the concept of sustainable fisheries as applied to the real world.

Peackock, T. and M. H. Alford, 2018. Is deep-sea mining worth it? *Scientific American,* vol. 318, no. 5, May, pp. 72–77. Deep-sea mining could ease demand for some minerals but it could cause serious environmental damage.

Royte, E., 2020. Surge engine. *Smithsonian,* vol. 51, no. 1, May, pp. 44–57, 100. A scheme to generate clean electricity from the Bay of Fundy, eastern Canada, which features the world's largest tidal range.

In Depth

Alleway, H. K., C. L., Gillies, M. J. Bishop, R. R. Gentry, S. J. Theuerkauf, and R. Jones, 2019. The ecosystem services of marine aquaculture: Valuing benefits to people and nature. *BioScience,* vol. 69, pp. 59–68.

Braña, C. B. C., K. Cerbule, P. Senff, and I. K. Stolz, 2021. Towards environmental sustainability in marine finfish aquaculture. *Frontiers in Marine Science* [https://doi.org/10.3389/fmars.2021.666662].

Carranza, A. and P. S. E. zu Ermgassen, 2020. A global overview of restorative shellfish mariculture. *Frontiers in Marine Science* [https://doi.org/10.3389/fmars.2020.00722].

Dayanidhi, D. L., B. C. Thomas, J. S. Osterberg, M. Vuong, G. Vargas, S. K. Kwartler, E. Schmaltz, M. M. Dunphy-Daly, T. F. Schultz, D. Rittschof, W. C. Eward, C. Roy, and J. A. Somarelli, 2021. Exploring the diversity of the marine environment for new anti-cancer compounds. *Frontiers in Marine Science* [https://doi.org/10.3389/fmars.2020.614766].

Gawarkiewicz, G. and A. Malek Mercer, 2019. Partnering with fishing fleets to monitor ocean conditions. *Annual Review of Marine Science,* vol. 11, pp. 391–411.

Gutiérrez, A. T. and S. K. Morgan, 2015. The influence of the sustainable seafood movement in the US and UK capture fisheries supply chain and fisheries governance. *Frontiers in Marine Science* [https://doi.org/10.3389/fmars.2015.00072].

Mackay, M., B. D. Hardesty, and C. Wilcox, 2020. The intersection between illegal fishing, crimes at sea, and social well-being. *Frontiers in Marine Science* [https://doi.org/10.3389/fmars.2020.589000].

Mintzer, V. J., K. Diniz, and T. K. Frazer, 2018. The use of aquatic mammals for bait in global fisheries. *Frontiers in Marine Science* [https://doi.org/10.3389/fmars.2018.00191].

Naylor, R. L., R. W. Hardy, A. H. Buschmann, S. R. Bush, L. Cao, D. H. Klinger, D. C. Little, J. Lubchenco, S. E. Shumway, and M. Troell, 2021. A 20-year retrospective review of global aquaculture. *Nature,* vol. 591, pp. 551–563.

Simon, P., M. F. Tlusty, A. L. Rhyne, and M. Metian, 2020. Aquaculture of marine ornamental fish: Overview of the production trends and the role of academia in research progress. *Reviews in Aquaculture,* vol. 12, pp. 1217–1230.

Smith, H. and X. Basurto, 2019. Defining small-scale fisheries and examining the role of science in shaping perceptions of who and what counts: A systematic review. *Frontiers in Marine Science* [https://doi.org/10.3389/fmars.2019.00236].

Sumaila, U. R. and T. C. Tai, 2020. End overfishing and increase the resilience of the ocean to climate change. *Frontiers in Marine Science* [https://doi.org/10.3389/fmars.2020.00523].

Thompson, K. F., K. A. Miller, D. Currie, P. Johnston, and D. Santillo, 2018. Seabed mining and approaches to governance of the deep seabed. *Frontiers in Marine Science* [https://doi.org/10.3389/fmars.2018.00480].

Sergi García Fernández/Getty Images

Sea turtles, like this green turtle (*Chelonia mydas*), often ingest plastic bags by mistake.

Everywhere, not just along cities and industrialized areas, humans are impacting the oceans. News about the effects of **global climate change,** vanishing marine life, and imperiled fisheries are all too familiar. Such news are, however, only a small sample of **anthropogenic impacts,** or the effects of human activities, on the marine environment (Fig. 18.1). Almost 8 billion people now live in our planet (see Fig. 17.2), and more than half of them live within 100 km (60 mi) of the coast, which is more than the population of the *whole* planet in 1950!

18.1 MODIFICATION AND DESTRUCTION OF HABITATS

Dredging, landfilling, and the use of explosives modify or destroy **habitats,** the places where organisms live. Increased coastal **sedimentation** resulting from human-induced soil erosion following deforestation, agriculture, and urbanization is a major problem, especially in regions with heavy rainfall. Particularly affected are coral reefs, seagrass meadows, and other shallow-water communities.

Low Impact ⟵─────────────────────⟶ Very High Impact

Source: Bill Ober

FIGURE 18.1 The impact of humans on the marine environment reaches practically every corner of the ocean planet, even the surface water farthest from land. The most impacted marine environments are along the coast near the densely populated regions of the Northern Hemisphere. Data was gathered from maps showing 17 different human activities like pollution, fishing, fertilizer runoff, and climate change, as well as maps for 14 marine ecosystems worldwide. A "vulnerability score" was used to quantify impact.

Increased sedimentation also decreases the penetration of light through the water column, decreasing **primary production**. The effects of such physical disturbances are direct and immediate, as opposed to indirect effects like those of pollutants released somewhere else. The indirect effects of destruction of habitats, however, can be over much larger areas, as when the nursery grounds of fishes are destroyed.

Most destruction of habitats takes place along the coast close to where people live, as in estuaries and mangrove forests (see 12.4, Human Impact on Estuarine Communities). It results mostly from unplanned or poorly planned coastal development (Fig. 18.2), and even from coral mining (Fig. 18.3). The problem is more acute in many developing nations, where population growth and the absence of effective management are harmfully combined. Growing cities, tourism, and development for industrial and recreational uses have radically altered the coastlines of the richer nations as well, as in the case of Singapore and Dubai, where artificial islands have been built for residential or industrial purposes (Fig. 18.4).

Dale Glantz

FIGURE 18.2 Salt marshes in Southern California and in many other locations around the globe have been obliterated by reclamation.

Trawling

Trawls that are dragged along the bottom for fish and shrimp, often illegally, are a major threat to subtidal habitats. It has been estimated that about 40,000 km² (15,400 mi²) of the bottom are scoured by trawls each day. Trawling scours the sea floor and leaves scars on soft sediments. It also causes the resuspension of sediment, which

kills suspension feeders. The release of bottom nutrients can induce the growth of bacteria and seaweeds, which deplete oxygen (see "Eutrophication," below). Trawling on hard bottoms breaks off many attached organisms, some of which, like sponges and tubeworms, offer shelter to juveniles of fishes and other animals. Trawling also displaces or overturns boulders, harming or killing organisms living on their surface and exposing others to predators. Repeated trawling gives bottom communities little chance for recovery. The total number of species ultimately decreases because the continuous disturbance favors short-living, fast-reproducing species like small worms, while long-living, slow-reproducing animals like sponges, clams, and sea stars tend to disappear. Deep-water trawling and ocean mining (see "Ocean Mining," in 17.2) also threaten many vulnerable species that inhabit Deep-water seamounts (see Box 16.2, "Biodiversity in the Deep Sea") and corals (see Box 14.3, "Deep-Water Coral Communities").

18.2 POLLUTION

Pollution—visible or invisible and on land, air, or water—is an unwanted but familiar part of our lives. **Marine pollution** can be

Kurt Amsler/Ardea.com

FIGURE 18.3 Coral mining in the Maldives, an island-group nation in the Indian Ocean. Reef-building corals are widely used as construction material in many parts. Coral was used in the Maldives to build part of a new airport runway, even though the islands rely on their coral reefs to attract tourists, an important sector of the economy. Two small islands between India and Sri Lanka, not far from the Maldives, sank, in part as a result of coral mining.

defined as the introduction by humans of substances, heat energy, or even sound that decrease the quality of the marine environment. Many of these substances, or **pollutants,** are human-made substances and materials that do not occur naturally. Some of these substances, however, have natural sources, like natural oil seeps and volcanic eruptions, and are not considered sources of pollution. By contrast, the liberation by humans of naturally occurring substances, as when mining releases metals that are naturally stored in rocks, is considered pollution.

The role of humans in decreasing the quality of the marine environment has been enormous. The potentially detrimental effects of pollution directly or indirectly affect all parts of the ocean, from beaches to great depths. Pollution often presents a hazard to human health when marine organisms are eaten or when we go swimming, diving, or surfing.

Delpixel/Shutterstock

FIGURE 18.4 The explosive expansion of Dubai, United Arab Emirates, has promoted the creation of artificial islands built from sand and other sediment dredged from the shallow Persian Gulf. Coral reefs, seagrass meadows, and other marine communities were buried by the sediment, and water visibility has been adversely affected.

Marine pollution is the introduction or release of substances or energy that decrease the quality of the environment. Many pollutants are toxic or harmful to marine life and humans.

There is considerable diversity in the types, distribution, sources, and effects of marine pollutants, but most pollution comes from land-based sources like urban development, agriculture, transport, industry, and power generation. The most important sea-based sources are shipping and offshore oil drilling, but these account for fewer than 20% of the total pollution that enters the ocean. Difficult to assess is **sound pollution** from

Nutrients Raw materials other than carbon dioxide and water that are needed by *primary producers* for *primary production.*
• 4.1, The Ingredients of Life

shipping and military testing. **Ocean noise**, which propagates fast and far in water, is known to interfere with whale echolocation (see "Behavior," in 9.3). Here we will briefly discuss only the most important types of marine pollutants and some of their effects on marine life.

Eutrophication

Fertilizers in agricultural and stormwater runoff and sewage are major anthropogenic sources of nitrate, phosphate, and other nutrients to the marine environment. Atmospheric input from fossil-fuel combustion is another major source of nitrogen, the largest to the open ocean. Anthropogenic inputs of nitrogen to the oceans now exceed natural inputs. Humans have come to dominate the global nitrogen cycle, and the situation will intensify because of the ever-expanding use of fertilizers, sewage from more people living along coasts, fossil-fuel combustion, and other human activities that increase nutrient inputs to the sea. **Stormwater runoff** not only carries fertilizers from lawns but harmful substances we deposit on land. Pesticides, oil, as well as bacteria, viruses, and other parasites from pet waste (see Box 13.3, "*Toxoplasma*: From Cats to Sea Otters"), get carried into the ocean when it rains.

Though nutrients are needed by marine primary producers, excessive amounts encourage too much algal growth, a phenomenon known as **eutrophication** (see Special Report, "Overwhelming the Nitrogen Cycle"). Eutrophication is primarily a problem of coastal waters, particularly in shallow, partially enclosed areas. Eutrophication can damage important habitats like seagrass beds and coral reefs by causing a chronic increase in **phytoplankton** abundance, reducing the penetration of sunlight to the bottom, and accelerating the growth of seaweeds that overgrow the bottom (see "The Kāne'ohe Bay Story," in 14.1). It can also trigger phytoplankton blooms, the short-term, explosive increases in the abundance of phytoplankton. Blooms of phytoplankton and particularly of bottom-dwelling cyanobacteria are sometimes toxic. **Red tides** are especially toxic (see Box 15.1, "Red Tides and Harmful Algal Blooms"). These events seem to be occurring more frequently in many coastal waters worldwide, being responsible for considerable damage to fisheries as well as adversely affecting tourism.

Organic matter in the form of the remains of the phytoplankton blooms and the feces of the **zooplankton** and fishes that feed on the plankton fall to the bottom. **Decay bacteria** then break down the organic matter and can completely use up the oxygen on the bottom, causing **anoxic conditions.** Seasonal **hypoxic** (or "dead") **zones,** areas where the water lacks oxygen, that result from the effects of agricultural runoff have become common in a number of areas, including the Gulf of Mexico (Fig. 18.5), Chesapeake Bay, and the Baltic Sea. About 150 hypoxic zones have been identified in oceans around the world (see Special Report, "The No-Zone," Fig. 16).

Agricultural and stormwater runoff, fossil-fuel combustion, and other sources of increased nutrient inputs to the ocean are responsible for eutrophication, the excessive growth of phytoplankton and seaweeds.

Sewage

Disposing of ever-increasing amounts of **sewage** is a major problem in cities around the world. **Domestic sewage** carries wastewater from homes and city buildings. It can also carry stormwater runoff. **Industrial sewage** contains a variety of wastes from factories and the like. Most sewage is discharged into the sea, or into rivers that flow to the sea.

Impacts of Sewage Sewage discharges into coastal waters are a serious health hazard. Sewage contains many viruses, bacteria, and other disease-carrying organisms. Infectious hepatitis, for example, is carried by viruses found in human feces. Several million worldwide cases of infectious hepatitis annually result from people eating oysters, clams, and other shellfish that concentrate the viruses as they filter the water for food. Swimming in sewage-polluted water can also be hazardous; people can get sick from swallowing contaminated water or develop ear, throat, and eye infections just from contact with the water.

The closing of beaches when sewers overflow after a rainstorm has now become routine in many areas. Contamination by failing septic systems that continually leak sewage materials is also a major source. The economic impact due to lost tourism and the closure of shellfish farms can be considerable.

Sewage can also be a hazard to marine life (Fig. 18.6). Chemicals found in prescription drugs and many health products adversely affect reproduction in some marine animals. Even hormones from the urine of anyone taking birth-control pills are known to cause sex changes in male fishes. Sewage that contains industrial waste invariably includes pesticides, heavy metals, and other toxic chemicals.

Sewage, discharged into the sea around the world, is a major health hazard to humans because it spreads disease.

Sewage Treatment and Sludge The harmful effects of sewage can be reduced by **sewage treatment,** and many countries require by law some form of treatment before sewage is discharged.

The sewage can simply be allowed to sit in a basin for a time, so that much of the solid matter settles out. A more advanced, but more expensive, option is to allow decay bacteria and other organisms to break down the organic matter in the sewage. The addition of chemicals or other steps can further purify the sewage. After treatment, the sewage is often disinfected by using chlorine to kill bacteria and viruses. Ozone treatment and UV irradiation are other methods of disinfection. Advanced forms of treatment can produce water that is pure enough to be used for irrigation or even drinking.

Sewage treatment reduces the impacts of sewage on the marine environment and human health, but it is not without drawbacks. The cost of sewage treatment increases as more advanced treatment methods are used, and many communities cannot afford it. Chlorine used for disinfection can remain in the discharged wastewater and is toxic to marine life. Sewage treatment also creates **sludge,** the wastes that are taken out of the sewage. This semiliquid material is more concentrated than the original sewage and often contains high levels of heavy metals and other toxic substances. Sludge smothers

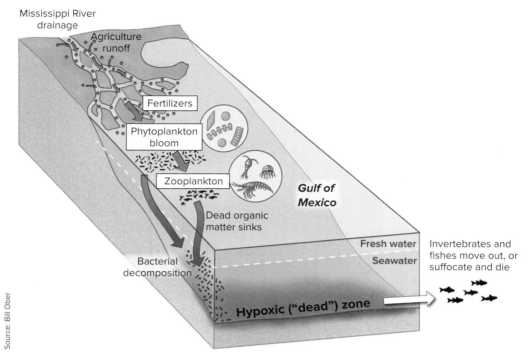

Source: Bill Ober

FIGURE 18.5 Hypoxic, oxygen-depleted (or "dead" zones) develop on the bottom of coastal waters due to increased bacterial decomposition caused by nutrient pollution, mostly from agricultural runoff as in the case of the Gulf of Mexico. Excessive nutrients stimulate the growth of phytoplankton and the organic matter they produce, which ultimately sink to the bottom. Their decomposition by bacteria depletes bottom oxygen. Surface fresh water from the Mississippi River causes stratification, which prevents the mixing of oxygen-rich surface water with oxygen-poor bottom water. Many fishes and other animals move out or die. "Dead" zones are not really devoid of life because many microbes and some invertebrates do thrive in these areas.

stockphoto-graf/Shutterstock

FIGURE 18.6 Raw or treated sewage can be very harmful to marine communities, even in moderate amounts like in this coral reef.

Anoxic Conditions Absence of oxygen that results in the accumulation of *hydrogen sulfide* (H_2S) in the sediment, which turns the sediment black.

• 11.2, Soft-Bottom Intertidal Communities; Figure 11.28

bottom communities, creating black deserts around outfalls or at best dominance by only a few species.

It is impossible for most detritus feeders to handle the massive amounts of organic matter contained in sludge. The organic matter is instead decomposed by bacteria that thrive under these conditions, using oxygen to such an extent that anoxic conditions develop. The total number of species decreases because many of the natural inhabitants disappear. They are replaced by hardier forms of life, like certain species of polychaete worms. Bottom fishes collected around sludge disposal sites tend to show skin tumors, erosion of fins, and other abnormalities, apparently a result of the high concentration of toxic substances, viruses, and bacteria.

It is possible to implement alternatives to the discharge of sewage into the sea. Some communities take advantage of the ability of marshes to naturally recycle nutrients by using the marshes for sewage treatment (Fig. 18.7). Ideally, we could recycle the large amounts of precious water and nutrients that go to waste. Sludge is sometimes recycled into landfill, construction blocks, and compost. It is also spread on farmlands as fertilizer, burned to generate electricity, and converted into fuel.

High volumes of sludge discharged into the sea greatly modify or destroy bottom communities.

Oil

Crude oil, or **petroleum,** is a complex mixture of **hydrocarbons,** long chains of carbon and hydrogen, and certain other chemicals.

Oil is one of the most widespread pollutants in the ocean. Nearly 700 million tons of oil and derivatives like fuel and lubricating oil enter the world oceans each year as a result of pollution. Oil from natural seepage, not a pollutant, contributes nearly 600 million tons worldwide. Land-based pollution is the most important source of oil in North American waters (Fig. 18.8). Over 90% of the polluting oil in North America comes from stormwater and river runoff, fuel from small boats and jet skis, and fuel jettisoned by planes.

The massive oil spills that result from the sinking or collision of supertankers and accidents from drilling platforms, however, are

FIGURE 18.7 This lush artificial marsh is part of a network of marshes where domestic sewage from the city of Arcata in northern California is naturally purified before it is piped into the ocean. Sewage, which is mostly water, is given preliminary treatment. It is then pumped into the marshes, where mud bacteria break down the organic matter. The released nutrients fertilize the marsh plants. The marshes prevent sewage pollution and attract many species of birds and other wildlife.

Sources of Oil Pollution	Estimated Amount (tons)	Percentage
Land-based pollution and recreational boating	1,200,000	91.6
Natural seeps	100,000	7.6
Exploration and extraction	9,500	0.7
Transportation of oil	818	<1

FIGURE 18.8 Annual sources of oil in the marine environment in North America, 2010–2019.

the most devastating to the marine environment. The 1978 grounding of a supertanker, the *Amoco Cadiz,* poured 230,000 tons of crude oil along the coasts of northwestern France. The 2010 blowout of the *Deepwater Horizon* drilling platform released an estimated 672,000 tons of crude oil into the Gulf of Mexico, so far the largest marine spill in the United States and second in the world after a Persian Gulf spill during the Iraqi War in 1991.

Most of the components of oil are insoluble in water and float on the surface. They appear as thin, iridescent slicks or as black deposits on the shore. Some of the other components sink and accumulate in sediments, especially after the lighter ones evaporate. Some residues remain on the surface and form **tar balls,** which are common along shipping lanes worldwide, but can persist for many years and have been observed in remote areas far from shipping traffic. Some even have barnacles living on them! Oil is ultimately broken down, or decomposed, by bacteria and thus is almost completely **biodegradable.** The breakdown rate is usually slow but varies among marine communities.

Accidents have prompted tighter restrictions, like having double hulls on tankers. Older tankers, however, do not necessarily have double hulls, and many still navigate busy shipping lines.

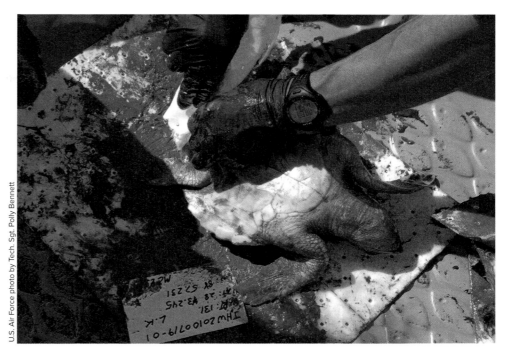

U.S. Air Force photo by Tech. Sgt. Polly Bennett

FIGURE 18.9 A Kemp's ridley sea turtle (*Lepidochelys kempii*) coated with oil from the 2010 *Deepwater Horizon* spill in the Gulf of Mexico. Long-term effects of the oil have been reported in this endangered sea turtle and in the bottlenose dolphin (*Tursiops truncatus*) and other cetaceans.

> Oil is a widespread pollutant that enters the sea as waste from land, from accidents during its extraction from the seabed, and as a result of its transportation across water.

Effects of Oil on Marine Life Crude oils vary markedly in their chemical composition, and therefore in their toxicity and environmental persistence. Refined products like fuel oils tend to be more toxic than crude oil. Even in small amounts, oil has a variety of effects on marine organisms. Organisms can accumulate oil components, many of which are toxic, from the water, sediments, and their food. There is evidence, for instance, that compounds found in oil interfere with the reproduction, development, growth, and behavior of many organisms. These compounds are released from oil for many decades. Oil also increases susceptibility to diseases in fishes and inhibits the growth of phytoplankton.

Seabirds and marine mammals like the sea otter are particularly susceptible. Many die of exposure when their feathers or hair is coated with oil, which affects their ability to maintain the thin layer of warm air needed for insulation. Birds that rely on flying to catch food are unable to do so and die of starvation. It is difficult to determine the number of birds killed by oil spills because many sink without reaching the coast, where the corpses can be counted. Sea turtles, crabs, and many other marine animals are simply overcome by the oil and die (Fig. 18.9). The 1989 *Exxon Valdez* spill in Alaska

is believed to have killed between 100,000 and 300,000 seabirds and 3,500 to 5,000 sea otters.

The effect of oil spills on exposed rocky shores is less devastating than it may appear. Initially, there is mortality among many attached inhabitants, but wave action and tides help clean away the oil. Rocky shore communities do recover, though recovery is dependent on factors like the amount of oil, wave action, and temperature. Experience has shown that recovery begins within months and that an apparently near-normal condition can occur as early as one or two years after the spill. Higher oil concentrations in sediments and isolated pockets, however, remain for 15 years or longer.

Large spills can have more catastrophic effects when they drift to salt marshes and mangrove forests, as shown by the *Deepwater Horizon* spill. These communities are characteristic of sheltered coasts and estuaries where oil cannot be dispersed by wave action. Oil is absorbed by the fine sediment of these communities and can persist for more than 30 years in salt marshes. Coral reefs and seagrass beds also are greatly affected by oil spills. Coral colonies show swollen tissues, excessive production of mucus, and exposed skeletons. Reproduction and feeding in surviving coral polyps are affected by oil, but there is little evidence of dramatic, long-term effects.

> Oil is harmful to most marine organisms. It is especially destructive to communities typical of shallow, sheltered waters.

Containing an oil spill is a major headache. Fencing off the spill with floating, fire-resistant booms can prevent the spill from moving into shore. "Skimmers," boats equipped with U-shaped booms, are used to recover some of the oil. These methods, however, cannot be used in heavy seas. Bacteria can degrade

rocky-shore oil more quickly if an oil-soluble fertilizer is added to the water or sprayed on the rocks. Chemical **dispersants** are added to the spill to break the surface oil into small droplets that can then disperse in the water. Unfortunately, dispersants also are harmful to marine life, as shown by the *Deepwater Horizon* spill. Furthermore, the dispersed oil still remains toxic underwater. The use of powerful streams of hot water to wash oil from beaches after the *Exxon Valdez* spill was also harmful to many forms of life, perhaps as harmful as the oil itself. Oil-soaked beaches are also disastrous to areas dependent on tourism.

The cost of oil spills to local economies can be enormous. Fish and filter-feeding shellfish like oysters and clams tainted with oil are unmarketable. The size of fish catches, particularly of bottom-dwelling species, can decrease because of the initial mortality of adults and juveniles or a drop in the abundance of their food. BP was fined $4.5 billion for damages caused by the *Deepwater Horizon* spill, but other issues, such as funding research into long-term effects, remain unresolved.

Persistent Toxic Substances

Many important pollutants that reach the sea from land are substances and materials that are said to be **persistent** because they remain in the environment for years, even many decades. Persistent substances are not readily broken down either by decay microorganisms (and for this reason the substances are known as **non-biodegradable**) or by physical or chemical means in the environment. The best-known toxic pollutants are the **persistent organic pollutants,** or **POPs.** They are all synthetic and do not occur naturally. Others are **inorganic** and do not contain carbon or are derived from living matter. They could occur naturally but in minute amounts.

Pesticides One group of non-biodegradable, persistent organic pollutants is the **chlorinated hydrocarbons**, which include many **pesticides,** chemicals used to kill insects and to control weeds, including DDT and many others. Millions of tons of these chlorinated hydrocarbons have been used since the 1940s. These pesticides have been used around the world to protect plant crops from insect pests and to control insects that carry diseases. Pesticides have saved millions of people from disease and starvation, but the unchecked use of chlorinated hydrocarbons has been shown to be harmful to many non-targeted forms of life.

These pesticides have not been used directly in the ocean. They are, however, carried there by rivers, stormwater runoff, and sewage, and are transported long distances, including the open ocean (Fig. 18.10). In the ocean they are absorbed by phytoplankton and particles suspended in the water and thus find their way into other organisms.

Chlorinated hydrocarbon pesticides dissolve in fats and are not excreted, so organisms tend to retain them almost indefinitely. Animals absorb and accumulate the pesticides in the organisms they eat, so their internal concentration of chlorinated hydrocarbons is higher than that in their food supply. At each level of the **food chain,** then, the chlorinated hydrocarbons become more concentrated. This phenomenon is known as **biological magnification.** Among marine animals, pesticide concentrations are higher in carnivorous

fishes, and even more so in the fish-eating birds and mammals at the top of the **trophic pyramid** (Fig. 18.10). Pesticides began to accumulate in top carnivores in concentrations that were thousands and even millions of times more than the amount found in seawater.

Chlorinated hydrocarbons, which include many widely used pesticides, are non-biodegradable and persistent. They accumulate in the food chain through biological magnification.

It was Rachel Carson, an American marine biologist, who in her 1962 book, *Silent Spring,* brought widespread attention of the environmental problems caused by the indiscriminate use of pesticides, and most especially their effects on wildlife and human health. Carson's work was most influential on the environmental movement not only in the United States but throughout the world.

The effects on seabirds were dramatic. The birds were not actually poisoned, but the high concentrations of chlorinated hydrocarbons in their body fat interfered with reproduction, specifically with the deposition of calcium in their eggshells. The eggshells became so thin that they broke during incubation before chicks became fully developed.

The once-abundant brown pelican (Fig. 18.11), for example, became a rare sight in most parts of the United States due to widespread reproductive failure during the late 1960s and early 1970s. Female pelicans sat on broken eggs, or adults simply did not attempt to nest. The Channel Islands off Southern California, the last remaining nesting colony on the Pacific north of Mexico, recorded only one chick in 1970 and seven in 1971. High amounts of DDT and related chemicals were found in the tissues of birds taken from these and other nesting colonies and in other marine animals in the area, from filter feeders like sand, or mole, crabs to top carnivores like sea lions.

By 1972 most uses of DDT and several other chlorinated hydrocarbons were banned in the United States and many other nations. DDT residues in marine animals and sediments then began to decrease. The brown pelican, once nearly extinct in the United States, has recovered, and its reproduction has returned to normal. DDT and related residues, however, can still be found in bottom-dwelling fishes. A 2000 international agreement restricting the production and use of certain toxic substances nevertheless allowed continued use of DDT because it provides inexpensive control of insects in developing nations, primarily to control the mosquitoes that transmit malaria.

PCBs and Other Persistent Organic Pollutants Another problematic group of toxic chlorinated hydrocarbons are the **PCBs,** the **polychlorinated biphenyls.** PCBs are non-biodegradable and persistent and thus show biological magnification. They were widely used in electrical transformers, in the manufacturing of plastics and paints, and in many other products. PCBs proved to be highly toxic, causing cancer and birth defects, and their production and use were gradually regulated or banned by many nations, including the United States in 1979.

This ban, however, came after PCBs had spread throughout the oceans. PCBs and other chlorinated hydrocarbons have been detected in the blubber of whales and other marine mammals,

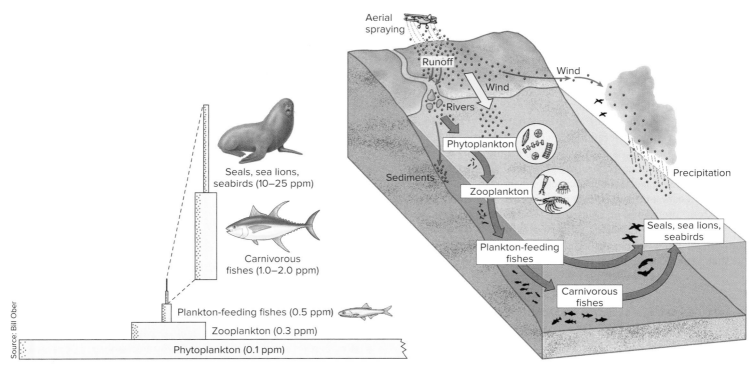

FIGURE 18.10 The concentration of chlorinated hydrocarbons increases with the relative position organisms have in the food chain, thus showing biological magnification. In the trophic pyramid that summarizes this generalized food chain, the concentration of pesticides is expressed in ppm, or parts per million.

and even in animals living in the deepest trenches of the Pacific. Farmed fish, like salmon, often have concentrations of PCBs and other contaminants that are higher than in wild fish. The farmed fish are fed contaminated fish meal, and PCBs in the food become concentrated in the farmed fish.

PCBs continue to be used in some parts of the world, and electrical equipment containing them is still around. Such equipment is required to remain sealed and the PCBs carefully disposed of when the equipment wears out. Invariably, though, PCBs are present in large amounts of hazardous wastes that accumulate and have to be disposed of somehow, somewhere, so they are widespread in landfills and waste dumps. Decades of use and disposal have also left significant amounts of these persistent pollutants in the marine environment, especially around sewage outfalls and in the sediment of harbors of industrial cities. Dredging to keep shipping lanes open releases persistent pollutants; the dredged material is another source.

Even at low concentrations years after being banned, PCBs and other chlorinated hydrocarbons have been implicated in abnormal sexual behavior and reproduction in seabirds, marine mammals, and fishes. These pollutants form chemicals that are similar to

FIGURE 18.11 The brown pelican (*Pelecanus occidentalis*) is again a common sight along the coasts of the United States and the Caribbean. Many, however, were affected by the 2010 Gulf of Mexico oil spill.

sex hormones (also called "environmental estrogen") and seem to disrupt reproduction.

Chlorinated **dioxins** and **furans,** two other groups of chlorinated hydrocarbons, also enter the marine environment from land. Pulp mills and waste incinerators are important sources, and these chemicals also occur naturally, for example, as a result of forest fires. Some dioxins are among the most toxic of all chemical pollutants. They are carcinogenic and cause birth defects and damage to the immune system in many vertebrates and humans. They also show biological magnification.

One metric ton of crude oil = **7.33 barrels (bbl),** or **308 U.S. gal.**

Food Chain The steps of transfer of energy from *producers,* the algae and plants, through *consumers,* the animals.

• 10.3, The Flow of Energy and Materials; Figure 10.13

Trophic Pyramid The pyramid-like relationship of energy, number of individuals, or biomass of the organisms found in a food chain.

• 10.3, The Flow of Energy and Materials; Figure 10.16

PCBs, a group of chemicals used as fire retardants (PBDEs), certain pesticides, and other toxic chemicals, evaporate into the atmosphere, where the wind can carry them considerable distances before they condense in the cool upper atmosphere. When they condense, they are carried in rain or snow back to the ground, where the process starts all over again. Because of wind patterns and the fact that more condensation of the chemicals takes place near the poles, where it is cold, the chemicals are concentrated in polar regions. This global system of evaporation and condensation of substances, many of which are toxic, is known as **global distillation.** Global distillation has been implicated in whale kills, and high levels of PCBs, mercury (see below), and other toxic chemicals have been found in seals, polar bears, and even the Inuit and other aboriginal peoples of the Arctic thousands of miles from where the pollutants were used. As ice melting increases in Antarctica and the Arctic as a result of **global climate change**, so is the release of the toxic pollutants that have accumulated in the ice through global distillation.

PCBs, dioxins, and furans are pollutants notable for their toxicity. They are persistent and carried to polar regions through global distillation.

Heavy Metals An additional category of chemical contaminants of the world's oceans is metals, particularly those classified as **heavy metals.** Very minute amounts of some metals are needed by most if not all organisms, but an excess can be toxic.

One particularly troublesome heavy metal is **mercury,** which reaches the ocean through several natural processes: the weathering of rocks, volcanic activity, rivers, and dust particles. Mercury is also used in batteries, fluorescent lamps, drugs, and even tooth fillings. Discharges from industries and cities and the burning of coal, which contains traces of mercury, have increased the concentration of mercury in the marine environment.

Pure, liquid mercury, like that in thermometers, is harmless unless its vapors are inhaled. It is a different story when mercury combines with organic chemicals, as when transformed by some bacteria and other microbes in the water or sediment. These organic compounds, like **methyl mercury,** are persistent and accumulate in the food chain. Levels of mercury too high for human consumption have been found in large fishes like tuna and swordfish. The older the fish, the higher the mercury content. Methyl mercury also can be found in coastal sediments, particularly around waste dumps. Mercury compounds also undergo global distillation. They are very difficult to eliminate and are highly toxic to practically all forms of life. In humans they can cause brain, kidney, and liver damage and birth defects. High levels of mercury in fish prompted the U.S. government to warn those pregnant and young children to limit their intake of canned tuna, swordfish, and other fishes.

Lead is another widespread heavy-metal pollutant. As with mercury, organic lead compounds are persistent and concentrate in the tissues of organisms. Lead is toxic to humans, causing nervous disorders and death. The principal source of lead pollution in the marine environment was the exhaust of vehicles run with leaded fuels. The lead reaches the water by way of rain and windblown dust. Lead is also found in all sorts of products, like paints and ceramics, that eventually make their way to the ocean. The removal of lead from gasoline has been responsible for a decrease in lead levels in surface water, especially in the North Atlantic, a success story that demonstrates that environmental problems can be addressed.

Mercury and lead compounds are highly toxic. They are persistent and accumulate in the food chain.

Cadmium and **copper** are other toxic heavy metals that are slowly concentrated in marine life. Mining and refining operations are major sources. Together with lead, mercury, and other toxic metals, cadmium is common in discarded computers and other electronic components, seeping into rivers or the ocean from disposal sites. Unlike lead and mercury, which are transported in the atmosphere, unnaturally high levels of cadmium, copper, and other heavy metals remain near their source.

Radioactive Wastes Pollution by radioactive substances has been an issue in the marine environment since the first atomic bomb explosions in the early 1940s. **Radioactivity** is a property exhibited by certain atoms that emit radiation in the form of energy or particular types of particles. Some radioactive **isotopes** occur in nature but in minute amounts, and some harmful radiation reaches us from outer space. Exposure to some types of radiation is harmful to all forms of life, and in humans it causes leukemia, other cancers, and various disorders. Radioactivity does not need to be ingested because it penetrates through living matter. Most radioactive materials emit radiation for thousands of years.

A source of radioactivity is the waste from nuclear power plants. Some of the waste used to be dumped into designated areas of the ocean. Sunken nuclear-powered submarines and ships, fallen satellites, and crashed planes carrying nuclear weapons are other potential sources of radioactive waste. Accidents in nuclear reactors along the coast, as in the case of the Fukushima power plant in Japan during the 2011 earthquake and tsunami, and radioactive waste in industrial effluents add to the risk. Nevertheless, the use of radioactive material is highly regulated, so it generally poses no major threat to the marine environment.

Plastic Waste

A look at the upper reaches of most beaches, even those in the Arctic or uninhabited Pacific islands far from populated areas, will reveal an amazing assortment of trash brought in by high water. Although rubber products and cans are common in beach trash, about 70% of the trash is plastic. Plastic is not limited to visible beach debris. Drifting plastic particles are found at every depth, being more abundant in water below the surface. Plastic waste still flows to sea at an alarming rate, even if dumping of solid waste and other pollutants is banned by the London Convention of 1972. A 2014 study estimated that 5.25 trillion pieces of plastic weighing about 270,000 metric tons (595 million lbs) were floating on the ocean. This amount increases annually. At least 8 million metric tons of plastic is added every year, and the figure is growing annually. The COVID-19 pandemic is responsible for a dramatic

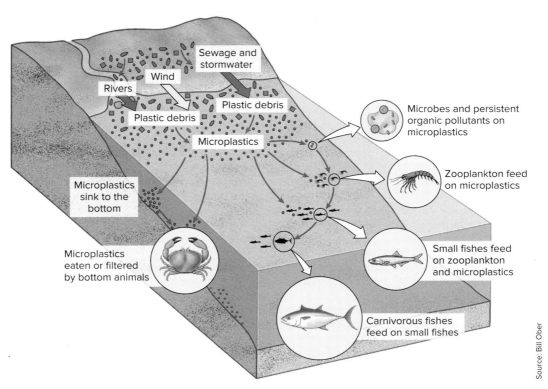

FIGURE 18.12 Plastics and microplastics entering the marine environment from many sources are further transported elsewhere by currents and organisms. Plastic is non-biodegradable and as such will remain in the environment indefinitely.

increase in plastic waste, from single-use test kits and containers to plastic-containing masks. East Asia is thought to be the source of most plastic in the ocean, with ten rivers, eight in Asia and two in Africa, discharging 90% of all marine plastic debris.

Plastics are particularly troublesome because although organic (made from chemicals derived from oil), they are synthetic (manufactured by us), non-biodegradable, and as such not broken down by microorganisms and thus extremely durable. Water bottles, bags, six-pack rings, packaging material, and countless other types of plastic debris are carried by from land, rivers, stormwater runoff, and wind (Fig. 18.12). Plastic products are also discarded by beach visitors, pleasure and fishing boats, and aquaculture operations. What's the biggest source of plastic waste? Packaging material. A huge patch of floating debris, the "great Pacific garbage patch," floats in the middle of the North Pacific gyre thousands of miles from land. Some have estimated the patch to be 1.6 km² (618,000 mi²) in size. At least four other giant patches are known elsewhere. Giant booms are being used to collect floating debris, but the task is not of much help.

Plastic bags kill sea turtles that swallow them, perhaps because sea turtles confuse them with jellyfishes or perhaps attracted by chemicals released by microorganisms living on the plastic (see photo at the beginning of the chapter). Six-pack rings and plastic fishing line easily ensnare seabirds and marine mammals, which, often unable to feed, face a slow death. It has been estimated that plastic debris kills at least 2 million seabirds and 100,000 marine mammals every year. Floating plastic also makes possible the

transport of potentially invasive species (see Box 18.2, "Biological Invasions: The Uninvited Guests") and perhaps spread diseases to corals and other marine organisms.

Plastics, especially polystyrene-foam packaging material and disposable cups, eventually break down by wave action and sunlight into **microplastics,** particles less than 5 mm (0.2 in) that are now found practically everywhere in the ocean, including the tissues of many marine organisms (see Box 18.1, "Microplastics in the Marine Environment"). Other sources of microplastics are toothpaste, exfoliant scrubs, and other personal-care products, tire rubber, cigarette filters, and microfibers from synthetic fabrics and face masks, all of which eventually enter the ocean, even by way of treated sewage. A 2015 study estimated that at least 5.25 trillion pieces of plastic were floating at sea, of which 4.5 trillion were between 0.33 and 4.75 mm (0.01 to 0.19 in).

Only a small fraction of the billions of plastic bags and water bottles used and discarded daily around the world is recycled. Recycling complex plastic polymers is still expensive, and removal of microplastics from car tires and other products is difficult. Only 5–6% of the 40 million plastic waste generated in the United States in 2021 was recycled (against 8.7% in 2018); 10% was incinerated (producing toxic and greenhouse gases), leaving 85% for landfills.

Isotopes Different atomic forms of an element.
• 2.2, The Origin and Structure of the Ocean Basins

EYE ON SCIENCE

Box 18.1 Microplastics in the Marine Environment

One of the major environmental problems facing the oceans is the widespread presence of microplastics (see "Plastic Waste," in 18.2). Most of these microplastics result from the degradation of the increasing quantities of plastic entering the oceans. Some microplastics sink to the bottom, some are locked up in sea ice, but considerable amounts remain in the water column (Fig. 18.12). Microplastics constitute 94% of the estimated 1.8 trillion pieces of plastic floating in the Great Pacific Garbage Patch. Deep underwater currents are responsible for the accumulation of microplastics in some ocean basins and trenches. All crustaceans taken from the Marianas Trench in the Pacific had microplastics in their guts. Surprisingly, we still don't know exactly how much microplastic is found in the marine environment, what effects it has on marine life and seafood-eating humans, and what is the eventual fate of these non-biodegradable particles.

Diatoms, bacteria, and other microbes have been found living on microplastics. These microbes grow in number and create microfilms, thin layers of cells and organic matter that provide a surface for other organisms to settle on the surface. The term **plastisphere** has been coined to refer to the community of organisms living on floating plastic, most especially microplastics. The type of microbes living on microplastics varies from place to place, and apparently with season as well. It has been suggested that certain water nutrients that are essential to the microbes, like nitrates and phosphates, concentrate on the surface of the microplastics.

Researchers have also found that diatoms living on microplastics release chemicals that are normally used by plankton-feeding fishes such as anchovies to locate their food. Anchovies feed on krill, which in turn feed on diatoms, so anchovies mistake diatom-coated microplastics as food—and thus concentrate microplastics in their tissues. Hundreds of species of fishes, including many eaten by humans, have been recorded as having ingested microplastics.

Microplastics have also been found on the gills of crabs and in many other invertebrates, both in the water column (like copepods, krill, and fish larvae) and on the bottom (everything from sponges to oysters). Microplastics excreted in the feces of marine animals are also ingested by filter and detritus feeders in the water and on the bottom. These non-biodegradable particles are thus transferred along the food chain.

The potential effects of microplastics on marine life and humans remains a major question, one that is stimulating research. The presence of microplastics in the fish meal used to feed farmed fishes and other animals has raised concern. The possibility has been raised that microplastics might interfere with the absorption of nutrients in fish intestines. There have been reports of changes in the behavior of fishes having microplastics in their tissues, and that particles release chemicals that might affect reproduction in fishes and other marine vertebrates due to their similarities to sex hormones, as in the case of some chemical pollutants (see "PCBs and Other Toxic Organic Chemicals," above). Another puzzling possibility is that microplastics could be involved in carrying and transporting chemical pollutants and disease-causing microbes clinging to the particles. There is evidence that persistent organic pollutants (POPs) (see "Persistent Toxic Substances," above) adhere to plastics. *Vibrio* bacteria, responsible for various diseases in marine invertebrates, fishes, and humans, have already been found inhabiting microplastics.

For more information, explore the links provided at the Marine Biology *Online Learning Center.*

Landfill plastics are eventually broken up as microplastics that pollute the soil and water. Perhaps a better solution is to ban, restrict, or reduce the use of plastics rather than undertaking the impossible task of removing all plastic from the environment. Plastic bags have already been banned by a number of countries. Changing consumer demand is another goal. A worldwide effort to such effects is beginning to take hold, including the 2015 United States ban on the use of microplastics in personal-care products.

Plastics, and particularly microplastics, have become one of the worst environmental problems in the marine environment.

Thermal Pollution

Seawater is often used as a coolant in coastal power plants, oil refineries, and other industries. The heated water that results from the cooling process is pumped back to sea, causing alterations to the environment known as **thermal pollution.** Local warm pockets can be created in poorly mixed bays. Even though some fishes can be attracted to the site, such temperature increases are known to adversely affect some organisms. Higher temperatures also decrease the ability of water to dissolve oxygen. The effects of thermal pollution on marine life are especially pronounced in the tropics. In contrast to temperate and polar species, corals and some other tropical species normally live just below the highest tolerable temperatures. Reef-building corals are particularly sensitive. **Saline brines** from plants used to obtain fresh water from seawater are a major pollutant in some coastal regions. Brines are typically warmer than coastal waters and highly saline as well.

18.3 THREATENED AND ENDANGERED SPECIES

The alteration or destruction of habitats by humans can have another disastrous effect: driving species to their eventual disappearance, or **extinction.** Organisms become adapted to changes in

Source: Bill Ober

FIGURE 18.13 As few as 10 vaquitas (*Phocoena sinus*), the smallest porpoise and the most endangered of all marine cetaceans, survive, thus being at the brink of extinction (see "Conservation of Cetaceans," in 9.3). Vaquitas are easily identified because of the dark rings around the eyes and the dark patches around the mouth.

the environment as a result of **natural selection**, but become extinct if they cannot adapt. Extinction can thus be a natural consequence of the process of evolution. To make a distinction, some biologists refer to human-induced extinction as **extermination.**

Species that face extinction are classified as **rare** when they are not in immediate danger but are at risk, **threatened** when their numbers have become low, and **endangered** when in immediate danger of disappearing.

Marine species can be threatened by overexploitation for human food, hides, blubber, tusks, and other products. Many species of fishes, sea turtles, and other animals are discarded as fisheries by-catch (Fig. 18.14; also see "Optimal Yields and Overfishing,"

in 17.1). Habitat destruction, pollution, and the introduction of pests (see Box 18.2, "Biological Invasions: The Uninvited Guests") and diseases also place species at risk.

Species are categorized as rare, threatened, or endangered when they face the possibility of extinction, or extermination.

The future of many marine species is at stake (Table 18.1). Examples can be found among many groups of marine animals.

Corals, which take decades to grow and are essential components of threatened coral reefs, are collected and bleached for sale. Giant clams (*Tridacna;* see Fig. 14.34) have become rare or even locally extinct in most of the tropical Pacific because they are taken in high numbers for food and for their shells, especially as ivory substitutes now that elephant tusks are harder to obtain in China and elsewhere. Marine snails like cowries (*Cypraea*) and cones (*Conus*), whose shells are eagerly sought by collectors, have similarly disappeared from many areas. Abalones (*Haliotis;* see Fig. 7.24*b*), once very common in California, are now rare because of overfishing. Two of the seven California species are now endangered. Chinese traditional medicine is responsible for indiscriminately killing, often

Natural Selection The production of more offspring by those individuals in a population that are genetically best adapted to the environment.
• 4.5, The Diversity of Life in the Sea

Jeffrey Rotman/Getty Images

FIGURE 18.14 Non-target species, or by-catch, are regularly caught by commercial fishers and discarded overboard to die. This by-catch from the Atlantic coast of the United States includes skates, flounders, crabs, and lobsters.

Box 18.2 Biological Invasions: The Uninvited Guests

FIVE SPINES

FLAT REAR LEG

Up to 3 inches wide across the back of the shell
Color variable, dark, mottled, often green or orange

The deliberate or accidental introduction of **invasive species**, also known as **introduced** or **alien species**, in areas where they do not naturally occur can have devastating effects by causing a drastic reduction in the number of individuals of **native**, or local, **species.** Invasive species, often prove to be strong competitors for food and space, and they can bring with them parasites that infect native species. There has been an increase in the frequency of invasive marine species as a result of growth in shipping, the introduction of shellfish and fish for farming, and the aquarium trade. Estimates are that at least 84% of coasts worldwide have been invaded by invasive species, mostly as accidental introductions.

Bays and estuaries, especially those with busy ports, are particularly vulnerable. Seaweeds and invertebrates like sponges, barnacles, and sea squirts that grow as **fouling organisms** that bore into or encrust on boats have become established around the world. Many other species have been introduced as planktonic larvae in ballast water, which is used to fill ships' ballast tanks for stability. Others have been introduced with shellfish. Oil platforms, which are often moved around, often transport attached organisms. Debris drifting in the Pacific as a result of the 2011 Japanese tsunami has been another source. As of 2021, about 300 living Japanese marine species representing 16 animal phyla, plus 84 species of Japanese seaweeds, have been transported to North American or Hawaiian shores. The "great Pacific garbage patch" (see above) has been found to be a potential source of invaders because it is populated with many coastal species.

More than 240 marine invasive species have so far been found in San Francisco Bay, California, considered the most

ALERT!
Have You Seen This Crab?

The green crab, *Carcinus maenas*, is a voracious predator of clams and oysters and a potential threat to these commercial species. Although not naturally occurring in B.C. water, green crab have now migrated here. As of 2010, green crabs have been trapped extensively along the west coast of Vancouver Island from Winter Harbour to Barkley Sound. We need your help to document their range, expansion, and growth rates.

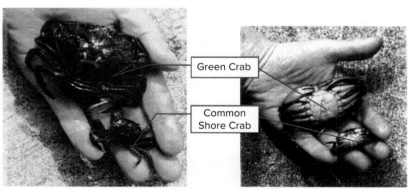

Green Crab

Common Shore Crab

Courtesy Glen Jamieson Department of Fisheries and Oceans, Nanaimo, British Columbia, Canada

invaded estuary in the world. It's actually difficult to find a native species in some parts of the bay. More than half of its fish species, for example, are invasive. Not only is San Francisco a busy port, but the bay is much disturbed. Many invaders do well in such unstable environments because they are often more tolerant than native species to wide fluctuations in factors like salinity.

illegally, a good number of species of marine animals. Seahorses, manta rays (for their gills), other fishes (for their swim bladders), and certain mollusk shells command high prices as unproven cures for a variety of ailments.

Intense commercial fishing to satisfy the growing markets for shark meat and fins, recreational fishing, and by-catch on longlines threatens many species of sharks, pushing some species to the brink of extinction (see Box 8.1, "Shark!"). The colorful anemonefishes,

or clownfishes (*Amphiprion;* Fig. 14.35), have become so popular because of the *Finding Nemo* film, that they have been collected to local extinction in some areas. Anemonefishes are bred in captivity but most are taken from the wild. All seven species of sea turtles are threatened. Adults as well as eggs have been exploited for food and tortoiseshell (Fig. 18.16; see Box 9.1, "The Endangered Sea Turtles"). Their nesting sites have been overrun by development, and they drown in fishing nets.

One of the more recent invaders to San Francisco Bay is the European green, or shore, crab (*Carcinus maenas;* see Fig. 7.40). It was first recorded in the bay in 1989, probably introduced as larvae in ballast water. It soon extended its range along stretches of the Pacific coast. The crab, which tolerates a wide range of salinities, has also been introduced, and become a pest, in the northeastern coast of the United States, Australia, South Africa, and South America. The green crab is a voracious predator, feeding on commercially valuable oysters and young Dungeness crabs, much sought for human food.

Another notorious guest, this one in the Black Sea, is a comb jelly (*Mnemiopsis leidyi;* see Fig. 7.13). It normally occurs in the Atlantic. First recorded in the Black Sea in 1982, it has become a monumental pest, practically taking over the sea. It not only competes with fish for zooplankton food but also feeds on fish eggs and larvae, causing huge economic losses.

Another example involves around 470 species of seaweeds, invertebrates, and fishes have invaded the Mediterranean Sea from their original home in the Red Sea and the Indian Ocean by way of the Suez Canal, which opened in 1869 to provide the shortest sea route between Europe and the Indian Ocean. The 160-km (100-mi) journey through the canal is getting easier because the high salinity of the lakes through which the canal passes has decreased, thus becoming less of a barrier to planktonic larvae brought in by tides. Most invaders have moved from the Red Sea to the Mediterranean because the high tide carries larvae up the canal from the Red Sea. The impact of these migrants has been enormous, with many of the species having reached the central Mediterranean.

Invasions involving Atlantic and Pacific species by way of the Panama Canal have not taken place (except one species of barnacle) because only fresh water flows through the canal, killing any marine life that is brought in by the tide (also see Fig. 9.4). A new, sea-level canal has nevertheless been proposed across Nicaragua north of Panamá.

Even the relatively isolated Galápagos Islands have not escaped from uninvited guests, with 53 marine invasive species of invertebrates recorded in 2019. Some have arrived on plastic debris. The list is expected to grow.

Seaweeds have also been accidentally introduced. *Codium fragile* (see Fig. 6.3), a green alga apparently brought over on oysters transplanted from Europe or the Pacific coast, has become a pest by growing in masses on rocks and oysters on the northeastern United States. Another green alga, *Caulerpa taxifolia,* was accidentally introduced in the Mediterranean from the Caribbean in 1984. It grows into branches as long as 3 m (9 ft), and has spread rapidly, particularly in the western Mediterranean, where it smothers seagrasses and depletes oxygen from the bottom. Unfortunately, the bright-green seaweed is widely used in marine aquaria. Its importation into the United States was banned in 1999, but in 2000 it was found in shallow water off Southern California, perhaps the result of someone emptying a fish tank into a storm drain. Other invasive seaweeds include *Caulerpa brachypus* in Florida and of *Kappaphycus* and *Eucheuma denticulatum;* see Fig. 14.14) introduced in Hawai'i, all of which smother corals.

The intentional introduction, or **transplantation,** of species for commercial purposes can also bring in invasive species. The Japanese oyster (*Crassostrea gigas*) was introduced as spat, or young individuals, on the Pacific coast of North America. It was a successful transplantation because the oyster is now of significant commercial value. Unfortunately, many species living on the spat shells were also introduced. A nasty invasive species is an oyster drill (*Ceratostoma inornatum*), a gastropod that preys on oysters and other native bivalves. Also introduced was *Sargassum muticum,* a Japanese brown seaweed that is now found from British Columbia to Southern California and even England. *Spartina alterniflora,* from the Atlantic coast of North America, is a cordgrass that has caused problems in salt marshes on the Pacific coast (see Box 12.2, "Restoration of Salt Marshes").

Marine aquaria are another source of invasive species. Fish escaping from a Florida aquarium are suspected of being the source of the venomous lionfish (*Pterois;* see Fig. 8.10c), native to the Indian and Pacific oceans. Two species of lionfishes are now rapidly reproducing and spreading throughout the eastern coast of the United States, the Caribbean, and South America. Lionfishes can live in fresh water a horror story in the making because native fishes and invertebrates cannot recognize these predators. There is little hope in that people have found that the lionfish is good to eat.

It is difficult to prevent the introduction of uninvited guests. The use of filtered or sterilized ballast water or the exchange of ballast water in mid-ocean far from land has been explored. The transplantation of species must also be strictly regulated. Rigorous studies of the biology of the species involved and those in the proposed new locations must also be undertaken before such transplantations are carried out.

Overfishing and plastic debris have been responsible for a decline in the number of seabirds in many parts of the world. Long-line fishing kills thousands of albatrosses (*Diomedea*) each year in Antarctic waters alone. Nine of the 22 species of albatrosses are critically endangered or endangered, and most of the remaining species are threatened.

Marine mammals, which have low reproductive rates, also face extermination. Some species of whales are still hunted (see "Conservation of Cetaceans," in 9.3). Other whales, although protected, are threatened by ship strikes. Some species of seals, sea lions, and the walrus have been decimated for their skins, meat, blubber, or the ivory of their tusks. The walrus and the polar bear are threatened by diminishing Arctic ice. Monk seals (*Monachus*) are endangered; one species, the Caribbean monk seal (*Monachus tropicalis),* is extinct. The sea otter (*Enhydra lutris;* see Fig. 9.12) had made a comeback but it is still threatened (see "Kelp Communities," in 13.3). Manatees (*Trichechus;*

Table 18.1 Endangered, Threatened, and Vulnerable Marine Species

Group of Marine Animals	Red List of Threatened Species, 2021[1] (Critically Endangered, and Vulnerable Species Only)	CITES List of Species Threatened with Extinction, 2021[2]	CITES List of Species Vulnerable to Exploitation, 2021[3]
Corals and other cnidarians	239	0	All scleractinian, black, blue, organ-pipe, and hydrozoan corals
Other invertebrates (mulluscs, crustaceans, echinoderms, etc.)	279	0	22
Sharks and rays	571	5	44
Marine bony fishes	525	5	74
Sea turtles	5	7 (all)	0
Sea snakes	3	0	0
Marine iguana	1	0	1
Seabirds	170	7	1
Sirenians	4 (all)	4 (all)	0
Seals, sea lions, walrus	10	3	9
Sea otter, marine otter	2	2	0
Polar bear	1	0	1
Whales, marine dolphins	19	31	0

[1]Compiled by the International Union for Conservation of Nature and Natural Resources (IUCN).

[2]Appendix I, Convention on International Trade in Endangered Species of Wild Flora and Fauna.

[3]Appendix II, Convention on International Trade in Endangered Species of Wild Flora and Fauna.

see Fig. 9.14) and the dugong (*Dugong dugon*), **sirenians** like the extinct Steller's sea cow (Fig. 18.15), are endangered.

Many marine species are at risk of extermination because of unregulated exploitation, destruction of habitats, global climate change, and other anthropogenic impacts.

18.4 CONSERVING AND ENHANCING THE MARINE ENVIRONMENT

The loss of biodiversity through the disappearance of species is mostly the result of the loss and degradation of habitats (see Box 10.1, "Biodiversity: All Creatures Great and Small"). Conservation of biodiversity aims at the conservation of a vast number of species, their habitats, and entire communities, not merely the preservation of a limited number of endangered species.

FIGURE 18.15 The Steller's sea cow (*Hydrodamalis gigas*), estimated to have weighed at least 10 tons, ate mostly kelp. It became known to science in 1741, when it inhabited the kelp beds of the Commander Islands in the western Bering Sea. Demand for its meat, which was considered "as good as the best cuts of beef," led to its extermination at the hands of whalers. The species was slaughtered to extinction soon after its discovery. The last known live individual was taken in 1768.

Conservation

The protection, or conservation, of coastal areas from the advancing wave of development is of crucial importance. A growing human population (see Fig. 17.2) and the increasing demands of practically everyone exert continuous pressure on the natural environment. The apparent conflict between economic development and the protection of marine resources, though especially intense in developing countries, occurs everywhere. Development must be **sustainable,** that is, it must meet the needs of today without affecting the ability of future generations to meet their needs. Laws have been passed by many governments, but there is still a lot to be done. **Coastal management** aims at promoting the wise use of our coasts while ensuring that the benefits of this use can be sustained for future generations. The multiple use of coastal resources and the need to manage them calls for judicious planning to accommodate the often conflicting interests of developers, fishers, surfers, beachgoers, and nesting seabirds. Coastal management deals with issues as varied as historical preservation, beach access, and tourism.

FIGURE 18.16 Endangered sea turtles (*Chelonia mydas*) confiscated from poachers in Bali, Indonesia. Poaching of protected and endangered or threatened marine animals is a problem worldwide, with many of these species being part of an illegal multimillion-dollar trade.

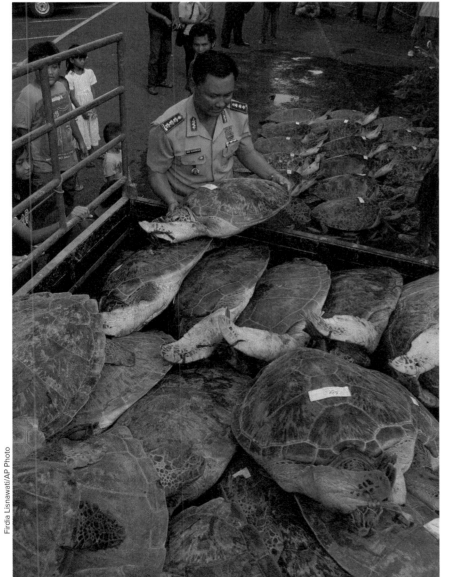

Firdia Lisnawati/AP Photo

Efforts to stop the deterioration of the marine environment include conservation and effective coastal management.

Conservation efforts include many local, national, and international projects and legislation dedicated to the protection of species and environments. Oil drilling, for instance, has been banned along some coasts, as in California. Commercial fisheries are regulated by national governments, partly as a result of the establishment of **exclusive economic zones,** or **EEZs,** and by international commissions (see "Managing the Resources," in 17.1), although many stocks are still being harvested at levels above **maximum sustainable yields** (see Fig. 17.9).

Governments have also established **marine protected areas** (**MPAs)** for the protection and management of areas of ecological significance (see Fig. 18.17 and map in Appendix D). The National Estuarine Reserve Research System of the United States, for example, designated 27 reserves in 21 states and Puerto Rico protecting almost 5,370 km^2 (2,073 mi^2) of estuaries, salt marshes, and mangrove forests. The largest MPA in the world is Antarctica's Ross Region Marine Protected Area, created in 2017, with a total area of 1.548 million km^2 (598,000 mi^2) (Fig. 18.17). The United States established the Pacific Remote Islands Marine National Monument, covering approximaely 1.058 km^2 (308,000 mi^2). Other MPAs have been proposed for Antarctica and elsewhere. Still, only about 7.7% of the world ocean received some type of protection by 2020.

MPAs are richer in the number of species and in the abundance of individuals in these species compared with unprotected waters around them. There is evidence that protected areas benefit surrounding waters through either "seeding," in which the offspring of individuals inside the protected area settle elsewhere, or "spillover," in which juveniles and adults move out of the protected area.

Many national and international organizations play an active role in marine conservation through education, the sponsoring of projects, and lobbying for legislation. Some concentrate on issues like biodiversity, habitat conservation, and sustainable fishing, whereas others aim at particular animal groups (cetaceans, sea turtles, and the like), environments (coral reefs, mangrove forests), or geographical regions.

Restoration of Habitats

Another strategy for improving the quality of the marine environment is to help habitats recover from modifications caused by habitat destruction and pollution. **Habitat restoration** helps recovery from stress by

Exclusive Economic Zone (EEZ) A zone 200 mi (370 km) wide along the coast, in which nations have exclusive rights to fishing and other resources.
• 17.1, The Living Resources of the Sea

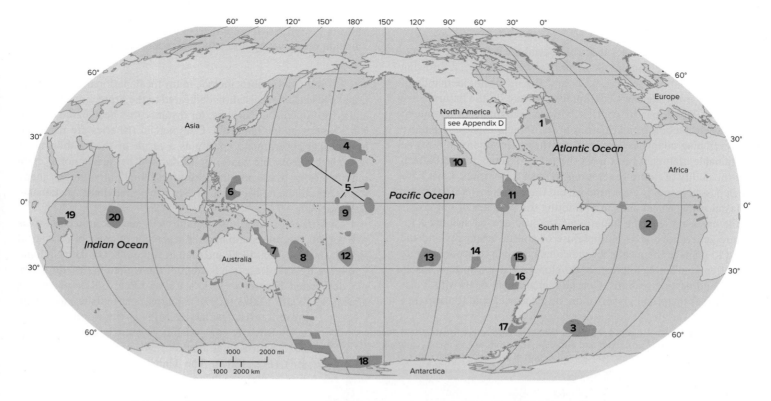

1. Northeast Canyons and Seamount Marine National Monument

2. Ascension Island Ocean Sanctuary

3. South Georgia and South Sandwich Islands Marine Protected Area

4. Papahānaumokuākea Marine National Monument

5. Pacific Remote Islands Marine National Monument

6. Palau National Marine Sanctuary

7. Coral Sea Marine Park (Australia)

8. Natural Park of the Coral Sea (France)

9. Phoenix Islands Protected Area

10. Revillagigedo Archipelago National Park

11. Galápagos Islands World Heritage Site (being extended as Hermandad Marine Reserve)

12. Niue Marine Protected Area

13. Pitcairn Islands Marine Reserve

14. Motu Motira Hiva Marine Park

15. Nazca-Desventuradas Marine Park

16. Juan Fernández Marine Park

17. Diego Ramirez Islands and Drake Passage Marine Park

18. Ross Region Marine Protected Area

19. Aldabra Group Marine National Park

20. Chagos Marine Protected Area

Source: Bill Ober

FIGURE 18.17 Some of the major Marine Protected Areas (MPAs) around the world.

transplanting, or restocking, key species from healthier areas. The loss of priceless salt marshes and mangrove forests through land-filling or the building of aquaculture ponds or boat marinas can be at least partially compensated for by creating or improving a similar but unstressed habitat elsewhere. These efforts, of course, assume that the new location meets the physical requirements (tides, salinity, type of substrate) for the development of a healthy biological community.

FIGURE 18.18 Restoration of marine habitats has included the transplantation of young giant kelp plants (*Macrocystis pyrifera*) into areas where kelp forests have diminished or vanished. Removal of grazing sea urchins by volunteers can also be effective.

Dale Glantz

Box 18.4 Ten Simple Things You Can Do to Save the Oceans

We all impact the oceans, no matter how far we live from the seashore. You can do a lot to help save the oceans and the rest of the planet. Here are 10 simple things inspired by *50 Ways to Save the Ocean* by D. Helvarg.

1. ***Take care of the environment***. Do not disturb the environment in any way if you go to the seashore or go snorkeling or diving. Respect natural habitats. Return any overturned rocks to their original positions. Leave all forms of life where they are.

2. ***Eat sustainably caught seafood***. Ask questions when buying fish or ordering it at a restaurant: Where is it from and how was it caught? Buy fish certified as caught or farmed in a sustainable way. Eat lower on the food chain (such as shellfish) and eat less or no swordfish, tuna, shark, or grouper (see Fig. 17.11). If you go fishing, target species that are abundant and not those that are overfished, even if it's legal. Know the regulations and take only what you really need for food. Return undersized fish and shellfish.

3. ***Beware of what you buy***. Never, ever buy products made from endangered or threatened species like tortoiseshell or ivory. Corals and shells should be left alone, and alive, in their natural home. Be sure to tell merchants you object to their sale or of that of other marine life, which were most probably collected alive and killed for sale. If you buy fishes, corals, and other marine life for your marine aquarium, be sure to check before buying if they were obtained in an environmentally responsible, sustainable way. Some aquarium fishes, like clownfishes, are captive-bred, but many other coral reef fishes are caught in the wild.

4. ***Reduce your footprint on planet Earth: Save gas***. Saving gas keeps carbon dioxide, which promotes global climate change and acidification of seawater, out of the atmosphere. Tailpipe pollutants add to the nitrogen nutrients that cause eutrophication of coastal waters. Use public transportation more often. Demand better and cheaper public transportation. If possible, use a bike, and, if you do need a car, get a small electric or hybrid one.

5. ***Save electricity***. Many power plants still burn coal to produce electricity, releasing more carbon dioxide (an electric drier produces an average of 3.6 pounds of carbon dioxide a day, but drying clothes on a clothesline produces none!) plus more nitrogen compounds as well as mercury. Saving gas and electricity also reduces the need for oil and thus the threats of more offshore oil drilling and oil spills.

6. ***Dispose of hazardous materials properly***. Reduce your use of toxic chemicals, which are in discarded computers and other electronics, batteries, motor oil, paints, cleaners, and many other household trash. Dumping them on the ground, in the trash can, down storm drains, or letting them accumulate in landfills will pollute wetlands, the ocean, and rivers, which drain into the ocean. Flushing them down the drain simply adds them to sewage, which in some places ultimately flushes, untreated, into the ocean. Your local recycling center can tell you how to recycle hazardous materials.

7. ***Use less plastics, recycle them***. Reduce the risk of plastics being washed to sea. Use reusable canvas bags to do your shopping instead of plastic bags; say no to plastic straws; use paper instead of plastic for packing. Wash and re-use plastic bottles and bags, if you actually need to use them. Drink tap water when safe to do so, not from plastic bottles, and carry drinking water in aluminum containers instead of plastic bottles. Buy and store food in glass containers instead of plastic bags or wrappings. Ban plastic plates and cups from your household. Pick up plastic trash from the beach. Cut open six-pack rings before disposal, and properly dispose of snarled fishing line; never toss it at sea or on shore.

8. ***Keep it clean***. Clean up after your pets. Their feces can carry parasites that, if washed to sea, can infect marine mammals (and humans).

9. ***Get involved. Keep informed***. Be aware of and keep up with environmental issues. Read, ask questions, and listen carefully. Numerous organizations, societies, and government agencies are committed to help save our planet. Hear what they have to say and sponsor them. Make your voice heard in coastal and conservation issues at local, state, and national levels. Vote for the oceans and the planet. Support marine protected areas.

10. ***Endorse a new ocean ethic***. Treat the ocean as a valuable resource, not as a garbage dump. Think globally and sustainably, act locally.

Successful examples of habitat restoration include the restoration of salt marshes (see Box 12.2, "Restoration of Salt Marshes") and of native oyster (*Crassostrea*) reefs in Chesapeake Bay, eastern United States, and elsewhere. Young giant kelp (*Macrocystis*), with their root-like holdfasts tied to concrete blocks or to submerged nylon lines (Fig. 18.18), have been used to help restore kelp forests, particularly in **artificial reefs** built of large rocks. Seabirds are even being attracted to old nesting grounds by using painted decoys and solar-powered tape recorders that play bird calls!

The irregular surfaces and the hiding places provided by artificial reefs attract fishes, lobsters, and other life. Shellfish and seaweeds can thrive on their surfaces. Everything from concrete blocks to toilets and scuttled ships have been used to build artificial reefs around the world.

Offshore oil rigs have been turned into artificial reefs after "reefing," the removal of the sections above the water. Life on and around these oil rigs has been shown to be far richer than in nearby rocky reefs, and can also serve as nursery grounds for fishes.

It has also been argued that artificial reefs only concentrate fishes and lobsters in one spot, making them easier to catch and thus contributing to their depletion. The use of long-lasting concrete modules for artificial reefs (Fig. 18.19), however, has been more successful. Round ones, called "reef balls," can be positioned to maximize photosynthesis and allow for an effective flow of plankton. A rough, more natural surface promotes the settlement of coral larvae in the tropics.

Several schemes are being investigated for the restoration of coral reefs. One such effort involves cross-breeding the healthiest, sturdiest corals, very much like crop plants, and ultimately using

FIGURE 18.19 Artificial reefs can be built of various types of prefabricated concrete blocks.

them to restore damaged reefs. Growing coral colonies in open-sea "nurseries" and transplanting them to damaged reefs is another approach.

Conservation of marine environments includes the establishment of marine protected areas and the restoration of habitats.

18.5 PROSPECTS FOR THE FUTURE

It is impossible to predict what lies ahead for our world ocean. Optimists have visions of cities built underwater or self-ruling cities built on floating islands, food from aquaculture, unlimited energy from the water and seabed, and no pollution to speak of. Many experts, however, are less confident. They point out that our impact on the marine environment will escalate as the world's population expands. Modern technology will lead to new means of exploitation, and for resources never imagined before.

The oceans, the legacy of all humankind, must be safeguarded to save them from overexploitation and pollution. This has been one of the aims of the **United Nations Convention on the Law of the Sea (UNCLOS),** the 1982 treaty that culminated many years of deliberations by the many nations that were represented. Most nations have ratified the treaty and implemented many of its provisions, but a few nations like the United States have yet to ratify it.

The treaty, for example, led to the establishment of the exclusive economic zones (EEZs) (see above). This agreement has had significant consequences for the management of marine resources, particularly fisheries (see "Managing the Resources," in 17.1). Nations that ratified the treaty could claim any extensions of their continental shelf beyond the 200 nautical miles as long as the extensions are not more than 100 nautical miles (185 km) from the point at which the sea reached a depth of 2,500 m (8,200 ft) and no more than 350 nautical miles (555 km) from land. Nations owning tiny islands and reefs barely above high water can now claim large portions of the surrounding seabed, which could hold a fortune in oil, gas, minerals, and fisheries. Such is the case of some islands and surrounding

waters in the South China Sea, now claimed by China and several nations in the region, and in potential conflicts over the exploitation of resources in the Arctic Ocean.

The United Nations Convention on the Law of the Sea initiated a series of international agreements in an effort to define the use of the oceans by all nations. They included the establishment of exclusive economic zones (EEZs).

Other international agreements have attempted to solve other problems. The United Nations Conference on Environment and Development at Rio de Janeiro, known as the Rio Earth Summit of 1992, is one example. It resulted in an agreement to preserve biodiversity on the planet (see Box 10.1, "Biodiversity: All Creatures Great and Small"). One commitment was to protect the interests of the traditional fisheries of indigenous people. The Paris Agreement, or **Paris Climate Agreement,** of the United Nations Framework Convention on Climate Change (UNFCCC), was signed by 197 nations that agreed to proceed with efforts to combat climate change. The 2021 26th United Nations Climate Change Conference (COP26) pledged to curb methane emissions, deforestation, and phase out carbon use. The United States, however, announced that it intends to withdraw from the agreement. Several states and Puerto Rico, however, challenged the federal decision and agreed to continue to abide by the objectives of the Paris Climate Agreement.

From the early beginnings the oceans have influenced humankind by providing food and avenues of commerce and culture. It is clear, however, that the relationship has been reversed. The future of the dynamic, ever-expanding field of marine biology is thus facing many challenges on the ocean we share. These challenges include global climate change and its effects on sea level and ocean acidification, a global food crisis that demands new and more efficient uses of food resources from the ocean, an energy crisis that similarly calls for innovative sources of renewable energy, the decrease in biodiversity and the disappearance of marine habitats brought about by humankind, and the effects of plastics, overfertilization and other types of pollution.

Interactive Exploration

McGraw-Hill Connect® is a great place to check your understanding of chapter material. Visit **www.mcgrawhillconnect.com** for access to interactive chapter summaries, chapter quizzing, and more! Further enhance your knowledge with video clips and web links to chapter-related material.

Critical Thinking

1. Wastes from duck farms used to wash into two shallow-water bays on Long Island, New York. The wastes, rich in nutrients such as nitrate and phosphate, polluted the water. What do you suppose was the immediate effect of the pollutants? Can you speculate on the likely effects on the commercially valuable shellfish of the area?

2. It is found that a chemical present in effluents from a factory is being stored in the tissues of herring, a plankton-feeding fish. What type of observations and possible experiments would you suggest to find out if the chemical is biodegradable? What is the significance of finding out if the chemical is biodegradable or not?

3. Tourism and its effects, like pollution from hotels and the impact of boats and tourists, on fragile habitats often clash with conservation efforts. Sometimes, however, tourism can help. The economic impact of banning the hunting of harp seals in eastern Canada has been compensated for, in part, by the influx of tourists who now go to see the seals. Can you think of other examples? What recommendations can you make to minimize the impact of tourism on unspoiled marine environments?

4. Why do you think that the possibility of a population of marine animals evolving resistance to a marine pollutant is not a solution to the problem of pollution by the pollutant in question?

5. Can you think of any disadvantages, if any, in the establishment of a marine protected area (MPA) along a coast?

For Further Reading

Some of the recommended reading may be available online. Look for live links on the *Marine Biology* Online Learning Center.

General Interest

Barnett, C., 2017. Saving the sea. *National Geographic,* vol. 231, no. 2, February, pp. 54–77. The United States has created a network of protected marine areas in the Pacific and Atlantic oceans.

Irwin, A., 2018. How to solve a problem like plastics. *New Scientist*, vol. 238, no. 3178, May 19, pp. 25–31. The recycling of plastics and even the use of biodegradable plastics are not free of complications.

Mole, B., 2015. An oil spill's aftermath. *Science News*, vol. 187, no. 8, April 18, pp. 22–26. There are still many unanswered questions about the *Deepwater Horizon*'s oil spill.

Nobel, J., 2017. The first line of defense. *Audubon,* vol. 119, no. 3, Fall, pp. 30–37. Louisiana's barrier islands are being restored using funds from fines for damage from the *Deepwater Horizon* oil spill.

Parker, L., 2018. Plastic. *National Geographic*, vol. 233, no. 6, June, pp. 40–91. Five articles on plastics: Sources, distribution in the marine environment, effects on marine life, and solutions.

Parker, L., 2019. Little pieces, big problems. *National Geographic*, vol. 235, no. 5, May, pp. 42–55. Microplastics of all shapes and composition are a common component of plankton tows across oceans.

Reed, C., 2018. The other plastic plague. *New Scientist*, vol. 239, no. 3186, 14 July, pp. 37–39. Plastic spreads microorganisms that cause diseases in corals and other marine life.

Reese, A., 2016. Sea level rise. *Discover*, vol. 37, no. 6, July/August, pp. 46–49. Coastal cities and other shores worldwide are at risk of rising sea levels.

Sumner, T., 2016. Changing climate. *Science News,* vol. 189, no. 8, pp. 22–29. Developments in the study of global climate change are reviewed 10 years after the release of Al Gore's *An Inconvenient Truth.*

Warne, K., 2020. The power of protection. *National Geographic*, vol. 238, no. 3, September, pp. 112–129. The establishment of additional marine protected areas can also improve fish stocks and help lessen the effects of climate change.

Welch, C., 2016. Heat wave. *National Geographic,* vol. 230, no. 3, September, pp. 54–75. Abnormally warm water has affected the Pacific Coast of North America due to the effects of algal blooms and the high mortality of some native species.

Wright, D. R., 2020. *Future sea: How to rescue and protect the world's oceans.* University of Chicago Press, Chicago, IL. A marine-policy specialist presents a readable account of the many problems currently faced by the oceans and the steps that anyone can take to help.

Zaleski, A., 2021. The godfather of pollution. *New Scientist*, vol. 250, no. 3334, May 15, pp. 41–45. Nitrogen compounds, the major culprit of eutrophication in the ocean, also pollute our air and soil.

In Depth

"Our plastic dilemma," 2021. *Science*, vol. 373, no. 6550, pp. 34–69 [special section of ten articles on plastic pollution].

Airoldi, L., M. W. Beck, L. B. Firth, A. B. Bugnot, P. D. Steinberg, and K. A. Dafforn, 2021. Emerging solutions to return nature to the urban ocean. *Annual Review of Marine Science*, vol. 13, pp. 445–477.

Giakoumi, S. and A. Pey, 2017. Assessing the effects of marine protected areas on biological invasions: A global review. *Frontiers in Marine Science* [https://doi.org/10.3389/fmars.2017.00049].

Gribben, P. E. and J. E. Byers, 2020. Comparative biogeography of marine invaders across their native and introduced ranges. *Oceanography and Marine Biology*: An Annual Review, vol. 58, pp. 395–440.

Grosell M. and C. Pasparakis, 2021. Physiological responses of fish to oil spills. *Annual Review of Marine Science*, vol. 13, pp. 137–160.

Knowlton, N., 2021. Ocean optimism: Moving beyond the obituaries in marine conservation. *Annual Review of Marine Science*, vol. 13, pp. 479–499.

Miatta, M., A. E. Bates, and P. V. R. Snelgrove, 2021. Incorporating biological traits into conservation strategies. *Annual Review of Marine Science*, vol. 13, pp. 421–443.

Müller, C., 2021. Not as bad as it seems? A literature review on the case of microplastic uptake in fish. *Frontiers in Marine Science* [https://doi.org/10.3389/fmars.2021.672768].

Oberbeckmann, S. and M. Labrenz, 2020. Marine microbial assemblages on microplastics: Diversity, adaptation, and role in degradation. *Annual Review of Marine Science*, vol. 12, pp. 209–232.

O'Hara, C. C., M. Frazier, and B. S. Halpern, 2021. At-risk marine biodiversity faces extensive, expanding, and intensifying human impacts. *Science*, vol. 372, no. 6537, pp. 84–87.

Passow, U. and E. B. Overton, 2021. The complexity of spills: The fate of the Deepwater Horizon oil. *Annual Review of Marine Science*, vol. 13, pp. 109–136.

Yu, S.-P., M. Cole, and B. K. K. Chan, 2020. Effects of microplastic on zooplankton survival and sublethal responses. *Oceanography and Marine Biology: An Annual Review*, vol. 58, pp. 351–393.

Design elements: chapter opener (ocean wave) ©EpicStockMedia/Shutterstock, (blue Parrotfish) ©ivvv1975/Shutterstock; Eye on Science box ©Westend61/ Getty Images; Evolutionary Perspective box ©vilainecrevette/123RF; end-of-chapter (beach): ©photoaraki.com/Getty Images

Appendix A

Units of Measurement

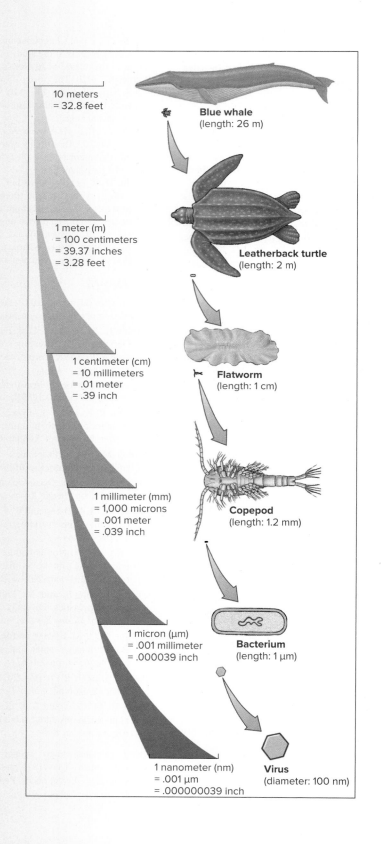

10 meters
= 32.8 feet

Blue whale
(length: 26 m)

1 meter (m)
= 100 centimeters
= 39.37 inches
= 3.28 feet

Leatherback turtle
(length: 2 m)

1 centimeter (cm)
= 10 millimeters
= .01 meter
= .39 inch

Flatworm
(length: 1 cm)

1 millimeter (mm)
= 1,000 microns
= .001 meter
= .039 inch

Copepod
(length: 1.2 mm)

1 micron (μm)
= .001 millimeter
= .000039 inch

Bacterium
(length: 1 μm)

1 nanometer (nm)
= .001 μm
= .000000039 inch

Virus
(diameter: 100 nm)

Appendix B

Selected Field Guides and Other References for the Identification of Marine Organisms in North America

General

Carwardine, M., 2020. *Handbook of whales, dolphins, and porpoises of the world.* Princeton University Press, Princeton, NJ.

Cole, B. and S. Michael, 2020. *Reef life: A guide to tropical marine life.* Firefly Books, Richmond Hill, ON, Canada.

Harrison, P., 2015. *Seabirds: The new identification guide.* Lynx Edicions, Barcelona, Spain.

Lieske, E. and R. Myers, 2002. *Coral reef fishes.* Princeton University Press, Princeton, NJ.

Meinkoth, N. A., 1981. *The Audubon Society field guide to North American seashore creatures.* Knopf, New York, NY.

Smith, D. L. and K. B. Johnson, 1996. *A guide to marine coastal plankton and marine invertebrate larvae.* Kendall-Hunt, Dubuque, IA.

Atlantic Coast of North America (Including the Gulf of Mexico, the Caribbean, and Bermuda)

Gosner, K. L., 1999. *A field guide to the Atlantic seashore.* Houghton Mifflin, Boston, MA.

Hoese, H. D. and R. H. Moore, 1998. *Fishes of the Gulf of Mexico.* Texas A&M Press, College Station, TX.

Johnson, W. S. and D. M. Allen, 2012. *Zooplankton of the Atlantic and Gulf Coasts: A guide to their identification and ecology.* Johns Hopkins University Press, Baltimore, MD.

Kaplan, E. H., 1999. *A field guide to coral reefs: Caribbean and Florida.* Houghton Mifflin, Boston, MA.

Kaplan, E. H., 1999. *A field guide to Southeastern and Caribbean seashores.* Houghton Mifflin, Boston, MA.

Katona, S. K., V. Rough, and D. T. Richardson, 1993. *A field guide to the whales, porpoises, and seals from Cape Cod to Newfoundland.* Smithsonian Institution Press, Washington, DC.

Lippson, A. J. and R. L. Lippson, 2006. *Life in the Chesapeake Bay.* Johns Hopkins University Press, Baltimore, MD.

Littler, D. S. and M. M. Littler, 2000. *Caribbean reef plants.* Offshore Graphics, Washington, DC.

Proctor, N. S. and P. J. Lynch, 2005. *A field guide to North Atlantic wildlife: marine mammals, seabirds, fish, and other sea life.* Yale University Press, New Haven, CT.

Proctor, N. S. and P. J. Lynch, 2012. *A field guide to the southeast coast & Gulf of Mexico.* Yale University Press, New Haven, CT.

Robins, C. R. and G. C. Ray, 1999. *A field guide to Atlantic coast fishes.* Houghton Mifflin, Boston, MA.

Ruppert, E. and R. Fox, 1988. *Seashore animals of the Southeast.* University of South Carolina Press, Columbia.

Schneider, C. W. and R. B. Searles, 1991. *Seaweeds of the Southeastern United States: Cape Hatteras to Cape Canaveral.* Duke University Press, Durham, NC.

Sept, J. D., 2016. *Atlantic seashore field guide.* Stackpole Books, Mechanicsburg, PA.

Smith, C. L., 1997. *National Audubon Society field guide to tropical marine fishes of the Caribbean, Gulf of Mexico, Florida, the Bahamas, and Bermuda.* Knopf, NY.

Snyderman, M. and C. Wiseman, 1996. *Guide to marine life: Caribbean, Bahamas, Florida.* Aqua Quest, Locust Valley, NY.

Spalding, M. D. and C. Ravilions, 2004. *A guide to the coral reefs of the Caribbean.* University of California Press, Berkeley, CA.

Watling, L., J. Fegley, and J. Moring, 2003. *Life between the tides. Marine plants and animals of the Northeast.* Tilbury House Publishing, Thomaston, ME.

Pacific Coast of North America (Including the Gulf of California and Hawai'i)

Allen, G., R. Steene, P. Humann, and N. Deloach, 2005. *Reef fish identification– Tropical Pacific.* New World Publications, Jacksonville, FL.

Allen, S. G., J. Mortenson, and S. Webb, 2011. *Field guide to marine mammals of the Pacific coast.* University of California Press, Berkeley, CA.

Brandon, J. L. and F. J. Rokop, 1985. *Life between the tides. The natural history of the common seashore life of Southern California.*

American Southwest Publishing, San Diego, CA.

Druhel, L. D. and B. Clarkston, 2016. *Pacific seaweeds.* Harbour Publishing, Madeira Park, BC, Canada.

Ebert, D. A., 2003. *Sharks, rays, and chimaeras of California.* University of California Press, Berkeley, CA.

Eschmeyer, W. N., E. S. Herald, and H. E. Hammann, 1999. *A field guide to Pacific coast fishes of North America.* Houghton Mifflin, Boston, MA.

Gotshall, D. W., 2005. *Guide to Marine invertebrates. Alaska to Baja California.* Sea Challengers, Monterey, CA.

Hinton, S., 1988. *Seashore life of Southern California.* University of California Press, Berkeley, CA.

Hoover, J. P., 1999. *Hawai'i's sea creatures. A guide to Hawai'i's marine invertebrates.* Mutual Publishing, Honolulu, HI.

Kells, V. A., L. A. Rocha, and L. G. Allen, 2016. *A field guide to coastal fishes: From Alaska to California.* Johns Hopkins Press, Baltimore, MD.

Kerstitch, A. and H. Bertsch, 2017. *Sea of Cortez marine invertebrates.* Sea Challengers, Monterey, CA.

Kozloff, E. N., 1993. *Seashore life of the Northern Pacific coast.* University of Washington Press, Seattle, WA.

Kozloff, E. N., 1996. *Marine invertebrates of the Pacific Northwest.* University of Washington Press, Seattle, WA.

Mondragon, J. and J. Mondragon, 2016. *Seaweeds of the Pacific coast. common marine algae from Alaska to Baja California.* Sea Challengers, Monterey, CA.

Ricketts, E. F., J. Calvin, J. W. Hedgpeth, and D. W. Phillips, 1985. *Between Pacific tides* (5th ed). Stanford University Press, Redwood City, CA.

Ûrandon, J. L. and F. J. Rokop, 1985. *Life between the tides. The natural history of the common seashore life of Southern California.* American Southwest Publishing, San Diego, CA.

Appendix C

The World Ocean

ARCTIC OCEAN

A

BARENTS SEA
▼374 m
KARA SEA
LAPTEV SEA
EAST SIBERIAN SEA
CHUKCHI SEA

Arctic Circle

S I B E R I A

Bering Strait

RUSSIA

MEIJI SEAMOUNT
BERING SEA
Aleutian Islands
ALASK
ALEUTIAN TR
ALEUTIAN PENIN

A S I A

SEA OF OKHOTSK
▼7,973 m

EMPEROR SEAMOUNTS

NORTH PACIFIC OCEAN

BLACK SEA
CASPIAN SEA
ARAL SEA

▼10,367 m
KURIL TRENCH
▼3,456 m

KOREA
JAPAN
SEA OF JAPAN
JAPAN TRENCH

NORTHWEST PACIFIC BASIN

CHINA

EAST CHINA SEA
▼10,211 m
IZU TRENCH

Midway Island
1,727 m

Suez Canal

Persian Gulf

INDIA

Tropic of Cancer

Taiwan
▼7,389 m
BONIN TRENCH
▼8,501 m

HAWAIIAN RIDGE

RED SEA

Gulf of Aden

ARABIAN SEA

Bay of Bengal

PHILIPPINE SEA

Philippine Islands

Mariana Islands
10,861 m
YAP TRENCH
MARIANA TRENCH

Marshall Islands

CHAGOS-LACCADIVE PLATEAU

SOUTH CHINA SEA

Gulf of Thailand

▼5,161 m

Maldive Islands

Sumatra

▼10,322 m
PHILIPPINE TRENCH

AFRICA
KENYA

Equator
▼5,035 m

MID-INDIAN RIDGE

Chagos Archipelago
▼6,139 m

NINETYEAST RIDGE

JAVA TRENCH

INDONESIA

Sulawesi

4,392 m ▼
Kiribati

Comoro Islands

MASCARENE PLATEAU

Krakatoa Island
▼7,333 m

New Guinea
▼8,999 m
BOUGAINVILLE TRENCH
VITYAZ TRENCH
Tuvalu

Mozambique Channel

▼6,235 m

Cocos Islands

GREAT BARRIER REEF

CORAL SEA

NEW HEBRIDES TRENCH

Fiji

MADAGASCAR

Tropic of Capricorn

New Caledonia
5,220 m ▼

TONGA TRENCH
▼10,711 m

9,988 m ▼

6,299 m ▼

INDIAN OCEAN

EAST INDIAMAN RIDGE

AUSTRALIA

SOUTHWEST INDIAN RIDGE

BROKEN RIDGE
▼4,402 m

PERTH BASIN

Great Australian Bight

5,581 m ▼

TASMAN SEA

KERMADEC TRENCH

Kerguélen
▼2,937 m

SOUTHEAST INDIAN RIDGE

SOUTH AUSTRALIAN BASIN

5,184 m ▼
▼

NEW ZEALAND

▼6,863 m
KERGUELEN PLATEAU

TASMAN PLATEAU

Auckland Islands

▼5,993 m

SOUTH INDIAN BASIN

ENDERBY PLAIN

SOUTHERN OCEAN

Antarctic Circle

PACIFIC-ANT

ROSS SEA

OCEAN

GREENLAND

2,102 m ▼ *Baffin Bay*

3,632 m ▼

NORWEGIAN SEA

ICELAND

Arctic Circle

NORWEGIAN BASIN

BALTIC SEA

Hudson Bay ▼ 296 m

LABRADOR SEA

Strait of Belle Isle

REYKJANES RIDGE

▼ 2,461 m

3,359 m ▼

234 m ▼

ENGLAND

NORTH SEA

EUROPE

60°

CANADA

LABRADOR

153 m ▼

NORTH ATLANTIC OCEAN

Newfoundland

GRAND BANKS OF NEWFOUNDLAND
▼ 6,210 m

NORTH AMERICA

UNITED STATES

Bay of Fundy
CAPE COD

CAPE HATTERAS

Bermuda

SARGASSO SEA

▼ 4,619 m

PORTUGAL SPAIN

Azores

▼ 3,573 m
▼ 2,281 m

40°

2,041 m ▼

MEDITERRANEAN SEA

3,124 m ▼

Columbia River

Mississippi River

▼ 5,376 m

NORTH AMERICAN BASIN

Madeira

Canary Islands

Gulf of Mexico

MEXICO

5,630 m ▼

MIDDLE AMERICA TRENCH

▼ 3,960 m

▼ 6,885 m

West Indies

PUERTO RICO TRENCH

MID-ATLANTIC RIDGE

Tropic of Cancer

20°

Cape Verde Islands

AFRICA

7,565 m ▼

CARIBBEAN SEA

▼ 5,335 m

ANDES MOUNTAINS

7,177 m ▼

COCOS RIDGE

Panama Canal
4,135 m ▼

5,130 m ▼

Gulf of Guinea

Equator 0°

Galapagos Islands

PERÚ-CHILE TRENCH

Amazon River

SOUTH AMERICA

6,434 m ▼

MID-ATLANTIC RIDGE

Ascension

Marquesas Islands

5,399 m ▼

4,763 m ▼

5,955 m ▼

French Polynesia

PERÚ

BRAZIL

EAST PACIFIC RISE

Easter Island (Rapa Nui)

NAZCA RIDGE

7,939 m ▼
▼ 324 m

CHILE

5,664 m ▼

RIO GRANDE RISE

Tropic of Capricorn

20°

NAMIBIA

SOUTH PACIFIC OCEAN

WALVIS RIDGE

SOUTH AFRICA

5,089 m ▼

5,183 m ▼

Tristan da Cunha

▼ 536 m

CAPE OF GOOD HOPE

2,274 m ▼

PACIFIC BASIN

3,915 m ▼

SOUTH ATLANTIC OCEAN

6,115 m ▼

40°

4,799 m ▼

Strait of Magellan
Falkland Islands

1,506 m ▼

ATLANTIC-INDIAN RIDGE

SOUTHERN OCEAN

CAPE HORN

SCOTIA SEA

South Georgia

SOUTH SANDWICH TRENCH

60°

5,158 m ▼

492 m ▼

...GSHAUSEN PLAIN

SOUTH SANDWICH TRENCH

827 m ▼

Antarctic Circle

WEDDELL PLAIN

WEDDELL SEA

▼ 4,754 m

ANTARCTICA

80°

120° 90° 60° 30° 0°

Appendix D

Major Coastal Communities and Marine Protected Areas in North America and the Caribbean

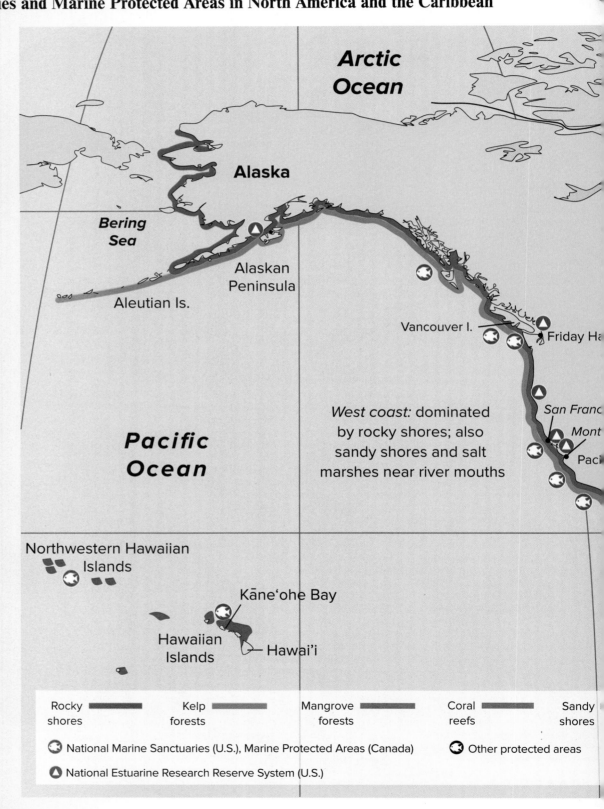

Arctic Ocean

Alaska

Bering Sea

Alaskan Peninsula

Aleutian Is.

Vancouver I.

Friday Ha

West coast: dominated by rocky shores; also sandy shores and salt marshes near river mouths

San Franc

Mont

Pac

Pacific Ocean

Northwestern Hawaiian Islands

Kāneʻohe Bay

Hawaiian Islands

Hawaiʻi

Rocky shores	Kelp forests	Mangrove forests	Coral reefs	Sandy shores

National Marine Sanctuaries (U.S.), Marine Protected Areas (Canada) Other protected areas

National Estuarine Research Reserve System (U.S.)

Northwest Passage

Greenland

Hudson Bay

Canada

Labrador

Newfoundland

St Lawrence River

Grand Banks

Shoals

Woods Hole

Nantucket I.

Chesapeake Bay

United States

East coast: dominated by sandy shores and salt marshes

Beaufort

Gulf of California

Bayous

Bermuda

Flower Gardens

Mexico

Gulf of Mexico

Bahamas

Atlantic Ocean

Belize

Jamaica

Puerto Rico

Central America

Caribbean Sea

Panama Canal

South America

Source: Bill Ober

447

Glossary

Words in **boldface** are defined separately in the glossary. Other key terms are given in *italics*.

A

abiotic A non-living (physical or chemical) component of the environment. Compare **biotic.**

aboral surface The surface opposite the mouth (or *oral surface*) in **cnidarians, comb jellies,** and **echinoderms.**

abyssal plain The nearly flat region of the deep-sea floor.

abyssal zone The bottom from a depth of approximately 4,000 m (13,000 ft) to 6,000 m (20,000 ft) (Fig. 10.12).

abyssopelagic zone The **pelagic** environment from a depth of 4,000 m (13,000 ft) to 6,000 m (20,000 ft) (Fig. 10.12).

accessory photosynthetic pigment Chemical compound that captures solar energy together with **chlorophyll.**

acorn worms (enteropneusts) See **hemichordates.**

active continental margin A **continental margin** that is colliding with another *tectonic plate* and as a result is geologically active (Fig. 2.23). Compare **passive continental margin.**

active transport The transfer of substances across membranes by a *cell* against a *concentration gradient.*

adenosine triphosphate See **ATP.**

adductor muscle One of two muscles that close a bivalve's shells (Fig. 7.25*d*).

aerenchyma Air-filled **tissue** in *cordgrasses, mangroves,* and *seagrasses.*

aerobic respiration The chemical process involved in the release of **energy** from organic matter (Fig. 4.5):

organic matter + $O_2 \rightarrow CO_2 + H_2O$
(glucose) energy

agar A commercially important **phycocolloid** extracted from **red algae.**

alga (pl. **algae**) Any of several groups of **eukaryotic, autotrophic protists** that lack the structural features (true leaves, roots, and stems) of plants.

algal ridge A ridge of **coralline algae** that is found on the outer edge of some **coral reefs.**

algal turf A dense growth of often filamentous **algae.**

algin A **phycocolloid** extracted from **brown algae** that is widely used in food processing.

alternation of generations A reproductive cycle in which a **sexual** stage alternates with

an **asexual** one, as in the case of a **gametophyte** alternating with a **sporophyte.**

ambergris Undigested material that accumulates in the intestine of the sperm whale.

ambulacral groove Each of the radiating channels of **echinoderms** through which **tube feet** protrude.

amino acid One of the 20 nitrogen-containing molecules that make up **proteins.**

amphibians (class *Amphibia*) **Vertebrates** that lay their eggs in fresh water: frogs, salamanders, and allies.

amphipods A group of small, laterally compressed **crustaceans** that includes *beach hoppers* (Fig. 7.34) and others.

ampulla (pl. **ampullae**) Each of the muscular sacs that extend inside the body opposite the **tube feet** of **echinoderms.**

ampulla (pl. **ampullae**) **of Lorenzini** One of several sensory structures in the head of sharks that detect weak electric fields (Figs. 8.3 and 8.19*b*).

anadromous Marine fishes that migrate to fresh water to breed. Compare **catadromous.**

anaerobic bacteria **Bacteria** that do not need oxygen.

anaerobic respiration The breaking down of organic matter by organisms in the absence of oxygen. Also see **aerobic respiration.**

anal fin The last **ventral** fin of fishes (Fig. 8.8).

angiosperms See **flowering plants.**

animals Members of the kingdom *Animalia,* which consists of **heterotrophic, eukaryotic,** multicellular organisms.

annelids See **segmented worms.**

anoxic Lacking oxygen. Compare **hypoxic.**

antenna A sensory appendage on the head of **arthropods.**

anthozoans (class *Anthozoa*) **Cnidarians** whose life cycle consists of a complex **polyp** and no **medusa.**

anthropogenic impact Disturbance to the natural environment caused by humans.

apneustic breathing Breathing pattern shown in many marine mammals that involves deep breaths followed by exhalation.

appendicularians See **larvaceans.**

aquaculture The farming of marine, brackish-water, and freshwater organisms. Also see **mariculture.**

archaea (sing. **archaeum**) **Prokaryotic,** unicellular microorganisms in the domain *Archaea.*

Aristotle's lantern The set of jaws and associated muscles used by **sea urchins** to bite off food (Fig. 7.49).

arrow worms (**chaetognaths;** phylum *Chaetognatha*) Planktonic **invertebrates** characterized by a streamlined, transparent body (Fig. 7.17).

arthropods (phylum *Arthropoda*) **Invertebrates** that have jointed appendages and a **chitinous,** segmented **exoskeleton.**

ascidians See **sea squirts.**

asexual (vegetative) reproduction The type of reproduction that takes place without the formation of **gametes.** Compare **sexual reproduction.**

assemblage A group of species that live in the same *habitat* but do not interact ecologically.

asthenosphere The layer of upper **mantle** that lies below the **lithosphere** (Fig. 2.3).

atoll A **coral reef** that develops as a ring around a central **lagoon** (Fig. 14.23).

atom The smallest unit into which an **element** can be divided and still retain its properties.

ATP (adenosine triphosphate) A molecule that stores **energy** and releases it to power chemical reactions in organisms.

autotroph An organism that manufactures its own organic matter by using **energy** from the sun or other sources. Compare **heterotroph.**

auxospore The resistant stage of **diatoms** that restores the maximum size characteristic to the species.

B

BCE (Before Common Era) Before year 1 in the *Gregorian calendar* we use today.

back reef The inner part of a **barrier reef** (Fig. 14.18) or an **atoll** (Fig. 14.23).

bacteria (sing. **bacterium**) **Prokaryotic,** unicellular microorganisms in the domain *Bacteria.*

bacteriophages **Viruses** that infect **bacteria** (Fig. 5.1).

baleen The filtering plates that hang from the upper jaws of **baleen whales.**

baleen whales The filter-feeding whales.

bar-built estuary An **estuary** that is formed when a **barrier island** or *sand bar* separates a section of the coast where fresh water enters (Fig. 12.1).

barnacles **Crustaceans** that live attached to surfaces and are typically enclosed by heavy **calcareous** plates (Fig. 7.33).

barophilic Pressure-loving. Applied to organisms or enzymes that grow or function best, or only, at high pressure.

barrier island A long and narrow island that is built by waves along the coast.

barrier reef A type of **coral reef** that develops at some distance from the coast (Fig. 14.18).

basalt The dark-colored rock that forms the sea floor, or oceanic **crust.**

bathyal zone The bottom between the **shelf break** and a depth of approximately 4,000 m (13,000 ft) (Fig. 10.12).

bathypelagic zone The **pelagic** environment from a depth of 1,000 m (3,000 ft) to 4,000 m (13,000 ft) (Fig. 10.12).

beard worms (pogonophorans) Tube-dwelling **annelids** that lack a digestive system (Fig. 7.20).

benthos Organisms that live on the bottom (Fig. 10.11).

Big Bang theory The theory that a cosmic explosion produced clouds of dust and gas from which Earth and the solar system originated.

bilateral symmetry The arrangement of body parts in such a way that there are only two identical halves, with different *anterior* and *posterior* ends and **dorsal** and **ventral** surfaces (Fig. 7.14*b*). Compare **radial symmetry.**

binomial nomenclature A system of naming species using two names, the first of which refers to the **genus.**

biodegradable Able to be broken down by bacteria or other organisms.

biofouling Unwanted settlement of organisms (*fouling organisms*) on submerged surfaces of boats, pilings, and other structures.

biofuel A fuel obtained from a biological **renewable resource.**

biogenous sediment Sediment that is made up of the skeletons and shells of marine organisms. Also see **calcareous** and **siliceous ooze.**

biological clock A repeated rhythm that is synchronized with time.

biological magnification The increased concentration of **non-biodegradable** chemicals in the higher levels of the **food chain.**

bioluminescence The production of light by living organisms.

biomass The total mass of living organisms.

biotic A living component of the environment. Compare **abiotic.**

bioturbator A member of the **infauna** that moves sediment while burrowing or feeding.

birds (class *Aves*) **Vertebrates** that have feathers and lay eggs with calcified shells on land.

bivalves (class *Bivalvia*) *Clams, mussels,* and other **molluscs** that possess a two-valved shell, filtering gills, and a shovel-like **foot.**

black corals (order *Antipatharia*) Colonial **anthozoans** that secrete a black protein skeleton.

black smoker A chimney-like accumulation of mineral deposits that is found at **hydrothermal vents** (Figs. 2.26 and 2.27).

blade The leaf-like portion of the **thallus** of a seaweed.

bleaching The expulsion of **zooxanthellae** by reef corals in response to stress.

bloom A sudden increase in the abundance of an **alga** or **phytoplankton.**

blowhole The nostrils, or nasal openings, of cetaceans.

blubber A thick layer of fat under the skin of many marine **mammals.**

blue carbon *Carbon* stored in marine and coastal *carbon sinks* (Box 10.3).

bony fishes Fishes with a skeleton made mostly of bone; they also have **opercula** and **fin rays.**

boring sponges **Sponges** that bore through **calcareous** skeletons and shells.

bottom layer See **deep layer.**

brachiopods See **lamp shells.**

bradychardia The slowing down of heart rate during diving in marine mammals.

breaching Leaping into the air by whales (Fig. 9.30).

brittle stars (class *Ophiuroidea*) **Echinoderms** with five flexible arms that radiate from a conspicuous central disk and **tube feet** that are used in feeding.

brown algae (phylum *Heterokontophyta,* class *Phaeophyta*) **Seaweeds** with a predominance of yellow and brown pigments.

bryozoans (phylum *Ectoprocta* or *Bryozoa*) Small, colonial, **encrusting invertebrates** with delicate, often lace-like skeletons (Fig. 7.44).

budding A type of **asexual reproduction** by which a separate, new individual is produced from a small outgrowth, or *bud.*

by-catch Non-target catch that is taken while fishing for other species.

byssal threads Strong fibers secreted by mussels for attachment.

C

calcareous Made of **calcium carbonate.**

calcareous green algae **Green algae** that deposit **calcium carbonate** in their **thallus.**

calcareous ooze A type of **biogenous sediment** that is made of the **calcium carbonate** shells and skeletons of marine organisms.

calcium carbonate (CaCO₃) A mineral that is the major component of the shell, skeleton, and other parts of many organisms.

capsid The outer protein coat of **viruses.**

carapace (1) The shield-like structure that covers the anterior portion of some **crustaceans.** (2) The shell of *sea turtles.*

carbohydrate An **organic compound** that consists of chains or rings of **carbon** with **hydrogen** and **oxygen** attached to them.

carbon (C) An **element** that is an essential constituent of all **organic compounds.**

carbon capture The storage of **carbon dioxide (CO_2)** away from the atmosphere.

carbon cycle The cyclic conversion of **carbon** between **carbon dioxide** and various **organic compounds** (Fig. 10.20).

carbon dating A procedure used to determine the age of recent fossils.

carbon dioxide (CO_2) A colorless gas that is required in the process of **photosynthesis.**

carbon fixation The conversion of inorganic **carbon** (CO_2) into energy-rich organic carbon, usually by **photosynthesis.**

carbon sink Environments that store *carbon* out of the atmosphere (Box 10.3).

carnivore An animal that eats other animals. A *top carnivore* is one that feeds at the top of the **food chain.** Also see **predation.** Also used for the order *Carnivora,* **mammals** with teeth that are adapted to eat other animals. The marine members of this group are the *sea otter* and the *polar bear.*

carotenoid One of a group of yellow, orange, and red plant pigments.

carposporophyte A **diploid** generation found in the **red algae.** It produces non-motile *carpospores.*

carrageenan A **phycocolloid** extracted from **red algae** that is widely used in food processing.

carrying capacity The maximum population size that can be sustained by the available resources in a given environment.

cartilaginous fishes Fishes with a skeleton made of *cartilage: sharks, rays, skates,* and *ratfishes* (or *chimaeras*).

catadromous Freshwater fishes that migrate to sea to breed. Compare **anadromous.**

caudal fin The posterior, or tail, fin of fishes.

cellulose A complex **carbohydrate** that is the main component of fibers and other support structures in plants.

central nervous system The *brain* (or a similar aggregation of **nerve cells**) and one or more **nerve cords.**

central rift valley A depression in the **mid-ocean ridge** (Fig. 2.25).

cephalopods (class *Cephalopoda*) *Octopuses, squids,* and other **molluscs** that possess a **foot** modified into arms that surround the head.

cephalothorax The anterior portion of the body of many **arthropods,** which consists of the head fused with other body segments.

cetaceans (order *Cetacea*) Marine **mammals** with anterior flippers, no posterior limbs, and a **dorsal** fin: *whales, dolphins,* and *porpoises.*

CFCs See **chlorofluorocarbons.**

chaetognaths See **arrow worms.**

chemosynthetic (*chemoautotrophic*) **prokaryotes** Autotrophic bacteria (like the *sulfur bacteria*) and **archaea** that use **energy** by releasing it from particular chemical compounds (Table 5.1, p. 87).

chitin A complex derivative of **carbohydrates** that is the main component of the skeleton of many animals.

chitons (class *Polyplacophora*) **Molluscs** that have a shell divided into eight overlapping plates (Fig. 7.30).

chloride cells *Cells* in the gills of fishes that are involved in the excretion of excess salts.

chlorinated hydrocarbons A group of **non-biodegradable persistent** organic pollutants (POPs).

chlorofluorocarbons (CFCs) Chemicals, used in sprays, air conditioners, and other products, that affect the **ozone layer.**

chlorophyll A green **photosynthetic pigment.**

chloroplast The **organelle** where **photosynthesis** takes place (Fig. 4.8b).

choanocyte See **collar cell.**

chordates (phylum *Chordata*) Animals that display a hollow **dorsal nerve cord, gill slits,** and a **notochord.** Includes the **protochordates** and the **vertebrates.**

chromatophore A skin *cell* that contains pigment.

chromosome The *cell* structure where **DNA** is located.

ciguatera A type of food poisoning contracted from eating certain tropical fishes. It results from a toxin produced by a **dinoflagellate.**

ciliary comb One of eight bands of **cilia** fused at the base that is found in **comb jellies.**

ciliates (phylum *Ciliophora,* or *Ciliata*) A group of **protozoans** that have **cilia.**

cilium (pl. **cilia**) A short, hair-like **flagellum** that is found in large numbers and used in movement, for pushing food particles, and in other functions.

clasper A copulatory organ along the inner edge of each **pelvic fin** in male sharks and other **cartilaginous fishes** (Fig. 8.26).

cleaning associations A **symbiotic** association in which a smaller partner regularly removes parasites from fishes.

climax community The final stage in an **ecological succession.**

cloaca The common opening for the intestine and the excretory and reproductive systems of **cartilaginous fishes** and other animals.

clone A series of genetically identical *cells* or individuals that have developed from a single *cell* or individual.

cnidarians (phylum *Cnidaria*) **Invertebrates** with **nematocysts** and **radial symmetry.**

cnidocyte A *cell* that contains a **nematocyst** (Fig. 7.10).

coastal management The use of coastal resources with the intention of preserving them.

coastal plain estuary See **drowned river valley estuary.**

coccolithophorids (phylum *Heterokontophyta,* class *Haptophyta*) Unicellular, **eukaryotic** members of the **phytoplankton** that have calcareous, button-like structures, or *coccoliths* (Fig. 5.10).

coelacanths A group of lobed-fin fishes. *Latimeria* was first discovered alive in 1952 (see figure on p. 173).

coelom The body cavity found in structurally complex animals (Fig. 7.18c).

coelomic fluid The fluid that fills the **coelom** of **echinoderms** and other **invertebrates.**

coevolution The process in which one **species** evolves in response to another.

collar cell (choanocyte) A flagellated, food-trapping *cell* of **sponges.**

colloblast Sticky *cell* used for the capture of small prey in **comb jellies.**

comb jellies (phylum *Ctenophora*) The **invertebrates** with a gelatinous body, **radial symmetry,** and eight rows of **ciliary combs** (Fig. 7.13).

commensalism The type of **symbiosis** in which one species obtains shelter, food, or other benefits without affecting the other, or *host.*

community The **populations** that live and interact in an area.

competition The interaction that results when a resource is in short supply and one organism uses the resource at the expense of another.

competitive exclusion The elimination of one species by another as a result of **competition.**

compound eye An eye typical of **arthropods** that consists of numerous light-sensitive units.

conditioning A form of learning in which a behavior is associated with a reward like food.

constant proportions, rule of A principle that states that the relative amounts of ions in seawater are always the same.

consumer A **heterotroph.** A *primary consumer* feeds directly on a **primary producer,** whereas a *secondary consumer* feeds on a primary consumer.

continental drift The movement of continental masses on the surface of Earth.

continental margin The edge of a continent; the zone between a continent and the deep-sea floor (Fig. 2.20). Also see **active** and **passive continental margins.**

continental rise The gently sloping area at the base of the **continental slope** (Fig. 2.20).

continental shelf The shallow, gently sloping section of the **continental margin** that extends from the shore to the point where the slope gets steeper (Fig. 2.20).

continental slope The steeper, seaward section of the **continental margin** (Fig. 2.20).

convection The movement that results when heat is transferred in a fluid, like the heat-driven motion observed in Earth's mantle.

convergent evolution **Evolution** in which two different species evolve similar structures because of similar lifestyles.

copepods Small, mostly planktonic **crustaceans** (Fig. 7.32).

copulation The sexual union undertaken to transfer **gametes.**

coral knoll (pinnacle) A column of coral within the **lagoon** of an **atoll** (Fig. 14.23).

coral reef A massive deposit of **calcium**

carbonate by colonial **stony corals** and other organisms.

coral rubble Coral fragments.

coralline algae **Red algae** that deposit **calcium carbonate** in their **thallus.**

coralline sponges See **sclerosponges.**

cordgrasses Salt-tolerant grasses, species of *Spartina,* that inhabit **salt marshes** (Fig. 12.7).

core The innermost layer of Earth (Fig. 2.3).

Coriolis effect The tendency of objects moving large distances on Earth's surface to bend to the right in the Northern Hemisphere and to the left in the Southern Hemisphere (Fig. 3.16).

counterillumination The emission of light by **midwater** animals to match the background light (Fig. 16.15).

countershading A color pattern that results in a dark back and a light belly; most common in **epipelagic fishes** (Fig. 15.18).

courtship Behavior related to attracting the opposite sex and mating.

crinoids (class *Crinoidea*) **Echinoderms** with a small, cup-shaped body and feathery arms: the *sea lilies* and *feather stars* (Fig. 7.51).

crown-of-thorns sea star (*Acanthaster planci*) A *predator* of reef corals (Fig. 14.31).

crust The outermost layer of Earth (Fig. 2.3).

crustaceans (subphylum *Crustacea*) **Arthropods** that have two pairs of **antennae** and an **exoskeleton** hardened by **calcium carbonate.**

cryptic coloration A color pattern that allows an organism to blend with the surroundings.

cryptophytes (phylum *Cryptophyta*) Unicellular, **eukaryotic** members of the **phytoplankton** that have two flagella and no skeleton.

crystal A solid that consists of a regular pattern of molecules.

crystalline style An **enzyme**-releasing rod in the stomach of **bivalves** (Fig. 7.25b).

ctenophores See **comb jellies.**

cubomedusae (class *Cubozoa*) **Cnidarians** having a cube-shaped **medusa** with only four tentacles.

current A horizontal movement of water.

cyanobacteria A group of generally **photosynthetic** bacteria. Formerly known as *blue-green algae.*

cytoskeleton A complex framework inside *cells* made of protein fibers.

D

decapods **Crustaceans** with five pairs of walking legs and a well-developed **carapace.** The group includes the *shrimps, lobsters, hermit crabs,* and *true crabs* (*brachyurans*).

decomposers Organisms like *decay* **bacteria** and **archaea** that break down dead organic matter into smaller molecules.

deduction Reasoning from general principles to specific conclusions.

deep (bottom) layer The deepest and coldest of the three layers of the ocean (Fig. 3.24).

deep scattering layer (DSL) A sound-reflecting layer made up of many types of organisms that migrate daily from the **mesopelagic zone** to the **epipelagic zone.**

deep sea The dark waters below the **mesopelagic zone** (Fig. 10.12).

deep-sea fan A fan-like accumulation of sediment at the base of a **submarine canyon.**

delayed implantation The delay in the attachment of the early **embryo** to the womb in **pinnipeds** and some other **mammals** in order to time birth with favorable conditions.

demersal fish A bottom-dwelling fish.

density The weight (or more correctly the *mass*) of a given volume of a substance.

deposit feeder An animal that feeds on organic matter that settles on the bottom (Fig. 7.4). Compare **suspension feeder.**

desalination The conversion of seawater into fresh water.

detritus Particles of dead organic matter.

diatomaceous ooze A biogenous sediment that consists mostly of the **siliceous frustules** of **diatoms.** It is known as *diatomaceous Earth* when found inland.

diatoms (phylum *Heterokontophyta,* class *Bacillariophyta*) Unicellular and **eukaryotic autotrophs** with a **siliceous frustule;** mostly **planktonic** (Figs. 5.6 and 15.3).

diffusion The movement of molecules from an area of high concentration to an area of low concentration.

digestive gland An **enzyme**-producing gland in several groups of **invertebrates** where digestion and absorption take place.

dinoflagellates (phylum *Dinophyta,* or *Dinoflagellata*) Unicellular, **eukaryotic,** mostly **autotrophic protists** with two unequal **flagella** (Fig. 5.8).

dioxins A group of toxic **chlorinated hydrocarbon** pollutants.

diploid (2n) cell A *cell,* like a body *cell,* that contains two similar sets of **chromosomes,** one from each parent. Compare **haploid.**

dispersal The manner in which organisms get from place to place.

disruptive coloration A color pattern that helps break the outline of an organism.

dissociation The breaking up of a salt molecule into **ions** when placed in water or other solvents (Fig. 3.5).

dissolved organic matter (DOM) Organic matter that is dissolved in water rather than being in particles.

diurnal tide A tidal pattern with a high and a low **tide** each day (Fig. 3.34c).

diversity The total number of species inhabiting a particular environment.

DNA (deoxyribonucleic acid) **Nucleic acids** that contain the inherited genetic code, or *genes,* that specifies the structure and function of an organism.

domestic sewage Wastewater from homes and non-industrial buildings. Compare **industrial sewage.**

domoic acid Toxin produced by some planktonic **diatoms.**

dorsal The upper or back surface of an animal with **bilateral symmetry** (Fig. 7.14b).

downwelling The sinking of surface water that is denser than underlying water layers.

drag Resistance to movement through water or any other medium.

drift net A fishing net that is allowed to drift for a long time before it is pulled on board.

drowned river valley (coastal plain) estuary An **estuary** that is formed when sea level rose at the end of the last glacial age.

E

ear stone (otolith) A calcareous body in the **inner ear** of fishes and other **vertebrates** that is used in the maintenance of equilibrium. Also see **statocyst.**

echinoderms (phylum *Echinodermata*) **Invertebrates** with five-way **radial symmetry** and a **water vascular system.**

echiurans (phylum *Annelida,* class *Echiura*) Burrowing **invertebrates** that have an unsegmented body and a non-retractable **proboscis** (Fig. 13.9).

echolocation The ability of some animals to sense their surroundings by analyzing the reflection of sound waves, or clicks, they emit.

ecological niche The full range of ecological characteristics of a species, like its feeding habits, specific **habitat,** and reproductive strategy.

ecological succession The regular replacement of **species** by others in a given area.

ecology The study of the interactions between organisms and their environment.

ecosystem A **community** or communities plus the physical environment, interacting in a large, more or less self-contained area.

ectoprocts See **bryozoans.**

ectotherm An organism that loses metabolic heat to the environment without it affecting its body temperature. Compare **endotherm.**

EEZ see **exclusive economic zone**

Ekman spiral The spiral change in the movement of water in the **water column** when the water is pushed by wind (Fig. 3.19). The *Ekman layer* is that part of the water column affected by wind; *Ekman transport* is the net water movement at 90° from the wind direction.

element A substance that consists of **atoms** of the same kind and that cannot be decomposed by ordinary chemical means.

El Niño–Southern Oscillation (ENSO) Large-scale changes in atmospheric and ocean current patterns in which, among other things, warm surface water in the Pacific Ocean moves further to the east than normal. *El Niño* refers specifically to the warming of the surface water in the Eastern Pacific. Compare **La Niña.**

embryo The early developmental stage that, through *embryological development,* ultimately becomes an adult individual.

encrusting Describing an organism that grows as a crust over rocks and other hard surfaces.

endangered species A species that is in immediate danger of **extermination.**

endolithic alga An alga that burrows into **calcareous** rocks or corals.

endophyte A photosynthetic organism that lives within the *cells* or **tissues** of algae or plants. Compare **epiphyte.**

endoplasmic reticulum An extensive system of folded membranes present in most **eukaryotic cells** (Fig. 4.8).

endoskeleton A skeleton under the external surface of an animal. Compare **exoskeleton.**

endotherm An organism that retains some metabolic heat, which raises its body temperature. Compare **ectotherm.**

energy The ability to do work.

enzyme A **protein** that speeds up a specific chemical reaction.

epifauna Animals that live on the surface of the **substrate.** Compare **infauna.**

epigenetic markers Small chemical compounds that attach to *DNA* and alter gene expression, often providing adaptation to environmental conditions.

epipelagic zone The **pelagic** environment from the surface to a depth of 100 to 200 m (350 to 650 ft) (Fig. 10.12).

epiphyte A photosynthetic organism that lives on algae or plants. Compare **endophyte.**

equatorial currents Major ocean currents that move parallel to the Equator (Fig. 3.20).

erythrocyte (red blood cell) A specialized type of blood *cell* that carries **hemoglobin** in **vertebrates.**

estuary A semi-enclosed area where fresh water and seawater meet and mix.

eukaryote An organism that consists of one or more **eukaryotic cells.**

eukaryotic cell A *cell* that contains a **nucleus** and other **organelles** (Fig. 4.8). Compare **prokaryotic cell.**

euryhaline An organism that can tolerate a wide range of salinities. Compare **stenohaline.**

eutrophication The process by which increased inputs of nutrients lead to an undesirable increase in algal growth.

evaporation The escape of molecules from the liquid phase into the gaseous phase, or vapor.

evaporative cooling The lower speed and hence lower temperature of molecules remaining in

the liquid phase after **evaporation** of the fastest molecules.

evisceration The expulsion of internal organs in **sea cucumbers.**

evolution A change in the genetic makeup of a species, usually as a result of **natural selection** favoring some individual characteristics over others.

evolutionary adaptation The genetic adaptation of a population to its environment through **evolution.**

exclusive economic zone (EEZ) A zone 200 nautical miles (370 km) wide along the coast where nations have exclusive rights to any resource. It was initiated by the *United Nations Convention on the Law of the Sea* (*UNCLOS*).

exoskeleton A skeleton that forms the external surface of an animal, as in **arthropods.** Compare **endoskeleton.**

experiment An artificially created situation that is used to test a **hypothesis.** In a *controlled experiment,* additional variables that might affect the experiment are prevented from doing so.

extermination (extirpation) The **extinction** of a species that is caused by humans.

extinction The disappearance of a species.

extracellular digestion Digestion that takes place outside *cells,* usually in a gut, or digestive cavity. Compare **intracellular digestion.**

F

fault A crack in Earth's crust usually formed when two pieces of crust are moving past each other.

feather stars See **crinoids.**

fertilization The union of **gametes.** It can be *external* and take place in the water or *internal* and take place within the body.

fetch The span of the sea surface over which the wind blows to form wind-driven **waves** (Fig. 3.28).

filter feeder A **suspension feeder** that actively filters food particles (Fig. 7.4). Compare **passive suspension feeder.**

fin ray Each of the bony spines in the fins of **bony fishes.**

fish meal A fish-protein supplement used in animal feeds.

fish protein concentrate (**FPC** or **fish flour**) A fish protein supplement for human consumption.

fission A type of **asexual reproduction** that results when one individual splits into two individuals.

fjord An **estuary** that is formed in a deep valley created by a retreating glacier (Fig. 12.2).

flagellum A long, whip-like **organelle** that is usually involved in locomotion.

flatworms (phylum *Platyhelminthes*) **Invertebrates** that are dorsoventrally flattened and have an incomplete digestive tract, true **organs,** and **organ systems.**

flowering plants (**angiosperms;** division *Anthophyta*) Plants that have flowers, seeds, and true leaves, stems, and roots.

fluke The fin-like tail of **cetaceans.**

flukes A group of parasitic **flatworms.**

food chain The steps of transfer of **energy** from **primary producers** through **consumers.**

food web All of the interconnecting feeding relationships in a **community.**

foot The muscular locomotory structure of **molluscs.**

foraminiferan ooze A **biogenous sediment** that consists mostly of the **calcareous** tests of **foraminiferans.**

foraminiferans (forams) (phylum *Foraminifera,* or *Granuloreticulosa*) **Protozoans** with a **calcareous** *test,* and **pseudopodia** (Fig. 5.11).

fore reef The outer part of a **barrier reef** (Fig. 14.18) or an **atoll** (Fig. 14.23).

fouling organisms Organisms that live attached to submerged surfaces like boats and pilings.

fringing reef A **coral reef** that develops as a narrow band close to a shore (Fig. 14.15).

frustule The **siliceous,** box-like *cell wall* of **diatoms.**

fucoxanthin The yellow to golden brown **photosynthetic pigment** of **brown algae.**

fungi (sing. **fungus**) Non-photosynthetic, mostly multicellular organisms, many of which are decomposers; members of the kingdom *Fungi.*

funnel See **siphon.**

G

gamete A **haploid** reproductive *cell* that develops into a new individual after its union with another gamete.

gametophyte The **haploid,** gamete-producing generation in many **seaweeds.** Compare **sporophyte.**

gas exchange The movement of **oxygen** and other gases between the atmosphere and the ocean, or between the water or atmosphere and living organisms, in which case it is often called **respiratory exchange.**

gastropods (class *Gastropoda*) Snails and other **molluscs** that typically possess a coiled **dorsal** shell and a **ventral** creeping **foot.**

genetic engineering The artificial alteration of the genetic information of an individual.

genital slit The genital opening of **cetaceans.**

genome The complete genetic information of an organism.

genomics The mapping of genetic information in individual **species.**

genus A group of similar **species.**

gestation The length of time between **fertilization** and birth in **mammals.**

gill Thin-walled extensions of the body that are used in **gas exchange.**

gill arch A supporting structure of fish **gills.**

gill cover See **operculum.**

gill filament The thin projection of a fish **gill** where **gas exchange** takes place (Fig. 8.17*b*).

gill raker Each of the projections along the inner surface of fish **gills** (Fig. 8.17*b*).

gill slit (pharyngeal slit) One of several pairs of openings along the **pharynx** in **chordates** (Figs. 7.52*b* and 7.54).

glass sponges Deep-water **sponges** with a skeleton of fused **silica spicules.**

global distillation **Evaporation** and condensation of substances on a global scale, leading to the net transport of certain pollutants to the poles.

global warming A long-term increase in the global average temperature. **Anthropogenic** (human-caused) global warming results from an intensified *greenhouse effect* due to human emissions of greenhouse gases.

glucose A **simple sugar** that plays an important role in the **metabolism** of most organisms.

Golgi apparatus An arrangement of sacs and membranes in many **eukaryotic cells** that is involved in collecting and transporting molecules (Fig. 4.8).

gonad An organ that contains the *germ tissue* that produces the **gametes:** *ovary* and *testis.*

Gondwana One of two large continents, the southern one, that formed when the supercontinent **Pangaea** broke up about 180 million years ago (Fig. 2.16*b*). Also see **Laurasia.**

gorgonians (order *Gorgonacea*) Colonial **anthozoans** that secrete a skeleton made of protein (Fig. 7.12).

granite The light-colored rock that forms most of the continental **crust.**

grazer An organism that feeds primarily on plants.

great ocean conveyor A global circulation pattern in which water cycles throughout the ocean basins (Fig. 3.25).

great whales Large whales: the sperm and the **baleen whales.**

green algae (phylum *Chlorophyta*) **Seaweeds** in which **chlorophyll** is not masked by other pigments.

greenhouse effect The retention of heat in the lower atmosphere due to the presence of **carbon dioxide,** *methane,* and other *greenhouse gases* that allow solar light energy to penetrate to Earth's surface but block the transmission of heat energy back into space.

guano The accumulation of the excrement of seabirds.

guyot A flat-topped **seamount.**

gyre A large, nearly circular system of wind-driven surface currents that center around latitude 30° in both hemispheres (Fig. 3.20).

H

habitat The natural environment where an organism lives.

habitat restoration The recovery of stressed or destroyed habitats.

hadal zone The bottom below 6,000 m (20,000 ft) (Fig. 10.12).

hadopelagic (hadal pelagic) zone The **pelagic** environment below 6,000 m (20,000 ft) (Fig. 10.12).

halophyte A salt-tolerant terrestrial plant.

haploid (*n*, or 1*n*) cell A **cell**, like a **gamete**, that contains only half the normal number of chromosomes found in **diploid**, or body, **cells**.

harem A large group of females herded by a large male **pinniped** for the purpose of mating; harems also occur in some fishes.

harmful algal blooms (HABs) Unusual population explosions, or **blooms**, of **phytoplankton** that are detrimental to humans.

heart urchins Burrowing **sea urchins** with a flattened test and short spines (Fig. 13.7).

heat capacity The amount of heat that must be added to a substance to raise its temperature by a given amount, which reflects the substance's ability to store heat.

heavy metals A group of toxic metals: *mercury, lead,* and others.

hemichordates (phylum *Hemichordata*) **Invertebrates** with a **dorsal nerve cord** and **gill slits.** Includes the *acorn worms,* or *enteropneusts.*

hemoglobin A blood **protein** that transports **oxygen** in many animals.

herbivore An animal that eats plants.

heredity The transmission of genetic characteristics from one generation to the next.

hermaphrodite An organism that has both male and female **gonads.** In *simultaneous hermaphroditism* sperm and eggs can be produced at the same time; in *sex reversal,* or *sequential hermaphroditism,* an individual begins life as a male but changes into a female (*protandry*) or as a female but changes into a male (*protogyny*).

hermatypic coral Corals that build **coral reefs.**

heterotroph An organism that obtains **energy** from organic matter.

holdfast The root-like portion of the **thallus** of a **seaweed.**

holoplankton Organisms that spend their entire lives in the **plankton.** Compare **meroplankton.**

homeotherm An organism that is able to keep its body temperature more or less constant regardless of the temperature of the environment. Compare **poikilotherm.**

homing The ability of an animal to find its home area.

hormone A substance that acts as a chemical messenger in an organism.

horseshoe crabs (class *Merostomata*) **Arthropods** with a large, horseshoe-shaped **carapace** (Fig. 7.42).

hydrogen An element that is one of the constituents of water, organic matter, and many other chemicals. Hydrogen gas (H_2) is composed of two hydrogen **atoms.**

hydrogen bond Weak bonds between water **molecules** that result from an attraction between the **hydrogen** atoms of one molecule and the **oxygen** atoms of adjacent molecules (Fig. 3.1).

hydrogen sulfide (H_2S) The gas that is produced in **anoxic** sediments.

hydrostatic skeleton A system that uses water pressure against the body wall to maintain body shape and aid in locomotion.

hydrothermal vent A deep-sea hot spring where heated seawater forces its way up through the **crust** (Figs. 2.26 and 2.27).

hydrozoans (class *Hydrozoa*) **Cnidarians** whose life cycle typically includes a **polyp,** which is often colonial, and a **medusa.**

hyphae Filaments of **fungi.**

hypothesis A statement that might be true.

hypoxic Sharp reduction of water oxygen as in *hypoxic* or *dead zones.* Compare **anoxic.**

I

ice age A period of time when significant amounts of ice form on the continents, inducing a fall in sea level.

Indo-West Pacific region The tropical Indian and western and central Pacific oceans.

inducible defenses Defense mechanisms that an organism uses only in response to predators.

induction Reasoning from specific observations to a general conclusion.

industrial sewage Wastewater from industries. Compare **domestic sewage.**

infauna Animals that burrow in the **substrate.** Compare **epifauna.**

ink sac A gland found in some **cephalopods** that secretes a dark fluid used to discourage predators.

inner ear A paired, sound-sensitive organ in **vertebrates.**

insects (class *Insecta*) **Arthropods** with three pairs of legs and one pair of **antennae.** Few are marine, an exception being the *water strider* (Fig. 15.17).

interglacial period A geological period between **ice ages** when, as at present, Earth's climate is relatively warm.

intermediate layer Of the three main layers of the ocean, the one below the **surface,** or **mixed,** layer. It includes the main **thermocline** (Fig. 3.24).

International Whaling Commission (IWC) An agency that regulates *whaling* around the world.

interspecific competition **Competition** among members of different species. Compare **intraspecific competition.**

interstitial fauna Animals living between sediment particles. Also see **meiofauna.**

interstitial water The water contained between sediment particles.

intertidal (littoral) zone The area between the highest and lowest tide (Fig. 10.12).

intracellular digestion Digestion that takes place within *cells,* usually those lining the gut or digestive tract. Compare **extracellular digestion.**

intraspecific competition **Competition** among members of the same species. Compare **interspecific competition.**

invasive species (introduced, alien, or **exotic species)** A species introduced into a new environment by humans. Compare **native species.**

invertebrates Animals that lack a backbone.

ion An atom or a group of atoms that is electrically charged.

iridophore A **chromatophore** with light-reflecting **crystals.**

island arc A curved chain of volcanic islands that form along a **trench.**

isopods Small, dorsoventrally flattened **crustaceans** like the *sea louse* (Fig. 7.35).

isotopes Different atomic forms of an **element.**

J

jawless fishes Fishes that lack jaws and paired fins: *hagfishes* (or *slime eels*) and *lampreys* (Fig. 8.2).

K

kelp **Brown algae** characterized by their large size and complexity. Some, like the giant kelp, form dense *kelp beds* or *kelp forests.*

keystone predator A predatory species whose effects on its community are proportionately much greater than its abundance.

krill (euphausiids) Planktonic **crustaceans** that are an important food of whales and other animals (Fig. 17.12).

L

lactic acid Harmful product of **anaerobic respiration** in muscles.

lagoon A shallow, sheltered body of water separated from the open sea by **coral reefs,** *sand bars,* and/or **barrier islands** (Figs. 14.18 and 14.23).

lamella (pl. **lamellae**) Each of the many thin plates that make up the **gill filaments** of fish gills (Fig. 8.17*c*).

La Niña Large-scale changes in atmospheric and ocean current patterns in which, among other things, warm surface water in the Pacific Ocean moves further to the west than normal. Compare **El Niño–Southern Oscillation.**

larva Immature stage of an animal that looks different from the adult.

larvaceans (appendicularians; class *Larvacea***)** Tunicates that retain the body of a **tadpole larva** throughout life (Fig. 15.9).

latent heat of evaporation The amount of heat **energy** that is needed to evaporate a substance, that is, to change it from a liquid to a gas.

latent heat of melting The amount of heat **energy** needed to melt a substance, that is, to change it from a solid to a liquid.

lateral line A system of canals and sensory *cells* on the sides of fishes that helps them detect vibrations in the water (Fig. 8.19).

Laurasia One of the two large continents, the northern one, that formed when the supercontinent **Pangaea** broke up about 180 million years ago (Fig. 2.16*b*). Also see **Gondwana.**

leptocephalous larva The leaf-shaped larva of freshwater eels and other fishes.

lichen The organism that results from the **symbiosis** of a **fungus** and an **autotroph** like a **green alga** (Fig. 5.14).

limiting resource An essential factor whose short supply limits the growth of a **population.**

lipid A group of **organic molecules** that are often used by organisms in the long-term storage of **energy,** waterproofing, buoyancy, and insulation.

lithogenous sediment Sediment that is derived from the breakdown, or **weathering,** of rocks. Also see **red clay.**

lithosphere The **crust** and the top part of the mantle that covers Earth's surface. It is broken into separate *lithospheric plates* (Fig. 2.10).

littoral zone See **intertidal zone.**

lophophore A feeding structure that consists of ciliated tentacles.

loriciferans (phylum *Loricifera***)** Tiny invertebrates that live among sediment particles and have a body enclosed by six plates.

lysogenic viruses Viruses that reproduce when their **nucleic acid** becomes part of the **genome** of the host *cells.*

M

macroplankton The component of the plankton that consists of large organisms 2 to 20 cm in size (Fig. 15.2).

madreporite A porous plate that connects the **water vascular system** of **echinoderms** to the exterior.

magnetic anomalies Magnetic bands in the sea floor that run parallel to the **mid-ocean ridge** (Fig. 2.8).

main thermocline See **thermocline.**

male parasitism The permanent attachment of a male to a female in some deep-sea fishes (Fig. 16.21).

mammals (class *Mammalia***)** Vertebrates that have hair and **mammary glands.**

mammary glands The milk-secreting glands of **mammals.**

mangroves Shrubs and trees that live along the seashore in tropical and subtropical regions and tolerate inundation by seawater (Fig. 6.16).

mantle (1) The semiliquid region between the **crust** and the **core** of Earth (Fig. 2.3). (2) The outer layer of **tissue** that secretes the shell of **molluscs** (Figs. 7.22, 7.27, and 7.29).

mantle cavity The space lined by the **mantle** of **molluscs** (Figs. 7.22, 7.27, and 7.29).

mariculture The culture of marine and brackish-water organisms. Also see **aquaculture.**

marine heatwaves Extended periods of much warmer than normal seawater temperatures over a wide region.

marine natural products Chemical compounds that are obtained from marine organisms.

marine snow Large, fluffy **detritus** particles that are found in the **water column.**

maxillipeds The food-sorting appendages of some **crustaceans.**

maximum sustainable yield The maximum catch of a **stock** that can be harvested year after year without diminishing the stock.

medusa The bell-shaped, free-swimming stage of **cnidarians.**

megaplankton The component of the plankton that consists of very large organisms over 20 cm in size (Fig. 15.2).

meiofauna Microscopic animals that live on the bottom; often used as a synonym of **interstitial fauna.**

meiosis Cell division that results in the formation of **gametes.**

melon A fatty structure on the forehead of some **cetaceans** that is used to direct sound waves emitted during **echolocation** (Fig. 9.28).

meroplankton Planktonic organisms that spend only part of their life in the **plankton.** Compare **holoplankton.**

mesenterial filament Any of the long, thin tubes attached to the gut of corals and other **cnidarians** that are involved in digestion and absorption.

mesoglea The layer between the *epidermis* and *gastrodermis* in **cnidarians** (Figs. 7.7 and 7.10).

mesopelagic zone The **pelagic** environment from a depth of approximately 100 to 200 m (350 to 650 ft) to 1,000 m (3,000 ft) (Fig. 10.12).

mesoplankton The component of the **plankton** that consists of organisms 0.2 to 2 mm in size (Fig. 15.2).

metabolism All the chemical reactions that take place in an organism.

metagenomics The study of **nucleic acids** from environmental samples, including the identification of new **species** and interactions between **species.**

metamorphosis A marked change in form during embryological development.

methane hydrate (clathrates) A potential source of energy in the form of *methane* trapped in frozen water.

microbial loop A component of **pelagic food webs** in which **dissolved organic matter** is cycled through the **picoplankton** and **nanoplankton** back into the main part of the food web (Fig. 15.25).

microfossils The microscopic shells and other remains of marine organisms that make up **biogenous sediments.**

microplankton The component of the **plankton** that consists of organisms 20 to 200 microns (μm) (0.02 to 0.2 mm) in size (Fig. 15.2).

microplastics Plastic particles less than 5 mm (0.2 in) in size (Fig. 18.12).

mid-ocean ridge The continuous chain of volcanic submarine mountains that extends around Earth. It includes the *Mid-Atlantic Ridge* and *East Pacific Rise* (Figs. 2.5 and 2.9).

midwater Pertaining to the **mesopelagic zone.**

migration The regular movement of one organism from one place to another.

mitochondrion The **organelle** in which **respiration** takes place in **eukaryotes** (Fig. 4.8).

mitosis The cell division in which a *cell* divides into two daughter *cells* that are identical to the original *cell.*

mixed layer See **surface layer.**

mixed semidiurnal tide A tidal pattern with two successive high **tides** of different heights each day (Fig. 3.34*b*).

molecule A combination of two or more **atoms.**

molluscs (phylum *Mollusca***)** Invertebrates with a soft, unsegmented body, a muscular **foot,** and, with some exceptions, a **calcareous** shell.

molt The **exoskeleton** that is shed during the *molting* process.

monsoon Winds in the northern Indian Ocean that blow from the southwest in summer and from the northeast in winter.

mudflat A muddy bottom that is exposed at low tide.

mutualism The type of **symbiosis** in which both partners benefit from the relationship.

myoglobin A type of muscle protein that stores **oxygen** in **vertebrates.**

myomere Each of the bands of muscles along the sides of fishes.

N

nanoplankton The component of the **plankton** that consists of very small organisms 2 to 20 microns (μm) (0.002 to 0.2 mm) in size (Fig. 15.2); they are too small to catch in a standard plankton net.

native species A species that naturally occurs in a given area. Compare **invasive species.**

natural selection A mechanism of evolutionary change that results when individuals that are better *adapted* than others in meeting the challenges of the environment produce more offspring.

nauplius A planktonic **larva** of many crustaceans (Figs. 7.41 and 15.11*e*).

neap tides The **tides** with a small **tidal range.** They occur around the times when the moon is in quarter. Compare **spring tides.**

negative estuaries **Estuaries** where loss of fresh water through evaporation is higher than fresh water input from rivers.

nekton Organisms that swim strongly enough to move against the current (Fig. 10.11).

nematocyst The stinging structure of **cnidarians.**

nematodes (roundworms; phylum *Nematoda*) **Invertebrates** with a cylindrical body, a conspicuous body cavity, and a complete digestive tract.

nemerteans See **ribbon worms.**

neritic zone The **pelagic** environment above the **continental shelf** (Fig. 10.12).

nerve cord A long, compact bundle of **neurons,** or *nerve cells,* that is part of the **central nervous system.**

nerve net The network of interconnecting **neurons,** or *nerve cells,* in **cnidarians** and other **invertebrates.**

net plankton **Plankton** that can be caught in a standard plankton net.

neuron A **cell,** or *nerve cell,* specialized to originate or transmit nerve impulses.

neuston Organisms that live right at the sea surface but remain underwater. Compare **pleuston.**

niche See **ecological niche.**

nictitating membrane A thin layer of **tissue** that can be drawn across the eye in sharks and some other **vertebrates.**

nitrate (NO_3^{-1}) An important **nutrient** in the ocean.

nitrogen (N_2) An **element** that is one of the constituents of **proteins.** Nitrogen gas (N_2) is composed of two nitrogen **atoms.**

nitrogen cycle The cycling of **nitrogen** among various nitrogen compounds (Fig. 10.21).

nitrogen fixation The conversion of gaseous **nitrogen (N_2)** into nitrogen compounds that can be utilized by **autotrophs.** It is performed by *nitrogen fixers* (Table 5.1, p. 87).

non-biodegradable Unable to be broken down by bacteria or other organisms.

non-renewable resource A resource that is not naturally replaced.

notochord A flexible rod that lies below the **nerve cord** of **chordates.**

nucleic acid **Organic molecules** that store and transmit genetic information. Also see **deoxyribonucleic acid, ribonucleic acid.**

nucleus The **organelle** of **eukaryotic cells** that contains the **chromosomes** (Fig. 4.8).

nudibranchs (sea slugs) **Gastropods** that lack a shell and have exposed **gills.**

nutrient A raw material other than **carbon dioxide** and water that is needed by an **autotroph** to produce **organic** matter. Examples are **nitrate** and **phosphate.**

nutrient regeneration The release of nutrients from organic matter by **decomposers.**

O

ocean acidification Decrease of seawater pH as a result of increased **carbon dioxide.**

ocean thermal energy conversion (OTEC) A process for obtaining **energy** by exploiting depth differences in temperature (Fig. 17.22).

oceanic zone The **pelagic** environment beyond the **shelf break** (Fig. 10.12).

olfactory sacs Structures on both sides of the head of fishes that are sensitive to chemical stimuli.

operculum (1) The tough lid that closes the shell opening of many **gastropods** when the body is withdrawn. (2) The flap of bony plates that covers the **gills** of **bony fishes.**

organ A group of **tissues** specialized for one function.

organelle A membrane-bound, specialized structure within a *cell* (Fig. 4.8).

organic compound A **molecule** that contains **carbon, hydrogen,** and usually **oxygen.**

organization, level of The extent of specialization and organization of the *cells* of an organism. Organization may be at the *cellular, tissue,* or *organ* level.

osculum A large opening in many **sponges.**

osmoconformer An organism that allows its internal **salt** concentration to change with the **salinity** of the surrounding water.

osmoregulator An organism that controls its internal **salt** concentration.

osmosis The movement of water across a *selectively permeable* membrane, like the *cell membrane,* which allows only certain molecules to pass through.

outwelling The export of **detritus** and other organic matter from estuaries to other ecosystems.

overturn The sinking of surface water that has become more dense than the water below (Fig. 3.23).

oviparous An animal that releases eggs.

ovoviviparous An animal that produces eggs that hatch inside the female immediately before birth.

ovulation The release of an egg from the ovary.

oxygen An **element** that is one of the constituents of water, organic matter, and many other chemicals. Oxygen gas (O_2), composed of two oxygen **atoms,** is needed for **respiration** and is produced by **photosynthesis.**

oxygen minimum zone (OMZ) A layer of water at a depth of approximately 500 m (1,600 ft) where **oxygen** is depleted (Fig. 16.18).

oyster reef A dense oyster bed present in some **estuaries** and other marine environments. Also called *shellfish reefs.*

ozone layer Ozone (O_3) in the atmosphere that deflects ultraviolet radiation, which is harmful to life.

P

Pangaea The single large landmass, or supercontinent, that broke up to form today's continents (Fig. 2.16a).

Panthalassa The large ocean that surrounded the supercontinent **Pangaea** and that was the ancestor of the modern Pacific Ocean (Figs. 2.16a and 2.16b).

parapodium A usually flat lateral extension present on each of the body segments of **polychaetes** (Fig. 7.18).

parasitism The type of **symbiosis** in which one partner, the *parasite,* derives benefit from the other, the *host.*

parthenogenesis Development of an egg into an embryo without fertilization by a sperm.

passive continental margin A **continental margin** that is located at the "trailing edge" of a continent and as a result shows little geological activity (Fig. 2.22). Compare **active continental margin.**

passive suspension feeder A **suspension feeder** that uses mucus or **cilia** to move food particles to the mouth (Fig. 7.4). Compare **filter feeder.**

patchiness The grouping of organisms in clumps or patches.

PCBs See **polychlorinated biphenyls.**

peanut worms (sipunculans; phylum *Annelida,* class *Sipuncula*) Burrowing **invertebrates** with an unsegmented body and an anterior end that can be pulled into the body (Fig. 7.21).

pectoral fin Each of the pair of fins just behind the head of fishes (Fig. 8.8).

pedicellaria One of the minute, pincer-like organs of some **echinoderms** that help keep the body surface clean.

pelagic organisms Organisms that live in the **water column,** away from the bottom, including the **plankton** and **nekton** (Fig. 10.11).

pelvic fin Each of the second pair of **ventral** fins of fishes (Fig. 8.8).

pen The reduced, thin shell of squids.

perennial A plant that lives more than two successive years.

Persistent chemicals Substances that are **non-biodegradable** and remain in the environment for a long time.

pharynx The anterior portion of the digestive tract of many animals. It is located directly behind the mouth cavity.

pheromone A chemical that organisms use to communicate with other members of their species.

phoronids (phylum *Phoronida*) Tube-dwelling, unsegmented **invertebrates** that possess a horseshoe-shaped or circular **lophophore.**

phosphate (PO_4^{-3}) A source of **phosphorus** important to marine **primary producers.**

phosphorus (P) An **element** that is essential to life.

phosphorus cycle The cycling of **phosphorus** among various phosphorus compounds.

photic zone The surface layer where there is enough light for **photosynthesis** to occur. Also see **epipelagic zone.**

photophore (light organ) An organ that produces **bioluminescence.**

photosynthesis The chemical process involved in the transformation of solar energy into **glucose** (Fig. 4.4):

$$CO_2 + H_2O + \text{sun energy} \rightarrow \text{organic matter} + O_2$$
$$(\text{glucose})$$

photosynthetic pigment A **molecule** like **chlorophyll** that is responsible for capturing solar **energy** in **photosynthesis.**

phycobilins A group of **photosynthetic pigments** that includes *phycocyanin,* a bluish pigment in **cyanobacteria,** and *phycoerythrin,* a red pigment in **red algae.**

phycocolloid One of several **starch**-like chemicals found in some **seaweeds.** They are of significant commercial importance. Also see **agar, algin,** and **carrageenan.**

phycocyanin See **phycobilins.**

phycoerythrin See **phycobilins.**

phylogeny The evolutionary history of a **species** or other **taxon.**

phylum The **taxon** that represents a main division of a kingdom. The equivalent term *division* is used in the kingdom Plantae.

physiological adaptation Non-inherited adaptation to the environment in an individual.

phytoplankton The photosynthetic component of **plankton** consisting primarily of single-celled algae and bacteria. Compare **zooplankton.**

picoplankton The component of the **plankton** that consists of extremely small organisms, 0.2 to 2 microns (μm) (0.0002 to 0.002 mm) in size (Fig. 15.2); they are too small to catch in a standard plankton net.

pinacocyte The flat *cells* on the outer surface of **sponges.**

pinnipeds (order *Pinnipedia*) **Mammals** with paddle-shaped flippers: *seals, eared seals* (*sea lions* and *fur seals*), and the *walrus.*

placenta A membrane that connects the **embryo** with the mother's womb to provide nourishment.

planktivore An animal that feeds on **plankton.**

plankton Organisms that drift in the water (Fig. 10.11).

plants Members of the kingdom *Plantae,* which consists of photosynthetic, **eukaryotic,** and multicellular organisms.

planula The ciliated **larva** of **cnidarians** (Fig. 7.9).

plate tectonics The process involved in the movement of large *tectonic plates* on Earth's crust.

Pleistocene A geological period, which began about 2.6 million years ago, characterized by a series of **ice ages.**

pleuston Organisms that live right at the sea surface, with part of the body projecting into the air. Compare **neuston.**

pneumatocyst A gas-filled bladder in **seaweeds** (Fig. 6.1).

pneumatophore Upward extension of roots of some **mangroves** (Fig. 12.19).

pod A **school** of **cetaceans.**

pogonophorans See **beard worms.**

poikilotherm An organism whose body temperature varies with that of its surroundings. Compare **homeotherm.**

polar easterlies Variable winds that blow at high latitudes (Fig. 3.18).

pollen The structure that produces the male **gamete** in **flowering plants.**

pollution The introduction of harmful substances, or *pollutants,* heat energy, or sound into the environment by humans.

polychaetes (class *Polychaeta*) **Segmented worms** that typically have **parapodia** (Figs. 7.18 and 7.19).

polychlorinated biphenyls (PCBs) A group of **chlorinated hydrocarbon persistent** organic pollutants (POPs).

polymetallic nodules Lumps of minerals (including manganese, nickel, and other valuable minerals) that are found on the sea floor beyond the **continental shelf.**

polyp The cylindrical, typically attached stage of **cnidarians** (Figs. 7.7 and 14.2).

population A group of organisms belonging to the same **species** and living in the same place.

pore cell (porocyte) The tube-like *cell* of **sponges** that forms a pore, or *ostium* (pl. *ostia*).

practical salinity units (PSUs) A measurement of seawater **salinity** based on electrical conductivity, numerically equivalent to parts per thousand.

precious corals Gorgonians that secrete a red or pink skeleton consisting of fused **calcareous spicules.**

predation The act of an animal, or *predator,* eating another organism, or *prey.* A *top predator* is one that feeds at the top of the **food chain.**

pressure The weight exerted over a unit area of surface. This is equal to 1 *atmosphere* (14.7 lb per square inch) at the sea surface and 1 atmosphere plus the pressure exerted by the **water column,** which is 1 atmosphere per 10 m (33 ft) of depth.

primary producer (producer) An **autotroph.** An organism that carries out **primary production.**

primary production The conversion of the inorganic carbon, usually in the form of **carbon dioxide,** into **organic compounds** by **autotrophs.**

primary productivity The rate of **primary production,** that is, the amount of carbon fixed under a square meter of sea surface in a day or in a year (Fig. 10.17).

proboscis An extension near the mouth that in some **invertebrates** helps in the capture or collection of food.

profile A graph that shows changes in temperature, salinity, or any other parameter with depth (Fig. 3.8).

prokaryote An organism, like bacteria, with a **prokaryotic cell.**

prokaryotic cell The simplest type of *cell,* one that lacks a **nucleus** and most other kinds of **organelles** (Fig. 4.7). Compare **eukaryotic cell.**

protective coloration Coloration that benefits the individual by providing concealment from predators.

protein A large group of complex **nitrogen**-containing **organic molecules** that play many crucial roles in organisms.

protists Collection of different groups of relatively simple **eukaryotes,** including unicellular forms and multicellular algae. Formerly members of the kingdom *Protista* but now grouped together mostly for convenience.

protochordates Chordates that lack a backbone.

protozoans Animal-like **protists;** the various groups of unicellular, **eukaryotic protists** that are mostly heterotrophic.

pseudopodium A thin or blunt extension of the cytoplasm.

psychrophilic Cold-temperature-loving. Applied to organisms or enzymes that grow or function best, or only, at cold temperatures.

pteropods Pelagic gastropods in which the **foot** is modified for swimming and the shell is reduced or absent (Fig. 15.10).

pyloric caecum (pl. **caeca**) Each of the slender, blind tubes found in the intestines of many **bony fishes.**

pyramid of biomass The decrease in biomass that is observed in each higher level of a **food chain.**

pyramid of energy The decrease in energy that is observed in each higher level of a **food chain.**

pyramid of numbers The decrease in the number of individuals that is observed in each higher level of a **food chain.**

R

radial symmetry The regular arrangement of similar body parts around a central axis (Figs. 7.7 and 7.14*a*). Compare **bilateral symmetry.**

radioactivity The emission of *radiation* by unstable **atoms** in the form of particles and rays.

radiolarian ooze A type of **biogenous sediment** that consists mostly of the **silica** skeletons of **radiolarians.**

radiolarians (phylum *Radiolaria*) **Protozoans** with a **silica** skeleton and **pseudopodia** (Fig. 5.11).

radula The ribbon-like band of teeth of **molluscs** (Figs. 7.22, 7.23, and 7.29).

recombination The formation of new genetic combinations, like the one that takes place during **fertilization.**

recruitment The entry of young individuals into a **population** or, in fisheries biology, into a fished stock.

rectal gland A gland in the **cloaca** of **cartilaginous fishes** that excretes excess salts.

red algae (phylum *Rhodophyta*) **Seaweeds** that contain characteristic red pigments.

red clay A fine sediment that is the most common type of **lithogenous sediment** in the open ocean floor.

red tide An extensive **bloom** of **phytoplankton** that discolors the water.

reef crest The shallow outer edge of the **reef slope** of a **coral reef** (Fig. 14.15).

reef flat The wide and shallow upper surface of a **coral reef** (Fig. 14.15).

reef slope The outer, steep margin of a coral reef (Fig. 14.15). Also see **fore reef.**

refraction The change in the direction of a wave as it moves into shallow water (Figs. 11.8 and 11.9).

regeneration The ability of an organism to grow a body part that has been lost.

renewable resource A resource that is naturally replaced.

replication The copying of a cell's **deoxyribonucleic acid (DNA)** before the *cell* divides.

reproductive isolation The inability of separate **populations** to interbreed.

reproductive strategy The reproductive patterns that are followed by a particular species.

reptiles (class *Reptilia*) **Vertebrates** with scales on their skin and leathery eggs that are laid on land. Marine reptiles include *sea turtles, sea snakes,* the *marine iguana,* the *saltwater crocodile,* and the *American crocodile.*

resource partitioning The sharing of resources by specialization.

respiration See **aerobic respiration.** In this text the term "respiration" by itself refers to aerobic respiration.

respiratory exchange See **gas exchange.**

respiratory tree The branched extensions of the posterior end of the digestive tract of **sea cucumbers** that are involved in **gas exchange.**

rete mirabile A network of blood vessels that in some fishes functions as a heat-exchange system to help keep the internal body temperature higher than that of the water (Fig. 15.22).

retroviruses **Viruses** that contain **RNA** instead of **DNA.**

ribbon (nemertean) worms (phylum *Nemertea*) **Invertebrates** with a complete digestive tract, a true circulatory system, and a long **proboscis** to capture prey (Fig. 7.16).

ribosomes **Organelles** where a cell's **proteins** are made.

rift A crack in Earth's crust formed as pieces of the crust separate.

RNA (ribonucleic acid) **Nucleic acids** that translate the genetic information contained in **DNA** (deoxyribonucleic acid) into **proteins** and that have many other functions in the *cell.*

rockweeds (wracks) Brown algae like *Fucus* that inhabit rocky shores in temperate areas.

rorquals Blue, fin, and the other **baleen whales** that display long grooves on the underside (Figs. 9.16 and 9.19).

roundworms See **nematodes.**

S

salinity The total amount of **salts** dissolved in seawater. It is generally expressed in parts per thousand (‰) or *practical salinity units (psu).*

salivary gland Any of the glands in **molluscs, vertebrates,** and other animals that release digestive **enzymes** into the mouth.

salmon ranching Practice in which cultured juvenile salmon are released into fresh water and allowed to migrate to sea so they can be harvested later when they return as adults.

salps (class *Thaliacea*) Pelagic **tunicates** with a transparent, cylindrical body, sometimes forming long colonies (Fig. 15.8).

salt A substance that consists of **ions** that have opposite electrical charges.

salt gland A gland that secretes excess salts in seabirds and sea turtles.

salt marsh A grassy area that extends along the shores of **estuaries** and sheltered coasts in temperate and subpolar regions.

salt wedge A layer of denser, saltier seawater that flows along the bottom in **estuaries** (Fig. 12.3).

sand dollars Sea urchins with a flat, round test and short spines that live partly buried in soft sediments (Fig. 7.48*b*).

Sargasso Sea The region of the Atlantic Ocean north of the West Indies that is characterized by floating masses of *Sargasso weed,* a **brown alga.**

scaphopods See **tusk shells.**

scavenger An animal that feeds on dead organic matter.

school A well-defined group of fishes or **cetaceans** of the same species. Also see **pod.**

scientific method The set of procedures by which scientists learn about the world (Fig. 1.20).

scleractinian corals Anthozoans with a solid **calcareous** skeleton that are the most important reef-building corals.

sclerosponges (coralline sponges) Sponges with a massive **calcareous** skeleton (Fig. 7.6*c*).

scuba (*s*elf-*c*ontained *u*nderwater *b*reathing *a*pparatus) Equipment that allows breathing underwater from tanks of compressed air.

scyphozoans (class *Scyphozoa*) **Cnidarians** whose life cycle includes a conspicuous **medusa** and a much reduced or absent **polyp.**

sea A **wave** that has a sharp peak and a relatively flat **wave trough.** Seas are found in areas where waves are generated by the wind (Fig. 3.29).

sea anemones Anthozoans that consist of one large **polyp.**

sea cows See **sirenians.**

sea cucumbers (class *Holothuroidea*) **Echinoderms** with a soft, elongated body that lacks spines.

sea-floor spreading The process by which new sea floor is formed as it moves away from *spreading centers* in **mid-ocean ridges.**

sea lilies See **crinoids.**

sea slugs See **nudibranchs.**

sea spiders (class *Pycnogonida*) **Arthropods** that have a reduced body and four pairs of legs (Fig. 7.43).

sea squirts (ascidians; class *Ascidiacea*) **Tunicates** with a typically sac-like, attached body as adults (Figs. 7.52a and 7.53).

sea stars (starfishes; class *Asteroidea*) **Echinoderms** with five or more radiating arms and **tube feet** that are used in locomotion.

sea urchins (class *Echinoidea*) **Echinoderms** with a round or flattened test and movable spines.

seagrasses Grass-like **flowering plants** like *eelgrass* that are adapted to live at sea (Fig. 6.13).

seamount A submarine volcano in the **abyssal plain.**

seaweeds (macrophytes) Large, multicellular **algae.**

sediment Loose material like sand and mud that settles on the bottom. Also see **biogenous** and **lithogenous sediments.**

seeding In **mariculture,** the release of cultured juvenile individuals to enrich a natural **stock.**

segmentation The division of the body into similar compartments, or *segments.*

segmented worms (annelids; phylum *Annelida*) **Invertebrates** that display an elongate body with distinct **segmentation** and a digestive tract that lies in a **coelom.**

seismic sea waves See **tsunami.**

self-regulating population A **population** with a growth rate that is dependent on its own numbers.

self-shading Reduction in the amount of light available to **phytoplankton** that live below other phytoplankton.

semidiurnal tide A tidal pattern with two high and two low **tides** each day (Fig. 3.34*a*).

septa The thin **tissue** partitions in the **polyp** of **anthozoans.**

sequence (of nucleic acids) The order in which *nucleotides* occur on a **nucleic acid** molecule, which specifies the information contained in the molecule.

sessile An organism that lives attached to the bottom or to a surface.

seta (pl. setae) The bristles of **polychaetes.**

sex hormone A **hormone** that controls the timing of reproduction and sexual characteristics in **vertebrates.**

sexual reproduction Reproduction that involves the union of **gametes.** Compare **asexual reproduction.**

shear boundary The boundary between two *tectonic plates* that move past each other on Earth's surface. Also see **fault.**

shelf break The section of the **continental shelf** where the slope abruptly becomes steeper, usually at a depth of 120 to 200 m (400 to 600 ft) (Figs. 2.19 and 2.20).

silica (SiO_2) A mineral similar to glass that is the major component of the *cell wall,* shell, or skeleton of many marine organisms.

siliceous Made of **silica.**

siliceous ooze A type of **biogenous sediment** that consists mostly of the **silica** shell and skeletons of marine organisms. Also see **diatomaceous ooze** and **radiolarian ooze.**

silicoflagellates (phylum *Heterokontophyta,* class *Chrysophyta*) Unicellular and **eukaryotic** members of the **phytoplankton** that have a star-shaped **silica** skeleton (Fig. 5.9).

simple sugar A sugar, like **glucose,** that cannot be broken down into simpler sugar molecules.

siphon (funnel) The tube-like extension through which water flows in and out of the **mantle cavity** in **bivalves** and **cephalopods,** and in **tunicates.**

siphonophores Hydrozoans that exist as drifting colonies.

sipunculans See **peanut worms.**

sirenians (sea cows; order *Sirenia*) Marine **mammals** with anterior flippers, no rear limbs, and a paddle-shaped tail (Fig. 9.14).

sludge Concentrated wastes extracted from sewage during sewage treatment.

soft corals (order *Alcyonacea*) Colonial **anthozoans** with no hard skeleton.

solute Any material dissolved in a *solvent.*

sonar (*s*ound *n*avigation and *r*anging) A technique or equipment used to locate objects underwater by the detection of echoes (Fig. 1.7).

Southern Ocean Body of water surrounding Antarctica.

Southern Oscillation See **El Niño–Southern Oscillation.**

spawning The release of **gametes** or eggs into the water.

species Individuals of the same kind that cannot breed with those belonging to other kinds.

spermaceti organ The **melon** of sperm whales. It contains *spermaceti,* an oil once widely used in candle making.

spermatophore A packet of sperm in **cephalopods.**

spicule Any of the small **calcareous** or **siliceous** bodies embedded among the *cells* of **sponges** or in the **tissues** of other **invertebrates.**

spiracle One of two openings behind the eyes of **cartilaginous fishes.**

spiral valve A spiral portion in the intestine of **cartilaginous fishes.**

sponges (phylum *Porifera*) **Invertebrates** that consist of a complex aggregation of *cells,* including **collar cells,** and have a skeleton of fibers and/or **spicules.**

spongin The resistant fibers of **sponges.**

spore The **asexual,** sometimes resistant structure produced by some **algae.** Also see **zoospore.**

sporophyte The **diploid, spore**-producing generation in many **seaweeds.** Compare **gametophyte.**

spout (blow) The water vapor and seawater that is observed when whales surface and exhale.

spring tides The **tides** with a large **tidal range;** they occur around the times of full or new moon. Compare **neap tides.**

standing stock (standing crop) The total amount, or **biomass,** of an organism at a given time.

starch A **carbohydrate** that consists of chains of **simple sugars.**

statocyst A fluid-filled cavity provided with sensitive hairs and a small free body that is used to orient animals with respect to gravity.

stenohaline Organism that can tolerate a narrow range of salinities. Compare **euryhaline.**

stipe The stem-like portion of the **thallus** of **seaweeds** (Fig. 6.1).

stock The size of a **population.**

stratification The separation of the **water column** into layers, with the most dense water at the bottom and the least dense water at the surface (Fig. 3.22). A stratified water column is said to be *stable.* An *unstable* column results when the surface water becomes more dense than the water below.

stromatolites Massive **calcareous** skeletons formed by **cyanobacteria** (Fig. 5.4).

structural color A color that results when light is reflected by a particular surface.

structural molecule A molecule, like **cellulose,** that provides support and protection.

subduction The downward movement of a *tectonic plate* into the mantle that occurs in **trenches,** which are also known as *subduction zones.*

sublittoral zone See **subtidal zone.**

submarine canyon A narrow, deep depression in the **continental shelf** formed by the erosion of rivers or glaciers before the shelf was submerged (Fig. 2.20).

subsidence The sinking of a landmass.

substrate The type of bottom or material on or in which an organism lives.

subtidal zone The bottom above the **continental shelf** (Fig. 10.12).

succession See **ecological succession.**

succulent A fleshy plant that accumulates water.

sulfide One of the minerals that is abundant in the hot water that seeps through **hydrothermal vents.**

surf A **wave** that becomes so high and steep as it approaches the shoreline that it breaks.

surface (mixed) layer The upper layer of water that is mixed by wind, waves, and currents (Fig. 3.24).

surface-to-volume ratio (S/V ratio) The amount of surface area relative to the total volume of an organism (Fig. 4.17).

suspension feeder An animal that feeds on particles suspended in the water (Fig. 7.4). Compare **deposit feeder, filter feeder, passive suspension feeder.**

swarming The aggregation of individuals for **spawning** or other purposes.

sweeper tentacle A type of **tentacle** in corals that is used to sting neighboring colonies.

swell A **wave** with a flatter, rounded **wave crest** and **trough.** Swells are found away from the area where waves are generated by the wind (Fig. 3.29).

swim bladder The gas-filled sac in the body cavity of **bony fishes** that is involved in the adjustment of buoyancy (Fig. 8.12).

symbiosis A close relationship between two species, including **commensalism, mutualism,** and **parasitism.**

system (organ system) A group of **organs** specialized for one function.

T

tadpole larva The larva of **tunicates.**

tapeworms Parasitic **flatworms,** typically consisting of a chain of repeated units.

taste buds Structures in the mouth and other locations of fishes that are sensitive to chemical stimuli.

taxon (pl. **taxa**) A group of organisms that share a common ancestry.

tectonic estuary An **estuary** that results from the sinking of land due to movements of the **crust.**

tentacle A flexible, elongated appendage.

territory A home area that is defended by an animal.

Tethys Sea A shallow sea that once separated the Eurasian and African sections of the super-continent **Pangaea.** It eventually gave rise to the modern Mediterranean Sea (Figs. 2.16*a* and 2.16*b*).

tetrapods **Vertebrates** that have two pairs of legs, a group that includes the **cetaceans.**

thallus The complete body of a **seaweed.**

theory (or **scientific theory**) A **hypothesis** that is accepted as "true" for the time being because it has passed test after test and is supported by a large body of evidence.

thermal pollution Pollution by heated water.

thermocline A zone in the **water column** that shows a sudden change in temperature with depth. The *main,* or *permanent, thermocline* is the zone where the temperature change marks the transition between the warm surface water and the cold deep water (Figs. 3.8 and 3.22).

thermohaline circulation Ocean circulation that is driven by differences in water density, due to variations in water temperature and salinity, rather than by the wind or tides.

threatened species A species that occurs in unnaturally low numbers.

tidal bore A steep wave generated as high tides move up some estuaries and rivers.

tidal current A **current** that is generated by **tides.**

tidal energy Energy that can be harnessed as a result of the movement of **tides.**

tidal marsh See **salt marsh.**

tidal range The difference in water level between successive high and low **tides.**

tide The periodic, rhythmic rise and fall of the sea surface.

tide pool A depression that holds seawater at low tide.

tide table A table that gives the predicted time and height of **tides** for particular points along a coast.

tintinnids **Ciliates** that secrete vase-like tests, or *loricas* (Fig. 5.13).

tissue A group of *cells* specialized for one function.

trade winds Steady winds that blow from east to west toward the Equator, replacing the hot air that rises at the Equator (Fig. 3.18).

transform fault A large horizontal displacement in the mid-ocean ridge.

transplantation The intentional introduction of a species.

trematodes See **flukes.**

trench A narrow, deep depression in the sea floor (Figs. 2.12 and 2.13).

trochophore A planktonic **larva** found in **poly-chaetes,** some **molluscs,** and other **invertebrates** (Fig. 15.11*d*).

trophic cascade When changes in the abundance of an organism result in changes at other **trophic levels** of the **food chain.**

trophic level Each of the steps in a **food chain.**

trophic pyramid The pyramid-like relationship found in the **pyramids of biomass, energy,** and **numbers** of organisms in a **food chain.**

tsunami (seismic sea waves) Long, fast waves produced by earthquakes and other seismic disturbances of the sea floor.

tube foot Any of the external muscular extensions of the **water vascular system** of **echinoderms.**

tubular eyes Specialized eyes of many **midwater** animals that allow acute upward or downward vision.

tunic The outer covering of **sea squirts** (Fig. 7.53*b*).

tunicates (subphylum *Urochordata*) **Chordates** that show the three basic chordate characteristics only in the larva.

turbellarians Mostly free-living **flatworms** (Fig. 7.15).

tusk shells (scaphopods; class *Scaphopoda*) **Molluscs** that have an elongated, tapered shell that is open at both ends.

U

umbo The region around the hinge of a bivalve's shell (Fig. 7.25).

upwelling The process by which colder water rich in **nutrients** rises from a lower to a higher depth. It includes *coastal* and *equatorial upwelling* (Figs. 15.30 to 15.33).

urea A toxic waste product of some vertebrates.

urogenital opening The common opening for urine and **gametes** in **bony fishes** and other animals.

uterus (womb) The portion of female mammals' reproductive tract in which the **embryo** develops.

V

valve Any of the two shells of **bivalves** and **lamp shells.**

vegetative reproduction See **asexual reproduction.**

veliger A planktonic **larva** in **gastropods** and **bivalves** (Fig. 15.11*a*).

ventral The underside or belly surface of an animal with **bilateral symmetry** (Fig. 7.14*b*).

vertebra (pl. **vertebrae**) Each of the bones that make up the backbone.

vertebrates (subphylum *Vertebrata*) **Chordates** with a backbone.

vestigial Undeveloped structure that is fully developed in ancestral species.

vestimentiferans **Polychaetes** that are common at **hydrothermal vents** (Fig. 16.29).

viruses Non-cellular particles containing **nucleic acid** but unable to reproduce unless infecting living *cells.*

viviparous An animal whose eggs develop inside the female while the **embryo** derives nutrition from the mother directly from the womb (*aplacental viviparity*) or by a **placenta** (*placental viviparity*) as in most **mammals.**

W

warning coloration Coloration that allows organisms to escape from predators by advertising something harmful or distasteful.

water column The vertical column of seawater that extends from the surface to the bottom.

water mass A body of water that can be identified by its temperature and salinity.

water vascular system A network of water-filled canals in **echinoderms** used in locomotion and food gathering (Figs. 7.45 and 7.49).

wave The undulation that forms as a disturbance moves along the surface of the water. Waves can be described by their *height* (the vertical distance between **wave crest** and **trough**), *wavelength* (the horizontal distance between adjacent **crests**), and *period* (the time the wave takes to move past a given point) (Fig. 3.26).

wave crest The highest part of a **wave** (Fig. 3.26).

wave shock The intensity of the impact of a **wave.**

wave trough The lowest part of a **wave** (Fig. 3.26).

weathering The physical and chemical breakdown of rocks.

westerlies The winds that blow from west to east at middle latitudes (Fig. 3.18).

wetlands Areas flooded by tides or with visible standing water like **salt marshes, mangrove forests,** and freshwater marshes.

world ocean A concept that is used to indicate that all oceans on Earth are interconnected.

Y

yolk sac A yolk-containing sac that is attached to the **embryo** of *fishes* and other **vertebrates.**

Z

zonation The presence of organisms within a particular range, or *zone,* as in the *vertical zonation* observed in the **intertidal.**

zooid Each member of a colony of **bryozoans** and other colonial **invertebrates.**

zooplankton The **heterotrophic,** animal and protozoan component of **plankton.** Compare **phytoplankton.**

zoospore A **spore** provided with one or more **flagella.**

zooxanthellae **Dinoflagellates** that live within the **tissues** of reef corals and other marine animals (Fig. 14.1).

zygote The **diploid** *cell* that results from **fertilization,** that is, a fertilized egg.

Index

Note: Page numbers followed by *f* refer to figures and *t* refer to tables.